Active Chemistry™

Arthur Eisenkraft, Ph.D.

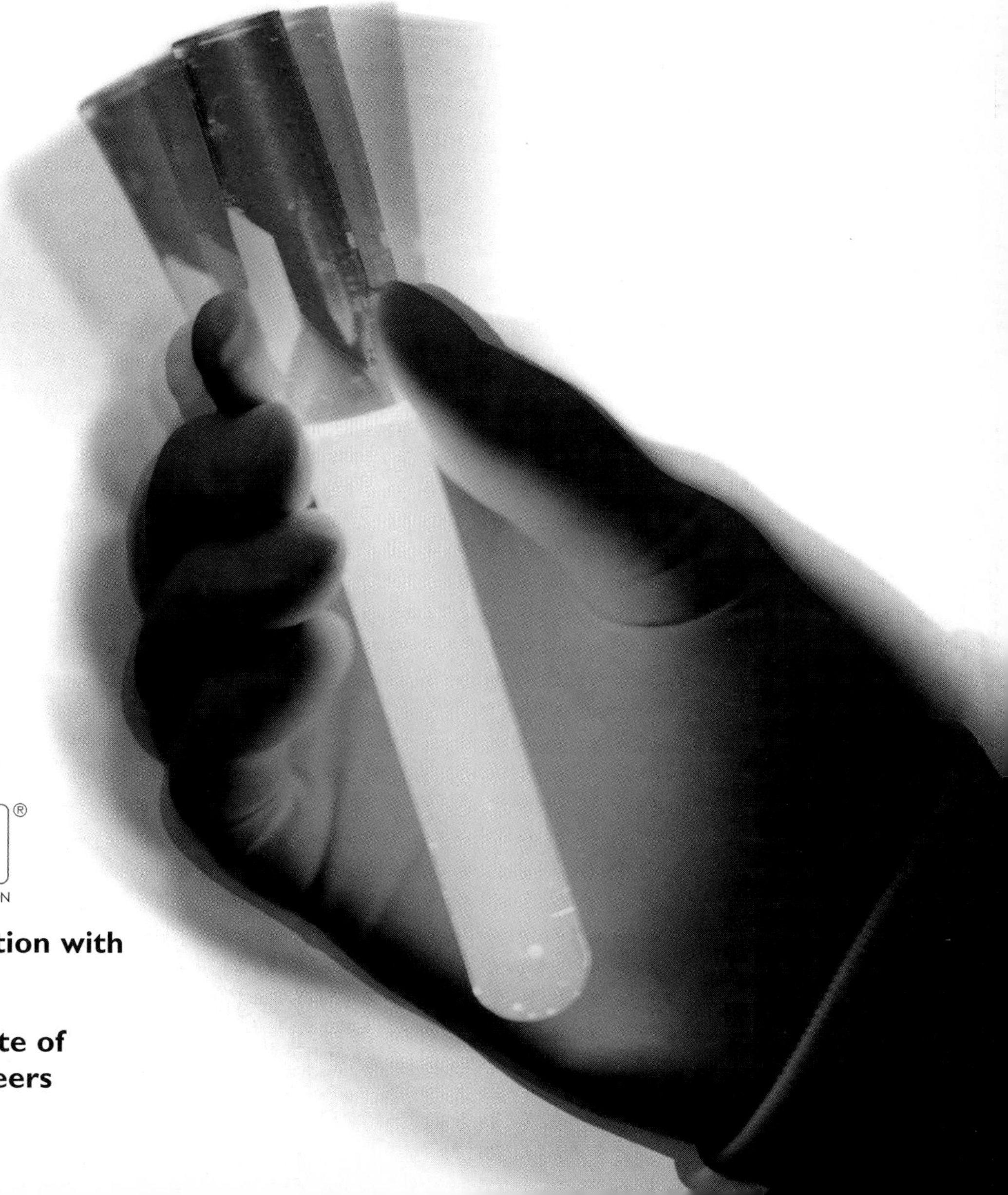

IT's ABOUT TIME®
HERFF JONES EDUCATION DIVISION

Developed in association with
AIChE®
American Institute of Chemical Engineers

IT's ABOUT TIME®
HERFF JONES EDUCATION DIVISION

84 Business Park Drive, Armonk, NY 10504
Phone (914) 273-2233 Fax (914) 273-2227
www.its-about-time.com

President
Tom Laster

Director of Product Development
Barbara Zahm, Ph.D.

Creative Director, Design
John Nordland

Project Development Editor
Ruta Demery

Project Coordinator
Gary Hickernell

Editorial Coordinator
Loretta Steeves

Associate Editors
Sampson Starkweather
Niki Lee
Todd Fishlin
Lydia D. Islan
Joseph C. DeMarco

Production/Studio Manager
Bob Schwalb

Layout and Production
Inkwell Publishing Solutions
Kadi Sarv
Tommaso A. Lorenzo

Creative Artwork
Tomas Bunk

Technical Art
Inkwell Publishing Solutions
Marie Killoran

Indexer
Caryn Sobel

Photo Research
Monica T. Rodriguez
Marie Killoran

Safety Reviewer
Edward Robeck

Printed and bound in the United States of America.

ISBN-13: 978-1-58591-451-7

1 2 3 4 5 VH 11 10 09 08 07

NSF

This project was supported, in part, by the
National Science Foundation under Grant No. 0137872.
Opinions expressed are those of the authors and not necessarily
those of the National Science Foundation.

Acknowledgments

Development Partner

The American Institute of Chemical Engineers (AIChE) is the world's leading organization for chemical engineers. It has more than 40,000 members in 93 countries. AIChE played a pivotal role in the development of *Active Chemistry* as one of the Co-Principal Investigators of the National Science Foundation Grant. AIChE's involvement has helped to ensure the accuracy of the program's chemistry content as well as its engineering design principles.

Project Director

Dr. Arthur Eisenkraft has taught high school physics for over 28 years and is currently the Distinguished Professor of Science Education and a Senior Research Fellow at the University of Massachusetts, Boston. Dr. Eisenkraft is the author of numerous science and educational publications. He holds U.S. Patent #4447141 for a Laser Vision Testing System (which tests visual acuity for spatial frequency).

Dr. Eisenkraft has been recognized with numerous awards including: Presidential Award for Excellence in Science Teaching, 1986 from President Reagan; American Association of Physics Teachers (AAPT) Excellence in Pre-College Teaching Award, 1999; AAPT Distinguished Service Citation for "excellent contributions to the teaching of physics," 1989; Science Teacher of the Year, Disney American Teacher Awards in their American Teacher Awards program, 1991; Honorary Doctor of Science degree from Rensselaer Polytechnic Institute, 1993; NSTA Distinguished Service Award to Science Education, 2005.

In 1999, Dr. Eisenkraft was elected to a three-year cycle as the President-Elect, President and Retiring President of the National Science Teachers Association (NSTA), the largest science teacher organization in the world. He also served on the content committee and helped to write the National Science Education Standards for the National Research Council. In 2003, he was elected a fellow of the American Association for the Advancement of Science (AAAS). Dr. Eisenkraft has been involved with a number of projects and chaired many competition programs, including: the Toshiba/NSTA ExploraVisions Awards (1991 to the present); the Toyota TAPESTRY Grants (1990 to 2005); the Duracell/NSTA Scholarship Competitions (1984 to 2000). In 1993, he served as Executive Director for the XXIV International Physics Olympiad after being Academic Director for the United States Team for six years. He is currently science consultant to ESPN Sports Figures.

Dr. Eisenkraft is a frequent presenter and keynote speaker at National Conventions. He has published over 100 articles and presented over 200 papers and workshops. He has been featured in articles in *The New York Times, Education Week, Physics Today, Scientific American, The American Journal of Physics* and *The Physics Teacher* and has appeared on The Today Show, National Public Radio (NPR), and many other radio and television broadcasts.

Content Specialists

Gary Freebury has been teaching chemistry for more than 35 years. He has been the Safety Advisor for Montana Schools, director of the Chemistry Olympiad, chairman of the Montana Section of the American Chemical Society (ACS), member of the Executive Committee of the Montana Section of the ACS, and a member of the Montana Science Advisory Council. Mr. Freebury has been the regional director and author of Scope, Sequence and Coordination (SS&C) – Integrated Science Curriculum and Co-director of the NSF supported Chemistry Concepts four-year program. He earned a B.S. degree at Eastern Montana College in mathematics and physical science, and an M.S. degree in chemistry at the University of Northern Iowa.

Dr. Gary Hickernell earned a B.S. degree in chemistry at Allegheny College and his Ph.D. in organic chemistry at the University of Washington in Seattle, and studied the chemistry of food flavors for nineteen years at the General Foods Technical Center in Tarrytown, NY, as a research scientist. During this period, he won two patents, a US patent for "Novel Sweetener Effects," and a Canadian patent for the "Resin Decaffeination of Coffee." His second career began at Vassar College in Poughkeepsie where he taught general and organic chemistry as an associate professor. During this period, he co-authored chapters in the NSF-funded series of engineering and environmental books, *Accident and Emergency Management: Problems and Solutions* and *Pollution Prevention: Problems and Solutions*. After two years at Vassar, Dr. Hickernell joined the science faculty at Keuka College, where he participated in the MADCAP project to bring project-based chemistry to college freshmen. Most recently, Dr. Hickernell joined the staff at It's About Time as the Project Coordinator for NSF-funded projects.

Acknowledgments — Active Chemistry Team

NSF Program Officer

Gerhard Salinger
Instructional Materials Development (IMD)

Principal Investigators

Arthur Eisenkraft
University of Massachusetts, Boston, MA

Gary Freebury
Kalispell High School
Kalispell, MT

Darlene Schuster
American Institute of Chemical Engineers
Washington, DC

Barbara Zahm,
It's About Time
Armonk, NY

Project Coordinators

Gary Hickernell
Project Coordinator
It's About Time,
Armonk, NY

Jean Pennycook
Field Test Coordinator
Fresno Unified School District, Fresno, CA

Writers

David Barry, Chelsea High School Chelsea, MA

Kristen Cacciatore
Dedham High School
Dedham, MA

James Clements
Atlantic High School
Port Orange, FL

Paul D. Dunbar
University of Kentucky
Paducah, KY

L.S. Fan
Ohio State University
Columbus, OH

Mary Gromko
Colorado Springs School District 11
Colorado Springs, CO

Himanshu Gupta
Ohio State University
Columbus, OH

Robert Hartshorn
University of Tennessee
Martin, TN

Carl Heltzel
Transylvania University
Lexington, KY

Diane Johnson
Lewis County High School
Vanceburg, KY

Maggie Matthews
Shorewood High School
Shoreline, WA

Sean Muller
Merrimack High School
Merrimack, NH

John Parson
Ohio State University
Columbus, OH

Stanford N. Peppenhorst
Germantown H.S.
Germantown, TN

Josh Pretzer
Culver Academy
Culver, IN

Brian Radcliffe
Bryan Station High School, Lexington, KY

John Roeder
The Calhoun School
New York, NY

Hannah Sevian
University of Massachusetts, Boston, MA

Peggy Sheets
Upper Arlington H.S.
Arlington, OH (Retired)

Sandra Smith
Colorado Springs, CO

Michael Tinnesand
American Chemical Society
Washington, D.C.

Alissa Watson
Bardstown High School
Bardstown, KY

Melissa Wickenkamp
San Rafael H.S., CA

Doug Yenney
Dayton High School
Dayton, WA

Board of Advisors

Jerry Bell
Senior Scientist
International Activities Division of ACS (American Chemical Society)

Rodger Bybee
Executive Director of BSCS (Biological Sciences Curriculum Study)

James Davis
Chemistry Professor Emeritus
Harvard University

Marilyn Decker
Senior Program Director of Science for Boston Public Schools

Dianne Dorland
Former President, AIChE and Dean of Engineering, Rowan University

Maria Alicia Lopez Freeman
Executive Director of CSP (California Science Project)

Mary Gromko
Science Supervisor K-12 for the Colorado Springs School District 11

David Lavallee
Provost Vice President of Academic Affairs
SUNY, New Paltz

Carlo Parravano
Executive Director
Merck Institute for Science Education and AAAS Fellow

Harold Pratt, NSTA President and BSCS Advisory Board member

Bryan Roberts, NSF Site Visitor, University of Pennsylvania, PA

Ethel Schultz, Science Education Consultant CESAME, trustee of the Noyce Foundation

Consultants

William Berlinghoff
Colby College, ME

Audrey Champagne
SUNY Albany, NY

Michael Hacker
Loudonville, NY

Martin Hughto
Horace Greeley H.S.
Chappaqua, NY

Inna Kasminskaya
Pace University, NY

Steve Long
Rogers High School, AR

George Miller
University of California at Irvine, Irvine, CA

Sr. Mary Virginia Orna
College of New Rochelle, NY

James Pellegrino
U. Illinois Chicago, IL

Mala Radhakrishnan
Graduate Student
MIT, Cambridge, MA

Maren Reeder
Merck Institute for Science Education
Rahway, NJ

Vladimir Shafirovich
New York University, NY

Ellen Weiser
Pace University, NY

Evaluation Team

Rachelle Haroldson
University of Minnesota, MN

Frances Lawrenz
University of Minnesota, MN

Nate Wood, University of Minnesota, MN

Field Test Teachers

Dawn Arnett
Titusville H.S., FL

Rachel Badnowski
Southfield H.S., MI

Patricia Barker
Hollywood H.S., CA

Nora Ann Bennett
Mt. Tabor H.S., NC

Kristen Cacciatore
Dedham H.S., MA

Isabel Camille
Coral Gables H.S., FL

Connie Celestine
Crossland H.S., MD

Ann Chatfield
Dalton H.S., GA

Jody Christophe
Lincoln H.S., PA

Grant Clark
Newton N. H.S., MA

James Clements
Atlantic H.S., FL

Linda Craig
Butler H.S., PA

Jeanene Crenshaw
Jeff. Davis H.S., AL

Carol Durso
Haverford H.S., PA

Frances Dziuma
St. Barnabas H.S., NY

Valerie Felger
DATA, TX

Brian Gagne
Newton N. H.S., MA

Marci Harvey
W. Forsythe H.S., NC

Gail Hermann
Quincy H.S., IL

Oscar Hernandez
Robert E.Lee H.S., TX

Angela Holcomb
Mt. Tabor H.S., NC

Solona Hollis
Miller Grove H.S., GA

Ray Hulse
Haverford H.S., PA

John Paul Jones
Crestview H.S., FL

James Kopchains
Flushing H.S., NY

Stephanie Levens
N. Broward Prep., FL

Arthur Logan
Clio Area H.S., MI

Charlotte Lum
Summit Prep. H.S., CA

Dan Mader
Kaukauna H.S., WI

Maggie Matthews
Shorewood H.S.,WA

Catherine McCluskey
E. Wake H.S., NC

Mitzi Moore
International School, TX

Sharona Moss
Selma High School, AL

Amy Murphy
Spain Park H.S., AL

Gerard Pepe
North Babylon H.S., NY

Alicia Peterson
Haverford H.S., PA

Vince Santo Pietro
Shorecrest H.S., WA

Richard Pimentel
Coachella Valley H.S., CA

Joshua Pretzer
Culver Academies, IN

Candace Purdom
Washington County H.S., KY

Richard Redman
Franklin H.S., CA

Veronica Riffle
Lake Ridge Acad., OH

Rosemary Riggs
Roosevelt H.S., TX

Brenda Rinehart
Thompson H.S., AL

Jocelyn Roger
Squalicum H.S., WA

Carol Smith
Van Alstyne H.S., TX

David Smith
Battle Creek H.S., MI

Karen Tokos
Newton N. H.S., MA

Jane Wallace
Dalton H.S., GA

Alissa Watson
Bardstown H.S., KY

Janice Weaver
Culver Academies, IN

Shanan Wheeler
Churchill H.S., MI

Rodney White
Shorecrest H.S., WA

Melissa Wickenkamp
San Rafael H.S., CA

James Wicks, Sr.
Garfield H.S., CA

Sarah Wilson
Caldwell H.S., ID

Doug Yenney
Dayton H.S., WA

Chem at Work

Todd Fishlin
Mount Kisco, NY

Equipment Development Manager

Dana Turner
Armonk, NY

Pilot Testers

Rob Adams
Wyoming, DE

Ina Ahern,
Plymouth Regional H.S.
Plymouth, NH

Yolanda Anderson
Wingfield H.S., MS

Susan Auld
Squalicum H.S., WA

Linda Barry
Skyview H.S., WA

Arthur Beauchamp
Will C. Wood H.S., CA

John Bibb
Georgetown, DE

Amy Biddle
Pinkerton Academy,
Derry, NH

Heidy Boyd
Grand Island H.S., NE

Fran Burkett
Forest Hill H.S., MS

Kristin Cacciatore
Dedham H.S., MA

Christine Carlson
Randolph H.S., NJ

Kelly Chaney
Cabot High School, AZ

Chris Clermont
Largo High School, MD

Sue Coluccio
Seattle Preparatory
High School, WA

Melissa Conrad
Hartford Academy
of Math & Science, CT

Marsha Crawford
Perry H.S., MI

Mary Cummane
Perspectives
Charter School, IL

Robert Dayton
Rush-Henrietta H.S.
Henrietta, NY

Deb Ditkowsky
Carl Schurz H.S., IL

Barbara Duch
Education Resource Ctr.
Newark, DE

Robert Dutch
South Shore
Vocational Tech, MA

Gabriel Duque
North Miami Sr. H.S.
Miami, FL

Kathleen Dwyer
Maplewood Richmond
Heights H.S., MO

Debra Edelman
Pueblo East H.S., CO

Julia Eichman
McDonald County
High School, MO

Louis Fraga
Hopedale H.S., MA

David Frantz
Bayshore H.S., FL

Shauna Friend
Webb City H.S., MO

Suzanne Fudold
Bowie High School, MD

Liz Garcia
Carson High School, CA

Bill Green
E.O. Smith H.S., CT

Jennifer Grivens
Eaton Rapids H.S., MI

Laura Hajdukiewicz
The Bromfield School
Harvard, MA

Jonathon Haraty
SAGE School
Springfield, MA

Curt Hart
Corbin High School, KY

Rachel Hechtman
Lyman Hall H.S., CT

Bill Heeren
D.C. Everest H.S., WI

Carl Heltzel
Transylvania University
Lexington, KY

Bernie Hermanson
Harlan Community
High School, IA

Alison Hess
Northwestern H.S., MD

Natalie Hiller
Philadelphia
Public Schools, PA

Nick Hoffman
Wallace Senior H.S., ID

Bronwyn Hogan
Meadowcreek H.S., GA

Penny Hood
Stanwood H.S., WA

Peg Huben
Somerville H.S., MA

Ray Hulse
Haverford H.S., PA

Tamilyn Ingram
Menifee County H.S.
Frenchburg, KY

John Jacoby
Upper Scioto Valley, OH

Amy James
Public Academy for the
Performing Arts, NM

Barbara Jeffries
Casey Co. High School
Liberty, KY

Diane Johnson
Lewis County High
School Vanceburg, KY

Lorraine Kelly
Hull High School, MA

Mary Kennedy
Texas Military Inst., TX

Elizabeth Kirkham
Chemawa Indian School,
OR

Steve Knight
Winthrop H.S., ME

Gerry LaFontaine
Toll Gate High School
Warwick, RI

Jo Larmore
Laurel, DE

Maria Lee-Alverez
Western Hills Design
Technology, OH

Jeffery Little
Pikeville H.S., KY

Kathy Lucas
Casey Co. High School
Liberty, KY

Neva Lyon
Jefferson H.S., OR

Barbara Malkas
Taconic H.S., MA

JoAnn Manor
Orchard View H.S., MI

Barbara Martin
Reading H.S., MA

Earl Martin
Garfield Sr. H.S., CA

Maggie Matthews
Shorewood H.S.,WA

Robert Mayton
Allen Central High School
Eastern, KY

Peggy McCoy
Alternative #1, CO

Jill McNew
Street School, OK

Vicki Mockbee
Caesar Rodney H.S.
Camden, DE

Dr. Judy Moody
Starkville H.S., MS

Guillermo Muhlman
PVPA High School, MA

Brenda Mullins
Knott Co. Central H.S.
Hindman, KY

Amy Murphy
Spain Park H.S., AL

Barbara Murphy
Benjamin School, FL

Barry North
Rivendell Interstate
Regional High School
Orford, NH

Mary Ollie
Caldwell H.S., ID

Angela Pence
Wolfe County H.S.
Campton, KY

Roy Penix
Prestonburg H.S., KY

Gerard Pepe
North Babylon H.S., NY

Alicia Peterson
Haverford H.S., PA

Frank Petkunas
Bradley-Bourbonnais
Community H.S., IL

Lou Pompilli
Abington Senior H.S., PA

Marcia Powell
Central City School
District, IA

Cindy Powell-Burgess
Affton H.S., MO

Genevieve Prendergast
Benedictine Academy, NJ

Hilary Reilly
Capitol Region Career &
Technical School, NY

Robin Ringland
Stanwood H.S., WA

George Robertson
Stanwood H.S., WA

Jocelyn Roger
Squalicum H.S., WA

Dena Rosenberger
El Capitan H.S., CA

Kabce Rudiger
Potsdam H.S., NY

John Scali
Newark, DE

Noreen Scarpitto
Reading H.S., MA

Sarah Schenk
East Syracuse-Minoa
High School, NY

Fred Schiess
Stanwood H.S., WA

James Senicola
Baldwin Senior H.S., NY

Hannah Sevian
Chelsea H.S., MA

Margaret Showalter
El Dorado H.S., NM

Angela Skaggs
Magoffin County H.S.
Salyersville, KY

Karin Skipper
Mid-Carolina H.S., SC

Mark Smith
Arcola High School, IL

Valerie Stone
Whitnall H.S., WI

Mary Stoukides
Toll Gate High School
Warwick, RI

Jim Swanson
Saugus H.S., MA

Kathy Swingle
Rehoboth, DE

Mary Thomaskutty
Owensboro H.S., KY

Karen Tokos
Newton North H.S., MA

Jeffert Scott Townsend
Powell Co. High School
Stanton, KY

Betsy Uhing
Grand Island Sr. H.S., NE

Josh Underwood
Deming High School
Mount Olivet, KY

Andrew Uy
Venice H.S., CA

Amy Voss
Grand Island Sr. H.S., NE

Elaine Weil
Berlin, MD

Jen Wilson
Wilmington, DE

Sarah Wilson
Caldwell H.S., ID

Carrie Woolfolk
Louisa Country H.S., VA

Doug Yenney
Dayton H.S., WA

Corey Zirker
Wahluke H.S., WA

Bruce ZuWalick
Lymann Hall H.S., CT

Table of Contents

Chapter 4 Chemical Dominoes

Chapter 5 Ideal Toy

Table of Contents

Chapter 9 It's Alimentary

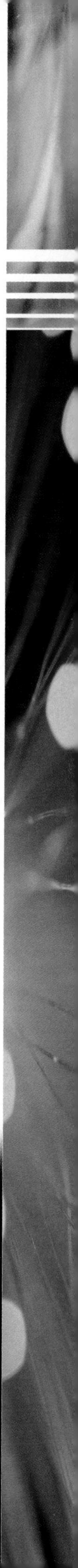

Table of Contents

The 7E Instructional Model Used in Active Chemistry

The 7E Model	At the Activity Level (Features in Red)	At the Chapter Level (Features in Red)
Engage • **Motivate students** • **Provide an anticipatory set**	What Do You See? illustration What Do You Think? introductory discussion	Scenario Your Challenge
Elicit • **Elicit prior knowledge** • **Uncover misconceptions**	What Do You See? What Do You Think?	Criteria Initial discussion of rubric
Explore • **Observe the physical and natural world** • **Provide a common experience** • **Participate in a laboratory investigation**	Investigate	Reflecting on the Activity and the Challenge Preparing for the Chapter Challenge
Explain • **Make sense of laboratory data** • **Provide opportunity for students to articulate concepts** • **Learning guided by the teacher**	Chem Talk Chem Words Student explanations of their observations and data Teacher explanation of how chemists view these topics	Chapter Challenge Chapter Assessment Completion of the Chapter Challenge including required written materials
Elaborate • **Further discussion and generalization of concepts**	What Do You Think Now? Checking Up Chem Essential Questions Chem to Go Chem You Learned	Contributions above the requirements of the Chapter Challenge Chem at Work
Extend • **Transfer of learning to new domains**	Reflecting on the Activity and the Challenge Preparing for the Chapter Challenge Inquiring Further	Chapter Challenge presentation Chapter Assessment of other teams' projects
Evaluate • **Assess what students know and are able to do**	Formative evaluation throughout the activity Lab reports Quizzes Chem to Go homework	Chapter Mini-Challenge Chapter Assessment End-of-Chapter Assessment Exam

From "Expanding the 5E Model," *The Science Teacher*, Vol. 70, No. 6.

Welcome to Active Chemistry: Your Guide to Success

Chemistry is involved in every aspect of your life – from the way your body works to the things you like to do. *Active Chemistry* makes learning chemistry relevant, fun, and exciting. Here's how you're going to learn about chemistry in this book.

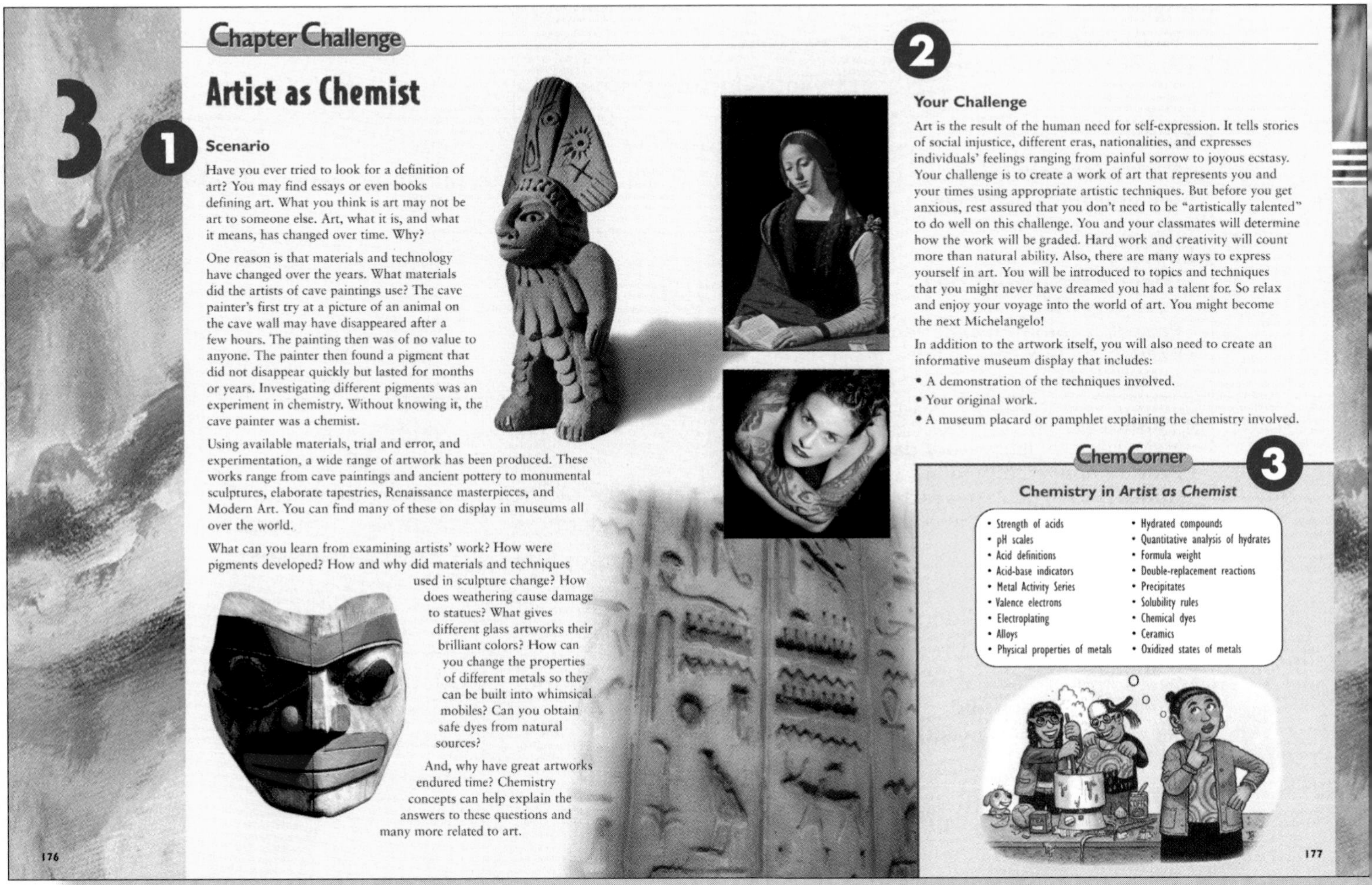

Chapter Challenge

3

Artist as Chemist

1 **Scenario**

Have you ever tried to look for a definition of art? You may find essays or even books defining art. What you think is art may not be art to someone else. Art, what it is, and what it means, has changed over time. Why?

One reason is that materials and technology have changed over the years. What materials did the artists of cave paintings use? The cave painter's first try at a picture of an animal on the cave wall may have disappeared after a few hours. The painting then was of no value to anyone. The painter then found a pigment that did not disappear quickly but lasted for months or years. Investigating different pigments was an experiment in chemistry. Without knowing it, the cave painter was a chemist.

Using available materials, trial and error, and experimentation, a wide range of artwork has been produced. These works range from cave paintings and ancient pottery to monumental sculptures, elaborate tapestries, Renaissance masterpieces, and Modern Art. You can find many of these on display in museums all over the world.

What can you learn from examining artists' work? How were pigments developed? How and why did materials and techniques used in sculpture change? How does weathering cause damage to statues? What gives different glass artworks their brilliant colors? How can you change the properties of different metals so they can be built into whimsical mobiles? Can you obtain safe dyes from natural sources?

And, why have great artworks endured time? Chemistry concepts can help explain the answers to these questions and many more related to art.

2 **Your Challenge**

Art is the result of the human need for self-expression. It tells stories of social injustice, different eras, nationalities, and expresses individuals' feelings ranging from painful sorrow to joyous ecstasy. Your challenge is to create a work of art that represents you and your times using appropriate artistic techniques. But before you get anxious, rest assured that you don't need to be "artistically talented" to do well on this challenge. You and your classmates will determine how the work will be graded. Hard work and creativity will count more than natural ability. Also, there are many ways to express yourself in art. You will be introduced to topics and techniques that you might never have dreamed you had a talent for. So relax and enjoy your voyage into the world of art. You might become the next Michelangelo!

In addition to the artwork itself, you will also need to create an informative museum display that includes:

- A demonstration of the techniques involved.
- Your original work.
- A museum placard or pamphlet explaining the chemistry involved.

ChemCorner 3

Chemistry in *Artist as Chemist*

- Strength of acids
- pH scales
- Acid definitions
- Acid-base indicators
- Metal Activity Series
- Valence electrons
- Electroplating
- Alloys
- Physical properties of metals
- Hydrated compounds
- Quantitative analysis of hydrates
- Formula weight
- Double-replacement reactions
- Precipitates
- Solubility rules
- Chemical dyes
- Ceramics
- Oxidized states of metals

176 177

1 Scenario

Each chapter begins with an event or situation that places chemistry in the context of a familiar everyday experience. Chances are that you can relate to each of these scenarios, but never thought about the chemistry involved! The topics involve things of interest to you and range from games to movies and from art to crime scene investigations.

2 Your Challenge

Each chapter gives you a challenge that will be your team's responsibility for the next month or so. Chemistry knowledge, application, and synthesis will be necessary for the successful completion of this project. However, chemistry content alone is not sufficient for success. Each challenge will require imagination and creativity. Your team's challenge project will be unique and will reflect the interests and talents of the members of your team.

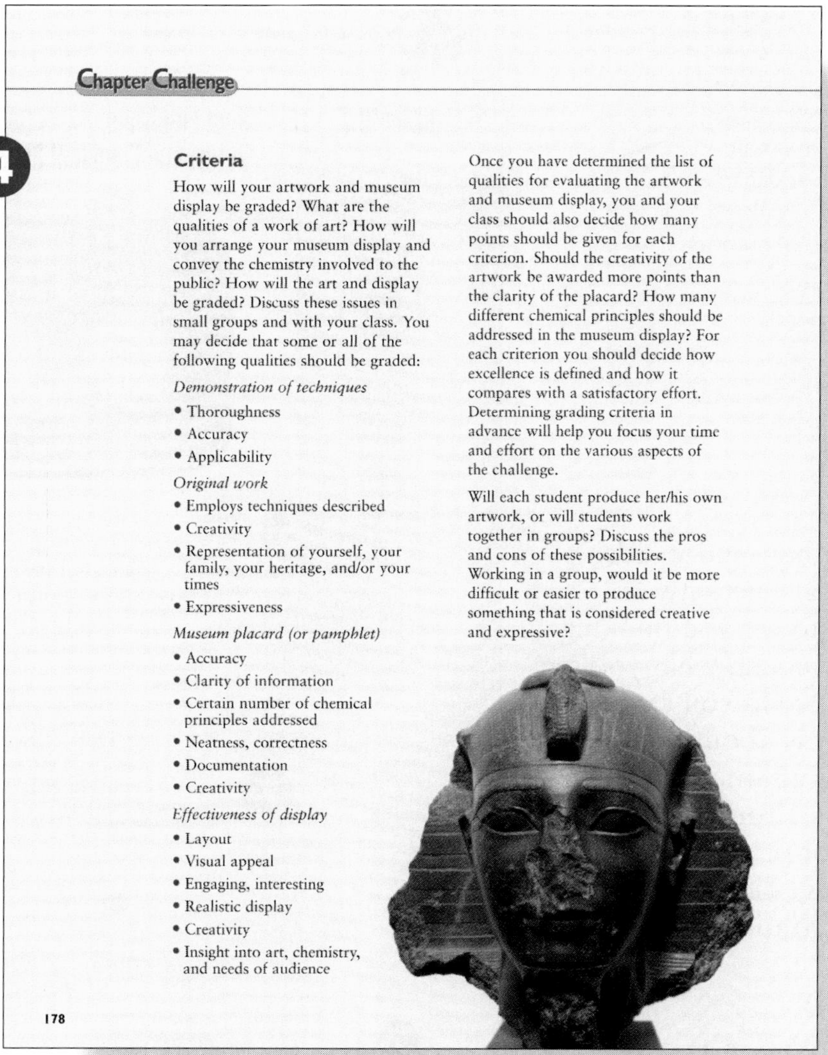

Chapter Challenge

4

Criteria

How will your artwork and museum display be graded? What are the qualities of a work of art? How will you arrange your museum display and convey the chemistry involved to the public? How will the art and display be graded? Discuss these issues in small groups and with your class. You may decide that some or all of the following qualities should be graded:

Demonstration of techniques

- Thoroughness
- Accuracy
- Applicability

Original work

- Employs techniques described
- Creativity
- Representation of yourself, your family, your heritage, and/or your times
- Expressiveness

Museum placard (or pamphlet)

- Accuracy
- Clarity of information
- Certain number of chemical principles addressed
- Neatness, correctness
- Documentation
- Creativity

Effectiveness of display

- Layout
- Visual appeal
- Engaging, interesting
- Realistic display
- Creativity
- Insight into art, chemistry, and needs of audience

Once you have determined the list of qualities for evaluating the artwork and museum display, you and your class should also decide how many points should be given for each criterion. Should the creativity of the artwork be awarded more points than the clarity of the placard? How many different chemical principles should be addressed in the museum display? For each criterion you should decide how excellence is defined and how it compares with a satisfactory effort. Determining grading criteria in advance will help you focus your time and effort on the various aspects of the challenge.

Will each student produce her/his own artwork, or will students work together in groups? Discuss the pros and cons of these possibilities. Working in a group, would it be more difficult or easier to produce something that is considered creative and expressive?

178

3 Chem Corner

As you enjoy learning the content necessary to create a special effect, invent a toy, or investigate a crime scene, you and your teacher will be impressed by how much chemistry content you are learning. The *Chem Corner* previews all the chemistry concepts that the chapter will present. You will be actively involved and your teacher will help you keep track of all the chemistry concepts you are learning.

4 Criteria

Before you begin your *Chapter Challenge*, you will be part of an important decision-making process. You and your class will decide what constitutes an excellent project. Your teacher will help guide you with your decisions. This rubric ensures that everybody knows the requirements of the challenge and how many points each component will be worth. It will help ensure that you are successful.

Your Guide to Success

Chem Poetry — Poems present the chemistry content in another form. These metaphors can help you see the chemistry in new ways. Mala Radhakrishnan, a former high-school chemistry teacher, wrote the poems. Chemistry is Mala's first love, but she is "hooked" on poetry!

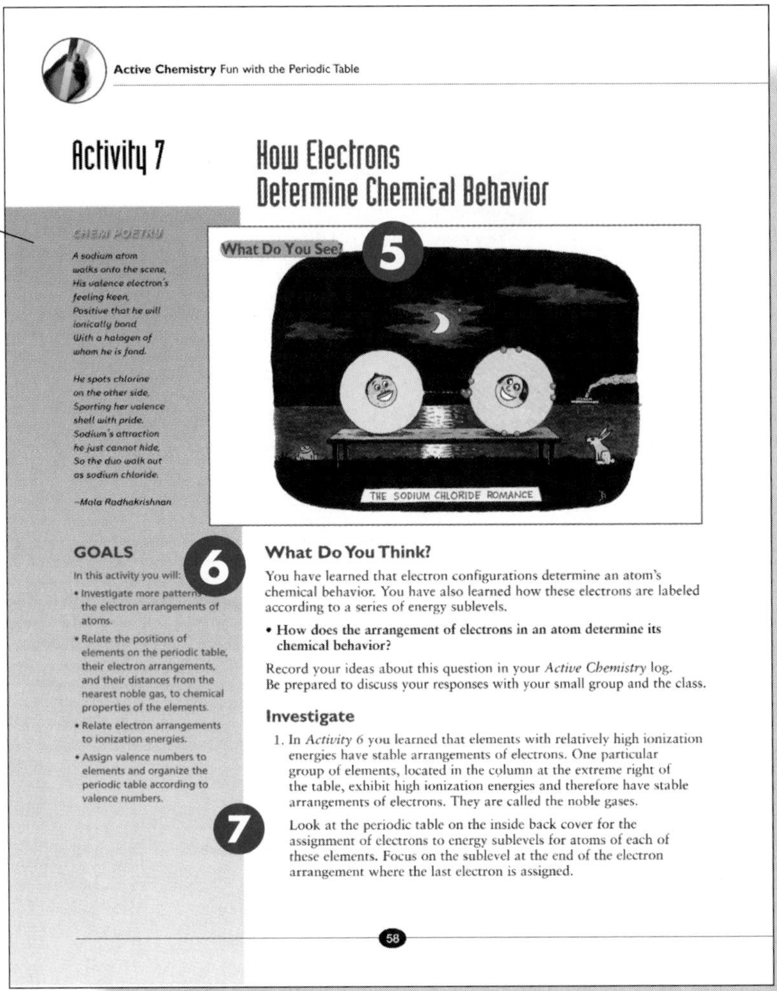
Active Chemistry Fun with the Periodic Table

Activity 7

How Electrons Determine Chemical Behavior

A sodium atom
walks onto the scene,
His valence electron's
feeling keen,
Positive that he will
ionically bond
With a halogen of
whom he is fond.

He spots chlorine
on the other side,
Sporting her valence
shell with pride.
Sodium's attraction
he just cannot hide,
So the duo walk out
as sodium chloride.

–Mala Radhakrishnan

What Do You See? 5

THE SODIUM CHLORIDE ROMANCE

GOALS

In this activity you will:

- Investigate more patterns the electron arrangements of atoms.
- Relate the positions of elements on the periodic table, their electron arrangements, and their distances from the nearest noble gas, to chemical properties of the elements.
- Relate electron arrangements to ionization energies.
- Assign valence numbers to elements and organize the periodic table according to valence numbers.

6

What Do You Think?

You have learned that electron configurations determine an atom's chemical behavior. You have also learned how these electrons are labeled according to a series of energy sublevels.

- **How does the arrangement of electrons in an atom determine its chemical behavior?**

Record your ideas about this question in your *Active Chemistry* log. Be prepared to discuss your responses with your small group and the class.

Investigate

7

1. In *Activity 6* you learned that elements with relatively high ionization energies have stable arrangements of electrons. One particular group of elements, located in the column at the extreme right of the table, exhibit high ionization energies and therefore have stable arrangements of electrons. They are called the noble gases.

   Look at the periodic table on the inside back cover for the assignment of electrons to energy sublevels for atoms of each of these elements. Focus on the sublevel at the end of the electron arrangement where the last electron is assigned.

58

❺ What Do You See?

A picture is worth a thousand words. At the beginning of each activity, an illustration is shown to get you thinking about chemistry. Discussing what you see in the illustration will help you reflect on what you already know about the topics in the activity. This is an important step in the learning process. Tomas Bunk, a well-known illustrator of *MAD* magazine, *Quantoons*, and *Garbage Pail Kids,* created the illustration.

❻ What Do You Think?

The *What Do You Think?* question(s) gives you a chance to explore what you already know or think you know. This is sometimes called "eliciting prior understandings." Your answers will help you become engaged and set the stage for the activity. Don't worry about being "right" or "wrong." Answering the questions as well as you can is another important step in the learning process.

❼ Investigate

Everyone learns better by doing than by watching. You can watch someone knitting a sweater for weeks, but you won't learn to knit if you never handle the knitting needles yourself. You can watch professional athletes play basketball, but you know that you won't ever play ball like they can, unless you practice, practice, and practice. Research says that you should explore a concept in an activity before your teacher tries to explain it in words. In *Active Chemistry*, the *Investigate* section is your opportunity to explore the world of chemistry.

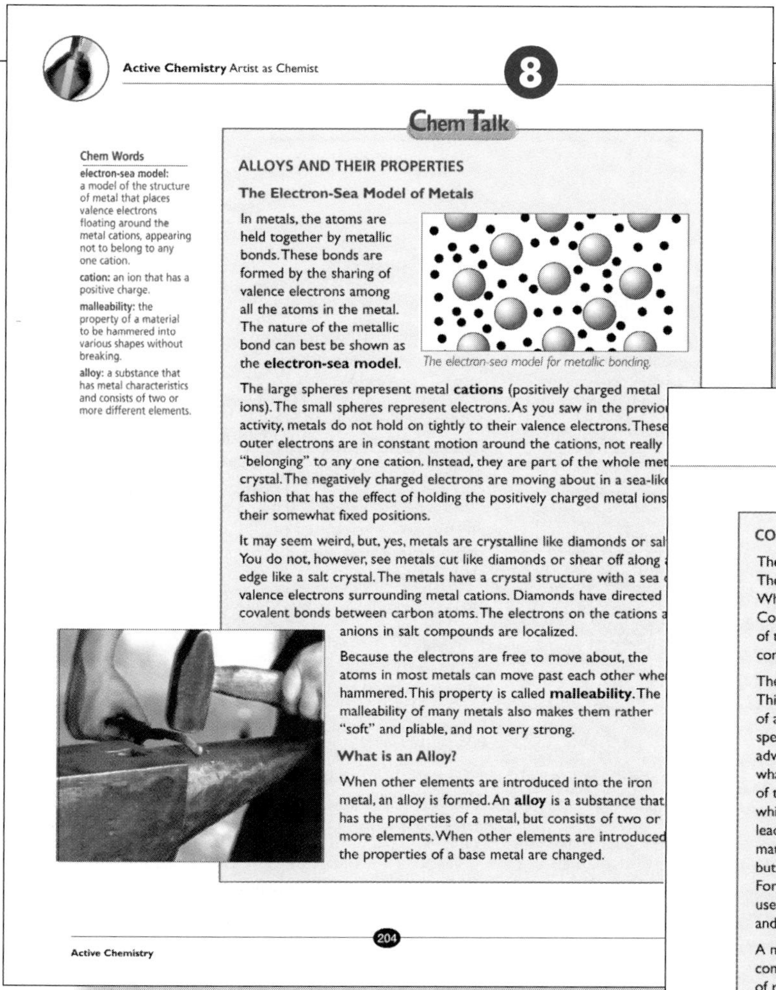

8

Chem Talk

Chem Words

electron-sea model: a model of the structure of metal that places valence electrons floating around the metal cations, appearing not to belong to any one cation.

cation: an ion that has a positive charge.

malleability: the property of a material to be hammered into various shapes without breaking.

alloy: a substance that has metal characteristics and consists of two or more different elements.

ALLOYS AND THEIR PROPERTIES

The Electron-Sea Model of Metals

In metals, the atoms are held together by metallic bonds. These bonds are formed by the sharing of valence electrons among all the atoms in the metal. The nature of the metallic bond can best be shown as the **electron-sea model.**

The electron-sea model for metallic bonding.

The large spheres represent metal **cations** (positively charged metal ions). The small spheres represent electrons. As you saw in the previo[us] activity, metals do not hold on tightly to their valence electrons. These outer electrons are in constant motion around the cations, not really "belonging" to any one cation. Instead, they are part of the whole met[al] crystal. The negatively charged electrons are moving about in a sea-lik[e] fashion that has the effect of holding the positively charged metal ions [in] their somewhat fixed positions.

It may seem weird, but, yes, metals are crystalline like diamonds or sal[t]. You do not, however, see metals cut like diamonds or shear off along [an] edge like a salt crystal. The metals have a crystal structure with a sea [of] valence electrons surrounding metal cations. Diamonds have directed covalent bonds between carbon atoms. The electrons on the cations a[nd] anions in salt compounds are localized.

Because the electrons are free to move about, the atoms in most metals can move past each other whe[n] hammered. This property is called **malleability.** The malleability of many metals also makes them rather "soft" and pliable, and not very strong.

What is an Alloy?

When other elements are introduced into the iron metal, an alloy is formed. An **alloy** is a substance that has the properties of a metal, but consists of two or more elements. When other elements are introduced the properties of a base metal are changed.

Chem Words — Concepts are often more efficiently communicated when vocabulary is introduced. *Chem Words* highlights the important terms you want to know. They are also briefly explained for you to make reading and comprehension easier.

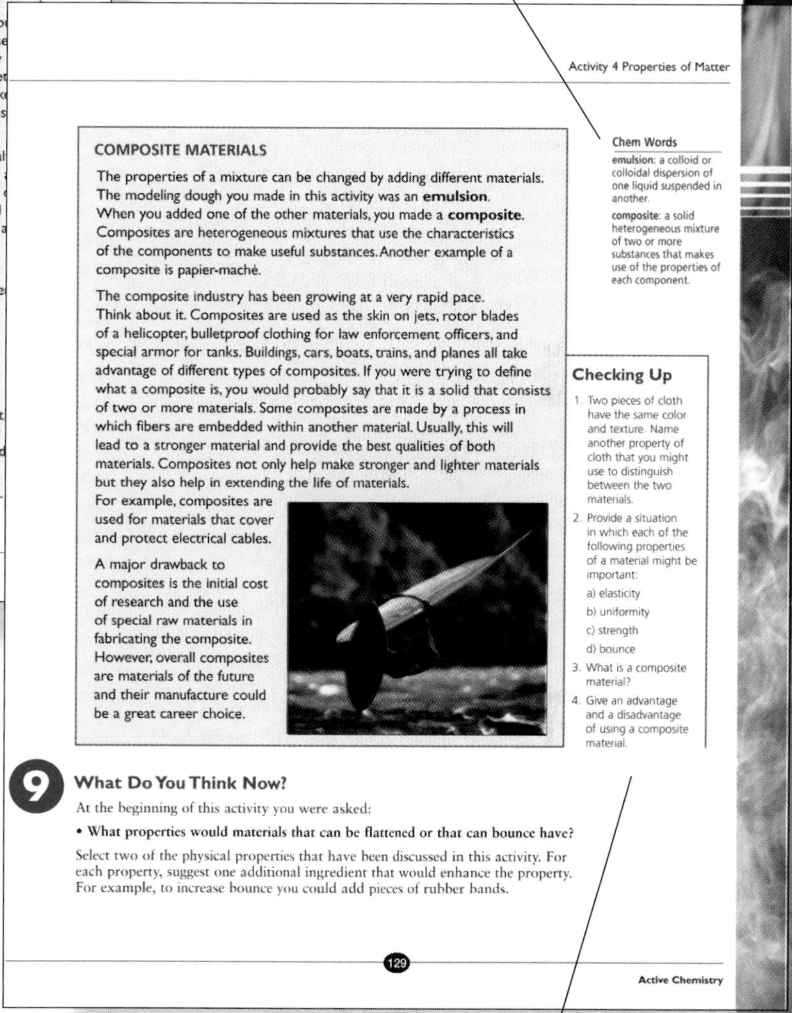

COMPOSITE MATERIALS

The properties of a mixture can be changed by adding different materials. The modeling dough you made in this activity was an **emulsion.** When you added one of the other materials, you made a **composite.** Composites are heterogeneous mixtures that use the characteristics of the components to make useful substances. Another example of a composite is papier-maché.

The composite industry has been growing at a very rapid pace. Think about it. Composites are used as the skin on jets, rotor blades of a helicopter, bulletproof clothing for law enforcement officers, and special armor for tanks. Buildings, cars, boats, trains, and planes all take advantage of different types of composites. If you were trying to define what a composite is, you would probably say that it is a solid that consists of two or more materials. Some composites are made by a process in which fibers are embedded within another material. Usually, this will lead to a stronger material and provide the best qualities of both materials. Composites not only help make stronger and lighter materials but they also help in extending the life of materials. For example, composites are used for materials that cover and protect electrical cables.

A major drawback to composites is the initial cost of research and the use of special raw materials in fabricating the composite. However, overall composites are materials of the future and their manufacture could be a great career choice.

Chem Words

emulsion: a colloid or colloidal dispersion of one liquid suspended in another.

composite: a solid heterogeneous mixture of two or more substances that makes use of the properties of each component.

Checking Up

1. Two pieces of cloth have the same color and texture. Name another property of cloth that you might use to distinguish between the two materials.
2. Provide a situation in which each of the following properties of a material might be important:
   a) elasticity
   b) uniformity
   c) strength
   d) bounce
3. What is a composite material?
4. Give an advantage and a disadvantage of using a composite material.

9 **What Do You Think Now?**

At the beginning of this activity you were asked:

• **What properties would materials that can be flattened or that can bounce have?**

Select two of the physical properties that have been discussed in this activity. For each property, suggest one additional ingredient that would enhance the property. For example, to increase bounce you could add pieces of rubber bands.

8 ChemTalk

The *Chem Talk* will help you make better sense of the investigation you completed. It will introduce you to the scientific way of explaining concepts. It will provide illustrations, charts, and chemical formulas to help guide your understanding. The *Chem Talk* is chock-full of chemistry content.

Checking Up — These questions are great tools for evaluating your understanding of the concepts that you have learned.

9 What Do You Think Now?

At the beginning of each activity, you were asked to think about one or two questions. At that point, you were not expected to come up with the chemistry answer. Now that you have completed the activity, you will be asked to think about these questions again. Compare your initial answers to the answers you give at the end of the activity.

Your Guide to Success

⑩ Chem Essential Questions

As a student chemist, you join the chemistry community by recognizing and understanding the organizing principles of chemistry. As a student chemist, you also need to focus on the essential questions of all scientific endeavors.

- What does it mean?
- How do you know?
- Why do you believe?
- Why should you care?

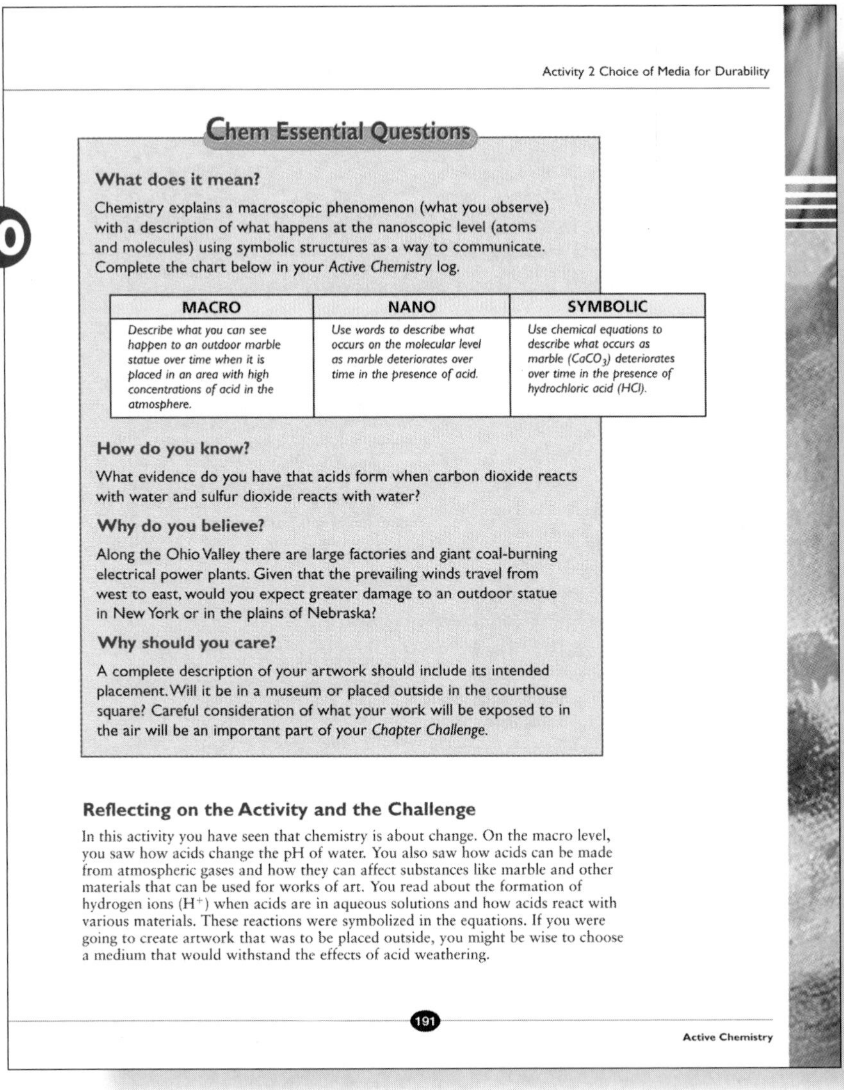
Activity 2 Choice of Media for Durability

Chem Essential Questions

10

What does it mean?

Chemistry explains a macroscopic phenomenon (what you observe) with a description of what happens at the nanoscopic level (atoms and molecules) using symbolic structures as a way to communicate. Complete the chart below in your *Active Chemistry* log.

MACRO	NANO	SYMBOLIC
Describe what you can see happen to an outdoor marble statue over time when it is placed in an area with high concentrations of acid in the atmosphere.	*Use words to describe what occurs on the molecular level as marble deteriorates over time in the presence of acid.*	*Use chemical equations to describe what occurs as marble ($CaCO_3$) deteriorates over time in the presence of hydrochloric acid (HCl).*

How do you know?

What evidence do you have that acids form when carbon dioxide reacts with water and sulfur dioxide reacts with water?

Why do you believe?

Along the Ohio Valley there are large factories and giant coal-burning electrical power plants. Given that the prevailing winds travel from west to east, would you expect greater damage to an outdoor statue in New York or in the plains of Nebraska?

Why should you care?

A complete description of your artwork should include its intended placement. Will it be in a museum or placed outside in the courthouse square? Careful consideration of what your work will be exposed to in the air will be an important part of your *Chapter Challenge.*

Reflecting on the Activity and the Challenge

In this activity you have seen that chemistry is about change. On the macro level, you saw how acids change the pH of water. You also saw how acids can be made from atmospheric gases and how they can affect substances like marble and other materials that can be used for works of art. You read about the formation of hydrogen ions (H^+) when acids are in aqueous solutions and how acids react with various materials. These reactions were symbolized in the equations. If you were going to create artwork that was to be placed outside, you might be wise to choose a medium that would withstand the effects of acid weathering.

191 Active Chemistry

The first essential question is: **What does it mean?** This question requires you to describe the content of the activity using a three-part organizing framework. This framework shows how chemistry explains *macroscopic* phenomena (what you observe) through a description of what happens at the *nanoscopic* level (atoms and molecules) using *symbolic* structures (graphs, models, diagrams, formula).

The second essential question is: **How do you know?** You answered this question by describing the experimental evidence that you have gathered from your investigations. You "know" because you have done an experiment.

The question **Why do you believe?** requires you to link the investigation you did in the lab to the world outside.

People learn better when new knowledge is relevant to their lives. **Why should you care?** asks you to explain how the present activity relates to the *Chapter Challenge* and how you can use the content of the activity in your team's project.

11

12

Active Chemistry Cookin' Chem

Reflecting on the Activity and the Challenge

Knowing how well a material conducts heat is the first step in making a cookware choice. Heat conductivity is most important for pots and skillets used on the stovetop, where uniform heating helps to prevent hot spots that burn food before it's completely cooked. The low specific heat capacity of metals means that it does not take much heat to increase the temperature of the metal. Consider how information such as this might be used in your cooking-show segment. For instance, you could describe why a chef might choose a copper-coated steel pan over an iron skillet for frying eggs. Your cooking show may also point out how some materials from the oven quickly cool to room temperature while others stay hot. A good restaurant must ensure that all foods are the right temperature when the food is served. This may be something that you want to highlight in your cooking show.

Chem to Go

1. If you had pans (of identical mass) made of each of the following metals—Al, Cu, and Fe—which would be the hottest after sitting on a burner for 1 min? Explain your answer.

Material	Specific heat (J/g °C)
copper	0.390
iron	0.470
aluminum	0.900
glass	0.840
stainless steel	0.500
water	4.18

2. a) If you had a 1000.0 g copper pot, how many calories of heat energy would it take to raise its temperature by 60.0°C?
   b) How many calories of heat energy would it take to raise an iron pot with the same mass by 60.0°C?
3. Why do confectioners use marble slabs to prepare candies and fudge?
4. When you pour hot water into a china cup, why should you have a spoon in the cup?
5. If you had water in either of the pots in *Question 2*, would the same amount of heat need to be supplied in order to bring about the same temperature change?
6. The heat capacity of a substance depends on:
   a) temperature only
   b) mass only
   c) temperature and mass
   d) mass and specific heat

566

Active Chemistry

11 Reflecting on the Activity and the Challenge

Research has shown that real learning takes place when people transfer their knowledge to a new domain. The chemistry content of each activity is another puzzle piece that you can put in place to create your *Chapter Challenge* project. *Reflecting on the Activity and the Challenge* provides guidance on how to transfer the knowledge and move forward on your project.

12 Chem to Go

Often given as homework assignments, *Chem to Go* is another opportunity for you to elaborate on the chemistry content of the activity. These are excellent study guide questions that help you to review and check your understanding.

Preparing for the Chapter Challenge – This feature helps you organize and synthesize the knowledge you have mastered from the chapter activities. It also serves as a guide to get another aspect of the *Chapter Challenge* completed.

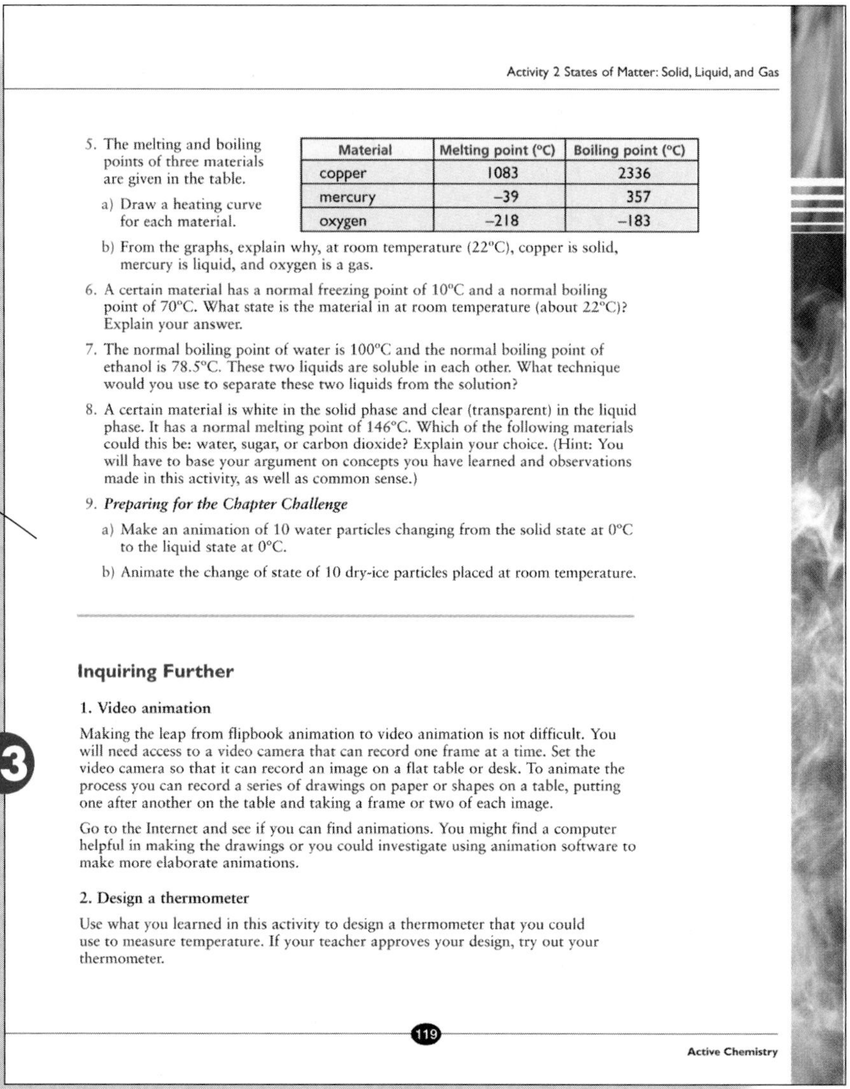
Activity 2 States of Matter: Solid, Liquid, and Gas

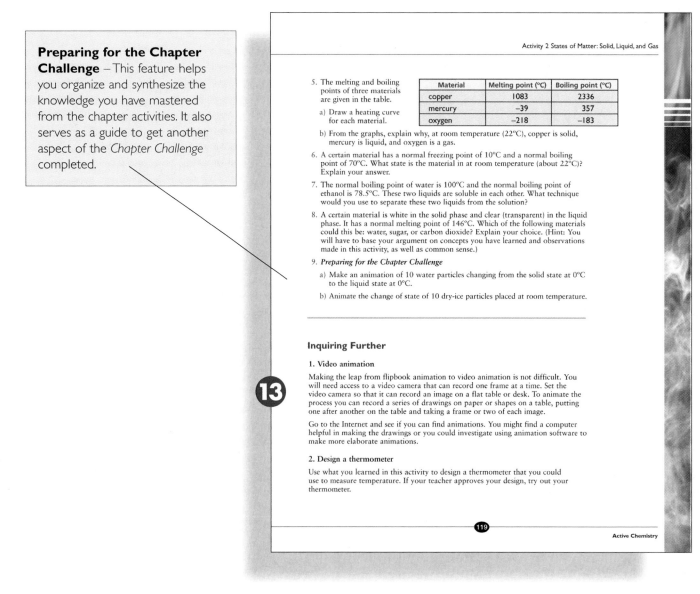

5. The melting and boiling points of three materials are given in the table.

Material	Melting point (°C)	Boiling point (°C)
copper	1083	2336
mercury	−39	357
oxygen	−218	−183

a) Draw a heating curve for each material.

b) From the graphs, explain why, at room temperature (22°C), copper is solid, mercury is liquid, and oxygen is a gas.

6. A certain material has a normal freezing point of 10°C and a normal boiling point of 70°C. What state is the material in at room temperature (about 22°C)? Explain your answer.

7. The normal boiling point of water is 100°C and the normal boiling point of ethanol is 78.5°C. These two liquids are soluble in each other. What technique would you use to separate these two liquids from the solution?

8. A certain material is white in the solid phase and clear (transparent) in the liquid phase. It has a normal melting point of 146°C. Which of the following materials could this be: water, sugar, or carbon dioxide? Explain your choice. (Hint: You will have to base your argument on concepts you have learned and observations made in this activity, as well as common sense.)

9. ***Preparing for the Chapter Challenge***

a) Make an animation of 10 water particles changing from the solid state at 0°C to the liquid state at 0°C.

b) Animate the change of state of 10 dry-ice particles placed at room temperature.

Inquiring Further

13

1. Video animation

Making the leap from flipbook animation to video animation is not difficult. You will need access to a video camera that can record one frame at a time. Set the video camera so that it can record an image on a flat table or desk. To animate the process you can record a series of drawings on paper or shapes on a table, putting one after another on the table and taking a frame or two of each image.

Go to the Internet and see if you can find animations. You might find a computer helpful in making the drawings or you could investigate using animation software to make more elaborate animations.

2. Design a thermometer

Use what you learned in this activity to design a thermometer that you could use to measure temperature. If your teacher approves your design, try out your thermometer.

119

Active Chemistry

13 Inquiring Further

Active Chemistry embraces inquiry as a way of learning. You are always involved in inquiry during the activity. You have another opportunity for open inquiry when you are asked to inquire further. *Inquiring Further* often requires you to design your own experiment and, with teacher approval, to continue to enhance your learning. *Inquiring Further* also provides more challenging in-depth problems, questions, and exercises for extra credit.

14

Chapter mini Challenge

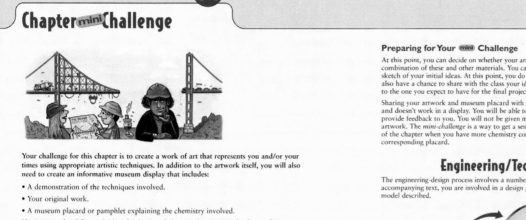

Your challenge for this chapter is to create a work of art that represents you and/or your times using appropriate artistic techniques. In addition to the artwork itself, you will also need to create an informative museum display that includes:

- A demonstration of the techniques involved.
- Your original work.
- A museum placard or pamphlet explaining the chemistry involved.

Having completed five activities, this is a good time to give your work of art a *first try*. It's time to provide a sketch of your artwork and describe it to your class. You should also preview your museum pamphlet or placard. Of course, being limited to the chemistry content of five activities will limit your art. This *first try*, however, will give you a good sense of what the challenge entails and how you and other teams are going to approach this task.

Chemistry Content

Your team should first review the chemistry content that may be included in this artwork and related pamphlet or placard.

Activity 1: You discussed art in general and what makes something a piece of art.

Activity 2: You learned about acids, pH, and how materials are affected by exposure to acids.

Activity 3: You investigated the chemical behavior of metals and learned how to electroplate a piece of metal.

Activity 4: You studied the physical behavior of metals and alloys.

Activity 5: You observed the effect of heat on hydrates and learned how clay could be part of your artwork. You were also introduced to the mole—the chemistry way of counting.

Criteria

Your team should also review the criteria that you discussed on the first day of this chapter. Your artwork and museum placard or pamphlet should be creative, artistic, and interesting as well as have accurate chemistry explanations.

222

Active Chemistry

Preparing for Your mini Challenge

At this point, you can decide on whether your artwork will include metal or clay or a combination of these and other materials. You can describe this artwork to the class or make a sketch of your initial ideas. At this point, you do not have to build the actual artwork. You will also have a chance to share with the class your idea for the museum placard. This can be similar to the one you expect to have for the final project.

Sharing your artwork and museum placard with your class will help you learn about what works and doesn't work in a display. You will be able to provide feedback to other teams and they will provide feedback to you. You will not be given much preparation time for the creation of this artwork. The *mini-challenge* is a way to get a sense of what you will be involved with at the end of the chapter when you have more chemistry content to include in your full artwork and its corresponding placard.

Engineering/Technology Design

The engineering-design process involves a number of distinct steps. In creating an art display and accompanying text, you are involved in a design process. Note how your efforts follow the design model described.

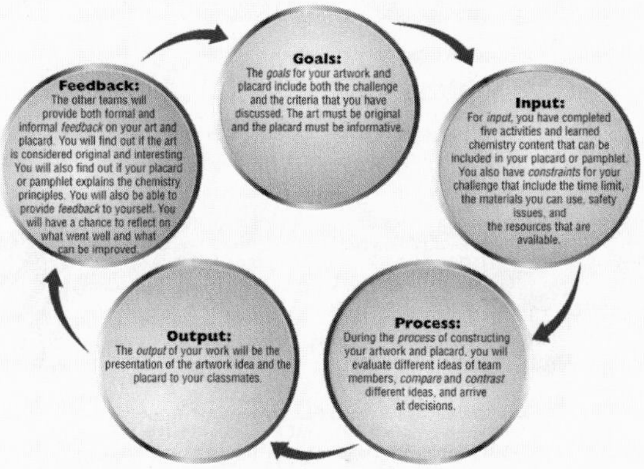

Goals:
The goals for your artwork and placard include both the challenge and the criteria that you have discussed. The art must be original and the placard must be informative.
Input:
For input, you have completed five activities and learned chemistry content that can be included in your placard or pamphlet. You also have constraints for your challenge that include the time limit, the materials you can use, safety issues, and the resources that are available.
Process:
During the process of constructing your artwork and placard, you will evaluate different ideas of team members, compare and contrast different ideas, and arrive at decisions.
Output:
The output of your work will be the presentation of the artwork idea and the placard to your classmates.
Feedback:
The other teams will provide both formal and informal feedback on your art and placard. You will find out if the art is considered original and interesting. You will also find out if your placard or pamphlet explains the chemistry principles. You will also be able to provide feedback to yourself. You will have a chance to reflect on what went well and what can be improved.

Remember: This is a *first try*. The feedback that you get from the art description and the placard will be extremely valuable when you create your original artwork and museum placard or pamphlet. At that point, you will have additional artistic techniques and materials to incorporate into your work. You will begin the entire design cycle again. That's why it is called a cycle. You keep going through it over and over to improve your design or, in this case, your original artwork.

223

Active Chemistry

14 Chapter Mini-Challenge

When engineers design a product, they follow a technology design cycle with several distinct steps. The *mini-challenge* takes you through a first cycle of this process. As part of this process, the *mini-challenge* will encourage you to give your *Chapter Challenge* a first try. In this way, you are actually involved in the engineering-design cycle and not just reading about it. As you create your "product" for your *Chapter Challenge*, you will become increasingly aware of the many benefits of using the Engineering/Technology Design cycle.

Your Guide to Success

Active Chemistry Movie Special Effects

Chem at Work

Mark Pollack

President, Flix FX, Hollywood, CA

"Everyone talks about 'Movie Magic,'" says Marc Pollack, president of the prestigious Hollywood special effects company Flix FX. "So I guess that makes me a magician." But Pollack is clearly more comedian than magician. The 'magic' he creates for movies like *Black Hawk Down*, *Men In Black*, and *Cast Away*, in addition to scores of television commercials, museum installments, and Las Vegas casinos, is the product not of mysterious hocus-pocus but rather fundamental principles of science.

"One of the most important aspects of our work," he continues, "is to push the limits of how chemicals are designed to be used." Among other things, Pollack and his crew at Flix FX use vacuum-forming thermo-plastics to make tin-based silicon molds for everything from prehistoric creatures to futuristic robots. Through a combination of trial and error experimentation and traditional research science, they've perfected the process. "Silicon is what we call an R.T.V.," Pollack explains. "That stands for room temperature vulcanization. So depending on the type and amount of catalyst we use, the mold will cure at different rates and with slightly differing properties." By manipulating the ratio of silicon to catalysts they can make strong, realistic molds in an efficient way. "Increasing the amount of catalyst will speed up the curing process but too much catalyst will shorten the life of the mold," he says. "Every job is different so determining that balance is one of our many challenges."

Pollack is a master in the art of using chemicals like silicon, polypropylene, urethane and urethane elastimers, and is not a chemist by trade. He actually graduated from film school at SUNY Purchase in the hopes of becoming "the next Steven Spielberg." Then, through a twist of fate, he became a special effects nut and eventually founded Flix FX in 1990. "Now," Pollack says, "Spielberg may one day come to me."

Rick Gonzales

Special Effects Designer, Orlando, FL

Rick Gonzales is a special effects designer who works on a lot of live stage shows. He works with polyurethanes, gelatins, silicone, and latex to make real-looking props and prosthetics. "Good special effects," he says, "are the ones where you can't tell what is fake and what is real."

Linda Stevenson

Drama Coordinator, Atlanta, GA

Linda Stevenson teaches her drama students at her north Atlanta performing arts school to be a "triple threat." She wants all 120 students to be able to sing, dance, and act at their best level. Stage effects, like smoke and fog made with dry ice, are added for the benefit of the audience.

170

Active Chemistry

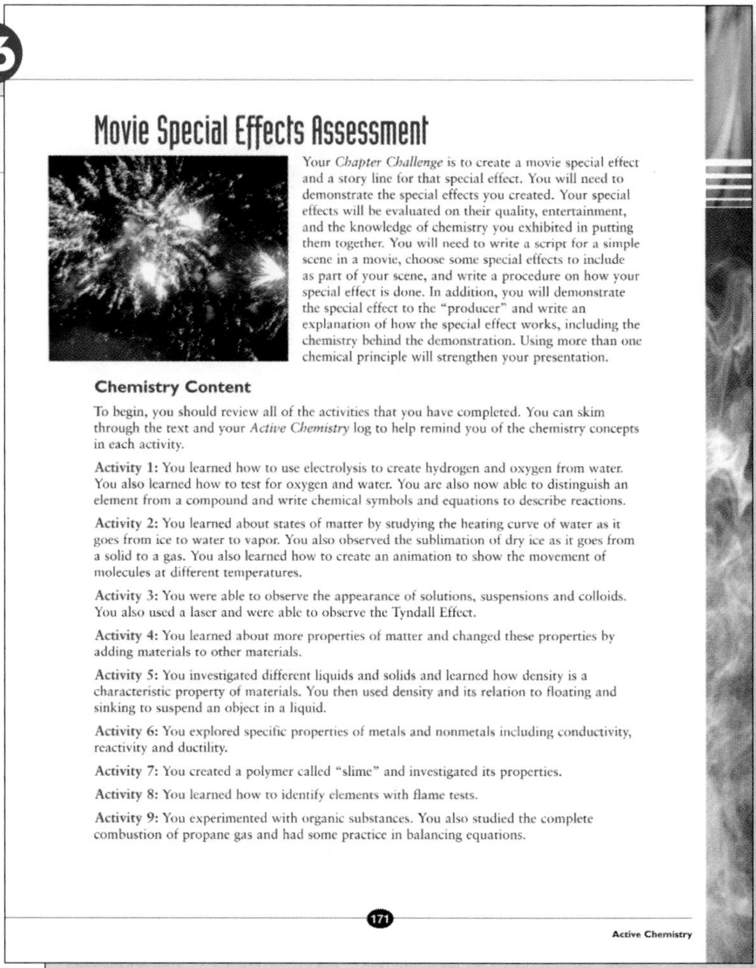

Movie Special Effects Assessment

Your *Chapter Challenge* is to create a movie special effect and a story line for that special effect. You will need to demonstrate the special effects you created. Your special effects will be evaluated on their quality, entertainment, and the knowledge of chemistry you exhibited in putting them together. You will need to write a script for a simple scene in a movie, choose some special effects to include as part of your scene, and write a procedure on how your special effect is done. In addition, you will demonstrate the special effect to the "producer" and write an explanation of how the special effect works, including the chemistry behind the demonstration. Using more than one chemical principle will strengthen your presentation.

Chemistry Content

To begin, you should review all of the activities that you have completed. You can skim through the text and your *Active Chemistry* log to help remind you of the chemistry concepts in each activity.

Activity 1: You learned how to use electrolysis to create hydrogen and oxygen from water. You also learned how to test for oxygen and water. You are also now able to distinguish an element from a compound and write chemical symbols and equations to describe reactions.

Activity 2: You learned about states of matter by studying the heating curve of water as it goes from ice to water to vapor. You also observed the sublimation of dry ice as it goes from a solid to a gas. You also learned how to create an animation to show the movement of molecules at different temperatures.

Activity 3: You were able to observe the appearance of solutions, suspensions and colloids. You also used a laser and were able to observe the Tyndall Effect.

Activity 4: You learned about more properties of matter and changed these properties by adding materials to other materials.

Activity 5: You investigated different liquids and solids and learned how density is a characteristic property of materials. You then used density and its relation to floating and sinking to suspend an object in a liquid.

Activity 6: You explored specific properties of metals and nonmetals including conductivity, reactivity and ductility.

Activity 7: You created a polymer called "slime" and investigated its properties.

Activity 8: You learned how to identify elements with flame tests.

Activity 9: You experimented with organic substances. You also studied the complete combustion of propane gas and had some practice in balancing equations.

171

Active Chemistry

15 Chem at Work

The projects that you complete for the *Chapter Challenges* are often the actual jobs of real people. *Chem at Work* introduces you to people who use the chemistry of the chapter as part of their career. Reading about their lives may get you thinking about careers that interest you and help you make a difference in the world.

16 Chapter Assessment

Business leaders want to hire people who know how to work effectively in groups and how to complete projects. The *Chapter Assessment* provides guidance on how to begin your work on the *Chapter Challenge* project, set deadlines, meet all the requirements, and combine the contributions of all members of the team. This section guides you without restricting you. Your team's creativity and imagination will be a major factor in your enjoyment and success. The best projects will reflect the diverse interests, backgrounds, and cultures of your team members.

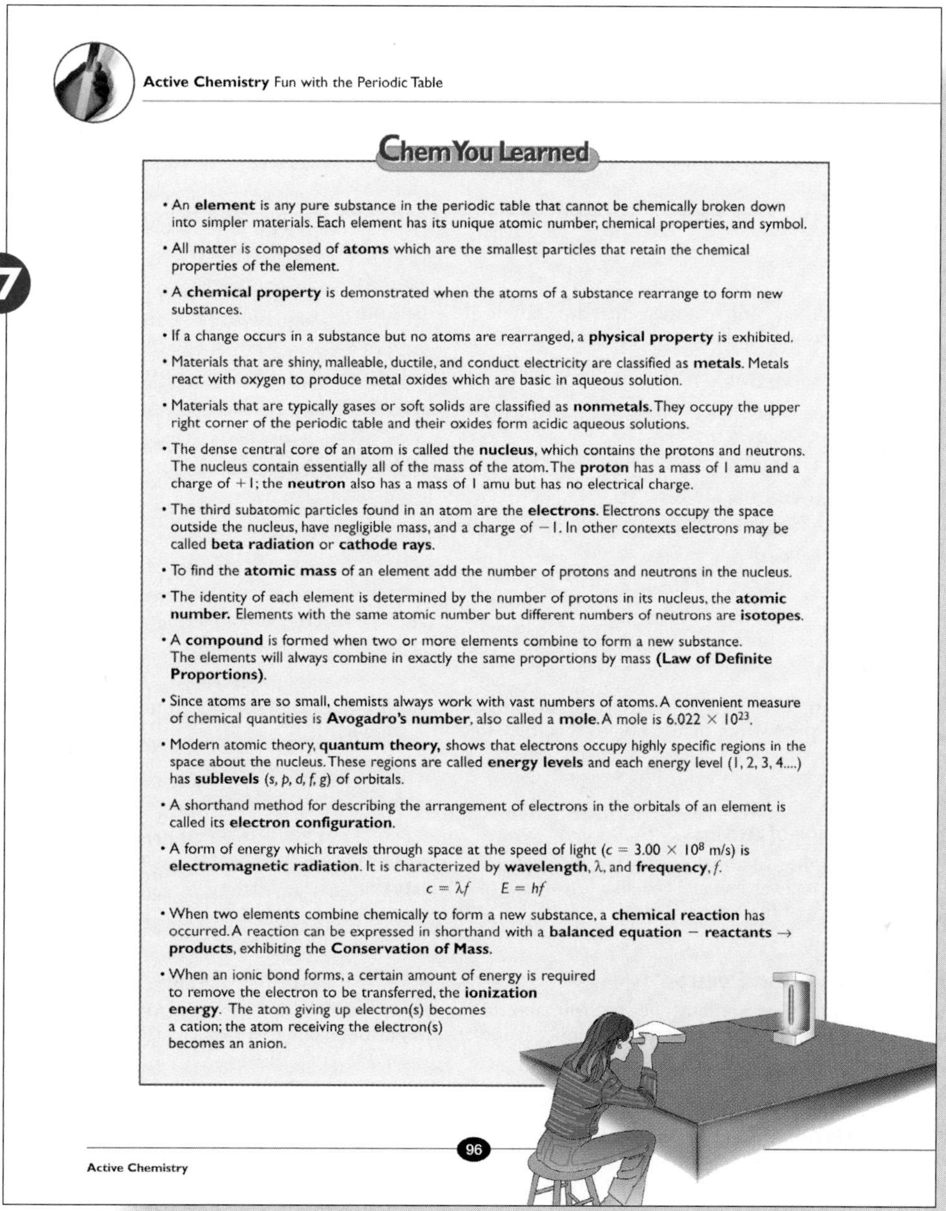
Active Chemistry Fun with the Periodic Table

Chem You Learned

- An **element** is any pure substance in the periodic table that cannot be chemically broken down into simpler materials. Each element has its unique atomic number, chemical properties, and symbol.
- All matter is composed of **atoms** which are the smallest particles that retain the chemical properties of the element.
- A **chemical property** is demonstrated when the atoms of a substance rearrange to form new substances.
- If a change occurs in a substance but no atoms are rearranged, a **physical property** is exhibited.
- Materials that are shiny, malleable, ductile, and conduct electricity are classified as **metals**. Metals react with oxygen to produce metal oxides which are basic in aqueous solution.
- Materials that are typically gases or soft solids are classified as **nonmetals**. They occupy the upper right corner of the periodic table and their oxides form acidic aqueous solutions.
- The dense central core of an atom is called the **nucleus**, which contains the protons and neutrons. The nucleus contain essentially all of the mass of the atom. The **proton** has a mass of 1 amu and a charge of +1; the **neutron** also has a mass of 1 amu but has no electrical charge.
- The third subatomic particles found in an atom are the **electrons**. Electrons occupy the space outside the nucleus, have negligible mass, and a charge of −1. In other contexts electrons may be called **beta radiation** or **cathode rays**.
- To find the **atomic mass** of an element add the number of protons and neutrons in the nucleus.
- The identity of each element is determined by the number of protons in its nucleus, the **atomic number.** Elements with the same atomic number but different numbers of neutrons are **isotopes**.
- A **compound** is formed when two or more elements combine to form a new substance. The elements will always combine in exactly the same proportions by mass **(Law of Definite Proportions)**.
- Since atoms are so small, chemists always work with vast numbers of atoms. A convenient measure of chemical quantities is **Avogadro's number**, also called a **mole**. A mole is 6.022×10^{23}.
- Modern atomic theory, **quantum theory,** shows that electrons occupy highly specific regions in the space about the nucleus. These regions are called **energy levels** and each energy level (1, 2, 3, 4....) has **sublevels** (*s, p, d, f, g*) of orbitals.
- A shorthand method for describing the arrangement of electrons in the orbitals of an element is called its **electron configuration**.
- A form of energy which travels through space at the speed of light ($c = 3.00 \times 10^8$ m/s) is **electromagnetic radiation**. It is characterized by **wavelength**, λ, and **frequency**, f.

  $$c = \lambda f \qquad E = hf$$
- When two elements combine chemically to form a new substance, a **chemical reaction** has occurred. A reaction can be expressed in shorthand with a **balanced equation** − **reactants** → **products**, exhibiting the **Conservation of Mass**.
- When an ionic bond forms, a certain amount of energy is required to remove the electron to be transferred, the **ionization energy**. The atom giving up electron(s) becomes a cation; the atom receiving the electron(s) becomes an anion.

96

Active Chemistry

17 Chem You Learned

To complete your *Chapter Challenge*, you will need to use the chemistry principles you learned as you completed each activity. For each chapter, you should review what you have learned and how you can use these concepts in your challenge. The *Chem You Learned* section lists many of the chemistry principles you investigated in the chapter. You can use this as a checklist to develop your own list.

Chapter 1: Fun with the Periodic Table

Chapter Challenge

As you study the properties of the elements, you become able to place them into categories. You will learn how Mendeleev was able to arrange the elements according to the chemical behavior that was known at his time. Your challenge is to develop a game that can be used to teach others how to learn and use the periodic table. These games are left up to your creativity. Card, computer, or board games are some choices that you may decide to use.

Activity Summaries	Chemistry Principles
Activity 1: Organizing a Store Students organize a store by categorizing the different items that are contained in the store and discover what to do with new items that had not been accounted for.	**Periodicity Trends Mendeleev**
Activity 2: Elements and Their Properties Students determine some of the physical and chemical properties of elements and learn how to use this information to organize elements into families.	**Atoms, Elements Physical properties Chemical properties Conductivity Reactivity, pH**
Activity 3: Atoms and Their Masses Students show why they believe in atoms and how the elements of different atoms interact with each other in a single-replacement reaction.	**Atoms, Atomic mass Single replacement Double-replacement reaction Law of Definite Proportions Compounds, Filtration Quantitative analysis Measurements Mole, Avogadro's number Dalton, Gay-Lussac, Proust**
Activity 4: Are Atoms Indivisible? Students learn through experimentation the properties of electrons and how Rutherford's experiment determined the location of the proton. In addition to this, they find that the nucleus is very dense.	**Cathode rays Properties of electrons Nucleus, Alpha particles Dalton's Atomic Theory Rutherford, Thomson Nagaoka, Millikan Coulomb's Law**
Activity 5: The Electronic Behavior of Atoms Students learn that when energy is supplied to a hydrogen atom, its electron is excited to higher levels and gives off light when it falls to lower levels. They also learn how to calculate the frequency of light waves and the energy of these waves.	**Hydrogen line spectrum Frequency, Wavelength Photons, Einstein Bohr's Atomic Model Electromagnetic spectrum Spectroscopic analysis Planck, Quantum**
Activity 6: Atoms with More than One Electron Students discover that each element produces a unique line spectrum and that the ionization potential of the elements helps them to understand why the elements occupy certain positions on the periodic table.	**Element line spectrum Ionization energy, Ion Electron configuration Period, Group, *s*, *p*, *d*, *f* orbitals Excited state, Ground state Heisenberg, Wave-particle duality Atomic number**
Activity 7: How Electrons Determine Chemical Behavior Students learn how to write the electron configuration for all of the elements. They also discover how the electron configuration can be used to show why families of elements behave the same with other elements.	**Electron configuration Inert gases, Noble gases Valence electrons Chemical families Transition elements Rayleigh, Cavendish, Ramsay**
Activity 8: How Atoms Interact with Each Other Students learn why atoms combine in certain proportions by transferring or sharing electrons from one atom to another. Students also learn the difference between an ionic and covalent bond.	**Octet rule, Bonding Ionic bonds, Covalent bonds Chemical formulas Binary compounds Electron dot structure Bonding electrons Nonbonding electrons**
Activity 9: What Determines and Limits an Atom's Mass? Students learn how to determine the atomic mass of an element and how the average atomic mass is determined from the common isotopes of an element. The activity also leads them through the factors that determine nuclear stability and how fission and fusion differ.	**Atomic mass Isotopes, Neutrons Nucleons, Beta particle Radioactivity, Half-life Binding energy Electrostatic forces Strong nuclear force Nuclear fission, Nuclear decay Nuclear fusion, Gamma ray**

Chapter 2: Movie Special Effects

Chapter Challenge

A movie producer has asked your class to create a movie scene using special effects that involve chemical concepts. You are asked to develop a script for the movie scene and to provide an explanation of the chemistry concepts you used to produce your special effect.

Activity Summaries	Chemistry Principles
Activity 1: Elements and Compounds The activity discusses the basic concept of what is matter and how we can change compounds back to the elements. Also, students will conduct some simple tests to identify hydrogen and oxygen gas.	Electrolysis Chemical reaction Elements Compounds Chemical properties Dissociation
Activity 2: States of Matter: Solid, Liquid, and Gas This activity helps the students develop an understanding of molecular motion in the different physical states: solid, liquid, and gas.	Heating curves, Melting point Boiling point, Vaporization Potential energy, Kinetic energy Physical states of matter Sublimation
Activity 3: Solutions, Suspensions, and Colloids This activity shows the students how to differentiate between solutions, suspensions, and colloids. The mixtures are tested for the Tyndall Effect and if they can be separated by simple filtration.	Tyndall Effect, Suspensions Emulsions, Filtration Homogeneous mixture Heterogeneous mixture Solutions, Solvent, Solute
Activity 4: Properties of Matter This activity helps the students understand how small models can be used to represent large structures. Models can be used to develop an understanding of the physical properties of a substance.	Composites Emulsions, Texture Elasticity, Malleability
Activity 5: Mass and Volume The students will determine the density of liquids and solids. The solids will be irregularly shaped, so that water displacement techniques need to be used to determine the densities.	Density, Estimation Displacement Measurements Uncertainty
Activity 6: Metals and Nonmetals This activity will study the physical properties of metals and will show how they can be differentiated from the nonmetals. They will also learn how the metals, metalloids, and nonmetals are arranged on the periodic table.	Metallic properties Nonmetals, Metalloids Oxidation Alloys
Activity 7: Polymers This activity shows the students how to make the polymer "slime" and how to test this non-Newtonian liquid. They will find that it has both solid and liquid characteristics.	Polymers, Proteins Starch, Cellulose Cross-linked polymers Commercial uses
Activity 8: Identifying Matter This activity uses flame tests to help identify metal cations. The principles of electron excitation are discussed and applied to fireworks and neon signs. Different metals can by used to produce the different colors.	Metal flame colors Electron excitation Ions, Flame tests
Activity 9: Organic Substances The students will learn what the term organic means to scientists and how the layman uses it incorrectly. They will study how to write organic structures and apply the Law of Conservation of Mass to combustion reactions.	Hydrocarbons Organic/Inorganic compounds Carbon bonding Alkanes, Alkenes Alkynes Combustion Law of Conservation of Mass

Chapter 3: Artist as Chemist

Chapter Challenge

Art is an activity found in every culture throughout history. Art can be expressed in a wide variety of media. You are asked to create a work of art that expresses yourself and to create a museum display around your artwork. The chemistry concepts you use to produce your artwork will be described in a museum placard.

Activity Summaries	Chemistry Principles
Activity 1: What Makes Something Art? The students view several examples of artwork and discuss the features which enable a work to be defined as "art."	Cultural role of chemistry Societal role of chemistry
Activity 2: Choice of Media for Durability This activity helps the students to understand the environmental impact of chemicals on sculptures. While doing this, they develop a working knowledge of acid/base chemistry by observing the effects of carbon dioxide and sulfur dioxide, followed by designing their own experiment.	Acid/base chemistry pH scale, Indicators Chemical reactions Displacement reactions Synthesis reactions Arrhenius, G.N.Lewis Brønsted-Lowry
Activity 3: Chemical Behavior of Metals This activity shows the students how to determine the relative reactivity of different metals and which are more durable against corrosion. Valence electrons are discussed and the concept of electroplating is demonstrated.	Reactivity of metals Valence electrons Ions, Octet rule Electroplating Electron configuration
Activity 4: Physical Behavior of Metals Beginning with making brass from a penny, this activity helps the students understand the common physical properties of metals. The electron-sea model is introduced to describe metallic bonding and the concepts of hardening, tempering, and annealing are explored.	Alloys, Brass, Bronze Electron sea model Cations, Annealing Tempering, Malleability Properties of metals
Activity 5: Clay Students will examine and dehydrate a hydrated compound as a model to better understand the chemistry of clay. From their dehydration data, students will determine the percent of water in the compound. The mole concept will be applied to determine the formula of the hydrate.	Nomenclature Mole, Molar mass Hydrate, Anhydrate Dessicants Ceramics
Activity 6: Paints The students will test various combinations of soluble compounds to determine which will produce precipitates in double-replacement reactions. This data will be tabulated and used to determine the best compounds to use as pigments for their paints.	Soluble, Insoluble Precipitate Suspension Anions Cations Double replacement Solubility rules
Activity 7: Dyes Students will determine a procedure for extracting dyes from natural materials and use them to dye pieces of wool. Then they will be introduced to the concept that the bonding of dyes to fibers is often pH-dependent. Students will observe the effect of changing pH on the colors of two natural dyes.	Organic compounds Mordant Chromophore Dye pH paper
Activity 8: How Does Stained Glass Get Its Color? In this activity, students will use borax as a glass substitute to observe how different compounds produce different colors in the "glass" as they are heated in a flame.	Borax, Minerals Metal oxides Ceramics, Glazes

Chapter 4: Chemical Dominoes

Chapter Challenge

You are challenged to create a prototype of a "chemical-dominoes sequence" that can be sold by a toy company to 10-15 year-old children. You are asked to demonstrate the product to company executives, as well as to explain the chemistry concepts behind each step. A detailed written explanation of the chemistry is also required.

Activity Summaries	Chemistry Principles
Activity 1: Alternative Pathways Students compare different ways of producing carbon dioxide gas to blow up a balloon that tips a lever. They brainstorm criteria for selecting which method might be best for using in the *Chemical Dominoes* apparatus. After an introduction to two chemical concepts (endothermic/exothermic changes, entropy increase/decrease) and drawings of arrangements of particles in different states (before/after), each student in the group becomes an expert in one of the carbon dioxide production methods.	**Reactants, Products** **Endothermic, Exothermic** **Energy, Entropy** **Engineering Design Process** **Covalent bond, Ionic bond** **Excited state**
Activity 2: Balancing Chemical Equations Students first learn to recognize whether a chemical equation is balanced. Then, they learn to balance simple chemical equations by an accounting method. Along the way, they practice identifying how many of a particular element there are in a formula, which involves reading parentheses and subscripts properly. They also balance the equation for Method 2 from the previous activity, prove that it's balanced, and then design an experiment and demonstrate that mass is conserved when the reaction is run.	**Conservation of matter** **Balancing chemical equations**
Activity 3: How Much Gas is Produced? In this activity, students use pennies and a balance to explore the concept of a mole. They also learn dimensional analysis with "chemical dominoes." The point of the activity, for students, is to be able to predict ahead of time how much baking soda will be necessary to use to make this happen. Then, after an empirical solution to the problem, they learn stoichiometry and test their "hypothesis." Finally, they participate in a discussion of error analysis to query why the prediction and reality are so different.	**Stoichiometry** **Dimensional analysis** **Mole, Molar mass** **Prediction** **Error analysis** **STP**
Activity 4: What Can Destroy a Metal? Students build a circuit to light the red LED using magnesium strip as wire. They then experimentally learn to turn off the circuit by destroying the magnesium strip using three "mystery" chemicals. By observing the effects of known chemicals on metals, they deduce the identity of the "mystery" chemicals. They practice writing and balancing oxidation-reduction reactions. In a short activity, students address the confusion between dissolving, melting, and reacting and learn to define the terms properly.	**Metal Activity Series** **Reactivity of metals** **Oxidation-reduction** **Balancing equations** **Half-reactions**
Activity 5: Producing and Harnessing Light Students view the spectrum of visible light by looking at an incandescent light through a diffraction grating. After seeing that "white" light is made of many colors, they view the red LED through the diffraction grating. They then determine the minimum operating voltages for a series of colors of LEDs, leading them to conclude that as the wavelength of light decreases, the voltage (energy) required to light the LED increases. Next, students determine which colors of light can cause a glow-in-the-dark toy to phosphoresce. They conclude that for the phosphorescence to occur, a minimum amount of light energy must be added.	**Matter-energy interactions** **Emission spectroscopy** **Absorption spectroscopy** **Energy vs. wavelength** **Electromagnetic spectrum** **Visible light, Fluorescence** **Conservation of energy** **Phosphorescence** **Excited state** **Ground state**
Activity 6: Electrochemical Cells Students use their red LED to build a conductivity tester. After testing several solutions, they determine which solutions conduct electricity, and therefore contain electrolytes. Students then construct a zinc-copper battery and use the LED to determine in which direction electricity flows. Afterward, students are introduced to two ways to create more voltage (so they can light LEDs that require greater voltage): connecting batteries in series, and changing the relative concentrations of the zinc and copper ion solutions.	**Electrochemical cells** **Half-reactions** **Spontaneity** **Electrolytes**
Activity 7: Reactions that Produce Heat Students interpret observations from a flameless heating unit, also known in the military as an MRE (Meal, Ready-to-Eat) heater. They operate the heating unit and make sense of their observations. They learn about factors that speed up reactions, including particle size and catalysts. Finally, they determine whether changes are endothermic or exothermic, and how much heat energy the reactions require or give off.	**Enthalpy changes** **Endothermic** **Exothermic** **Effects of catalysts,** **Bond energy** **Reaction diagrams** **Activation Energy** **Activated complex** **Spontaneous reaction**
Activity 8: Rubber Bands and Spontaneity Students experiment with a rubber band, stretched and unstretched, to learn about enthalpy and entropy. They then build models to explain the behavior of the rubber bands. They formalize ideas of enthalpy and entropy change, and relate these ideas back to other activities in this chapter.	**Reaction driving forces** **System vs.Surroundings** **Spontaneity** **Exothermic, Endothermic** **Degree of disorder** **Gibbs free energy** **Law of Conservation of Energy** **Polymers, Monomers**

Chapter 5: Ideal Toy

Chapter Challenge

You are challenged to create a toy that uses various chemical and/or gas principles. Your toy should appeal to an age group of your choice. Your final presentation to the board of a major toy company will include a written proposal, either a detailed drawing or a mock prototype of the toy, a statement of any potential hazards or waste-disposal issues, and a cost analysis of the item for manufacturing. An oral and written explanation of the chemistry principles used is a key part of the proposal.

Activity Summaries	Chemistry Principles
Activity 1: Batteries In this three-part activity students will first explore what they already know about batteries and examine several types of batteries. Starting on the macro level, they will make observations about commercial batteries. Then they will use the Metal Activity Series to guide them as they build their own electrochemical cells. They will learn the nanoscopic concepts of redox reactions and electrochemical cell chemistry. They then return to the macroscopic level as they attempt to power a toy with the cells they have created.	**Chemical properties of matter Metal Activity Series Electrochemistry Redox reactions Matter/energy interactions Qualitative observations Quantitative observations Spectator ions, Cathode Anode, Voltage, Current**
Activity 2: Solid, Liquid, or Gas? In this two-part activity, students will use the free ChemSketch and 3D Viewer programs from ACD Labs to create representations of different molecules. The focus is on the fact that the size and shape of a molecule have an important effect on the properties of the molecule. Properties examined are boiling points and melting points of organic compounds.	**Kinetics Particle nature of matter Molecular size, shape, polarity Polar, Non-polar Electronegativity Intermolecular forces London dispersion forces**
Activity 3: Cartesian Divers This activity involves two parts. In Part A, students rotate through two stations and explore the effect of pressure on gas volume. In one station, students will simply explore pressure changes on volume using a syringe. At another station, students will explore pressure changes on buoyancy of a Cartesian diver, without using their hands. In Part B, students will use the Pressure Sensor probe and their graphing calculators to derive Boyle's Law ($P_1V_1 = P_2V_2$).	**Natural laws Units of pressure Boyle's Law Gas constant mm Hg**
Activity 4: Hot-Air Balloons Students will use an indirect measure of gas volumes at decreasing temperatures to determine the relationship between gas volume and temperature. From this data, they will graphically determine absolute zero and gain an understanding of the Kelvin scale versus the Celsius scale. Then, students will apply their understanding of temperature and gas volumes by constructing and testing hot-air balloons.	**Kelvin sscale Charles's law Kinetic theoryof matter Absolute zero**
Activity 5: How Are Gases Produced? In this two-part activity students will generate and test for hydrogen, oxygen, and carbon dioxide gases. They will then determine an effective ratio of hydrogen/oxygen gases to use in the propulsion of a small rocket.	**Molar relationships Reaction types, Catalysts Decomposition reactions Single-replacement reaction Double-replacement reaction Balanced equations**
Activity 6: Ideal Gas Law for the Ideal Toy This activity gives students an opportunity to use knowledge gained from the preceding activities in order to determine the volume of one mole of hydrogen gas. With this information in hand they will then calculate the gas law constant "*R*."	**STP, Gas law constant Combined gas law Ideal gas law**
Activity 7: Moving Molecules First, students will use pictorial and physical models to determine the effect of mass on gas effusion rates. Then, students will apply stoichiometric relationships to determine the amount of HCl and Zn needed to completely inflate a baggie with hydrogen gas. Finally, students will explain the observations made using the balloon/baggie model and the molecular weights of the gases generated.	**Kinetic Molecular Theory Graham's Law Limiting reagents Balanced equations Diffusion, Effusion**
Activity 8: Plastics This activity has three parts. In Parts A and B, students will make and explore a thermoplastic and a thermoset polymer. They will note the differences between the two types of plastics and construct an item, which could be a part of their prototype, from each type. In Part C, students will test different types of plastics to determine the best choice for its function. Students will identify two important criteria of the plastic needed for their toy, and then they will design tests to determine which plastic best fits their criteria.	**Types of polymers Thermoset Thermoplastic Organic compounds Polymers, Monomers**

Chapter 6: Cool Chemistry Show

Chapter Challenge

One of the best ways to demonstrate that you understand the chemical concepts that you have studied is to teach those concepts to others. Your challenge in the *Cool Chemistry Show* chapter is to demonstrate chemistry concepts to grade school children. You not only demonstrate the concepts, but also have to be able to explain them and to answer questions on the concept you are presenting.

Activity Summaries	Chemistry Principles
Activity 1: Chemical and Physical Changes Students learn what conditions are necessary in order to determine whether the process is a physical or chemical change.	**Chemical change Physical change Chemical reaction Chemical tests Reactant, Product Solution, Solvent, Solute Molarity, Concentration Saturated solution, Unsaturated Precipitate, Polymer**
Activity 2: More Chemical Changes Students learn what characteristics are used to identify a chemical reaction taking place, how indicators are used to identify acids and bases, and tests used to identify gases.	**Chemical tests Acid-Base indicators Precipitates**
Activity 3: Chemical Names and Formulas Students learn how to use the symbols from the periodic table and how to write the correct formulas of compounds. In addition to writing formulas, they will also learn how to name compounds.	**Chemical symbols Chemical formulas Chemical compounds Chemical names Anions, Cations, Polyatomic ions Covalent bond Oxidation number**
Activity 4: Chemical Equations Students practice writing chemical changes by using word equations and chemical equations. In addition to learning how to express an equation, they will also study single-replacement and double-replacement reactions.	**Chemical equations Balancing equations Single replacement Double replacement Synthesis Decomposition Metal Activity Series Solubility rules**
Activity 5: Chemical Energy Students learn how to use chemical thermodynamics to produce products that use endothermic and exothermic reactions.	**Heat energy Endothermic reactions Exothermic reactions Conservation of energy Activation energy Heat vs. Temperature**
Activity 6: Reaction Rates Students study those factors that can alter the rate of a chemical reaction. The factors studied are temperature, concentration, the nature of the reactants, and catalysts.	**Reaction rates Concentration Kinetic energy Collision theory Catalysts, Surface area**
Activity 7: Acids, Bases, and Indicators—Colorful Chemistry Students study the special properties of acids and bases. Special properties that the students will need to understand: how they react with metals, how they feel, how they taste (however, remember that you do not taste chemicals in the laboratory), and how they can be tested for using indicators.	**Acids/Bases Arrhenius acids and bases Indicators, Buffers pH Scale Titration Neutralization**
Activity 8: Color Reactions that Involve the Transfer of Electrons Students investigate metal activity. They study oxidation and reduction and how we might be able to control them to our benefit.	**Oxidation, Reduction Ions, Spectator Ions Polyatomic ions Single replacement Galvanization Metal plating, Rust**

Chapter 7: Cookin' Chem

Chapter Challenge

This chapter challenges you to create a segment of a television cooking show that explains in detail the chemistry behind the cooking involved. This can be videotaped, live, or a voice-over of a popular television program. In your final presentation, you must discuss the chemical principles in each part of the food preparation that you select.

Activity Summaries	Chemistry Principles
Activity 1: What is Heat? By studying the heat from a light bulb, students learn the three ways in which heat can be transferred. A distinction is made between heat and temperature. Heat transfer is also discussed by examining a partially cooked potato. Students find examples in their homes that demonstrate convection, conduction, and radiation.	Heat vs. temperature Convection, Conduction Radiation, Heat energy Kelvin scale, Absolute zero Calories
Activity 2: Safety and Types of Fires By observing an unlit and lit candle, students learn the necessary features that support combustion. This knowledge is used to discuss the control of combustion reactions.	Combustion reactions Balancing equations Hydrocarbons, Catalysts Law of Conservation of Mass
Activity 3: Cooking Fuels Using an insulated container containing water, students measure the heat content of several fuels. This leads to a discussion of how energy is stored in fuels and how it is released.	Thermochemistry Exothermic, Endothermic Activation energy Bond energy, Joules Mole concept Hydroxyl group, Alcohols Specific heat capacity
Activity 4: Boiling Water By taking data and graphing a heating curve, students learn about the heat of vaporization, and phase changes. The students also learn the effect of pressure on the boiling point.	Heating curves Phase changes Heat of vaporization Boiling point Energy of phase changes
Activity 5: Freezing Water By taking data and graphing a cooling curve, students learn about the heat of fusion, and phase changes. The students also practice their skills of graphing.	Cooling curves Phase changes Heat of fusion Melting point Energy of phase changes
Activity 6: How Do You Choose Cookware? The students examine the properties of several substances (Cu, Fe, Al, plastics, glass, ceramics) and learn about specific heat and the principles of heat transfer.	Specific heat Calorimetry Conduction Alloys
Activity 7: How Do Proteins in Foods React? Students denature raw egg protein in two ways—with heat by boiling in water and by pH change with acid. The structure of proteins is studied: primary, secondary, and tertiary.	Organic molecules Denaturation Functional groups Proteins, Amino acids Primary, secondary, tertiary structure
Activity 8: How Does the Home Canning Process Work? Students observe the effects of pressure on a heated can which is suddenly cooled. The principles are investigated more quantitatively in a simulated canning experiment using a rubber balloon as the "canned food."	Boyle's Law Kinetic theory Atmospheric pressure Inverse proportion

Chapter 8: CSI Chemistry

Chapter Challenge

You are challenged to create a crime scene and to prepare evidence that requires the use of at least three forensic chemistry techniques learned in this chapter in order to solve the crime. Before developing the story for the crime-show episode, you will need to analyze the evidence created in the laboratory and to determine which pieces the detectives in the show will use to solve the crime. Your crime story should include a police report, description of the crime, a diagram of the crime scene, a list of all the evidence found at the scene, and a thorough discussion of the chemical concepts used.

Activity Summaries	Chemistry Principles
Activity 1: Clue Me In In this activity, students use their deductive reasoning skills to identify elements based on clues about their properties, names, position on the periodic table, and history. Next, students work collaboratively to gather evidence and solve a crime using deductive reasoning.	Elements Periodic table Categorization Chemical families Group, period, series Deductive reasoning Halogens, Metals Nonmetals, Metalloids Alkali, Alkaline earth Transition metals
Activity 2: Distinguishing Glass Fragments In this activity, students determine the density of a glass sample using the slope method. They compare the density of their sample to the density of another group's sample to determine if they have the same type of glass.	Density, Measurements Graphing Chemical properties Physical properties Extensive properties Intensive properties
Activity 3: Presumptive Blood Testing: The Luminol Reaction In this activity, students learn the principles of chemiluminescence while testing bovine hemoglobin with luminol reagent. These principles include ground state, excited state, energy levels and catalysis. They also study the formation of ions through the gain or loss of electrons.	Atomic structure Spectroscopy Chemiluminescence Ions, Reactants Products, Catalyst Ground state, Excited state Energy levels
Activity 4: Identification of White Powders In this activity students learn how to use and read a flowchart. They will also create a flowchart that will identify six white powders. The creation of the flowchart will be based on the chemical and physical properties of the six white powders with which they experiment.	Anions, Cations Polyatomic ions Ionic bonds Solubility rules Double replacement Word equations Flowcharts Qualitative analysis
Activity 5: Developing Latent Prints Students learn how to use a double-replacement reaction and an oxidation-reduction reaction to develop invisible fingerprints on paper.	Solvents, Solutes Oxidation Reduction Fingerprint analysis Crystalline structure
Activity 6: Metal Activity Series Students add metals to different ionic solutions to create a smaller version of the activity series.	Oxidizing agent Reducing agent Single replacement Double replacement Oxidation number Valence electrons Transition metals
Activity 7: Serial-Number Etching In this activity, students stamp a serial number into a piece of metal and then apply what they have learned about single-replacement reactions to restore that serial number after it has been obliterated. Next, they build and manipulate a clay model in order to understand what happens to metal atoms when they are stamped and how the changes caused by stamping allow restoration of serial numbers.	Redox reactions Properties of metals Nanostructure of metals Etching, Grain of metal
Activity 8: Chromatographic Capers In Part A, students perform a separation of black marker dye. In Part B, they create a model of the separation process to learn how it separates the different dyes in the ink. In this model a felt board is used to represent the paper and different colored poker chips represent the dyes in the marker ink. Finally, in Part C, they create a set of standard chromatograms R_f value of different black inks. They are then given an unknown sample of black ink and asked to determine the brand of ink.	Chromatography Mixtures Pure substances Separation methods Mobile phase Stationary phase R_f value

Chapter 9: It's Alimentary

Chapter Challenge

In this chapter you are challenged to learn the chemistry involved in the digestion of food as it passes down the alimentary canal. You will demonstrate your understanding in a skit depicting the perils you would encounter in a trip down the alimentary canal, assuming you had become one-billionth of your current size. The vehicles you ride in this futuristic theme park called Anatomy World must be a portion of food from a recently ingested meal. Most of the chemical substances that you encounter will be much larger than they are in this "nano-world." In order to survive you will have to understand chemistry at its molecular level, instead of observing only what you can see and manipulate in the "macro-world" of a chemistry laboratory.

Activity Summaries	Chemistry Principles
Activity 1: The Upper End of the Alimentary Canal The effect of salivary amylase is examined in the mouth and in the test tube. Tests for both starch and sugars are conducted on crackers that have been hydrolyzed. Rate of reaction is studied.	**Hydrolysis Starch test Sugar test Benedict's reagent Reaction rates Enzyme/catalyst Amylase**
Activity 2: Antacids in the Stomach The purpose of antacids is examined. Are all antacids the same? A comparison of standard antacids' neutralizing capacity is performed. The nature of a new acid-base indicator is explored in these titrations. Heartburn and acid indigestion are compared.	**Acids Bases pH Titration Neutralization Indicators**
Activity 3: Studying Carbon Dioxide How can carbon dioxide be identified? A bottle of carbonated beverage is degassed and the volume measured. The volume is studied at three different temperatures. The need for an absolute temperature scale is developed and Charles's Law is introduced.	**Gas collections CO_2 test, Limewater Charles's Law Kelvin scale Precipitate**
Activity 4: Observing Real Food in Artificial Stomachs Four foods are subjected to differing conditions in artificial "stomachs" with the goal of finding out the optimum set of conditions needed to digest food in the stomach. Evidence for the type of food that can be digested in the stomach is also collected.	**Hydrolysis Catalytic action Pepsin Enzyme activity with pH Peristalsis Proteins, Amino acids**
Activity 5: Gas Pressure The relationship between pressure and temperature is experimentally determined by monitoring the pressure generated by carbon dioxide being produced from reaction of an effervescent antacid tablet and water. Quantitative methods are developed to calculate volume, pressure, and temperature using Gay-Lussac's Law and Charles's Law. The fundamental principles of the Kinetic-Molecular theory of gases is examined.	**Gas pressure Atmospheric pressure Gay-Lussac's Law Reaction rates Charles's Law Kinetic theory Ideal gas**
Activity 6: Size of Molecules A scale will be developed for common biochemical molecules assuming they could be enlarged from their nano-world size into the macro-world.	**Scale and models Nanometer**
Activity 7: Hydrolysis of Lactose The cause and treatment for lactose intolerance will be studied. The fate of certain monsaccharides and disaccharides in the presence of lactase will be explored.	**Lactose intolerance Disaccharides Monosaccharides Testing for glucose Enzymes**

TICKETS

Chapter 10: Soap Sense

Chapter Challenge

In this chapter, you are challenged to create a soap from natural sources that are readily available. In working through the activities, you explore variations in the two main ingredients of soap and their effect on the properties of your target soap. At the conclusion, you will prepare two presentations—one for corporate executives of a soap company and a second for the marketing department of that company.

Activity Summaries	Chemistry Principles
Activity 1: What Makes a Good Soap? Students list different cleaners and soaps and describe their characteristics. They design and administer a survey to identify the most important characteristics. They choose a characteristic they want to measure quantitatively, and design an experiment to do so. After running the experiment, they discuss possible revisions.	Experimental design Cleaning agents Soaps vs. other cleaners Market research Detergents, Soap scum Quantitative tests Qualitative tests
Activity 2: Modeling Molecules Students build organic molecules of steadily increasing complexity, and examine the chemical bonding rules which determine these structures. A fat molecule is modeled and subjected to saponification and a skit is performed to demonstrate this reaction.	Molecular models Lewis diagrams Organic molecules Covalent bonding Saponification Fat, Fatty acid Bohr model, Quantum mechanics Valence electrons Functional group Carboxylic acid group Bonding and nonbonding electrons Cis/trans double bonds
Activity 3: How Do You Clean Dirty Laundry? Students test different cleaning solutions of varying polarity on different types of "dirt" to see which ones are most effective. They will discover that most types of dirt fall into one of two categories (polar or non-polar) and that laundry detergent in water will wash out most of them. Students perform a couple of quick experiments involving static electricity, observing that water behaves like a charged object and kerosene does not.	Electrostatic forces Hydrophilic interactions Hydrophobic interactions Polar molecules Non-polar molecules Polar covalent bonds Electronegativity Surfactant
Activity 4: How Does Soap Work? Students explore surface tension and the effect of soap on it. They then separate various liquids and solids according to their polarity. Models to describe the behavior of interactions between polar and non-polar substances are designed. The effect of adding a surfactant is considered, and students will also observe the characteristics of a mixture of water and oil.	Polar molecules Non-polar molecules Surface tension Surfactants Micelles
Activity 5: Changing the Fat: How Does Chain Length Affect Properties? Students determine the melting points of three saturated fatty acids of increasing chain length, identifying the trend. They examine a heating curve to help understand the phase transition between the solid and liquid states, and generate an explanation for this behavior. They examine three soaps made with high percentages of these three fatty acids, looking for trends between the properties and increasing chain length.	Melting point/freezing point Heating/cooling curves Phase transitions Structural effects on properties Intermolecular forces van der Waals forces Saponification, Fats Fatty acids
Activity 6: Changing the Fat: Does Unsaturation Make a Difference? Students use paper clips to model the overall shapes of a related series of fatty acids with increasing numbers of double bonds and examine the relationship between shape and melting point. They model the packing behavior of each acid, then predict and measure their melting points. Students will examine the properties of soaps containing large amounts of these fatty acids in terms of the number of double bonds. They will then predict the attributes of other soaps with these fatty acids.	Melting points Molecular packing Molecular structure Single and double bonds Saturated/unsaturated van der Waals forces Animal fat Vegetable fat Polyunsaturated
Activity 7: Soap, Other Bases, and pH Students measure the pH of an array of different soaps brought from home, and use acid to neutralize the pH of the soap. Then they measure the pH of an acid solution and try to dilute the acid enough to change the pH by 1 unit. After they discover the amount of water required to change the pH by 1 unit, they make predictions for more pH changes and carry them out.	pH scale, Logarithms Acids/Bases Arrhenius definition Brønsted definition Neutralization Dilution Mole, Molarity Weak acids and bases Strong acids and bases
Activity 8: Making Soap Functional and Appealing Students test and compare the soap they bought as a target to the soaps they made before beginning the chapter. They consider the properties of the various fats available and choose one or more as the basis for the soap they will design. After learning about moisturizers, thickeners, pH adjustments, and foaming agents, they decide whether to include any of them or not. Finally, they make the soap they have designed.	Experimental design Soap additives Marketing Moisturizers Humectants Thickeners, Waxes Foaming agents Esters

Chapter 11: H_2Woes

Chapter Challenge

You have been assigned by an international health organization, such as UNESCO, to improve the water supplies of communities in Latin America. The communities are of three types: **1. mining** and logging areas that have drawn water from mountain streams; **2. farming** areas that rely on wells, rivers, swamps, or lakes as sources of water; **3. industrialized** areas that depend on water reservoirs fed by rivers and wells. You will develop a flowchart for their recommended purification procedures, explain the chemistry behind the procedures, and present your plan to the class.

Activity Summaries / Chemistry Principles

Activity 1: What's in Natural Water?

Students learn some of the minerals common to natural waters and that they are composed of ions. They also study the reactions involved when gases dissolve in water and how to measure concentrations. Different sources of pollution, such as agricultural runoff and industrial discharge, are encountered.

Chemistry Principles:
- Hydrological cycle
- Aquifer
- Naming compounds
- Ionic substances
- Molecular compounds
- Polar covalent bonds
- Concentration units, ppm
- Electronegativity
- Hydrogen bonds
- Solubility rules

Activity 2: Factors Affecting Solubility of Solids

Students explore solubility for ionic compounds and develop a set of rules for various combinations of cations and anions. The solubility of covalent compounds is also investigated and the importance of hydrogen bonds is discovered. The effect of temperature on solubility is observed, as well as the exothermic or endothermic nature of solution formation.

Chemistry Principles:
- Solubility rules
- Chemical bonding
- Electrostatic forces
- Energy changes, Enthalpy
- Disorder changes
- Thermodynamics
- Gibbs free energy
- Ion dissolution
- Saturated solutions
- Disorder changes, Spontaneity

Activity 3: How Much Solute Is in the Water?

Students learn several common measurements for substances found in water. These include nitrates, iron, and the alkaline earth elements, magnesium and calcium. These quantitative analysis techniques will use colorimetry and titration.

Chemistry Principles:
- Periodic trends
- Classes of substances
- Solubility
- Colorimetric analysis
- Precipitation reactions
- Acids and bases, pH
- Titration, EDTA
- Water hardness
- Indicators, Endpoint
- Ion-specific electrodes

Activity 4: Aqueous Balance: Equilibrium

Students generate calcium oxalate in a micro-lab experiment and calculate the K_{sp} for the equilibrium. Similarly, the K_W of water is explored. The concept of a shift in equilibrium and methods for causing a shift are learned.

Chemistry Principles:
- Equilibrium
- Equilibrium constant, K_{eq}
- Solubility Product, K_{sp}
- Acid/base equilibria, pH
- Law of Mass Action
- LeChatelier's principle
- Total ionic equation
- Net-ionic equation
- Spectator ions

Activity 5: Removing Suspended Particles and Iron

As a model, students construct a filtration column using a syringe and use it to filter iron (as its hydroxide) from water. In a second experiment, iron is removed in a batch process and the results of the two experiments are compared. Suspended particles are removed using a gel of aluminum hydroxide.

Chemistry Principles:
- Colloids, Tyndall Effect
- Suspensions, Filtration
- Coagulation, Alum
- Rate of reaction
- Properties of fluids
- Batch method, Flow method

Activity 6: Water Softening

Students study the removal of magnesium and calcium ions in the water softening process using a precipitation reaction. Quantitative results are obtained and compared to removal by an ion exchange resin.

Chemistry Principles:
- Ionic equilibrium
- Precipitation reactions
- Separation methods
- Soda-lime process
- Water hardness
- Ion exchange resins

Activity 7: Removing Toxic-Metal Ions

Students learn the toxic heavy metals which must be removed from a water supply and what the maximum allowed concentrations are. Copper, cadmium, and nickel are removed as their sulfides by precipitation. Also by precipitation, chromium, lead, tin, or zinc concentrations can be lowered by formation of their hydroxides.

Chemistry Principles:
- Human toxicity limits
- Incomplete precipitation
- Precipitation reactions
- Solubility
- Heavy metals
- Distillation, Reverse osmosis

Activity 8: Disinfection

Students complete their study of water purification methods by examining the final steps of the process. Bacteria are killed by administering hypochlorite solution and the effectiveness is measured by comparing tests from agar jelly. Other bacteriocides are studied and compared with regard to safety and cost. Finally, the pH is adjusted with acid or base.

Chemistry Principles:
- Toxic bacteria, Pathogens
- Bacterial origins in water
- Chlorination reactions
- Acids and bases, pH, Acid rain
- Chlorinated organic pollutants
- Ozone, Activated carbon

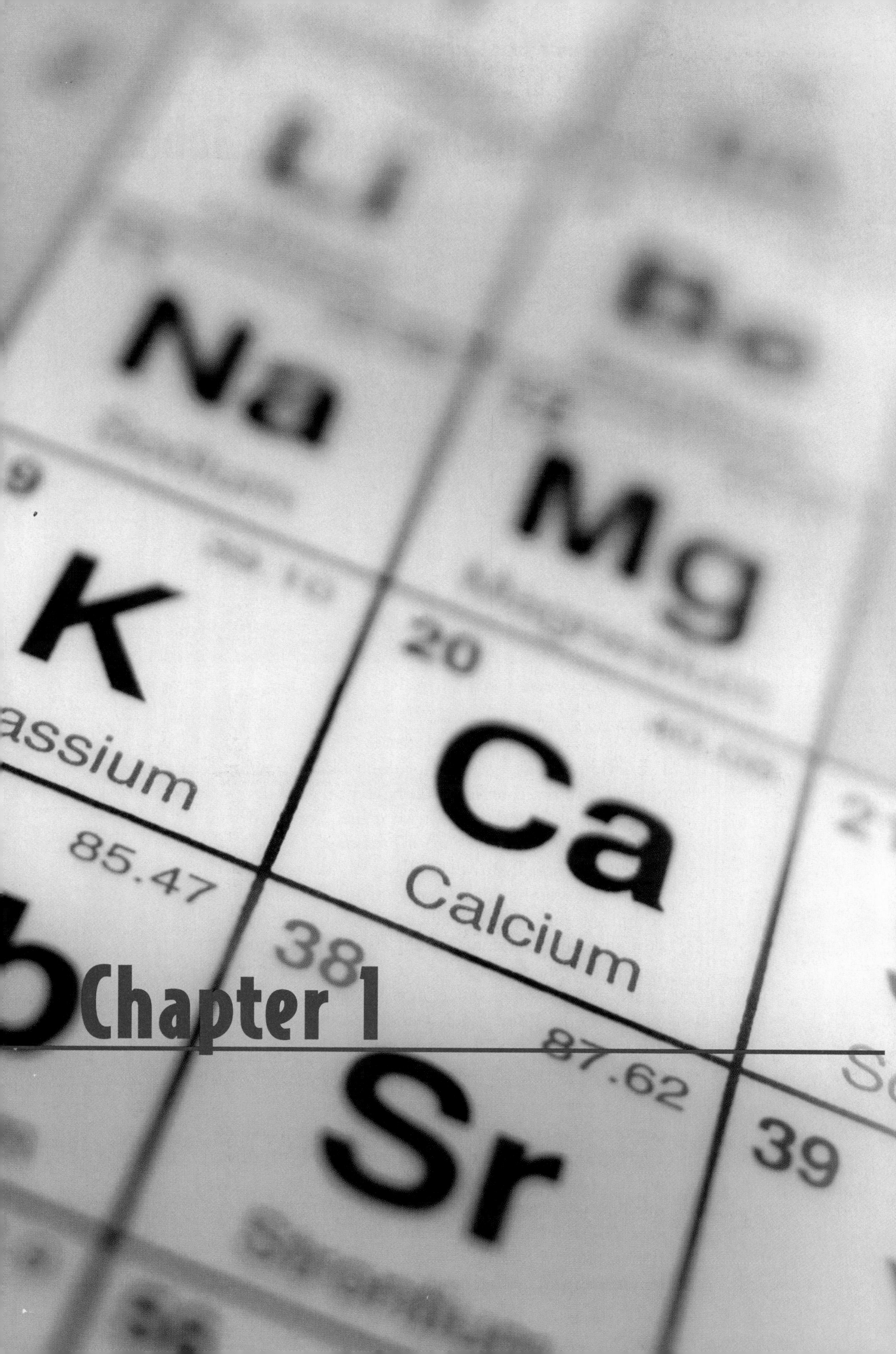
Na
Mg
K
20
Ca
Calcium
85.47
38
87.62
Sr
39

Chapter 1

FUN WITH THE PERIODIC TABLE

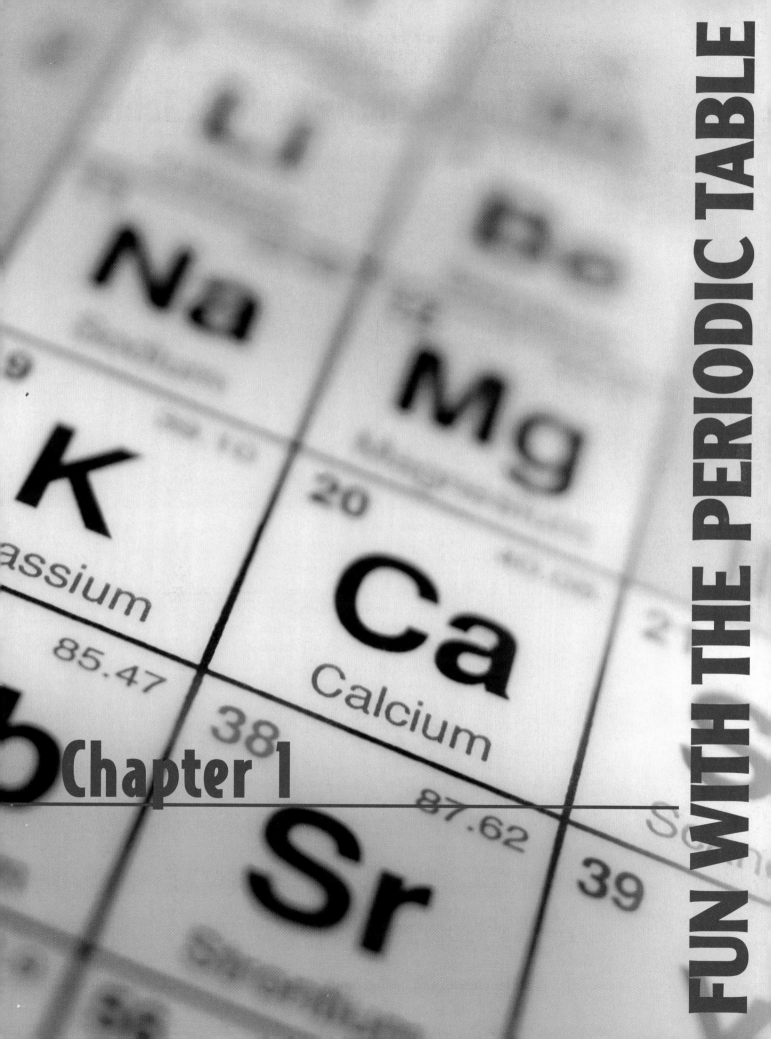

Ca
87.62

1

Fun with the Periodic Table

Scenario

Every time you say you like or don't like something, you are putting it into a category. You have probably developed categories for many things in your life. You may have categories for food you eat for breakfast, as opposed to dinner, or clothes you wear to school, as opposed to at home. Can you imagine what your life would be like if nothing were sorted into categories? What if you went shopping in a supermarket that displayed milk next to shoe polish, next to oranges, next to oatmeal, next to hams, next to orange juice, next to detergent? Where would you look for yogurt, shoelaces, corn flakes, ground beef, lemonade, and soap?

That kind of supermarket display pretty much describes the state of chemistry in the mid-19th century. By then chemists had identified and isolated a large number of chemical elements. However, they needed a way to sort elements into categories—much as a supermarket groups milk with yogurt, shoe polish with shoe laces, oatmeal with corn flakes, ham with ground beef, orange juice with lemonade, and detergent with soap.

Like similar items in a supermarket, some chemical elements were recognized to share similar chemical properties. The chemists that are given credit for arranging these elements successfully into a pattern according to their properties are the Russian, Dimitri Mendeleev, and a German, Julius Lothar Meyer.

Dimitri Mendeleev

One of the things Mendeleev did was to write down everything that was known about each element on a small card. Then he moved the cards around until he got an arrangement that showed the groups of elements with similar properties.

In Mendeleev's time, the periodic table was developed as a way to arrange elements according to their chemical behavior. Surprisingly, 50 years later it revealed information about the structure of the atoms of those elements as well.

By writing the properties of the elements onto separate cards and arranging them, Mendeleev created a puzzle. He solved that puzzle when he arranged the first version of what is now known as the Periodic Table of the Elements. Meyer independently created the table at the same time.

ChemCorner

Chemistry in *Fun with the Periodic Table*

- Elements
- Atoms
- Chemical and physical properties
- Metals and nonmetals
- Nucleus and orbitals
- Proton, neutron, electron
- Atomic mass
- Atomic number
- Isotopes
- Compound
- The mole and Avogadro's number
- Electron configuration
- Electromagnetic radiation
- Wavelength and frequency
- $c = \lambda f$
- Conservation of mass
- Ionization energy
- Cations and anions

BATTERY

Chapter Challenge

Your Challenge

Your challenge in this chapter is to develop a game related to Mendeleev's Periodic Table of the Elements.

How the game is played, whether on a table, with cards, on a computer, or with equipment that only you might choose, is up to you. You might choose to emphasize some aspects of the periodic table over others, such as why the elements are grouped the way they are, how atomic masses are determined, or how the electrons of the elements are configured. Or you may choose to focus on some types of information related to the table like the history of the discovery of atomic structure, how the elements combine to form compounds and why some are radioactive. However, you need to keep in mind the criteria you and your teacher establish.

Criteria

How will your game be graded? What qualities should a good game have? Discuss these issues in small groups and with your class. You may decide that some or all of the following qualities should be graded:

- how well the game shows your understanding of the periodic table
- how well the game enables players to learn about the periodic table
- how interesting the game is to play
- how long the game takes to play
- whether the game is sequential or can be continued.

Once you have determined the list of qualities for evaluating the game, you and your class should also decide how many points should be given for each criterion. Make sure that you understand all the criteria as well as you can before you begin. Your teacher may provide you with a sample rubric to help you get started.

54
Xe
Xeno
13
32
G
Germ
7
28
Ni
Nick
59
35
Br
Bromine
80
51
Sb
Antimon
122
63
Eu
Europium
152

Activity 1 Organizing a Store

What Do You See?

AISLE 36
ELECTRONICS
CDs
BIKES
CHEESE
CANOES
WINE
CARPETS
AISLE 32
FIGS
APRICOTS
ONIONS
GARDEN TOOLS
FRESH FISH
CHEESE

GOALS

In this activity you will:

- Plan the arrangement of the items for sale in a store.
- Analyze trends in the arrangement of the store.
- Relate the arrangement of items in the store to the arrangement of elements in the periodic table.

What Do You Think?

Some supermarkets now sell books, flowers, and prescription drugs in addition to eggs, meat, and cereal.

- **How many different items do you think that a supermarket has?**

The *What Do You Think?* question is meant to get you thinking about what you already know or think you know. Don't worry about being right or wrong. Discussing what you think you know is an important step in learning.

Record your ideas about this question in your *Active Chemistry* log. Be prepared to discuss your responses with your small group and the class.

Investigate

1. Suppose that you decided to go into the business of opening and running a supermarket. In your group, brainstorm a list of between 50 and 100 items you would sell at your supermarket.

   A member of your group should volunteer to record the items suggested by all members of the group. Everyone, including the person serving as recorder, should participate.

   a) Make a map showing the locations of all of the items in your store. Give some thought to what will be at the front of each aisle, and what will be at the back. Consider how the store will be arranged from left to right.

b) Keep in mind which items you want shoppers to see as they enter the store and which should be near as they approach the cash register. Would either of these factors alter your arrangement?

c) Consider the items from left to right across your store. Why did you choose to arrange the items that way?

Your teacher may decide to supply you with copies of flyers from a supermarket. Cut out all the items from the flyer and arrange them as if they were being sold in your store.

What Do You Think Now?

At the beginning of the activity, you were asked to think about the question:

- **How many different items do you think that a supermarket has?**

When you get used to one supermarket, it becomes easier to navigate your way. Would your supermarket be easy to navigate? Why?

Reflecting on the Activity and the Challenge

Organizing 50 to 100 items in your store is not unlike the problem faced by Mendeleev when he organized about the same number of chemical elements into the periodic table. This activity was designed to get you to understand some of the problems Mendeleev faced. It is hoped that you can better appreciate what he did. You may wish to build this experience into the game you design.

Chem to Go

1. What is the pattern or arrangement in your store's aisles?
2. Choose one aisle in your store. Describe the arrangement of items going from the front of the store to the back of the store. What is the trend (or general drift) in that aisle?
3. A new item is brought into the store — chocolate-covered peanuts. Where would you place this item? Provide an explanation for your decision.
4. Your store decides to sell napkins, plates, and decorations for Thanksgiving. How will you adapt your store arrangement to make room for these items?
5. You would like people to purchase a certain item because it gives you a big profit. Where would you place it in your store and why?
6. One of the characteristics of Mendeleev's original periodic table was a series of blank spots. Mendeleev expected these would eventually be filled with elements yet to be discovered. What would such a "blank" correspond to in your store?
7. Many supermarkets have the fruits and vegetables at the entrance to the market because these items are large profit items. Many supermarkets put magazines by the check-out counter hoping that shoppers will make an "impulse buy" before they leave. Did your supermarket map include these considerations? How would you change the map if profits were a new characteristic of the items?

Activity 2 Elements and Their Properties

What Do You See?

GOALS

In this activity you will:

- Apply ancient definitions of elements to materials you believe are elements.
- Test some properties of several common elements.
- Classify elements as metals, nonmetals, or metalloids.
- Learn to differentiate between chemical and physical properties of materials.
- Organize a table of the elements you tested based on their properties.
- Practice safe handling of corrosive chemicals in the laboratory.

What Do You Think?

Throughout history, philosophers and scientists have talked about "the elements." Reference to elements is most frequent today in the field of chemistry.

- **What is an element?**

The *What Do You Think?* question is meant to get you thinking about what you already know or think you know. Don't worry about being right or wrong. Discussing what you think you know is an important step in learning.

Record your ideas about this question in your *Active Chemistry* log. Be prepared to discuss your responses with your small group and the class.

Investigate

1. Work individually first and then with your group.

   a) Make a list of four or more substances you use or see every day that meet your definition of an element.

2. The ancient Greeks believed that the four elements were earth, air, fire, and water. The alchemists of the early Renaissance identified a limited number of elements including: mercury, sulfur, and salt.

   a) Does each of the above "elements" satisfy your definition of an element? Why or why not?

Element	Initial observation	Conducts electricity	Reacts with HCl	Magnetic or nonmagnetic	Metal or nonmetal
aluminum					
carbon					
copper					
iodine					
iron					
magnesium					
silicon					
sulfur					
zinc					

Safety goggles and a lab apron must be worn *at all times* in a chemistry lab.

Be sure the terminals are kept apart between trials.

3. Your teacher will provide watch glasses containing several common elements: aluminum, carbon, copper, iodine, iron, magnesium, silicon, sulfur, and zinc.

   You will investigate the properties of these elements. By observing common properties, you may gain an insight into how an organizational chart can be created for all of the known elements. Observe the sample of the chemical element in each jar (without removing any). You can describe this initial observation of each element in the first column of a table similar to the one shown.

   a) Record your observations in a table.

4. One of the properties of the elements on Mendeleev's cards was the ability of the element to conduct electric current. Some materials can conduct electricity while others cannot. Using a conductivity meter, you will be able to complete the third column of the chart.

   Insert the terminals of the electrical conductivity apparatus into the jar containing each element. If the light on the apparatus goes on, that means that a complete circuit is created, and an electric current is passing through both the light bulb (LED) and the sample of the element in the jar.

   It is important to make sure that the part of the apparatus immersed into the elements stays dry and is not contaminated by any of the other elements in which it has been immersed. Also, your teacher will provide you with steel wool to polish the metal strips before you test them. The steel wool removes the non-conducting oxides from the surface, especially on the aluminum, copper, and zinc.

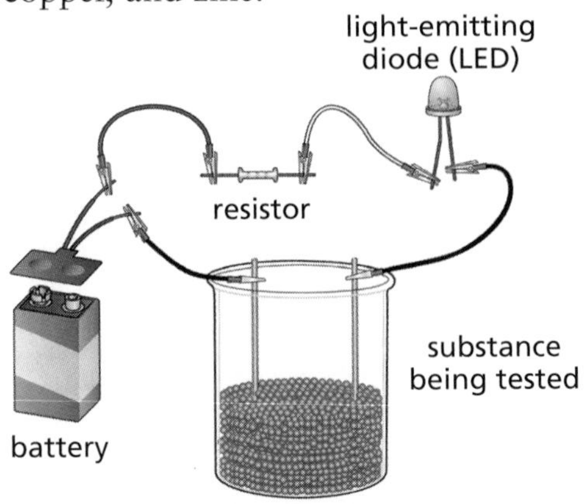
light-emitting diode (LED)
resistor
substance being tested
battery

a) Test the samples of each element with the electrical conductivity apparatus. Record whether the element conducts electric current, (yes) or (no).

b) Based on your initial observation and the results of the conductivity test, can you suggest a way to group the elements? Describe an arrangement in your log.

5. Another property of each element known to Mendeleev was how it reacts with an acid.

Pour 5 mL of 1 *M* hydrochloric acid (HCl) into each of nine small test tubes. (1 *M* is an indication of the concentration of the acid.) Use a scoop or tongs to remove a small portion of each element from the jar and add it to the hydrochloric acid. It is important to add the hydrochloric acid to the test tube first so that you will not be surprised by a reaction that occurs when you pour acid over a reactive element. Place a piece of white paper in the background behind the test tube and observe the reaction between the element and hydrochloric acid by looking through the side of the test tube.

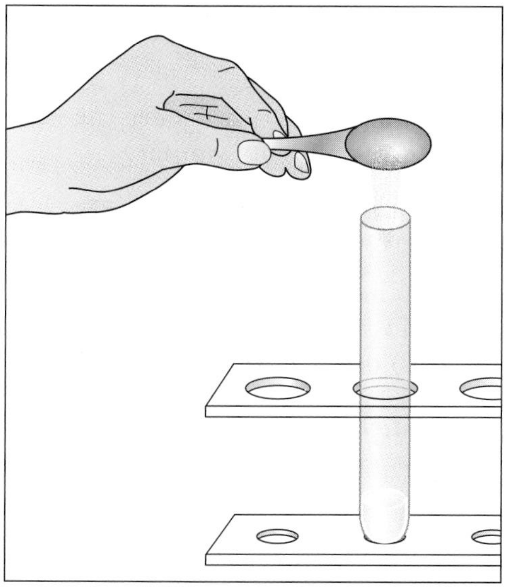

a) Test a small sample of each element for its reaction with hydrochloric acid (HCl). Record whether it reacts with the acid, (yes) or (no).

b) For those elements that do react, try to determine whether all show the same type of reaction. (Do they all do the same thing?) Compare the relative vigor of the reactions. If the reaction is vigorous, include a + sign next to your "yes." If the reaction is weak, place a – sign next to your "yes."

6. Dispose of the contents of the test tubes and clean the test tubes as directed by your teacher.

a) Now that three columns of observations are included in the table, describe a way to arrange the different elements.

7. Place a small amount of each sample on a watch glass. Use a magnet and test the element to see if it is attracted to the magnet.

a) Record your observations in your table.

8. A metal is generally a solid that is shiny, malleable, and a good conductor of heat and electricity. Nonmetals have a wide range of properties. Some are dull and brittle, but others, like diamond, are hard and brilliant, and still others are gases or liquids. Most are poor conductors of electricity. Classify each of the elements you observed as either a metal or nonmetal.

a) Record your observations in the table in your *Active Chemistry* log.

9. When elements combine with oxygen they form oxides. Another way to determine whether an element is a metal or nonmetal is to see how the oxide reacts with pH paper.

The term pH is a way of describing how acidic or basic a solution is. A pH of 7 is neutral, below 7 is acidic, and above 7 is basic. Most oxides of metals will produce a pH greater than 7 (base). Most oxides of nonmetals will produce a pH less than 7 (acid). The pH paper comes with a key of pH number and color.

You will now investigate the pH of the oxides to see if your initial determination of metal versus nonmetal was correct. The elements that you have been investigating form common oxides (compounds containing oxygen), as shown in the table below.

If the oxide is a solid, add a small amount of the oxide to a test tube. Then add about 10 mL of deionized water. Stir the mixture to get some of the oxide to dissolve. Some of the oxides may already be in solution. Transfer 10 mL of the solution to the test tube in which you will be determining the pH.

a) Make a table to record your observations in your *Active Chemistry* log. Complete the table.

Wash your hands and arms thoroughly after the activity.

Oxides of elements	pH test
aluminum oxide	
carbon dioxide	
copper oxide	
iron (III) oxide	
magnesium oxide	
silicon dioxide	
sulfur dioxide	
zinc oxide	

b) Were all of the oxides that had a pH more than 7 identified in your table as metals?

c) Were all of the oxides that had a pH less than 7 identified in your table as nonmetals?

The pH observation is the one you rely on to tell the difference between metals and nonmetals. (There are some exceptions to this.)

10. Create an index card for each element. Find a way to sort them based on their properties. You may try arranging them and/or color coding them. Your method of sorting will be successful if you can quickly find an element and know from its position whether it:

- conducts electricity
- reacts with hydrochloric acid (HCl)
- is metallic or nonmetallic.

a) Record your method of sorting the cards in your *Active Chemistry* log.

11. Dispose of the materials as directed by your teacher. Clean up your workstation.

12. Compare and contrast your arrangement with that of another group.

a) In what two ways are the arrangements similar?

b) In what two ways are the arrangements different?

c) Which of these two arrangements do you think better allows you to quickly find if an element conducts electricity, reacts with HCl, or is metallic?

Chem Talk

PHYSICAL AND CHEMICAL PROPERTIES

Classifying Elements Using Properties

You began this activity by trying to define the meaning of an **element**. The ancient Greek philosopher Aristotle defined an element as "a body into which other bodies may be analyzed . . . and not itself divisible into bodies different in form." The first modern definition of element, which is not much different, is from Robert Boyle: "Bodies, which not being made of any other bodies, or of one another, are the ingredients of which all those . . . mixed bodies are . . . compounded." Scientists now state that an element is any material that cannot be broken down by chemical means into simpler materials.

Before the mid-19th century, scientists were busy discovering elements and observing and recording their properties. Then they tried to organize the elements they had discovered in a useful way. At first, they listed the elements alphabetically. However, every time a new element was discovered, the whole list had to be changed. They tried other methods. Could elements be organized by properties like state (solid, liquid, or gas), color, or taste? None of these methods appeared practical or safe! However, chemists worldwide were sure that elements existed in families that had similar physical and chemical properties.

To the Russian scientist, Dimitri Mendeleev (1843–1907), the development of a tool to organize the elements began the same way that so much of science inquiry begins. He began with a simple question. The question Mendeleev wanted answered was: "What is the relationship of the elements to one another and to the chemical families to which they belong?" At that time there were 63 known elements. To help him with his organization, he developed a card system, much the same as you did in this activity. He wrote the properties of each known element on a different card. Then he spent many hours arranging and rearranging the cards. He was looking for patterns or trends in the data in front of him. Mendeleev, however, had more information on his cards than you presently have. In the following activities, you will look at additional properties of elements that will help you organize your game.

Physical and Chemical Properties

In this activity, you observed several properties of the elements you were provided. You probably initially observed the color of the element and whether the element was a liquid or a solid. You then

Chem Words

element: any material that cannot be broken down into simpler materials.

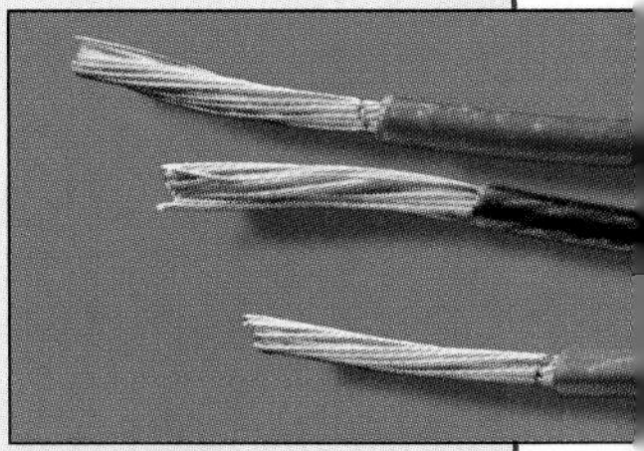

investigated whether or not the element conducted electricity. You could have also observed the luster, measured the density (its mass/volume relationship) or the strength, or determined the malleability of each element. In each case, you would not have changed the element itself. In this *Investigation*, the element in the jar still looked the same after you removed the electrical conductivity apparatus as it did when you initially inserted it. It was unchanged. If measuring a property of a substance does not change the chemical identity of the substance, you are measuring a **physical property**.

On the other hand, when you observed whether the element reacted with hydrochloric acid, the element clearly changed. A **chemical property** is a property that is displayed when matter undergoes a change in composition (it undergoes a chemical reaction).

When elements combine with oxygen they form oxides. In the investigation, you saw that the oxides of metals are basic (have a pH greater than 7) and the oxides of nonmetals are acidic (have a pH less than 7) when tested with pH paper. You know that cars and coal-generating power plants emit sulfur dioxide and carbon dioxide into the atmosphere. When these nonmetal oxides combine with water they produce acid rain. Your tests on the nonmetal oxides should have confirmed this observation.

Chem Words

physical property: a property of matter that can be measured without causing chemical change or composition of the material. Density is a physical property of a substance.

chemical property: a property that is displayed when matter undergoes a change in composition (it undergoes a chemical reaction). The burning of wood is a chemical property.

Checking Up

1. Define an element.
2. What question did Mendeleev use to guide his science inquiry?
3. In your own words, describe the difference between a physical and a chemical property.

What Do You Think Now?

At the beginning of the activity you were asked to think about the question:

- **What is an element?**

The question was used to find out what you already know or think you know about elements.

At this point in the activity, it is time to reflect on what you think now. Has your definition of an element been enriched? If you were given several more elements, would you be able to classify them as either metals or nonmetals?

Chem Essential Questions

What does it mean?

Chemistry explains a macroscopic phenomenon (what you observe) with a description of what happens at the nanoscopic level (atoms and molecules) using symbolic structures as a way to communicate. Complete the first column of the chart in your *Active Chemistry* log.

MACRO	NANO	SYMBOLIC
What observations did you make of elements in this activity?	*In chemistry, you try to explain what you see with your eyes about what is happening at the molecular level. You have not yet looked at elements at this level. However, this is the chemist's goal. A nanometer is one-billionth of a meter. It is used to describe the size of atoms and molecules. That is why we call this the nanoscopic level.*	*Symbols are used to represent elements. Aluminum is represented as Al, and zinc has the symbol Zn. These symbols can also be used to represent interactions the elements have with other substances. In this activity, you used pH to see if a material is an acid or a base. The pH is a symbol that chemists use to "talk about" acids and bases.*

How do you know?

A new element is given to you for testing. Describe the tests that you would perform to determine if an element conducted electricity or reacted with hydrochloric acid.

Why do you believe?

Because different elements possess different properties, they have many different uses. For example, since copper metal is a good electrical conductor, it is used in speaker wiring. Choose two of the elements you worked with in this activity and suggest a use for them based on a particular property they exhibit.

Why should you care?

Knowledge of how the elements are classified or grouped might be an important component of your game. How can arranging elements by conductivity and other properties be a part of a game?

Reflecting on the Activity and the Challenge

In this activity, you learned not only the definition of an element but also some of the properties of elements. Measuring these properties not only enabled Mendeleev to place the elements in his periodic table but also allowed other chemists to identify the elements. You have tried to sort the cards of elements in the same way that Mendeleev did. Perhaps your periodic-table game can have sorting cards as one part of the strategy.

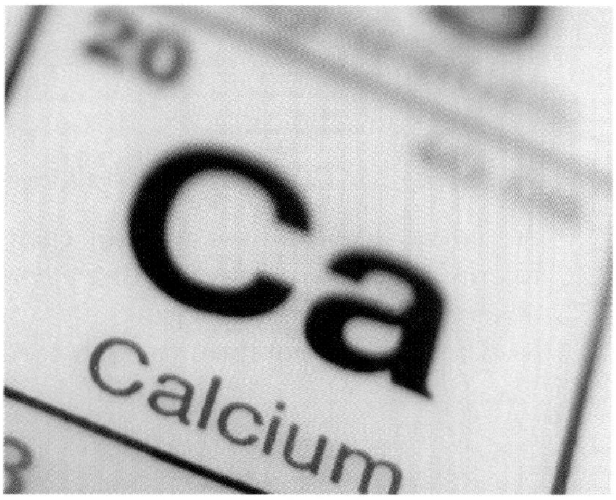
20
Ca
Calcium

Chem to Go

1. Make a list of three more physical properties of an element that you can observe.
2. Make a list of three more chemical properties of an element that you can measure.
3. Why did you want the metals to be clean or polished before you tested them for electrical conductivity?
4. What criteria did you use to differentiate metals from nonmetals in this investigation?
   a) Is this a valid statement of a trend you saw: as the color of the element becomes darker, the element is less metallic? Support your assessment of this statement with evidence that you observed in your investigation.
   b) Is this a valid statement of a trend you saw: the elements react with hydrochloric acid more as you move down a list of the elements in alphabetical order? Support your assessment of this statement with evidence that you observed in your investigation.
5. Which statement describes a chemical property?
   a) Its crystals are a metallic gray. c) It forms a violet-colored gas.
   b) It has a "chemical-like" smell. d) It reacts with hydrochloric acid to form a gas.
6. A student investigated the physical and chemical properties of a sample of unknown gas. Which statement represents a conclusion rather than an experimental observation?
   a) The gas is colorless.
   b) The gas is carbon dioxide.
   c) When the gas is bubbled in limewater, the liquid becomes cloudy.
   d) When placed in the gas, a flaming splint stops burning.
7. Which element is most likely to be a good conductor of electricity?
   a) copper c) sodium
   b) carbon d) neon
8. The pH test for tin oxide would show that it is:
   a) acidic (pH less than 7)
   b) basic (pH greater than 7)

   Explain your choice.
9. ***Preparing for the Chapter Challenge***

   Prepare a set of index cards for each of the elements with which you are familiar. Record as many properties of each element you know on the card. Use your observations in the following activities and any research you complete on your own to add information to each card.

Activity 3 Atoms and Their Masses

What Do You See?

GOALS

In this activity you will:

- Explore the idea of atoms by trying to isolate a single atom.
- Measure how many times greater the mass of a copper atom is than a magnesium atom.
- Practice careful laboratory technique with measuring masses and filtration.
- Locate sources of the variation in the class's experimental results.
- Compare Dalton's experimental results to the masses of atoms known today.
- See that atoms react in definite proportions of mass when forming a compound.
- Relate the mole concept to real quantities.
- Use scientific notation in calculations.

What Do You Think?

Atoms are the smallest, indivisible part of an element.

- **When did you first hear of atoms? What did they mean to you then, and what do they mean to you now?**
- **State three comments about atoms and place them under the headings given below. (You can place one comment under each heading or all three comments under one heading.)**

Use the following three headings: Things I Know about Atoms, Things I Think I Know about Atoms, Things I Would Like to Know about Atoms.

Record your ideas in your *Active Chemistry* log. Be prepared to discuss your responses with your small group and the class.

Investigate

1. One way to think about an atom is to imagine trying to isolate a single atom from a large number of atoms.

   Take a piece of aluminum foil (5 cm by 5 cm) and cut it in half. Take one of the resulting pieces and cut it in half again. Repeat this process with each successive half until you cannot make another cut.

   a) Record how many cuts you were able to make.

Safety goggles and a lab apron must be worn *at all times* in a chemistry lab.

b) How does the size of the smallest piece of aluminum compare to the size of the original piece?

c) Does the smallest piece of aluminum have the same properties as the original piece of aluminum foil? How could you test this assumption?

2. An atom is the smallest part of an element. Since you can still cut the aluminum in pieces, you have not reached the size of a single atom. Now imagine that there may be a way to cut the smallest piece of aluminum you have into even smaller and smaller pieces.

   a) How small can the smallest piece be and still retain the properties of aluminum? Could you cut the piece in half and half again 10 more times? 100 more times? 1000 more times?

   Using your imagination of cutting and cutting, you will eventually get to one atom of aluminum.

3. Chemists combine elements to form new substances. Each of the original elements has different properties. The new substance has properties different from either of the combined elements. By measuring the amounts of elements used and substances formed, they are able to draw conclusions about the properties of the elements involved. You will study the reaction between magnesium metal and a solution of copper (II) chloride.

   Read through the procedure below.

   a) Make a table in your *Active Chemistry* log for the data you will be collecting. You will need room for measurements (mass) and observations. You can use a table similar to the one provided below.

4. Check your balance to make sure that it reads zero with nothing on it. Then measure the mass of a 50-mL beaker to the precision of your balance.

   a) Record the mass in your *Active Chemistry* log.

Finding the mass of the magnesium metal	
1. Mass of empty 50-mL beaker	g
2. Mass of beaker and magnesium metal	g
3. Calculate the mass of magnesium metal from 1 and 2 above.	g
Finding the mass of copper (II) chloride	
4. Mass of weighing paper	g
5. Mass of paper and copper (II) chloride	g
6. Calculate the mass of copper (II) chloride from 4 and 5 above.	g
Finding the mass of the product	
7. Mass of dry filter paper	g
8. Mass of filter paper with product, after drying	g
9. Calculate the mass of the product material from 7 and 8 above.	g

5. Measure out approximately 0.20 g of magnesium metal into the empty beaker. Try to get your mass measurement close to the assigned value.

   If you have a centigram balance, you'll need to adjust the balance to read 0.20 more grams than the beaker alone. Then add pieces of magnesium metal until it rebalances.

   If you have an electronic balance, simply add pieces of magnesium until the display indicates 0.20 g more than the empty beaker.

   a) Record the value that you obtain, even though you might not hit the target value.

6. Measure the mass of a piece of weighing paper.

   Place approximately 2.00 g of copper (II) chloride on the weighing paper. (The elements you would expect to find in copper (II) chloride are copper and chlorine.) Again, remember that your target value is 2.00 g and that you may be slightly over or under this value.

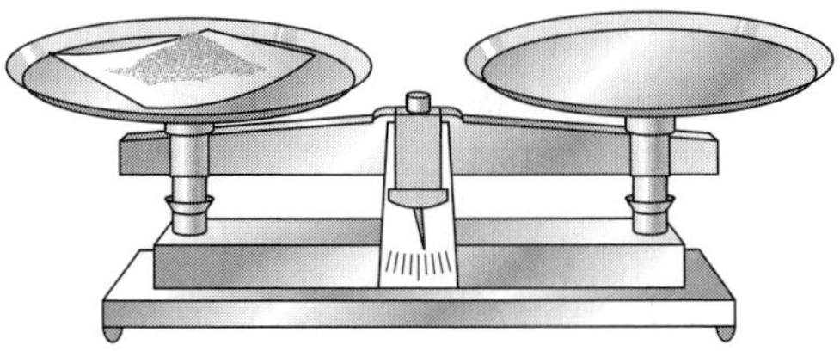

   a) Record the masses in your *Active Chemistry* log.

7. Add the copper (II) chloride to the beaker with the magnesium metal. Next add water to the beaker until it is approximately half full.

   a) Record your observations in your *Active Chemistry* log. Consider including the following: how the beaker feels when you touch it; what you hear when you listen closely to the beaker; what you see happening in the beaker.

   b) What color forms on the magnesium metal? What do you think is responsible for this color? Where is the color coming from?

8. You will now need to find the mass of the substance formed in the chemical reaction. You can filter out this substance and then find its mass. First measure the mass of a piece of dry, clean filter paper.

   a) Record the mass in your log.

9. Set up a filtration system, as shown in the diagram.

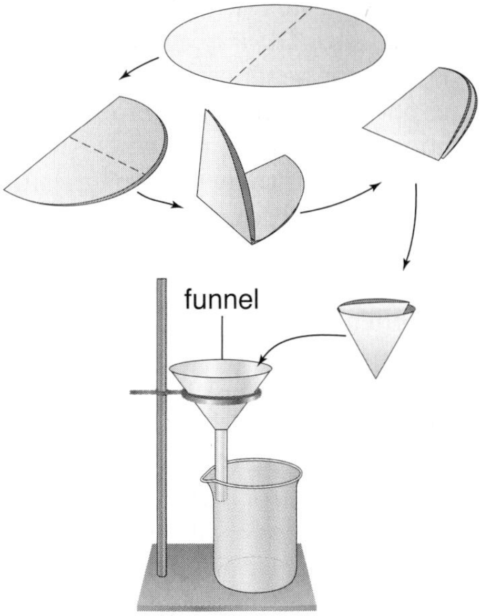
funnel

10. Wait until you no longer see or hear any reaction and the liquid begins to clear. Pour the contents of the 50-mL beaker through the filter paper into a second beaker. Rinse the first beaker a couple of times with some distilled water to be sure that all of the contents of the beaker are transferred. Carefully remove the filter from the funnel and place it on a piece of folded paper towel. Allow it to dry overnight or use a drying oven. Label the paper

Wipe up any spills immediately.

Wash your hands and arms thoroughly after the activity.

Safety goggles and a lab apron must be worn *at all times* in a chemistry lab.

Wash your hands and arms thoroughly after the activity.

towel so that you can identify your filter paper. Clean and put away your equipment and dispose of your chemicals as directed by your teacher.

11. When the filter paper is dry, measure the mass of the filter paper and its contents. Dispose of the filter paper and its contents as directed by your teacher.

    a) Record the mass in your *Active Chemistry* log. Determine and record the mass of the contents of the filter paper.

12. The element on the filter paper appears by its color to be copper. The reaction you witnessed is called a *single-replacement reaction.* Before the reaction, there was copper (II) chloride compound and the magnesium metal. After the reaction, there was magnesium chloride compound and copper metal. In this reaction, a single element (magnesium) replaces another element (copper) in its combined form (copper (II) chloride). As a result of this reaction, the copper leaves its combined form to become an uncombined, or free, element. The magnesium leaves its uncombined form to join with the chlorine to form a new compound, magnesium chloride. It's time to look at your data and see if you can make some sense of the numbers.

    a) How many grams of magnesium metal did you start with? How many grams of copper did you end up with (contents of the dry filter paper)?

    b) How many times as great is the mass of the copper as compared to the mass of magnesium you originally used? (What is the ratio of mass of copper to mass of magnesium?)

    c) If one atom of copper is released for each atom of magnesium that becomes combined (with chlorine), the masses of copper and magnesium determined in (a) should contain the same number of atoms. What does this tell you about the relative masses of copper and magnesium atoms?

    d) If the data you recorded showed 0.20 g of magnesium and 0.52 g of copper, then the number of atoms in 0.20 g of magnesium *equals* the number of atoms in 0.52 g of copper. From your data, how many times more massive is a copper atom than a magnesium atom? (You may wish to compare objects that you are familiar with: a dozen bowling balls of mass 60.0 kg can be compared to a dozen eggs of mass 0.50 kg. Since there are a dozen bowling balls and a dozen eggs, you can find that the bowling balls are 60.0/0.50 or 120 times as heavy as the eggs.)

13. Recall that every group in your class reacted the same mass of magnesium with the same mass of copper (II) chloride. Discuss the similarities and differences in the data and calculations among the groups in the class.

    a) Record your thoughts on how and why the results are similar and/or different.

Chem Talk

ATOMIC MASS

Atoms

Aristotle

In *Activity* 2, you defined the term element and explored the properties of some common elements. In this activity, you focused on atoms. An **atom** is the smallest representative part of an element. The ancient Greek philosopher Aristotle did not believe in the existence of atoms. In his thinking, if atoms did exist, there would have to be empty space between them.

Aristotle did not believe it was possible to have empty space. Not everyone agreed with Aristotle. Another ancient Greek named Democritus believed that matter was made up of tiny particles that could not be broken down further. He called the particles atoms, from the Greek word *atomos*, meaning indivisible.

If you could have continued cutting the aluminum foil until it could no longer be cut, by any method, you would have reached one atom of aluminum. A mind-expanding fact is that if you started with 27 g of aluminum, you would find that there are 6.02×10^{23} atoms of aluminum (that is, 602,000,000,000,000,000,000,000 atoms). Nobody has ever counted this nor could they. Scientists have determined this number by other means and are very confident that it is correct.

Masses of Elements and Compounds in a Reaction

By the turn of the 19th century, chemists were combining elements to form new substances. The new substance was called a **compound**, because the atoms of the elements were believed to combine to form what was called a compound atom. The chemists were also particularly interested in measuring the amounts of elements used and substances formed. Their first attempts in determining masses were wrong, possibly due to the equipment that they had available at that time.

Chem Words

atom: the smallest, representative part of an element.

compound: a material that can be dissociated chemically into two or more kinds of atoms.

John Dalton was an early 19th century chemist born in England. He did much to advance the belief in the existence of atoms. He expected that atoms combined in the simplest possible relationship. He reported that seven parts of oxygen reacted with one part of hydrogen to form water. Accurate modern experiments give eight parts to one. (We will use modern values rather than historical ones to avoid confusion.) He also reported that eight parts of oxygen reacted with seven parts of nitrogen to form a compound he called nitrous gas.

Gay-Lussac

Joseph Gay-Lussac was a French chemist and physicist. In 1809, he reported that the hydrogen reacting with oxygen to form water occupied twice as much volume as the oxygen. He also noted that the hydrogen reacting with nitrogen to form ammonia occupied three times as much volume as the nitrogen. Furthermore, he found that equal volumes of nitrogen and oxygen reacted to form nitrous gas. (This gas is now known as nitric oxide or nitrogen monoxide, NO.)

Avogadro

Gay-Lussac's data did not agree with Dalton's idea that water, ammonia, and nitrous gas are formed from one atom of each of the combining elements. Amedeo Avogadro, an Italian scientist, later resolved this disagreement. He furthered the understanding of the correct chemical formulas and atomic masses.

This historical information shows how difficult it was to learn about atoms. The chemists who did this research were very intelligent people. They devoted most of their lives to trying to make sense of experiments like the one you did with magnesium and copper chloride. You can benefit from their hard work and insights.

This is how knowledge evolves. That is why you are able to have the world that you live in with chemicals being used in transportation, food, medicines, clothing, and every other aspect of your life. By becoming student chemists, you are able to better understand how scientists have come to understand the world of atoms.

Relative Mass of Atoms

Eventually, chemists determined a scale of relative masses of atoms. They did this through the organized study of chemical reactions. They measured the masses of two elements reacting with each other, as you did in the activity. This allowed them to find relative masses. They could find out which elements were more massive than others, given the same number of atoms of each. Chemists were able to determine, for example, that one element has twice the mass of a second element. Relative mass does not tell you the exact mass measured in kilograms. It does provide a relative scale. Comparison of many reactions resulted in a scale of relative masses. Atoms of carbon were found to have a mass 12 times greater than the mass of hydrogen atoms. Oxygen atoms were found to have a mass 16 times greater than the mass of hydrogen. The units for this scale are called **atomic mass units**. They are defined in such a way that the mass of one type of carbon (carbon-12) is exactly 12 atomic mass units. The average mass of an atom of a given element in atomic mass units is known as the **atomic mass**. Atoms of hydrogen have an atomic mass of one unit. As he organized his table, Mendeleev understood the physical and chemical properties of elements. He also knew the relative mass of each element. The atomic mass is still one of the important pieces of information provided for each element on the periodic table. The table shown gives the relative atomic masses of the nine elements that you observed in *Activity 2*, plus hydrogen. (The elements are in alphabetical order.)

Element	Relative atomic mass
aluminum	26.98
carbon	12.01
copper	63.55
hydrogen	1.01
iodine	126.90
iron	55.85
magnesium	24.31
silicon	28.09
sulfur	32.06
zinc	65.38

Chem Words

atomic mass unit (amu): a unit of mass defined as the mass of $\frac{1}{12}$ of a carbon-12 atom.

atomic mass: the average mass of an atom of a given element in atomic mass units.

Chem Words

Law of Definite Proportions: a law that states that whenever two elements combine to form a compound, they do so in a definite proportion by mass.

The Law of Definite Proportions

Joseph Proust

Chemists at the beginning of the 19th century noted that eight parts of oxygen always reacted with one part of hydrogen to form nine parts of water. This observation is an example of **the Law of Definite Proportions.** Joseph Proust, a French chemist, first stated this law in 1799. The law says that whenever two elements combine to form a compound, they do so in a definite proportion by mass. Proust based this statement on his observations. (He observed that 100 g of copper, dissolved in nitric acid and precipitated by carbonates of soda (sodium) or potash (potassium), gave 180 g of green carbonate.) The Law of Definite Proportions is not a direct proof of the existence of atoms. However, if you believe in the existence of atoms it does make it easier to explain why the Law of Definite Proportions should hold. The existence of atoms can also help explain why a given mass of magnesium reacting with sufficient copper (II) chloride in solution should always produce a specific mass of copper.

Checking Up

1. What is the difference between an element and a compound?
2. What is an atom?
3. How is an atomic mass unit defined?
4. How can the existence of atoms help to explain the Law of Definite Proportions?

What Do You Think Now?

At the beginning of the activity you were asked to:

- **State three comments about atoms and place them under the appropriate heading.**

Return to your chart. Would you like to move any of your comments to different columns or add items to the list? Try to add at least two comments based on what you have learned from this activity.

Chem Essential Questions

What does it mean?

Chemistry explains a macroscopic phenomenon (what you observe) with a description of what happens at the nanoscopic level (atoms and molecules) using symbolic structures as a way to communicate. Complete the chart below in your *Active Chemistry* log.

MACRO	NANO	SYMBOLIC
Explain what you observed when the magnesium metal was added to the copper solution.	*Explain the single replacement of magnesium metal with copper solution at the nanoscopic level (atoms and molecules).*	*Math is often used as a symbolic way of describing relationships. Give an example of how math was used or described in this activity to relate atoms and mass.*

How do you know?

What evidence do you have about the reaction of magnesium and copper chloride? How do you know that the mass of magnesium and the mass of copper were not identical in the reaction?

Why do you believe?

Baking a cake is a chemical reaction. How do you use the concept of definite proportions in the recipe for baking a cake?

Why should you care?

The challenge in this chapter is to create a game that will help people understand the periodic table. The atomic mass of elements is another property that will be added to your cards and help you to better understand the periodic table. Describe how you can creatively use atomic masses as part of a game and not require players to memorize these numbers.

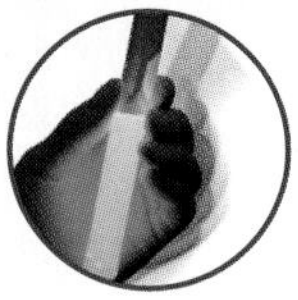

Reflecting on the Activity and the Challenge

In this activity, you learned how chemists measured elements in chemical reactions to determine the relative masses of atoms and how these masses were assembled into a scale of atomic masses. The atomic mass is one of the most important pieces of information listed for each element on the periodic table. When you incorporate atomic mass into your game about the periodic table, you will have to decide whether you will test players' ability simply to identify the atomic mass from a periodic table or require that players understand how the relative scale was determined.

Chem to Go

1. John Dalton believed that water was formed from the simplest combination of hydrogen and oxygen atoms—one of each. Observations today show that 8 g of oxygen react with 1 g of hydrogen to form water.

John Dalton

   a) Based on these two statements, what conclusion could Dalton draw about the relative masses of oxygen and hydrogen atoms? How many times more massive is an oxygen atom than a hydrogen atom?

   b) The atomic mass of oxygen is 16 and the atomic mass of hydrogen is 1. How do the current atomic masses of oxygen and hydrogen compare to Dalton's?

   c) You know that water molecules are not made from one atom of hydrogen and one atom of oxygen. Water is H_2O. A water molecule is made up of two atoms of hydrogen and one atom of oxygen. The gram of hydrogen reacting with eight grams of oxygen is due to the fact that there are twice as many hydrogen atoms as there are oxygen atoms. How many times more massive is an oxygen atom than a hydrogen atom?

   d) Are the values of these revised masses closer to the current atomic masses of oxygen and hydrogen atoms?

2. In Dalton's time, it was observed that ammonia formed when nitrogen reacted with hydrogen. Today's values show that fourteen grams of nitrogen react with three grams of hydrogen.

   a) If ammonia were formed from Dalton's simplest formula of one atom of each element, what would he have concluded about the relative masses of nitrogen and hydrogen atoms?

   b) Ammonia molecules are actually made from three atoms of hydrogen and one atom of nitrogen. If the three grams of hydrogen reacting with fourteen grams of nitrogen is due to three times as many hydrogen atoms as there are nitrogen atoms, how many times more massive is a nitrogen atom than a hydrogen atom?

3. Instead of magnesium, a student uses aluminum in this activity and obtains the following data:

   Mass of beaker: 30.20 g

   Mass of beaker + aluminum: 30.40 g

   Mass of beaker + aluminum + copper (II) chloride: 32.40 g

   Mass of beaker + aluminum + copper (II) chloride + water: 57.40 g

   Mass of dry filter paper: 0.67 g

   Mass of new beaker: 30.50 g

   Mass of beaker + wet filter and residue + solution: 58.37 g

   Mass of dry filter + residue: 1.38 g

   a) How many grams of aluminum did the student use in this experiment?

   b) How many grams of copper did the student measure in the dry filter paper?

   c) How many times as great is the mass of the copper as the mass of aluminum the student originally used? (What is the ratio of mass of copper to mass of aluminum?)

   d) If three atoms of copper were released for two atoms of aluminum that become combined (with chlorine), the masses of copper and aluminum determined in (a) and (b) should contain the same number ratio of atoms (3:2). What does this tell you about the relative masses of copper and aluminum atoms? How many times more massive is a copper atom than an aluminum atom?

4. Look at the table. It gives the atomic masses of the nine elements that you observed in *Activity* 2, plus hydrogen. Add this data to your element cards. Can you now improve upon the way you sorted the cards in the previous activity taking this new information about relative masses into account?

Element	Relative atomic mass
aluminum	26.98
carbon	12.01
copper	63.55
hydrogen	1.01
iodine	126.90
iron	55.85
magnesium	24.31
silicon	28.09
sulfur	32.06
zinc	65.38

5. If you cut a piece of aluminum into two equal pieces and cut those pieces into two equal pieces and repeat this 10 times, the tiny piece of aluminum is about 1000 (2^{10}) times smaller than the original piece. How many cuts would it take to get down to 1 atom of aluminum if the size of an atom was one billion times smaller than a 1-cm piece of aluminum?

6. ***Preparing for the Chapter Challenge***

   In a paragraph, explain how the relative scale of atomic masses is determined.

Activity 4 Are Atoms Indivisible?

What Do You See?

Do not try this at home. It may ruin your TV.

GOALS

In this activity you will:

- Observe or learn the behavior of a cathode ray in the presence of a magnet.
- Discuss Thomson's conclusions from 1897 about cathode rays.
- Simulate an experiment from 1911 by Rutherford in which he learned more about the structure of atoms.
- Organize your understanding of some of the different particles that comprise matter.

What Do You Think?

Ever since Democritus from ancient Greece hypothesized the existence of atoms, a major question was how atoms of different elements were different.

- **If you could observe a single atom of gold and a single atom of lead, how do you think they would be different? What might they have in common?**

Record your ideas about these questions in your *Active Chemistry* log. Be prepared to discuss your responses with your small group and the class.

Investigate

1. Your teacher will demonstrate the behavior of what were called cathode rays a hundred years ago. They were called cathode rays because they were emitted from the negative terminal, or cathode of what was known as a cathode-ray tube. This tube was a forerunner of the television and the computer monitor. Alternatively, your teacher may show you a video demonstrating the effect of a magnetic field on a cathode-ray tube.

a) What happens to the path of the cathode rays when a horseshoe magnet is placed near the tube? Record your observation in your *Active Chemistry* log.

b) Record what happens to the path of the cathode rays when the orientation of the horseshoe magnet is reversed.

2. For the particles that make up the cathode rays to change direction, the magnet must be exerting a force on these electrically charged particles. In 1897, Joseph John (J. J.) Thomson showed that the cathode rays were made of electrons. Electrons are negatively charged, tiny particles. He also discovered that identical electrons were emitted regardless of the metal of which the cathode was made.

Discovery of electrons emerging from the atoms of any metal gave scientists new information about the atom. The atom is divisible. It has internal parts, one of which is the electron.

a) In a sentence or two, describe the relationship between cathode rays, the electron, and the structure of atoms.

3. To investigate the other components of an atom, you will take part in the following simulation. It is similar to the game *Battleship*. You will work with a partner for this activity.

You and your classmate should each construct an 8-by-10 grid of squares as shown on the following page. You can label the columns of the grid with letters A, B, C... Label the rows of the grid 1, 2, 3... Without letting your classmate see your grid, color in a section of ten squares. The squares must touch each other. To make the simulation relatively simple, begin with a compact design. This shape (colored region) represents your target.

You and your partner will try to guess the shape of each other's target by sending "missiles" onto any of the 80 squares in this array. For the purpose of this description, designate one person to be Player X and the other person to be Player Y. To begin, Player X will tell Player Y the destination (number and letter) of the missile being sent. Player Y will respond, indicating that the missile "hit" or "missed" the target shape. Player X will make note of the response. Then Player Y

Always use the minimum voltage and current necessary to operate the Crooke's tube to limit the hazard of x-ray production. In addition, maximize distance and minimize time for the demonstration.

Cathode-ray tube with electrons being deflected by a magnetic field

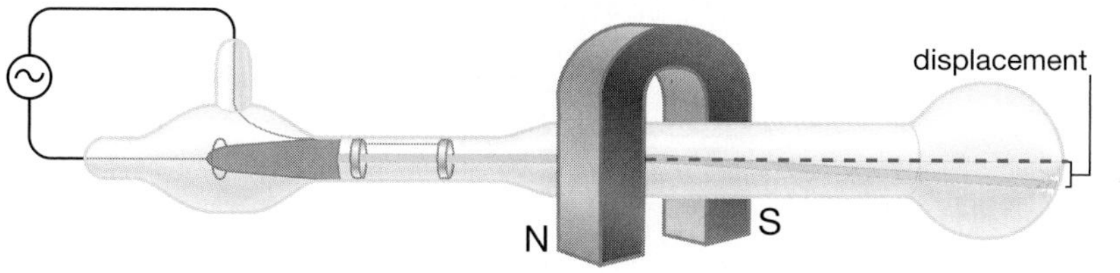
displacement
N
S

sends the next missile, noting the response. Continue this process until one player identifies the other player's target.

a) Record the number of turns taken to complete the game.

b) Repeat the game with a target of only two adjacent squares. Record the number of turns taken.

4. Now do a thought experiment. The same-size game grid is divided into smaller squares. Suppose there are 100 squares across and 100 squares down. There are now 10,000 squares in the same size board as before. A target of only one square is chosen.

a) Record an estimate of how many turns will be required to identify the target square amongst the 10,000 squares in the game grid.

5. Now modify the thought experiment. The same-size grid is now 1000 rows across and 1000 squares down. That is 1,000,000 squares.

a) Record an estimate of how many turns will be required to identify the target square among the 1,000,000 squares in the grid.

6. In 1911, Lord Ernest Rutherford conducted an experiment similar to your game of battleship. Rutherford sought to learn something about the structure of the atom by bombarding gold atoms with energetic particles given off by certain atoms.

	A	B	C	D	E	F	G	H	I	J
1										
2										
3										
4										
5										
6										
7										
8										

In Rutherford's game of battleship, it seemed that he was required to send an incredibly large number of missiles to get a "hit." He concluded that the grid of the atom must be composed of very tiny cells and only one cell contains all of the positive charge of the atom.

a) In your *Active Chemistry* log, explain why you think he concluded this.

Chem Talk

THE CHANGING MODEL OF AN ATOM

J.J. Thomson's Model of an Atom

As was noted in this activity, in the late 1800s J.J. Thomson, an English physicist, found evidence for the existence of negatively charged particles that could be removed from atoms. He called these subatomic particles with negative charges **electrons**. Using this new information, Thomson then proposed a model of an atom. This model was a positive sphere, with electrons evenly distributed and embedded in it, as shown in diagram (a). Using the same evidence, H. Nagaoka, a Japanese scientist, modeled the atom as a large positively charged sphere surrounded by a ring of negative electrons, as shown in diagram (b). These models show that scientists agreed that atoms contain electrons. They also agreed that atoms were electrically neutral. To maintain this electric neutrality, an atom must contain an equal number of positive and negative charges.

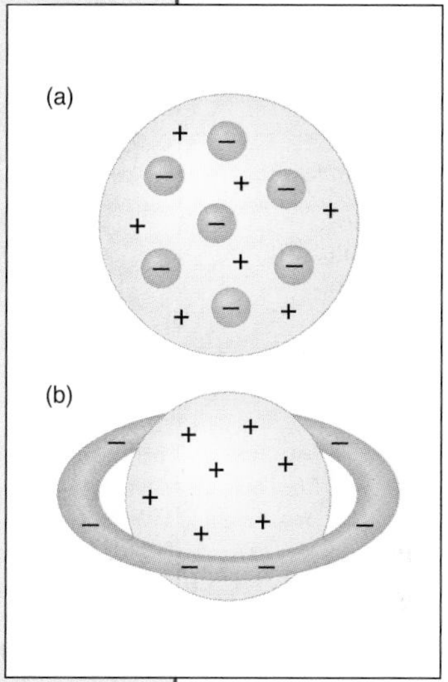
(a)
(b)

Chem Words

electron: the negatively charged subatomic particle of an atom.

Millikan Determines the Mass and Charge of an Electron

Thomson was able to measure only the ratio of mass-to-charge for an electron, not the mass itself. The American physicist Robert A. Millikan devised a method for determining the mass of an electron. His famous experiment is called the Millikan oil-drop experiment.

First, Millikan produced small droplets of oil by spraying them from a nozzle into a box. The tiny mist of negatively charged droplets was allowed to fall between two charged metal plates. It was possible to stop the drops from falling by having the plates exert an upward electrical force on the drops. Millikan was able to calculate the charge of an electron as 1.6×10^{-19} C (coulombs). He then used Thomson's charge-to-mass ratio to determine the mass of an electron to be 9.10×10^{-28} g. This is about 1/2000 of the mass of a proton. Thomson remarked that these electrons were very, very tiny.

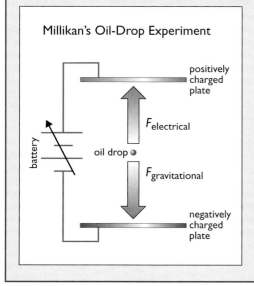

Millikan's Oil-Drop Experiment

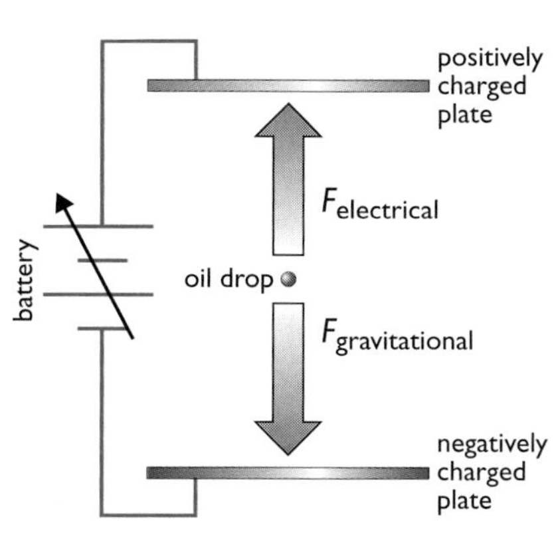
positively charged plate
$F_{electrical}$
battery
oil drop
$F_{gravitational}$
negatively charged plate

Chem Words

alpha particle: helium ions that are positively charged.

nucleus: the very small dense region in the center of an atom that contains all the positive charge and most of the mass.

proton: the positively charged subatomic particle contained in the nucleus of an atom.

Ernest Rutherford

Rutherford's Discovery of the Nucleus

For several years there was no evidence to contradict either Thomson's or Nagaoka's atomic models. However, in the early 1900s, Ernest Rutherford, a New Zealand-born scientist, designed experiments to test the current model of an atom. In Rutherford's experiment, positively charged **alpha particles** were sent as "missiles" toward a thin sheet of gold. Gold was used because it is malleable and could be hammered into a very thin sheet. Most of the positively charged alpha particles went through the sheet and were not deflected. It is as if they missed the target. This was expected since it was assumed that the atom's charge and mass was spread evenly throughout the gold. Some of the alpha particles were deflected slightly. However, most interesting to Rutherford was that occasionally one of the alpha particles "hit" the gold sheet and bounced straight back at the source. This was unexpected. The conclusion was that there must be tiny places containing lots of charge and mass. Since the bouncing back was so unusual, it was assumed that the places where all the charge and mass were concentrated were only 1/100,000 of the area of the gold. Rutherford concluded that almost all the mass and all of the positive charge of the atom is concentrated in an extremely small part at the center. He called this center part the **nucleus**. He used the term **proton** to name the smallest unit of positive charge in the nucleus.

Rutherford's Experiment

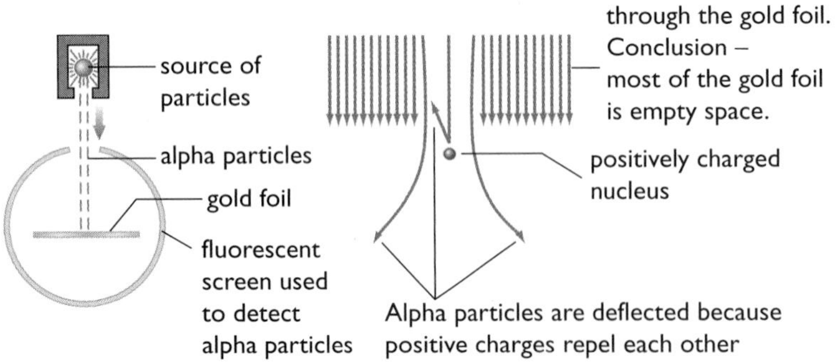
source of particles
alpha particles
gold foil
fluorescent screen used to detect alpha particles
Most alpha particles pass straight through the gold foil. Conclusion – most of the gold foil is empty space.
positively charged nucleus
Alpha particles are deflected because positive charges repel each other

Experimental setup **Observed results**

The story of Rutherford's discovery of the atomic nucleus is best told by Rutherford himself. Examining the deflection of high-speed alpha particles as they passed through sheets of gold foil, Rutherford and his student Hans Geiger noticed that some particles were scattered through larger angles than predicted by the existing theory of atomic structure.

Fascinated, Rutherford asked Geiger's research student Ernest Marsden to search for more large-angle alpha scattering. Rutherford did not think that any of the alpha particles in his experiment would actually bounce backward. "Then I remember two or three days later Geiger coming to me in great excitement and saying, 'We have been able to get some of the alpha particles coming backwards . . . ' It was quite the most incredible event that has ever happened to me in my life. It was almost as incredible as if you fired a 15-inch shell (a missile) at a piece of tissue paper and it came back and hit you."

A Physics Connection

What was responsible for the wide-angle scattering of the alpha particles and their bouncing back? Well, the major forces involved in chemistry are electrical. They are based on the physics associated with Coulomb's Law of electrostatics.

The force between two charged particles (q_1 and q_2) is inversely proportional to the square of the distance (d) between them.

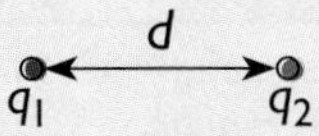
d
q1
q2

where k is a constant $= 9.0 \times 10^9 \mathrm{N{\cdot}m^2/C^2}$

$$F = \frac{kq_1q_2}{d^2}$$

If the particles are of opposite charge, then the force is attractive. If the particles are of the same charge, then the force is repulsive. Opposite charges attract, and like charges repel. The closer the positively charged alpha particle gets to the positively charged nucleus, the larger the force. This causes a larger deflection of the alpha particle.

In this activity, you learned about experimental evidence for the existence of electrons and a nucleus. Think back to when you first heard about electrons and the nucleus. Was it in elementary school? Often, theories about the structure of the atom are presented as facts without explaining any of the evidence that led to the theory. Science involves the accumulation of evidence and the building of a model and theory. It is not memorizing a set of facts.

Checking Up

1. What is an electron?
2. Why was Rutherford surprised that some alpha particles bounced back from the gold foil?
3. What is the nucleus of an atom?

What Do You Think Now?

At the beginning of the activity you were asked:

- **If you could observe a single atom of gold and a single atom of lead, how do you think they would be different? What might they have in common?**

Compare and contrast an atom of gold and an atom of lead using what you learned in this activity.

Chem Essential Questions

What does it mean?

Chemistry explains the macroscopic phenomenon (what you observe) with an explanation of what happens at the nanoscopic level (atoms and molecules) using symbolic structures as a way to communicate. Complete the chart below in your *Active Chemistry* log.

MACRO	NANO	SYMBOLIC
Describe your observations of the cathode rays and their interaction with a magnet.	*Chemistry uses the structure of the atom to describe reactions of one material with another. What explanations at the atomic level did Thomson and Rutherford each make based on their evidence?*	*In chemistry, you create symbolic structures. How could you build a model that shows a tiny positively charged nucleus that takes up only 1/100,000 of the total space?*

How do you know?

What evidence do you have for the existence of a nucleus in the atom?

Why do you believe?

The electrons in a cathode ray are also used to create a picture on your TV screen and your computer monitor. How could you test to see if those electrons behave similarly to those in the cathode-ray tube?

Do not carry out your idea without your teacher's permission. You can damage the TV.

Why should you care?

The periodic table will be a symbolic structure that summarizes much of what you know about atoms. What three things would you want the players of your periodic-table game to know at the end of the game?

Reflecting on the Activity and the Challenge

In this activity, you learned of evidence that atoms are made of a positively charged nucleus and negatively charged electrons. Mendeleev's Periodic Table of the Elements provided insights into the structure of matter and atoms. Your periodic-table game will also reveal information about the structure of the atom and the role of evidence in creating models.

Chem to Go

1. Since the electron has a negative electric charge and the nucleus has a positive electric charge, where would you expect to find electrons in atoms?
2. Are atoms indivisible? Support your answer using information from this activity.
3. Construct a chart or diagram to summarize what you have learned in this activity about the particles that make up an atom. Include electric charge and location of the particles.
4. Lead has an atomic number (the number of protons) of 82; iron has an atomic number of 26; and copper has an atomic number of 29. How do the charges of the nuclei of these three elements compare?
5. An atom is neutral and an electron has a charge of -1.6×10^{-19} C. What is the charge of a proton? Explain why you chose this value.
6. Sketch the outside outline of three grids. Pretend that each grid has 100,000 squares.
   a) If the target was 50,000 squares, draw the target.
   b) If the target was 25,000 squares, draw the target.
   c) If the target was only 1 square, draw the target.
   d) Which grid most closely relates to the nucleus found in Rutherford's experiment? Explain your answer.
7. Cathode rays (electrons) originate at the cathode (negative) terminal. They move in a straight line.
   a) What will happen when you bring a magnet near the cathode ray?
   b) How can you get it to deflect it in the opposite direction?
   c) If the cathode-ray beam travels between a positive and a negative plate, which plate will the cathode rays be attracted towards?
8. In Millikan's oil-drop experiment, you wish to suspend the negatively charged oil drop. Since gravity pulls the oil drop down, should the negative plate be placed above or below the negatively charged oil drop?

Inquiring Further

1. An atomic timeline

Construct a timeline that reflects how scientists' views of the atom have changed through the ages. Identify significant scientists, their beliefs, and experimental findings as mentioned in this chapter. You may also wish to consult other resources. Add information to your timeline as you continue to work through this chapter.

2. John Dalton's Atomic Theory

John Dalton, an English scientist, developed his atomic theory in the early 1800s. This theory was based on the Greek concept of atoms and the studies of Joseph Proust's Law of Definite Proportions or Law of Constant Composition. Dalton's Atomic Theory contained a series of postulates (hypotheses). They were based on the data of his time and his observations:

- **Matter consists of small particles called atoms.**
- **Atoms of one particular element are identical and the properties are identical.**
- **Atoms are indestructible. In chemical reactions, the atoms rearrange or combine, but they are not destroyed.**
- **Atoms of different elements have a different set of properties.**
- **When atoms of different elements combine to form compounds, they combine a ratio of small whole numbers.**

From his postulates, the Law of Conservation of Mass would be supported. His postulates state that atoms cannot be destroyed but they can be moved around and combine with other atoms to form compounds. That means that the mass of the compound must be the sum of the atoms of the compound. This law still exists with a slight change for nuclear reactions.

Investigate whether all of Dalton's postulates are presently accepted or describe how some have been changed based on current understanding.

3. Avogadro's number and a mole

Chemists are interested in keeping track of quantities of particles. However, the particles are very small so chemists use a particular quantity that is convenient for counting particles. The quantity is called a *mole*. The quantity of particles in a mole is 602,000,000,000,000,000,000,000. The mole can be represented more easily in scientific notation as 6.02×10^{23}. This is a very large number because many, many small particles (atoms or molecules) make up a mole. The number 6.02×10^{23} is sometimes called Avogadro's number.

Research to find the significance of Avogadro's number and a mole. Record your findings in your *Active Chemistry* log.

Then, to appreciate how huge a mole is, answer the following question:
Imagine there are 7 billion people (7×10^9 people, which is approximately the human population of the world) and they are given the task of dropping $1-bills once every second into a large hole. How long will it take 7×10^9 people to drop one mole of dollar bills into the hole? How old will you be when they complete this task?

Activity 5 The Electronic Behavior of Atoms

What Do You See?

ARGON
Ar
HELIUM
He
NEON
Ne
CHLORINE
Cl

GOALS

In this activity you will:

- View the spectrum of hydrogen.
- Interpret changes in electron energies in the hydrogen atom to develop an explanation for where the colored light in the hydrogen spectrum comes from.
- Use Bohr's model of the atom to predict parts of the hydrogen-atom spectrum.
- Compare the wavelengths, energies, and frequencies of light of different colors.
- Identify regions in the electromagnetic spectrum.
- Explain the photoelectric effect.

What Do You Think?

Neon signs make up some of the lights of Broadway in New York City. They are also used in advertising signs throughout the world.

- **How is the color produced in a neon sign?**

Record your ideas about this question in your *Active Chemistry* log. Be prepared to discuss your response with your small group and the class.

Investigate

1. In order to directly observe the behavior of atoms, you can observe the spectrum of light given off when atoms are excited by a high-voltage, electric-power supply. You probably have already seen this effect in the familiar red color of neon signs.

   For this demonstration, your teacher will set up a tube of hydrogen gas connected to a high-voltage power supply. This light can be viewed through a spectroscope or a diffraction grating, as shown in the diagram. When the slit at the end of the spectroscope is aimed towards the light, the colors of the spectrum appear separately off to the sides of the slit.

a) What colors do you see in the spectrum of light given off by hydrogen gas?

b) Make a colored diagram in your *Active Chemistry* log of what you see inside the spectroscope. Make sure to draw and label the colors in the proper order and spacing between them that you observe.

2. When you observed the spectrum of light given off by hydrogen gas, you probably saw three or four distinct lines, each having a different color. The color of light is a measure of its energy. The colors closer to red in the spectrum have the least energy and the colors closer to violet have the greatest energy.

   a) List the colors that you observed from lowest energy to highest energy.

3. In 1913, Niels Bohr, a Danish physicist, tried to explain the line spectrum of hydrogen. He hypothesized that the electron in the hydrogen atom is allowed to have only certain amounts of energy. These energy levels would be orbits in which the electron in hydrogen could circle the nucleus of hydrogen.

   The diagram shows a sketch of some of the possible orbits of the hydrogen electron with their corresponding energies.

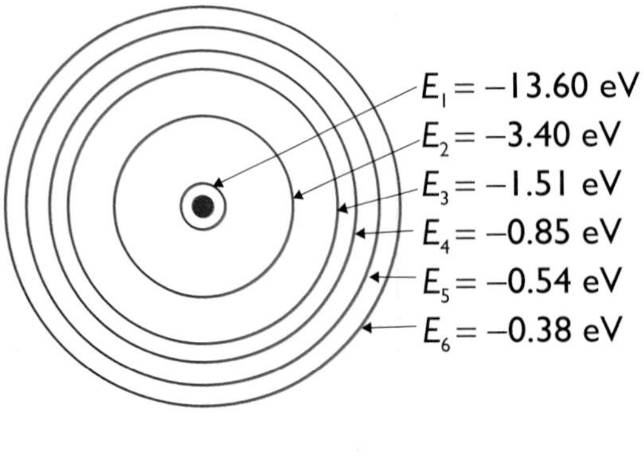

E1 = −13.60 eV
E2 = −3.40 eV
E3 = −1.51 eV
E4 = −0.85 eV
E5 = −0.54 eV
E6 = −0.38 eV

   a) Think of the energy values as being on a number line. Which orbit has the greatest energy?

   b) Which orbit has the least energy?

4. Bohr believed that an electron in a higher energy level would give off light when it jumps to a lower energy level. The amount of energy in the light would be the difference in these energy levels. When an electron jumps from E_2 to E_1, the amount of energy in the light would be $E_2 - E_1 = (-3.4) - (-13.6) = +10.2$ units of energy. Note that E_2 has a larger energy than E_1 (that's because $-3.4 > -13.6$).

   Calculate the amount of energy in the light when an electron jumps from the following energy levels.

   a) E_3 to E_1

   b) E_3 to E_2

   c) E_4 to E_2

   d) E_5 to E_2

5. Picture the electron in orbit about the nucleus of the hydrogen atom as Bohr did. Allowing the electron to have only certain amounts of energy would mean that the electron could be allowed in orbits of only certain distances from the nucleus. As the electron "jumps" from one energy level to another, it behaves something like a ball falling down a flight of uneven stairs. It is allowed to rest only on one of the steps, nowhere in between.

   a) Every possible jump corresponds to light of a different energy. How many different energies of light can be emitted from hydrogen when the electron jumps down to E_1 from E_2, E_3, E_4, E_5, and E_6?

   b) How many different energies of light can be emitted from hydrogen when the electron jumps down to E_2 from E_3, E_4, E_5, and E_6?

ARCH #2
The Nugget

c) An electron can also jump from E_5 to E_3 to E_2. Calculate the two energies of light that would be emitted in these two jumps.

6. Each energy of light corresponds to a specific color. The four colors of light that you observed in the hydrogen spectrum corresponded to four specific energies and therefore four specific jumps. Bohr found that the four colors of light had energies that corresponded to the energy differences when electrons jumped from a higher level to the E_2 level. However, Bohr was unable to find light colors corresponding to jumps to the E_1 level or the E_3 level.

   a) Why do you think he was unable to find light colors corresponding to the jumps in the E_1 level?

7. The colors corresponding to jumps to the E_1 level have higher energies and are not seen by the eye. They do not correspond to visible light. When detectors were built that could see into the ultraviolet portion of the spectrum, the wavelengths of light corresponded to the energy levels that Bohr predicted when the electron jumped down to the E_1 level.

   a) Why do you *now* think that Bohr was not able to find light colors corresponding to the jumps to the E_3 level? (Hint: Compare the energies of these jumps to the energies when the electron jumped to the E_2 level.)

   Prediction of the energies of the light given off when the electrons jumped from higher energy states to the E_1 level and the E_3 level demonstrated what a powerful model Bohr had invented. He was able to predict accurately some light given off that nobody had ever measured.

8. The electrons can get "excited" and move from lower energy levels to higher energy levels by absorbing light of just the right energy. An electron in the E_1 orbit can absorb 10.2 units of energy and jump to the E_2 level. Refer back to the energies of the different levels. Provide the energies of light that can be absorbed by an electron to move it through each of the following.

   a) E_1 to E_3

   b) E_2 to E_3

   c) E_2 to E_4

9. You now have grasped the basics of the Bohr model of the atom. The electron of hydrogen is able to orbit the nucleus in specific orbits. Each of these orbits corresponds to a specific energy. When the electron jumps from a higher energy level (further from the nucleus) to a lower energy level (closer to the nucleus), the electron loses energy. Light of exactly this energy is given off. Each jump corresponds to a different energy of light. Some of these light energies can be detected by the human eye and are called visible light. You see these different energies as different colors. Other jumps correspond to energies of light that are not detected by the human eye. However, they can be detected by instruments. These energies correspond to light in the infrared or ultraviolet parts of the spectrum. When electrons jump to lower energy levels, light is given off. When electrons absorb light, they jump to higher energy levels.

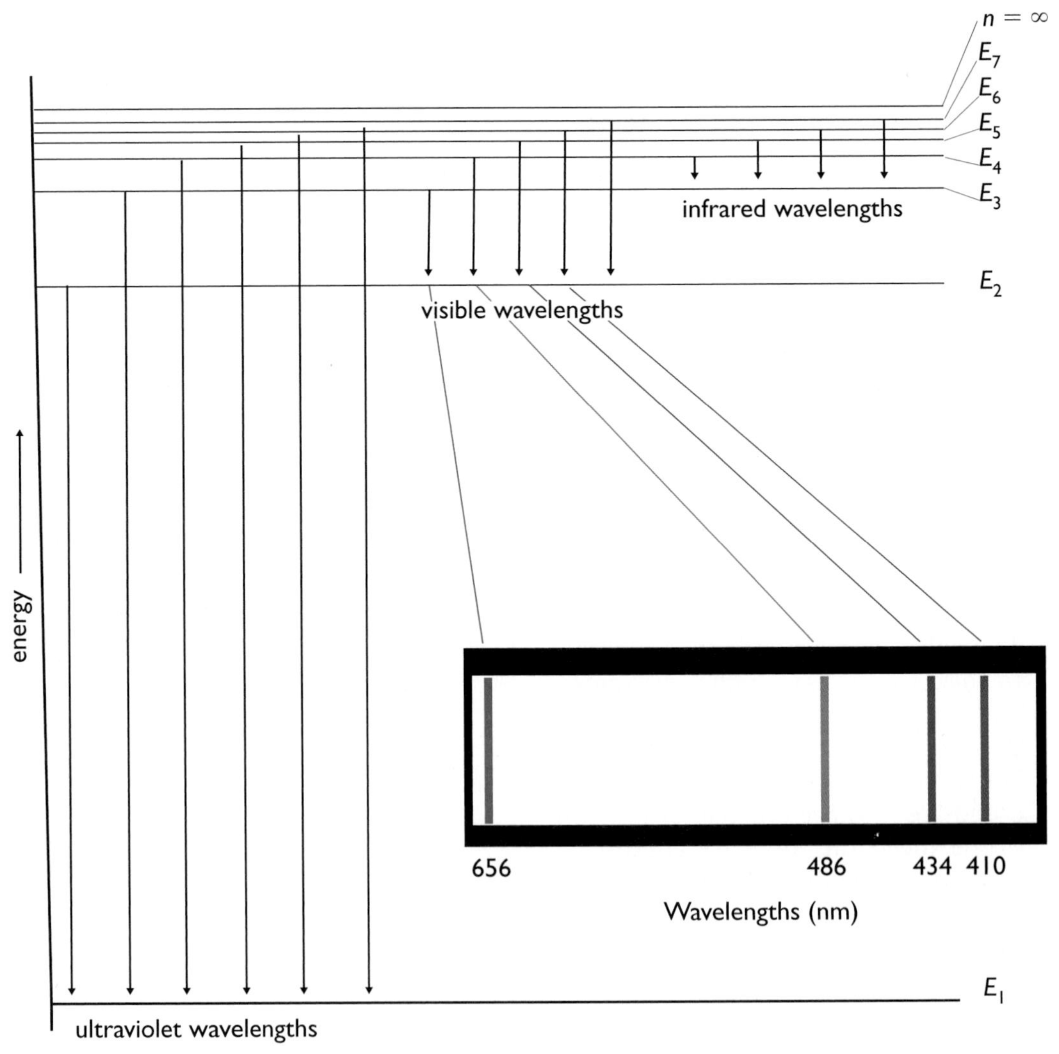

n = ∞
E7
E6
E5
E4
E3
infrared wavelengths
E2
visible wavelengths
energy
656
486
434
410
Wavelengths (nm)
E1
ultraviolet wavelengths

Chem Talk

BOHR'S MODEL OF AN ATOM

Electron Orbits

Niels Bohr

Niels Bohr was a brilliant Danish physicist. He proposed a "planetary" model of the atom. He theorized that electrons travel in nearly circular paths, called **orbits**, around the nucleus. Each electron orbit has a definite amount of energy. The farther away the electron is from the nucleus, the greater is its energy. Bohr suggested the revolutionary idea that electrons "jump" between energy levels (orbits) in a *quantum* fashion. This means that they can never exist in an in-between level. Thus, when an atom absorbs or gives off energy (as in light or heat), the electron jumps to higher or lower orbits. Electrons are the most stable when they are at lower energy levels closer to the nucleus.

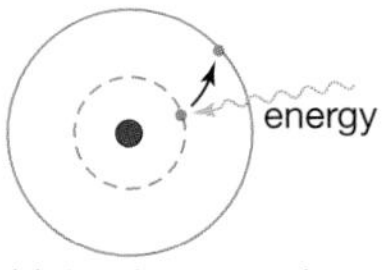
energy

(a) An electron gains a quantum of energy.

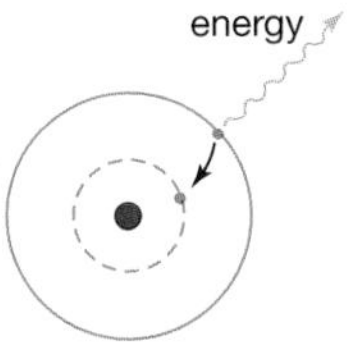
energy

(b) An electron loses a quantum of energy.

The Electromagnetic Spectrum

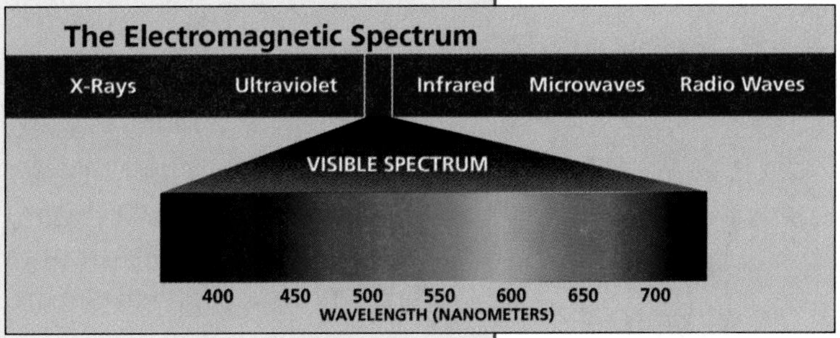
The Electromagnetic Spectrum
X-Rays
Ultraviolet
Infrared
Microwaves
Radio Waves
VISIBLE SPECTRUM
400
450
500
550
600
650
700
WAVELENGTH (NANOMETERS)

You observed light when hydrogen gas was given a large voltage. This visible light is only one part of the **electromagnetic spectrum**. You have probably heard of some of the other parts. These include ultraviolet, infrared, x-rays, gamma rays, microwaves, and radio waves. As you demonstrated in calculations using Bohr's model, the light from some of the transitions is in the ultraviolet region. Infrared light is also emitted as the electron jumps from E_4 to E_3 and E_5 to E_3 and other higher energy levels.

Many people do not think of radio waves as being similar to light waves. However, they are part of the electromagnetic spectrum. Your eyes can only see a very small part of the electromagnetic spectrum. Often, you hear radio announcers say that they are broadcasting at a certain **frequency**. Your FM radio dial may have MHz (megahertz) printed on the side. This tells you that the numbers correspond to frequencies in units of MHz or 10^6 Hz. Frequency tells you the number of cycles or waves that are being produced per second. The unit for frequency is a hertz (Hz). 1 Hz = 1 cycle/s = 1 s^{-1}. Normally, frequency is read as per second and the cycles are dropped from the terminology.

Chem Words

orbit: in Bohr's model of the hydrogen atom, the circular path of an electron traveling around the nucleus (similar to the planet's orbit around the Sun).

electromagnetic spectrum: the complete spectrum of electromagnetic radiation, such as radio waves, microwaves, infrared, visible, ultraviolet, x-rays, and gamma rays.

frequency: the number of waves per second or cycles per second or Hertz (Hz).

Chem Words

wavelength: the distance measured from crest to crest of one complete wave.

photon: a fixed packet of electromagnetic radiation that has a given amount of energy.

Wavelength is the distance from crest to crest of a wave. The symbol for wavelength is λ, the Greek letter *lambda*. The speed of electromagnetic radiation is constant and it is called the speed of light, *c*. Its value is 2.998×10^8 m/s. This is often approximated to 3.00×10^8 m/s.

Frequency and wavelength are related through the speed of light:

$$c = \lambda f$$

From this information, you can calculate the frequency of light of a given wavelength. The equation that is used for this is:

$$f = \frac{c}{\lambda}$$

As an example, if the wavelength is 434.2 nm, then the frequency is:

$$f = \frac{2.998 \times 10^8 \text{ m/s}}{434.2 \times 10^{-9} \text{ m}}$$

$$= 6.905 \times 10^{14} \text{ cycles/s}$$

$$= 6.905 \times 10^{14} \text{ Hz}$$

As you go across the electromagnetic spectrum you should note that the wavelength continues to get smaller as the frequency increases. Also, you should understand that the energy of the spectrum increases as you go from radio waves to x-rays or gamma rays. Max Planck, a German physicist, found that light comes in fixed packets called **photons**. The energy of a specific wavelength or frequency of light could be calculated.

The equation he developed is

$$E = hf$$

where h is Planck's constant and is 6.63×10^{-34} J·s and f is the frequency.

The corresponding energy of the red light above would be:

$$E = hf$$

$$= (6.63 \times 10^{-34} \text{ J·s})(4.567 \times 10^{14} \text{ Hz})$$

$$= 3.03 \times 10^{-19} \text{ J}$$

So, the next time that you are standing around a campfire, you can inform your fellow campers that red light has less energy than blue light. You can also tell them how to calculate these values.

Example:

In hydrogen the energy change of an electron jumping from E_3 to E_2 is 3.03×10^{-19} J. Conservation of energy insists that this is equal to the energy of the light that is emitted.

You can find the frequency of the light.

$$E = hf$$

$$3.03 \times 10^{-19}\ \text{J} = (6.63 \times 10^{-34}\ \text{J·s})\ (f)$$

$$f = 4.57 \times 10^{14}\ \text{Hz}$$

Knowing the frequency of light, you can find the wavelength.

$$c = f\lambda$$

$$3 \times 10^{8}\ \text{m/s} = (4.57 \times 10^{14}\ \text{Hz})\ \lambda$$

$$\lambda = 6.56 \times 10^{-7}\ \text{m}$$

Referring to a chart that shows wavelength and color, you find that this is red light. It is the red light that you observed when looking at the hydrogen spectrum.

The Photoelectric Effect

Light has wave-like properties like wavelength and frequency. These wave-like properties were seen in the activity as you observed the spectrum of hydrogen. Light also has particle-like properties like momentum and can be seen in collisions with matter. The photoelectric effect is a collision between a particle of light (a photon) and an electron on the surface of a metal. The energy of this photon is calculated using the equation $E=hf$. The energy of light is *quantized.* That means that it comes in fixed amounts. In Einstein's explanation of the photoelectric effect, he showed that light must behave like a particle with fixed energies that depend on the frequency. For this he was awarded the Nobel Prize in 1921.

The Problem with Bohr's Atomic Theory

Niels Bohr was aware that his theory of electron jumps had incredible success but also raised some problems. Bohr's theory could only account for the spectrum of hydrogen. It could not account for the spectra of any other element. Bohr's theory could not explain why only certain orbits were allowed. It could also not explain how the electron could jump from one orbit to another. Other scientists improved on Bohr's model as they discovered more about the atom and quantum mechanics.

Checking Up

1. How are visible light, ultraviolet light, infrared light, x-rays, gamma rays, microwaves, and radio waves related?
2. Explain the meaning of wavelength.
3. Why is "planetary" model an appropriate name for Bohr's model of the atom?
4. How do the energy levels of different electron orbits compare?
5. Why do elements produce certain color light when heated?
6. What two particles collide in the photoelectric effect?

What Do You Think Now?

At the beginning of the activity you were asked:

- **How is the color produced in a neon sign?**

You now know why light of certain wavelength (and color) is given off when energy is applied to neon gas. How would you explain to a friend how a neon light works?

Chem Essential Questions

What does it mean?

Chemistry explains a macroscopic phenomenon (what you observe) with a description of what happens at the nanoscopic level (atoms and molecules) using symbolic structures as a way to communicate. Complete the chart below in your *Active Chemistry* log.

MACRO	NANO	SYMBOLIC
Describe what you saw through the spectroscope or the diffraction grating when the tube of hydrogen gas was subjected to a large voltage.	*Explain how the light is created in the hydrogen atom. Why are only certain colors emitted?*	*Make a sketch to represent what is occurring at the atomic level when the line spectrum for hydrogen is produced. What equation is used to measure the different electron energy levels?*

How do you know?

The excitation of hydrogen atoms produces a visible line spectrum that allows you to measure the wavelength and then determine the energy of that specific wavelength of light. How well did the calculations of the energy correspond to the energy (or wavelength) measured in the lab?

Why do you believe?

The Sun is primarily made of hydrogen. What colors (or wavelengths) of light would you expect to see?

Why should you care?

Understanding what causes the line spectrum of hydrogen atoms will help to understand the behavior of hydrogen's electron. This in turn will help you to understand many of hydrogen's properties, and will be an excellent addition to your game.

Reflecting on the Activity and the Challenge

In this activity you learned that the electrons in an atom are responsible for the colors of light emitted. Bohr explained the spectrum of light given off by excited hydrogen atoms. He hypothesized that each hydrogen atom's electron was allowed in only certain energy levels. Mendeleev knew nothing about electrons or energy levels when he *first* developed the periodic table. Yet, the periodic table today is seen as a reflection of the number of electrons in an atom of each element and the energy levels those electrons occupy. Continue to think about how the electronic structure of an atom could be included in the game you are designing.

Chem to Go

1. In this activity you were told that light with greater frequency has greater energy.
   a) Which color in the visible spectrum of hydrogen has the greatest energy? The least energy?
   b) Which color in the visible spectrum of hydrogen has the highest frequency? The lowest frequency?
2. If an electron were to fall down to the E_1 level from the E_3 level, how would its energy compare to one that only fell to the E_2 level? Explain.
3. What is the difference measured in energy when an electron falls from E_3 to E_1? How many times greater is this value as compared to the difference of the electron falling from E_3 to E_2?
4. A wavelength of light is 389.0 nm and its frequency is 7.707×10^{14} Hz. Show how this frequency value was calculated.
5. Show that the wavelength of 389.0 nm has an energy of 5.11×10^{-19} J.
6. a) Microwave radiation is absorbed by the water in food. As the water absorbs the heat it causes the food to get hot. If the λ of a microwave is 10 cm, calculate the frequency of the microwave and the energy of each photon.
   b) The red light you observed in the hydrogen spectrum had a $\lambda = 656.5$ nm. The energy of the red light was 3.03×10^{-19} J. How many times greater is this value when compared to the energy value that you found for the microwave energy?
7. Describe how the Bohr model explains the spectra emitted by hydrogen.
8. Describe all possible energy transitions that can be emitted from an electron in the E_4 level as it moves to the E_1 level.
9. What are two limitations of the Bohr model for the atom?
10. Draw the set of energy levels of hydrogen to scale. Which transition produces the highest energy light?
11. What do you think happens when an electron in a hydrogen atom moves from a higher energy level to the lowest E_1 level? This series is known as the *Lyman series* (ultraviolet light).

Chapter mini Challenge

HONK
THE BRIDGE

Your challenge for this chapter is to create a game that will both entertain and teach people about the periodic table. Since you have completed five activities, this is a good time to give your game a *first try*.

Your *mini-challenge* is to create or adapt a game that has chemistry content as part of its structure. You will only be providing the class with a two-minute explanation of the game that you are developing. Within your two minutes, you should explain some of the rules of the game and some of the chemistry content that a player will get to learn from the game.

Chemistry Content

Your team should first review the chemistry content that may be included in this periodic-table game challenge.

Activity 1: You learned about organization. The periodic table is a way in which your knowledge about the properties of matter can be organized.

Activity 2: You investigated the properties of some elements. These properties included the ability to conduct electricity, whether the element reacted with HCl, and whether the material was a metal or nonmetal. You also attempted to organize the elements in terms of these properties.

Activity 3: You learned how to compare and contrast elements and compounds. You were also able to determine the relative masses of elements. The mass of elements is another property by which elements can be organized.

Activity 4: The game of battleship helped you learn about the structure of the atom. You learned that the nucleus takes up a very, very small part of the atom. That tiny space holds all of the positive charge and almost all of the mass of the atom. You also learned about the discovery of the electron and its place in the atom.

Activity 5: You observed the specific colors of the light given off by hydrogen gas. By investigating these colors (and energies) of light, you learned how Bohr developed a model of the atom. You learned that electrons jumping from a higher energy orbit to a lower energy orbit emitted light of a specific energy and color.

Criteria

Your team should also review the criteria that you discussed on the first day of this chapter. Your periodic-table game should be creative and fun. It should demonstrate an understanding of chemistry concepts and help teach these concepts.

Preparing for Your mini Challenge

Your team should begin the process of creating a game by brainstorming ideas about games that you enjoy that may be adapted for this purpose. You should then discuss how you could include chemistry concepts from at least two of the activities in the game. You can then decide on the rules of the game.

Engineering/Technology Design

The engineering-design process involves a number of distinct steps. In creating a game, you are involved in a design process. Note how your efforts follow the design model described.

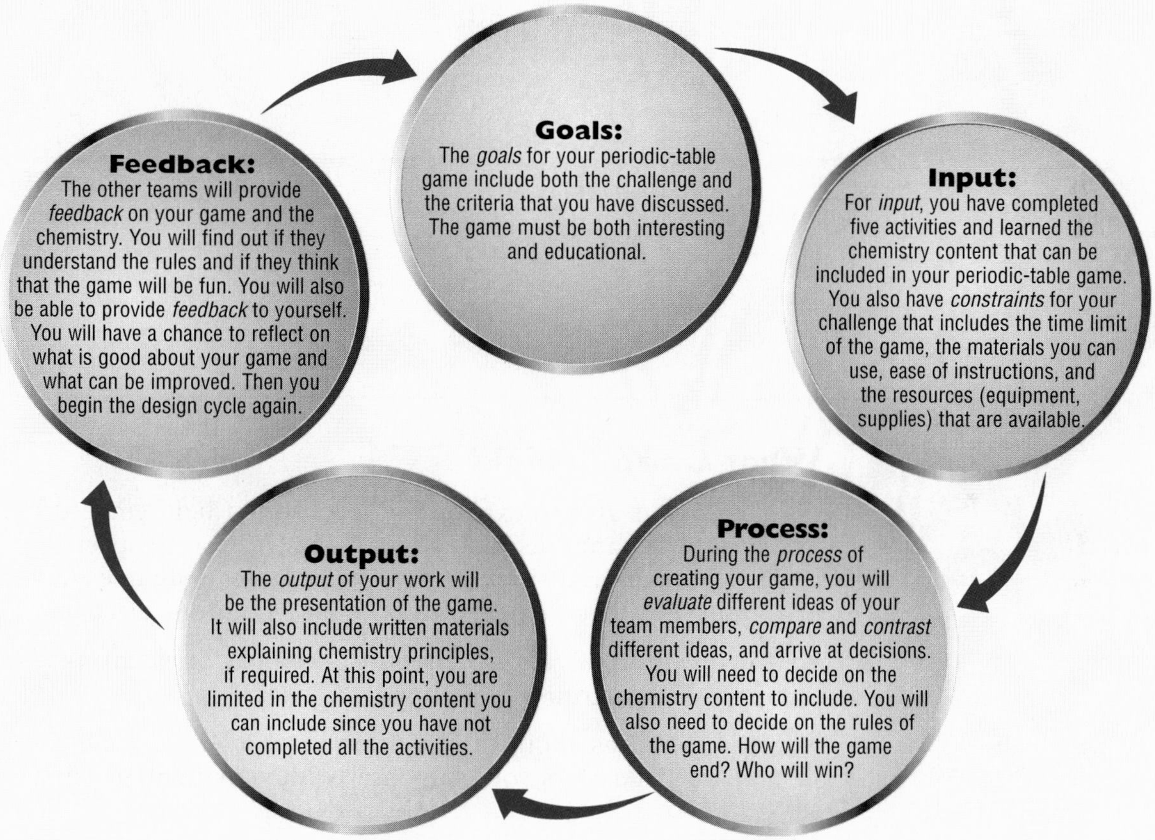
Goals:
The *goals* for your periodic-table game include both the challenge and the criteria that you have discussed. The game must be both interesting and educational.
Input:
For *input*, you have completed five activities and learned the chemistry content that can be included in your periodic-table game. You also have *constraints* for your challenge that includes the time limit of the game, the materials you can use, ease of instructions, and the resources (equipment, supplies) that are available.
Process:
During the *process* of creating your game, you will *evaluate* different ideas of your team members, *compare* and *contrast* different ideas, and arrive at decisions. You will need to decide on the chemistry content to include. You will also need to decide on the rules of the game. How will the game end? Who will win?
Output:
The *output* of your work will be the presentation of the game. It will also include written materials explaining chemistry principles, if required. At this point, you are limited in the chemistry content you can include since you have not completed all the activities.
Feedback:
The other teams will provide *feedback* on your game and the chemistry. You will find out if they understand the rules and if they think that the game will be fun. You will also be able to provide *feedback* to yourself. You will have a chance to reflect on what is good about your game and what can be improved. Then you begin the design cycle again.

Remember: This is a *first try*. The feedback that you get from this brief presentation of your game will be extremely valuable when you prepare for the full periodic-table game that you will develop at the end of the chapter. At that point, you will begin the entire design cycle again. That's why it is called a cycle. You keep going through it over and over to improve your design or, in this case, the periodic-table game.

Activity 6 Atoms with More than One Electron

What Do You See?

POP!
He
Li

GOALS

In this activity you will:

- View the spectra of various materials.
- Graphically analyze patterns in the amounts of energy required to remove electrons from different kinds of atoms.
- Compare trends in stability of atoms in the periodic table.
- Compare the structure of the periodic table with the patterns of levels and sublevels to which electrons can be assigned.
- Develop a shorthand notation to describe the configuration of electrons in an atom.

What Do You Think?

Niels Bohr was able to explain the spectrum of light emitted by hydrogen using a model that assigned the electron to specific energy levels. Hydrogen is a simple atom that contains only one electron. The atoms of other elements contain more than one electron.

- **How do you think an increase in the number of electrons would impact the spectrum of an atom?**

Record your ideas about this question in your *Active Chemistry* log. Be prepared to discuss your responses with your small group and the class.

Investigate

1. In *Activity 5* you observed the visible spectrum of hydrogen gas as its electron moved from a higher energy level to a lower energy level. You also explored a model that used Bohr's theory to explain this spectrum. Now it's time to look at the spectra of some other elements.

   a) Your teacher will connect a tube containing an element other than hydrogen to a high-voltage supply. Record the name of the element in your *Active Chemistry* log. Look at the spectrum of light of this element through the spectroscope.

   b) What colors do you see? Make a diagram in your log of the spectrum (pattern of colors) you see inside the spectroscope.

c) Record how this spectrum is similar to and different from the hydrogen spectrum you observed in *Activity 5*.

d) Repeat *Steps (a), (b),* and *(c)* for other samples of elements as available.

2. Spectra of such elements as helium and neon are very beautiful. However, they cannot be explained by Bohr's simple theory for the single electron in the hydrogen atom. The basic idea is still true. Light is emitted when electrons jump from a higher energy level to a lower energy level. The energy levels, however, are more complex if there are additional electrons. A more elaborate labeling of electron energy levels is necessary. In this activity you will explore the pattern of electron energy levels in atoms containing more than one electron.

When multiple electrons are present, some are easier (i.e., require less energy) to remove from the atom than others. The chart of ionization energies provides information about the amount of energy required to remove the two highest energy electrons. These are the outermost electrons and are easiest to remove. These energies are called the first and second ionization energies. They are given in units of joules. Notice that all values are multiplied by 10^{-19}.

a) Make a graph that shows how the ionization energies vary with atomic number. Since the atomic numbers range from 1 to 36, label the *x*-axis with atomic numbers from 1 to 36. Since the ionization energies range from 7 to 121.2, label the *y*-axis with ionization energies from 0 to 130. Plot the first ionization energy data from the chart in one color, connecting the data points as you go along.

b) Plot the values for the second ionization energies in a different color.

c) Include a title and legend on your graph.

Atomic number	Element (symbol)	1st ionization energy J ($\times 10^{-19}$)	2nd ionization energy J ($\times 10^{-19}$)
1	H	21.8	
2	He	39.4	87.2
3	Li	8.6	121.2
4	Be	14.9	29.2
5	B	13.3	40.3
6	C	18.0	39.1
7	N	23.3	47.4
8	O	21.8	56.3
9	F	27.9	56.0
10	Ne	34.6	65.6
11	Na	8.2	75.8
12	Mg	12.3	24.1
13	Al	9.6	30.2
14	Si	13.1	26.2
15	P	16.8	31.7
16	S	16.6	37.4
17	Cl	20.8	38.2
18	Ar	25.2	44.3
19	K	7.0	50.7
20	Ca	9.8	19.0
21	Sc	10.5	20.5
22	Ti	10.9	21.8
23	V	10.8	23.5
24	Cr	10.8	26.4
25	Mn	11.9	25.1
26	Fe	12.7	25.9
27	Co	12.6	27.3
28	Ni	12.2	29.1
29	Cu	12.4	32.5
30	Zn	15.1	28.8
31	Ga	9.6	32.9
32	Ge	12.7	25.5
33	As	15.7	29.9
34	Se	15.6	34.0
35	Br	18.9	34.9
36	Kr	22.4	39.0

3. Look at the graph of the first ionization energies and answer the following questions:

   a) What kinds of patterns do you see? How could you quickly relate the shape of the graph to someone who had not seen it? If you were given a piece of blank paper and only five seconds, how would you sketch the pattern of ionization energies?

   b) Where are the ionization energies the largest? The smallest?

   c) What happens to the ionization energies as the atomic number increases?

   d) Group the elements by their ionization energies into four consecutive "periods." List the range of atomic numbers in each group.

   e) Is there any interruption in the general trend of ionization energies as the atomic number increases for a "period"? If so, describe it.

4. Look at the second colored graph line you drew.

   a) Describe how the two graphs are alike and/or different. Do you see similarities between the two graphs?

5. If a large amount of energy is needed to remove an electron from an atom, the arrangement of electrons in that atom is considered to be especially stable. Thus, a high first ionization energy means that a lot of energy must be supplied to remove an electron from an atom and that the electron arrangement in that atom is especially stable. Any element that has a larger first ionization energy than its neighboring elements has an electron arrangement in its atoms that is more stable than its neighboring elements.

   a) Which element in the first period (atomic numbers 1 and 2) has the most stable arrangements of electrons in its atoms? (Remember, you are looking for elements that have larger ionization energies than their neighbors. In reality, you are looking for peaks in your graph, not just those elements with higher values.)

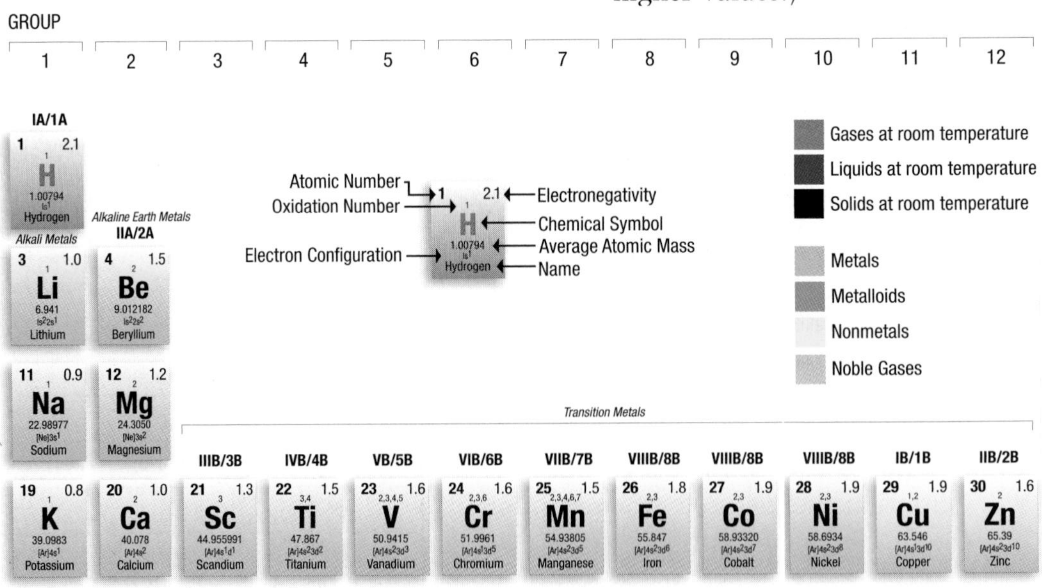

GROUP
1
2
3
4
5
6
7
8
9
10
11
12
IA/1A
Alkali Metals
Alkaline Earth Metals
IIA/2A
Atomic Number
Oxidation Number
Electron Configuration
Electronegativity
Chemical Symbol
Average Atomic Mass
Name
Gases at room temperature
Liquids at room temperature
Solids at room temperature
Metals
Metalloids
Nonmetals
Noble Gases
Transition Metals
IIIB/3B
IVB/4B
VB/5B
VIB/6B
VIIB/7B
VIIIB/8B
VIIIB/8B
VIIIB/8B
IB/1B
IIB/2B
H Hydrogen 1.00794
Li Lithium 6.941
Be Beryllium 9.012182
Na Sodium 22.98977
Mg Magnesium 24.3050
K Potassium 39.0983
Ca Calcium 40.078
Sc Scandium 44.955991
Ti Titanium 47.867
V Vanadium 50.9415
Cr Chromium 51.9961
Mn Manganese 54.93805
Fe Iron 55.847
Co Cobalt 58.93320
Ni Nickel 58.6934
Cu Copper 63.546
Zn Zinc 65.39

b) Which elements in the second period (atomic numbers 3 through 10) of the periodic table have the most stable arrangements of electrons in their atoms?

c) Which elements in the third period (atomic numbers 11 through 18) of the periodic table have the most stable arrangements of electrons in their atoms?

d) Which elements in the fourth period (atomic numbers 19 through 36) of the periodic table have the most stable arrangements of electrons in their atoms?

6. As mentioned earlier, the Bohr model was not able to account for the spectrum of an element containing more than one electron. A more elaborate model was needed. In this new model, the energy levels are broken down into sublevels. When these sublevels are filled, the atom exhibits a higher degree of stability. In this model, the sublevels are designated by the four letters *s*, *p*, *d*, and *f*.

	13	14	15	16	17	18
				Chalcogens	*Halogens*	*Noble Gases*
PERIOD	IIIA/3A	IVA/4A	VA/5A	VIA/6A	VIIA/7A	VIIIA/8A or 0
1						2 He 4.002602 $1s^2$ Helium
2	5 2.0 1 B 10.811 $1s^22s^22p^1$ Boron	6 2.5 -4,2,4 C 12.011 $1s^22s^22p^2$ Carbon	7 3.0 -3,2,3,4,5 N 14.00674 $1s^22s^22p^3$ Nitrogen	8 3.5 -2 O 15.9994 $1s^22s^22p^4$ Oxygen	9 4.0 -1 F 18.998403 $1s^22s^22p^5$ Fluorine	10 Ne 20.1797 $1s^22s^22p^6$ Neon
3	13 1.5 3 Al 26.981539 $[Ne]3s^23p^1$ Aluminum	14 1.8 2,4 Si 28.0855 $[Ne]3s^23p^2$ Silicon	15 2.1 -3,3,4,5 P 30.973762 $[Ne]3s^23p^3$ Phosphorus	16 2.5 -2,2,4,6 S 32.066 $[Ne]3s^23p^4$ Sulfur	17 3.0 -1,1,3,5,7 Cl 35.44527 $[Ne]3s^23p^5$ Chlorine	18 Ar 39.948 $[Ne]3s^23p^6$ Argon
4	31 1.6 3 Ga 69.723 $[Ar]4s^23d^{10}4p^1$ Gallium	32 1.8 4 Ge 72.61 $[Ar]4s^23d^{10}4p^2$ Germanium	33 2.0 -3.3.5 As 74.92159 $[Ar]4s^23d^{10}4p^3$ Arsenic	34 2.4 -2,4,6 Se 78.96 $[Ar]4s^23d^{10}4p^4$ Selenium	35 2.8 -1,1,5,7 Br 79.904 $[Ar]4s^23d^{10}4p^5$ Bromine	36 Kr 83.80 $[Ar]4s^23d^{10}4p^6$ Krypton

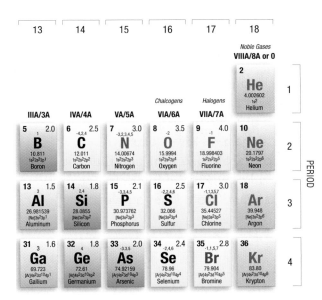

The periodic table shows the atomic number, the chemical symbol, and how many electrons in an atom of each element are in each sublevel. The total number of electrons is equal to the atomic number of the element. This is because the atoms are neutral and therefore have a number of electrons equivalent to the number of protons. Remember that the atomic number is equal to the number of protons, since all protons are positively charged. This arrangement of the electrons in each sublevel will be referred to as the electron assignment or electron configuration of the element. Use the periodic table below to answer the following questions:

a) In which sublevels (include number and letter) are the one electron in hydrogen and the two electrons in helium?

As you move to the second period (second row on the periodic table), each new element has one more proton in its nucleus and one more electron. The electrons must find a place to stay—an energy level and a sublevel within that energy level. As you move along in the periodic table to increasing atomic numbers, you see that the additional electrons fill the sublevel. A completed sublevel is one that is holding the maximum number of electrons allowed to it before electrons must be placed in the next higher sublevel.

b) In which region of the periodic table are electrons added in an *s* sublevel? What is the greatest number of electrons found in any *s* sublevel?

c) In which region of the periodic table are electrons added in a *p* sublevel? What is the greatest number of electrons found in the *p* sublevel?

d) In which region of the periodic table are electrons added in a *d* sublevel? What is the greatest number of electrons found in the *d* sublevel?

e) Select a column in the periodic table. (A column of elements on the periodic table is called a family or group.) Look at the electron configuration for each element within the column. Take special note of the last entry, the sublevel to which the last electron in an atom of each element in that column is added. What do all of these sublevels have in common? How many electrons are in these particular sublevels?

f) Mendeleev assigned elements to the same column of the periodic table because the elements had similar properties, both physical and chemical. For example, elements may have had similar electrical conductivity or similar reactions with acid, or were metals. These were the properties that you explored in *Activity 2*. How, then, does the number and location of the electrons in the outermost sublevel relate to chemical properties? You can now acknowledge that electrons (as opposed to the nucleus) are the key to the chemical properties of elements. Write this statement in your log using your own words.

7. At the beginning of this activity, you constructed a graph of the ionization energy versus the atomic number. If you take this graph and rotate it 90°, you will find that the graph reminds you of the periodic table, constructed by Mendeleev because of similar chemical and physical properties of elements.

   a) What is the relationship between ionization energies and the rows of the periodic table?

Chem Talk

A PERIODIC TABLE REVEALED

Ions and Ionization Energy

In the table in the *Investigate* section, the amount of energy required to remove an electron from an atom was called **ionization energy**. Atoms are neutral. That is, the number of electrons is equal to the number of protons. However, atoms can gain or lose electrons. Atoms that have lost or gained electrons are called **ions** and thus the energy used to remove the electrons is known as the ionization energy. A sodium (Na) ion is formed when a sodium atom loses an electron:

$$Na + \text{energy} \longrightarrow Na^{+} + e^{-}$$

Chem Words

ionization energy: the amount of energy needed to totally remove an electron from an atom.

ions: atoms that have lost or gained electrons.

The energy required to remove a single electron from the highest occupied energy level is called the first ionization energy. The energy needed to remove a second electron from the same atom, after the first one has already been removed, is called the second ionization energy. For another example, look at the removal of two electrons from a calcium (Ca) atom:

$$Ca + energy \longrightarrow Ca^{+} + e^{-}$$

This equation represents the 1st ionization energy.

$$Ca^{+} + energy \longrightarrow Ca^{2+} + e^{-}$$

This equation represents the 2nd ionization energy.

The second electron to be removed from the nucleus is more tightly bound. This is because of a greater electrostatic attraction to the positively charged nucleus. Therefore, it takes more energy to remove this electron. The second ionization energy is always higher than the first.

Measuring the atomic radii of the elements correlates with the ionization energies. As you go left to right across a row of the periodic table, the atomic radius of each element becomes smaller. Consider this in light of the ionization energies. Moving from left to right across a row in the periodic table, the ionization energies increase. The nuclear charge (the number of protons) is increasing so the electrons are held more tightly. As the electrons are held more tightly, you would expect the size of the atoms to decrease.

Also, as you go down a column, the atomic radius for each element becomes larger. This is because the electrons are now being placed in orbitals farther from the nucleus.

Electron Configuration and Energy Levels

As you discovered, the Bohr model was not able to account for the spectrum of an element containing more than one electron. In the new model you investigated, the energy levels are broken down into sublevels. This arrangement of the electrons in each sublevel is called the electron assignment or **electron configuration** of the element. When these sublevels are filled, the atom exhibits a higher degree of stability. The sublevels are designated by the four letters *s, p, d,* and *f.* The letters come from the words that the early scientists used to describe some of the observed features of the line spectra. The sublevels are governed by the following rules:

(i) The first energy level (corresponding to E_1 in *Activity 5*) has only →

Chem Words

electron configuration: the arrangement of the electrons of an atom in its different energy sublevel(s).

one type of orbital, labeled 1*s*, where 1 identifies the energy level and *s* identifies the orbital.

(ii) The second energy level (corresponding to E_2 in *Activity 5*) has two types of orbitals (an *s* orbital and *p* orbitals) which are labeled the 2*s* and 2*p* orbitals.

(iii) The third energy level (corresponding to E_3 in *Activity 5*) has three types of orbitals (an *s* orbital, *p* orbitals, and *d* orbitals) and are labeled as the 3*s*, 3*p*, and 3*d* orbitals.

(iv) The number of orbitals corresponds to the energy level you are considering. For example: E_4 has four types of orbitals (*s, p, d,* and *f*); E_5 has five types of orbitals (*s, p, d, f,* and *g*).

(v) The *s* orbital has a maximum of two electrons. The *p* orbitals have a maximum of six electrons. The number of electrons is indicated by a superscript following the orbital designation. For example, $2p^5$ means that in the 2nd energy level and the *p* orbitals there are five electrons. $1s^2$ means that in the 1st energy level and the *s* orbital there are two electrons.

Electron configuration is determined as follows. Electrons are placed into the lowest energy levels first and "built up" from there. For example, a neutral carbon atom has six electrons. The first electron is placed in the 1st energy level and the *s* orbital. The second electron is placed in the 1st energy level and the *s* orbital. You can represent these two electrons as $1s^2$. The 1*s* orbital is now filled. There are no more orbitals in the 1*s* level. The next two electrons are placed in the 2nd energy level and the *s* orbital. You can signify these two electrons as $2s^2$. The 2nd energy level also has the *p* orbitals. The final two electrons are placed in the 2nd energy level and the *p* orbitals. You can signify these two electrons as $2p^2$. The resulting configuration is $1s^2 2s^2 2p^2$.

The electron configuration for Argon (Ar, with 18 electrons) is:

$1s^2 2s^2 2p^6 3s^2 3p^6$. To be sure that all 18 electrons are accounted for, add the superscript numbers to see that they do add up to 18 $(2 + 2 + 6 + 2 + 6 = 18)$.

The electron configuration for arsenic (As, with 33 electrons) is:

$1s^2 2s^2 2p^6 3s^2 3p^6 4s^2 3d^{10} 4p^3$ or a shorthand designation as [Ar] $4s^2 3d^{10} 4p^3$.

The [Ar] simply implies the electron configuration is the same as argon up to the point just before $4s^2$.

Example:

What is the element with an electron configuration $1s^2 2s^2 2p^6 3s^2 3p^6 4s^1$?

You can find the number of electrons by adding the electrons in each orbital (2 in the 1*s* orbital, 2 in the 2*s* orbital, 6 in the 2*p* orbital, etc.) That is, $2 + 2 + 6 + 2 + 6 + 1 = 19$. This element has 19 electrons. Referring to the periodic table, you find that potassium (K) has 19 electrons and is the element with that electronic configuration.

Stability is an important feature for all matter. Remember the excited electron of the hydrogen atom? If the electron were in energy level 3, it would drop down to energy level 2 and give off a specific wavelength of light. Alternatively, the electron in energy level 3 could drop down to energy level 1 and give off a different, specific wavelength of light. The word "excited" is used to describe an electron that has absorbed enough energy to move to a higher energy level, before it falls back down to its original state. The electron in the **excited state** was unstable and lost energy by giving off light in order to get to a more stable form. Particles arranged in an unstable way will move to a more stable arrangement. The most stable arrangement is called the **ground state** and this is where electrons occupy the lowest orbitals possible.

Electrons: Where Are They, Really?

The atomic orbitals designated as *s, p, d,* and *f* are regions in space. Each has its own shape. They are mathematical descriptions of a *probability* of locating an electron at any given time. The quantum mechanical model of modern physics concentrates on the electron's wavelike properties. This is not easily understood in terms of your everyday experiences. The concept of wave/particle duality is simply a model. It is a highly mathematical model. You cannot see atoms and electrons and observe their behavior directly. The best you can do is construct a set of mathematical models that best fit atomic properties that you see experimentally.

Describing the location of an electron in terms of probability resulted from an idea of Werner Heisenberg, a German physicist. He proposed what is now called the **Heisenberg uncertainty principle**. It basically says that it is impossible to precisely determine the exact position and momentum of an electron at the same time. This is why scientists speak of orbitals instead of orbits (like in Bohr's model). They refer to average distance from the nucleus, not actual distance.

→

Chem Words

excited state: an electron of an atom that has absorbed enough energy to be raised to a higher energy sublevel.

ground state: the lowest energy sublevel that an electron of an atom can occupy.

Heisenberg uncertainty principle: states that it is impossible to precisely determine the exact position and momentum of an electron at the same time.

Chem Words

period: a horizontal row of elements in the periodic table.

chemical group: a family of elements in the periodic table that have similar electron configurations.

If you know the position of an electron with a high degree of certainty, then you can't know its momentum. This principle is stated mathematically as:

$$(\Delta x)(\Delta p) \geq \frac{h}{2\pi}$$

where Δx is the uncertainty in the electron's position, and

Δp is the uncertainty in the momentum, and

h is Planck's constant.

Here's another way to look at this concept. In order to "see" an electron, it is necessary to shine light (a photon with a certain energy) on it. This energy will be passed on to the electron, increasing its energy and its momentum. So, the very process of looking at an electron causes it to be somewhere else!

Werner Heisenberg

The Periodic Table

In previous activities you tried to organize elements by their properties and then by their atomic number. When elements are arranged according to their atomic numbers a pattern emerges in which similar properties occur regularly. This is the periodic law. The horizontal rows of elements in the periodic table are called **periods**. The set of elements in the same vertical column in the periodic table is called a **chemical group**. As you discovered, elements in a group share similar physical and chemical properties. They also form similar kinds of compounds when they combine with other elements. This behavior is due to the fact that elements in one chemical group have the same number of electrons in their outer energy levels and tend to form ions by gaining or losing the same number of electrons.

Checking Up

1. What is an ion?
2. What is ionization energy?
3. Explain the term chemical group.
4. Name three elements in a chemical group.
5. Provide the complete electron configuration for the atom argon (Ar).

What Do You Think Now?

At the beginning of the activity you were asked:

- **How do you think an increase in the number of electrons would impact the spectrum of an atom?**

Your response might have been along the lines of "it will become more complicated, more complex." Now that you have additional information about line spectra, describe what you would see and why you would see it when you have more than one electron in an atom.

Chem Essential Questions

What does it mean?

Chemistry explains a macroscopic phenomenon (what you observe) with a description of what happens at the nanoscopic level (atoms and molecules) using symbolic structures as a way to communicate. Complete the chart below in your *Active Chemistry* log.

MACRO	NANO	SYMBOLIC
Describe what you see when an atom other than hydrogen emits light.	*Describe how electron behavior is able to account for the specific wavelengths of emitted light.*	*A symbolic structure is used to describe the electron configuration of an atom. Explain what the symbols* $1s^2$, $2s^2$, *and* $2p^5$ *tell you about the electron and the atom.*

How do you know?

Calcium and strontium are close to one another on the periodic table. What do you know about their ionization energies, their electron configurations, and their characteristics based on their position on the periodic table?

Why do you believe?

In viewing a fireworks display, how can you determine the chemicals being used?

Why should you care?

Understanding the ionization potentials of the elements helps you understand the electron configuration of the elements. It also helps you to understand why the atomic size decreases as you go from left to right and also why it increases as you go down a column. How can information about electron configurations and their relation to the periodic table be an interesting part of your game?

Reflecting on the Activity and the Challenge

In this activity you learned that electrons in atoms are assigned not only to energy levels but also to sublevels, labeled *s, p, d,* and *f*. You have also learned that the electron configuration of atoms of all elements in the same column of the periodic table end with the same sublevel and number of electrons in that sublevel. Mendeleev organized elements into columns based on similar chemical properties. Thus, electron energy sublevels are clearly associated with chemical properties of elements and their position on the periodic table. You may wish to incorporate the information about electron configuration in your game to meet the *Chapter Challenge*.

Chem to Go

1. Write the complete configuration of electron energy levels, from 1*s* to 4*s*.
2. Consider the element boron (B) as an example.
   a) What is boron's atomic number?
   b) How many electrons does boron have?
   c) What is the complete electron configuration for boron? (Be sure to include the number and letter of the appropriate sublevels, as well as the number of electrons in each sublevel.)
3. Answer the following questions for the element zinc.
   a) What is zinc's atomic number?
   b) How many electrons does zinc have?
   c) What other elements might you expect to have chemical properties similar to zinc? Explain your choices.

30 2 1.6
Zn
65.39
$[Ar]4s^2 3d^{10}$
Zinc

4. Answer the following questions for the element calcium.
   a) What is calcium's atomic number?
   b) How many electrons does calcium have?
   c) What is the complete electron configuration for calcium? (Be sure to include the number and letter of the appropriate sublevels, as well as the number of electrons in each sublevel.)

20 2 1.0
Ca
40.078
$[Ar]4s^2$
Calcium

d) What is the last sublevel (number and letter, please) to which electrons are added? How many electrons are in this sublevel?

e) Where would you expect to find calcium on the periodic table? Support your prediction with your answers from (d).

f) What other elements would you expect to have chemical properties similar to calcium? Explain your choices.

5. A chemist has synthesized a heavy element in the laboratory and found that it had an electron configuration:

$1s^2 2s^2 2p^6 3s^2 3p^6 4s^2 3d^{10} 4p^6 5s^2 4d^{10} 5p^6 6s^2 4f^{14} 5d^{10} 6p^6 7s^2 5f^{14} 6d^8$

a) What is the number of electrons in this element?

b) What is the atomic number?

c) What might you predict about this element?

6. If the electron configuration is given, you should be able to determine what element it is. Identify the following element from its electron configuration:

$1s^2 2s^2 2p^6 3s^2 3p^6 4s^2 3d^6$

7. Which list of elements is arranged in order of increasing atomic radii?

a) Li, Na, Mg, Be

b) Na, Mg, Be, Li

c) Li, Be, Na, Mg

d) Be, Mg, Li, Na

8. Which is smaller, Br or Br^-? Explain your choice.

9. ***Preparing for the Chapter Challenge***

Write a sentence or two to explain in words the pattern you noticed between any group and the electron configurations of the elements belonging to that group.

Inquiring Further

Determining electron configuration

In this activity, you were able to look at the electron configuration for a given element provided in the periodic table. Research other ways that the electron configuration can be determined.

Activity 7

How Electrons Determine Chemical Behavior

What Do You See?

THE SODIUM CHLORIDE ROMANCE

CHEM POETRY

A sodium atom
walks onto the scene,
His valence electron's
feeling keen,
Positive that he will
ionically bond
With a halogen of
whom he is fond.

He spots chlorine
on the other side,
Sporting her valence
shell with pride.
Sodium's attraction
he just cannot hide,
So the duo walk out
as sodium chloride.

—Mala Radhakrishnan

GOALS

In this activity you will:

- Investigate more patterns in the electron arrangements of atoms.
- Relate the positions of elements on the periodic table, their electron arrangements, and their distances from the nearest noble gas, to chemical properties of the elements.
- Relate electron arrangements to ionization energies.
- Assign valence numbers to elements and organize the periodic table according to valence numbers.

What Do You Think?

You have learned that electron configurations determine an atom's chemical behavior. You have also learned how these electrons are labeled according to a series of energy sublevels.

- **How does the arrangement of electrons in an atom determine its chemical behavior?**

Record your ideas about this question in your *Active Chemistry* log. Be prepared to discuss your responses with your small group and the class.

Investigate

1. In *Activity 6* you learned that elements with relatively high ionization energies have stable arrangements of electrons. One particular group of elements, located in the column at the extreme right of the table, exhibit high ionization energies and therefore have stable arrangements of electrons. They are called the noble gases.

   Look at the periodic table on the inside back cover for the assignment of electrons to energy sublevels for atoms of each of these elements. Focus on the sublevel at the end of the electron arrangement where the last electron is assigned.

a) Make and complete a chart like the one below in your *Active Chemistry* log. An example has been provided for you.

Element	Column A Energy level (number) to which the last electron is assigned	Column B Sublevel (letter) to which the last electron is assigned	Column C Number of electrons in the sublevel to which the last electron is assigned	Column D Total number of all electrons of the energy level in Column A
helium				
neon				
argon	3	*p*	6	8
krypton				
xenon				
radon				

b) Look at the numbers in Column A in your chart. How are these numbers related to the respective rows of the periodic table in which each of the elements is located?

c) What pattern do you notice in Columns B and C?

d) What pattern do you notice in Column D?

2. The chemical behavior of an element can be understood by looking at the electron assignment of an atom of the element as compared to the electron assignments of neighboring noble gas atoms. The chemical inactivity of noble gas atoms reflects the stable arrangement of their electrons, one which other atoms cannot easily disturb. In the following questions you will compare the electron assignments in atoms with those of noble gases.

a) Make and complete a chart like the following one in your *Active Chemistry* log. In this chart you will compare the electron assignments of lithium, beryllium, and boron to the electron assignment of helium ($1s^2$), the closest noble gas. An example has been provided for you.

Element being compared	Number of electrons *more* than those found in closest noble gas (He)	Energy level (number) to which the last electron is assigned	Energy sublevel (letter) to which the last electron is assigned	Location of element (row) in the periodic table	Location of element (column) in the periodic table
lithium	1	2	s	*Row 2*	*Column 1*
beryllium					
boron					

b) Make and complete another chart like the one below in your *Active Chemistry* log. This time you will compare the electron assignments of sodium, magnesium, and aluminum to the electron assignment of neon ($1s^22s^22p^6$), the closest noble gas.

Element being compared	Number of electrons *more* than those found in closest noble gas (Ne)	Energy level (number) to which the last electron is assigned	Energy sublevel (letter) to which the last electron is assigned	Location of element (row) in the periodic table	Location of element (column) in the periodic table
sodium					
magnesium					
aluminum					

c) Describe any patterns you notice in the charts in 2(a) and/or 2(b) above.

d) Make and complete a chart like the one below in your *Active Chemistry* log. In this chart you will compare the electron assignments of nitrogen, oxygen, and fluorine to the electron assignment of neon ($1s^22s^22p^6$), the closest noble gas. An example has been provided for you.

Element being compared	Number of electrons *less* than those found in closest noble gas (Ne)	Energy level (number) to which the last electron is assigned	Energy sublevel (letter) to which the last electron is assigned	Location of element (row) in the periodic table	Location of element (column) in the periodic table
nitrogen	3	2	*p*	*Row 2*	*Column 5*
oxygen					
fluorine					

e) Make and complete another chart like the one below in your *Active Chemistry* log. This time you will compare the electron assignments of phosphorus, sulfur, and chlorine to the electron assignment of argon ($1s^22s^22p^63s^23p^6$), the closest noble gas.

Element being compared	Number of electrons *less* than those found in closest noble gas (Ar)	Energy level (number) to which the last electron is assigned	Energy sublevel (letter) to which the last electron is assigned	Location of element (row) in the periodic table	Location of element (column) in the periodic table
phosphorus					
sulfur					
chlorine					

f) Describe any patterns you notice in the charts 2(d) and/or 2(e) above.

3. In your *Active Chemistry* log, draw a simplified periodic table that contains only the first three rows of the periodic table. Your table should have 3 rows and 8 columns, and should contain the elements with atomic numbers 1 through 18.

a) Write the symbol for each element in each appropriate box.

b) In the columns headed by lithium, beryllium, and boron indicate how many more electrons are found in atoms of those elements than in an atom of the nearest noble gas. Place a plus sign in front of these numbers to indicate that these elements contain more electrons than their nearest noble gas element.

c) In the columns headed by nitrogen, oxygen, and fluorine indicate how many fewer electrons are found in atoms of those elements than in an atom of the nearest noble gas. Place a minus sign in front of these numbers to indicate that these elements contain fewer electrons than their nearest noble gas element.

d) The carbon column was not listed in the table. How many fewer electrons are found in atoms of these elements than in an atom of the nearest noble gas? How many more electrons are found in atoms of these elements than in an atom of the last noble gas? What can you conclude about the position of the carbon column in respect to the other columns that you have examined?

4. The questions in *Step 2* asked you to compare the electron assignments in atoms of the second and third rows with the electron assignments of the noble gas that was closest in atomic number to those elements. You noted that electrons are added to the *s* and *p* sublevels of the energy level whose number is the same as the row of the periodic table the elements are found in. For instance, lithium has one more electron than its closest noble gas element. That additional electron is added to the *s* sublevel of the second energy level, corresponding to the second row, where lithium is located.

The number of an electron energy level is significant, because the higher the number, the greater the average distance between the nucleus and the electron. The electrons in the energy levels with the highest number are, on average, the farthest from the nucleus. Because differences in electrons located in the outermost level distinguish an atom from its nearest noble gas, these are the electrons responsible for the atom's chemical behavior. These electrons are often called valence electrons.

Valence electrons are those electrons found in the outermost energy in level *s* and *p* orbitals. The maximum number of valence electrons that you can have is 8 for the representative elements (2 in the *s* and 6 in *p* sublevel). For example, sodium contains one valence electron since its outermost level is 3 and sublevel is *s*. It does not have any electrons in the *p* sublevel. Bromine would have seven valence electrons, since its outermost energy level is 4 and it contains 2 electrons in *s* sublevel and 5 electrons in *p* sublevel.

Use the assignment of electrons to energy sublevels in the periodic table on the inside back cover and your answers to the questions in *Steps 1* and *2* to answer the following questions:

a) How many valence electrons are in an atom of helium? Neon? Argon? Krypton? Xenon? Radon?

b) How many valence electrons are in an atom of lithium? Sodium? Potassium? Rubidium? Cesium? This family of elements is known as the alkali metals.

c) How many valence electrons are in an atom of beryllium? Magnesium? Calcium? Strontium? Barium? This family of elements is known as the alkaline earth metals.

d) How many valence electrons are in an atom of boron? Aluminum?

e) How many valence electrons are in an atom of carbon? Silicon?

f) How many valence electrons are in an atom of nitrogen? Phosphorus?

g) How many valence electrons are in an atom of oxygen? Sulfur?

h) How many valence electrons are in an atom of fluorine? Chlorine? Bromine? Iodine? This family of elements is known as the halogens.

Chem Talk

THE NOBLE GASES

The Discovery of Argon

Imagine that you prepared two samples of nitrogen, each one liter in volume. You found one to have a mass of 1.250 g and the other a mass of 1.257 g. You might be tempted to attribute the difference to experimental error. Lord Rayleigh didn't! In 1892 he decomposed ammonia to generate one liter of nitrogen with a mass of 1.250 g. In another preparation method, he isolated one liter of nitrogen with a mass of 1.257 g by removing what he thought were all the other gases from a sample of air.

Lord Rayleigh

What accounted for the difference in masses of the two samples? Could there be yet another gas in the air that Rayleigh didn't know about? William Ramsay, a colleague of Rayleigh, looked to the experiments conducted by Henry Cavendish a hundred years earlier. Henry Cavendish (the discoverer of hydrogen) had been puzzled by a small bubble of gas remaining after he had chemically absorbed all of a sample of nitrogen he had similarly extracted from the atmosphere.

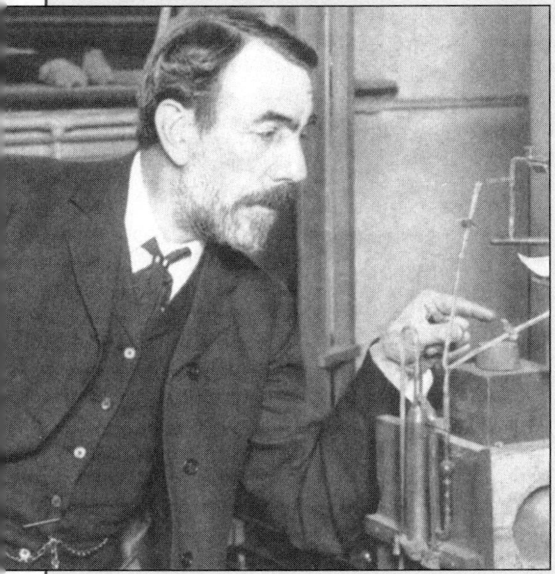

William Ramsay

As Cavendish had done, Ramsay extracted a sample of nitrogen from the atmosphere and then chemically absorbed all of the nitrogen in that sample. He looked at the spectrum of the remaining bubble of gas, just as you have looked at the spectra of various gases in *Activity 4* and *5*. The new spectral lines of color he saw showed him that the bubble of gas was a new element, which today is called argon. It had previously escaped notice because of its rarity and lack of chemical activity.

Chem Words

noble gas (also rare or inert gas): a family of elements (Group 18 or VIIIA of the periodic table), all of which are gases that are not chemically reactive.

valence electrons: the electrons in the outermost energy levels of an atom.

A New Family

When Mendeleev formulated the first periodic table, argon had not been discovered, and therefore, it had not been placed in the periodic table. There was no obvious place for argon. A new column was created. A prediction was therefore made that there would be other elements with similar properties to argon. The other elements of this family (He, Ne, and Kr) were subsequently discovered by the end of the 19th century. Good scientific theories are able to predict things that nobody is aware of at the time. When people perform additional observations, they then discover these predicted things with the very properties that were described. This is one means by which the value of a theory can be judged.

Unlike atoms of the other chemical elements, atoms of elements in this column are so stable that they either do not react at all, or they react only in unusual circumstances, with other elements. For this reason, this family has been known as **rare** gases (because they are rare in abundance), **inert** gases (because they are not very reactive), or **noble** gases.

Valence Electrons

The energy level of an electron is important. The greater the number, the larger is the average distance between the electron and the nucleus. The electrons in the highest energy levels are usually the farthest from the nucleus. The differences in the electrons in the outermost level identify an atom from its nearest noble gas. It is these electrons that are responsible for the chemical behavior of the atom. They are called **valence electrons.** The maximum number of valence electrons that you can have is 8 for the representative elements (2 in the *s* and 6 in *p* sublevel).

A simple way to determine the number of valence electrons for the representative elements is to look at the element's group number. All elements in group IA have one valence electron. All elements in group 2A have two valance electrons. Those in 3A have three valence electrons, and so on. The noble gases in group 8A all have 8 electrons in their outermost energy levels with the exception of helium. Helium has only two electrons total.

Checking Up

1. Why did one liter of nitrogen prepared by Lord Rayleigh appear to have a greater mass than the other liter prepared by a different method?
2. What are two reasons that the noble gases had escaped notice?

What Do You Think Now?

At the beginning of the activity you were asked to think about the question:

- **How does the arrangement of electrons in an atom determine its chemical behavior?**

You are now able to look at the periodic table and know how many valence electrons any representative element has. You also know that having a full outer energy level imparts stability to an atom; think of the noble gases. It is these outermost electrons that are responsible for the chemical behavior of the elements. Knowing all these facts, predict what ions would likely form for the elements Cl, Mg, and Na.

Chem Essential Questions

What does it mean?

Chemistry explains a macroscopic phenomenon (what you observe) with a description of what happens at the nanoscopic level (atoms and molecules) using symbolic structures as a way to communicate. Complete the chart below in your *Active Chemistry* log.

MACRO	NANO	SYMBOLIC
How was the noble gas argon discovered?	*Compare and contrast the electron configurations of K, Cl and Ar.*	*Since the elements in any row have similar electron configurations as the inert gas in the preceding row, the electron configuration can be written more symbolically using a notion like K = [Ar]4s^1. Show how this can be used in describing the electron configuration of magnesium.*

How do you know?

What evidence do you have that the noble gases do not react with other substances under normal conditions?

Why do you believe?

Helium was predicted as an element for a blank space on the periodic table before it was discovered on Earth. In fact, helium was discovered in the Sun's spectra before it was discovered on Earth. How can you know so much about helium before you have even observed it?

Why should you care?

Knowledge of chemical formula writing is a basic need of chemistry. Understanding element's valence electrons will make it easy in determining correct formulas of different compounds. How might the filled levels of the noble gases and the lack of the reaction of the noble gases with other elements become a part of your game?

Reflecting on the Activity and the Challenge

In this activity, you have learned that the electrons in the energy sublevels with the highest number are, on the average, the farthest from the nucleus of an atom. These electrons, also known as valence electrons, determine the atom's chemical behavior. This chemical behavior is best understood in relationship to the arrangement of electrons in energy sublevels in atoms of noble gases, which, by virtue of their chemical inactivity, have a stability which is unmatched by other chemical elements. The key is an atom's excess or deficiency of electrons compared to an atom of the nearest noble gas on the periodic table. This excess or deficiency is readily indicated by the position of an element on the periodic table. How will you include this in your game about the periodic table?

Chem to Go

1. From the periodic table on the back inside cover, identify the excess or deficiency of electrons in an atom of a given element relative to an atom of the closest noble gas. Be sure to indicate both the number of electrons and a sign (plus or minus) to indicate whether the electrons are in excess or deficiency.

   a) calcium
   b) arsenic
   c) potassium
   d) iodine

2. Listed below are groups of three elements. For each group determine which two elements have more in common in terms of electron arrangement and therefore exhibit more similar chemical behavior. Give a reason for your selection.

   a) carbon, nitrogen, silicon
   b) fluorine, chlorine, neon
   c) sulfur, bromine, oxygen
   d) sodium, magnesium, sulfur
   e) helium, neon, hydrogen

3. Listed below are pairs of elements. For each pair determine which of the two has the most stable arrangement of electrons. You may refer to the table of first ionization energies in *Activity* 6 and the periodic table on the back inside cover. Provide a statement explaining your choice in terms of ionization energy and electron arrangement.

   a) helium and lithium
   b) lithium and beryllium
   c) magnesium and chlorine
   d) magnesium and argon
   e) neon and krypton

4. a) Write the electron configuration for magnesium.

   b) Determine how many valence electrons magnesium contains.

   c) Write the electron configuration for barium.

   d) Determine how many valence electrons barium contains.

   e) How does the number of valence electrons of magnesium compare to the number of valence electrons of barium?

   f) What general statement can you make about the number of valence electrons of each element of the alkaline earth metals?

5. a) Write the electron configuration for cobalt.

   b) How many valence electrons does cobalt contain?

Inquiring Further

1. **Valence electrons of transition elements**

   How many valence electrons are there in an atom of iron (Fe, atomic number 26 and called a transition element)? When you look at the periodic table on the back inside cover, you see that iron has all the electrons in an atom of calcium plus six additional electrons in the 3*d* sublevel. Relative to the 2 electrons in the 4*s* sublevel in calcium, do these 3*d* electrons qualify as valence electrons? Explain your thinking. What can you say about the number of valence electrons in the other transition elements, from scandium to copper?

2. **Ionization energies of beryllium (Be) atoms**

   The first three ionization energies of beryllium atoms are as follows:

   1st = 1.49×10^{-18} J

   2nd = 2.92×10^{-18} J

   3rd = 2.49×10^{-17} J

   Explain the magnitudes of the energies in terms of electron configurations and from this information determine how many valence electrons are contained in beryllium.

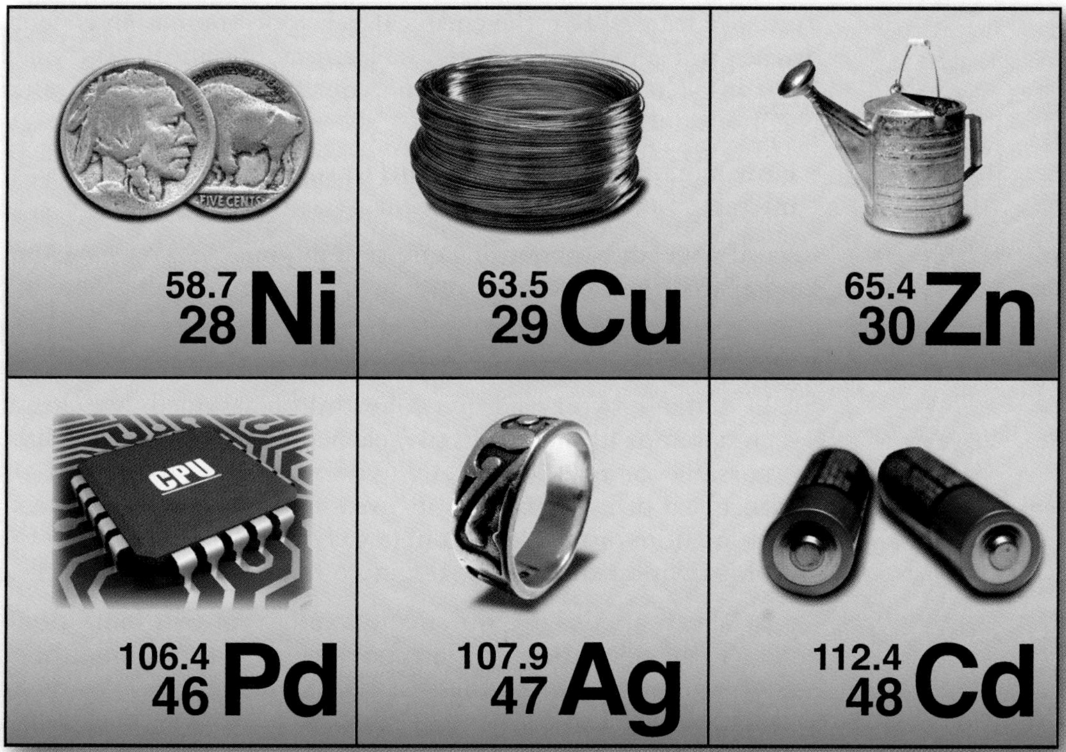
58.7 28 Ni
63.5 29 Cu
65.4 30 Zn
CPU
106.4 46 Pd
107.9 47 Ag
112.4 48 Cd

Activity 8 How Atoms Interact with Each Other

What Do You See?

CuCl2

GOALS

In this activity you will:

- Relate patterns in ionization energies of elements to patterns in their electron arrangements.
- Use your knowledge of electron arrangements and valence electrons to predict formulas for compounds formed by two elements.
- Contrast ionic bonding and covalent bonding.
- Draw electron-dot diagrams for simple molecules with covalent bonding.

What Do You Think?

You have learned that the chemical behavior of an atom is determined by the arrangement of the atom's electrons, specifically the valence electrons. The salt that you put on your food is chemically referred to as NaCl—sodium chloride.

- **How might the valence electrons of sodium (Na) and chlorine (Cl) interact to create the bond in NaCl?**

Record your ideas about this question in your *Active Chemistry* log. Be prepared to discuss your responses with your small group and the class.

Investigate

1. In *Activity 3* you read that John Dalton assumed that chemical compounds formed from two elements combined in the simplest possible combination. In *Activity 6* you began to see that an atom's chemical behavior reflects its excess or deficiency of electrons relative to an atom of the closest noble gas on the periodic table. Use the list of ionization energies in *Activity 6* to answer the following questions:

   a) Which atoms have the smallest values for first ionization energies? (Remember, the first ionization energy is the amount of energy required to remove the first electron.)

b) Where are these atoms located on the periodic table?

c) What do you observe about the amount of energy required to remove the second electron from atoms of the elements identified in (a)?

d) Use your understanding of the arrangement of electrons in this group of elements to suggest a reason for the pattern you noted in (c).

e) Which atoms have the smallest values for second ionization energies? Where are these atoms located on the periodic table?

f) Use your understanding of the arrangement of electrons in this group of elements to suggest a reason for the pattern you noted in (e).

2. Once you recognize the role of an atom's electron arrangement—especially the valence electrons—in an atom's chemical activity, you can often predict formulas for compounds formed by two chemical elements. (Recall that valence electrons are the electrons located in the highest energy level, the levels designated by the sublevel having the highest numbers.)

Sodium (Na) has one valence electron in the 3*s* sublevel. By losing that electron, the sodium atom becomes a sodium ion and it has the same stable electron arrangement as neon.

a) What is the stable electron arrangement of neon?

b) What is the stable electron arrangement of sodium after the 3*s* sublevel electron has been removed?

c) What is the electric charge on the resulting Na ion?

Consider a chlorine atom.

d) How many valence electrons does a chlorine atom have?

e) How many electrons would a chlorine atom have to lose in order to have a stable electron arrangement like neon?

f) How many electrons does a chlorine atom need to gain to have the same number of electrons as an argon atom?

g) Gaining one electron is much easier than losing seven electrons. When a chlorine atom gains an electron, a chloride ion is formed. The original chlorine atom was electrically neutral. It gained a negative electron to form the ion. What is the electric charge (sign and value) on the resulting ion?

Sodium reacts violently with chlorine gas.

h) Each chlorine atom is capable of accepting one electron to become more stable. Each sodium atom is capable of losing one electron to become more stable. It certainly sounds as if a relationship is in store for the chlorine and sodium atoms. Describe how you think the compound sodium chloride (NaCl) is formed.

i) Look at the *What Do You See?* illustration at the beginning of *Activity* 7. Describe what you see in terms of bonding.

3. Consider the reaction between aluminum and zinc chloride (similar to the reaction in *Activity* 3). The zinc atom in zinc chloride has two valence electrons located in the 4*s* sublevel. You can note the two valence electrons in the electron arrangement marked on the periodic table.

   In order to acquire the rather stable electron configuration of argon atoms, the zinc atoms give up their two valence electrons to form zinc ions. Since the original zinc atom was electrically neutral and it lost two negative electrons to form the ion, the resulting ion has a positive charge with a magnitude two times the charge on the electron. It has a plus two charge.

   a) Each chlorine atom is capable of accepting one electron. How many chlorine atoms are needed to accept the two electrons that zinc atoms have to give?

   b) When writing the formula for a compound, the number of atoms necessary to balance the loss and gain of electrons can be designated through the use of a subscript, such as the 2 in H_2O. There are 2 hydrogen atoms linked to every oxygen atom. How would you write the formula for the compound zinc chloride?

   c) Look at the *What Do You See?* illustration at the beginning of this activity. Describe what you see in terms of bonding.

4. Aluminum chloride is another material formed in reactions.

   a) Consider an atom of aluminum. How many valence electrons does an aluminum atom have?

   b) How many electrons does an aluminum atom need to give up to reach the same chemical stability as a neon atom?

   c) What are aluminum atoms called after they give up their valence electrons? What is their electric charge (sign and value)?

   d) How many chlorine atoms are needed to accept the electrons given up by an aluminum atom?

   e) How would you write the formula for the compound aluminum chloride?

5. In a reaction between aluminum and zinc chloride, aluminum replaces the zinc in the zinc chloride, forming aluminum chloride and zinc.

   The reaction is:

   $2Al(s) + 3ZnCl_2(aq) \rightarrow$
   $2AlCl_3(aq) + 3Zn(s)$

   Create a model to explain how the valence electrons change places during the reaction.

Chem Talk

FORMING COMPOUNDS

The Octet Rule

In this activity you explained the formation of the compounds that you investigated by how the electrons are transferred or shared between atoms. Some scientists explain these observations using the **octet rule**. This rule states that atoms tend to gain or lose electrons during chemical reactions so that the atoms have an outer shell configuration of eight electrons. The exceptions to this are the transition elements. The octet rule works well with almost all of the elements found in the first three rows of the periodic table.

You should note that the name of all of the compounds that you have studied have all started with the name of the metal and then followed with the nonmetal part. The second thing that you should note is that all of these compounds are binary (meaning two parts). **Binary compounds** always end with the suffix "ide" (except for a few compounds with common names like water and ammonia).

Covalent and Ionic Bonds

You may have noticed that the column headed by carbon in the periodic table has not received a lot of attention so far. In *Activity* 7 you learned that atoms of these elements contain four valence electrons. Atoms with a small number of valence electrons give up electrons, and atoms with a large number of valence electrons gain additional electrons to have the same electron arrangement as an atom of the nearest noble gas. Except for helium, with two valence electrons, the noble gases each have eight valence electrons. What do atoms of carbon do? Do they give up their four valence electrons, or gain four more?

In actuality, atoms of carbon do neither. Instead of giving or taking electrons to form what are called **ionic bonds**, carbon atoms share electrons with other carbon atoms as well as with other elements. The result is the formation of what are called **covalent bonds**. In fact, all nonmetallic elements whose atoms have four or more valence electrons can form covalent bonds by sharing electrons. This sharing results in a situation in which each atom is associated with eight valence electrons, as is characteristic of an atom of a noble gas.

Chem Words

octet rule: the rule that states that atoms tend to gain or lose electrons during chemical reactions so that the atoms have an outer shell configuration of eight electrons.

binary compound: a compound formed from the combining of two different elements.

ionic bond: the attraction between oppositely charged ions.

covalent bond: a bond produced by sharing of a pair of electrons between two atoms.

Chem Words

bonding electrons: the two electrons that are shared between two atoms.

nonbonding electron pair (or lone pair): a pair of electrons that are not used in forming a bond, but are located as a pair on the atom.

Covalent bonding can be illustrated using electron-dot diagrams (sometimes called Lewis structures). In these diagrams each valence electron is indicated by a dot (or other appropriate symbol) around the chemical symbol for the element in question. Consider the following covalent compound illustrations:

Hydrogen chloride contains one hydrogen atom and one chlorine atom.

Water contains two hydrogen atoms and one oxygen atom.

Carbon dioxide contains one carbon atom and two oxygen atoms.

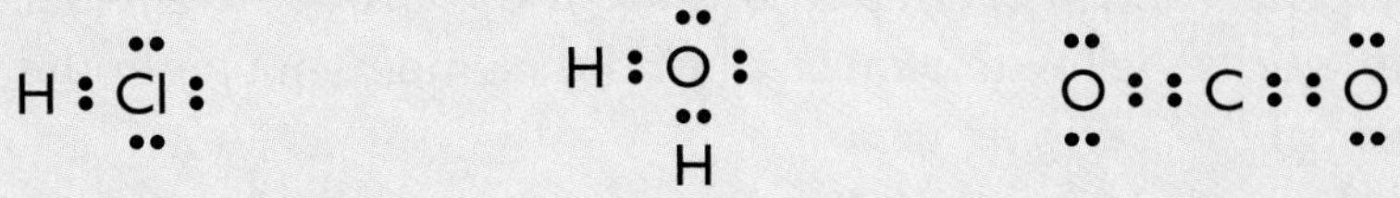

You can count eight electrons around the chlorine in hydrogen chloride (note that hydrogen can only have two electrons). In water the oxygen has eight electrons around it and hydrogen again has only two electrons. Carbon dioxide shows that oxygen contains eight electrons and carbon has eight electrons as well. These shared electrons in these examples all produce stable covalent compounds.

Let's take a look at how the electron-dot structures were formed.

The electron-dot structure of hydrogen has a single dot for its only electron and looks like this: H•.

When two hydrogen atoms combine to form molecular hydrogen (H_2), you draw the resulting electron-dot structure like this: H:H.

You can represent the two electrons forming the bond with two dots as shown, or with a dash (H—H).

The table below shows the electron-dot structures for the first 20 elements.

H•							He:
Li•	•Be•	•B•	•C•	•N•	•O:	:F•	:Ne:
Na•	•Mg•	•Al•	•Si•	•P•	•S:	:Cl•	:Ar:
K•	•Ca•						

Notice that the electrons shown are only the valence electrons, not all the electrons of the element. Notice also that the electron-dot structures are identical for elements in columns. This is why Li and Na and K have such similar characteristics, as do F and Cl.

To write electron-dot structures for molecules, you can follow these simple guidelines using water as an example:

1. Start with the dot structure of each atom. Determine where bonding can occur (look for unpaired electrons).

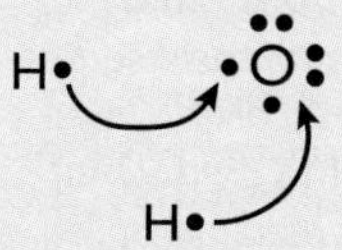

2. Redraw the structure showing bonds as pairs of electrons between the elements. Any unbonded electron pairs remain with the original element.

nonbonding pairs
bonding pairs

Note that the two electrons forming the bond between the oxygen and the hydrogen (which can also be represented as a dash as in second structure) are called **bonding electrons.** The two pairs of electrons placed on the oxygen are called **nonbonding electron pairs**, or **lone pairs.** The oxygen has a total of eight electrons around it. This follows the octet rule.

Checking Up

1. When naming a binary compound, which element is named first, the metal or the nonmetal? Give an example to explain your answer.
2. Explain the difference between an ionic and a covalent bond.
3. Draw electron-dot diagrams showing covalent bonding in the following compounds:

a) water (two atoms of hydrogen, one atom of oxygen). Note: Since the noble gas nearest hydrogen is helium, with only two valence electrons, hydrogen atoms need be associated with only two valence electrons.

b) methane (four atoms of hydrogen, one atom of carbon)

c) ammonia (three atoms of hydrogen, one atom of nitrogen)

d) carbon tetrachloride (four atoms of chlorine, one atom of carbon)

What Do You Think Now?

At the beginning of the activity you were asked:

- **How might the valence electrons of sodium (Na) and chlorine (Cl) interact to create the bond in NaCl?**

In the *Investigate* you described how sodium chloride (NaCl) forms. Describe how calcium bromide ($CaBr_2$) forms. That is, for this binary compound, show which element will lose electron(s) and which one will gain electron(s).

Chem Essential Questions

What does it mean?

Chemistry explains a macroscopic phenomenon (what you observe) with a description of what happens at the nanoscopic level (atoms and molecules) using symbolic structures as a way to communicate. Complete the chart below in your *Active Chemistry* log.

MACRO	NANO	SYMBOLIC
Sodium and chlorine can combine to make salt. Hydrogen and oxygen can combine to make water. From the Investigate *sections in this chapter, list one chemical reaction that you have observed.*	*The sharing of electrons between two atoms is a covalent bond. When the electron(s) of one element is transferred to another atom it is called an ionic bond. Describe what happens to the electrons when sodium and chlorine combine to create NaCl.*	*In order to help you keep track of the electrons during bond formation you can use a symbolic structure called Lewis diagrams. Show the creation of NaCl using a Lewis diagram.*

How do you know?

Sodium chloride is written as NaCl and is composed of one sodium ion and one chloride ion. Calcium chloride is written as $CaCl_2$ and is composed of one calcium ion and two chloride ions. How would you know that two chloride ions are required to create calcium chloride?

Why do you believe?

The recipe to make brownies requires one cup of sugar and 8 oz of chocolate and one oven. If you wanted to double the recipe, how much sugar, chocolate and oven(s) are required?

Why should you care?

Knowing the number of valence electrons for the elements will make it easy to write correct formulas for compounds. How will your game include fun and creative ways for naming compounds as they form?

Reflecting on the Activity and the Challenge

In this activity, you learned that atoms of two chemical elements will interact with each other in order to achieve a stable electron arrangement like that of nearby noble gases. The way in which atoms interact is based on their excess or deficiency of electrons relative to atoms of the closest noble gas on the periodic table. An atom's excess or deficiency of electrons relative to the closest noble gas is readily indicated by the position of an element on the periodic table. In this way, the periodic table can be used to predict the chemical formulas when two elements interact to form a compound. This information can be deduced from the periodic table. Perhaps you can invent a way to make this more explicit as you create your periodic-table game. How might you incorporate this information into your game to meet the *Chapter Challenge*?

Chem to Go

1. Find the following pairs of elements in the periodic table on the back inside cover. Identify the excess or deficiency of electrons in each atom relative to an atom of the closest noble gas. Then predict the formula of the compound formed when these elements interact:

   a) sodium and chlorine (to form sodium chloride)

   b) calcium and oxygen (to form calcium oxide)

   c) magnesium and chlorine (to form magnesium chloride)

   d) aluminum and oxygen (to form aluminum oxide)

2. a) In your *Active Chemistry* log, draw a simplified periodic table that contains only the first three rows of the periodic table. Your table should have three rows and eight columns. It should contain the elements with atomic numbers 1 through 18.

   b) In the box for each element, write the symbol for the element.

   c) In the columns headed by lithium, beryllium, and boron, indicate the charge (sign and value) of the ion formed when atoms of these elements give up electrons to get a more stable electron arrangement.

   d) In the columns headed by nitrogen, oxygen, and fluorine, indicate how many electrons atoms of those elements gain to get a more stable electron arrangement.

3. You know the formula for sodium chloride (NaCl). From this knowledge you can also write the formula for potassium chloride, cesium bromide, lithium iodide, and sodium fluoride.

   a) What tool makes it possible for you to do this, even though you may have never investigated these compounds?

   b) Using the periodic table, explain what information you used to help explain how you arrived at the formulas.

4. The formula for calcium chloride is $CaCl_2$. From this knowledge you should be able to write the formulas of the alkaline earth metals (Group 2) and halogens combining.

   a) Write the formula for magnesium bromide, strontium iodide, beryllium fluoride, barium chloride, and calcium iodide.

   b) What information from the periodic table did you use to write the formulas of these compounds?

5. A compound that was used previously is aluminum chloride ($AlCl_3$). Use your understanding of why elements are grouped together and are called a family to write the formula for each of the following compounds:

   a) boron fluoride

   b) aluminum bromide

   c) gallium iodide

   d) indium (III) chloride

   e) thallium (III) bromide

6. You have explored how the alkali, alkaline earth metals, and IIIA group (boron, aluminum, gallium, indium, and thallium) combine with the halogens. How do these metals combine with the group VIA elements (oxygen, sulfur, selenium, tellurium, and polonium)? Look at a few compounds such as sodium oxide that has a formula of Na_2O. Alkali metals like sodium have low ionization energy values. When they react to form an ionic compound, an electron is lost and they become the positive ion (cation) of the new compound. A nonmetal like oxygen has a high ionization energy value. In reacting to form an ionic compound it gains electrons, becoming the negative ion (anion) of the compound. Therefore, when the alkali metals combine with oxygen or other elements of group VIA, they should have a similar formula.

   a) Write the formula for each of the following compounds:

      i) potassium sulfide ii) rubidium selenide iii) lithium telluride

      iv) sodium sulfide v) cesium oxide

   You can do the same thing with the alkaline earth metals combining with the group VIA elements. Calcium oxide has the formula CaO. The alkaline earth metals have low ionization energies and react to form the positive ion with a +2 charge. Again, the nonmetal oxygen will form an anion with a charge of −2. Thus, the alkaline earth metals and the group VI elements will combine in a 1:1 ratio.

   b) Write the formula for each of the following compounds:

      i) magnesium sulfide ii) strontium selenide iii) barium oxide

      iv) beryllium telluride v) calcium sulfide

   Finally, look at the group IIIA elements combining with the group VIA elements. Aluminum oxide has the formula Al_2O_3. The group IIIA elements have lower ionization energies than the Group VIA elements and form cations with a charge of +3. The oxygen or the Group VIA nonmetals like oxygen have a −2 charge in the ionic compounds. In order to make a whole-number exchange of electrons, six electrons must be transferred. (Remember to make sure that your formula has the correct number of electrons being transferred.)

   c) Write the formula for the following compounds:

      i) boron sulfide ii) aluminum selenide iii) gallium telluride

      iv) indium (III) oxide v) thallium (III) sulfide

Inquiring Further

Creating compounds with "inert" gases

For a long period of time the noble gases were called the inert elements because it was assumed that they were non-reactive and did not want to gain or lose electrons. Research to find out if compounds can be formed with the noble gases. Record your finding in your *Active Chemistry* log. If time permits, share your findings with the class.

Activity 9 What Determines and Limits an Atom's Mass?

CHEM POETRY

My Dearest Love,
I'm writing you
To tell you all
that I've been through.
I've changed my
whole identity,
But loved I can't
pretend to be.

When I was Uranium-238,
You were on my case to
start losing weight.
For five billion years I'd
hope and I'd pray,
And finally, I had
an alpha decay.

Two protons, two neutrons
went right out the door
And now I was Thorium-234.
But my nucleus was still
unfit for your eyes,
Not positive enough for its
large size.
protactinium.

–Mala Radhakrishnan

GOALS

In this activity you will:

- Investigate the composition of the atom's nucleus.
- Explain why the atomic masses of some elements are not whole numbers.
- Use symbols to represent different isotopes of an element.
- Determine the composition of the nucleus of an atom from its isotope symbol.
- Calculate the average atomic mass of an element from the percent abundance of its isotopes.

What Do You See?

37
35
THE AMAZING CHLORINE TWINS
ACTIVE SCIENCE SHOW

What Do You Think?

In *Activity 4* you learned that the structure of an atom includes a nucleus surrounded by electrons. Most of the mass of an atom is concentrated in the small nucleus. In a neutral atom, this positive electric charge is equal to the negative charge of all the electrons around the nucleus.

- **What do you think makes up the nucleus of the atom?**

Record your ideas about this question in your *Active Chemistry* log. Be prepared to discuss your responses with your small group and the class.

Investigate

Part A: What's in the Nucleus?

1. Atomic number indicates the number of electrons in the atom and the number of protons located in the nucleus needed to produce a neutral atom. Refer to the periodic table to answer the following questions. How many protons are there:

   a) in a hydrogen atom?

   b) in a sodium atom?

   c) in a carbon atom?

   d) in a uranium atom?

2. Atomic mass is the average mass of atoms of each element. A proton has a mass of 1.67×10^{-24} g. Chemists often refer to this as approximately one atomic mass unit or 1 amu or 1 u.

   a) To the nearest whole number, what is the atomic mass of a hydrogen atom?

   b) How many protons are there in a helium atom?

   c) The mass of an electron is negligible, compared to the nucleus. What would you expect the atomic mass of a helium atom to be? Explain your answer.

   d) Refer to the periodic table and estimate to the nearest whole number the atomic mass of a helium atom.

3. In *Step 2*, you found that the helium atom has a mass that is four times the mass of a hydrogen atom. However, the electric charge on the helium nucleus is only twice that of the hydrogen atom. This suggests the presence of another particle in the nucleus, with about the same mass as the proton but no electric charge. It is called a ***neutron***.

   Example:

   Boron has atomic number 5. This informs you that there are 5 electrons and that the nucleus contains 5 protons. The average atomic mass of boron is 10.811 amu. You can round this number to 11 amu. Since the mass is the sum of the protons and the neutrons (electrons have very, very little mass) then you can conclude that boron has 5 protons and 6 neutrons in the nucleus.

   Refer to your table of atomic numbers and atomic masses to answer the following questions:

   a) How many protons would you expect to find in the nucleus of a helium atom? (Recall that the number of protons needs to balance the number of electrons.)

   b) How many neutrons would you expect to find in helium? (The atomic mass is a combination of the mass of the protons and the mass of the neutrons.)

   c) How many protons and neutrons would you expect to find in the nucleus of an atom of each of the following elements:

   - lithium
   - beryllium
   - boron
   - carbon
   - nitrogen
   - oxygen
   - fluorine
   - neon

4. Refer again to the periodic table. Take a closer look at boron. The atomic mass is 10.811 amu and not 11 amu. Subtracting the mass of the protons from the actual total mass would indicate that there are 5.811 neutrons in the nucleus of boron. You cannot have pieces of neutrons. There must be a different explanation. Most boron has 11 amu and some boron has 10 amu. The average atomic mass is 10.811 amu. All boron atoms have exactly 5 protons. The number of neutrons can vary.

   a) What are the atomic masses of magnesium, chlorine, sodium, and fluorine?

   b) What are the probable number of protons and neutrons in each of these four elements?

5. The fact that some atomic masses are not close to whole number multiples of the atomic mass of hydrogen is now explained by the fact that the number of neutrons is not the same in all atoms of a given element. Only the number

of protons, the atomic number, is the same in all atoms of a given element. Atoms of the same element with different number of neutrons in the nucleus are known as ***isotopes***. (Isotope implies "same number of protons.") Isotopes are identified by their mass number, the sum of the number of neutrons plus protons.

Example:

Lithium has an atomic number of 3 and an average atomic mass of 6.941 amu. All lithium atoms have 3 protons in the nucleus. A neutral atom of lithium always has 3 electrons to balance the charge of the 3 protons. The average atomic mass of a lithium atom is 6.941 amu. This indicates that some naturally occuring lithium atoms have 3 neutrons, to make a total atomic mass of 6 amu. Others have 4 neutrons, to make a total atomic mass of 7 amu. These two isotopes are designated lithium-6 and lithium-7. Since there are so many more lithium-7 atoms, the average of all of the atoms is very close to 7 amu.

Refer to your list of atomic masses to answer the following questions:

a) What isotopes (as indicated by their mass numbers) do you expect to account for the known atomic masses of the following elements?

For example, carbon (carbon-12 atoms with 6 neutrons and carbon-13 atoms with 7 neutrons; more carbon-12 atoms).

- hydrogen
- boron
- magnesium
- beryllium
- sodium

b) The mass number is written at the upper left of the chemical symbol of the element. The atomic number is written at the lower left of the chemical symbol of the element as shown below. How many neutrons and protons are present in the following isotopes?

i) $^{3}_{2}\text{He}$ and $^{4}_{2}\text{He}$

ii) $^{6}_{3}\text{Li}$ and $^{7}_{3}\text{Li}$

iii) $^{12}_{6}\text{C}$ and $^{13}_{6}\text{C}$

iv) $^{14}_{7}\text{N}$ and $^{15}_{7}\text{N}$

Part B: Forces within the Atom

1. There are two very different forces acting on the electrons, protons, and neutrons in the atom. In order to better understand the atom, you must first understand these forces.

Cut two strips of transparent tape about 12 cm long. Bend one end of each strip under to form a tab. Place one strip sticky-side down on a table and label the tab "B," for "bottom." Place the other strip sticky-side down on top of the first strip and label the tab "T," for "top."

Safety goggles and apron must be worn *at all times* in the laboratory.

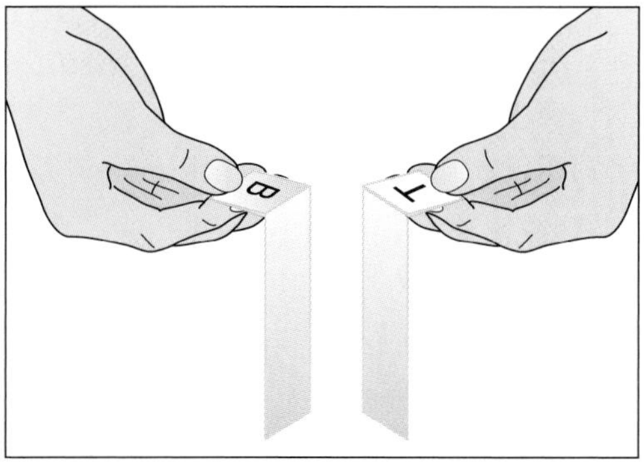
B
T

With one hand peel off the top strip, using the tab. Then pick up the bottom strip with the other hand. Hold both strips apart, allowing them to hang down.

Slowly bring the hanging strips toward each other, but do not let them touch.

a) Record your observations.

b) The strips may have moved (accelerated) toward or away from each other. If this happened, Newton's Second Law tells you that there must be a force. Is the force between the two strips of tape attractive or repulsive?

2. Make a second set of strips as in *Step 1*.

a) Predict what you think will happen if the two top strips are picked up, one from each set and brought toward each other. Record your prediction.

Pick up the two top strips by the tabs, allowing both strips to hang down. Slowly bring them toward each other.

b) Record your observations.

c) Was the force attractive or repulsive? Explain.

d) Predict what you think will happen if the two bottom strips of tape are picked up and brought toward each other. Record your prediction.

Pick up the two bottom strips by the tabs, allowing both strips to hang down. Slowly bring them toward each other.

e) Record your observations.

f) Was the force attractive or repulsive? Explain.

3. The two different strips of tape have different charges. The top strips have a positive electric charge. They have lost some of their electrons. Since the number of protons has remained the same, the strips are positive. The bottom strips have a negative charge. The bottom strips have gained some electrons. Since the number of protons has remained the same, the strips are negative. The force between the strips is called the electric force.

a) Is the force between two positive strips repulsive or attractive? Use evidence to justify your answer.

b) Is the force between two negative strips repulsive or attractive? Use evidence to justify your answer.

c) When a positive and a negative strip come near each other, is the force attractive or repulsive? Justify your answer.

4. The nucleus has a positive charge due to all of the protons there. The electrons surrounding the nucleus have negative charges.

a) What kind of electric force (attractive or repulsive) exists between the nucleus of an atom and its electrons?

b) What kind of electric force exists between pairs of protons in the nucleus?

5. The nucleus is a very crowded place. The protons in the nucleus are very close to one another. If these protons are repelling each other by an electrostatic force (and they are!), there must be another force, an attractive force, which keeps them there. The attractive force is the nuclear force, also called the strong force. This force is much stronger than the electric force. It acts between pairs of protons, pairs of neutrons, and protons and neutrons. The electron is not affected by the nuclear force.

a) Copy and complete the table below. The first row has been completed for you.

Particles	Coulomb electrostatic force	Strong nuclear force
electron-proton	attractive	none
electron-neutron		
proton-proton		
proton-neutron		
neutron-neutron		

6. If the nucleus were too large, the protons on one side of the nucleus would be too far away to attract the protons on the other side of the nucleus. The protons can still repel one another since the coulomb electrostatic force is long-range. The repulsive electrostatic force wins over the strong nuclear force and the nucleus won't form.

   A large nucleus will break apart when the electrostatic repulsion between the protons is too great. The repulsion pushes the fragments of the nucleus apart, releasing a great amount of energy. This process of splitting an atom into smaller atoms is called ***fission***. It occurs in uranium when an additional neutron is added and causes instability.

   One example of the fission process is when uranium breaks into krypton and barium. Three neutrons and energy are released. This can be represented as follows:

   $^{235}_{92}\text{U} + ^{1}_{0}\text{n} \rightarrow ^{94}_{36}\text{Kr} + ^{139}_{56}\text{Ba} + 3\,^{1}_{0}\text{n} +$ energy

   a) What is the total mass number on each side? Is the mass number (the top number) conserved on both sides of the reaction?

   b) What is the total atomic number on each side? Is the atomic number (the bottom number) conserved on both sides of the reaction?

   c) Why does the neutron have a mass number of 1?

   d) Why is the atomic number of a neutron equal to 0?

7. Small nuclei can also combine to form a larger nucleus and release energy. This process is called ***fusion***. An example of fusion is the combining of hydrogen to make helium in three steps on the Sun. In the first step of the process, two hydrogens produce an isotope of hydrogen (deuterium) with one neutron. In the second step, a hydrogen combines with a deuterium to produce a helium isotope with one neutron. In the third step, two helium isotopes produce a helium with two protons and two neutrons and two hydrogens. Along the way, other particles and energy are also released. The corresponding nuclear equations are shown below.

   Step 1:

   $^{1}_{1}\text{H} + ^{1}_{1}\text{H} \rightarrow ^{2}_{1}\text{H} + ^{0}_{1}\text{e} +$ neutrino

   (*positron:* particle with a mass equal to that of an electron but with a positive charge)
   (*neutrino:* a very energetic subatomic particle with zero charge and near zero mass)

   Step 2:

   $^{1}_{1}\text{H} + ^{2}_{1}\text{H} \rightarrow ^{3}_{2}\text{He} +$ gamma radiation

   Step 3:

   $^{3}_{2}\text{He} + ^{3}_{2}\text{He} \rightarrow ^{4}_{2}\text{He} + ^{1}_{1}\text{H} + ^{1}_{1}\text{H}$

   a) Is the atomic mass number conserved on both sides of the reaction?

   b) Is the atomic number conserved on both sides of the reaction?

8. The neutrons and protons in the nucleus have a substructure and consist of particles called quarks. Quarks come up in many types. The ones that combine to make protons and neutrons are "up" quarks with a charge of +2/3 and "down" quarks with a charge of −1/3. These combine in sets of three quarks to make protons and neutrons.

   a) Show how a proton (charge = +1) can be made up of a combination of up and down quarks.

   b) Show how a neutron (charge = 0) can be made up of a combination of up and down quarks.

Chem Talk

Chem Words

neutron: a neutral particle located in the nucleus of an atom.

nucleon: either a proton or neutron in the nucleus of an atom.

THE NUCLEUS OF AN ATOM

Discovery of the Neutron

The average atomic masses of some elements were known in Mendeleev's time, even though scientists didn't know much about the actual structure of an atom. In *Part A* of this activity you explored the idea of how the atomic mass relates to the atomic number. Mendeleev began organizing his periodic table by listing all the known elements in order of atomic mass. However, he found that organizing the elements in this way did not always make sense in terms of the behavior of the elements. He concluded that his measurements of atomic mass were incorrect. In those situations he used the properties of the elements to place them in the table.

As it turned out, Mendeleev's measurements were not necessarily flawed. Although early models of the nucleus included the proton, the proton alone could not account for the fact that the mass of a helium atom is four times the mass of a hydrogen atom while the electric charge on the helium nucleus is only twice that of the hydrogen atom. Lord Rutherford (after discovering that atoms had a nucleus) addressed this problem. He suggested that another particle was present in the nucleus with about the same mass as the proton but no electric charge. He named this particle the **neutron**.

J. Chadwick

The English scientist J. Chadwick confirmed the presence of this particle in 1932. He was awarded the Nobel Prize in Physics in 1935 for his discovery. This discovery added a great deal to the understanding of the nucleus of the atom. It did not, however, solve all of the mysteries concerning the atomic masses of some elements. Scientists today refer to protons and neutrons as **nucleons.** They both reside in the nucleus and are almost identical in mass. The mass number tells you the number of nucleons.

Isotopes

In *Part A* of this activity you also investigated why the atomic mass of an element is not a whole number. Not all atoms of a given element have the same number of neutrons in the nucleus. (Think about the chlorine twins in *What Do You See?*) Only the number of protons, the atomic number, is the same in all atoms of a given element. Atoms of the same element with different number of neutrons in the nucleus are known as **isotopes**. Isotope implies "same number of protons." Isotopes are identified by their mass number, the sum of the number of neutrons plus protons.

You can refer to an element by its name (chlorine), by its atomic symbol (Cl), or by its atomic number (17). All three identifications are equivalent and used interchangeably in chemistry. The same element can have a different number of neutrons in the nucleus. Chlorine, which must have 17 protons in the nucleus, can have 18 or 20 neutrons. Chlorine with 18 neutrons and chlorine with 20 neutrons are the two isotopes of chlorine ($^{35}_{17}Cl$ and $^{37}_{17}Cl$, respectively).

Electrostatic and Nuclear Forces

In *Part B* of this activity, you brought two positive strips near each other. They experienced a repulsive force. This was true for two negative strips as well. When a positive and a negative strip were brought close together, the force was attractive. As you have heard, "opposites attract!"

Inside the nucleus, the protons are repelling one another. Every pair of protons has a repulsive force between them. The force is very large because the distances within the nucleus are very small. The nucleus is between 10,000 and 100,000 times smaller than the atom. As you saw in *Activity 4*, the electrical force can be described mathematically.

$$F = \frac{kq_1q_2}{d^2}$$

where F is the force,

k is Coulomb's constant, (a number $= 9 \times 10^9$ N·m²/C²),

q_1 and q_2 are the charges, and

d is the distance between the charges.

As the distance between the charges increases the force weakens. Since the distance in the denominator is squared, if the distance triples the electrical force is one-ninth ($\frac{1}{3^2}$) as strong.

Chem Words

isotope: atoms of the same element that have different masses due to a different number of neutrons.

The question then becomes, what holds the protons together in the nucleus? The protons do have an electrical force pushing them apart. However, they have the larger nuclear force holding them together. The nuclear force is strong at short range. Anywhere beyond a distance of approximately 10^{-14}m (that's less than one 10 millionth of one 10 millionth of a meter), the nuclear force is zero. Neutrons in the nucleus are also attracted to each other and to protons with the nuclear force. Electrons are not affected by the nuclear force. Electrons belong to a different class of particles than protons and neutrons. They do not interact with the strong nuclear force.

A new force, the strong nuclear force, holds the nucleus together. The nuclear force:

- is very, very strong at small distances
- acts only between nucleons (proton-proton, proton-neutron, neutron-neutron)
- is always attractive
- is very short range (if nucleons are more than 10^{-14}m apart, the nuclear force is zero).

The electrostatic coulomb force holds the atom together. The electrostatic force:

- is strong at small distances, weak at large distances
- acts only between charged particles (proton-proton, electron-electron, proton-electron)
- is attractive or repulsive
- is long range (the force gets weaker at large distances, but is never zero).

All the nucleons are attracted by the nuclear force. The electrostatic force repelling protons in the nucleus is overwhelmed by the attractive nuclear force between these protons.

Unstable Atoms

Nuclei of atoms have a wide range of numbers of protons and neutrons. All possibilities do not occur in nature. For example, although you could probably assume that an element exists with 20 protons and 20 neutrons, you can also assume that no element exists with 50 protons and only one neutron. In addition, scientists have found that elements do not occur in nature with atomic number greater than 92. In the lab, scientists have been able to create heavier elements (up to 117 as of this writing) and continue to explore this area of nuclear chemistry.

Chlorine has two stable isotopes. Both have the same atomic number of 17. However, one has a mass of 35 amu and the other has a mass of 37 amu. Chlorine-35 has 17 protons and 18 neutrons. Chlorine-37 has 17 protons and 20 neutrons. There are other isotopes of chlorine such as chlorine-36, but it is not stable. Unstable isotopes decay into other elements in ways that have been investigated over the past 100 years.

Three of the ways in which unstable nuclei decay are alpha, beta, and gamma emission. In alpha emission, the nucleus "spits out" a particle that has two neutrons and two protons. This is identical to the nucleus of helium. Its chemical symbol is ${}^{4}_{2}\mathrm{He}$ and it is referred to as an alpha particle. Alpha particles are what Rutherford used in his "battleship" experiment.

$${}^{238}_{92}\mathrm{U} \rightarrow {}^{4}_{2}\mathrm{He} + {}^{234}_{90}\mathrm{Th}$$

In beta emission, the nucleus "spits out" a high-speed electron. The electron was not residing in the nucleus. A neutron in the nucleus decayed into a proton and an electron and the electron was ejected. The symbol for this high-speed electron is ${}^{0}_{-1}\mathrm{e}$ and it is referred to as a beta particle.

$${}^{40}_{19}\mathrm{K} \rightarrow {}^{0}_{-1}\mathrm{e} + {}^{40}_{20}\mathrm{Ca}$$

In gamma emission, the nucleus "spits out" a packet of electromagnetic radiation. This does not change the atomic number or atomic mass of the element. The symbol for this emission is γ and it is referred to as a gamma particle or gamma ray.

$${}^{99}_{43}\mathrm{Tc} \rightarrow {}^{99}_{43}\mathrm{Tc} + \gamma$$

RADIOACTIVE

Alpha, beta and gamma emissions can be a health risk or a medical therapy. Radiation can harm both cancer cells and healthy cells. A thin sheet of material can usually block alpha particles. A thicker shield is required to block beta particles. An even thicker shield is required to block gamma particles.

Radioactive decay of large numbers of nuclei occurs with incredible precision and can be used as clocks to date items.

Understanding why certain elements are **radioactive** requires a deeper understanding of the structure of the nucleus. Scientists are still trying to fully understand stability of the elements.

If the nucleus of an atom is too large, the protons on one side of the nucleus are too far away to attract the protons on the other

Chem Words

radioactive: an atom that has an unstable nucleus and will emit alpha, positron, or beta particles in order to achieve more stable nucleus.

Chem Words

fusion: nuclei of lighter atoms combining to form nuclei with greater mass and releasing a large amount of energy.

fission: the process of breaking apart nuclei into smaller nuclei and with the release of a large amount of energy.

side of the nucleus. The protons can still repel one another since the coulomb electrostatic force is long-range. The interaction between the repulsive electrostatic force and the attractive nuclear force is one determining factor of the maximum size of a nucleus.

Within a star, the stability of an atom varies with the nucleus. Light elements become more stable as the atomic mass (the number of nucleons) increases. The most stable element is iron (atomic number 26) with an atomic mass of 56 amu. Elements with larger atomic masses become less stable.

In general, elements with nuclear mass much, much less than 56 amu can combine to gain mass, become more stable, and give off energy. This process is called **fusion**. Elements with nuclear mass much, much greater than 56 amu can break apart to lose mass, become more stable, and give off energy. This process is called **fission**.

Fusion is the process of small nuclei combining to increase their mass. The best example of fusion processes is what occurs in the Sun and other stars. Theoretically, the fusion process is ideal for supplying safe energy because it releases very large amounts of energy without leaving much dangerous radioactive residue. However, it is very difficult to accomplish this on an industrial level at the present time. In the future we hope scientists will figure out how to harness the energy of nuclear fusion, because it would be an excellent source of energy for society.

The process of splitting an atom into smaller atoms is called fission. This is the process that is used to produce nuclear energy. It is used to power nuclear submarines and to produce electrical energy in nuclear power plants all over the world. The energy given off upon nuclear fission can be determined according to the famous equation $E = mc^2$, where m stands for mass deflect and c is the speed of light. The energy is liberated in this process because the total mass of the reactants is not equal to that of the products. There is a very small loss of mass; think of the process as one where a small amount of mass is converted into energy. Since the square of the speed of light (9×10^{16} m^2/s^2) is a tremendously large number, a very small amount of mass can generate a huge amount of energy. The energy released in nuclear reactions can be millions of times greater than in chemical reactions.

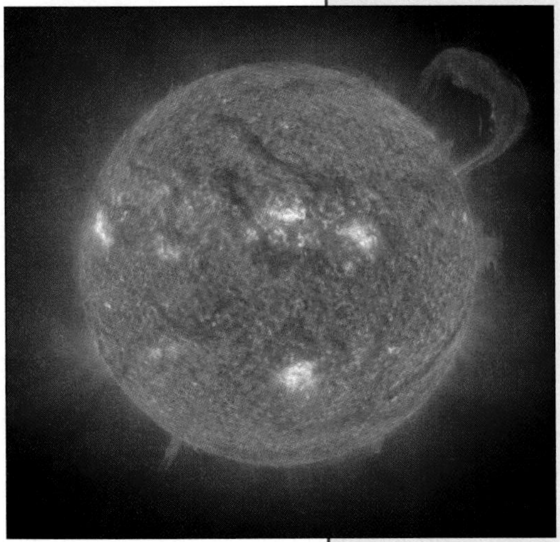

The use of nuclear energy for the production of electricity is quite apparent as you look at the numerous states that depend on nuclear energy. For example, over 40% of Illinois's electricity is produced by nuclear energy. Nuclear fission does create some major problems. These include security, safety, radiation, removal of spent rods, and disposal of waste.

The disposal of nuclear waste has its own particular set of problems, and probably the most important of these is the half-life of the by-products of nuclear-power generation. The fission process creates many radioactive isotopes, each emitting its own hazardous radiation at its own particular rate. The **half-life** of a radioactive isotope is the length of time it takes for half of any quantity of that isotope to decay. The unstable isotopes decay by emitting radiation. They do so until a stable isotope is formed. The stability of an isotope has to do with the ratio of protons to neutrons in the nucleus, and will not be discussed further here. Half-lives of isotopes can be as short as less than a second and as long as tens of thousands of years. The uranium-238 that is a radioactive by-product of nuclear-power production will decay through a series of other radioactive isotopes until a stable isotope (Pb-206) is formed. The half-life of U-238 is 4.5×10^9 years. This means that it will take that many years for half of the U-238 to decay into Pb-206. The half-life of Kr-93, one of the many products of U-235 fission is 1.3 s. For any radioactive material, after two half-lives one quarter of the original sample remains. After four half-lives, 1/16 of the original sample remains.

Half-lives of Kr-93

Elapsed time (s)	0	1.3 s	2.6 s	3.9 s	5.2 s
Elapsed time (half-lives)	0	1 half-life	2 half-lives	3 half-lives	4 half-lives
Mass of Kr-93 remaining	60 g	30 g	15 g	7.5 g	3.75 g

Chem Words

half-life: the length of time it takes for half of any quantity of a given radioactive isotope to decay.

With the problems facing nuclear energy, and the problems we continue to experience with our dependence on oil for energy, there is a need for continued research. Numerous universities and government facilities are trying to improve the efficiency of nuclear fission and at the same time, trying to develop nuclear fusion for commercial use.

This ongoing research is expensive and depends on the government, industry, and other organizations for continued support. This research and the use of nuclear energy itself must be directed by a careful risk-benefit analysis. Nuclear radiation can be both extremely beneficial and extremely dangerous. It just depends on how you use it.

Used as a medical tool, radiation has extended the lives of many cancer patients. This process is also important for generating electrical power. However, there are high costs in terms of waste disposal and other problems. If scientists can learn how to harness nuclear fusion they can alleviate the nation's electrical problems while decreasing pollution. The field of nuclear science is going to continue to grow. The future will provide great opportunities for a student scientist like you to get involved.

Our most recent view of the nucleus reveals that the protons and neutrons within it have an internal substructure. Experiments similar to the Rutherford scattering experiment (see *Activity 4*) reveal this substructure. Theories have shown that two "up" quarks (each with a charge of $+2/3$) and one "down" quark (with a charge of $-1/3$) combine to create a proton (with a charge of $+1$). Similarly, one "up" quark and two "down" quarks combine to create a neutron (with a charge of 0).

Checking Up

1. Explain the difference between atomic mass and atomic number.
2. What two forces are at work in the nucleus of an atom? Explain the characteristics of each.
3. What is an isotope?
4. Why are some isotopes unstable?
5. What percentage of a radioactive sample remains after three half-lives?
6. Suppose you have 500 g of a radioactive sample with a half-life of 100 years. How much of the sample would be radioactive after 400 years?
7. Construct a table or diagram to compare and contrast the nuclear processes of fission and fusion.

What Do You Think Now?

At the beginning of the activity you were asked:

- **What do you think makes up the nucleus of the atom?**

You now know that the nucleus is made up of protons and neutrons. Protons repel protons and neutrons are neutral. Then why is the nucleus so small and why doesn't it just fall apart? Explain this in terms of the electrostatic force and strong nuclear force.

Chem Essential Questions

What does it mean?

Chemistry explains a macroscopic phenomenon (what you observe) with a description of what happens at the nanoscopic level (atoms and molecules) using symbolic structures as a way to communicate. Complete the chart below in your *Active Chemistry* log.

MACRO	NANO	SYMBOLIC
Describe what happened when you placed two charged pieces of tape near each other.	*The pieces of tape repel each other when each tape has a negative charge – due to an excess of electrons. Explain why the nucleus of the atom does not "blow itself up" due to the repulsion of all the positive charges in such a small space.*	*Formulas are used to show the mass of different isotopes. For example, Cl-35 and Cl-37 would be expressed as* $^{35}_{17}Cl$ *and* $^{37}_{17}Cl$*. Compare and contrast Cl-35 and Cl-37.*

How do you know?

The periodic table is ordered by atomic number, which corresponds to the number of protons in the element. How do you know that it should not be ordered by the atomic mass, which corresponds to the total number of protons and neutrons in the element?

Why do you believe?

You know that in nuclear fission, uranium-235 is bombarded with neutrons and this reaction will cause the nuclei to split to smaller elements, releasing a large amount of energy. How does the Sun create energy using fusion?

Why should you care?

The future depends on a continued increase in producing energy for a growing population. Nuclear reactions such as fission and fusion will be expected to meet this demand, but there will be costs to bear. How can your game include fission, fusion, the nuclear force, isotopes, or radioactivity as an interesting component?

Reflecting on the Activity and the Challenge

In *Part A* of this activity you learned that the mass of an atom, concentrated in the nucleus, is due to two types of particles, the proton and the neutron. Elements are identified by their atomic number, the number of protons in the nucleus.

The atomic mass, the average mass of the isotopes of a given element, listed on the periodic table is a reflection of the variety of isotopes of a given element that exist. You will probably want to incorporate your expanded understanding of the contents of an atom's nucleus, average atomic masses, and isotopes into your game about the periodic table.

In *Part B* of this activity you also learned that only some combinations of neutrons and protons in a nucleus are stable, depending on the balance between the strong force holding the nuclear particles together and the electric force pushing them apart. The nuclear force is a short-range force. Beyond a distance of approximately 10^{-14} m, the nuclear force has no strength. Within that distance, this force between protons and protons, protons and neutrons, and neutrons and neutrons is quite strong. Recognizing the interplay between the electric force in the nucleus and the strong, attractive nuclear force provides an insight into the size of nuclei and the maximum size of a nucleus. These insights can be incorporated into your periodic table game in a creative way.

Chem to Go

1. If lithium loses an electron to become Li^+, what is the average atomic mass of the lithium ion? Explain how you arrived at your answer.
2. Hydrogen has three isotopes with mass numbers of 1, 2, and 3. Write the complete chemical symbol for each isotope.
3. Give the complete chemical symbol for the element that contains 16 protons, 16 electrons, and 17 neutrons.
4. Use the periodic table to complete the table below:

Chemical symbol	$^{39}_{19}K$			
Atomic number		9		
Number of protons			15	
Number of electrons				53
Number of neutrons		10	16	
Atomic mass				127

5. Neutrons can be used to bombard the nucleus of an atom like uranium. Why would it be more difficult to inject the nucleus of uranium with a proton?
6. Complete the following reaction: $^{235}_{92}U + ^{1}_{0}n \rightarrow ^{94}_{38}Sr +$ ______ $+ 2\,^{1}_{0}n$.
7. Radon is a threat to the health of people in their homes. It emits radioactive particles at a significant rate. Complete the following radioactive decay equation:
$^{222}_{86}Rn \rightarrow ^{218}_{84}Po +$ ________ .
8. Explain why a helium atom is able to exist. What keeps the two electrons, two protons, and two neutrons together?

9. Which of the following may be used to decrease the half-life of a radioactive isotope?

   a) increase surface area b) increase concentration

   c) increase temperature d) none of the above

10. What percent of a radioactive isotope would remain after two half-lives?

   a) 50.0% b) 6.25% c) 12.5% d) 25.0%

Inquiring Further

Calculating average atomic mass

If you know the percentages of abundance for the isotopes of a chemical element and the known masses of those isotopes, you can calculate the average atomic mass of that element. The process is similar to calculating the average age of students in your class — add up each person's age and divide by the number of students in your class. However, if you had to average the age of all of the students in your high school, you might choose another route. It would be easier to find out how many students are fourteen, how many are fifteen, and so on. Then you could multiply the number of students in each age group by that age. Then you would add these subsets together and divide by the total number of students.

A similar process is used to average the masses of different isotopes of an element. Consider the element chlorine. There are two stable isotopes of chlorine, chlorine-35 and chlorine-37. Of all the chlorine atoms on Earth, 75.77% of them are the isotope chlorine-35, each having a mass of 34.97 amu. The other 24.23% of stable chlorine atoms are the isotope chlorine-37, each having a mass of 36.97 amu. This means that 75.77 out of 100 chlorine atoms have a mass of 34.97 amu and 24.23 atoms have a mass of 36.97 amu. To find the average mass, the number of each isotope is multiplied by that isotope's mass. Then the products are added together. The sum is divided by 100, since the information pertained to 100 chlorine atoms. The result is an average atomic mass of 35.45 for chlorine, the same value stated in the periodic table. The math is shown below:

Chlorine-35 $34.97 \times 75.77 = 2649.6$

Chlorine-37 $36.97 \times 24.23 = \underline{895.5}$

3545.1

$3545 \div 100 = 35.45$

Magnesium, another isotope you investigated, has three stable isotopes as follows:

mass number	isotopic mass	% abundance
24	23.99	78.99
25	24.99	10.00
26	25.98	11.01

Calculate the average atomic mass for magnesium. Describe how you arrived at your answer. You may use the process described above or challenge yourself to develop your own process.

Chem at Work

Scott Kim

Puzzle Designer, San Francisco, CA

"A real puzzle master is rare," says Scott Kim. "There aren't many of us in the world." Scott is a full-time puzzle master, living in San Francisco, California. He creates all kinds of brainteasers. Scott has designed three-dimensional puzzles based on the art of M.C. Escher. He has also designed puzzles for computer and video games, like the web game "Bejeweled." He even writes a monthly column on puzzles for *Discover Magazine*.

Scott designs each puzzle to test a specific set of knowledge. Does that sound familiar to you? That's because the *Chapter Challenge* for *Fun with the Periodic Table* is to create a game to do just that. Fun is also a goal in Scott's puzzles, just as it is for your game. According to Scott, the biggest mistake that new puzzle masters make is to be too complicated. "Keep it fun and use simple concepts. The concept should be easy for you to explain in the directions." Also, it is helpful for the instructions to include examples. Did you do that in your game?

Scott teaches others how to be puzzle masters. He advises new masters to design a puzzle around a subject. "Think about what's important to understand about your puzzle. If you're trying to make a puzzle out of the periodic table for example, it might be useful that all the elements have letter symbols. Acronyms are a good tool for letter puzzles."

The testing phase is a crucial trial for a new puzzle. "The single most important aspect of puzzle design is to test your product. Give the puzzle to your friends and *restrain yourself*. Don't give them hints. Let them struggle. Everything you need to know is in that process. Then revise your puzzle and test it again."

Tom Lensch

Woodworker, Dayton, OH

Tom Lensch has been carving wood since he was a little boy. His specialty is making puzzles. He has made over 75 different puzzle designs come to life. Puzzle masters from around the world design the puzzles. Tom shares his work with students for free because he feels that the challenges puzzles present are important to education.

Thuyanh (Ann) Nguyen

Senior Clinical Safety Specialist, Durham, NC

Thuyanh Nguyen works at Quintiles Transnational Corp. Before a new drug is sold to the public, it must undergo years of tests. She makes sure that when patients take a new drug in a clinical trial, all adverse effects are recorded. Her puzzle is to solve what combination of chemicals caused the bad reaction.

Fun with the Periodic Table Assessment

Your *Chapter Challenge* is to create a game that will both entertain and teach people about the periodic table. How the game is played, whether on a table, with cards, on a computer, or with equipment that only you might choose is up to you. You might want to emphasize some aspects of the periodic table over others, such as why the elements are grouped the way they are, how atomic masses are determined, or how the electrons of the elements are configured. Or you may choose to focus on some types of information related to the table like the history of the discovery of atomic structure, how the elements combine to form compounds, and why some are radioactive.

Chemistry Content

To begin, you should review all of the activities that you have completed. You can skim through the text and your *Active Chemistry* log to help remind you of the chemistry concepts in each activity.

Activity 1: You learned about organization. The periodic table is a way in which our knowledge about the properties of matter can be organized.

Activity 2: You investigated the properties of some elements. These properties included the ability to conduct electricity, whether the element reacted with HCl and whether the material was a metal or nonmetal. You also attempted to organize the elements in terms of these properties.

Activity 3: You learned how to compare and contrast elements and compounds. You were also able to determine the relative masses of elements. The mass of elements is another property by which elements can be organized.

Activity 4: The game of battleship was used as a tool to help you learn about the structure of the atom. You learned that the nucleus takes up a very, very small part of the atom. That tiny space holds all of the positive charge and almost all of the mass of the atom. You also learned about the discovery of the electron and its place in the atom.

Activity 5: You observed the specific colors of the light given off by hydrogen gas. By investigating these colors (and energies) of light, you learned how Bohr developed a model of the atom. You learned that electrons jumping from a higher energy orbit to a lower energy orbit emitted light of a specific energy and color.

Activity 6: You analyzed the ionization energies of elements and were introduced to the periodic table. You found out that the rows or periods of the periodic table were closely related to the ionization energies. You also recognized that the columns or chemical groups were comprised of elements with similar properties.

Activity 7: You investigated how electrons determine the chemical behavior of atoms. You paid particular attention to the valence electrons of each element.

Activity 8: You learned how atoms interact with each other. You also were introduced to the octet rule. You then learned how to differentiate between ionic and covalent bonds between atoms.

Activity 9: You investigated the electrostatic force that holds the electrons to the nucleus and holds atoms together. You also learned that the nucleus is made up of protons and neutrons. The nucleus is able to withstand the large electrostatic force of repulsion because an even larger nuclear force exists between nucleons (protons and neutrons). You were introduced to isotopes and their relation to the atomic mass of an element.

You may want to make a chart that shows the activity number, some chemistry concepts in the activity, and some ideas as to how you can use these concepts as part of your periodic-table game. Your chart may include whether the concept will be part of the rules or part of the equipment or part of the play. You should pay particular attention to the *Reflecting on the Activity and the Challenge, Chem Essential Questions*, and *Preparing for the Chapter Challenge* sections. You should also compare your list with that given in the *Chem You Learned* summary.

Activity #	Chemistry concepts	How to use concepts

You may decide to do the first activity as a group to ensure that everybody understands how to proceed. After completing the first activity, each team member can be assigned two or three activities. You can then review all of the activities as a group with the activity expert reviewing each summary.

Criteria

You and your team should review the criteria by which you will be graded. Before beginning the chapter, your teacher led a class discussion to get a sense of what criteria should be used to judge the quality of work for this periodic-table game. It is time to revisit that discussion since you now have considerable understanding of the chemistry concepts that you can include in your presentation. Think about and discuss what would make a great game. How will you both entertain and help players learn concepts at the same time?

How will your game be graded? What qualities should a good game have? Your rubric should assign points to how well the game shows your understanding of the periodic table and how well the game enables players to learn about the periodic table. You may also wish to assign points to how interesting the game is to play and how long the game takes to play. This rubric can be a useful tool for your team to check the quality of your work and to ensure that you have included all necessary parts of the project.

Preparing for the Chapter Challenge

- Chemistry Concepts

Your team's next step would then be to decide on what kind of game you want to play and how you will incorporate the chemistry into the game. Will it be a board game or a physical game or a video game? Will individuals compete against one another or will teams be involved? How will the game end? How does someone win the game? How can your game include chemistry concepts?

- Practice Playing Your Game

You need to practice playing your game to ensure that the rules of the game make sense. You want to get a sense of how difficult the game is to learn and how long it takes to complete it. It may be helpful to call in some classmates who have not helped to develop the game to find out if the rules make sense. This "focus group" may be able to point out some facets of the game that need more work.

- Chemistry content is necessary, but not sufficient.

Games are about challenges and fun. You must create a game that people will want to play. You don't want to make it too easy nor too difficult. You want people to look forward to the game. You also want them to complete the game and want to play another round. The game should help people learn chemistry concepts but it shouldn't be identical to a school quiz or test. Being creative and making the game both fun, challenging and educational is what makes this periodic table game such an exciting challenge.

- Manage Your Time

You have a sense of how you want to proceed and what you want the final product to be. You now have to allocate the work. How much time do you have to complete the project? When is the presentation? How will you get everything done in this timeframe? Who will be working on the game equipment and who will be working on the instructions? How will you ensure that each member's work meets the standard of excellence so that everybody on the team gets an A? Create a time chart for the challenge. Divide the responsibilities. How much time will each take? Some work can be done individually as homework. Leave time to review each other's work.

Planning a project well does not ensure success, but poor planning almost always leads to disappointment.

Engineering/Technology Design

Reflect on the engineering/technology design process. Recall the successes and disappointments from the *mini-challenge*. How can you use the feedback that you received to improve your show? At this point, you are starting the design cycle again.

Have fun with the periodic-table game!

Chem You Learned

- An **element** is any pure substance in the periodic table that cannot be chemically broken down into simpler materials. Each element has its unique atomic number, chemical properties, and symbol.
- All matter is composed of **atoms** which are the smallest particles that retain the chemical properties of the element.
- A **chemical property** is demonstrated when the atoms of a substance rearrange to form new substances.
- If a change occurs in a substance but no atoms are rearranged, a **physical property** is exhibited.
- Materials that are shiny, malleable, ductile, and conduct electricity are classified as **metals**. Metals react with oxygen to produce metal oxides which are basic in aqueous solution.
- Materials that are typically gases or soft solids are classified as **nonmetals.** They occupy the upper right corner of the periodic table and their oxides form acidic aqueous solutions.
- The dense central core of an atom is called the **nucleus,** which contains the protons and neutrons. The nucleus contain essentially all of the mass of the atom. The **proton** has a mass of 1 amu and a charge of +1; the **neutron** also has a mass of 1 amu but has no electrical charge.
- The third subatomic particles found in an atom are the **electrons**. Electrons occupy the space outside the nucleus, have negligible mass, and a charge of −1. In other contexts electrons may be called **beta radiation** or **cathode rays**.
- To find the **atomic mass** of an element add the number of protons and neutrons in the nucleus.
- The identity of each element is determined by the number of protons in its nucleus, the **atomic number.** Elements with the same atomic number but different numbers of neutrons are **isotopes**.
- A **compound** is formed when two or more elements combine to form a new substance. The elements will always combine in exactly the same proportions by mass **(Law of Definite Proportions)**.
- Since atoms are so small, chemists always work with vast numbers of atoms. A convenient measure of chemical quantities is **Avogadro's number**, also called a **mole.** A mole is 6.022×10^{23}.
- Modern atomic theory, **quantum theory,** shows that electrons occupy highly specific regions in the space about the nucleus. These regions are called **energy levels** and each energy level (1, 2, 3, 4....) has **sublevels** (*s, p, d, f, g*) of orbitals.
- A shorthand method for describing the arrangement of electrons in the orbitals of an element is called its **electron configuration**.
- A form of energy which travels through space at the speed of light ($c = 3.00 \times 10^8$ m/s) is **electromagnetic radiation**. It is characterized by **wavelength**, λ, and **frequency**, f.

$$c = \lambda f \qquad E = hf$$

- When two elements combine chemically to form a new substance, a **chemical reaction** has occurred. A reaction can be expressed in shorthand with a **balanced equation** − **reactants** → **products**, exhibiting the **Conservation of Mass**.
- When an ionic bond forms, a certain amount of energy is required to remove the electron to be transferred, the **ionization energy**. The atom giving up electron(s) becomes a cation; the atom receiving the electron(s) becomes an anion.

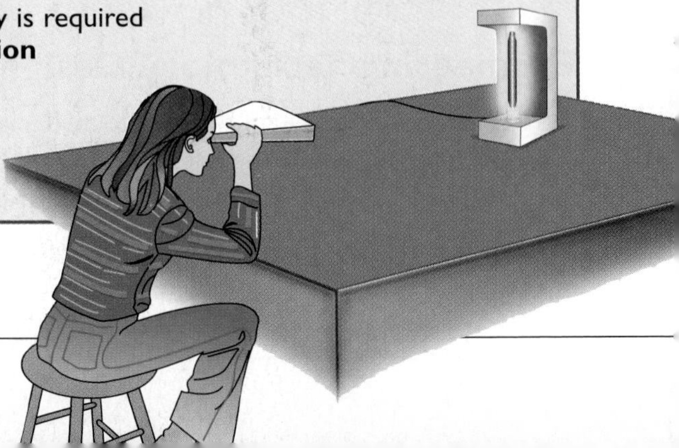

Chapter 2

MOVIE SPECIAL EFFECTS

Chapter Challenge

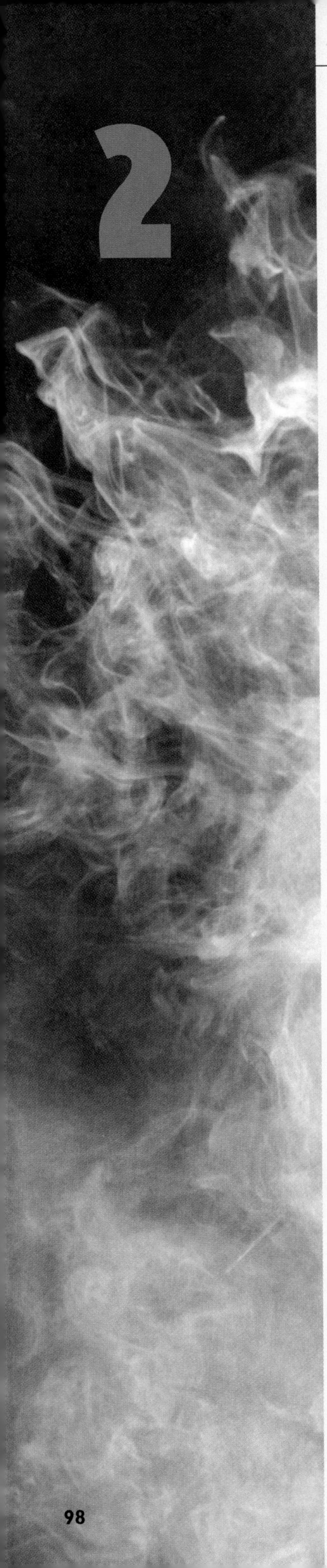

2

Movie Special Effects

Scenario

You have all been captivated and entertained by special effects in movies. The explosions, makeup, animation, and props in the "blockbuster" features take months and millions of dollars to put together. Many special effects are the result of the application of science and technology.

Your *Active Chemistry* class has been asked to participate in the production of a low-budget movie. However, to make the film exciting, the movie producer would still like to use some awesome special effects. You are being asked to write a simple scene in which you can incorporate some special effects. Of course, in addition to cost, safety is also a major concern.

Your Challenge

Your challenge is to create a storyline and produce special effects based on the chemistry you have learned in your *Active Chemistry* class. You will need to demonstrate the special effects you created. Your special effects will be evaluated on their quality, entertainment, and the knowledge of chemistry you exhibited in putting them together.

You will need to complete the following tasks:

- Write a script for a simple scene in a movie.
- Choose some special effects to include as part of your scene.
- Write a procedure on how your special effect is done.
- Demonstrate the special effect to the "producer."
- Write an explanation of how the special effect works, including the chemistry behind the demonstration.

Using more than one chemical principle will strengthen your presentation.

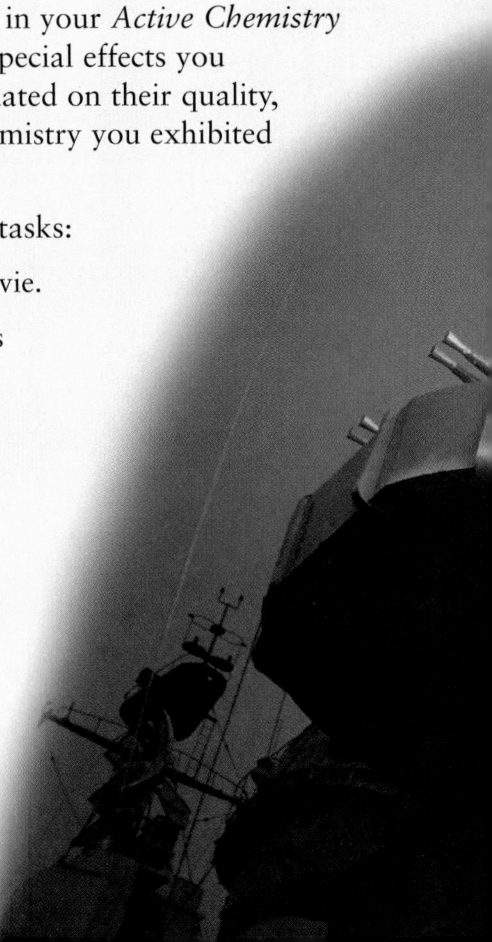

Criteria

How will your special effect be graded? What qualities should an effective special effect have? How will your demonstration and supporting documentation be graded? Discuss these issues in small groups and with your class. You may decide that some or all of the following qualities should be graded:

- Demonstration
- Safety
- Quality
- Interest and appeal to an audience
- Supporting documentation
- Script—creativity
- Procedure—clarity, safety, accuracy
- Chemistry explanation—accuracy and quantity of chemical principles incorporated

ChemCorner

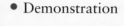

Chemistry in *Movie Special Effects*

- Electrolysis of water
- Density
- Hydrocarbons
- Tyndall Effect
- Accuracy
- Precision
- Flame tests
- Polymers
- Phase changes
- Sublimation
- Scientific notation
- Hydrogen gas experiments
- Boiling point
- Freezing point
- Heating curves
- Physical states of matter
- Composites

Once you have determined the list of qualities for evaluating the documentation and demonstration, you and your classmates should also decide how many points should be given for each criterion. How many points should be assigned to the documentation and how many to the demonstration? Should more points go to the chemistry explanation than to the movie script? How many different chemical principles should be incorporated in your special effect?

Determining grading criteria might be a time-consuming task, but knowing the point values in advance will help you focus your time and effort on the most important aspects of your special-effect documentation and demonstration.

Will each student produce his/her own special effect, will students be required to work in groups, or will both options be offered? Discuss the pros and cons of these possibilities. Keep in mind that if you are going to be working in groups, it is important to discuss, before the work begins, how each member of the group will be graded. Determine grading criteria that will reward each individual in the group for his/her contribution and also reward the group for the final project. You should discuss different strategies and choose the strategy that is best suited to your situation. Make sure that you understand all the criteria as well as you can before you begin. Your teacher may provide you with a sample rubric to help you get started.

Activity 1 Elements and Compounds

What Do You See?

SUGAR

GOALS

In this activity you will:

- Decompose water by electrolysis into the two elements from which it is composed.
- Test the two elements to determine their identities.
- Learn one way to determine the chemical formula of a material.
- Compare characteristic properties of a material to those of its constituent elements.
- Represent materials with chemical formulas using numbers and the symbols of elements.
- Practice safe laboratory techniques with flames and explosions.

What Do You Think?

Matter is the name for all the "stuff" in the universe. Anything that has mass and occupies space is called matter.

- **How many kinds of matter are there in the universe: 1, 10, 100, 1000, 10 000, 100 000 or 1 000 000?**
- **What makes up matter?**

The *What Do You Think?* questions are meant to get you thinking about what you already know or think you know. Don't worry about being right or wrong. Discussing what you think you know is an important step in learning.

Record your ideas in your *Active Chemistry* log. Be prepared to discuss your responses with your small group and the class.

Investigate

1. Look around your classroom at the kinds of matter that make up the things you see.

   a) Make a list of 10 kinds of materials that make up the objects you see. For example, you might list the wood in your pencil, or the glass in the windows.

   b) To understand the nature of matter, it helps to know if it is simple or complex. Is the matter made from only one kind of material or is it a mixture of various materials? Classify each of the 10 materials you listed as pure or mixtures.

c) For each material you thought was a mixture, write your best guess about what materials make it up.

Safety goggles and a lab apron must be worn *at all times* in a chemistry lab.

2. Sometimes the materials that make up a substance are not obvious. Early scientists thought that water was an element. In other words, they thought that there was only one kind of material in water. They had not discovered a way of breaking it down further. Water, however, can be broken down further.

a) Carefully observe the characteristic properties of water. Record at least three observations of water in your log.

3. Assemble the apparatus for decomposing water as shown in the diagram. Fill two test tubes with water. Submerge them in the water in the beaker and invert them. Make sure you do not allow any air to enter the test tubes. The ends of the wires should be stripped. Polish them with steel wool. Insert the ends of the wires into the test tubes. Add about 1 to 2 mL of sodium sulfate solution to the water in the beaker.

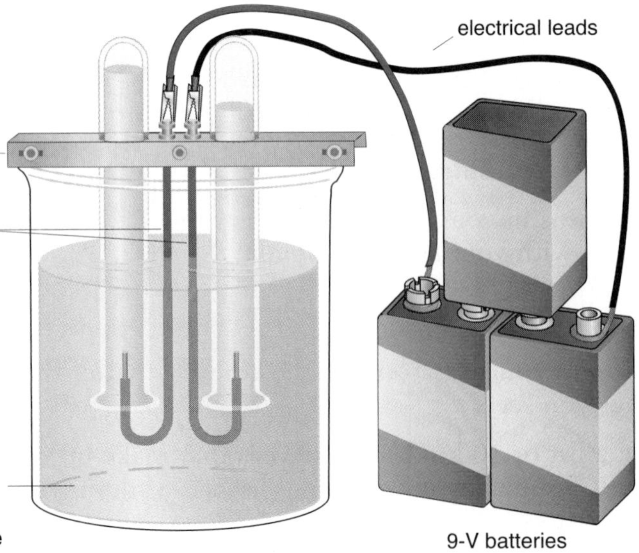
electrical leads
electrolysis apparatus
stainless steel or platinum electrodes
water containing dissolved sodium sulfate
9-V batteries

4. Plug in the set of three 9-V batteries in series or use a power supply. Let the reaction run until a test tube is half-full of gas. (Your teacher may decide to have you stop the reaction sooner.)

a) Note what happens when the power is turned on. Record your observations in your *Active Chemistry* log.

b) How do the relative amounts of gas formed in the test tubes compare?

5. Disconnect the batteries or power source. While inverted, place stoppers in the test tubes and remove them from the water.

a) What gas do you think is contained in each test tube? (Hint: You've probably heard that water is H-2-O, written H_2O.) Record your prediction, and give reasons for your prediction.

b) Observe the physical properties of each gas. Record these properties in your log.

6. Remove the stopper while the test tube is inverted. Drain the water and replace the stopper. You are going to use a lighted wooden splint to identify the gas in each test tube. First, examine the test tube with the smaller volume of gas. Light a wooden splint. Blow out the flame, but leave the splint glowing. Hold the test tube with its mouth up. Remove the stopper. Quickly bring the glowing splint to the mouth of the test tube.

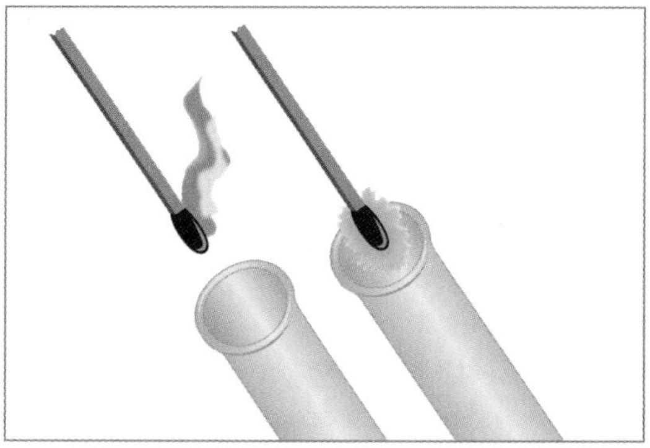

a) Observe what happens to the splint and record your observations.

b) What gas do you think was produced in this test tube?

c) In your log record any additional properties of the gas that you discovered.

7. Next, examine the test tube that contains the larger volume of gas. Light a wooden splint. Keep the test tube inverted. Remove the stopper. Quickly bring the burning splint to the mouth of the test tube.

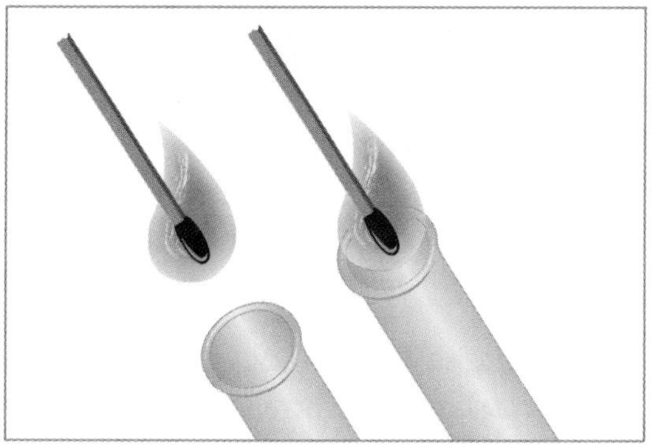

a) Record your observations.

b) What gas do you think was produced in this test tube?

c) In your log record any additional properties of the gas that you discovered.

8. Return the splints and equipment as directed by your teacher. Clean up your workstation.

9. You may have deduced that the water (H_2O) decomposed into hydrogen gas and oxygen gas.

a) How would you write an equation to show this decomposition?

10. You may think of ways of using the tests (glowing splint and burning splint) as special effects in your show. Your teacher will demonstrate an additional way you can use what you investigated to produce a special effect. Your teacher will set up a gas generator, similar to the one shown in the diagram.

The test tube contains 10 mL of 6 *M* HCl (hydrochloric acid is a compound of hydrogen and chlorine) and 3 g of zinc.

a) What gas do you think is being produced in the test tube? Give a reason for your answer.

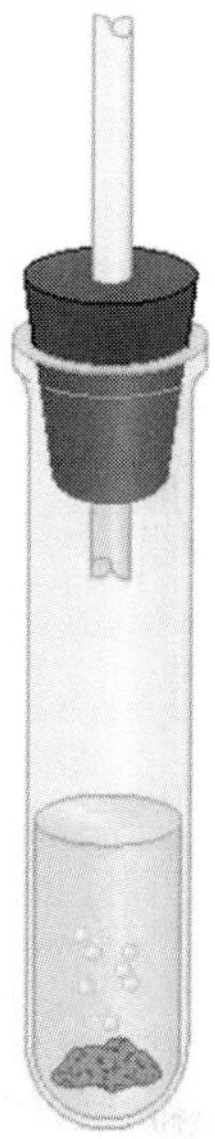

11. An egg has been emptied out. There is a small hole in the top and another in the bottom of the egg. The top hole is taped. The bottom hole in the egg will be placed over the gas generator, and gas will be collected in the egg for several minutes.

12. The egg will then be mounted in an egg holder behind a shield. If you have a video camera available, be prepared to start recording. Your teacher will remove the tape, and light the top of the egg with a burning splint. Begin recording or observing the reaction until it is over.

a) Record your observations in your log.

b) If the gas in the egg was hydrogen and air contains oxygen, what substance do you think may have been created in this process?

c) Write an equation that shows how the two gases produced this new substance.

Be certain that the mouth of the test tube is pointed away from everyone.

Clean up spills immediately.

Wash your hands and arms thoroughly after the activity.

Both the teacher and the students must be shielded during this part of the activity.

Chem Talk

Chem Words

element: any material that cannot be broken down into simpler materials.

THE STRUCTURE OF MATTER

In this investigation you used electricity to decompose water into two gases. You learned that the gases were different because they reacted differently to the burning and glowing splints. Since water is referred to as H_2O, a first guess would be that hydrogen (H) and oxygen (O) were produced in the experiment. The test for hydrogen is a small explosion when exposed to a burning splint. The test for oxygen is the re-ignition of a glowing splint. If you look back on the results of the experiment, you find that the volume of the hydrogen gas was twice as much as the oxygen gas. There was twice as much hydrogen as oxygen; that's where the "2" comes from in the chemical formula H_2O.

Hydrogen and oxygen are elements. An **element** is any material that cannot be broken down into simpler materials by chemical means. You are probably familiar with many elements like hydrogen, oxygen, zinc, gold, or helium. Other elements like strontium and beryllium are more exotic and less likely to be familiar to you. Every kind of matter you observe in your everyday life is made up of the chemical elements. There are only a little more than a hundred different kinds of chemical elements. This is an amazing discovery of chemistry—everything you observe in the world is made of different combinations of a hundred elements. Chemistry is the study of the properties of these elements, how these elements combine, the new properties of these combinations, and the energy changes that result from these combinations.

PUBLIC
MARKET
CENTER
FARMERS MARK

Elements are represented by symbols. The periodic table shows that the symbol used for each element is one or two letters to represent the name. It's easier to write O than to write oxygen. It's easier to write H than to write hydrogen. The symbols come from many different sources. However, the same symbols are used for each element in all countries of the world.

When elements combine, they form new substances called **compounds**. These compounds have entirely new characteristics. It is like combining the letters of the alphabet to make words. Twenty-six letters can be combined to make thousands of different words. Water is an example of a compound. A water molecule, H_2O, is composed of two atoms of hydrogen and one atom of oxygen. (For now, think of an atom as the smallest particle of an element and a molecule as the smallest unit of a compound.) In this activity you used electricity to decompose water into its elements, hydrogen and oxygen. This process is called **electrolysis**. You observed that oxygen gas made a glowing splint burst into flame, and that hydrogen gas was explosive. However, to extinguish a burning splint, you could use liquid water. The compound has very different characteristics from the elements from which it is made.

Symbols for Some Elements

Name of element	Symbol
aluminum	Al
bromine	Br
calcium	Ca
carbon	C
chlorine	Cl
copper	Cu
gold	Au
helium	He
hydrogen	H
iodine	I
iron	Fe
lead	Pb
magnesium	Mg
mercury	Hg
neon	Ne
nickel	Ni
nitrogen	N
oxygen	O
phosphorus	P
potassium	K
silicon	Si
sodium	Na
sulfur	S
tin	Sn
zinc	Zn

Compounds are represented by **chemical formulas**. A chemical formula shows the symbols of the elements that are combined to make the compound. If there is more than one atom of an element, a subscript is added after the symbol indicating how many atoms of that element there are. For example, as you discovered in this activity, the chemical

Chem Words

compound: a substance that consists of two or more elements bonded together in definite proportion.

electrolysis: the conduction of electricity through a solution (that contains ions) or a molten (ionic) substance that results in a chemical change.

chemical formula: the combination of the symbols of the elements in a definite numerical proportion used to represent molecules, compounds, radicals, ions, etc.

Examples of Some Chemical Formulas		
Compound	**Common name**	**Chemical formula**
calcium carbonate	chalk	$CaCO_3$
carbon dioxide	dry ice	CO_2
hydrochloric acid	muriatic acid	HCl
hydrogen sulfide	rotten-egg gas	H_2S
sodium hydrogen carbonate (or sodium bicarbonate)	baking soda	$NaHCO_3$
sodium chloride	table salt	$NaCl$
sodium nitrate	fertilizer	$NaNO_3$
sulfuric acid	battery acid	H_2SO_4

formula for water is H_2O. Two hydrogen atoms combine with one oxygen atom to produce one molecule of water. You could call H_2O dihydrogen monoxide but you use the common name water. In chemistry, there are common names for some familiar chemical compounds.

From the table of chemical formulas, you can see that carbon dioxide (CO_2) is a compound of carbon and oxygen. There are two atoms of oxygen for every atom of carbon. Sodium hydrogen carbonate or sodium bicarbonate ($NaHCO_3$) is a compound of sodium, hydrogen, carbon, and oxygen. There are three atoms of oxygen for every atom of the other elements. Also, there are a total of three atoms in the carbon dioxide formula and a total of six atoms in sodium hydrogen carbonate.

Many elements appear as single atoms in nature. There are seven common elements that exist in diatomic form. They are: Hydrogen (H_2), Oxygen (O_2), Nitrogen (N_2), Fluorine (F_2), Chlorine (Cl_2), Bromine (Br_2), and Iodine (I_2).

For example, hydrogen may be found as a single atom in a compound like HCl and oxygen may be found as a single atom in H_2O. When hydrogen is not combined with any other element, it always appears as H_2, two hydrogen atoms combined together.

You can write an equation that summarizes the electrolysis of water:

$$H_2O_{(l)} + \text{energy} \rightarrow H_{2(g)} + O_{2(g)}$$

Notice that the letters "g" and "l" are used. The "g" means gaseous state and the "l" means liquid state. Also notice that the elements are written in their diatomic form. **Conservation of mass** and elements states that the number of hydrogen atoms must be equal before and after the reaction. In addition, the number of oxygen atoms must be

Chem Words

conservation of mass: states that matter can neither be destroyed or created in a chemical reaction.

equal before and after the reaction. In the previous equation, you have one oxygen atom before the reaction and two oxygen atoms after the equation. You can fix this problem by "balancing the equation."

$$2H_2O_{(l)} + \text{energy} \rightarrow 2H_{2(g)} + O_{2(g)}$$

You now have 2 water molecules before the reaction (4 hydrogens and 2 oxygens). You also have 4 hydrogens and 2 oxygens after the reaction. You balanced the equation because you know that mass and elements must be conserved. By balancing the equation, you found that in electrolysis 2 water molecules decompose into 2 hydrogen molecules and 1 oxygen molecule. This is why you saw that there was twice as much hydrogen in one test tube than oxygen in the other test tube.

To generate the gas to fill the empty eggshell in this activity (the teacher demonstration), zinc was placed in hydrochloric acid. Zinc is an element. Hydrochloric acid (HCl) is a compound of hydrogen and chlorine. The reaction of the zinc and hydrochloric acid created a gas. Given the explosion you observed, you can guess that the gas produced was hydrogen. The hydrogen gas came from the hydrogen in the hydrochloric acid. You can write this reaction as an equation:

$$HCl_{(aq)} + Zn_{(s)} \rightarrow ZnCl_{2(aq)} + H_{2(g)}$$

The sub letter "s" means that the substance is in the solid state. The sub letters "aq" stands for aqueous, meaning that the substance (HCl) is dissolved in water. The zinc combined with the chlorine and hydrogen was released. Once again, conservation of mass and elements requires you to balance the equation:

$$2HCl_{(aq)} + Zn_{(s)} \rightarrow ZnCl_{2(aq)} + H_{2(g)}$$

There's much more to the structure of matter than you can discover in just one activity. However, this activity may have raised some new questions in your mind. For example:

- Can all compounds be decomposed into their elements?
- What techniques can be used to decompose compounds?
- What are elements made of?
- What are atoms?
- What are molecules?

These questions and many more are answered in other *Active Chemistry* activities.

Checking Up

1. In your own words, explain the difference between an element and a compound.
2. Why are symbols useful in describing chemical elements?
3. What are the symbols for the following elements: carbon, copper, gold, and helium?
4. What information does a chemical formula of a compound provide?

What Do You Think Now?

At the beginning of the activity you were asked:

- **How many kinds of matter are there in the universe: 1, 10, 100, 1000, 10 000, 100 000 or 1 000 000?**
- **What makes up matter?**

Matter is all of the stuff in the universe and it can either be a compound or an element. How many kinds of elements are there? How many kinds of compounds are there? Give an example of each.

Chem Essential Questions

What does it mean?

Chemistry explains a macroscopic phenomenon (what you observe) with a description of what happens at the nanoscopic level (atoms and molecules) using symbolic structures as a way to communicate. Complete the chart below in your *Active Chemistry* log.

MACRO	NANO	SYMBOLIC
Describe what you observed in the decomposition of water and while generating hydrogen.	*In words, describe what is happening to the compounds during the two separate experiments (electrolysis of water and zinc reacting with hydrochloric acid) in this activity.*	*Draw a picture that represents the decomposition of water (H_2O) into hydrogen (H_2) and oxygen (O_2). Beneath the picture, write the chemical formulas that are used to symbolically represent the elements.*

How do you know?

Water is often referred to as H_2O. What evidence do you have that water is composed of hydrogen and oxygen?

Why do you believe?

Individual elements will behave one way when they are alone and another way when they are combined with other elements. Create an analogy that is true from your life to show how a compound can behave differently from its parts.

Why should you care?

You will be writing a movie scene for your challenge in this unit. Write a short scene using an egg explosion and describe how the hydrogen was generated.

Reflecting on the Activity and the Challenge

Part of the problem you are facing in creating a special effect is understanding what matter is made of and how it can change. In this activity you broke a chemical compound down into its component elements using electrolysis. In another part of the activity a compound was made from chemical elements through a fast and noisy reaction. There are only about one hundred elements, but there are far more than a million compounds. You should begin thinking of ways in which some of the reactions you observe could be made to appear more dramatic on screen, without making them any larger in real life. You can now use the concepts of elements and compounds to provide the chemistry description of what is occurring.

Chem to Go

Common name	Formula
table sugar	$C_{12}H_{22}O_{11}$
marble	$CaCO_3$
natural gas	CH_4
rubbing alcohol	C_3H_8O
glass	SiO_2

1. The table shown contains several common compounds that are probably familiar to you.

   For each compound:

   a) List the names of the elements present.

   b) State the number of atoms of each element present.

   c) Give the total number of atoms present in each compound.

2. Write a chemical formula for nitrous oxide (laughing gas) that is made up of two atoms of nitrogen and one atom of oxygen.

3. Choose one compound from the table in *Question 1*.

   a) Investigate and record the properties of each element in the compound.

   b) Explain how the property of the compound is different from the property of each element.

4. ***Preparing for the Chapter Challenge***

   In a short paragraph, summarize the difference between an element and a compound and describe how the properties of a compound can be very different from the properties of the elements that make it up. Explain why knowing these differences is important when designing special effects for a movie set.

Inquiring Further

How is electrolysis used in industry?

Use the reference materials available to you to explore how electrolysis is used in industry to produce hydrogen gas and other elements from compounds.

Activity 2 States of Matter: Solid, Liquid, and Gas

What Do You See?
DRY ICE
THE HOUND OF BASKETVILLE

GOALS

In this activity you will:

- Create an animation to illustrate the behavior of particles in different phases of matter, and as the material changes phase.
- Observe changes of state of water and describe the process graphically.
- Observe a change of state of carbon dioxide and describe the energy transformations involved.
- Describe the energy transformations and the roles of kinetic and potential energy as heat energy is transferred to or away from a material.
- Describe the behavior of gas particles, based on your observations of how the temperature, pressure, and volume of the gas are affected as heat energy is transferred to or away from the gas.
- Characterize materials by their unique phase-change temperatures.
- Practice safe laboratory techniques in working with temperature extremes.

What Do You Think?

You know that materials can exist as solids, liquids, or gases. Ice is a solid that melts and becomes water and boils or evaporates and becomes water vapor. Each state of matter has its own characteristics.

- **Draw three circles. In the first circle, draw what you think particles of material look like in the solid state. In the next circle, draw the particles of the same material as a liquid. In the final circle, illustrate the same material as a gas.**

Record your ideas in your *Active Chemistry* log. Be prepared to discuss your responses with your small group and the class.

Investigate

Part A: The Heating Curve of Water

1. In this activity, you will be heating a beaker of crushed ice while the ice becomes water and the water becomes vapor. Record the temperature once every minute.
   a) Construct a graph and label the *x*-axis "time" and the *y*-axis "temperature." Sketch what you expect the graph will look like.
2. Half-fill a 250-mL beaker with crushed ice.
3. Set up your equipment as shown in the diagram. Your teacher may have you use a heat probe instead of a thermometer.

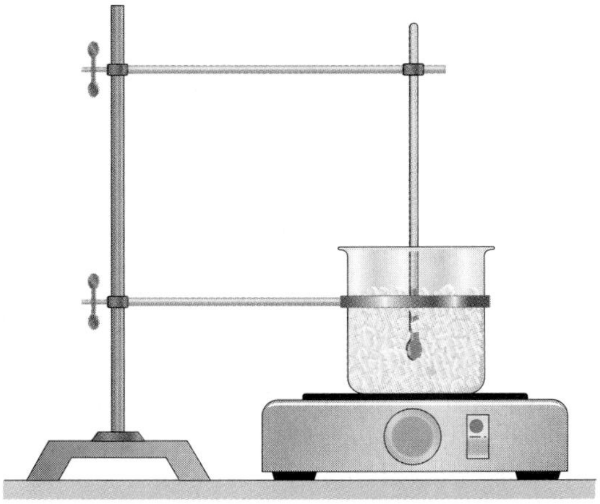

If you use a hot plate, you should provide a few minutes for the hot plate to heat up before placing the beaker on the hot plate. Use a medium-low setting, or one suggested by your teacher.

You may be asked to heat the ice and water with a heating coil that is placed directly in the beaker. If a heating coil is available, remember that the coil must be in the ice or water any time it is plugged in. Never plug in the coil or unplug the coil when it is outside the ice or water.

When you clamp the thermometer or probe into place, be sure that the bulb is in the center of the ice and is not touching the bottom of the beaker.

4. Observe the thermometer closely until it appears to have reached its lowest reading.
   a) Prepare a data table similar to the one shown. Record the minimum temperature at time 0 min.

5. Place the beaker on the heated hot plate.

6. Gently stir the ice and water mixture with a stirring rod.
   a) Record the temperature once every minute along with observations of state.

7. Continue to record the temperature until the water reaches 120°C or when there is too little water or your teacher tells you it is okay to stop.
   a) Name all the changes of state that you observed. A change of state refers to a change from a solid to a liquid, a liquid to a gas, a solid to a gas, and vice versa.

8. Turn off the hot plate. When the water has cooled, discard it. Return all equipment as directed and clean up your station.

9. Use your data to answer the following:
   a) What was the temperature at which all the ice had melted?
   b) What was the boiling point of the water?
   c) Plot a graph of the data with time along the x-axis and temperature on the y-axis. You may wish to use a computer or a calculator to plot your graph. If you are using a heat probe, this graph will be generated for you.
   d) Describe your graph. Consider: What is happening at the various points along the graph? Heat energy is being continually transferred to the system by

Time (min)	Temperature (°C)	Observations
0		
1		

Safety goggles and a lab apron must be worn *at all times* in a chemistry lab.

Clean up spills immediately.

Report any broken or cracked glassware to your teacher.

Never use a thermometer as a stirring rod.

Hot plates may remain hot for some time after they are turned off.

Wash your hands and arms thoroughly after the activity.

the hot plate. At which point is the heat energy causing the temperature to increase? What is the heat energy doing if it is not acting to raise the temperature of the water?

Safety goggles and a lab apron must be worn *at all times* in a chemistry lab.

Part B: Making Particles Shake

1. Your teacher will assemble or have you assemble a small booklet with many blank pages.
2. Use only the right-hand pages of the booklet. At the very bottom right of the last page of the booklet, draw a dot. To make the dot appear to move from the top left to the bottom right at a constant speed, draw another dot on the previous page slightly to the left and up. Continue this until you reach the first page of the booklet. Now, as you flip through the booklet from the front to the back, the dot will appear to move. The smaller the movements from one page to the next, the smoother the animation effect will appear.
3. Matter can be in a solid state, a liquid state, or a gaseous state. Each state of matter has its own typical motion of particles. The physical properties of each state are a result of how the particles move relative to one another. Use animation to model the movement of particles in each state of matter. Consider using different colors to keep track of the particles.
   a) In a solid the particles stay in the same position but vibrate. Use your flipbook to model the movement of particles in a solid.
   b) In a liquid the particles are about the same distance apart as in the solid, but they are not confined to fixed positions and can move more freely. Use animation to model a liquid.
4. The molecules in a gas (at 1 atm) are about eight diameters apart on the average and move very quickly.
   a) What problems would you face if you tried to make a flipbook for gases?

Part C: Volume Changes

1. Draw up a water plug about 1 cm long in a 30-cm long acrylic tube that has been previously inserted into a rubber stopper. One method is to put your finger on the bottom and then add a drop of water into the top with an eyedropper. Insert the glass tube and rubber stopper into the test tube keeping your finger on the end of the tubing. Invert the test tube. Remove your finger. The air pressure then supports the water droplet.

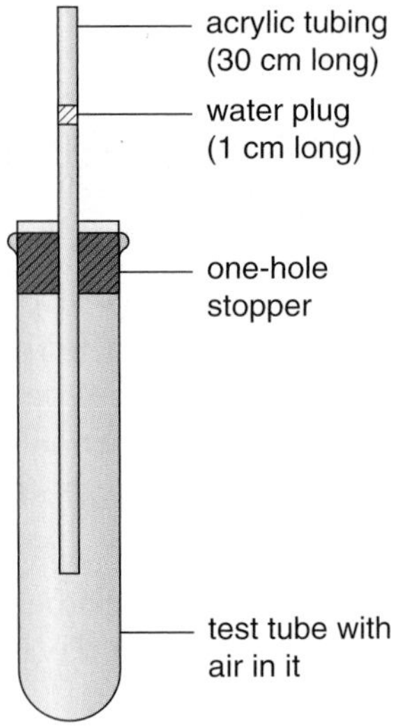
acrylic tubing (30 cm long)
water plug (1 cm long)
one-hole stopper
test tube with air in it

   a) Observe and describe the movement, if any, of the water plug.
2. Place the test tube into a beaker of warm water.
   a) Record your observations in your *Active Chemistry* log.

b) How does the warm water affect the volume of the air in the test tube? What evidence did you observe that suggested a volume change?

c) The warm water was a source of heat energy. What effect did this heat energy have on the volume of air?

3. Place the test tube into a beaker of ice water.

a) Record your observations in your *Active Chemistry* log.

4. In physics you've learned that for the drop of water to stay in place, the forces must be equal and opposite. The force of gravity pulling down on the water plug must be equal to the upward force of the gas. When the air in the test tube was heated, the upward force on the water plug must have increased, because the water rose in the tube. Since no additional air molecules were added, the molecules must have moved faster as a result of the additional heat. As the temperature of the air increased, the molecules of air increased their speed and therefore applied a greater force to the drop of water. Once the drop of water rose high enough, the larger volume and fewer air molecules hitting the drop per second compensated for the increased speed of the molecules. The forces of gravity and pressure were equal once again.

a) Pressure is force per area. What happened to the pressure on each wall of the test tube as you heated up the air (gas)?

b) Draw a box with a moveable piston, as shown in the diagram.

c) Use animation or a series of diagrams to show what would happen to the piston if the temperature of the gas inside the cylinder and below the piston were increased.

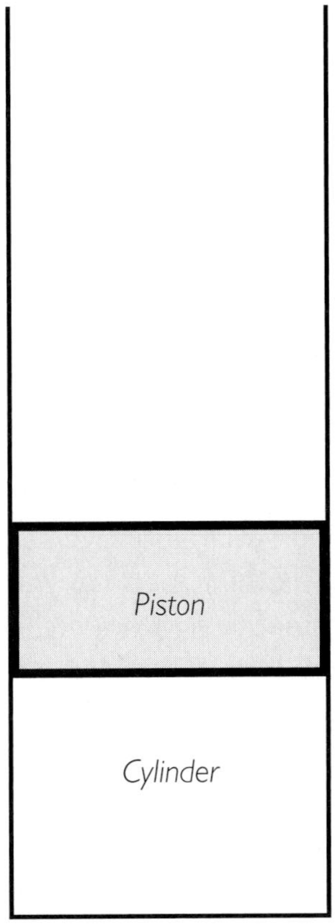
Piston
Cylinder

The water should not be too hot to touch. Glassware is slippery when wet. Handle with care.

Wash your hands and arms thoroughly after the activity.

Part D: "Special" Ice

1. Your teacher will place a small piece of dry ice (solid carbon dioxide) in an empty beaker.

a) Record your observations in your *Active Chemistry* log.

b) Is heat energy being transferred to or away from the dry ice by the surrounding air?

c) What change of state is taking place?

The carbon dioxide vapor formed from sublimation of solid dry ice is invisible. However, it is so cold that it condenses water vapor in the air to form the "cloud."

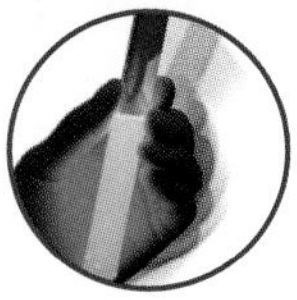

Chem Talk

CHANGES OF STATE

In this activity you have investigated changes of state as ice became water and water became vapor. All matter is made up of tiny particles called atoms or molecules. Generally, different substances are made of different kinds of molecules. Molecules are always moving, and there are spaces between them. The more energy the molecules have, the faster they move. There are also attractive forces among the molecules. The closer the molecules are together, the greater the attractive forces.

Temperature

You get an intuitive sense of **temperature** by how hot or cold something feels on your skin. Your body is at 37°C (98.6°F). When something with a higher temperature comes in contact with your skin, you know that it is "hot." When something with a lower temperature comes in contact with your skin, you know that it is "cold." How cold something feels to your skin is not the best way to talk about temperature. Thermometers are used to give a number corresponding to the temperature. As you observed in the activity, when the temperature of the air increased, the drop of water lifted. This drop of water could be a crude thermometer. As the drop rises, you know that the temperature of the air is higher. Liquids like alcohol expand when they get hot and are used for the thermometers with which you are most familiar.

The movement of the water drop gives you an insight into another interpretation of temperature. The air molecules inside the tube were moving faster as the temperature of the air increased. The temperature of the air is a measure of the speed of the molecules. In physics, you learned that kinetic energy is related to speed. **Kinetic energy** is equal to one-half the mass times the square of the speed of the particles ($KE = \frac{1}{2}mv^2$). Observing the behavior of many gases, scientists have concluded that temperature is a measure of the average kinetic energy of the molecules of the gas.

Melting and Boiling Points

In this activity you may have started with a beaker of crushed ice that was at a temperature less than 0°C. As you heated the ice it did not initially melt, but the temperature of the ice began to rise. As the temperature of any solid increases, the kinetic energy (energy of motion) of the particles of the material increases.

Chem Words

temperature: a measure of the average kinetic energy of molecules and atoms.

kinetic energy: energy associated with the motion of an object ($KE = \frac{1}{2}mv^2$).

This motion is mainly vibrational where the molecules vibrate around a fixed point. As heat energy continued to be transferred, the temperature of the ice increased until it reached 0°C. This is called the **normal melting point** of water. It is the temperature at which water changes from a solid to a liquid state at 1 atm (atmospheric pressure at sea level). It is also the **normal freezing point** of water, when water changes from a liquid to a solid at 1 atm. Each material has its own characteristic normal melting/freezing point.

The temperature then remained at 0°C as the solid water changed to a liquid. At the phase change, you continued to add heat energy to the system but the temperature did not change. The energy that was being absorbed overcomes the attractive forces that hold the neighboring ice molecules together. There was a change in the **potential energy**. If there is a change in kinetic energy you will see a change in temperature. However, with a change in potential energy during a phase change, the temperature will remain constant while heat energy is transferred to a material.

When all of the water had melted at 0°C, the temperature of the liquid water increased until it reached 100°C. This is called the **normal boiling point** of water at 1 atm.

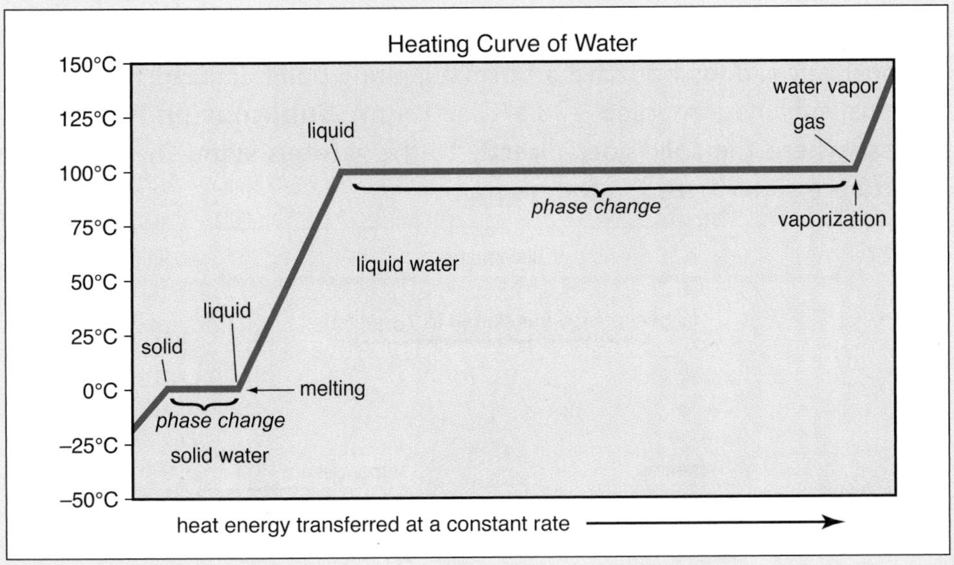
Heating Curve of Water
150°C
125°C
100°C
75°C
50°C
25°C
0°C
–25°C
–50°C
water vapor
gas
liquid
phase change
vaporization
liquid water
liquid
solid
melting
phase change
solid water
heat energy transferred at a constant rate

If the atmospheric pressure is less than 1 atm, then the water will boil at less than 100°C. This temperature is simply called the boiling point of the liquid. For example, on Mt. Rainier in Washington State, at an altitude of about 4393 m (14,411 ft), the atmospheric pressure is less than 1 atm.

Chem Words

normal melting point: the characteristic temperature, at 1 atm, at which a material changes from a solid state to its liquid state.

normal freezing point: the characteristic temperature, at 1 atm, at which a material changes from a liquid state to its solid state.

potential energy: stored energy of a material as a result of its position in an electric, magnetic, or gravitational field.

normal boiling point: the characteristic temperature, at 1 atm, at which a material changes from a liquid state to a gaseous state.

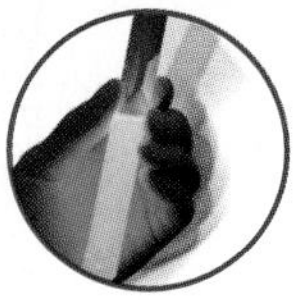

Chem Words

vaporization: the change of state from a liquid to a gas.

sublimation: the change of state of a solid material to a gas without going through the liquid state.

You would find that water boils at a lower temperature at the top of the mountain.

When the water arrived at the boiling point, you again noted that the temperature remained the same, even though heat energy was still being transferred to the water. The temperature would remain the same until all of the liquid is **vaporized**. Then, with additional heat energy, the temperature would again increase and the gas molecules of water would have greater average kinetic energy.

Heating Curve of Water

These changes in the temperature of a material, as heat energy is transferred to it, can be summarized in a graph, similar to the one you constructed. The heating curve of water is shown in the graph on the previous page. The length of the first horizontal section corresponds to the amount of heat energy required to make the material change from solid to liquid. Since heat is being transferred to the beaker at a constant rate, then the length of the horizontal section of the heating curve corresponds to the amount of energy required.

Dry ice (solid carbon dioxide), which your teacher used in the demonstration, does not have a normal melting point. Instead, it has a normal sublimation point (–78.5°C at 1 atm). **Sublimation** is the process where the solid goes directly to the gaseous state. The changes of state are summarized in the diagram.

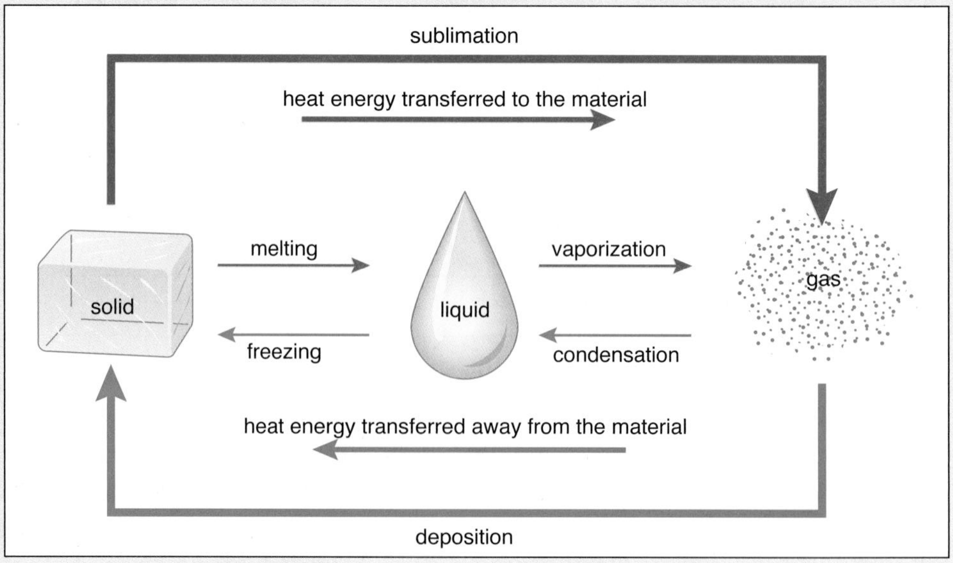
sublimation
heat energy transferred to the material
melting
vaporization
solid
liquid
gas
freezing
condensation
heat energy transferred away from the material
deposition

Checking Up

1. What does temperature measure?
2. Describe what is happening to particles of a material when heat energy is transferred to the material and the temperature increases.
3. What happens to the temperature of a material when it is undergoing a change of state?
4. What is the difference between the normal boiling point of water and the temperature at which water might boil?

What Do You Think Now?

At the beginning of this activity you were asked to:

- **Draw three circles. In the first circle, draw what you think particles of material look like in the solid state. In the next circle, draw the particles of the same material as a liquid. In the final circle, illustrate the same material as a gas.**

Now draw five circles. In the first circle, draw many particles as a gas. In the second circle, draw condensation of these particles. In the third circle, draw liquid particles. In the fourth circle, draw solidification of these particles from liquid into solid. Finally, in the fifth circle, draw the particles in the solid state.

Chem Essential Questions

What does it mean?

Chemistry explains a macroscopic phenomenon (what you observe) with a description of what happens at the nanoscopic level (atoms and molecules) using symbolic structures as a way to communicate. Complete the chart below in your *Active Chemistry* log.

MACRO	NANO	SYMBOLIC
Describe what you observed happening as you added heat to the ice in Part A, to the gas in Part C, and to the dry ice in Part D.	*In words, describe what is happening to the particles of these substances.*	*A heating-curve graph can be used to summarize the change from solid to liquid to gas. Draw a heating-curve graph and indicate where you would find water, ice, and ice water.*

How do you know?

Refer to the graph that you made for the heating curve of water. At one point the temperature stayed constant, even though you were still adding heat. Where did the heat energy go, and why didn't the temperature increase?

Why do you believe?

Can you make frozen popsicles out of hot cocoa? Would it still be hot cocoa or would it change into something new? Explain your reasoning.

Why should you care?

You will be writing a movie scene for your challenge in this unit. How might you use dry ice or a drop of rising water in a tube as a special effect in your movie?

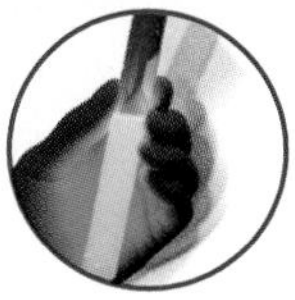

Reflecting on the Activity and the Challenge

In this activity you focused on very simple chemistry: the motions of particles in solids, liquids, and gases. You can use the techniques learned in this activity to animate more complicated chemical systems. Consider how you could illustrate a phase change, like boiling or freezing. Dry ice converting directly to a gas (sublimation) may be a good way to add a mysterious cloud to your special effect. (The carbon dioxide vapor formed from sublimation of solid dry ice is invisible, but it is so cold that it condenses water vapor in the air to form the "cloud.") With research you might be able to use animation to explain the chemistry you use in staging your special effect.

Chem to Go

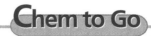

1. Copy and complete the following table summarizing the changes of state in your *Active Chemistry* log.

Change of state	From	To	Heat energy (gained or lost)
boiling	liquid	gas	gained
condensation	gas	liquid	lost
evaporation			
freezing			
melting			
deposition	gas		
sublimation	solid		
vaporization			

2. Copy and complete the following table in your *Active Chemistry* log.

Definite or indefinite?	Solid	Liquid	Gas
shape			
volume			

3. The heating curve for water was given in the *Chem Talk* reading section. Create the cooling curve for water when water is placed in the freezer. Describe each part of the curve.

4. Create a heating curve for water when you have twice the amount of water you used in the *Investigate* section. How does this heating curve compare with the original curve?

5. The melting and boiling points of three materials are given in the table.

Material	Melting point (°C)	Boiling point (°C)
copper	1083	2336
mercury	–39	357
oxygen	–218	–183

   a) Draw a heating curve for each material.

   b) From the graphs, explain why, at room temperature (22°C), copper is solid, mercury is liquid, and oxygen is a gas.

6. A certain material has a normal freezing point of 10°C and a normal boiling point of 70°C. What state is the material in at room temperature (about 22°C)? Explain your answer.

7. The normal boiling point of water is 100°C and the normal boiling point of ethanol is 78.5°C. These two liquids are soluble in each other. What technique would you use to separate these two liquids from the solution?

8. A certain material is white in the solid phase and clear (transparent) in the liquid phase. It has a normal melting point of 146°C. Which of the following materials could this be: water, sugar, or carbon dioxide? Explain your choice. (Hint: You will have to base your argument on concepts you have learned and observations made in this activity, as well as common sense.)

9. ***Preparing for the Chapter Challenge***

   a) Make an animation of 10 water particles changing from the solid state at 0°C to the liquid state at 0°C.

   b) Animate the change of state of 10 dry-ice particles placed at room temperature.

Inquiring Further

1. Video animation

Making the leap from flipbook animation to video animation is not difficult. You will need access to a video camera that can record one frame at a time. Set the video camera so that it can record an image on a flat table or desk. To animate the process you can record a series of drawings on paper or shapes on a table, putting one after another on the table and taking a frame or two of each image.

Go to the Internet and see if you can find animations. You might find a computer helpful in making the drawings or you could investigate using animation software to make more elaborate animations.

2. Design a thermometer

Use what you learned in this activity to design a thermometer that you could use to measure temperature. If your teacher approves your design, try out your thermometer.

Activity 3 Solutions, Suspensions, and Colloids

What Do You See?
SOIL
BROTH
MILK
CEREAL
SUGAR
TRAIL MIX
AIR
$CuSO_4$
OLIVE OIL

GOALS

In this activity you will:

- Explore different ways that materials can be mixed together to make new materials.
- Test some materials to determine what kinds of mixtures they are.
- Determine why certain kinds of mixtures are manufactured for commercial use in particular situations.

Safety goggles and a lab apron must be worn *at all times* in a chemistry lab.

What Do You Think?

One way to get different types of materials is to just mix them together. Lots of different things can happen when materials are mixed. You can get some good food or you can get dynamite. Each kind of mixture has its own characteristics. Taking mixtures apart is a different story.

- **Is it easier to separate milk from coffee or milk from a bowl of cereal? Why?**

Record your ideas about these questions in your *Active Chemistry* log. Be prepared to discuss your responses with your group and the class.

Investigate

1. Half-fill six test tubes with water. Number the test tubes.
   a) In your *Active Chemistry* log, prepare a table for your observations. You may wish to use a table similar to the one shown on the next page.

No.	Materials mixed with water	Observations before mixing	Observations after mixing		
			Homogeneous or heterogeneous	Effect on laser beam	Passes through filter paper
#1	water only				
#2	0.5 g salt				
#3	drops of milk				

2. Add the following materials to the test tubes:

   #1—water only

   #2—0.5 g salt

   #3—a few drops of milk

   #4—0.5 g $CuSO_4$ (copper sulfate)

   #5—2 mL olive oil

   #6—0.5 g soil

   a) Describe each material before mixing.

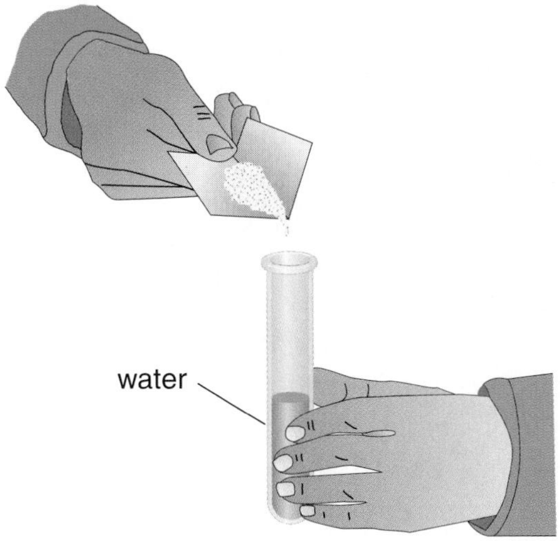
water

3. Stopper each test tube. Place your finger over the stopper and shake each for several minutes to make a mixture.

   Observe each mixture.

4. Consider the following characteristics of the mixtures:

- What is the appearance of each mixture after the vigorous mixing? Which ones have visible particles suspended in them? Which ones look totally uniform (homogeneous) throughout?
- Which mixtures separate (are heterogeneous) after sitting a few moments after vigorous mixing? Which remain mixed?
- Shine a laser pointer through each mixture. In which mixtures is the laser beam clearly visible? In which mixtures does it pass through with little effect?
- For each mixture place a small beaker below a funnel to catch the filtrate, as shown in the diagram. Pour the contents of each test tube into a funnel with filter paper. Which mixtures pass through? Which leave material behind on the filter paper?

   a) Record all your observations in the table in your log.

5. Discard materials and return all equipment as directed by your teacher. Clean up your station.

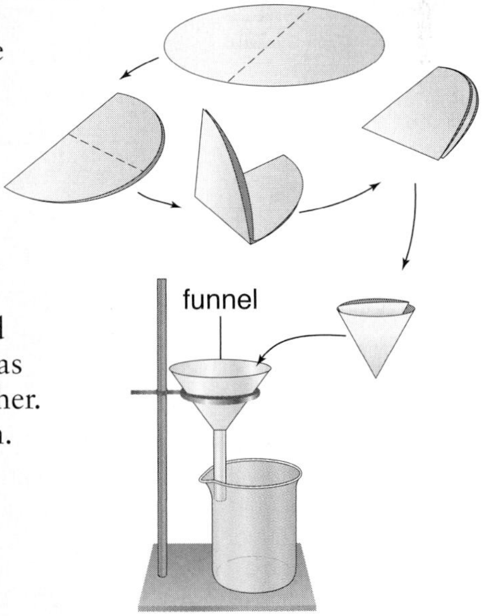
funnel

Wipe up spills immediately.

Report any broken or cracked glassware to your teacher.

Never look directly at a laser beam. Be sure the laser is pointed away from other people's eyes.

Wash your hands and arms thoroughly after the activity.

Chem Talk

CLASSIFYING MIXTURES

In this activity you mixed together water and several different materials to produce different kinds of mixtures. In some cases the materials you used were **pure substances**. A pure substance contains only one kind of particle throughout. For example, sugar is a pure substance. A mixture contains at least two pure substances. You may think of water as a pure substance; however, most water found in nature has different materials mixed with it, and is in fact a mixture.

Most materials that you find in nature, as well as most human-made materials, are mixtures of one or more pure substances. You made one kind of mixture, called a **solution**, when you added salt to water. In a solution, the particles that dissolve are so tiny they can't be seen with the naked eye. The mixture is said to be homogeneous. The dissolved particles (called the **solute**) remain mixed with the solvent indefinitely. The water, in this case, is the **solvent** and the salt is the solute. If a solution is filtered, everything passes through. Light passing through a solution has no special effect.

When you added milk to water, the water appeared cloudy. However, the tiny drops of milk remained suspended in the water and did not settle out over time. You could see the laser beam as it passed through the mixture, and when you filtered the mixture, it all passed through the filter paper. This kind of mixture is a **colloid**. In colloids, the dispersed particles are larger than those in solution and may be visible on close inspection with a microscope. The particles will also stay suspended indefinitely. All parts of the colloid will pass through a filter. Light, or any other form of electromagnetic radiation, is most effectively scattered when particles are about the same size as the wavelength of the light. In a colloid, many of the particles, which are made up of a great many molecules clumped together, may be just about the same size as light waves. When light passes through a colloid it is scattered and you can see where the light beam passes through. This is known as the **Tyndall Effect**.

When you added soil to water, you created a suspension. **Suspensions** have the largest of all the dispersed particles. The particles are visible to the eye and will settle out in time. The suspended particles can be separated by filtration. The mixture is said to be heterogeneous. A light beam shining through a suspension may be scattered, but the suspension is definitely not transparent.

Chem Words

pure substance: a substance that contains only one kind of particle and cannot be separated into simpler components without chemical change.

solution: a homogeneous mixture of two or more substances.

solute: the substance that interacts with a solvent to form a solution.

solvent: a substance present in a larger amount that interacts with the solute to make a solution.

colloid: a mixture containing particles larger than the solute but small enough to remain suspended in the continuous phase of another component. This is also called a colloidal dispersion.

Tyndall Effect: the scattering of a light beam as it passes through a colloid.

suspension: heterogeneous mixture that contains fine solid or liquid particles in a fluid that will settle out spontaneously. By shaking the container, they will again be dispersed throughout the fluid.

Checking Up

1. In your own words, describe how you would distinguish among a solution, a colloid, and a suspension.
2. What is the Tyndall Effect?

What Do You Think Now?

At the beginning of this activity you were asked:

- **Is it easier to separate milk from coffee or milk from a bowl of cereal? Why?**

Use what you know to develop a procedure to separate a mixture of salt, sand, and iron filings. Think about the following:

- **Which item is magnetic and how would you remove it from the mixture?**
- **What will dissolve in water and pass through a filter?**
- **What item is not magnetic and will not dissolve in water?**

Chem Essential Questions

What does it mean?

Chemistry explains a macroscopic phenomenon (what you observe) with a description of what happens at the nanoscopic level (atoms and molecules) using symbolic structures as a way to communicate. Complete the chart below in your *Active Chemistry* log.

MACRO	NANO	SYMBOLIC
Describe what you observed after preparing a solution, a suspension, and a colloid.	*In words, describe what is happening to the particles in a solution, a suspension, and a colloid.*	*Draw a picture to show how and why the Tyndall Effect appears in a colloid and not in a solution or a suspension.*

How do you know?

Look back at your data table and determine the visual clue that will help distinguish solutions, suspensions, and colloids.

Why do you believe?

On some days it is possible to see rays of light from the Sun distinctly coming through breaks in clouds. What atmospheric difference allows you to see the light rays on some days and not on others?

Why should you care?

You will be writing a movie scene for your challenge in this unit. How could you use lasers in the video and make them visible to the camera?

Reflecting on the Activity and the Challenge

In this activity you made mixtures with solid or liquid solutes and water as the solvent. The same basic principles apply regardless of the states of matter involved. For example, it is possible to have solid solutions. Metal alloys such as brass or bronze are such solutions. Fog, smoke, and clouds are mixtures that show the Tyndall Effect. A common stage effect is to produce smoke or fog to give an eerie setting. Many movies have used the Tyndall Effect to show the path of laser beams or flashlights. One easy way to produce this effect is to use a spray bottle of water to mist the air in a darkened room. Another way is to use chalk dust from an eraser. When a flashlight or laser pointer is directed through the mist, it shows up nicely, thanks to the Tyndall Effect.

Brass is a solid solution.

Chem to Go

1. Classify each of the following as a suspension, colloid, or solution. Explain your reasoning. (Hint: In some cases more than one answer may be possible.)
   a) A mixture is poured through a filter, and the entire mixture passes through.
   b) A mixture is left to stand for a while and small particles settle out.
   c) When viewed under a microscope, small particles are visible in the mixture.
   d) A beam of light passed through the mixture is scattered.
   e) The mixture is blue and transparent.
2. Suggest a method by which you could separate the various materials in each of the following mixtures:
   a) solutions
   b) colloids
   c) suspensions

3. Look in your kitchen at home and choose five products. Make your best guess as to the type of mixture they represent. Elaborate on the evidence that you used to classify the products into their respective categories. Explain what would happen to each product that you have chosen if it were in a different kind of mixture. For example, milk would settle if it was a suspension instead of a colloid. (Old-fashioned milk, before homogenization, did separate into the cream (oily) phase and the water phase.)

4. *Preparing for the Chapter Challenge*

   Consider how you could use the properties of a solution, colloid, or suspension to produce a special effect for a movie scene. In a few sentences establish the setting for the scene, and describe the mood you want to create. In a paragraph or two, describe the chemistry required to understand the differences between the different types of mixtures and how they produce the special effect.

Inquiring Further

Cooking and mixtures

Cooking is a practical application of mixtures. One such application is the recipe for making mayonnaise. Mayonnaise is classified as a colloid. A liquid—liquid colloid is also called an emulsion. If you have access to the following materials, try making mayonnaise *at home*.

COLAVITA
ANOLA HARVEST

Recipe for Mayonnaise

Combine in a blender:

2 tablespoons beaten egg

1 large egg yolk

1/4 teaspoon dry mustard

1 teaspoon lemon juice

Blend the mixture for 20 s. While the blender is still running, add 3/4 cup of vegetable oil slowly in the thinnest stream you can manage. Serve immediately or keep for one to two days in the refrigerator.

Investigate the properties of the ingredients of mayonnaise that allow them to form this colloidal emulsion. What other substances are classified as emulsions? How could emulsions be used in a movie special effect?

Metals in cooking utensils are also examples of mixtures. Investigate the kinds of materials used in making metal cooking utensils. Why are some mixtures more suitable for cooking than others?

Do this only with the approval of a responsible adult.

Activity 4 Properties of Matter

What Do You See?
ALICE IN CLAYLAND
CLAY

GOALS

In this activity you will:

- Make modeling dough from common kitchen materials.
- Adjust the properties of the modeling dough by adding another material to it.
- Compare the properties of an emulsion to those of a composite material.
- Recommend whether an emulsion or a composite would be best for certain applications.
- Consider the advantages and disadvantages of using composites for industrial applications.

What Do You Think?

Frequently in movies, models of characters or sets are built to achieve specific effects. A character might be flattened by a falling object or bounced off a wall when tossed.

- **What properties would materials that can be flattened or that can bounce have?**

Record your ideas about this question in your *Active Chemistry* log. Be prepared to discuss your responses with your small group and the class.

Investigate

1. Use the following ingredients and directions to prepare a batch of modeling dough.

Ingredients:

1 cup flour

$\frac{1}{2}$ cup salt

3 tablespoons cooking oil

2 tablespoons cream of tartar

1 cup water

Directions:

- Warm the oil in a saucepan or large beaker on a hot plate set at medium-low.
- Add the other ingredients and cook 3 to 5 min while stirring constantly.
- Using tongs, drop the mixture onto waxed paper or aluminum foil.
- Cool until the modeling dough is easy to handle.
- Knead the dough until the texture is consistent.
- Add a drop of food coloring, if desired.

2. Divide the dough into two samples. Set aside one sample.

   Add a new material (tissue paper or paper towel strips, sand, gravel, pieces of twine, marbles) to the other sample, as directed by your teacher. Knead the mixture well until the new material is well incorporated into the dough.

3. You will now observe and compare the properties of the original sample and the new sample that you made. In your group, discuss how you will test for each of the following properties: texture, elasticity, uniformity, bounce, strength, and malleability.

   If you are not sure what characteristics you should be testing for, each property is explained in the *Chem Talk* reading section.

   a) Record in your log the procedure you will use to test for each property.

   b) Make a table in your *Active Chemistry* log to record your observations.

4. When your teacher has approved your procedure, test each property.

   a) Record your observations in your log.

   b) In a few sentences, describe the differences between the two kinds of mixtures.

   c) Speculate on why your new mixture behaved differently from the original modeling dough.

5. Compare the properties of your new mixture with the mixtures of other groups.

   a) What new or useful properties did each mixture have?

6. Dispose of materials and return all equipment as directed by your teacher. Clean up your station.

Safety goggles and a lab apron must be worn *at all times* in a chemistry lab.

Do not overheat the oil. Do not heat the oil above 100°C.

Wash your hands and arms thoroughly after the activity.

Chem Words

texture: the characteristics of the surface of a material, like how smooth, rough, or coarse it is.

uniformity: the property of how consistent a material is throughout.

strength: the property of how well a material withstands the application of a force.

elasticity: the property of a material to resist deformation and return to its normal size or shape after a force has been applied to it.

bounce: the ability of an object to rebound to its original position when dropped from a given height.

malleability: the property of a material to be able to be hammered into various shapes without breaking.

Chem Talk

PHYSICAL PROPERTIES

In this activity you examined a variety of physical properties of a mixture. In addition to the state and color of the mixture, you also observed the **texture** of the material. Texture is defined as the feel or appearance of a surface or substance. For example, if you were looking at a photograph, you may be interested in the texture of the surface of the paper used, or if you were looking at cloth, you might be interested in how the material is woven together. **Uniformity** describes how consistent a material is throughout. Does everything in the material seem to be evenly distributed? **Strength** determines how durable the material is. How well the material withstands the application of a force establishes how strong it is. **Elasticity** determines how well the material will resist deformation and return to its normal size or shape after a force has been applied to it. **Bounce** refers to the material's ability to return to its original position when it is dropped from a given height. Another way to think about bounce is to consider how much it behaves like a ball. **Malleability** determines how easy it is to roll or hammer out the material without breaking it apart. Can the material be reshaped without breaking it apart? Lead is an example of a metal that can easily be shaped into other forms without breaking. Brittle objects shatter easily.

COMPOSITE MATERIALS

The properties of a mixture can be changed by adding different materials. The modeling dough you made in this activity was an **emulsion**. When you added one of the other materials, you made a **composite**. Composites are heterogeneous mixtures that use the characteristics of the components to make useful substances. Another example of a composite is papier-maché.

The composite industry has been growing at a very rapid pace. Think about it. Composites are used as the skin on jets, rotor blades of a helicopter, bulletproof clothing for law enforcement officers, and special armor for tanks. Buildings, cars, boats, trains, and planes all take advantage of different types of composites. If you were trying to define what a composite is, you would probably say that it is a solid that consists of two or more materials. Some composites are made by a process in which fibers are embedded within another material. Usually, this will lead to a stronger material and provide the best qualities of both materials. Composites not only help make stronger and lighter materials but they also help in extending the life of materials. For example, composites are used for materials that cover and protect electrical cables.

A major drawback to composites is the initial cost of research and the use of special raw materials in fabricating the composite. However, overall composites are materials of the future and their manufacture could be a great career choice.

Chem Words

emulsion: a colloid or colloidal dispersion of one liquid suspended in another.

composite: a solid heterogeneous mixture of two or more substances that makes use of the properties of each component.

Checking Up

1. Two pieces of cloth have the same color and texture. Name another property of cloth that you might use to distinguish between the two materials.
2. Provide a situation in which each of the following properties of a material might be important:
   a) elasticity
   b) uniformity
   c) strength
   d) bounce
3. What is a composite material?
4. Give an advantage and a disadvantage of using a composite material.

What Do You Think Now?

At the beginning of this activity you were asked:

- **What properties would materials that can be flattened or that can bounce have?**

Select two of the physical properties that have been discussed in this activity. For each property, suggest one additional ingredient that would enhance the property. For example, to increase bounce you could add pieces of rubber bands.

Chem Essential Questions

What does it mean?

Chemistry explains a macroscopic phenomenon (what you observe) with a description of what happens at the nanoscopic level (atoms and molecules) using symbolic structures as a way to communicate. Complete the chart below in your *Active Chemistry* log.

MACRO	NANO	SYMBOLIC
Describe what you observed when you added the new material to the dough.	*In words, compare the uniformity of the emulsion (the original dough) and the composite at the molecular level.*	*Draw a picture to illustrate the difference between homogeneous and heterogeneous mixtures.*

How do you know?

Refer to the observations on uniformity. Explain how to distinguish between homogeneous and heterogeneous mixtures.

Why do you believe?

Sometimes when roads or driveways are repaved, the builders choose between cement and concrete. Cement is a mixture of clay, lime, and water used to bind substances together. Concrete is cement with sand or rocks added. Builders often choose concrete over cement. Why do you think they do this?

Why should you care?

You will be writing a movie scene for your challenge in this unit. You may choose to have dangerous scenes for your characters in which you could use models. By adding materials to your dough, you can create the effect for the scene.

Reflecting on the Activity and the Challenge

One part of making a special effect for a movie is finding materials that could be used for making models. In this activity you learned to make a material that has many characteristics that make it ideal for making models. Consider how each of the properties you investigated is important to a special effect. A malleable material is easy to shape. To construct a large building, you will want to use a composite that is strong. You could also construct a small model of a tall building, and then make a model of a character that can bounce 10 stories high.

Chem to Go

1. A composite when tested bounces half as high as the original material. How can you create another composite that bounces only one-quarter as high?
2. Pure, 24-K gold is very malleable. By mixing gold with other metals it becomes harder and less malleable. In what situations would you want to use gold that is not as malleable?
3. Plastics are made of one type of material. Why are they not classified as a composite?
4. When road contractors are laying cement, they first place a series of steel rods in a specific pattern. Then they pour the cement on the rods and allow it to cure. The composite is called reinforced concrete. What is the purpose of the steel rods?
5. Give two examples of special effects in movies where each of the following properties is important: strength, elasticity, bounce, uniformity, malleability.
6. ***Preparing for the Chapter Challenge***

   Each kind of modeling dough that you made in this activity could be used in making sets for a movie special effect. In your log list the kinds of structures each might be useful in constructing.

Inquiring Further

1. Other modeling materials

Many other types of modeling materials, such as plaster of Paris or polymer clay, are available in crafts and art stores. Research these substances and consider their usefulness as modeling materials for your movie special effect.

2. Different composites

Investigate different composites. Learn about the special properties of these materials. List the items of products that are constructed from composites.

3. Investigating other techniques with modeling dough

Color and appearance of models are crucial to making them look authentic in a movie scene. With the supervision of an adult, try some alternative means of coloring your modeling dough. Try painting the surface of the dough, or using other substances to add color and texture. How do the various techniques affect the characteristics of the dough?

Chapter mini Challenge

THE BRIDGE
HONK

Your challenge for this chapter is to create a movie special effect and a story line for that special effect. Since you have completed four activities, this is a good time to give your special effect a *first try*.

Your *mini-challenge* is to create a one-minute script with a special effect. In the *mini-challenge*, you will be required to explain the scene to the class and explain the special effect that you could demonstrate. You will have to mention safety requirements as if you were performing the demonstration. You will have to explain the procedure for performing your special effect and act it out as if you were actually performing. You will also have to explain the chemistry principle. You will not be given much preparation time for your *mini-challenge*. It is a way to get a sense of what you will be involved with at the end of the chapter when you have more chemistry content to include in your full script and movie special effect.

Chemistry Content

Your team should first review the chemistry content that may be included in this movie special effect. Each content area can be creatively used as a special effect.

Activity 1: You learned how to use electrolysis to create hydrogen and oxygen from water. You also learned how to test for oxygen and water. You are also able to distinguish an element from a compound and write chemical symbols and equations to describe reactions.

Activity 2: You learned about states of matter by studying the heating curve of water as it goes from ice to water to vapor. You also observed the sublimation of dry ice as it goes from a solid to a gas. You also learned how to create an animation to show the movement of molecules at different temperatures.

Activity 3: You were able to observe the appearance of solutions, suspensions and colloids. You also used a laser and were able to observe the Tyndall Effect.

Activity 4: You learned about more properties of matter and changed these properties by adding materials to other materials.

Criteria

Your team should review the criteria that you discussed on the first day of this chapter. Your special effects show and script should be creative, fun, and engaging, as well as having accurate chemistry explanations.

Preparing for Your mini Challenge

Your team should begin the process of creating the special effect by brainstorming ideas about possible story lines you may use while keeping in mind that your special effect must be from one of the four activities. You can try to imitate movies or television shows that you have seen or adopt a theme from a book that you have read. You can also use recent news items or video games or songs to help you find the right subject matter.

Engineering/Technology Design

The engineering-design process involves a number of distinct steps. In creating a special effect for a movie, you are involved in a design process. Note how your efforts follow the design model described.

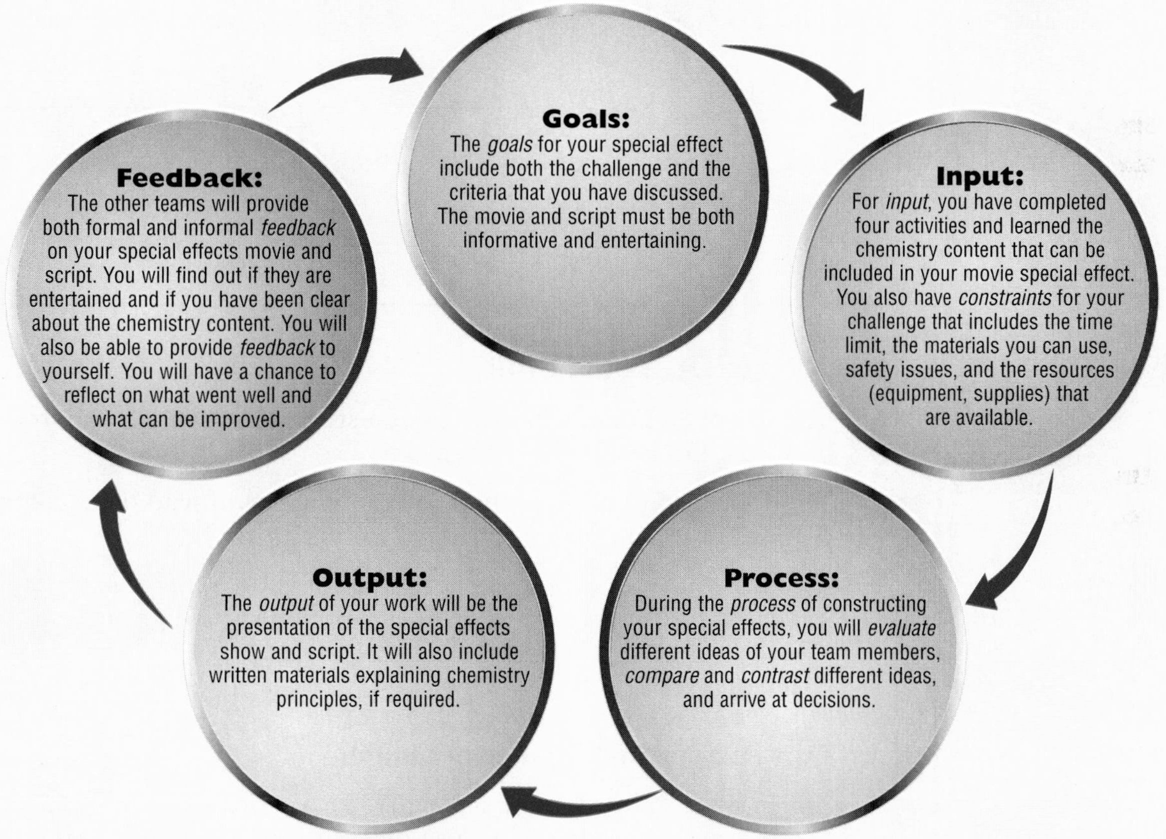

Goals:
The *goals* for your special effect include both the challenge and the criteria that you have discussed. The movie and script must be both informative and entertaining.
Input:
For *input*, you have completed four activities and learned the chemistry content that can be included in your movie special effect. You also have *constraints* for your challenge that includes the time limit, the materials you can use, safety issues, and the resources (equipment, supplies) that are available.
Process:
During the *process* of constructing your special effects, you will *evaluate* different ideas of your team members, *compare* and *contrast* different ideas, and arrive at decisions.
Output:
The *output* of your work will be the presentation of the special effects show and script. It will also include written materials explaining chemistry principles, if required.
Feedback:
The other teams will provide both formal and informal *feedback* on your special effects movie and script. You will find out if they are entertained and if you have been clear about the chemistry content. You will also be able to provide *feedback* to yourself. You will have a chance to reflect on what went well and what can be improved.

Remember: This is a *first try*. The feedback that you get from this brief presentation of a script and special effect will be extremely valuable when you prepare for the full special effects show at the end of the chapter. At that point, you will begin the entire design cycle again. That's why it is called a cycle. You keep going through it over and over to improve your design or, in this case, your movie special effects.

Activity 5 Mass and Volume

What Do You See?

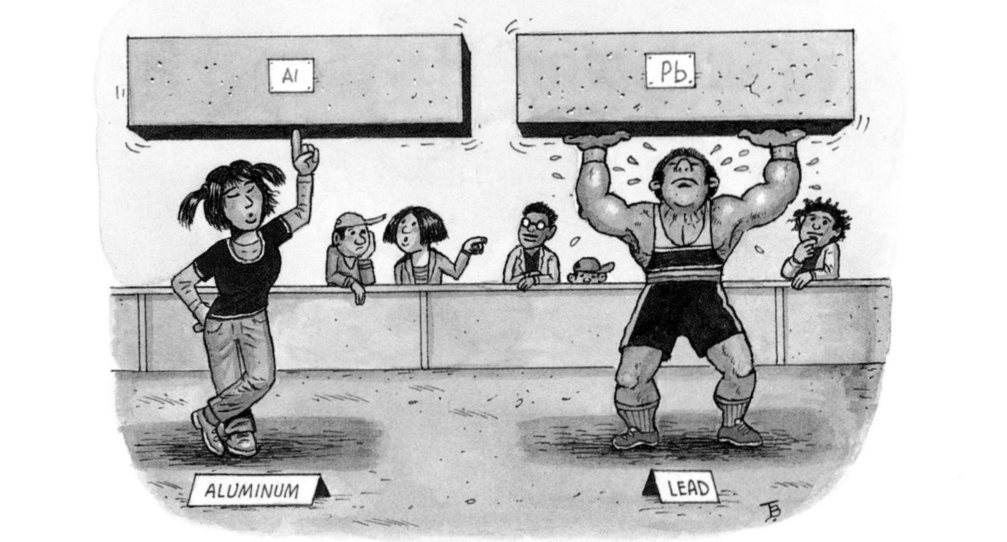
Al
Pb
ALUMINUM
LEAD

GOALS

In this activity you will:

- Determine the densities of various liquid and solid materials.
- Make measurements in the laboratory to the precision of the instruments used.
- Learn the difference between accuracy and precision in experimental measurements.
- Retain significant figures in calculations involving experimental measurements.
- Use density measurements to determine the identity of a material.
- Locate sources of the variation in the class's experimental results.

What Do You Think?

A piece of steel sinks in water, but a steel boat floats. A tiny rock sinks in water, but a large log floats.

- **Since a kilogram of feathers and a kilogram of lead have the same mass, how do they appear different and why?**

Record your ideas about this question in your *Active Chemistry* log. Be prepared to discuss your responses with your small group and the class.

Investigate

Part A: Mass and Volume of Liquids

1. In your *Active Chemistry* log create a table to record your data for this part of the activity. You may wish to use a table similar to the one shown.

Volume and Mass of Water				
Mass of graduated cylinder (g)	Volume of water (mL)	Mass of graduated cylinder and water (g)	Mass of water (g)	$\frac{\text{Mass}}{\text{Volume}}$ (g/mL)

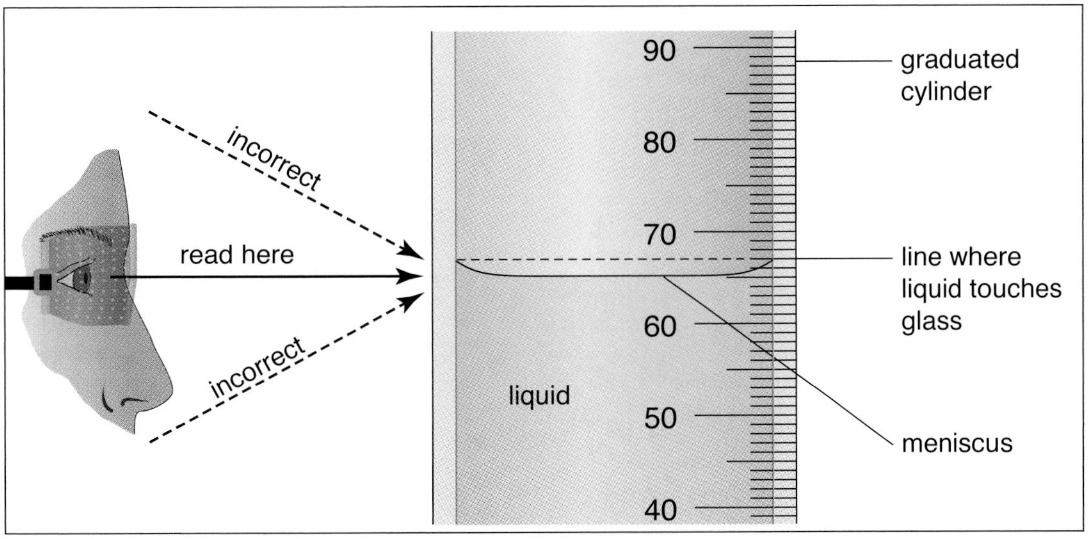
incorrect
read here
incorrect
liquid
90
80
70
60
50
40
graduated cylinder
line where liquid touches glass
meniscus

2. Measure the mass of an empty, dry graduated cylinder.

   a) Record the mass of the cylinder in your *Active Chemistry* log.

3. Add 10 mL of water to the graduated cylinder. Remember when reading the volume, take the reading at the lowest part of the meniscus, as shown in the diagram.

   a) Record the volume of water in your table. Remember to consider the uncertainty of your measurement when recording your data.

4. Measure the mass of the graduated cylinder and 10 mL of water.

   a) Record the measurement in the table in your log.

   b) Calculate the mass of the water and record this in your table.

5. Add another 10 mL to the graduated cylinder and measure the mass. Calculate the mass of 20 mL of water.

   Repeat this step for five more volumes of water.

   a) Record all your measurements and calculations in the table in your log.

6. Use the data you obtained.

   a) Plot a graph of the mass versus the volume of water. Plot volume on the x-axis (horizontal axis) and mass on the y-axis (vertical axis).

   b) As the volume of the water increases, what happens to the mass?

   Since the graph you created is a straight line (or close to a straight line), you should draw the best-fit line through the data points. Do not connect the points with small segments but draw one line that comes closest to all of the individual points. The line you draw should pass through or close to the zero.

   c) From your graph predict the mass of 55 mL of water. What would be the volume of 25 g of water? Predicting values from within a graph is called interpolation. Predicting values beyond the measured values is called extrapolation.

   d) An important attribute of a straight-line graph is its slope. How steep is the graph? Calculate the slope of the graph you plotted. Remember, to calculate slope you divide the "rise" by

Safety goggles and a lab apron must be worn *at all times* in a chemistry lab.

the "run." What does the "rise" of the graph represent? What does the "run" represent?

e) Divide the mass of each sample of water by the volume. What do you notice about the relationship between the mass and the volume and the mass to volume ratio?

f) How does the slope of the graph compare to the values you calculated in this step?

Ethanol is very flammable and is a poison. Keep it away from sparks or flames. Do not ingest!

Wash your hands and arms thoroughly after the activity.

Safety goggles and a lab apron must be worn *at all times* in a chemistry lab.

7. Your teacher will provide you with a sample of a liquid such as ethanol. Use the procedure you used to find the mass and corresponding volumes of water to determine the slope of the ethanol's mass/volume graph and the mass to volume ratio.

   a) Record all your data and calculations in your *Active Chemistry* log.

8. Dispose of your ethanol sample as directed by your teacher. Clean up your workstation.

9. Someone tells you the mass and volume of a liquid that is either water or ethanol.

   a) Would you be able to determine what the liquid was?

   b) How would you make that determination?

Part B: Mass and Volume of Solids

1. Your teacher will provide you with three samples each of two different solid materials or a sample of a material like clay that can easily be divided into pieces.

2. As a group, decide on a procedure to calculate the mass/volume ratio and slope of the graph of each material.

   You can consider using either method shown in the diagrams on this and the next page for measuring

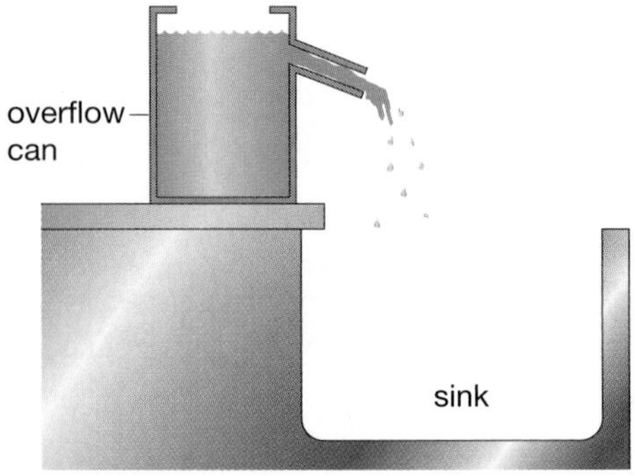
overflow can
sink

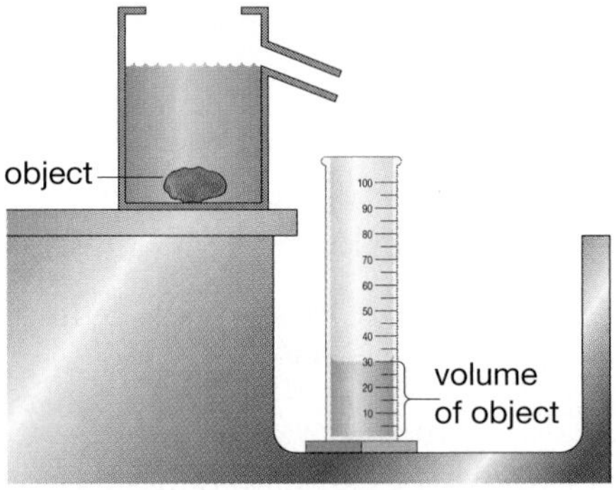
object
volume of object

the volume of each solid. Volume of solids is usually expressed in cubic centimeters. One milliliter is equivalent to one cubic centimeter (1 mL = 1 cm^3).

   a) Record your procedure in your *Active Chemistry* log. Be sure to include what measurements you need to make, what equipment you will need, what safety precautions you must use, and what calculations you have to do.

3. When your teacher has approved your procedure, carry out your activity.

   a) Carefully record all your data.

4. Use the data you collected.

   a) Plot a mass versus volume graph for each solid. Plot both solids on the same graph.

   b) How do the slopes for the two solids compare? Which solid has the larger mass for the same volume?

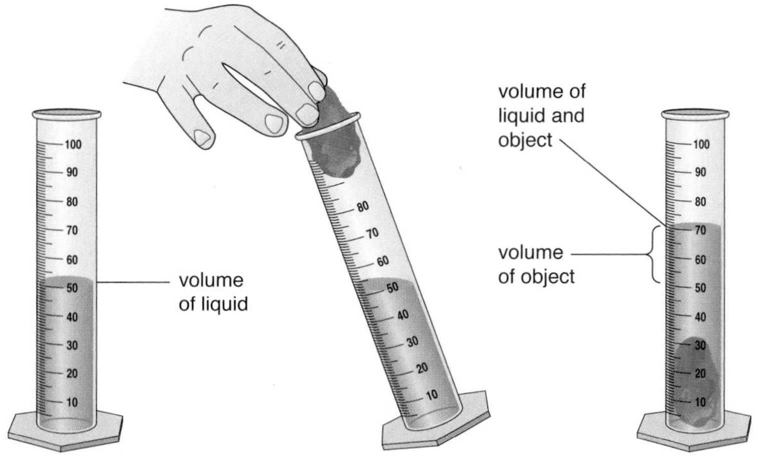
volume of liquid
volume of liquid and object
volume of object

5. You are given the mass and volume of a mystery material. How could you determine if the material is one of the liquids or solids that you used in this activity?

6. The mass of a unit volume of a material is called its density. You found the density of water by calculating the slope of the mass versus volume graph. You can also calculate density by dividing the mass of a sample of a material by the volume.

$$\text{density } (D) = \frac{\text{mass } (m)}{\text{volume } (V)}$$

a) Find the densities of water, the other liquid, and the two solid materials.

b) Compare your answers with another lab group.

Part C: Density and Special Effects

1. You will now try to make a plastic cap of a pen float in liquid.

a) Place the pen cap in a beaker of distilled water. Does the pen cap float or sink?

b) Place the pen cap in a beaker of ethanol. Does the pen cap float or sink?

c) Slowly add distilled water to the ethanol until the pen cap floats.

2. Use the concept of density.

a) Explain the results of your observations of the pen cap in water, ethanol, and the mixture of the two.

3. Your teacher may display a set of four colored liquids that float on one another or have you refer to a picture. The densities of each of the liquids were measured. The top layer has a density of 0.8 g/mL. The next layer has a density of 0.9 g/mL. The following layer has a density of 1.39 g/mL. The bottom layer has a density of 1.49 g/mL.

a) What do you notice about the densities of the liquids and their position in the display?

4. Your teacher will drop a pen cap into the liquids.

a) What would you predict will happen to the pen cap? Write your prediction in your *Active Chemistry* log.

b) Observe and record the movement of the pen cap as your teacher places it in the liquid.

Wash your hands and arms thoroughly after the activity.

Chem Talk

Chem Words

density: the mass per unit volume of a material.

DENSITY

Density as a Property of Matter

If you were to compare a 1 cm^3 cube of iron to a 1 cm^3 cube of wood, you would probably say that the iron is "heavier." However, if you compared a tree trunk to iron shavings, the tree trunk is obviously heavier. As you discovered in this activity, a "fair" comparison of the "heaviness" of two materials is a comparison of their densities. **Density** is the mass of the same volume of each material. In this activity you measured the density of water and ethanol. You found that each sample of the same liquid had the same density and each different liquid had its own characteristic density. You also found that each solid material you investigated had its own characteristic density. Density can be expressed in grams per milliliter (g/mL) or grams per cubic centimeter (g/cm^3). The units g/mL and g/cm^3 are equal, since 1 mL = 1 cm^3. The table shows the densities of some common liquids and solids.

Approximate Densities of Some Common Liquids and Solids

Material	Density (g/cm^3)
wood (balsa)	0.12
wood (birch)	0.66
gasoline	0.69
isopropanol	0.79
vegetable oil	0.92
distilled water	1.00
glycerol	1.26
magnesium	1.70
aluminium	2.70
iron	7.90
copper	8.90
nickel	8.90
silver	10.50
mercury	13.50
gold	19.30

You used the slope of the mass versus volume graph of a material to calculate density. You also calculated density using the equation:

$$\text{density } (D) = \frac{\text{mass } (m)}{\text{volume } (V)}$$

Density and Flotation

In this activity you further observed that materials with a greater density than a given liquid will sink, and materials with less density than a given liquid will float. In a column of colored liquids, the liquid with the highest density will be on the bottom, and the liquid with the lowest density will be on the top. The pen cap sank in ethanol and floated in water. When you added ethanol to the water you created just the right density to have the pen cap float within the liquid. The point at which the pen cap will neither rise nor sink is where the density of the pen cap is equal to the density of the ethanol/water. The pen cap "found" the place where the density of the liquid was identical to the density of the pen cap.

The most famous story about density is when Archimedes jumped out of the bath, ran through the town naked, and shouted "Eureka!" As the story supposedly goes, Archimedes was asked by the king to determine if his crown was solid gold. Archimedes knew the density of gold. He also knew that he could correctly determine if the crown were gold if he knew the density of the crown. The mass of the king's crown was easy to measure. The volume posed a real problem because it had such an unusual shape, and of course the king did not want his crown altered. When Archimedes submerged himself in the bathtub, he realized that the displacement of water would provide him with the volume. *Eureka* is Greek for "I found it."

MAKING MEASUREMENTS AND USING THE MEASUREMENTS TO MAKE CALCULATIONS

Uncertainty of Measurements

Every measurement that you make involves some uncertainty. When you measured the volume of water using a graduated cylinder, you used the division of units marked on the side of the cylinder to make your measurements. Suppose the smallest precision division marked on the graduated cylinder was a milliliter. This means that you can estimate the measure to the nearest tenth of a milliliter, because you can see if the level of the water is at, above, or below the mark. When you record your measurement of volume, you can record it as 10.0 mL, because you can see that the meniscus is at the 10 mL mark.

Remember always to look at the instrument that you are using and determine the smallest precision mark it has. When you make your measurement using the instrument you can only estimate to the →

next place. If you are using an electric balance to measure mass, it will do the estimating work for you. Most school balances will measure to the tenth or the hundredth of a gram.

Calculations

When you perform calculations using the measurements that you made in an investigation, you need to express the result of your calculations in a way that makes sense of the certainty of the measurements you made. For example, when calculating the density of a 10.1 mL sample of liquid with a mass of 9.8 g, you may obtain a value of 0.9702770... g/mL using a calculator. The precision of this value does not seem reasonable when considering limitations of your measurements.

There are rules that you can use when making your calculations:

Adding and Subtracting

When adding or subtracting numbers, arrange the numbers in columns so that the decimals line up. Complete the addition or subtraction problem and draw a vertical line to mark the end of your least precise number. The final answer should have the same number of decimal places as the number with the least decimal places.

Multiplying and Dividing

In multiplication and division, the result should have no more significant digits than the factor having the fewest number of significant digits. In order to determine the number of significant digits there are a few rules. First you must count all non-zero digits as significant (735 has 3 significant digits). Then all zeroes that are sandwiched by non-zero digits are significant (2008 has 4 significant digits). Finally, if zeroes are on the left they are not significant (00.0076 has 2 significant digits), and if they are on the right they are significant (820.00 has 5 significant digits). You can remember this rule with two words: "Not Significant." If the zeroes are on the left, they are not significant. If the zeroes are on the right, they are significant. (Exception: zeroes on the right are not significant if they do not have a decimal point. For example, 230 has only 2 significant digits and if you want 230 to have 3 significant digits, then write it in scientific notation, 2.30×10^2.) After you have determined the number of significant digits in each of your starting numbers, your final answer is limited to the least number of significant digits.

Checking Up

1. Explain the meaning of density.
2. Explain the difference between feathers and lead, using the concept of density.
3. Why is balsa instead of birch wood used in the construction of model airplanes?
4. In an investigation, the volume of a material is measured as 80.0 cm^3 and its mass is measured as 253 g. Which calculation of density correctly uses the precision rules: 3.1625 g/cm^3, 3.163 g/cm^3, 3.16 g/cm^3, 3.2 g/cm^3, or 3 g/cm^3?

What Do You Think Now?

At the beginning of this activity you were asked:

- **Since a kilogram of feathers and a kilogram of lead have the same mass, how do they appear different and why?**

You answered this question using density in *Checking Up*. If there were a statue made out of pure gold (density = 19.30 g/cm^3) and you built a replacement out of copper (density = 8.90 g/cm^3) and painted it gold, you know that the volumes would be identical. Discuss how you could tell the difference between the two statues.

Chem Essential Questions

What does it mean?

Chemistry explains a macroscopic phenomenon (what you observe) with a description of what happens at the nanoscopic level (atoms and molecules) using symbolic structures as a way to communicate. Complete the chart below in your *Active Chemistry* log.

MACRO	NANO	SYMBOLIC
Describe what you would see when comparing liquids of different densities.	*In words, describe at the particle level the difference between two liquids of different densities.*	*How can you find density mathematically?*

How do you know?

Look at the graph of the mass and volume of a liquid. Use your data to show that density is an intensive property. An intensive property is one that does not depend on the amount of the material.

Why do you believe?

Everyone has experienced density at some point in his or her life. How have you experienced this property in the course of life? Explain how density related to this life experience.

Why should you care?

You will be writing a movie scene for your challenge in this unit. You can make objects appear to float by suspending them in a liquid of equal density. Alternatively, you can also create an object from a less dense material and make it appear like a dense material (e.g., foam can be made to look like rocks). Write about an object that you could include for a special effect in your movie.

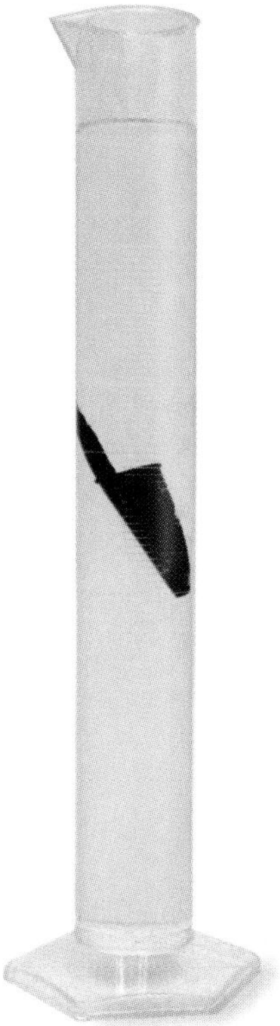

Reflecting on the Activity and the Challenge

In this activity, you discovered that the ratio of mass to volume (m/V) is a special number associated with each material. The ratio m/V is called the density and is a characteristic property of matter. You can identify whether a piece of metal is gold or gold-plated by measuring the density. You can distinguish one material from another by comparing densities. Objects of greater density than a liquid will sink, while objects of lesser density will float. Objects of the same density will appear suspended. You can make use of these conclusions in your challenge. For instance, you may want to have a movie special effect where a material appears suspended in space. The concept of density will help you create this special effect. You can compare the density of different materials and decide which materials will float and which materials will sink, and also how to make them appear to be suspended somewhere between the top and bottom of a liquid. Foam with its low density could also be made to look like dense rocks. The strength of a super-hero character can then be part of your special effect.

Chem to Go

1. Look at the table in the *Chem Talk* reading section. Use density to identify the liquid and solid samples you investigated in this activity.
2. Calculate the density of a solid from the following data:

   Volume of water: 48.4 mL (or cm^3)
   Volume of water and solid: 62.7 mL (or cm^3)
   Mass of solid: 123.4 g
3. Determine the density of a liquid from the following data:

   Mass of the graduated cylinder: 33.79 g
   Mass of the cylinder and liquid: 40.14 g
   Volume of liquid: 13.3 mL
4. Methanol has a density of 0.79 g/mL. What would be the mass of 589 mL of methanol?
5. Copper has a density of 8.90 g/cm^3. What would be the volume of a 746 g sample of copper?
6. In a well-known movie, *Raiders of the Lost Ark*, there is a famous scene in which the hero tries to outwit the designers of a trap by replacing a gold statue with a bag of sand of about the same volume.
   a) Given that the density of gold is 19.3 g/mL and sand is 3.1 g/mL, does this seem like a scientifically reasonable plan?
   b) In the movie, the hero grabs the gold statue with one hand and appears to handle it quite easily. Given that the volume of the statue appears to be about one liter, what would be the mass of the statue?
   c) A mass of 454 g has a gravitational weight of about 4.45 N (newtons) which is about 1 lb. How many pounds would the statue weigh?
   d) One gallon of milk has a mass of 3.7 kg and a weight equivalent of approximately 8 lb. How many gallons of milk would be equivalent to the gold statue?

7. In each of the following pairs, which has the greater mass:
   a) 1 kg lead or 1 kg feathers?
   b) 1 L gold or 1 L water?
   c) 1 L copper or 1 L silver?
8. Which of the following has the greater volume:
   a) 1 kg lead or 1 kg feathers?
   b) 1 kg gold or 1 kg water?
   c) 1 kg copper or 1 kg silver?
9. Review the measurements you made for mass and volume. How certain were your measurements? If you were to make the measurements again, could you be more certain? Explain your answer.
10. In calculating density you divided the mass of the material by the volume. Review the calculations you made. Adjust the precision of your answers using the rule for division given in the *Chem Talk* reading section.
11. ***Preparing for the Chapter Challenge***

    Design a special effect in which an object is suspended in a liquid. Consider the density of the material you will suspend and the density of the liquid you will use. Show the calculations that you used to make your choice of materials.

Inquiring Further

1. Is it real gold?

The new United States dollar coin has a golden color. Could it be made of real gold? Devise a method to determine if the new golden coin is any of the metals in the table in the *Chem Talk* reading section.

2. Density of gas

Devise an investigation that you could do to determine the density of air.

Activity 6 Metals and Nonmetals

What Do You See?

CHAR COAL
BATTERY

GOALS

In this activity you will:

- Observe some chemical and physical properties of various materials.
- Classify the materials as metals or nonmetals.
- Identify the metals that make up common alloys and learn about some special properties and uses of the alloys.
- Make generalizations about the properties that differentiate metals from nonmetals.
- Explore how heat treatments can alter the properties of metals.

What Do You Think?

If you look around your house you will see hundreds of objects made from dozens of kinds of materials. Have you ever wondered why the manufacturer chose the materials they did for each item?

- **Why are frying pans made of metal and baking dishes often made of glass or ceramic?**
- **Could a baking dish be made of metal? Could a frying pan be made of glass or ceramic?**

Record your ideas about these questions in your *Active Chemistry* log. Be prepared to discuss your responses with your small group and the class.

Investigate

1. Your teacher will provide you with samples of a number of materials: iron, copper, zinc, magnesium, tin, aluminum, brass, solder, chalk, graphite or charcoal, wood, glass, plastic, and concrete.

   Choose two of the materials that are obviously different. In your group, brainstorm at least five characteristics or properties of each material.

a) In your *Active Chemistry* log, use the characteristics to describe each material. Could someone else reading your log be able to identify the material?

2. Chemists use specific characteristics or properties to describe and distinguish among materials. You investigated some of these properties in *Activity 4* (e.g., strength, elasticity, malleability) and *Activity 5* (e.g., density). Additional properties used by chemists are described below.

   a) In your log, prepare a table for recording your observations.

3. **Luster:** Is the material shiny or dull in appearance? Does it look more like a mirror or more like mud? If a material has lots of luster it reflects light and you may be able to see images reflected from the surface. Polished metal has high luster. Dull surfaces don't reflect as much light. They have a matte appearance and no images can be reflected.

   a) In the table in your log, record whether the material has a high or low luster.

4. **Electrical conductivity:** Test each substance with a conductivity tester or multi-meter. To test each substance, touch the two leads to each end of the sample. Do not allow the leads to touch each other, or it will give a false reading. In the example shown in the diagram, the bulb will glow if the material is conductive. Your teacher will demonstrate how the specific conductivity tester works.

   a) In the table in your log, record whether the material is conductive. You can use words like nonconductive, slightly conductive, or very conductive to reflect this. If you are using a meter, you can record the reading.

5. **Malleability:** Wrap the material being tested in heavy plastic or a cloth to prevent pieces from flying off the sample. Place the material on a hard, flat surface. Using a hammer, try to pound the material flat. If the sample can be pounded into a flatter shape it is called malleable. If it breaks or doesn't change it is called nonmalleable.

Safety goggles and a lab apron must be worn *at all times* in a chemistry lab.

Be sure the terminals of your conductivity tester are kept apart between trials.

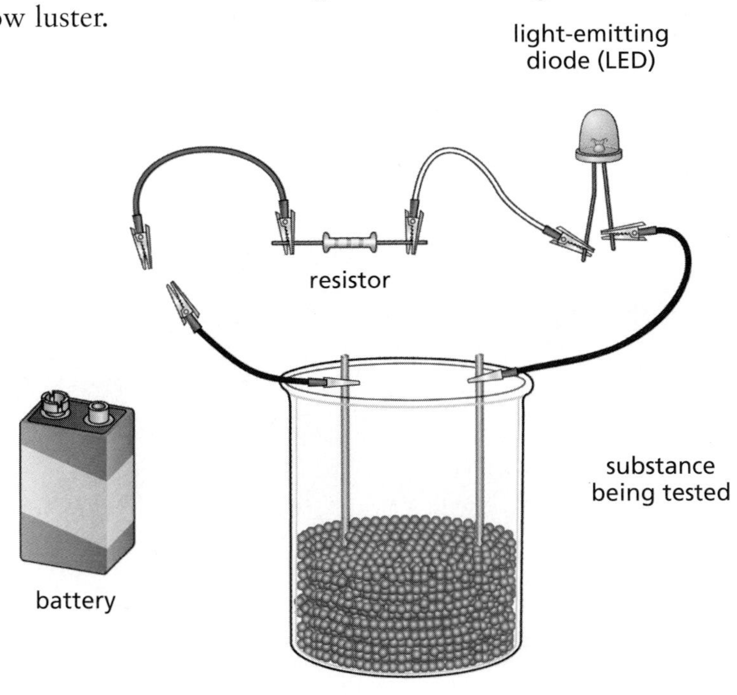
light-emitting diode (LED)
resistor
battery
substance being tested

a) In the table in your log, record whether the material is malleable or nonmalleable.

6. **Reactivity:** Try scraping or sanding a small part of each sample. Is the surface underneath the same in appearance or different? If the surface is different, that means the sample has reacted with the air.

   a) In the table in your log, record whether the material is reactive or non-reactive.

7. **Ductility:** Ductility refers to how easily the substance can be pulled out into a wire or how bendable it is. Try bending each piece to determine how ductile it is.

   a) In the table in your log, record whether or not the material is ductile.

8. **Color:**

   a) Record the color of each sample material in the table in your log.

9. Once you have completed the table, compare your list of characteristics of each substance with those recorded by the other students in your class. Have each member of your group pair off with a student from another group. If there is a difference in the results go back to the material and review your observations until everyone agrees on the most accurate list of properties for each material.

   a) Be sure to record any changes you make in your log.

Wash your hands and arms thoroughly after the activity.

10. Classify the substances into two groups. Use any property you have observed to divide the samples into groups that have the most in common. For example, you could divide the materials into those that do have a luster and those that do not.

    a) Record your classification of the materials in your log.

11. Most metals have a shiny and lustrous surface. They conduct electricity and heat. They are malleable and ductile and they are often relatively reactive. Nonmetals have characteristics that are generally opposite to metals in every way. Instead of being lustrous their surfaces are dull in appearance. They are nonconductive, brittle, and non-ductile. Now separate your samples into metals and nonmetals. If you have any samples that do not fit clearly as either a metal or a nonmetal, set them aside.

    a) Make a list of the samples in each category in your *Active Chemistry* log.

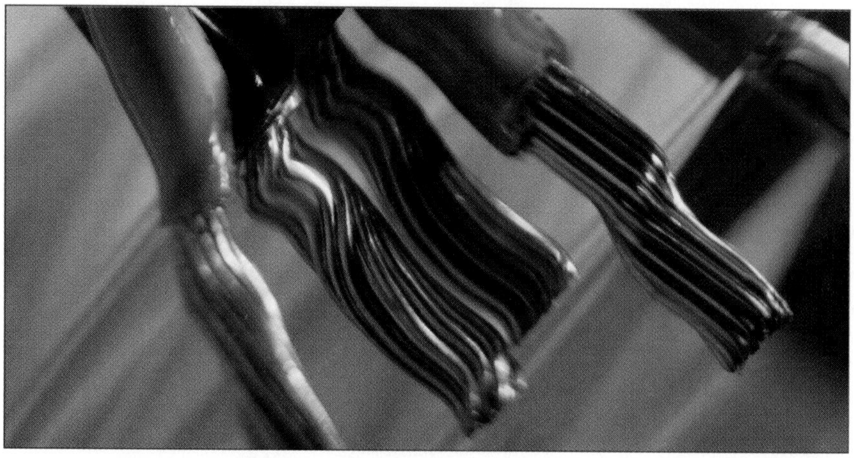

Chem Talk

METALS, NONMETALS, AND METALLOIDS

In this activity you investigated specific properties of materials. You then used your observations to classify a material as a **metal** or a **nonmetal**. Metals have **luster**. They exhibit **conductivity**. They conduct electricity and heat. They are malleable and **ductile** and they are often relatively **reactive**. Many metals form a compound on their surface that results from reactions with air. When you scrape or sand a piece of metal you are removing that coating of metal compound. Sometimes that natural coating can prevent further reacting and will preserve the metal underneath.

Look at the drawing of the electron-sea model of copper. You can see that in solid copper metal, the centers of the copper atoms are in fixed locations but a sea of electrons surrounds them. If an electric circuit is set up, the electrons are free to move. This is the basis of the metallic property of electrical conductivity.

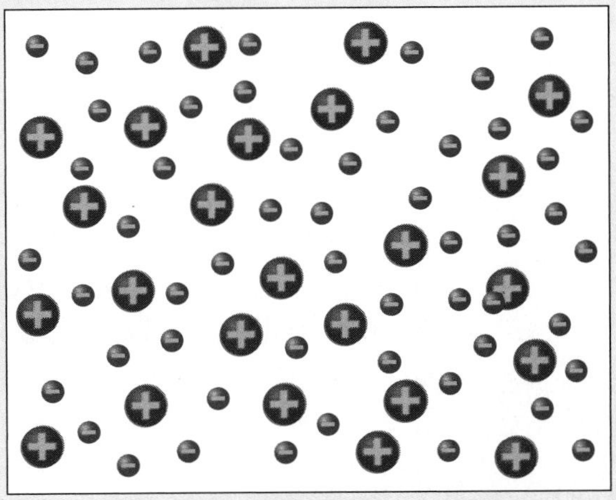

Electron-sea model of copper metal.

On the other hand, silicon dioxide is an **amorphous solid;** you know it as glass. In glass, electrons are fixed into position and are held tightly by each atom due to covalent bonding (sharing of electrons) between silicon and oxygen atoms. Since the electrons are not mobile, the glass does not conduct an electric current like copper metal does. Glass is a nonconductor of electricity.

Preserving metal and preventing its reaction with some of the components in the air is a major task. When metals react with oxygen in the air it is called **oxidation**. This type of reaction is what happens when iron rusts. Preventing rust is important. While a metal like steel is very strong and makes excellent building material, once it rusts it loses all strength and flakes away. Millions of structures, tools, and vehicles are made primarily of metal. Preventing oxidation (also called corrosion) is essential if they are to remain in good operating condition. In order to prevent oxidation, metal surfaces can be painted, coated, or →

Chem Words

metal: class of materials that exhibit the properties of conductivity, malleability, reactivity, and ductility. Metal elements readily lose electrons to form positive ions.

nonmetal: an element that does not exhibit the properties of conductivity, malleability, reactivity, and ductility. Nonmetals tend to form negative ions. The oxides of these elements are acidic.

luster: the reflection of light from the surface of a material described by its quality and intensity.

conductivity: the property of transmitting heat and electricity within a substance.

ductility: the property of a material to be pulled out into a wire.

reactivity: a property that describes how readily a material will react with other materials.

oxidation: the chemical process of reacting with oxygen. More generally, the loss of one or more electrons by a substance.

amorphous solid: any noncrystalline solid in which the atoms and molecules are not organized in a definite fixed pattern.

Chem Words

metalloid: an element that exhibits some properties of metals and some of nonmetals.

alloy: a substance that has metal characteristics and consists of two or more different elements.

Rusting is an oxidation reaction.

combined with another metal to make them less reactive. (Oxidation is part of an oxidation-reduction reaction in which an element loses one or more electrons. You will learn more about this type of reaction in later chapters.)

Nonmetals have characteristics that are generally opposite to those of metals in every way. Instead of being lustrous, their surfaces are dull in appearance. They are nonconductive, brittle, and non-ductile. Over the past 150 years, chemists developed the Periodic Table of the Elements for classifying and organizing the chemical elements. Elements are classified as metals and as nonmetals.

Silicon is used in computer chips.

Some other elements are called **metalloids**. On the periodic table they can be found along the zigzag line that separates metals from nonmetals. Boron (B), silicon (Si), germanium (Ge), arsenic (As), antimony (Sb), tellurium (Te), and polonium (Po) are metalloids. They share some characteristics of metals and some of nonmetals. Metalloids are solids. They can be either shiny or dull. Some metalloids are semiconductors. A semiconductor is a substance that can conduct electrical charge under certain conditions. Silicon and germanium are semiconductors and are used in computer chips as well as many other electronic devices.

Brass and solder are not elements but they are still classified as metals. They are commonly called **alloys**. Alloys are materials that contain more than one metal element and still maintain the characteristic properties of metals. Many metals are not practically useful because they may be too soft and are hard to work with. Gold is a good example of a metal that is too soft for jewelers to work with so they make an alloy of gold, silver, and copper. The alloy is harder and will hold its shape. Iron combined with chromium, nickel, and carbon makes the alloy called steel. This gives it the strength that it needs in construction. The brass that you investigated contains $\frac{2}{3}$ copper and $\frac{1}{3}$ zinc. Solder contains $\frac{2}{3}$ lead and $\frac{1}{3}$ tin. (There are several different recipes for solder and brass.) Alloys are classified as metal solutions and if they are uniformly mixed then they are homogeneous mixtures called solution alloys.

Checking Up

1. List five properties of metals and five properties of nonmetals.
2. Why is it important to prevent the oxidation of metals used in construction?
3. What is a metalloid?
4. Explain the meaning of an alloy.
5. Why are alloys used?

What Do You Think Now?

At the beginning of this activity you were asked:

- **Why are frying pans made of metal and baking dishes often made of glass or ceramic?**
- **Could a baking dish be made of metal? Could a frying pan be made of glass or ceramic?**

Using what you now know about metals and nonmetals, answer these questions. Then, classify the following unknown element as a metal or a nonmetal and explain your reasoning.

Unknown element: nonconductive, brittle, and non-reactive.

Chem Essential Questions

What does it mean?

Chemistry explains a macroscopic phenomenon (what you observe) with a description of what happens at the nanoscopic level (atoms and molecules) using symbolic structures as a way to communicate. Complete the chart below in your *Active Chemistry* log.

MACRO	NANO	SYMBOLIC
What did you see when a substance conducted electricity?	*In words, describe what is happening to the electrons in a metal when it conducts electricity.*	*Draw a picture to show the conductivity of electricity in a metal.*

How do you know?

List the elements from the lab that did conduct electricity.

Why do you believe?

To keep small children safe, adults will use plastic covers for electrical outlets. Explain why they use plastic (and not another material) for the covers on electrical outlets.

Why should you care?

You will be writing a movie scene for your challenge in this unit. During the filming you will probably need to construct backgrounds and props for the scene. List one metal and one nonmetal that you plan to use in the scene. For each, explain what would happen if you substituted a different item.

Reflecting on the Activity and the Challenge

As you are creating your movie special effect, you may have to build a stage set, model, or prop. It is important to consider the nature of the materials you choose before you start construction. You need to match the characteristics of the material you choose with the object you are trying to build. You need to decide if the building material should be heavy or light, flexible or rigid. Each of the characteristics of the substance is important. The characteristics required will probably vary with each construction project. Whichever materials you choose, you will strengthen your report by discussing the specific properties of the materials and classifying them as metals, nonmetals, or metalloids.

Chem to Go

1. a) List the names of three metals you are familiar with in your daily life.
   b) For each metal you listed in (a), describe two different uses for each.
2. a) List the names of three nonmetals you are familiar with in your daily life.
   b) For each nonmetal you listed in (a), describe two different uses for each.
3. Examine the following objects or machines that you use every day:
   a) backpack
   b) bicycle
   c) car

   Make a list of the metals and nonmetals that make up the major components of the object. List the function and characteristics of each component.
4. a) List two properties of a material that you can observe using your senses.
   b) List two properties of a material that require tests to observe.
5. Classify each of the following as a metal, nonmetal, or metalloid:
   a) aluminum (Al)
   b) iron (Fe)
   c) boron (B)
   d) oxygen (O)
   e) carbon (C)
   f) silicon (Si)
   g) mercury (Hg)
6. The way materials are used can change with time. Milk was originally delivered in glass bottles. Now cartons made from wax-coated paper and plastic jugs are used for milk. Snow skis used to be made of wood. Now they are made from fiberglass or graphite. What factors go into decisions about changing what materials should be used when building a product?

Inquiring Further

The effect of heat treatment on the property of a metal

It is possible to change the characteristics of a material by treating them in various ways. Determine the effect of heat on a metal. Obtain a few paper clips or bobby pins from your teacher. As a control, determine how many times it takes to bend the clip or pin back and forth in order to break it. The stress at the point of bending causes the paper clip or bobby pin to break.

Now try some various types of heat treatment to see what effect they have on the metal. Try heating the piece in the flame of a burner until it is red. To do this, hold the piece with tongs or forceps. Allow the piece to cool on its own until it is safe to handle. Then try to break it again, being careful to bend it back and forth exactly as you did with the control. Record your results and try another heating scheme.

Consider the following treatments:

- **heating to redness and then cooling by plunging into water**
- **heating and cooling several times**
- **heating only a moderate amount.**

Record your observations and summarize what seems to be the relationship of heat treatment to the characteristics of the metal.

What characteristic of metals do you think is demonstrated by bending the metals back and forth until breaking?

Safety goggles and a lab apron must be worn *at all times* in a chemistry lab.

Have an adult with you at all times when heating materials. The adult should check for safety before you begin.

If you are doing this activity in class, make sure your teacher approves and supervises your procedure.

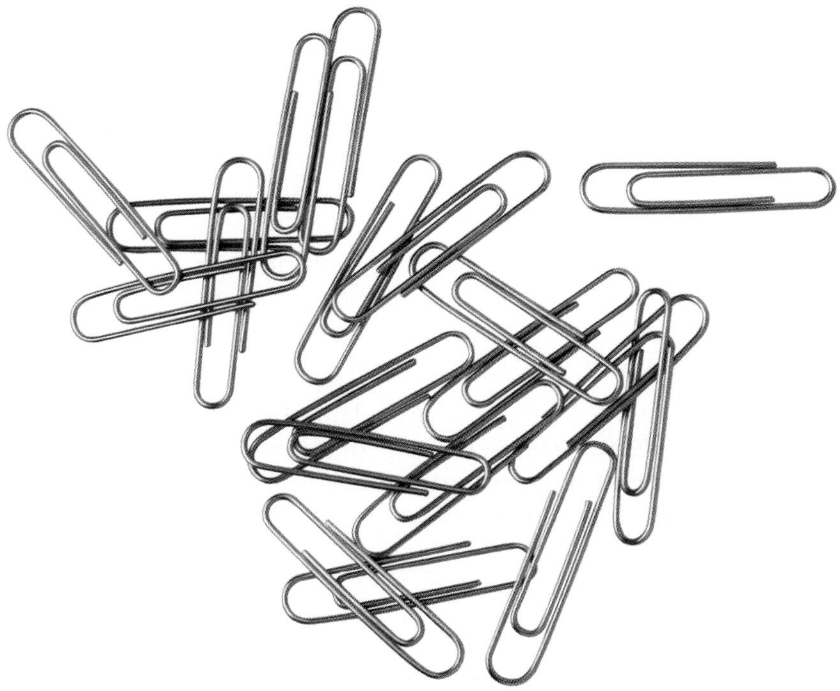

Activity 7 Polymers

What Do You See?

HOW TO
MAKE
POLYMERS

GOALS

In this activity you will:

- Make a polymer-based material that has properties different from other states of matter that you have studied.
- Observe the material's properties and compare them to those of solids and liquids.
- Describe the process of cross-linking in polymeric materials.
- Discuss and invent new commercial uses for water-soluble polymers.
- Compare the viscosities of two non-Newtonian fluids.

What Do You Think?

In ancient times, humans made most of the objects they needed for daily life from natural substances. Relatively little processing was done between harvesting and use. For much of history, people have used metals, cotton, wood, and other natural materials for building, clothing, and tools. In the 1900s things changed dramatically as scientists were able to create new materials.

- **What is a polymer?**
- **How are polymers made?**

Record your ideas about these questions in your *Active Chemistry* log. Be prepared to discuss your responses with your small group and the class.

Investigate

1. Measure 50 mL of polyvinyl alcohol (PVA) solution into a 250-mL beaker. Observe closely the properties of the PVA solution. Refer to the different types of properties you investigated in previous activities to make your observations.

   a) Record your observations in your *Active Chemistry* log.

2. Measure 10 mL of sodium tetraborate (borax) solution into another beaker. Observe the properties of borax.

   a) Record your observations in your *Active Chemistry* log.

3. Add one drop of food coloring to the sodium tetraborate solution.

4. Add the sodium tetraborate solution to the PVA solution while stirring with a wooden stick. Keep stirring until the mixture thickens.

   When the mixture has thickened, remove the stick. Place a few paper towels on your desktop and use your hands to remove the thickened mixture.

   Mold and stretch the new material while you observe its characteristics.

   a) Record your observations in your log.

5. Test your new "slime" and see if it behaves more like a solid or more like a liquid. Try holding the slime in your fingers and dangling it downward. Wait for a few minutes to see what happens.

   Place your slime back in the beaker and see what happens as it sits for a few minutes.

   Try pulling the slime out slowly and see what happens. Now try the same thing but pull quickly.

   Roll the slime into a ball and try bouncing it gently on the tabletop.

   a) Record all your observations in your log.

6. It was easy to label the PVA solution as a solid or a liquid. Similarly, it was easy to label borax. Liquids have very different characteristics from solids. Liquids flow while solids have a rigid shape. Liquids assume the shape of their container and solids have their own shape. Slime blurred the line between the definitions. Liquids spread out when force is applied, but solids break. Liquids splatter when dropped, while solids may bounce.

   a) In what ways does your slime behave like a liquid?

   b) In what ways does it behave like a solid?

7. The PVA molecules are relatively long, slender molecules. The sodium tetraborate molecules are shorter and can form bonds on both ends.

   a) Draw a sketch to represent how the substances act in this reaction. Use the model in the diagram to draw PVA molecules alone that can account for it being a liquid. The molecules in a liquid slide past one another easily.

   b) Draw sodium tetraborate molecules alone that can account for it being a solid. In a solid the bonds prevent molecules from moving too far from their original positions.

   c) Finally, draw the reaction of sodium tetraborate cross-linking the PVA molecules that can account for it being somewhat solid and somewhat liquid. Remember your drawing is just a representation of the molecules.

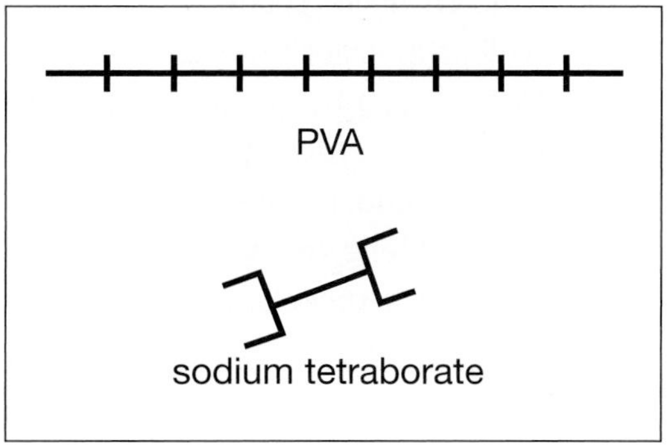
PVA
sodium tetraborate

Safety goggles and a lab apron must be worn *at all times* in a chemistry lab.

Wash your hands and arms thoroughly after the activity.

Do not inhale or ingest borax!

Chem Talk

Chem Words

polymer: a substance that is a macromolecule consisting of many similar small molecules (monomers) linked together in long chains.

viscosity: a property related to the resistance of a fluid to flow.

polymerization: a chemical reaction that converts small molecules (monomers) into large molecules (polymers).

POLYMERS

In this activity you made "slime." This substance is a **polymer** that has unique characteristics. It is classified as a non-Newtonian liquid. Liquids resist flow. This phenomenon is known as **viscosity**. Newton devised a simple model for fluid flow. You will learn more about this model in later chemistry and physics courses. Liquids like water and gasoline behave according to Newton's model. They are called Newtonian fluids. Ketchup, blood, yogurt, gravy, pie fillings, mud, and slime do not follow the model. They are classified as non-Newtonian liquids. Slime has some characteristics of liquids such as being fluid and taking the shape of its container. On the other hand it bounces and breaks when pulled quickly, as solids do. The unique characteristics of slime are due to the two substances that make it up. The borax solution forms cross-links among the polyvinyl alcohol molecules. These cross-links make the resulting polymer slower to flow and change shape. The formation of very large molecules from many smaller molecular units is called **polymerization**. Polymers are materials that are made up of many similar small molecules, called monomers, linked together in long chains. These materials have always existed in nature, but they have only been produced by industrial processes in the 20th century.

Proteins are natural polymers. They are the basic structural unit of plants and animals. There are more than ten thousand different proteins found in nature, yet they are all made up of combinations of about 20 different amino acids. Starch and cellulose are examples of carbohydrates that are polymers. The human digestive system is able to break apart the bonds that form starch molecules, releasing glucose, which the body uses as a source of energy. Humans cannot digest cellulose.

Polyethylene (polyethene) is a polymer made up of ethylene molecules linked together. It is one of many chemicals manufactured from crude oil. It is used to make plastic milk bottles as well as a variety of other objects. Other examples of polymers include polyesters, nylon, polyvinyl chloride, polystyrene, natural rubber, and polyethylene terephthalate (PET), which is a recyclable thermoplastic.

Checking Up

1. Describe polymers and polymerization in your own words.
2. Name two natural-occurring polymers.
3. Give examples of five polymers that are manufactured using technological processes.

What Do You Think Now?

At the beginning of the activity you were asked:

- **What is a polymer?**
- **How are polymers made?**

Now that you know what a polymer is, how would you update your earlier response? Create an animation that shows the process of polymerization.

Chem Essential Questions

What does it mean?

Chemistry explains a macroscopic phenomenon (what you observe) with a description of what happens at the nanoscopic level (atoms and molecules) using symbolic structures as a way to communicate. Complete the chart below in your *Active Chemistry* log.

MACRO	NANO	SYMBOLIC
Describe your observations when you mixed polyvinyl alcohol and borax.	*In words, describe what is happening to the PVA and the borax molecules.*	*Draw a picture that shows the binding of PVA and borax.*

How do you know?

Look back at your observations of the PVA and borax before they were mixed. What changes happened to the liquids after they were mixed?

Why do you believe?

Manufacturers describe polymers by their physical macroscopic properties. Chemists describe polymers by their chemical structure. As a student chemist, can you give one reason why each description is important?

Why should you care?

You will be writing a movie scene for your challenge in this unit. Write a short scene using slime and explain the procedure for making slime.

Reflecting on the Activity and the Challenge

What monster movie is complete without slime? Now you know how to make slime. Supplies for making slime are relatively expensive. Keep costs in mind as you plan for your special effect.

Chem to Go

1. List three ways you could modify the properties of your slime. If the slime you made in this activity is not quite correct for the special effect you have in mind, how might you modify it for use in your movie?
2. List five other uses that might be possible for the slime substance, in addition to its use as a movie special effect.
3. Thin sheets of solid PVA slime have been used in several new commercial products. Since the sheets are soluble in water, they are ideal recyclable containers. Seed manufacturers have made long tapes of PVA sheets with seeds imbedded inside. When the tapes are planted in the ground the PVA dissolves and the seeds are free to grow. Another use is collecting dirty laundry in hospitals. The solid laundry is placed into PVA bags. When it is time to wash the clothing the entire bag is thrown into the washing machine. It is not necessary for workers to handle the dirty clothes again. What two other uses can you think of for PVA sheet material?

Inquiring Further

1. Self-siphoning slime

Spread your slime on a piece of plastic wrap or waxed paper and let it dry completely. This may take a day or two. Compare the characteristics of the dry slime to the wet slime.

PVA slime has been reported to be "self-siphoning." To siphon most substances, a tube is placed in a liquid and the siphon is started by sucking the liquid out of the container, over the edge and down the tube. The mass of the water flowing out of the tube creates a pressure difference and draws the remainder of the liquid with it. Slime is supposed to have the same effect, but without the tube! Try demonstrating this self-siphoning effect with your slime.

2. Viscosity of non-Newtonian liquids

Ketchup is classified as a non-Newtonian liquid. Determine which non-Newtonian liquid is the most viscous (resistant to flow).

Safety goggles and a lab apron must be worn *at all times* in a chemistry lab.

- Set up a retort stand with a ring to hold a long-stem funnel.
- On the funnel place two marks with a pen at about 2 cm apart.
- Pour one of the liquids into the funnel and allow it to flow through the stem into a beaker.
- Let the liquid level come down to your top mark on the side of the funnel and stop the flow with your finger.
- Using a stopwatch, time how long it takes for the liquid to flow before it reaches the second line after you remove your finger.

Activity 8 Identifying Matter

What Do You See?
LiCl
$BaCl_2$
NaCl
$SrCl_2$
KCl
$CaCl_2$

GOALS

In this activity you will:

- Produce colored flames.
- Identify the metal ions present in materials by the colors of light a material gives off when held in a flame.
- Describe how atoms create the colored light.
- Investigate ways of producing new colors not among those produced by the materials you test.
- Practice safe laboratory techniques in working with laboratory burners.

What Do You Think?

You may have read how royalty, suspicious of enemies, had their food tested for poison by having someone else taste it first. That's not a job anyone would enjoy for very long!

- **How else could you test for a poisonous substance (other than by eating it)?**

Record your ideas about this question in your *Active Chemistry* log. Be prepared to discuss your response with your small group and the class.

Investigate

1. Your teacher will supply you with seven numbered wooden splints that have been soaked in various solutions. Some are harmful, and some are not.

   a) How could you distinguish one splint from another?

2. Light your Bunsen burner. Immediately make observations about the color of the burner flame.

   a) Record your observations in your *Active Chemistry* log.

Safety goggles and a lab apron must be worn *at all times* in a chemistry lab.

Follow all safety precautions for working with an open flame.

3. Take one of the wooden splints and hold it in the hot part of the flame using forceps, tongs, or a fireproof glove. Note the color of the flame when the solution-soaked wooden splint is heated.

   As soon as the flame from the splint is no longer strongly colored, extinguish the splint by placing it in a beaker of water.

   a) Organize a table to record your data.

   b) Record your observations in your table.

4. Repeat *Step 3* for the remaining six splints.

   a) Record all your observations.

5. Refer to your data table. The salt solutions in which the splints were soaked are metal compounds of the elements lithium, barium, sodium, strontium, potassium, and calcium. One splint was soaked in water.

   a) What do you notice that was different about each splint?

   b) Your teacher will identify the solution each splint was soaked in. Record this information in your data table.

Wash your hands and arms thoroughly after the activity.

6. Obtain another splint soaked in an unknown solution. Hold the wooden splint soaked in the unknown solution in the burner flame. Observe what happens.

   a) Record your observations in your log.

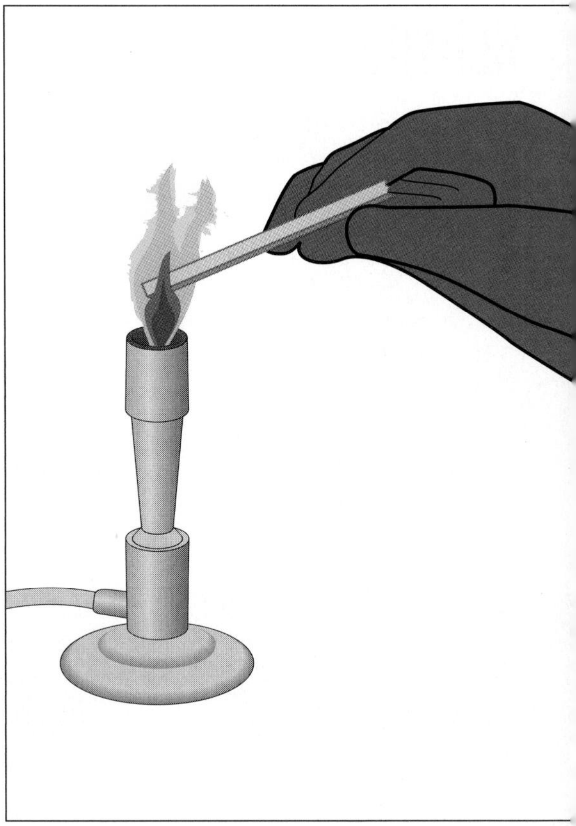

   b) Use your observations to decide what metal ions are on the splint. Confirm your results with your teacher.

   c) Did you correctly identify the metal ion?

   d) In your log describe how you decided what the identity of your compound was, and how sure you are that you were correct.

7. Clean up your workstation and return all your equipment as directed by your teacher.

Chem Talk

IDENTIFYING ELEMENTS USING FLAME TESTS

In this activity you were able to create unique colors. Each color was an identifying characteristic of the solution on the splint. The colors are the result of the electron structure of each solution. When the metal **ions** are placed in the hot flame their **electrons** absorb the energy and move to higher energy levels around the nucleus. When these electrons fall back to their original level, they give off the light you see in the **flame test**. Since each atom has a unique arrangement of electrons, each gives a unique color. This experimental technique is called a flame test. It is the basis for identifying the composition of the salt solutions. This same effect is responsible for the burst of color in fireworks. In this experiment only the metal ions are changed. The negatively charged ion (chloride) is not affected.

The flames produced in this activity have interesting colors. The structure of matter is the key to the colors. The metal compounds are made of atoms that have **nuclei** surrounded by electrons. When electrons fall from a higher energy level to a lower energy level, they give off radiation. In this case, the electrons were able to get to a higher energy level by absorbing heat energy from the Bunsen-burner flame. Each compound has a different configuration of electrons and electron energy levels. The change in energy levels represents the color of the light given off. If you refer to the higher energy level as E_h and to the lower energy level as E_l, then you can state:

The energy of the emitted light is equal to $E_h - E_l$. The total amount of energy remains the same as it is conserved. The energy the electron gains from the heat energy of the Bunsen burner flame raises the electron to a higher energy state. When the electron drops down to the lower energy state, it gives off that energy as light energy.

The process you observed in this activity is not a chemical reaction. In a chemical reaction, the product of the reaction is different from the original materials. In the flame test, the heat did not chemically alter the metal compound on the splint.

Chem Words

ion: an electrically charged atom or group of atoms that has acquired a net charge, either negative or positive.

electron: a subatomic particle that occurs outside of the nucleus and has a charge of –1 and mass of 9.109×10^{-28} g.

flame test: an experimental technique or process in identifying a metal from its characteristic flame color.

nucleus: the very dense core of the atom that contains the neutrons and protons.

Checking Up

1. Explain what is meant by a flame test.
2. Explain how energy is conserved during the flame test.

What Do You Think Now?

At the beginning of the activity you were asked:

- **How could you test for a poisonous substance (other than by eating it)?**

Suppose that you were going to try to test food samples using a flame test to see if they had been poisoned. How would you know for sure that the food had been contaminated? How do you know what color the pure food would have when it burned?

Chem Essential Questions

What does it mean?

Chemistry explains a macroscopic phenomenon (what you observe) with a description of what happens at the nanoscopic level (atoms and molecules) using symbolic structures as a way to communicate. Complete the chart below in your *Active Chemistry* log.

MACRO	NANO	SYMBOLIC
Describe what you saw during the flame test.	*In words, describe what is happening to the electrons as they are heated in the Bunsen burner flame.*	*Draw a set of slides showing an electron starting at ground state, becoming excited, and falling to emit light.*

How do you know?

Look back at your data table. Are there any elements that you cannot distinguish between?

Why do you believe?

Energy is conserved in a chemical process. This means that when you put energy in (from the flame) you will get energy out (in the form of light). Where is the energy input to produce light in your home?

Why should you care?

You will be writing a movie scene for your challenge in this unit. Add a part to your scene that could involve a colored flame. What is the significance in the movie of using a colored flame? (For example, a red flame could mean that the characters are in danger.)

Reflecting on the Activity and the Challenge

Most of the common fuels are primarily hydrocarbons, which do not contain metal ions. Therefore, you are most familiar with flames that are yellow-orange or occasionally a light blue. The bright colors of the excited metals are a surprise and tend to look "out-of-this-world."

Colors could play an interesting part in a plot line of a movie script. Perhaps an unusually colored flame could be taken as a mystical sign. A sudden change in the color of campfires could be a sign that danger is near. Consider how you might use flame tests to create unusually colored flames for your movie special effect.

Chem to Go

1. Compare the colors you observed in your flame tests to the colors you have seen in fireworks displays. Identify what metals are used in producing the different colors in fireworks.
2. Develop a series of sketches showing how an electron of an atom can give off light. Your first sketch should have the electron in the ground state. The next sketch should show the electron excited when you apply energy to the atom and the third sketch should show how light is emitted when the electron falls to a lower energy state.
3. ***Preparing for the Chapter Challenge***

   Name three new colors of light that could be produced by combining some of the metal salts that you tested in the lab, and identify which metal salts you would combine to produce these colors. If time and your teacher permit it, test your predictions.

Inquiring Further

Fireworks

Fireworks have been around for centuries. They were used long before anyone knew why they produced the stunning effects they do. Investigate the manufacturing of fireworks and find the specific compounds used to produce the many colors presented during fireworks displays.

Are all colors equally represented in fireworks displays, or are some colors easier to obtain than others? Research what colors are available and which, if any, do not seem possible given the range of substances readily available.

Activity 9 Organic Substances

What Do You See?
ORANGES

GOALS

In this activity you will:

- Combust a material present in fruit rinds.
- Represent the combustion of hydrocarbons as chemical equations.
- Learn the formulas and proper names for simple hydrocarbons.
- Make two-dimensional drawings showing the chemical bonding structure in simple hydrocarbons.
- Classify materials as organic or inorganic.
- Explore various definitions of the term "organic."

What Do You Think?

At a grocery store or market, "regular" apples might cost about 79 cents per pound, while "organic" apples may cost as much as or even more than $1.93 per pound.

- **Why do people buy organic apples if they are so much more expensive?**
- **Does organic mean one thing to shoppers and another to chemists? Explain your answer.**

Record your ideas about these questions in your *Active Chemistry* log. Be prepared to discuss your responses with your small group and the class.

Investigate

1. Obtain a piece of orange peel from your teacher. Make observations of its texture, color, smell, and any other characteristics you notice.

   a) Record your observations in your log.

2. Take one piece of the orange peel and hold it in your hand between your thumb and index finger. Fold the orange peel in half.

   Using forceps or tongs, hold it with the smooth fold pointing away from you.

Safety goggles and a lab apron must be worn *at all times* in a chemistry lab.

Hold the surface of the orange peel near the flame of a candle. Pinch or squeeze hard.

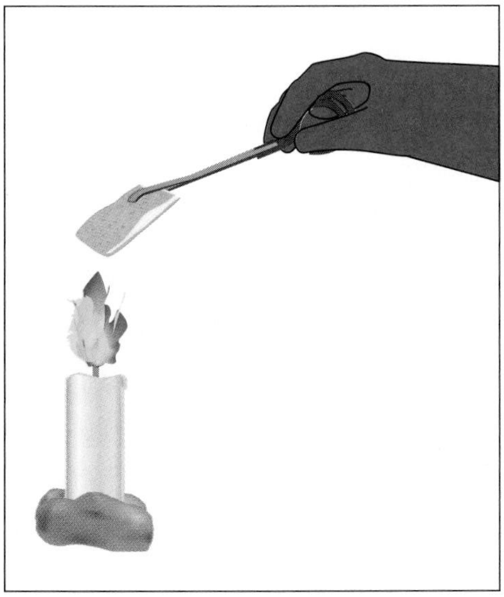

Repeat using fresh pieces of orange peel.

a) Record your observations in your *Active Chemistry* log.

3. Repeat *Step 2* with other types of fruit and vegetable skins. Use pieces that are the same approximate size and shape as the orange peel.

a) Record your observations in your log.

4. Organic chemistry is the study of molecular compounds of carbon. The gas and liquid that you ignited in the previous steps are carbon compounds. They belong to a class of organic compounds called hydrocarbons. That means it is a compound composed only of carbon and hydrogen.

a) Draw what the molecules of some simple hydrocarbons might look like. Each carbon atom can form four chemical bonds. Each hydrogen atom can form one bond. Carbon can link to another carbon atom or to hydrogen. Look at a structure for a hydrocarbon containing one carbon and 4 hydrogens and a second structure for 2 carbons and 6 hydrogens in the diagram.

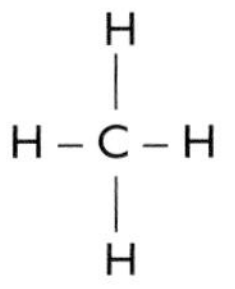

CH_4

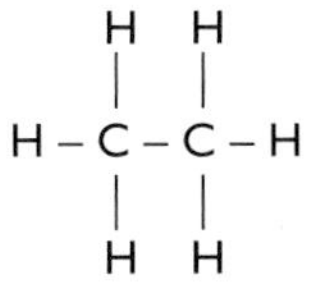

C_2H_6

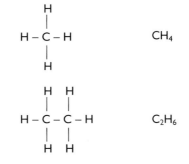

b) In these two structures, does each carbon atom have 4 bonds? Does each hydrogen atom have 1 bond?

c) Draw structures for 3 carbons, 4 carbons, 5 carbons, and 10 carbons, adding hydrogen as necessary to fill the bonds.

5. In the case of ethene (ethylene), a chemical that stimulates the ripening of fruit, the carbons share two bonds between them. The chemical formula for ethylene is C_2H_4. Its structural formula is shown below.

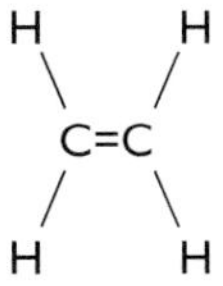

a) Write some chemical formulas for carbon compounds containing two, three, and four carbons that contain a carbon—carbon double bond. Draw the structural formula beside the chemical formula. Remember that each carbon can still only have a total of four bonds. If it shares two bonds with another carbon atom, that leaves only two others to share.

6. In addition to chemical formulas and structural formulas, chemists use other symbolic structures to help visualize molecules. Pictured are ball-and-stick models for methane (CH_4) and ethylene (C_2H_4) as well as space-filling models. In the ball-and-stick model, balls represent atoms and sticks represent chemical bonds. The balls are labeled or are given specific colors (e.g., hydrogen is white, carbon is black, nitrogen is blue). In the space-filling model, the atom is shown as a distorted sphere as a way to indicate that the electrons spend most of the time in the space between the different nuclei.

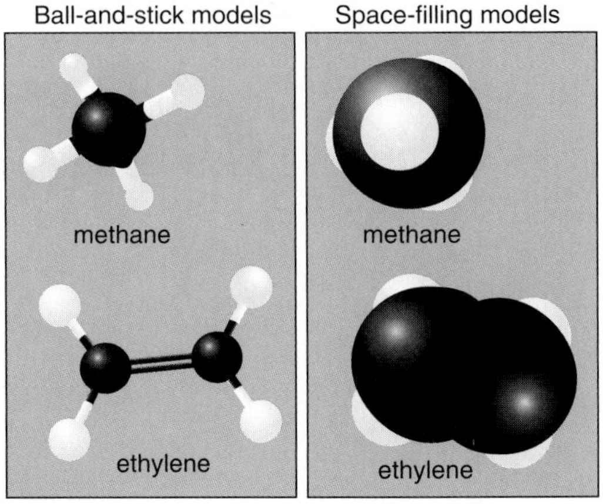
Ball-and-stick models
Space-filling models
methane
methane
ethylene
ethylene

Chem Talk

THE CHEMISTRY OF MOLECULAR COMPOUNDS OF CARBON

Chemistry attempts to explain nanoscopic events through an understanding of macroscopic phenomena. Chemists rationalize how the world they see works by describing how things they cannot see function. In this activity you found evidence of a gas. This gas is called ethylene and is responsible for the ripening of fruits.

As plants age, they release ethylene gas (C_2H_4), which acts as a plant hormone to begin the ripening process. Unripened fruit can be made to ripen faster by bathing it in ethene (ethylene) gas. Absorbing the gas from fruit storage areas can stop the ripening process. This activity demonstrated the presence of the ethylene gas, which is flammable, in the skin of the fruit.

Ethylene is one of many materials classified as organic. To a chemist the term organic means "based on carbon molecules." Everything that is not organic is termed inorganic. In the very early 19th century, compounds were classified into two categories: **organic**, which were those compounds that came from living (or once living) organisms; and **inorganic**, which were obtained from mineral sources. A theory, called "vitalism," proposed that a "vital force" was required to produce organic compounds. This

Chem Words

organic compound: a molecular compound of carbon.

inorganic compound: a compound not based on molecular compounds of carbon.

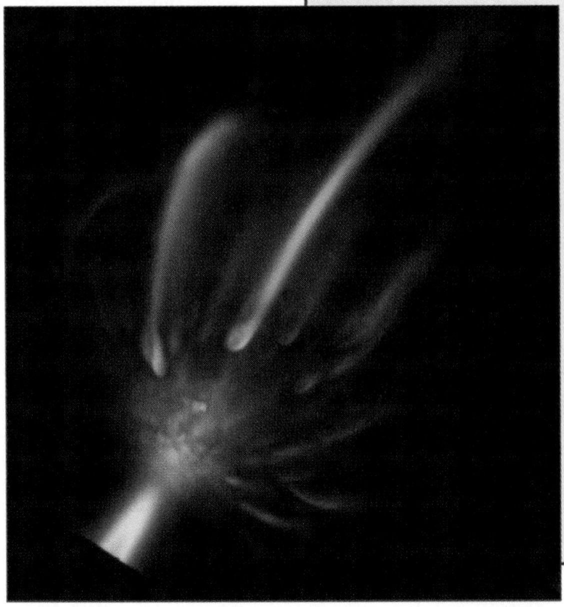

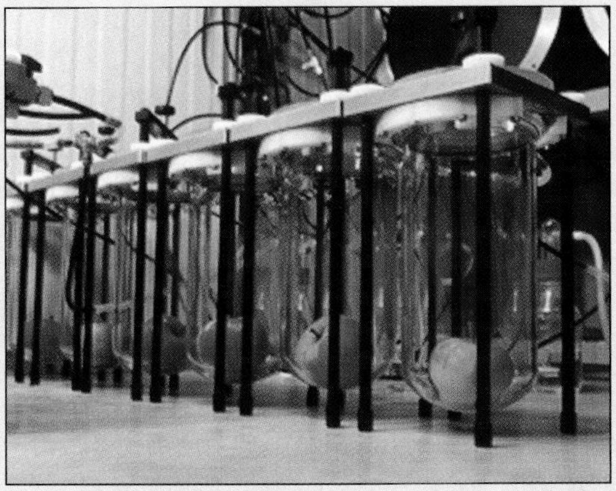

theory was disproved when an organic compound was synthesized in the laboratory. Today, organic chemistry refers to the study of carbon compounds. This is the largest area of study in chemistry. In the natural world alone, plants and animals synthesize millions of carbon compounds. Many manufactured chemicals are facsimiles of these natural products. Chemists have also invented processes that synthesize similar, new chemicals for use in society and technology. Examples of synthesized chemicals include gasoline, artificial sweeteners and flavors, and a variety of medicines.

The popular use of the word "organic" implies totally natural or not human-made. Organic farms do not use synthetic pesticides or fertilizers. Chemists do not use the word in this way, and would consider a molecule organic if it came from either a test tube or a tomato plant. They would also argue that all apples are organic, no matter how they are cultivated.

Ethylene belongs to a class of organic compounds called **hydrocarbons**. A hydrocarbon is a compound composed only of carbon and hydrogen. Most fuels, such as gasoline, kerosene, candle wax, propane, and natural gas are hydrocarbons too. The burning of a hydrocarbon in the presence of oxygen is an example of **combustion**. In combustion, a substance is combined with oxygen, accompanied by the generation of heat, carbon dioxide, and water.

Chem Words

hydrocarbon: a molecular compound containing only hydrogen and carbon.

combustion: the rapid reaction of a material with oxygen accompanied by rapid evolution of flame and heat.

Chem Words

Law of Conservation of Mass: the law that states that the total mass of the products of a chemical reaction is the same as the total mass of the reactants entering into the reaction.

Consider the complete combustion of propane gas:

$$C_3H_8 \quad + \quad O_2 \quad \rightarrow \quad CO_2 \quad + \quad H_2O$$

reactants (total of 3 C atoms, 8 H atoms, 2 O atoms) *products* (total of 1 C atom, 2 H atoms, and 3 O atoms)

Careful examination of the chemical equation reveals that there are different numbers of atoms on both sides of the equation. On the reactant side, there are 3 carbon atoms, 8 hydrogen atoms, and 2 oxygen atoms. On the product side of the equation, there is only 1 carbon atom, 2 hydrogen atoms, and 3 oxygen atoms. This is in violation of the **Law of Conservation of Mass** that states that the total mass of the products of a chemical reaction is the same as the total mass of the reactants entering into the reaction. The types of elements must also be identical. Since there are different numbers of atoms before and after the reaction, the total mass of the atoms involved is not equal. To fix this, you need to balance the equation.

Atoms are rearranged during a chemical reaction. This is the nature of a chemical change. It is *not* required that both sides of an equation contain the same number of molecules. It *is* required that they have the same number and type of atoms though.

You can balance this equation by adding appropriate coefficients in front of the molecular formulas of the reactants and products. *It is important that you change only coefficients, not the molecular formulas.* If you were to change the molecular formulas, you would no longer be working with the same chemical reaction. If you place a 3 in front of the CO_2 product, you will now have three carbon atoms on both sides of the equation. Placing a 4 in front of the H_2O product will bring the total number of H atoms on both sides to 8. However, this now makes a total number of 10 oxygen atoms on the right side of the equation. If you place a 5 in front of the O_2 reactant, this will make the total number of O atoms on both sides equal.

You now have a balanced equation that is represented as:

$$C_3H_8(g) \quad + \quad 5O_2(g) \quad \rightarrow \quad 3CO_2(g) \quad + \quad 4H_2O(g)$$

Reactants	Products
3 carbon atoms	3 carbon atoms
8 hydrogen atoms	8 hydrogen atoms
10 oxygen atoms	10 oxygen atoms

This suggests that one molecule of propane reacts with 5 molecules of oxygen to yield 3 molecules of carbon dioxide and 4 molecules of water.

Checking Up

1. What does a chemist mean by an organic compound?
2. How did the meaning of "organic" change during the 19th century?
3. What is a hydrocarbon?

What Do You Think Now?

At the beginning of the activity you were asked:

- **Does organic mean one thing to shoppers and another to chemists? Explain your answer.**

ORGANIC
Spinach
Organic Baby Spinach
Organic
Broccoli

Organic compounds are molecular compounds of carbon that could come from living or once-living things. However, they also can be made from inorganic compounds. Why do you think that grocery stores use the term "organic" for a certain group of products, even though all plants are chemically organic?

Chem Essential Questions

What does it mean?

Chemistry explains a macroscopic phenomenon (what you observe) with a description of what happens at the nanoscopic level (atoms and molecules) using symbolic structures as a way to communicate. Complete the chart below in your *Active Chemistry* log.

MACRO	NANO	SYMBOLIC
Describe what you saw when you squeezed the fruit peels near the flame.	*In words, describe the combustion reaction of ethylene.*	*Write a chemical reaction (or draw molecules) to show the combustion of ethylene.*

How do you know?

Ethylene is flammable and changes into CO_2 and H_2O, which are not flammable. After all of the ethylene has burned, there will only be CO_2 and H_2O remaining. What would happen if you attempted to light these on fire?

Why do you believe?

All combustion reactions require oxygen. Think of an example from your experience where a fire was extinguished because oxygen was removed.

Why should you care?

You will be writing a movie scene for your challenge in this unit. Think of how you could use "orange-peel fireworks" in your movie scene.

Reflecting on the Activity and the Challenge

When you held the orange peel near the flame and squeezed it, you forced a natural material made by the orange to be released. The material that comes from the skin of the orange peel is a hydrocarbon fuel. It is similar to the fuel used in barbecues and portable lighters. This material burns very quickly and is quite like the fuels used in movies to make huge explosions and fires. Of course, explosions and fires can be quite dangerous. Often, movie directors will film an explosion on a small scale, by using models, and then make it appear huge on the screen. Think of some ways you could use this very small explosion to represent a larger effect on the screen.

Chem to Go

1. Write two or three examples of the use of the word organic to mean natural.
2. Classify each of the following materials as inorganic or organic:
   a) salt (NaCl)
   b) gasoline (C_8H_{18})
   c) sugar ($C_{12}H_{22}O_{11}$)
   d) sand (SiO_2)
   e) vinegar (CH_3COOH)
   f) oxygen (O_2)
3. Draw an example of a simple hydrocarbon that contains five carbon atoms, all with single bonds.
4. a) Draw an example of a hydrocarbon compound containing seven carbons that contain at least two carbon—carbon double bonds.
   b) Is there more than one answer possible in (a)? Explain your answer.
5. Acetylene (C_2H_2) is also a hydrocarbon. The carbons in this case share three bonds between them. Again, remember that a carbon atom can only have a total of four bonds. Draw the structure for acetylene (also called ethyne).
6. In addition to chains, carbon atoms can bond together to form rings and other shapes. Draw a hydrocarbon that is made up of six carbon atoms, all with single bonds, that forms a ring.
7. Some products or processes claim to be "chemical free" or say "no chemicals added." Based on your understanding of chemistry, what are the arguments for and against such statements?
8. Draw the structural formula for isoprene (the building block of rubber). It should satisfy the molecular formula for isoprene of C_5H_8.

Inquiring Further

Organic produce and federal regulations

The federal government has proposed standards for food products bearing the label "organic." The National Organic Standards Board of the United States Department of Agriculture has issued the following definition of an organic food:

"Organic is a labeling term that denotes products produced under the authority of the Organic Foods Production Act. The principal guidelines for organic production are to use materials and practices that enhance the ecological balance of natural systems and that integrate the parts of the farming system into an ecological whole."

- How does this definition of the term "organic" compare with the chemical definition?
- Investigate the other proposed USDA standards and evaluate them relative to the chemical definition of organic.

Nutrition Facts

Serv Size 1 cup shredded (70g)
Servings Per Container about 3

Calories 35
Calories from Fat 0

* Percent Daily Values (DV) are based on a 2,000 calorie diet.

Amount Per Serving	%DV	Amount Per Serving	%DV*
Total Fat 0 g	**0%**	**Total Carb** 8g	**0%**
Sat Fat 0g	**0%**	Dietary Fiber 4g	**16%**
Trans Fat 0g		Sugar 0g	
Cholesterol 0mg	**0%**	**Protein** 2g	
Sodium 130mg	5%		
Vitamin A 60%	•	Vitamin C 20%	
Calcium 4%	•	Iron 15%	

INGREDIENTS: ORGANIC BABY SPINACH.
DISTRIBUTED BY IAT FOODS U.S.A., LLC
ARMONK, NY 10504
Certified Organic by QAI.

© 2005 MR Brands, Inc.
Produce of USA or Mexico.
Processed in the USA.

Quality guaranteed or your money back.

Chem at Work

Mark Pollack

President, Flix FX, Hollywood, CA

"Everyone talks about 'Movie Magic,'" says Marc Pollack, president of the prestigious Hollywood special effects company Flix FX. "So I guess that makes me a magician." But Pollack is clearly more comedian than magician. The 'magic' he creates for movies like *Black Hawk Down*, *Men In Black*, and *Cast Away*, in addition to scores of television commercials, museum installments, and Las Vegas casinos, is the product not of mysterious hocus-pocus but rather fundamental principles of science.

"One of the most important aspects of our work," he continues, "is to push the limits of how chemicals are designed to be used." Among other things, Pollack and his crew at Flix FX use vacuum-forming thermo-plastics to make tin-based silicon molds for everything from prehistoric creatures to futuristic robots. Through a combination of trial and error experimentation and traditional research science, they've perfected the process. "Silicon is what we call an R.T.V.," Pollack explains. "That stands for room temperature vulcanization. So depending on the type and amount of catalyst we use, the mold will cure at different rates and with slightly differing properties." By manipulating the ratio of silicon to catalysts they can make strong, realistic molds in an efficient way. "Increasing the amount of catalyst will speed up the curing process but too much catalyst will shorten the life of the mold," he says. "Every job is different so determining that balance is one of our many challenges."

Pollack is a master in the art of using chemicals like silicon, polypropylene, urethane and urethane elastimers, and is not a chemist by trade. He actually graduated from film school at SUNY Purchase in the hopes of becoming "the next Steven Spielberg." Then, through a twist of fate, he became a special effects nut and eventually founded Flix FX in 1990. "Now," Pollack says, "Spielberg may one day come to me."

Rick Gonzales

Special Effects Designer, Orlando, FL

Rick Gonzales is a special effects designer who works on a lot of live stage shows. He works with polyurethanes, gelatins, silicone, and latex to make real-looking props and prosthetics. "Good special effects," he says, "are the ones where you can't tell what is fake and what is real."

Linda Stevenson

Drama Coordinator, Atlanta, GA

Linda Stevenson teaches her drama students at her north Atlanta performing arts school to be a "triple threat." She wants all 120 students to be able to sing, dance, and act at their best level. Stage effects, like smoke and fog made with dry ice, are added for the benefit of the audience.

Movie Special Effects Assessment

Your *Chapter Challenge* is to create a movie special effect and a story line for that special effect. You will need to demonstrate the special effects you created. Your special effects will be evaluated on their quality, entertainment, and the knowledge of chemistry you exhibited in putting them together. You will need to write a script for a simple scene in a movie, choose some special effects to include as part of your scene, and write a procedure on how your special effect is done. In addition, you will demonstrate the special effect to the "producer" and write an explanation of how the special effect works, including the chemistry behind the demonstration. Using more than one chemical principle will strengthen your presentation.

Chemistry Content

To begin, you should review all of the activities that you have completed. You can skim through the text and your *Active Chemistry* log to help remind you of the chemistry concepts in each activity.

Activity 1: You learned how to use electrolysis to create hydrogen and oxygen from water. You also learned how to test for oxygen and water. You are also now able to distinguish an element from a compound and write chemical symbols and equations to describe reactions.

Activity 2: You learned about states of matter by studying the heating curve of water as it goes from ice to water to vapor. You also observed the sublimation of dry ice as it goes from a solid to a gas. You also learned how to create an animation to show the movement of molecules at different temperatures.

Activity 3: You were able to observe the appearance of solutions, suspensions and colloids. You also used a laser and were able to observe the Tyndall Effect.

Activity 4: You learned about more properties of matter and changed these properties by adding materials to other materials.

Activity 5: You investigated different liquids and solids and learned how density is a characteristic property of materials. You then used density and its relation to floating and sinking to suspend an object in a liquid.

Activity 6: You explored specific properties of metals and nonmetals including conductivity, reactivity and ductility.

Activity 7: You created a polymer called "slime" and investigated its properties.

Activity 8: You learned how to identify elements with flame tests.

Activity 9: You experimented with organic substances. You also studied the complete combustion of propane gas and had some practice in balancing equations.

You may want to make a chart that shows the activity number, some chemistry concepts in the activity, and some ideas as to how you can use these concepts as part of your movie special effect. Your chart may include whether the concept will be part of the demonstration and how it may be a part of the movie plot. You should pay particular attention to the *Reflecting on the Activity and the Challenge, Chem Essential Questions,* and *Preparing for the Chapter Challenge* sections. You should also compare your list with that given in the *Chem You Learned* summary.

Activity #	Chemistry concepts	How to use concepts

You may decide to do the first activity as a group to ensure that everybody understands how to proceed. After completing the first activity, each team member can be assigned two or three activities. You can then review all of the activities as a group with the activity expert reviewing each summary.

Criteria

You and your team should review the criteria by which you will be graded. Before beginning the chapter, your teacher led a class discussion to get a sense of what criteria should be used to judge the quality of work for this movie special effect. It is time to revisit that discussion since you now have considerable understanding of the chemistry concepts that you can include in your presentation. Think about and discuss what would make a great script and movie special effect. Remember you must also have documentation including the procedure and the chemistry explanation for your chemical principles.

How will your special effect be graded? What qualities should an impressive special effect have? How will your demonstration and supporting documentation be graded? Discuss these issues in small groups and with your class. You may decide that safety and interest are as important as the script. How many chemical principles are required for an A?

Preparing for the Chapter Challenge

- Choose Your Movie Special Effect

Your team's next step would then be to decide on what kind of movie and movie special effect you will create. Will it be a "disaster movie," a thriller, or a comedy? Will you use a favorite movie or a book you've read or a recent newspaper article as the basis for your plot? Will you first decide on the movie script and then introduce the special effects or will you first decide on the special effects and then build a script about that chemistry phenomenon?

• Practice Your Movie Special Effect

You need to practice your presentation to the class. You will have to show the special effect and describe or act out the plot of the scene. You will also have to show an awareness of safety issues. You may also have to summarize the chemical principles as part of your presentation as well as in your documentation.

• Chemistry content is necessary, but not sufficient.

Movies are about entertainment. Will your movie make your fellow students react in the way you anticipate? Can you create a tension for a serious movie plot or laughs for a comedy spoof? Will your dialog be well acted? Setting the stage for the scene will help with people's enjoyment of your movie special effect. Chemistry content is required, but creativity is desired.

• Manage Your Time

You have a sense of how you want to proceed and what you want the final product to be. You now have to allocate the work. How much time do you have to complete the project? When is the presentation? How will you get everything done in this time frame? Who will be working on the special effect and who will be working on the chemistry principle and safety documentation? How will you ensure that each member's work meets the standard of excellence so that everybody on the team gets an A? Create a time chart for the challenge. Divide the responsibilities. How much time will each take? Some work can be done individually as homework. Leave time to review each other's work.

Planning a project well does not ensure success, but poor planning almost always leads to disappointment.

Engineering/Technology Design

Reflect on the engineering/technology design process. Recall the successes and disappointments from the *mini-challenge*. How can you use the feedback that you received to improve your show? At this point, you are starting the design cycle again.

Enjoy your movie special effect!

Chem You Learned

- **Electrolysis** of water is a technique that uses electricity to decompose water into 2 parts of hydrogen gas and 1 part of oxygen gas.
- The **Law of Conservation of Mass** states that the number and type of atoms on the reactant side must be the same as the atoms on the product side of a reaction.
- The subscripts in the **chemical formula** for a substance, such as Al_2O_3, give the number of atoms of each element in that substance.
- The three **states of matter** are solid, liquid, and gas.
- During any **phase change** from solid to liquid, and from liquid to gas, **heat energy** is required but the temperature does not change.
- An **energy curve** of Temperature vs. Heat can be plotted using time in the *x*-axis if a constant source of heat is used.
- As heat energy is added to a substance, the average **kinetic energy** of its particles increases. Kinetic energy (KE) = $1/2\ mv^2$.
- During a **phase change**, energy is absorbed to overcome the **intermolecular attractive forces** which hold the substance in the solid or liquid phase.
- When the vapor pressure of a liquid equals the atmospheric pressure, a liquid will boil. At STP this temperature is called the **normal boiling point** of a liquid.
- Fog is an example of a **colloidal dispersion** or **colloid.** The observation that a beam of light passing through a colloid is visible is called the **Tyndall Effect**.
- **Density** is a physical property of all substances which is determine by mass and volume. The mathematical expression is: $D = m/V$.
- **Precision** of measurements is a term used to show the reproducibility of a measurement.
- **Accuracy** is the term used to show how close the measurements are to the true value.
- **Scientific notation** uses powers of ten to simplify working with very large and very small numbers.
- All of the elements of the periodic table fall into one of three groups: **metals, nonmetals,** and **metalloids.**
- **Alloys** are solutions of one (or more) metal in another. The alloy, such as brass, has superior properties to any of the components.
- **Polymers** are very large molecules which are built from repeating units of **monomers.** Starch and plastics are common **polymers** used on a daily basis.
- **Metal cations** can be identified by the color that they emit when they are excited in a flame.
- Carbon has unique bonding capabilities which leads to the enormous field of **organic chemistry**, the study of the molecular compounds of carbon.
- The simplest family of compounds in organic chemistry, **hydrocarbons**, are used for **combustion**.

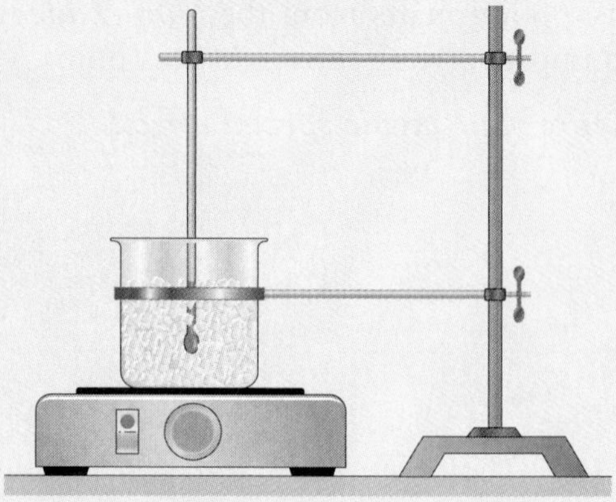

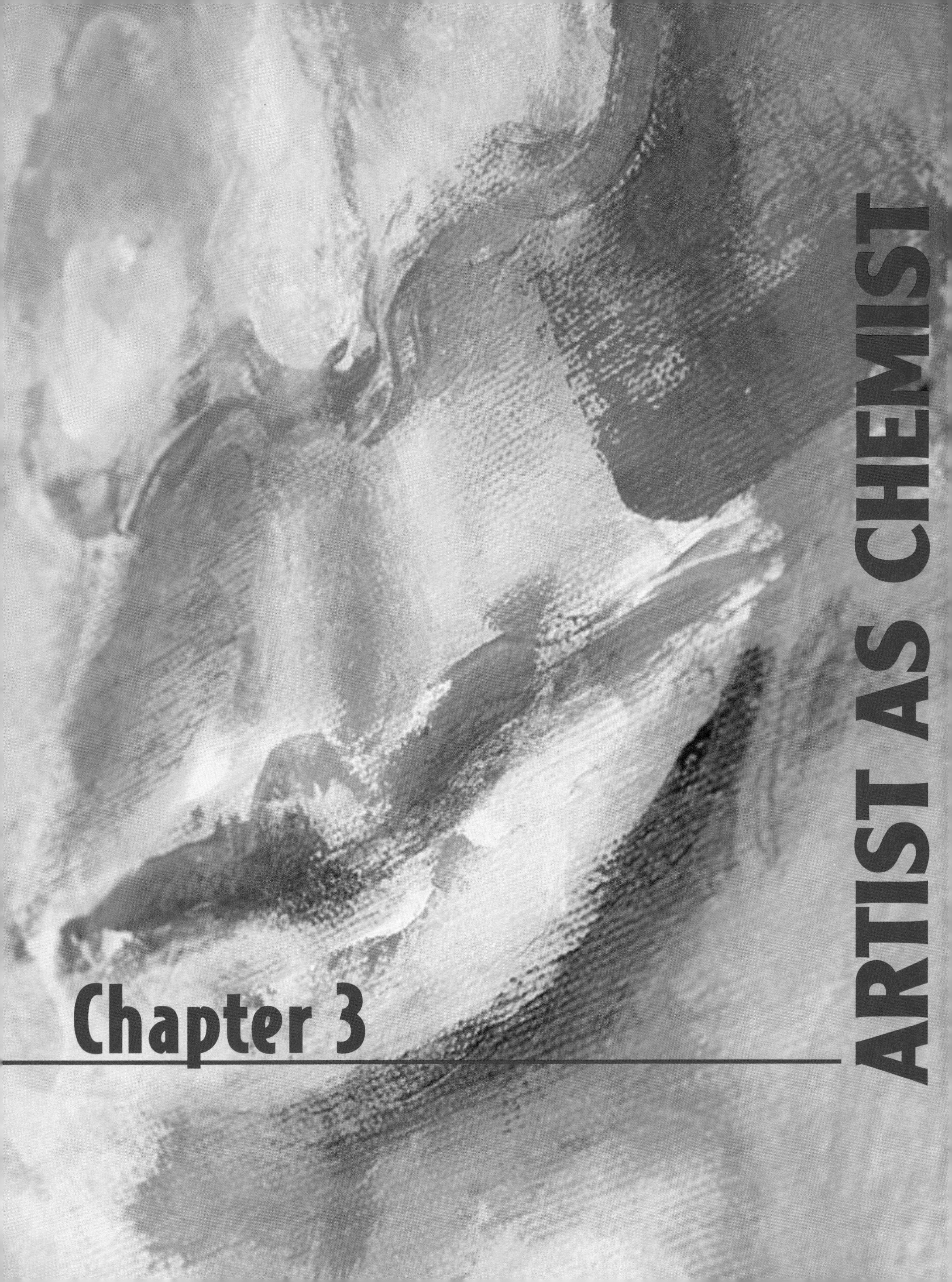

Chapter 3

ARTIST AS CHEMIST

3

Artist as Chemist

Scenario

Have you ever tried to look for a definition of art? You may find essays or even books defining art. What you think is art may not be art to someone else. Art, what it is, and what it means, has changed over time. Why?

One reason is that materials and technology have changed over the years. What materials did the artists of cave paintings use? The cave painter's first try at a picture of an animal on the cave wall may have disappeared after a few hours. The painting then was of no value to anyone. The painter then found a pigment that did not disappear quickly but lasted for months or years. Investigating different pigments was an experiment in chemistry. Without knowing it, the cave painter was a chemist.

Using available materials, trial and error, and experimentation, a wide range of artwork has been produced. These works range from cave paintings and ancient pottery to monumental sculptures, elaborate tapestries, Renaissance masterpieces, and Modern Art. You can find many of these on display in museums all over the world.

What can you learn from examining artists' work? How were pigments developed? How and why did materials and techniques used in sculpture change? How does weathering cause damage to statues? What gives different glass artworks their brilliant colors? How can you change the properties of different metals so they can be built into whimsical mobiles? Can you obtain safe dyes from natural sources?

And, why have great artworks endured time? Chemistry concepts can help explain the answers to these questions and many more related to art.

Your Challenge

Art is the result of the human need for self-expression. It tells stories of social injustice, different eras, nationalities, and expresses individuals' feelings ranging from painful sorrow to joyous ecstasy. Your challenge is to create a work of art that represents you and your times using appropriate artistic techniques. But before you get anxious, rest assured that you don't need to be "artistically talented" to do well on this challenge. You and your classmates will determine how the work will be graded. Hard work and creativity will count more than natural ability. Also, there are many ways to express yourself in art. You will be introduced to topics and techniques that you might never have dreamed you had a talent for. So relax and enjoy your voyage into the world of art. You might become the next Michelangelo!

In addition to the artwork itself, you will also need to create an informative museum display that includes:

- A demonstration of the techniques involved.
- Your original work.
- A museum placard or pamphlet explaining the chemistry involved.

ChemCorner

Chemistry in *Artist as Chemist*

- Strength of acids
- pH scales
- Acid definitions
- Acid-base indicators
- Metal Activity Series
- Valence electrons
- Electroplating
- Alloys
- Physical properties of metals
- Hydrated compounds
- Quantitative analysis of hydrates
- Formula weight
- Double-replacement reactions
- Precipitates
- Solubility rules
- Chemical dyes
- Ceramics
- Oxidized states of metals

TEA
COFFE

Criteria

How will your artwork and museum display be graded? What are the qualities of a work of art? How will you arrange your museum display and convey the chemistry involved to the public? How will the art and display be graded? Discuss these issues in small groups and with your class. You may decide that some or all of the following qualities should be graded:

Demonstration of techniques

- Thoroughness
- Accuracy
- Applicability

Original work

- Employs techniques described
- Creativity
- Representation of yourself, your family, your heritage, and/or your times
- Expressiveness

Museum placard (or pamphlet)

- Accuracy
- Clarity of information
- Certain number of chemical principles addressed
- Neatness, correctness
- Documentation
- Creativity

Effectiveness of display

- Layout
- Visual appeal
- Engaging, interesting
- Realistic display
- Creativity
- Insight into art, chemistry, and needs of audience

Once you have determined the list of qualities for evaluating the artwork and museum display, you and your class should also decide how many points should be given for each criterion. Should the creativity of the artwork be awarded more points than the clarity of the placard? How many different chemical principles should be addressed in the museum display? For each criterion you should decide how excellence is defined and how it compares with a satisfactory effort. Determining grading criteria in advance will help you focus your time and effort on the various aspects of the challenge.

Will each student produce her/his own artwork, or will students work together in groups? Discuss the pros and cons of these possibilities. Working in a group, would it be more difficult or easier to produce something that is considered creative and expressive?

Activity 1 What Makes Something Art?

What Do You See?
ART ROCKS

GOALS

In this activity you will:

- Create a class definition of art.
- List some materials used to make art.
- Describe how chemistry is related to art.

What Do You Think?

"The art of a people is a true mirror of their minds."

Nehru

"Every child is an artist. The problem is how to remain an artist once he grows up."

Picasso

"Art is either plagiarism or revolution."

Gauguin

"We must never forget that art is not a form of propaganda; it is a form of truth."

John F. Kennedy

- **What makes something art?**

The *What Do You Think?* question is meant to get you thinking about what you already know or think you know. Don't worry about being right or wrong. Discussing what you think you know is an important step in learning.

Record your ideas about this question in your *Active Chemistry* log. Be prepared to discuss your responses with your group and the class.

Investigate

1. Look at the photographs of artwork on these pages. Then answer the following questions on your own in your *Active Chemistry* log.

   a) List at least 10 different forms or types of art.

   b) Write down some of the materials used to make art.

   c) For each material you listed in (b), consider what properties of the material make it useful for creating artwork.

2. Share your ideas with your small group.

   a) Make a list of the different art forms your group suggested.

   b) Make a group list of the different materials used in art.

   c) Write down why your group thinks each material is useful.

   d) Write down a group definition of art.

3. Over the next few weeks, become aware of the art around you. Look for examples of art in parks, as part of buildings, in your neighborhood, in magazines or posters, and in your school. As you examine artwork, look at it from two perspectives—that of an artist and that of a materials chemist.

   a) Keep a record of what you observe.

Chem to Go

1. *Preparing for the Chapter Challenge*

   The pictures on these pages contain a wide variety of types of art. They show some of the earliest known forms of art along with some of today's most innovative artworks.

   a) Discuss how you could use these to express something about yourself and/or your times.

   b) Describe what information you might need to find out about these artworks in order to create your museum display.

Inquiring Further

1. Impact of technology on art

Research the major art movements. List characteristics of each movement and some of its most notable artists and their works. Explain how you could distinguish between art of one movement and that of another. Discuss any relationships between art movements and advancements in technology. Reflect on how you can incorporate this knowledge into your museum display.

2. Timeline of art movements

Create a timeline depicting the major art movements throughout human history. Illustrate your timeline with examples from that movement. Identify areas where chemistry might be involved in creating different types of art and add that information to your timeline.

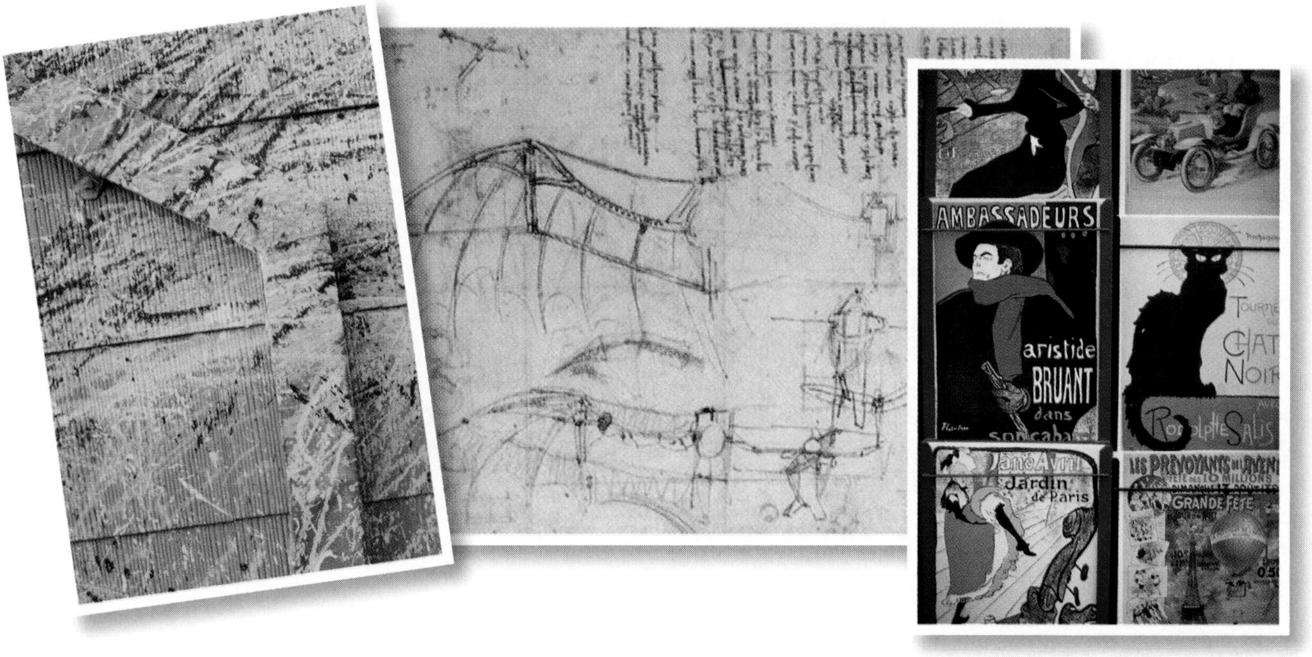
AMBASSADEURS
aristide
BRUANT
dans
Jardin
de Paris
GRANDE FETE

Activity 2 Choice of Media for Durability

CHEM POETRY

She looked in the mirror and
stared at her face,
It just wasn't easy being
a base.
All that she wanted was
a shoulder to cry on,
And a way to remove her
hydroxide ion.

Because of its stigma, her
life was a mess,
She thought that she'd
never feel another's
caress.
The guys she'd ask out
would always say no,
"I ain't goin' out with no
bottle of Drano!"

All of her neighbors
managed to hate her,
Except for her one friend, an
indicator.
Her friend would say,
"It's tough knowing you.
Wherever we go, you keep
me so blue."

–Mala Radhakrishnan

What Do You See?

What Do You Think?

Outdoor statues can be damaged from exposure to the atmosphere.

- **What is in the air that can cause this damage?**
- **What factors must be considered when you want to create art that endures time?**

Record your ideas about these questions in your *Active Chemistry* log. Be prepared to discuss your responses with your group and the class.

GOALS

In this activity you will:

- Learn about acids and the pH scale.
- Determine the effect of sulfur dioxide and carbon dioxide on the pH of water.
- Design and carry out an investigation to determine what media will hold up under acidic conditions.
- Read about different theories of acids.

Investigate

There are different types of acids. In this activity you will investigate the relative strengths of acids.

Part A: Solutions and pH

1. Universal indicator is used to determine a property of solutions called pH. This is a measurement used to represent how acidic a solution is. Your teacher will show you solutions with different pH values.

   a) Record in your *Active Chemistry* log the color of each solution and the corresponding pH.

   b) Which colors indicate an acidic pH (below 7)? Which colors show a basic pH (above 7)?

Part B: Formation of Sulfur Dioxide (SO_2)

1. In the fume hood, place about 2 g of sodium sulfite (Na_2SO_3) in the bottom corner of a 500 mL (about 1 pint) heavy-duty zipper bag. If a fume hood is not available for each group to use, you will need to skip this part of the activity.
2. Fill a plastic transfer pipette with 6 *M* sulfuric acid.
3. Place the transfer pipette with the sulfuric acid in the plastic bag with the Na_2SO_3. Smooth out the bag so it contains a minimum amount of air and then seal the bag. (Do not press the acid out of the pipette.)

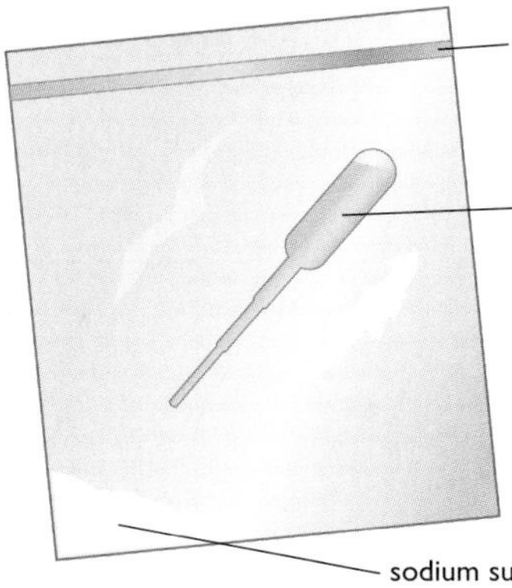
sealed bag
plastic pipette
sodium sulfite

4. Hold the sealed plastic bag and slowly squeeze the transfer pipette so that the acid drops onto the Na_2SO_3. **Keep the bag sealed and in the fume hood.**
   a) Record your observations in your *Active Chemistry* log.

Part C: The Properties of Sulfur Dioxide (SO_2)

1. Use a fresh plastic pipette and work in the fume hood to remove a sample of the SO_2 gas.

   To get a pipette filled with the gas, squeeze the bulb of the pipette to expel the air inside.

   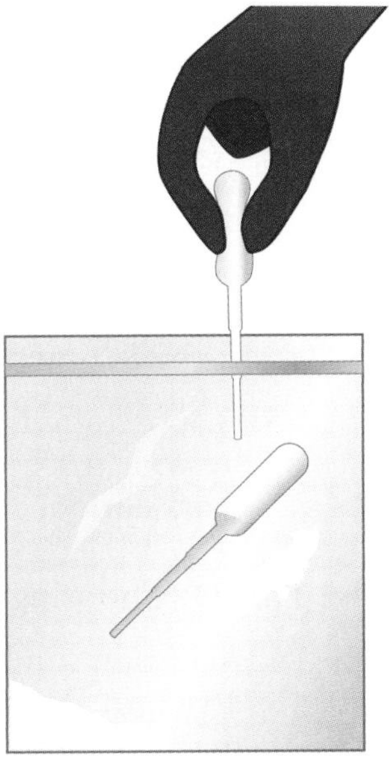

   Then, keep squeezing the bulb as you carefully push the tip of the pipette into a small opening in the seal of the bag. You may be able to use the tip of the pipette to force a small opening in the seal.

   Once the tip of the pipette is inside the bag, release the bulb so that the gas enters the pipette.

   Remove the pipette and reseal the bag. Be careful that you do not place the pipette tip against the solid or liquid in the bag.
2. Place the tip of the pipette into a well of a well plate containing 10 drops of distilled water and two drops of universal indicator. Gently squeeze the pipette. This will slowly bubble the gas through the solution. Determine the change in pH of the gaseous solution by observing the color of the solution.
   a) Record your observations in your *Active Chemistry* log. If no significant change is immediate, repeat this step.
3. For comparison, repeat *Step 2* with a clean air-filled pipette.
   a) Record the pH of the resulting gaseous solution in your *Active Chemistry* log.
4. Using a straw, exhale a breath of air into a flask of water containing universal indicator.

Safety goggles and apron must be worn *at all times* in a chemistry lab.

Sulfuric acid is caustic and should be handled with care.

Be prepared to wash skin that contacts the acid with soap and plenty of water.

SO_2 gas is toxic and should be handled only in the fume hood.

Your teacher may supply you with the SO_2 gas dissolved in water to test in *Part C.* Follow instructions outlined by your teacher.

Be careful not to swallow any fluid from the flask. Alert your teacher to any problems.

Wash your hands and arms thoroughly after each activity.

Be sure to follow all your safety precautions.

Clean up spills immediately. Alert your teacher to spills, especially on your skin.

The exhaled air has a higher concentration of carbon dioxide (CO_2) than the inhaled air.

a) Was there a change in the pH? Record your observations in your *Active Chemistry* log.

b) Compare the change in pH with the SO_2 and the CO_2.

5. Dispose of all materials as directed by your teacher. Clean up your workstation.

Part D: Choosing Durable Materials

1. Acid rain can harm outdoor artwork. Design a procedure that will allow you to determine if marble, limestone, sandstone, granite, gypsum, copper, or zinc will be more durable as an outdoor work of art by testing their reactivity with acid. Acid and pieces of these materials will be supplied.

   a) Record your experiment procedure as well as any safety concerns in your *Active Chemistry* log. You may need to set aside the experiment and make your observations over several days.

2. Have your procedure approved by your teacher.
3. Carry out your experiment.

   a) Record all your observations.

4. Present your findings to the class.

   a) How do your findings compare with those of other teams?

Chem Talk

ACIDS AND BASES

Properties of Acids and Bases

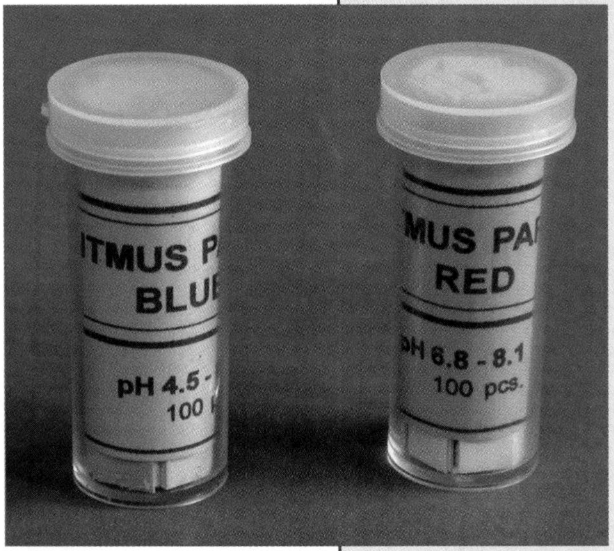
RED
pH 6.8 - 8.1
100 pcs.

Blue and red litmus paper.

In this activity you observed different acid and base solutions. You were able to tell the difference between the solutions because you used an indicator. An **acid-base indicator** is a substance that changes color when exposed to either an acid or a base. You may have used red and blue litmus paper before. A base turns red litmus paper blue, and an acid turns blue litmus paper red. In the activity you used a **universal indicator**. A universal indicator is a mixture of acid-base indicators used to indicate how acidic or basic a solution is.

You are probably familiar with acids like battery acid (sulfuric acid) or vinegar (acetic acid). Acids tend to have a sour taste, neutralize bases, react with

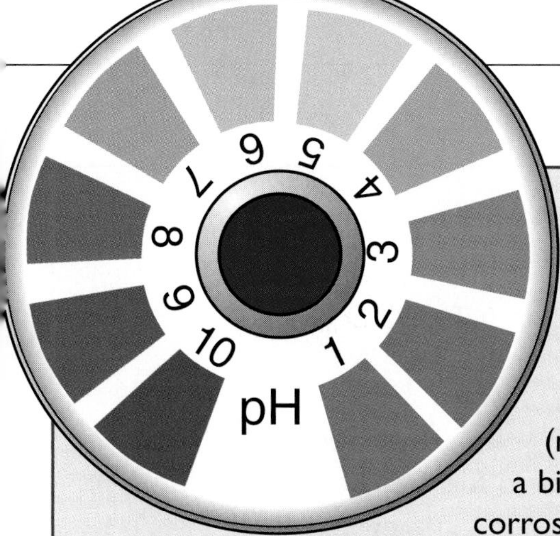
pH
1
2
3
4
5
6
7
8
9
10

most metals, and react with certain indicators to produce a color change.

Bases that you may be familiar with include household ammonia (ammonium hydroxide) and antacids (magnesium hydroxide). Bases have a bitter taste and a slippery feel, are corrosive, neutralize acids, and cause certain indicators to produce a color change.

Universal-indicator paper.

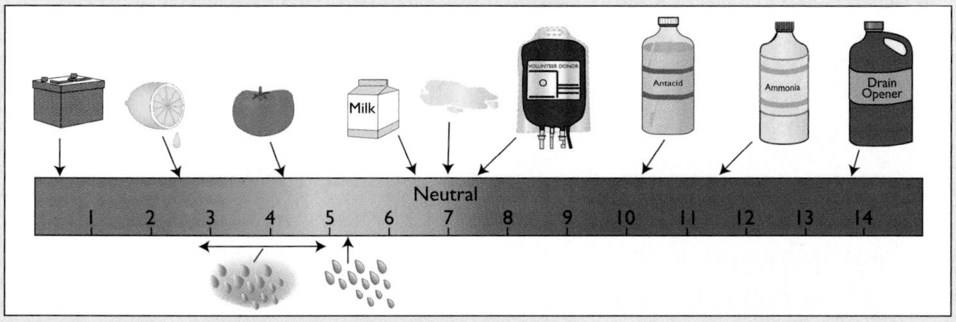
Milk
Antacid
Ammonia
Drain Opener
Neutral
1 2 3 4 5 6 7 8 9 10 11 12 13 14

The Strength of Acids and Bases

The **pH** of a solution is a measure of the concentration of **hydrogen ions (H^+)** in that solution. (Recall that an ion is an atom that has gained or lost an electron. A hydrogen ion is a hydrogen atom that has lost its only electron.) A *high* concentration of H^+ ions (an acidic solution) is indicated by a *low* pH. If the pH of a solution is less than 7, the solution is acidic. If the pH of a solution is greater than 7, the solution is basic. If a solution has a pH of 7 it is neutral. It is neither acidic nor basic.

Hydrochloric acid (HCl) and sulfuric acid (H_2SO_4) produce many hydrogen ions (H^+) in aqueous (water) solution. They are considered to be strong acids, with low pH. Weak acids, like acetic acid (CH_3COOH) and carbonic acid (H_2CO_3), produce few H^+ ions in aqueous solutions. Their pH is higher.

Some common acids and their behavior in aqueous solutions are described below. Notice in all cases H^+ ions are produced in the aqueous solutions:

$HCl(aq)$	$\rightarrow$	$H^+(aq)$	+	$Cl^-(aq)$
hydrochloric acid		*hydrogen ions*		*chloride ions*

Chem Words

acid-base indicator: a substance that changes color when exposed to either an acid or a base.

universal indicator: a mixture of various acid-base indicators that give color changes over a wide range of pH values.

pH: a measure of the concentration of hydrogen (H^+) ions in a solution. Acidic solutions have a pH less than 7. Basic solutions have a pH greater than 7. A neutral solution has a pH of 7.

hydrogen ion (H^+): a hydrogen atom that has lost its electron, sometimes referred to as a proton. Acids release hydrogen ions (H^+).

Acetic acid is a weak acid because a very small number of H^+ ions are formed in aqueous solution.

$$\underset{\textit{acetic acid}}{CH_3COOH(aq)} \leftrightarrows \underset{\textit{hydrogen ions}}{H^+(aq)} + \underset{\textit{acetate ions}}{CH_3COO^-(aq)}$$

How did the carbon dioxide (CO_2) from your breath affect the pH of water? Carbon dioxide reacts with water to form carbonic acid (H_2CO_3):

$$\underset{\textit{carbon dioxide}}{CO_{2(g)}} + \underset{\textit{water}}{H_2O(l)} \rightarrow \underset{\textit{carbonic acid}}{H_2CO_3(aq)}$$

Carbonic acid is a weak acid that forms hydrogen ions and hydrogen carbonate ions (HCO_3^-) in aqueous solution:

$$\underset{\textit{carbonic acid}}{H_2CO_3(aq)} \leftrightarrows \underset{\textit{hydrogen ions}}{H^+(aq)} + \underset{\textit{hydrogen carbonate ions}}{HCO_3^-(aq)}$$

The change in pH you noted in *Part B* was due to the formation of carbonic acid and the resulting release of H^+ ions into the water. The CO_2 was present in your breath. The atmosphere naturally contains CO_2, therefore all rain is naturally slightly acidic.

There are other, stronger acids that form in the atmosphere. The sulfur dioxide gas you made was formed according to the following reaction: sulfuric acid reacts with sodium sulfite to produce sodium sulfate plus water and sulfur dioxide gas.

$$\underset{\textit{sulfuric acid}}{H_2SO_4(aq)} + \underset{\textit{sodium sulfite}}{Na_2SO_3(s)} \rightarrow \underset{\textit{sodium sulfate}}{Na_2SO_4(aq)} + H_2O(l) + \underset{\textit{sulfur dioxide}}{SO_2(g)}$$

Sulfur dioxide gas is formed from the combustion of coal in power plants that generate electricity for use around the nation.

Changing Definitions of Acids and Bases

In this activity and *Chem Talk* section, you have seen how compounds act as acids in solution. Arrhenius, a Swedish chemist, was interested in the formation of ions. He defined acids as compounds that release hydrogen ions (H^+) in a water solution. Svante August Arrhenius (1859–1927) won the Nobel Prize for chemistry in 1903 for his work on ionic dissociation. (Amazingly, he also predicted the "greenhouse effect" in 1896, although he didn't foresee its potentially disastrous results.) According to his definition, although HCl releases large quantities of H^+ in solution and acetic acid (CH_3COOH) releases smaller amounts, both are acids.

He also defined bases as compounds that release hydroxide ions (OH^-) in solution. Sodium hydroxide (NaOH) is an example of a compound that will release hydroxide ions in solution. You did not focus on bases in this activity, but hydroxide ions are always present in water solutions. Water is neutral, even though pure water contains acid and base in small quantities.

The following equation shows the dissociation of water:

$$H—O—H \leftrightarrows H^+ + OH^-$$

Note that the formula for water (H_2O) is written to show which atoms are bonded to each other. When the amounts of H^+ and OH^- are the same, the solution is neutral and the pH is seven.

It is important to note that H^+ is a proton. Hydrogen has one proton and one electron. If the electron has been removed, the H^+ ion is identical to a single proton. It just has a different name.

One water molecule in every 10 million dissociates and becomes an H^+ ion and an OH^- ion. This happens when one H in the H_2O (HOH) loses an electron and the OH in the H_2O (HOH) gains an electron. However, in a water solution, the H^+, an isolated proton, is never found. It attaches itself to a molecule of water. The H^+ attaches to the H_2O and becomes H_3O^+. You can write this as:

$$H—O—H + H_2O \leftrightarrows H_3O^+ + OH^-$$

or as:

$$H—O—H + H\text{-}O\text{-}H \leftrightarrows H_3O^+ + OH^-$$

This ion, H_3O^+, is called the hydronium ion.

The Arrhenius definition was very useful. However, there are many cases where it is not adequate. The definition is not useful when water is not present, or when compounds containing ionizable H^+ or OH^- are not present. For these situations, a slightly different definition of acids and bases is needed. That definition was proposed by two men in 1923. A Danish chemist, Johannes Nicolaus Brønsted, and an English chemist, Thomas Martin Lowry, working independently, proposed what is now called the Brønsted-Lowry theory of acids and bases.

Brønsted and Lowry defined an acid as a substance that can transfer a proton to another substance. For example, hydrogen chloride gas will donate a proton to ammonia gas (NH_3):

$$HCl + NH_3 \rightarrow NH_4^+ + Cl^-$$

This reaction occurs in the absence of water and H^+ is never formed. HCl is the proton donor and the acid in this reaction. According to the Brønsted-Lowry theory, a base is a proton acceptor. In this reaction, ammonia is accepting the proton from HCl and is therefore the base. Another example is the reaction of NH_3 with water:

$$HOH + NH_3 \leftrightarrows NH_4^+ + OH^-$$

Water (HOH or H_2O) is acting as a proton donor (acid) and the ammonia is acting as a proton acceptor (base).

The Brønsted-Lowry definition is more general than the Arrhenius definition because it includes the Arrhenius definition and extends it to reactions not covered by Arrhenius.

Unfortunately, there are still other acid-base reactions in chemistry that are not covered by either definition. These reactions are frequently found in organic chemistry and need not involve either H^+ or OH^-.
In 1923, the same year that Brønsted and Lowry published their theory about acids and bases, G. N. Lewis proposed a far more universal definition that includes most reactions. An American chemist, Gilbert Newton Lewis (1875–1946) believed that the simplest definition of acids and bases would focus on the electron pairs found in ions and compounds. In the course of most reactions, some molecules or ions donate electron pairs and others accept. His contribution to the definition of acids and bases was to label the electron-pair donor as a base. An acid, therefore, would be an electron-pair acceptor. Incidentally, Lewis made many contributions to chemistry, including the "Lewis-dot structures" that show bonding between atoms and help to explain how reactions proceed.

In the reaction of ammonia with hydrochloric acid, it is the ammonia molecule that donates the electron pair and is the base. The proton (H^+) from HCl accepts the electron pair and is the acid.

$$HCl + :NH_3 \rightarrow NH_4^+ + Cl^-$$

The reaction between water and ammonia shows that once again, the ammonia serves as the base and the proton of a water molecule serves as the acid.

$$HOH + :NH_3 \leftrightarrows NH_4^+ + OH^-$$

The Lewis definition of acids and bases is by far the most universal of these three since it includes most reactions.

$$CH_3Cl + :\ddot{\underset{..}{Br}}:^- \rightarrow CH_3Br + :\ddot{\underset{..}{Cl}}:^-$$

The three definitions are summarized in the table below.

Theory	Acid definition	Base definition
Arrhenius	releases H^+ in water solution	releases OH^- in water solution
Brønsted-Lowry	H^+ donor	H^+ acceptor
Lewis	electron-pair acceptor	electron-pair donor

Acid Deposition and Outdoor Art

The gas SO_2 is released into the atmosphere when coal and petroleum products are burned (coal is 1–3% sulfur). Another source of atmospheric SO_2 is volcanic eruptions. Mt. Kilauea in Hawaii has spewed an estimated 350,000 tons of SO_2 each year since 1986.

In the atmosphere, sulfur dioxide can react with water to produce sulfurous acid:

$$\underset{\text{sulfur dioxide}}{SO_2(g)} + H_2O(l) \rightarrow \underset{\text{sulfurous acid}}{H_2SO_3(aq)}$$

Sulfur trioxide is formed when coal is burned or can be formed from the reaction of SO_2 and oxygen in the air. This gas can react with water vapor to form sulfuric acid, a very strong acid.

$$\underset{\text{sulfur trioxide}}{SO_3(g)} + H_2O(l) \rightarrow \underset{\text{sulfuric acid}}{H_2SO_4(aq)}$$

Sulfuric acid and sulfurous acid will form hydronium ions in water.

$$\underset{\text{sulfurous acid}}{H_2SO_3(aq)} \rightarrow \underset{\text{hydrogen ion}}{H^+(aq)} + \underset{\text{hydrogen sulfite ion}}{HSO_3^-(aq)}$$

Both H_2SO_3 and H_2SO_4 can fall out of the sky in liquid form as rain, sleet, or snow. The technical term for this phenomenon is **acid deposition**. **Acid rain** is a form of acid deposition. When rain has a pH lower than 5.6, it is considered to be acidic. Acid deposition can damage buildings and statues and make lakes and streams unsuitable for life.

Chem Words

acid deposition: a deposition of acidic substances from the atmosphere onto the surface of the Earth.

acid rain: rain that has a pH less than 5.6.

Buildings and statues can be damaged by acid rain. The building and sculpting materials, limestone and marble, are made of calcium carbonate ($CaCO_3$). When exposed to acid rain, the following reaction can occur:

$$H_2SO_{4}(aq) + CaCO_{3}(s) \rightarrow CaSO_{4}(aq) + H_2O(l) + CO_{2}(g)$$

sulfuric acid — *calcium carbonate* — *calcium sulfate* — *water* — *carbon dioxide*

The $CaSO_4$ (calcium sulfate) is soluble in water and is removed from the marble, causing it to deteriorate.

Sandstone and granite are mainly made of oxides of silicon. These materials do not react readily with acid.

$$SiO_{2}(s) + H_2SO_{4}(aq) \rightarrow \text{no reaction}$$

silicon dioxide — *sulfuric acid*

Metals are often used in sculptures that may be placed outdoors. When a metal like zinc reacts with an acid like H_2SO_4, the following reaction occurs:

$$Zn(s) + H_2SO_{4}(aq) \rightarrow ZnSO_{4}(aq) + H_{2}(g)$$

zinc — *sulfuric acid* — *zinc sulfate* — *hydrogen*

Unfortunately, zinc sulfate is also soluble in water and causes the outdoor sculpture to deteriorate.

Checking Up

1. How can you determine the pH of a solution?
2. Write a chemical equation for the reaction of CO_2 with water.
3. Write the equation for the dissociation of sulfuric acid in water.
4. What is meant by the term "acid deposition"?

What Do You Think Now?

At the beginning of this activity you were asked:

- **What is in the air that can cause this damage?**
- **What factors must be considered when you want to create art that endures time?**

Using what you learned in this activity, how would you answer these questions now?

Chem Essential Questions

What does it mean?

Chemistry explains a macroscopic phenomenon (what you observe) with a description of what happens at the nanoscopic level (atoms and molecules) using symbolic structures as a way to communicate. Complete the chart below in your *Active Chemistry* log.

MACRO	NANO	SYMBOLIC
Describe what you can see happen to an outdoor marble statue over time when it is placed in an area with high concentrations of acid in the atmosphere.	*Use words to describe what occurs on the molecular level as marble deteriorates over time in the presence of acid.*	*Use chemical equations to describe what occurs as marble ($CaCO_3$) deteriorates over time in the presence of hydrochloric acid (HCl).*

How do you know?

What evidence do you have that acids form when carbon dioxide reacts with water and sulfur dioxide reacts with water?

Why do you believe?

Along the Ohio Valley there are large factories and giant coal-burning electrical power plants. Given that the prevailing winds travel from west to east, would you expect greater damage to an outdoor statue in New York or in the plains of Nebraska?

Why should you care?

A complete description of your artwork should include its intended placement. Will it be in a museum or placed outside in the courthouse square? Careful consideration of what your work will be exposed to in the air will be an important part of your *Chapter Challenge*.

Reflecting on the Activity and the Challenge

In this activity you have seen that chemistry is about change. On the macro level, you saw how acids change the pH of water. You also saw how acids can be made from atmospheric gases and how they can affect substances like marble and other materials that can be used for works of art. You read about the formation of hydrogen ions (H^+) when acids are in aqueous solutions and how acids react with various materials. These reactions were symbolized in the equations. If you were going to create artwork that was to be placed outside, you might be wise to choose a medium that would withstand the effects of acid weathering.

Chem to Go

1. Define acids and bases.
2. How is pH related to hydrogen ion concentration?
3. An acidic solution could have a pH of ________________.

   a) 4 b) 8 c) 10 d) 16
4. The pH of vinegar solution is ________________________.

   a) equal to zero b) less than 7 c) 7 d) greater than 7
5. Write a chemical equation for the reaction of SO_2 with water.
6. Is the pH of a water sample lowered more when equal amounts of CO_2 or SO_2 are introduced? Why?
7. What are the sources of sulfur dioxide in the air?
8. Military gravestones are made out of marble (calcium carbonate). Why are old military gravestones difficult to read? Write an equation to explain your answer.
9. What are some other materials that might be used for artwork placed outdoors and how might they be affected by the environment?
10. In a museum setting, identify other factors that could cause artwork to deteriorate. Provide suggestions on how to preserve the artwork from these factors.
11. When nonmetal oxides (like sulfur dioxide) are dissolved in water, the pH will be ____________________________.

    a) acidic b) neutral c) basic d) the same as the distilled water's pH
12. *Preparing for the Chapter Challenge*

    Sketch an idea for a sculpture that would be placed outdoors. Describe the material you would use and explain how it would resist deterioration caused by the environment.

Inquiring Further

Acid deposition and Earth science

Research to find why some areas of the U.S. are more susceptible than others to the effects of acid deposition.

Activity 3 Chemical Behavior of Metals

What Do You See?

BATTERY

GOALS

In this activity you will:

- Test different metals to determine their relative reactivity.
- Explore the concept of valence electrons.
- Use the process of electroplating to coat a nickel strip with copper atoms.

What Do You Think?

Various metals have been used since ancient times for works of art. The properties of metals determine their uses.

- **How might the properties of metals be related to the atomic structure of the metal's atoms?**

Record your ideas about this question in your *Active Chemistry* log. Be prepared to discuss your responses with your group and the class.

Investigate

Part A: Losing Electrons

In this activity you will investigate the chemical reactivity of metals.

1. Your teacher will provide you with a voltmeter, connecting wires, samples of several metals, and a salt-water solution. Among the metals you may find copper, aluminum, tin, iron, zinc, magnesium, and silver. If two different metals are connected by a wire and the metals are placed in the salt-water solution, electrons may flow through the wire from one metal to the other, creating an electric current in the wire. The potential difference (voltage) creating this current can be measured with the voltmeter.

Safety goggles and apron must be worn *at all times* in a chemistry lab.

Wash your hands and arms thoroughly after the activity.

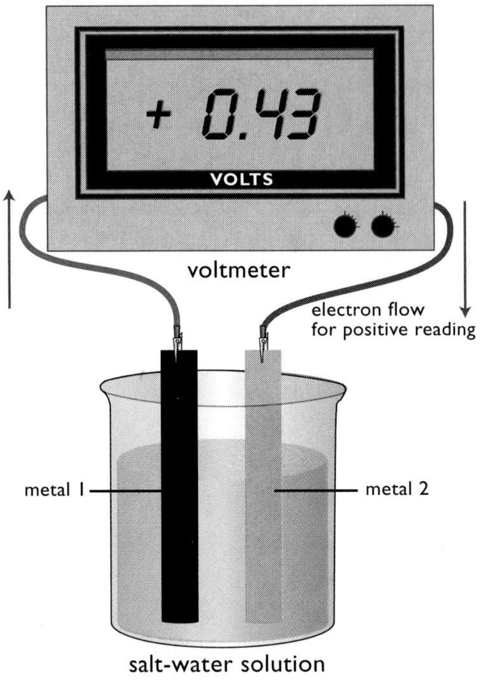
+ 0.43
VOLTS
voltmeter
electron flow
for positive reading
metal 1
metal 2
salt-water solution

Attach a wire to each of two metals. Attach the wire from one of the metals to the voltmeter terminal marked positive "+". Attach the wire from the other to the terminal marked negative "−".

2. Place the metals in the salt-water solution (be sure to place only the metals in the solution, not the ends of the wire clips). Decide which metal will be metal 1.

   a) What happens to the reading on the voltmeter? If the reading is positive, the metal connected to the negative side is losing electrons more easily than the other metal. The electrons are flowing through the voltmeter to the plus side. If the reading is negative, the metal connected to the plus side is losing its electrons more easily and electrons are flowing in the opposite direction to the metal connected to the minus side. In either case, it is the same metal that is losing electrons more easily.

   Switch the wires to the opposite terminals.

   b) What happens to the reading on the voltmeter now?

3. Make a table in your *Active Chemistry* log for the data you will be collecting. You can use one similar to the one shown.

Negative terminal	Positive terminal	Reading
metal 1	metal 2	
metal 1	metal 3	
metal 1	metal 4	
metal 1	metal 5	
metal 1	metal 6	

   a) Record the reading for each combination of metals when placed in the salt-water solution. Be sure to identify whether the reading is positive or negative.

4. Repeat *Step* 2, using a different metal on the negative terminal each time. Continue this until you have tested all possible combinations.

   a) Record all your readings.

5. Dispose of the salt-water solution and rinse and dry all metal samples when the investigation is completed. Clean up your workstation.

6. Answer the following questions in your *Active Chemistry* log.

   a) Which metal lost its electrons most easily?

   b) Which one had the most difficulty losing its electrons?

   c) Rank the rest of the metals in between. Begin with the ones that lose their electrons most easily.

Part B: Reactivity with Acids

1. Use the information you gained in *Part A* and in *Activity 2 (Part D)* to predict which metals are more reactive with acids.

a) Record your predictions in your *Active Chemistry* log.

2. Place a small piece of each polished metal provided in a separate well in a spot plate. Add 10–15 drops of 3 *M* hydrochloric acid to each well.

   a) Record your observations. Discuss the results in small groups.

   b) Rank the metals in order of increasing reactivity with acid.

   c) How does this ranking compare with the ranking of the metals in *Part A*?

3. Dispose of the materials as directed by your teacher. Clean up your workstation.

Part C: Electroplating

1. You can electroplate copper onto a nickel strip by using a 27-V battery (made up of three 9-V batteries in series), wires, a solution of copper (II) sulfate, a piece of copper, and a nickel strip. Electroplating is the deposition of a thin layer of a metal on an object by electrolysis.

   Attach wires to the positive and negative terminals of the batteries.

   Attach the copper to the other end of the wire attached to the positive terminal of the battery with an alligator clip. Attach the nickel strip to the other end of the wire connected to the negative terminal with an alligator clip. Place the copper into the solution of copper (II) sulfate and dip the nickel strip into the solution several times. Remove and rinse off the nickel strip.

   a) Make a sketch in your *Active Chemistry* log of the nickel strip after electroplating.

   b) What has been deposited on the nickel? Where did it come from?

   c) What was the purpose of the three 9-V batteries?

   d) How might an artist use this process?

2. Dispose of the materials as directed by your teacher. Clean up your workstation.

Safety goggles and apron must be worn *at all times* in a chemistry lab.

Wash your hands and arms thoroughly after the activity.

Be careful not to breathe any gases coming from the beaker.

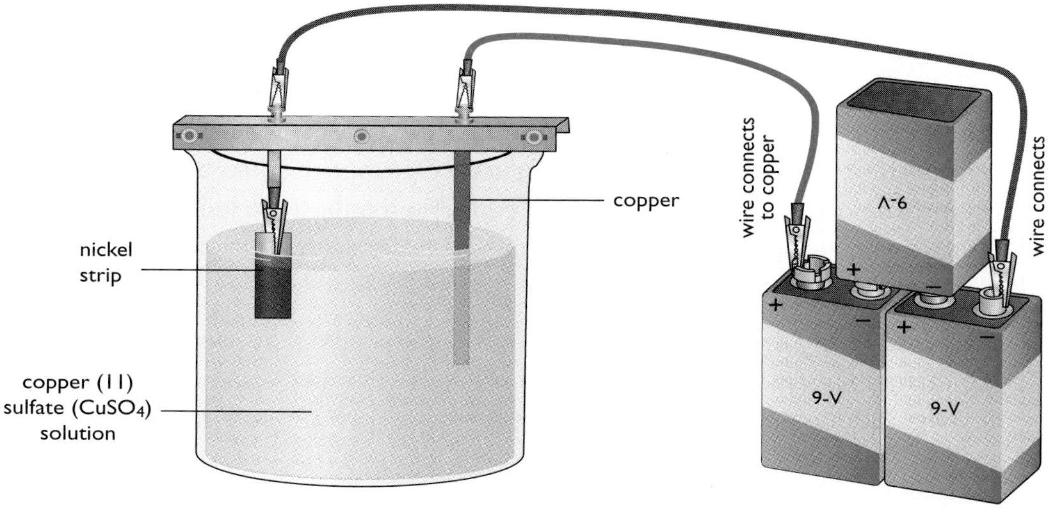
copper
nickel strip
copper (II) sulfate ($CuSO_4$) solution
wire connects to copper
wire connects to nickel
9-V
9-V
9-V
+
–
+
–
+
–

Chem Talk

REACTIVITY OF METALS

Valence Electrons and the Octet Rule

In this activity you looked at the chemical reactivity of metals. This reactivity depends on the **valence electrons**. (Recall that you first learned about valence electrons in the *Fun with the Periodic Table* chapter.) In the modern model of atomic structure, protons and neutrons are located in the nucleus. The electrons are in some predictable cloudlike energy level (called an orbital) outside of the nucleus. The electrons in the outermost electron shell that are furthest from the nucleus are the valence electrons. These electrons are responsible for the reactivity of an element.

Metals tend to lose these electrons in chemical reactions with other substances. When a metal atom loses electrons, it becomes a positively charged particle, or an ion. **Ion** is the name for a charged atom or charged group of atoms. Cation is the name for a positively charged ion. Some metals are better than others at losing their valence electrons. In this activity, you determined which metals tend to lose electrons easily and which ones do not. This property relates to the reactivity of the metal and therefore to its usefulness as material for works of art.

You can determine the number of valence electrons an element has by examining its location on the periodic table. The metals that belong to group 1A all have one valence electron. Those metals in group 2A all have two valence electrons. Elements in groups 3A, 4A, 5A, 6A, 7A, and 8A similarly have 3, 4, 5, 6, 7, and 8 valence electrons, respectively.

When you examine the noble gases in group 8A you see that, except for helium, all of these "inert" or nonreactive elements have eight valence electrons. Having eight valence electrons gives certain stability to an element. Elements other than the noble gases have a tendency to lose or gain electrons so that they too will have eight valence electrons. This phenomenon is referred to as the **octet rule**. The root "oct" means eight. An octagon is an eight-sided figure. (October used to be the eighth month, before July and August were added in a tribute to Julius and Augustus Caesar.) Helium is a notable exception, achieving stability with two valence electrons.

Fluorine, with seven valence electrons, typically gains one electron to form a fluoride ion with a charge of -1. Remember the electron configuration of fluorine's nine electrons is $1s^2\ 2s^2\ 2p^5$ so if it gains one

Chem Words

valence electrons: the electrons of an atom that are located in the outermost energy level.

octet rule: the rule that states that atoms tend to gain or lose electrons during chemical reactions so that the atoms have an outer shell configuration of eight electrons.

ion: an atom or molecule that has acquired a charge by either gaining (anion) or losing (cation) electron(s).

electron, the second energy level will have eight electrons: $1s^2\ 2s^2\ 2p^6$

$$F + e^- \rightarrow F^-$$

Sodium, with only one valence electron, will "give" it away to form a sodium ion with a +1 charge. Its electron configuration is $1s^2\ 2s^2\ 2p^6\ 3s^1$. Losing that one electron in the 3s shell will create an ion with a full outer shell (eight electrons in the second energy level).

$$\underset{1s^2\ 2s^2\ 2p^6\ 3s^1}{Na} \rightarrow \underset{1s^2\ 2s^2\ 2p^6}{Na^+} + e^-$$

Metals in group 2A all have two valence electrons, and if one loses these two electrons an ion with a +2 charge will form.

$$Mg \rightarrow Mg^{2+} + 2\ e^-$$

For example, when the zinc metal was attached to the negative terminal of the voltmeter, the electrons flowed through the voltmeter to the copper terminal, giving a positive reading. When you reversed the wires of the system you got the opposite flow and a negative reading. From the investigation, you were then able to determine which metal is the easiest to oxidize (lose electrons). This metal is referred to as most active. Looking at all of the combinations that you investigated, you should now be able to place the metals in a reactivity order of easiest to most difficult to oxidize (lose electrons).

Here is a list of metals, including the ones you tested in the activity, from most active to least active:

Most active → lithium (Li), potassium (K), calcium (Ca), sodium (Na), magnesium (Mg), aluminum (Al), zinc (Zn), iron (Fe), nickel (Ni), tin (Sn), lead (Pb), hydrogen (H), copper (Cu), mercury (Hg), silver (Ag), platinum (Pt), gold (Au) → least active

Reactivity of Metal and Art

Reactive metals lose electrons easily and form compounds readily. Sometimes the properties of these new compounds are detrimental to the metal. For example, formation of rust (iron oxide) causes iron metal to deteriorate. In other metals, the new compounds that form can protect the underlying metal from further deterioration. For example, when aluminum is exposed to air, it forms aluminum oxide (Al_2O_3), which is less reactive than aluminum itself. This forms a protective coating, preventing the underlying aluminum from deteriorating.

→

Chem Words

patina: a surface coating that develops on metals and protects them from further corrosion.

electroplating: the deposition of a thin layer of a metal on an object by electrolysis.

Even copper, which is fairly low in reactivity, will react with substances in the air to form a protective coating. The natural protective coating of a blue-green patina is found on many old copper roofs, statues, and other copper surfaces. The Statue of Liberty is covered with a green **patina** finish. A patina, from the Latin word "to plate," is a surface coating that develops on metals and protects them from further corrosion.

The main constituent of the patina found is a mixture of basic copper carbonate and basic copper sulfate. The color variations from greenish to blue-gray depend on differences in chemical composition. The decorative coating protects the underlying copper from further corrosion by acting as a barrier between the atmospheric chemicals and the copper.

In this activity, you coated the nickel with copper. This process is called **electroplating**. Some of the copper was released from the positive (+) terminal as copper ions and went into the solution of copper (II) sulfate. Then some of the copper ions from the copper (II) sulfate moved toward the negative terminal where it gained electrons and the copper atoms adhered to the nickel.

Metal ions in solution (like the solution of copper (II) sulfate) can accept electrons and turn back into metal atoms (copper) that no longer dissolve in water. Voltage applied to metals placed in a solution containing ions (electrolyte) will cause the metal connected to the positive terminal to dissolve. The positive ions of this metal flow through the solution and accept any excess electrons from the second metal connected to the minus terminal. Thus, the atoms of the first metal can be plated on the second. Electroplating is often used by sculptors and jewelers.

Checking Up

1. How many valence electrons does an oxygen (O) atom have?
2. How many valence electrons does a calcium (Ca) atom have?
3. What will be the typical charge on a calcium ion?
4. What is the electron configuration of a neutral magnesium (Mg) atom?

What Do You Think Now?

At the beginning of the activity, you were asked:

- **How might the properties of metals be related to the atomic structure of the metal's atoms?**

How would you answer this question now?

Chem Essential Questions

What does it mean?

Chemistry explains a macroscopic phenomenon (what you observe) with a description of what happens at the nanoscopic level (atoms and molecules) using symbolic structures as a way to communicate. Complete the chart below in your *Active Chemistry* log.

MACRO	NANO	SYMBOLIC
Which metal appeared to be the most reactive? The least? How did you measure this?	*When two metals are connected to different terminals of a battery and placed in a solution containing ions, what happens at the molecular level?*	*Make a list of the reactivity of the metals you tested, from the most reactive to the least.*

How do you know?

What evidence do you have to support the idea that one metal is more reactive than another? Use your data to explain how copper made its way onto nickel in *Part C.*

Why do you believe?

Report on a situation in your life where you would need to choose a less (or more) reactive metal for some everyday purpose.

Why should you care?

Understanding the reactivity of metals will help guide you as you create your work of art, should you choose to incorporate metal into it. The reasons may be for beauty or protection, but either way a meaningful explanation of your choice of metal will add credibility to your museum display.

Reflecting on the Activity and the Challenge

You have now seen that some metals lose their electrons more easily than others. This determines their reactivity with other substances. You saw this when you used different metals to produce a current that you measured with the voltmeter. You then used the octet rule of valence electrons to help explain this property of metals. Equations can also be written to show the loss of electrons.

Metals are often used in various ways when creating artwork. When an artist decides to incorporate some metal into her work it is important for her to understand the chemical reactivity of the metal. You saw that some metals react with acids; this phenomenon is used in creating etched metals for printmaking and other artwork. The use of patinas to enhance and protect the beauty of metals is used in sculpture and jewelry. Perhaps you might choose to create a work of art that incorporates a metal. It would be essential to have knowledge about the chemical reactivity of this metal for your project's explanation.

Chem to Go

1. Using the periodic table, determine how many valence electrons the following elements have?

   a) Na b) F c) Mg d) Ne e) P f) Al

2. For each of the atoms in *Question 1*:

   a) How many electrons will each atom either gain or lose in order to satisfy the octet rule?

   b) What will be the charge on each resulting ion?

3. State in your own words the octet rule.
4. In this activity you plated copper onto nickel. Describe the conditions you would use to perform the opposite process–nickel-plating a piece of copper metal.
5. Show an equation for the formation of a typical Mg (magnesium) ion from a neutral Mg atom.
6. Show an equation for the formation of a typical Cl (chlorine) ion from a neutral Cl atom.
7. Why are some items silver- or gold-plated rather than solid silver or gold?
8. Why might an artist choose to electroplate a sculpture?
9. ***Preparing for the Chapter Challenge***

   Propose how you might electroplate some metal to change or enhance its appearance so that it might be used as a work of art. Be sure to make use of your data regarding the relative reactivities of metals when making your proposal.

Inquiring Further

Protecting metals in the ground

Protection of metal in the ground uses the principles of electroplating in a special way. This process is called cathodic protection. Research this process and report to your class.

Activity 4 Physical Behavior of Metals

What Do You See?

GOALS

In this activity you will:

- Discover what an alloy is.
- Make a brass-coated penny.
- Determine how the properties of a metal are affected by making it into an alloy.

What Do You Think?

In the previous activity, you found that the chemical properties of metals are dependent upon their valence electrons.

- **How can the physical properties of metals be modified?**
- **What properties of metals make them useful as works of art or tools for creating art?**

Record your ideas about these questions in your *Active Chemistry* log. Be prepared to discuss your responses with your group and the class.

Investigate

Part A: Making Brass

In the first part of this activity, you will attempt to make brass from a penny with a mint date after 1982.

Safety goggles and a lab apron must be worn *at all times* in a chemistry lab.

Follow all safety rules for working with an open flame.

1. Get a shiny new penny. If it is not shiny, use steel wool to shine it. Wear gloves when shining the penny.
2. Fill a beaker with water and set it near a Bunsen burner. Light the burner and adjust the flame to get the inner blue cone.
3. Hold the edge of a penny with tongs. Place the penny in the Bunsen burner flame just above the inner blue cone. Heat the penny, turning it in the flame. Look for a color change.

Safety goggles and a lab apron must be worn *at all times* in a chemistry lab.

Follow all safety rules for working with an open flame.

The penny and the bobby pin can get very hot. Use extreme caution.

Do not touch the heated bobby pin until you are sure it has cooled.

Wash your hands and arms thoroughly after the activity.

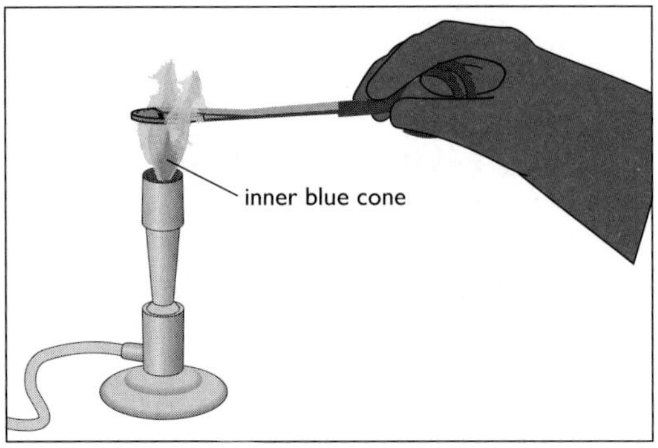
inner blue cone

4. When a color change occurs, quickly put the penny in the water.
5. Remove the penny from the water and observe the penny closely.
   a) Record your observations in your *Active Chemistry* log.
   b) What color did the penny turn?

   Pennies minted since 1982 have a core of zinc with a layer of copper covering it. The melting point of zinc is low enough for the flame of a Bunsen burner to melt it. Copper becomes very soft in the flame, but won't quite melt. The resulting copper-zinc mixture (called an alloy) is brass.

   c) Lower percentages of zinc with the copper produce a yellow color. With more zinc, the color is redder. Does the penny have a higher percentage or a lower percentage of zinc?
6. Dispose of the materials as directed by your teacher. Clean up your workstation.

Part B: Properties of Steel

In this part of the activity, you will determine how to change the properties of iron by introducing carbon and changing the way it is heated and cooled.

"Spring" steel	Annealed steel	Hardened steel	Tempered steel

1. Make a table in your *Active Chemistry* log similar to the one shown to record your observations and answers to questions.
2. Your teacher will provide you with several bobby pins. These are made of steel, which is an alloy of iron and carbon. The bobby pins are made of ***"spring"*** steel. Examine one of the bobby pins by trying to bend it. Open it up, close it, and generally manipulate it for a few minutes.
   a) Describe its properties in your *Active Chemistry* log.
3. Light a Bunsen burner. Adjust the flame until you see a light blue cone in the center. Hold a second bobby pin by the ends using tongs or heat-proof gloves. Place the bent portion of the bobby pin at the tip of the inner blue flame.
4. When the bend is red hot, gently pull the ends apart to straighten the bobby pin. Remove the bobby pin from the flame. Do not touch the middle of the bobby pin.
   a) When the bobby pin was red hot, was it easier or more difficult to open it?
5. Using tongs, hold one end of the open bobby pin in the flame to burn off the plastic tip. Let it cool and repeat with the other end.

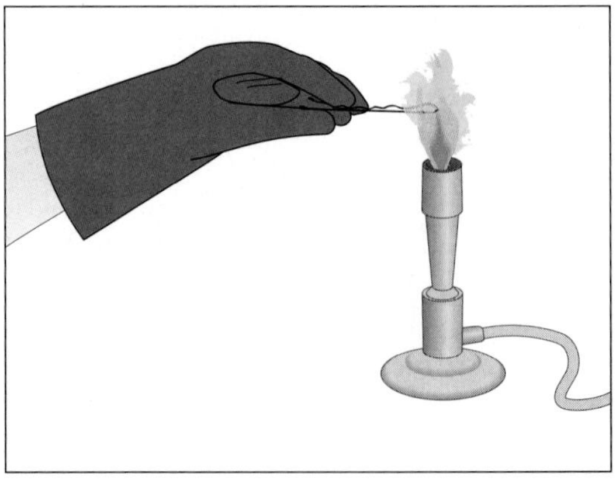

6. Heat the entire bobby pin to red-hot. Let it cool slowly on a porcelain dish on the counter. When the pin is cool, again observe the properties by manipulating the bobby pin.

   This process is called ***annealing***. Heating the bobby pin to red-hot introduces carbon atoms into the iron-crystal structure. The flame from the burner is the source of the carbon. As the iron slowly cools, many of the carbon atoms are squeezed out of the crystal. You can wipe these off the surface.

   a) Compare and contrast this annealed steel with the original spring steel.

   b) Would annealed steel be useful for tools? Why or why not?

7. Fill a 250-mL beaker with water. Take the annealed bobby pin and bend the end around your finger to form a J-shaped hook.

8. Hold the other end of the bobby pin with tongs and heat the hook to red-hot. This time quickly immerse the entire hook in the beaker of cold water to cool it off quickly. Examine the hook end of the bobby pin. Try to bend it. What happens?

   a) Record your observations in your *Active Chemistry* log.

   b) How can you explain your observations?

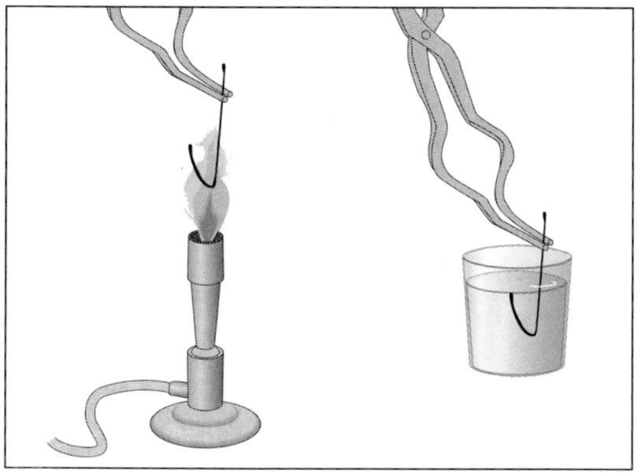

   This process is called ***hardening***. When the iron is cooled quickly after introducing additional carbon atoms, the carbon atoms do not have a chance to escape and become trapped with the iron. The extra carbon atoms can hold onto electrons and make the metal less malleable.

   c) Would hardened steel be useful for tools? Why or why not?

9. Open up another bobby pin. Burn off the plastic tips and heat the entire length to red hot, and then let it cool slowly on the counter.

   a) What type of steel have you made again?

10 When the bobby pin is cool, form the J-hook and reheat it to red-hot and then immerse it in cold water.

   a) What type of steel is it now?

11. The next step is to ***temper*** the steel. This will allow some of the bonds that the carbon atoms have to loosen up and relieve some of the stresses in the steel.

12. Use tongs to hold the bobby pin. Slowly run the entire bobby pin through the flame without heating it to red-hot. You should see a bluish sheen appear on the bobby pin if it is done correctly. Let the bobby pin cool on a porcelain dish on the counter when heating is completed.

13. Manipulate the hook. What has changed?

   a) Describe the properties of this steel.

   b) Is tempered steel useful for making tools? Explain your answer.

14. Be sure to turn off the burner. Dispose of the bobby pins as directed by your teacher.

Wash your hands and arms thoroughly after the activity.

Chem Talk

Chem Words

electron-sea model: a model of the structure of metal that places valence electrons floating around the metal cations, appearing not to belong to any one cation.

cation: an ion that has a positive charge.

malleability: the property of a material to be hammered into various shapes without breaking.

alloy: a substance that has metal characteristics and consists of two or more different elements.

ALLOYS AND THEIR PROPERTIES

The Electron-Sea Model of Metals

In metals, the atoms are held together by metallic bonds. These bonds are formed by the sharing of valence electrons among all the atoms in the metal. The nature of the metallic bond can best be shown as the **electron-sea model**.

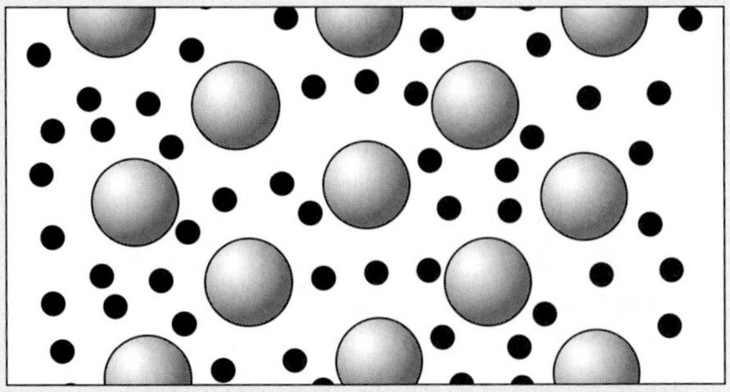

The electron-sea model for metallic bonding.

The large spheres represent metal **cations** (positively charged metal ions). The small spheres represent electrons. As you saw in the previous activity, metals do not hold on tightly to their valence electrons. These outer electrons are in constant motion around the cations, not really "belonging" to any one cation. Instead, they are part of the whole metal crystal. The negatively charged electrons are moving about in a sea-like fashion that has the effect of holding the positively charged metal ions in their somewhat fixed positions.

It may seem weird, but, yes, metals are crystalline like diamonds or salt. You do not, however, see metals cut like diamonds or shear off along an edge like a salt crystal. The metals have a crystal structure with a sea of valence electrons surrounding metal cations. Diamonds have directed covalent bonds between carbon atoms. The electrons on the cations and anions in salt compounds are localized.

Because the electrons are free to move about, the atoms in most metals can move past each other when hammered. This property is called **malleability**. The malleability of many metals also makes them rather "soft" and pliable, and not very strong.

What is an Alloy?

When other elements are introduced into the iron metal, an alloy is formed. An **alloy** is a substance that has the properties of a metal, but consists of two or more elements. When other elements are introduced, the properties of a base metal are changed.

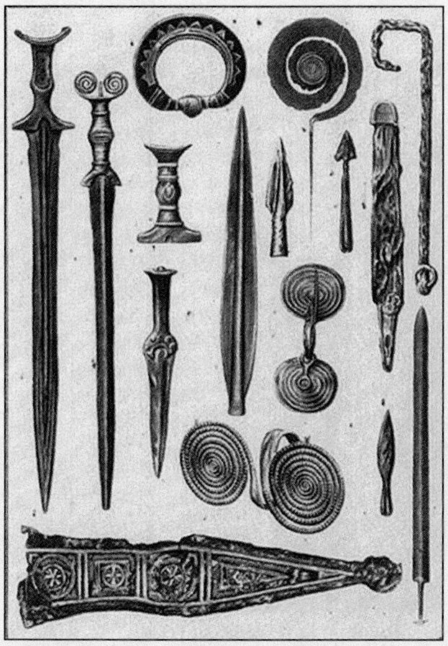
Tools from the Bronze Age.

It is difficult to say precisely when the human species started to use and adapt materials to its benefit. However, different types of blades and cutting tools were certainly being developed about 100,000 years ago, during the late Stone Age. One of the earliest alloys used by humans was bronze, a mixture of copper and tin. A second important alloy was brass, a mixture of copper and zinc. The alloys were more durable than copper, which allowed for better tools. Over time, even stronger alloys were formed from iron, which brought about tremendous changes in human culture—warfare, agriculture and art.

Properties of Different Types of Steel

In the activity you used three processes to change the properties of steel. Through these processes, you altered the arrangement of iron atoms as carbon atoms were introduced into the crystal structure. (Recall that steel is an alloy of iron and carbon.)

As the iron slowly cooled, the crystalline structure was rearranged and excess carbon was squeezed out. The **annealed steel** contains fewer carbon atoms between the iron atoms and the result is a softer, more malleable, and more pliable steel. If the steel is cooled quickly after being heated to red hot, the carbon atoms are locked into the crystalline structure. Since carbon atoms tend to hold onto electrons, the iron atoms have a more difficult time sliding past each other. The resulting **hardened steel** is hard and brittle. If the hardened steel is gently heated, the crystalline structure again changes, relieving some of the bonds between the carbon atoms and electrons. This results in **tempered steel** that has properties of both the annealed and hardened steels. It is hard, malleable, and useful for tools and building materials.

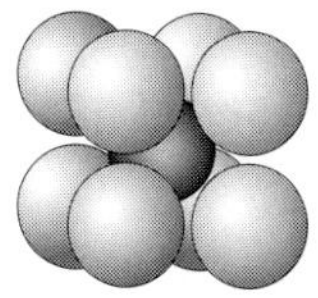
cold iron
body-centered cubic

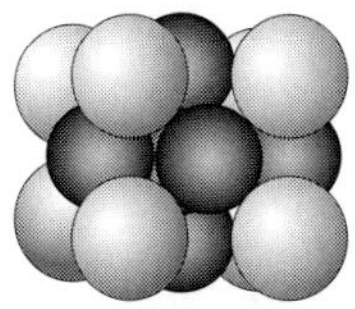
hot iron
face-centered cubic

Chem Words

annealed steel: steel that contains fewer carbon atoms between the iron atoms and is a softer, more malleable, and more pliable steel. It is formed as iron is slowly cooled.

hardened steel: a hard and brittle type of steel that results when steel is cooled quickly after being heated to red hot, causing the carbon atoms to be locked into the crystalline structure.

tempered steel: steel that is heated to an appropriate temperature for a short period of time and then cooled rapidly to give it properties of both hardened and annealed steel.

Chem Words

brass: an alloy that consists of copper and zinc.

bronze: an alloy that is primarily made up of copper and tin.

Alloys in the World of Art

Pure gold (also referred to as 24-carat gold) is a deep-yellow color, soft, and very malleable. Because pure gold is so soft, the "gold" used in jewelry and artworks is made of gold-silver-copper alloys to increase its strength. That is why most gold jewelry is only 18-carat, 16-carat, 14-carat, etc., gold. The variation of color of gold jewelry from yellow to pink is determined by the metals added to increase strength. The malleability of gold is very important in art. It is seen in the use of gold leaf, which has a range of thicknesses of 0.1 to 0.3 μm (millionths of a meter).

Brass alloys are made of copper and zinc (generally 5% to 40%). They may also contain small amounts of other elements. Additions of aluminum, iron, and manganese to brass improves its strength. Adding silicon improves its resistance to wear.

Bronze is an alloy of copper and tin, sometimes containing small amounts of other elements like zinc or phosphorus. It is stronger, harder, and more durable than brass, and has been used since antiquity for sculpture. Bronze has desirable properties that also make it useful for symbols and gongs. Bronze alloys vary in color from a silvery hue to a rich, coppery red. The U.S. has set a standard for bronze that is 90% copper, 7% tin, and 3% zinc.

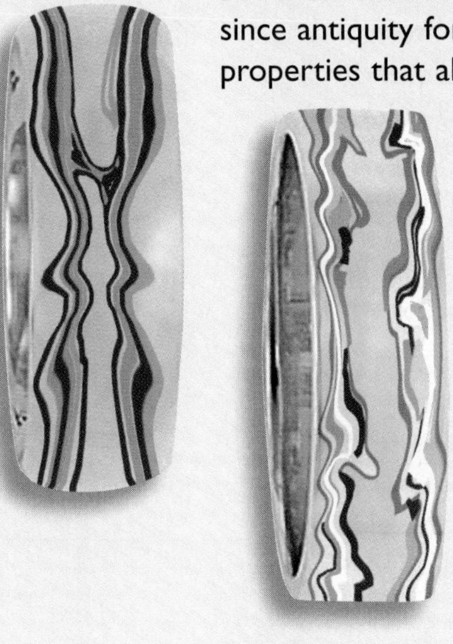

While alloys like bronze have been used for ages, more recently the art world has seen the use of exciting types of alloys called shape-memory alloys (SMAs). They are sometimes referred to as "smart materials." They are

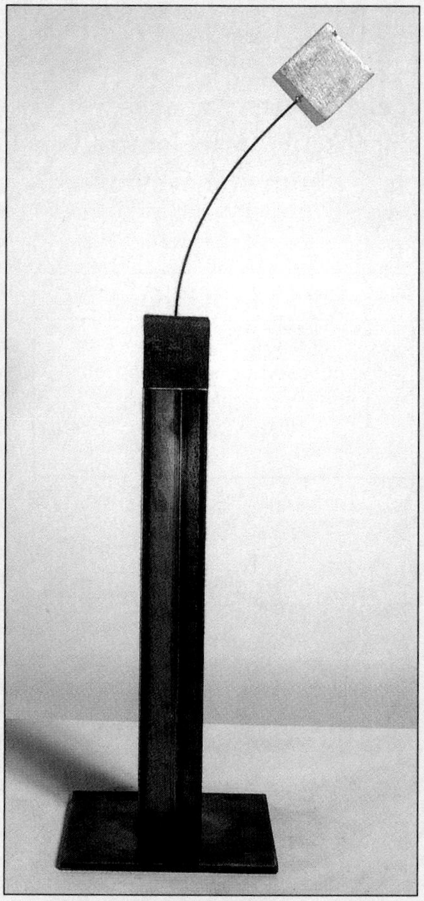

metal alloys that, after being strained at a certain temperature, revert back to their original shape. After being bent, these alloys revert back to their original shape upon heating. This is caused by a reversion to the original crystal structure at their transformation temperature.

The most effective and widely used SMAs include NiTi (nickel-titanium), CuZnAl (copper-zinc-aluminum), and CuAlNi (copper-aluminum-nickel). A Swiss artist named Etienne Krähenbühl has used nickel titanium and other SMAs to create sculptures that can remember and return to their original shapes even after being severely deformed. Krähenbühl makes sculptures that play with viewers' perceptions, moving and reacting to wind and temperature. Some of them are musical, and all of them are designed to be touched and handled.

Checking Up

1. Explain the electron-sea model.
2. What is meant by malleability?
3. Describe the properties of three different types of steel.

What Do You Think Now?

At the beginning of the activity you were asked:

- **How can the physical properties of metals be modified?**
- **What properties of metals make them useful as works of art or tools for creating art?**

What are alloys? Why are they made? What are some properties of metals that make them useful as works of art or tools to create art? Record your answers in your *Active Chemistry* log.

Chem Essential Questions

What does it mean?

Chemistry explains a macroscopic phenomenon (what you observe) with a description of what happens at the nanoscopic level (atoms and molecules) using symbolic structures as a way to communicate. Complete the chart below in your *Active Chemistry* log.

MACRO	NANO	SYMBOLIC
Referring to your experiences in this activity, explain how you were able to observe how the properties of a metal were modified.	*Explain the modified properties of the metal in terms of what happened at the molecular level.*	*Create a drawing to show the introduction of new atoms into a metal's crystal structure.*

How do you know?

Explain how you were able to see the different properties of annealed, hardened, and tempered steel.

Why do you believe?

Alloys surround you in your daily lives—jewelry, tools, auto parts, and other everyday objects are made of alloys. What are some examples of alloys that you come across in the course of an average day?

Why should you care?

Your work of art might have some metal or alloy incorporated into it. Having a good understanding of the physical properties of metals at the atomic level will enhance your explanation in your museum placard. How flexible will the metal be that you decide to use in your art display?

Reflecting on the Activity and the Challenge

Once again, you have seen that chemistry involves change. On the macro level you learned how to manipulate the properties of metal by subjecting it to various changes in temperature. Introducing other elements into the metal also caused changes in the properties of the metal. On the nano and symbolic level, you can use the electron-sea model of metals to help explain the changes in behavior of the metals.

As humans learned more about the chemistry of metals, the tools and materials they used for creating sculpture changed over time. Think about how materials used for sculpture changed through the ages. Explaining the chemistry behind this may be an important part of your museum display.

Chem to Go

1. What are the differences in composition of bronze and brass?
2. What are the components of steel? List some different uses for steel and explain why an alloy is better for the job.
3. a) Provide a summary of the formation and properties of each type of steel—annealed, hardened, and tempered.

   b) Describe a use for each type of steel.
4. What is the difference between 24-carat gold and gold used for normal jewelry?
5. Is there a connection between the tools used for creating art and the technology of the time? Explain your answer.
6. ***Preparing for the Chapter Challenge***

   Sculpting artworks has changed over time from simply carving out an image from some soft material to forming molds and casting to the use of high temperatures to weld metals together. Create a small sculpture either out of metal materials or some other material using a metal tool. What properties of the materials allowed you to create the effect you sought?

Inquiring Further

1. The changing composition of alloys

The composition of alloys of pewter and solder has changed in recent times. What is different in these alloys and why have they changed? (Hint: Think in terms of health concerns.)

2. The difference between soldering and welding

For what purpose is solder used? How is this different from welding? How can each process be used in creating art?

Activity 5 Clay

What Do You See?
CLAY

GOALS

In this activity you will:

- Identify an unknown hydrate.
- Distinguish between a hydrated and an anhydrous compound.
- Examine and describe the effects of heat on clay.

What Do You Think?

Ceramics are materials made from clay and have been used by humans for both practical and artistic purposes dating back almost 13,000 years. However, ceramics are far from being antiquated. In fact, they are used in some of our most "high-tech" materials today.

- **List as many ceramic materials and products as you can.**
- **What are some properties of ceramic materials that make them so useful?**
- **What are some properties of ceramic materials that can limit their usefulness?**

Record your ideas about these questions in your *Active Chemistry* log. Be prepared to discuss your responses with your group and the class.

Investigate

Part A: Heating a Hydrate

If a substance contains water as part of its crystalline structure, it is called a ***hydrate***. The solid that is left when the water is removed from a hydrate is called an ***anhydrate***. In this part of the activity, you will remove the water from a mystery hydrate. By measuring the amount of water removed, you will be able to identify the hydrate.

1. You will use heat to drive off the water from a hydrate. Dehydrating the hydrated compound requires intense heating for a period of time. You will use a clean, dry crucible and cover to do this. Set up your equipment as shown in the diagram.

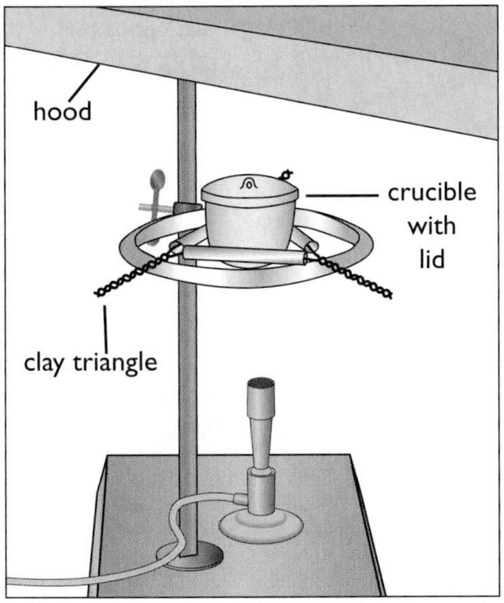
hood
crucible with lid
clay triangle

2. You will need to determine the mass of water in your hydrate.

   a) What information will you need to collect in order to calculate this? Design a procedure you will follow to obtain the information. Use the following steps to guide you.

   b) Construct a data table for recording this information in your *Active Chemistry* log. Make sure that you identify on your data table which unknown you are testing.

   Have your procedure and data table approved by your teacher before starting.

3. Light the burner. Heat the crucible with its cover in the hottest part of the flame for 3 min in order to remove any moisture that might be present in the crucible or cover. Remove the crucible carefully using tongs. Place it on a heat-resistant surface on your lab table to cool. Turn off the burner.

4. Obtain your unknown hydrate. You will not need more than 2.00 g of the hydrate. Observe the hydrated compound with a hand lens.

   a) Record the letter of your unknown on your data table.

   b) Describe the crystalline structure of the hydrate in your *Active Chemistry* log.

5. Place the hydrate in the crucible and then on the clay triangle. The cover should tilt slightly, which will allow water vapor to escape as it forms. Light your Bunsen burner and adjust flame.

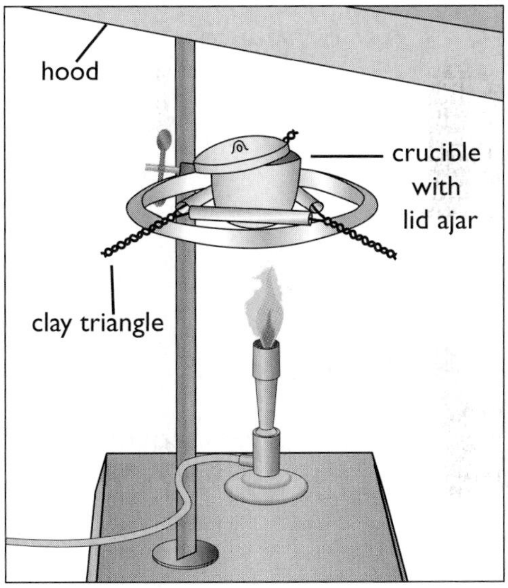
hood
crucible with lid ajar
clay triangle

6. Begin heating gently, gradually increasing the heat until there is no more popping or spattering. Remove the cover using tongs and examine the material in the crucible. If the edges of the solid are turning brown, reduce the heat momentarily and then begin heating again at a slower rate.

7. Use tongs to remove the crucible, lid, and contents. Allow them to cool before making any measurements. Some anhydrous compounds will readily absorb moisture from the air so it is important that you quickly determine the mass as soon as it has cooled down. If a desiccator is available, place your crucible inside the desiccator to let it cool.

Safety goggles and a lab apron must be worn *at all times* in a chemistry lab.

Follow all safety rules for working with an open flame.

Handle objects with care once they have been heated. Objects look the same whether they are hot or cool.

8. Using good technique and making accurate measurements will be critical in obtaining accurate calculations. Make sure you record mass to the nearest 0.01 g.

   a) How can you be sure that all of the water has been removed from the hydrated compound?

   b) Adjust the procedure as needed to ensure that you have removed all of the water.

9. Observe the dehydrated compound with a hand lens.

   a) Describe the crystalline structure. Note any changes in your observations before and after heating.

   b) Explain what might be responsible for any changes that you noted. Record these observations and thoughts in your *Active Chemistry* log.

Wash your hands and arms thoroughly after the activity.

10. Dispose of the materials as directed by your teacher. Clean up your workstation.

Part B: Using Calculations to Find the Formula of a Hydrate

In this part of the activity, you will determine the formula of the unknown hydrate.

1. Using the original mass of the hydrate and the final mass of the anhydrate, calculate the mass of the water removed.

2. To determine the identity of the unknown hydrate, you will have to know the amount of water and the amount of hydrate in your original sample. You already know the amount as measured in grams. What you will need to calculate is the amount in moles—the wonderful chemistry way of counting.

The ***mole*** is a specific unit of measurement that chemists use. A mole is simply a quantity of something. It happens to be a very large quantity. Just like a pair means two items and a dozen means 12 items, a mole means 6.022×10^{23} items! This odd unit is used because it makes calculations easier. Typically, it will refer to a number of particles—atoms, molecules, and ions.

One mole of any element is also equal to its atomic mass *in grams*. From the periodic table, you find that one mole of hydrogen atoms has a mass of 1.008 g. A mole of carbon atoms has a mass of 12.01 g, and a mole of oxygen atoms has a mass of 16.00 g. You can determine the ***molar mass*** of a molecular or ionic compound by simply adding up the atomic masses (in grams) of each element present in the molecules or ions.

Thus, the molar mass of water is 18.0 g. One mole of H_2O contains two moles of hydrogen (2.0 g, rounded off) and one mole of oxygen (16.0 g) for a total molar mass of 18.0 g/mol.

   a) Calculate the amount of water removed from your sample in moles. If you had removed 18 g of water, that would have been 1 mol. If you had removed 0.18 g, that would have been 0.01 mol.

$$\_\ \text{g of water} \times \frac{1\ \text{mol}\ H_2O}{18.0\,\text{g}} = \_\ \text{mol}\ H_2O$$

3. You do not know which anhydrate you have out of the following four possibilities shown in the table. Therefore, you will need to calculate the number of moles of each possible anhydrate.

   a) Prepare a similar table in your log.

b) Calculate and record the molar mass for each of the possible anhydrates.

Suppose your unknown has the formula $MgSO_4$. The formula tells you several things. The formula indicates that for every one unit of this compound, there is 1 magnesium atom, 1 sulfur atom, and 4 oxygen atoms. You can look up these atomic masses on the periodic table. The first entry is already listed for you, so that you can check your procedure. You can now proceed to calculate the molar masses for the other anhydrates.

Anhydrate	Molar mass (g/mol)	Number of moles
$MgSO_4$	120.3	
Na_2CO_3		
$CaSO_4$		
$CuSO_4$		

c) Calculate and record the amount of anhydrate in moles. The number of moles must be based on the amount of anhydrate you had divided by the molar mass of each anhydrate. For example, if the mass of the anhydrate was 1.2 g and the anhydrate was $MgSO_4$, then the amount in moles is 0.01 mol since 1.2 g/(120 g/mol) = 0.01 mol.

$$\_\_ \text{ g of } MgSO_4 \times \frac{1 \text{ mol } MgSO_4}{120.3 \text{ g}} = \_\_ \text{ mol } MgSO_4$$

d) Calculate the amount of anhydrate in moles for each of the possible anhydrates. Use the number of grams of the anhydrate that you measured in the activity and the molar mass that you just determined. Place these values in the second column of the table. The same number of grams will correspond to a different number of moles for each of the four possible anhydrates.

4. You will now make a prediction of your anhydrate based on one more bit of information. Hydrates are formed with specific ratios of the anhydrate and water.

$MgSO_4{\cdot}7H_2O$

1 mol of magnesium sulfate combines with 7 mol of water

$Na_2CO_3{\cdot}H_2O$

1 mol of sodium carbonate combines with 1 mol of water

$CaSO_4{\cdot}2H_2O$

1 mol of calcium sulfate combines with 2 mol of water

$CuSO_4{\cdot}5H_2O$

1 mol of copper sulfate combines with 5 mol of water

Using your calculated quantities for moles of water and moles of the possible anhydrates, determine which of the hydrates you began with by computing which of these anhydrates have the correct ratio of anhydrate to water. The ratio is a ratio of moles—the chemist's way of counting.

a) Record your answer in your *Active Chemistry* log.

5. Compare your results with other members of your class with the same unknown.

a) Are there differences? What reasons could account for those differences?

Safety goggles and a lab apron must be worn *at all times* in a chemistry lab.

Wash your hands and arms thoroughly after the activity.

Part C: Clay

1. Obtain a sample of artist's clay from your teacher. Observe the hydrated compound with a hand lens.

   a) Describe any solid structures you see.

2. Measure the mass of the hydrated clay.

   a) Record the mass in your *Active Chemistry* log.

3. Create an object from the clay. You may wish to create something that you will be able to use in your museum display or a replica of another object made of clay. Or you may want to just be creative and make something unique with your clay.

4. Let your object air-dry overnight, or, if available, set it in a low-heat drying oven overnight.

   You now have dehydrated clay. (We limit the use of the word anhydrate for pure compounds. This clay is composed of many different compounds.) Observe your dried object with a hand lens. Note any changes compared to dehydrated clay, the hydrated clay, and the dehydrated clay object.

   a) How might you explain any differences that you noted?

5. Measure the mass of the dehydrated clay object.

   a) Record the mass in your *Active Chemistry* log.

6. Calculate the mass percent of water in your sample:

$$\frac{\text{mass of water removed}}{\text{starting mass of hydrate}} \times 100\% = \_\% \text{ water}$$

   a) Record the mass percent of water in your log.

   b) If you had fired your clay in a kiln, how might that affect the calculated percentage of water?

7. Dispose of the materials as directed by your teacher. Clean up your workstation.

Chem Talk

HYDRATES AND ANHYDRATES

Defining Hydrate and Anhydrate

Many compounds form as a result of reactions that occur in water solutions. These compounds appear to be dry, but when they are heated, water is released. The water molecules are a part of the crystalline structure and are weakly bonded to the ions or molecules that make up the compound. When a potter fires his clay in a kiln, water is removed from the clay, resulting in a change in the nature of the clay. If a substance contains water as part of its crystal structure, it is called a **hydrate**. The solid that is left when the water is removed from a hydrate is called an **anhydrate**.

The Chemistry Way of Counting – Moles

Since atoms are so incredibly small and samples of matter typically contain so many atoms, chemists needed to establish a method for counting atoms. The method is the same one employed by food manufacturers everywhere. No one at the factory would want to have to count the candies that go in a 454-g bag each time. Instead, if they know that 10 candies have a mass of 8.9 g, they can estimate that there will be about 510 candies in a 454-g bag. They can simply use the mass to determine the number of items in the bag.

Chemists routinely use a unit of measurement called the **mole**. A mole is simply a quantity of something, just like an octet is a specific quantity of something. An octet means eight and a mole happens to mean 6.022×10^{23}.

1 dozen = 12	**1 mole = 6.022×10^{23}**
1 dozen pots = 12 pots	1 mole pots = 6.022×10^{23} pots
1 dozen atoms = 12 atoms	1 mole atoms = 6.022×10^{23} atoms
1 dozen molecules = 12 molecules	1 mole molecules = 6.022×10^{23} molecules
6.022×10^{23} = 602,200,000,000,000,000,000,000	

Chem Words

hydrate: a compound that has water attached to it.

anhydrate: a compound that does not have any water attached to it.

mole: the number equal to the number of carbon atoms in exactly 12 g of pure ^{12}C.

Chem Words

Avogadro's number: the number equal to the number of carbon atoms in exactly 12 g of pure ^{12}C, 6.022×10^{23} units.

Furthermore, if a student has two dozen brushes, you know she has 24 brushes. You carry out the mathematics of this in your head with no trouble. The math looks like this:

$$2 \text{ dozen brushes} \times \frac{12 \text{ brushes}}{1 \text{ dozen brushes}} = 24 \text{ brushes}$$

If you have 2 mol of atoms:

$$2 \text{ mol atoms} \times \frac{6.022 \times 10^{23} \text{ atoms}}{1 \text{ mol atoms}} = 2(6.022 \times 10^{23} \text{ atoms}) = 1.204 \times 10^{24} \text{ atoms}$$

Amedeo Avogadro

By definition, one mole is equal to the number of carbon atoms in exactly 12 g of pure carbon-12 (the isotope carbon-12, or ^{12}C). Various techniques have been used to determine this number as 6.022×10^{23}. This number is called **Avogadro's number** to honor Amedeo Avogadro's contributions to chemistry.

It is also true that 12 g of ^{12}C contains 6.022×10^{23} atoms. One mole of any substance will always contain 6.022×10^{23} chemical units of that substance. The masses of one mole of two different substances will not be the same because the atoms making up those substances have different atomic masses.

The mass of one mole is equal to an element's atomic mass expressed in grams.

This means that:

- 1 mol of He contains 6.022×10^{23} atoms of He and has a mass of 4.003 g
- 1 mol of Al contains 6.022×10^{23} atoms of Al and has a mass of 26.98 g
- 1 mol of U contains 6.022×10^{23} atoms of U and has a mass of 238.0 g
- 2 mol of U contains 1.2044×10^{24} atoms of U and has a mass of 476.0 g
- 1 mol of H_2O contains 6.022×10^{23} molecules of H_2O and has a mass of 18 g:

  $2 [H (1 g)] + 1 [O (16 g)] = 18 g$
- 1 mol of SiO_2 contains 6.022×10^{23} molecules of SiO_2 and has a mass of 60 g:

  $1 Si (28 g) + 2 [O (16 g)] = 60 g$
- 1 mol of $ZnSO_4 \cdot 2H_2O$ contains 6.022×10^{23} formula units of $ZnSO_4 \cdot 2H_2O$ and has a mass of 197 g:

- 1 Zn (65 g) + 1 S (32 g) + 4 [O (16 g)] + 2 [H_2O (18 g)] = 197 g

See the pattern? You just add up the masses of all the elements present in a compound to determine the mass of one mole of that compound. This is called the **molar mass**.

This means that anything less than that mass will be only part of a mole.

For example, if you weighed out 2.00 g of $ZnSO_4 \cdot 2H_2O$, you would have 0.0102 mol of $ZnSO_4 \cdot 2H_2O$, as shown below.

$$2.00 \text{ g } ZnSO_4 \cdot 2H_2O \times \frac{1 \text{ mol } ZnSO_4 \cdot 2H_2O}{197 \text{ g}} = 0.0102 \text{ mol } ZnSO_4 \cdot 2H_2O$$

If you have 500.0 g of $ZnSO_4 \cdot 2H_2O$, that would be:

$$500.0 \text{ g } ZnSO_4 \cdot 2H_2O \times \frac{1 \text{ mol } ZnSO_4 \cdot 2H_2O}{197 \text{ g}} = 2.54 \text{ mol } ZnSO_4 \cdot 2H_2O$$

In order to determine the identity of your unknown hydrate, you have to understand a few things about chemical formulas. Suppose your unknown has the formula $CaSO_4 \cdot 2H_2O$. The formula tells you several things. First, the formula indicates that for every one unit of this compound, there is 1 calcium atom, 1 sulfur atom, 6 oxygen atoms (4 from the $CaSO_4$ and 2 from the H_2O), and 4 hydrogen atoms. Most commonly, this compound would be described as a dihydrate. That is, there are two water molecules for every calcium sulfate group. Its name is therefore calcium sulfate dihydrate. The formula also indicates that for every 1 mol of this compound, there will be 1 mol of calcium atoms, 1 mol of sulfur atoms, 6 mol of oxygen atoms, and 4 mol of hydrogen atoms.

5 lbs
Copper Sulphate

Number of Moles of Each Atom in $CaSO_4 \cdot 2H_2O$

Hydrogen atoms	Oxygen atoms	Sulfur atom	Calcium atom	$CaSO_4 \cdot 2H_2O$

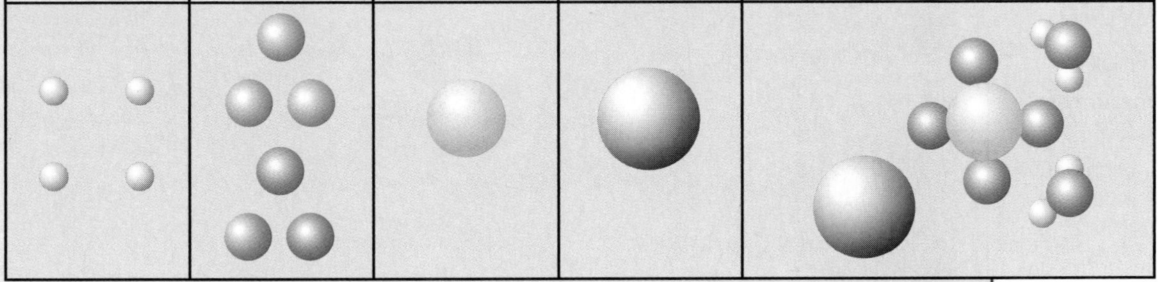

Chem Words

molar mass: the mass of one mole of a pure substance.

Putting Hydrates and Anhydrates to Work

Gypsum is a natural mineral whose chemical name is calcium sulfate dihydrate. The formula is represented as $CaSO_4 \cdot 2H_2O$. This tells you that each molecule of calcium sulfate has two water molecules attached to it.

If you have ever had a broken bone, the doctor may have made a cast out of gypsum to fit over the broken area. Improved materials have replaced gypsum in many places. Gypsum is also called plaster of Paris from gypsum quarries located near Paris. To make plaster of Paris you start with powdered gypsum by heating the hydrated calcium sulfate to about 160°C to drive off some of the water to form the hemi-hydrate calcium sulfate ($CaSO_4 \cdot \frac{1}{2}H_2O$). Hemi means $\frac{1}{2}$. Now when you mix it with water it makes a paste that you can apply to the area that has the broken bone. A hard cast is formed when the hemi-hydrate ($CaSO_4 \cdot \frac{1}{2}H_2O$) reacts with the water to return to the original dihydrate ($CaSO_4 \cdot 2H_2O$).

$$2CaSO_4 \cdot \tfrac{1}{2}H_2O + 3H_2O \rightarrow 2CaSO_4 \cdot 2H_2O$$

This process takes about 30 min to set.

Plaster has many uses in the world of art as well. Plaster is used to produce intricate details in interior architecture. Plaster can be poured into casts to create sculptures or other pieces of art. Plaster is often used as an intermediate stage for large bronze sculptures. Plaster can also have other substances like cement, sand, and even wood fibers added to it to give it more strength.

Checking Up

1. What is a mole?
2. What is molar mass?
3. What is the difference between a compound that is hydrated or anhydrous?
4. How many grams are there in 1.5 mol of water?

What Do You Think Now?

At the beginning of the activity you were asked:

- **What are some properties of ceramic materials that make them so useful?**
- **What are some properties of ceramic materials that can limit their usefulness?**

What is a potter doing when she is firing her pottery? What effect does this have on the pottery?

Chem Essential Questions

What does it mean?

Chemistry explains a macroscopic phenomenon (what you observe) with a description of what happens at the nanoscopic level (atoms and molecules) using symbolic structures as a way to communicate. Complete the chart below in your *Active Chemistry* log.

MACRO	NANO	SYMBOLIC
How did the mass measurement of the unknown compound that you investigated convince you that the compound was hydrated?	*Explain how an anhydrous compound becomes hydrated at the nano level.*	*Use formulas to show the difference between a hydrated and a dehydrated compound.*

How do you know?

Draw a model of the copper sulfate pentahydrate ($CuSO_4 \cdot 5H_2O$) and copper sulfate anhydride using diamonds to represent the anhydride and circles to represent H_2O molecules.

Why do you believe?

When measuring anhydrous compounds on the balance, why must you always remember to immediately replace the lid on the reagent container?

Why should you care?

Would it be possible to incorporate an anhydrate/hydrate chemical system into a work of art? That is, can you imagine a scenario where a color change takes place in a piece of art? Design a simple system based on this concept to be used in some art form.

Reflecting on the Activity and the Challenge

So far, you have examined several different artistic media, and some of the chemistry behind each one. In this activity you investigated hydrated compounds and saw the changes they undergo upon dehydration and re-hydration. You learned that removing water from a hydrated compound affects the crystalline structure of the compound and in turn its properties. You showed these changes by writing formulas and determining the molar masses of the hydrated and anhydrous compounds.

Since your challenge is to create a museum display (including a work of art) and to explain the chemistry related to creating it, consider how you might use the knowledge gained from this activity in your display.

Chem to Go

1. How is knowing the percentage by mass of water different from knowing the mole ratio of water to the hydrate?
2. Why do chemists use the unit *moles*?
3. What is the gram-molecular mass of $NaN_{3(s)}$?
4. What is the total number of moles of $NaN_{3(s)}$ in a 52-g sample of the compound?
5. A sample of a compound contains 65.4 g of zinc, 12.0 g of carbon, and 48.0 g of oxygen. What is the mole ratio (simplest formula) of zinc to carbon to oxygen in this compound?
6. A sample of a substance containing only magnesium and chlorine was tested in the laboratory and was found to be composed of 74.5% chlorine by mass. If the total mass of the sample was 190.2 g, what was the mass of the magnesium?
7. Kaolinite is a type of clay commonly used for making china. Its formula is $Al_2Si_2O_5(OH)_4$. Suppose you were given approximately 250 g of kaolinite for creating an object. How many moles of kaolinite did you have?
8. You may have noticed that most electronic equipment comes packed with small packets of desiccants (drying agents that pick up water molecules). Speculate about what you think these desiccants might be made of and why they are placed in packaged electronic equipment.
9. In *Part A*, if the empty crucible was not heated long enough to completely dry it prior to weighing, what would be the effect on the calculated percent water in the unknown (larger or smaller)? Explain.

10. Explain how determining the percent composition of water might be useful to a potter.

11. Calculate the mass of water removed in forming the anhydrate from 3.22 g of $Na_2SO_4 \cdot (10H_2O)$.

12. ***Preparing for the Chapter Challenge***

Your challenge for this chapter involves the creation of a work of art. In *Part C* of this activity you made an object out of clay. How could you use this object in your final work of art? Consider the object and come up with some ideas for how you might add another element to the object to make it more useful or aesthetically pleasing. Take one of your ideas for adding on to the clay object and then do it.

Inquiring Further

1. History of ceramics

Research the history of ceramics. What can archaeologists discern about a culture or a society from its pottery? How does the history of ceramics also mirror the advancements in technology for a culture? What are some of the newest uses for ceramics today? What is it about the properties of clay that make it so useful?

2. Desiccants

Desiccants are used for a variety of purposes because of their tendency to absorb moisture. Conduct some research, both in and out of the lab, to determine if there is a relationship between the percent of water in a hydrate and its water-absorbing capacity. Based on your findings, make some recommendations about which anhydrous salts make the best desiccants.

Chapter mini Challenge

THE BRIDGE
HONK

Your challenge for this chapter is to create a work of art that represents you and/or your times using appropriate artistic techniques. In addition to the artwork itself, you will also need to create an informative museum display that includes:

- A demonstration of the techniques involved.
- Your original work.
- A museum placard or pamphlet explaining the chemistry involved.

Having completed five activities, this is a good time to give your work of art a *first try*. It's time to provide a sketch of your artwork and describe it to your class. You should also preview your museum pamphlet or placard. Of course, being limited to the chemistry content of five activities will limit your art. This *first try*, however, will give you a good sense of what the challenge entails and how you and other teams are going to approach this task.

Chemistry Content

Your team should first review the chemistry content that may be included in this artwork and related pamphlet or placard.

Activity 1: You discussed art in general and what makes something a piece of art.

Activity 2: You learned about acids, pH, and how materials are affected by exposure to acids.

Activity 3: You investigated the chemical behavior of metals and learned how to electroplate a piece of metal.

Activity 4: You studied the physical behavior of metals and alloys.

Activity 5: You observed the effect of heat on hydrates and learned how clay could be part of your artwork. You were also introduced to the mole—the chemistry way of counting.

Criteria

Your team should also review the criteria that you discussed on the first day of this chapter. Your artwork and museum placard or pamphlet should be creative, artistic, and interesting as well as have accurate chemistry explanations.

Preparing for Your mini Challenge

At this point, you can decide on whether your artwork will include metal or clay or a combination of these and other materials. You can describe this artwork to the class or make a sketch of your initial ideas. At this point, you do not have to build the actual artwork. You will also have a chance to share with the class your idea for the museum placard. This can be similar to the one you expect to have for the final project.

Sharing your artwork and museum placard with your class will help you learn about what works and doesn't work in a display. You will be able to provide feedback to other teams and they will provide feedback to you. You will not be given much preparation time for the creation of this artwork. The *mini-challenge* is a way to get a sense of what you will be involved with at the end of the chapter when you have more chemistry content to include in your full artwork and its corresponding placard.

Engineering/Technology Design

The engineering-design process involves a number of distinct steps. In creating an art display and accompanying text, you are involved in a design process. Note how your efforts follow the design model described.

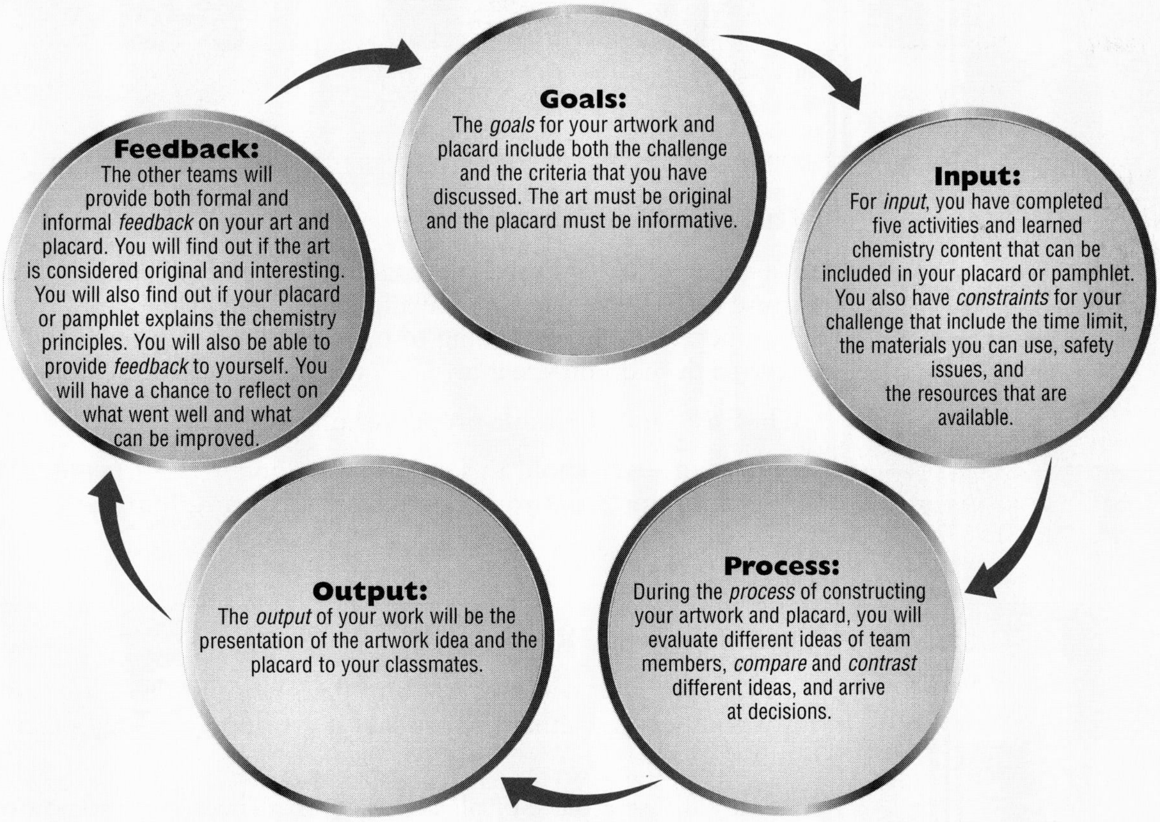
Goals:
The goals for your artwork and placard include both the challenge and the criteria that you have discussed. The art must be original and the placard must be informative.
Input:
For input, you have completed five activities and learned chemistry content that can be included in your placard or pamphlet. You also have constraints for your challenge that include the time limit, the materials you can use, safety issues, and the resources that are available.
Process:
During the process of constructing your artwork and placard, you will evaluate different ideas of team members, compare and contrast different ideas, and arrive at decisions.
Output:
The output of your work will be the presentation of the artwork idea and the placard to your classmates.
Feedback:
The other teams will provide both formal and informal feedback on your art and placard. You will find out if the art is considered original and interesting. You will also find out if your placard or pamphlet explains the chemistry principles. You will also be able to provide feedback to yourself. You will have a chance to reflect on what went well and what can be improved.

Remember: This is a *first try*. The feedback that you get from the art description and the placard will be extremely valuable when you create your original artwork and museum placard or pamphlet. At that point, you will have additional artistic techniques and materials to incorporate into your work. You will begin the entire design cycle again. That's why it is called a cycle. You keep going through it over and over to improve your design or, in this case, your original artwork.

Activity 6 Paints

What Do You See?

H₂O
ASSORTED PIGMENTS FOR ARTISTS
GUAR GUM
LINSEED OIL

GOALS

In this activity you will:

- Identify and predict properties of double-replacement reactions.
- Observe reactions that produce precipitates.
- Understand how insoluble compounds can be used as pigments.

What Do You Think?

Ancient cave dwellers used charcoal and minerals for their drawings because that is what they had available to them at the time. As time went by, an increased understanding of pigments (coloring agents) allowed people to develop different artwork with more brilliant colors.

- **What are some desirable properties of a pigment?**

Record your ideas about this question in your *Active Chemistry* log. Be prepared to discuss your responses with your group and the class.

Investigate

Part A: Precipitate Reactions

In this activity you will mix different pairs of solutions. After mixing, you will observe whether the product is a solution, a solid precipitate, or both.

1. You will use a piece of plastic wrap or a sheet of plastic on which to test your solutions. You will want to mix every possible pair of solutions.

   Prepare a copy of the table shown to place beneath the plastic sheet. Make a second copy in your log to record your results.

	$FeCl_3$	NaOH	$Zn(NO_3)_2$	KI	Na_2CO_3	NaCl	K_2SO_4	$CuSO_4$
$FeCl_3$ iron(III)chloride	X							
NaOH sodium hydroxide		X						
$Zn(NO_3)_2$ zinc nitrate			X					
KI potassium iodide				X				
Na_2CO_3 sodium carbonate					X			
NaCl sodium chloride						X		
K_2SO_4 potassium sulfate							X	
$CuSO_4$ copper sulfate								X

For the first reaction, you will mix $FeCl_3$ with NaOH and record whether a solid precipitate has formed. You will then continue along the first row and mix $FeCl_3$ with $Zn(NO_3)_2$ and record whether a solid precipitate is formed. You will then mix $FeCl_3$ with each of the other solutions and record the results in the first row of the table.

a) Why is an X noted in the first box?

2. The different solutions you will use are in dropper bottles. Using only one or two drops of each, react each solution with the others. Do not allow the tip of the dropper of one solution to come in contact with the other solution.

a) If a precipitate forms, record its color in the table in your log by using the notation "Ppt (color)." If no precipitate forms, record "Sol" (for solution) in the table.

3. To analyze the results, you must understand how the reactions proceed. All of these reactions are double-replacement reactions. The general equation for this type of reaction is:

$$AB + CD \rightarrow AD + CB$$

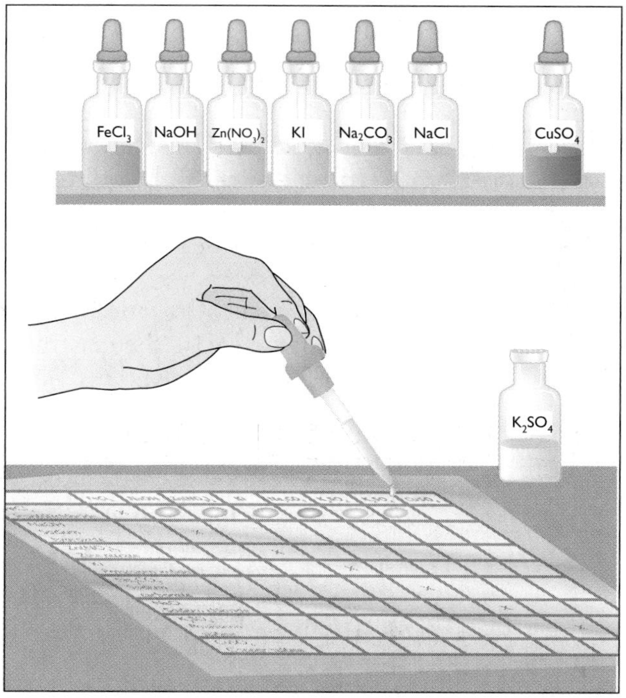
FeCl3
NaOH
Zn(NO3)2
KI
Na2CO3
NaCl
CuSO4
K2SO4

Safety goggles and a lab apron must be worn *at all times* in a chemistry lab.

For example, the first reaction you investigated was:

Iron (III) chloride(aq) + sodium hydroxide(aq) →
iron (III) hydroxide(s) + sodium chloride(aq)

$FeCl_3(aq) + 3NaOH(aq) \rightarrow$
$Fe(OH)_3(s) + 3NaCl(aq)$

The ionic equation would be:

$Fe^{3+}(aq) + 3Cl^{-}(aq) + 3Na^{+}(aq) + 3OH^{-}(aq) \rightarrow$
$Fe(OH)_3(s) + 3Na^{+}(aq) + 3Cl^{-}(aq)$

Notice that the symbol (aq) has been added to the solutions to indicate that the chemical is dissolved in water (aqueous solution). The symbol (s) has been added to identify the solid precipitate.

The equation has also been balanced in order to conserve mass. For example, the three chlorine atoms in the reactant, iron (III) chloride ($FeCl_3$) must also be present as three chlorine atoms in the product, sodium chloride (NaCl).

In this reaction, one of the products, iron hydroxide, [$Fe(OH)_3$], was not soluble. You observed it as a solid precipitate.

a) Write word equations [e.g., iron (III) chloride(aq) + sodium hydroxide(aq) → iron (III) hydroxide(s) + sodium chloride(aq)] for each of the double-replacement reactions that you investigated. Use the general format AB + CD → AD + CB.

   There were 64 boxes in the grid. Eight of the reactions (along the diagonal) were not carried out. Of the remaining 56 boxes, there are only 28 reactions. Why are the reactions above the diagonal identical to the reactions below the diagonal? You are therefore required to write 28 double-replacement reactions.

b) Make a list of all soluble compounds that you observed in these reactions. The first eight soluble compounds in your list will be the ones that you began with (e.g., iron (III) chloride, sodium hydroxide, zinc nitrate, etc.).

   The next set of soluble compounds is the products of the reactions that did not produce a solid precipitate (from the chart of reactions).

c) For each reaction that produced a precipitate, indicate which product is the precipitate by placing an (s) after the name of the compound. Remember that for the reactions that produced a precipitate, one of the products should be on your soluble list. The other is the precipitate.

4. Dispose of the materials as directed by your teacher.

5. In your *Active Chemistry* log, answer the following:

   a) Identify types of compounds that were found on the soluble list (for example: sodium compounds).

   b) Identify types of compounds that were generally insoluble.

Part B: Paints

In this part of this activity, you will attempt to determine which compounds make good pigments and which liquids make good binders to carry the pigments.

Your teacher will supply you with some compounds or have you prepare larger amounts of compounds from *Part A*.

The compounds may include some of the following:

Oxides	Carbonates	Sulfates
copper	copper	copper
iron	iron	iron
zinc	zinc	zinc
nickel	nickel	nickel

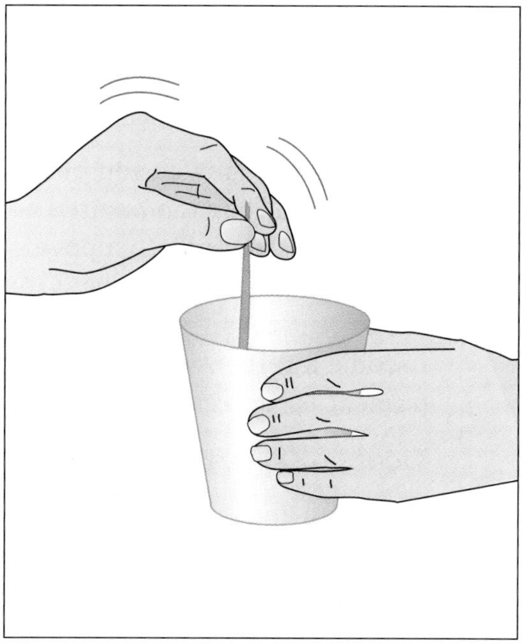

1. Make a table in your *Active Chemistry* log similar to the one shown below.
2. Using each medium (water, egg white and linseed oil) and a small mixing container, add a small quantity of the compound to be tested and mix thoroughly with a toothpick. Record the color of the paint in the table.
   a) Record your observations to these questions in your *Active Chemistry* log.
3. After you finish with single compounds, try mixing some of the compounds to make new colors. Try to make at least four or five different colors.
   a) Record your observations in your *Active Chemistry* log.
   b) Which medium seems to keep the color of the solid the best? Which medium is poorest? Which change the color?
   c) Which colors were difficult to produce?

	Medium		
	Water	Egg white	Linseed oil
Compound A			
Compound B			
Compound C			

Chem Talk

Chem Words

cation: an ion that has a positive charge.

anion: an ion that has a negative charge.

precipitate: an insoluble salt that is formed when two solutions are mixed together.

ionic compound: a compound that is composed of positive ions (cations) and negative ions (anions).

salt: an ionic compound that is a product of neutralization reaction.

double-replacement reaction: a reaction in which two elements or groups of elements in two different compounds exchange places to form new compounds.

THE CHEMISTRY OF COLOR PIGMENTS

Using Solid Precipitates as Pigments

The solid precipitates you observed in this activity are insoluble compounds. They can be used as pigments for paints. In making paint, the pigment is crushed into a powder and mixed with a liquid (called the binder). The liquid could be water or some other liquid such as linseed oil, turpentine, or guar gum. If the pigment is insoluble in the liquid, it will become a suspension of particles in the liquid. When the paint dries, the pigment particles are left behind.

Double-Replacement Reactions

There are thousands upon thousands of reactions that occur in the world, and most of them take place in water (aqueous) solutions. When certain **cations** and **anions** are combined, water-insoluble ionic compounds may form. (Cations are positively charged ions and anions are negatively charged ions.) When these ions are in separate aqueous solutions and then brought together, an insoluble solid, or precipitate forms. The precipitate is an **ionic compound** (often called a **salt**) that forms because certain ions attract each other so strongly that they are removed from the water solution as the product of a chemical reaction. A **double-replacement reaction** is one type of precipitation reaction where a precipitate forms when one of the products is insoluble.

Look at the example of the reaction between solutions of zinc nitrate and sodium carbonate that you observed in the activity:

$$\text{Zinc nitrate}_{(aq)} + \text{sodium carbonate}_{(aq)} \rightarrow \text{sodium nitrate}_{(aq)} + \text{zinc carbonate}_{(s)}$$

$$Zn(NO_3)_{2(aq)} + Na_2CO_{3(aq)} \rightarrow 2NaNO_{3(aq)} + ZnCO_{3(s)}$$

Note that (aq) means a compound is in aqueous solution, and (s) means that a solid has formed (the precipitate).

In solution, you have ions, according to the ionic equation:

$$Zn^{2+}{(aq)} + 2NO_3^-{(aq)} + 2Na^+{(aq)} + CO_3^{2-}{(aq)} \rightarrow 2Na^+{(aq)} + 2NO_3^-{(aq)} + ZnCO_{3(s)}$$

The zinc ions and carbonate ions are strongly attracted to each other and form a solid that no longer stays in solution. Zinc carbonate is the precipitate in this reaction.

The Na^+ and NO_3^- ions do not undergo any change; they remain in solution before and after the reaction. Ions that do not participate in the reaction are called **spectator ions**. If you removed them from the total ionic equation, the net result would be:

$$Zn^{2+}(aq) + CO_3^{2-}(aq) \rightarrow ZnCO_3(s)$$

which is called the **Net Ionic Equation.**

It is possible, based on experience, to predict whether or not a precipitate will form in a double-replacement reaction. The following solubility rules will help you to predict the products of precipitation reactions. Chemists do not memorize these rules but refer to them when needed. Some of these simple rules may have come from the analysis of the double-replacement reactions that you conducted in this activity.

Simple Rules for Solubility of Ionic Compounds in Water

1. Most nitrate (NO_3^-), acetate (CH_3COO^-), and perchlorate (ClO_4^-) compounds are soluble.
2. Group 1A metal (Li^+, Na^+, and K^+) and ammonium (NH_4^+) compounds are soluble.
3. Most chloride (Cl^-), bromide (Br^-), and iodide (I^-) compounds are soluble. The most notable exceptions are when these anions are combined with Cu^+, Ag^+, Pb^{2+}, Hg^{2+}, and Hg_2^{2+}.
4. Most sulfate (SO_4^{2-}) compounds are soluble, except when they are combined with Ba^{2+}, Hg_2^{2+}, Sr^{2+}, and Pb^{2+}. Ca^{2+} compounds are slightly soluble.
5. Carbonate (CO_3^{2-}) and phosphate (PO_4^{3-}) compounds are only slightly soluble.
6. Most hydroxide (OH^-) compounds are insoluble except when combined with group 1A cations. $Ca(OH)_2$ is slightly soluble.

An ionic compound is said to be **soluble** if a large amount of it dissolves in water. How much is a "large amount"? Typically, this means a solution with a concentration of at least 0.1 mol/L (mole per liter) at room temperature. An **insoluble** ionic compound is defined as one that will not dissolve in water, typically producing an aqueous solution of less than 0.001 mol/L at room temperature. A slightly soluble compound falls somewhere between these two boundaries, usually forming a precipitate in water.

Chem Words

soluble: a substance that dissolves in a liquid.

insoluble: a substance that will not dissolve in a liquid.

spectator ion: ions that do not participate in the reaction and remain in solution before and after the reaction.

Net Ionic Equation: chemical equation for a reaction that lists only those compounds participating in the reaction.

Checking Up

1. Predict the products when the following aqueous solutions are combined; write the entire reaction as a word equation and then again using symbols.
   a) copper sulfate plus sodium hydroxide
   b) potassium iodide plus iron (III) bromide
2. Use the solubility rules to determine which of the following are insoluble in water:
   a) lithium acetate
   b) ammonium chloride
   c) silver bromide

What Do You Think Now?

At the beginning of the activity, you were asked:

- **What are some desirable properties of a pigment?**

What makes a compound a good paint pigment? Will different binders give different results?

Chem Essential Questions

What does it mean?

Chemistry explains a macroscopic phenomenon (what you observe) with a description of what happens at the nanoscopic level (atoms and molecules) using symbolic structures as a way to communicate. Complete the chart below in your *Active Chemistry* log.

MACRO	NANO	SYMBOLIC
What visual evidence do you have to prove that a double-replacement reaction has occurred?	*How can mixing two clear solutions produce a solid material? What is happening at the molecular level? Provide a specific example in your discussion.*	*Use symbols in a chemical equation to explain what happens during a double-replacement reaction.*

How do you know?

What experimental data do you have that shows how a pigment can form from a precipitation reaction?

Why do you believe?

Silver bromide (AgBr) is used in photography. Finely divided silver bromide is suspended in a solution of gelatin, which is used to coat a plastic film. When light strikes the film, silver atoms are formed, creating what is known as the latent image. This is then subjected to the development process. Afterwards, excess AgBr must be washed off the negative. This is done by washing the negative with sodium thiosulphate ($Na_2S_2O_3$) solution. Based on the knowledge you gained from this activity, explain why sodium thiosulphate dissolves the AgBr. Use a balanced equation in your discussion.

Why should you care?

Preparing your own pigments to be used as paints in your *Chapter Challenge* would be very interesting to many people. Creating a work of art about yourself with paints that you created yourself would be a significant addition to your *Chapter Challenge*. What color do you want your pigment to possess?

Reflecting on the Activity and the Challenge

You have seen on the macro level how some precipitates are formed. You have looked at the solubility of certain chemicals. On the micro level, you have read about the ions in solution and the fact that some combinations of ions will form precipitates. You can now predict the formation of precipitates from double-replacement reactions. The reactions can be represented symbolically in word equations and formula equations. There is chemistry behind the development of various colored pigments. For example, the solubility of pigments and the use of different pigments in watercolors, oil paints and acrylics will vary.

Precipitation reactions are also responsible for the formation of the patina on copper and its alloys. The opposite of a precipitation reaction occurs when an acid reacts with calcium carbonate. In this case, an insoluble substance (calcium carbonate) is made soluble by the reaction with the acid. This can cause the deterioration of statues and other artwork (refer back to *Activity 2*). Consider how you might incorporate this information in your artwork and museum display.

Chem to Go

Using the Simple Rules for Solubility in *Chem Talk*, answer the following questions.

1. Describe the difference between salts that are water soluble, slightly soluble, and insoluble.
2. Which of the following compounds are soluble in water?
   a) $NaOH$
   b) $CuCl_2$
   c) $PbSO_4$
   d) KCl
   e) $Mg(OH)_2$
3. Predict whether precipitation will occur when the following compounds in aqueous solution are combined. If so, what is the formula of the precipitate?
   a) barium chloride + aluminum sulfate
   b) silver nitrate + potassium chloride
4. Predict whether precipitation will occur when the following solutions are combined. If so, what is the formula of the precipitate?
   a) $AgNO_3(aq) + KBr(aq)$
   b) $Na_2SO_4(aq) + MgCl_2(aq)$
   c) $KOH(aq) + Fe(NO_3)_3(aq)$

5. Which set of compounds contains a salt that is insoluble in water?
   a) $BaCl_2$, $ZnCO_3$, $LiOH$
   b) Cs_2SO_4, KOH, $MgBr_2$
   c) $(NH_4)_2SO_4$, Li_3PO_4, $KC_2H_3O_2$
   d) $NaNO_3$, $MgCl_2$, Li_2CO_3
6. Which of the following would most likely be a precipitate formed in a double-replacement reaction?
   a) $AgCl$ b) $AgNO_3$ c) $NaCl$ d) $LiNO_3$
7. Which of the following shows the general equation of a double-replacement reaction?
   a) $AB + CD \rightarrow ABDC$ b) $AB + CD \rightarrow AD + CB$
   c) $AB + CD \rightarrow BA + DC$ d) $AB + CD \rightarrow AD + CD$
8. If a solid forms from a double-replacement reaction, it is called:
   a) precipitate b) reactant c) product d) pigment
9. For the following reaction, write the products in a balanced equation, and then give the total ionic equation and the net ionic equation.
   $LiOH(aq) + AgHCO_3 \rightarrow ?$
10. In photography, silver halide (e.g., silver bromide or chloride) salts are used as described in the *Why do you believe?* section. One way to produce AgCl is by reacting aqueous silver nitrate with aqueous potassium chloride. What is the other product of this reaction, and what are the "spectator" ions?

Inquiring Further

Paint pigments over time

Research the formulas for various paint pigments. How have their origins and ingredients changed over time? Compile your findings in an article for an art magazine.

Activity 7 Dyes

What Do You See?

COFFEE
Tea
BLACK
CABBAGE
CARROTS

GOALS

In this activity you will:

- Extract dyes from natural sources.
- Examine factors that affect the color and colorfastness of dyes.

What Do You Think?

Look around the room at the colors of your classmates' clothing. Notice the variety of colors, shadings, and intensity. A dye is simply a substance used to color materials. Humans have been using dyes for over 5000 years.

- **List some desirable properties of a dye.**
- **Identify as many natural sources of dyes as you can.**

Record your ideas about these questions in your *Active Chemistry* log. Be prepared to discuss your responses with your group and the class.

Investigate

Each team will be doing *Parts A* and *B* at the same time. You will be assigned a particular solution and a special procedure. Read both *Parts A* and *B* before proceeding so that you can get both parts done at the same time.

Part A: Colors and pH

The bonding of dyes to fibers is often pH-dependent. In this part of the investigation, you will observe the effect of changing the pH on the colors of two natural dyes.

1. Your teacher has prepared two solutions. One solution was made with the green tops of carrots. The second contains onion

Safety goggles and apron must be worn *at all times* in a chemistry lab.

Clean up any spills immediately.

The hot plate will remain hot for a period of time even after it is turned off.

skins. These materials have been simmering for at least 30 min in distilled water.

2. Your teacher will assign you a group number. Follow these steps for *Part A*.
   - Pour about 100 mL of your group's solution into a 150-mL beaker. The solution for your group is shown in the table.
   - Label the beaker using your group's number.
   - Use hydrion paper to measure the pH and adjust as indicated.
   - Place a piece of yarn in the beaker.
   - Place the beaker on a hot plate at medium and heat for 15 min. There should always be some liquid in the beaker.
   - Fill a 250-mL beaker two-thirds full of warm tap water.
   - Use a glass stirring rod to remove the yarn from the dye bath.
   - Rinse the sample yarn thoroughly in the warm water and lay it on a paper towel to dry.
   - Summarize your results.

Group number	Solution	pH adjustment
A1	carrot top	Adjust the pH to 3–4 by adding vinegar to the solution.
A2	carrot top	Determine the pH of the solution.
A3	carrot top	Adjust the pH to 10 by adding ammonia to the solution.
A4	onion	Adjust the pH to 3–4 by adding vinegar to the solution.
A5	onion	Determine the pH of the solution.
A6	onion	Adjust the pH to 10 by adding ammonia to the solution.

3. Present your data to the other groups. Complete a chart that shows the natural dye used (carrot top or onion skin), the pH, and the color of the yarn. From your chart, comment on your observations.
   a) Did pH have an effect on the color of the dyed material?
   b) Why might it be useful to know how pH affects dyes?

Part B: Mordants

The color from natural dyes often fades upon repeated washings or from exposure to light. Early in dyeing history, it was discovered that if certain metallic salts were added to wool, the dyeing became less likely to wash out. A mordant is a chemical that fixes a dye.

1. Your teacher has prepared the following dye solutions. They have been simmering for at least 30 min.

   Dye beaker 1: onion skins in 200 mL of distilled water

   Dye beaker 2: carrot greens torn into pieces in 200 mL of distilled water

   Dye beaker 3: rose hip and hibiscus tea bags in 200 mL of distilled water

   Dye beaker 4: chamomile tea bags in 200 mL of distilled water

2. Your teacher has also prepared the following mordant solutions. These 100-mL beakers also contain four pieces of yarn each that have a special knot for identification purposes and have also been simmering for 30 min. The mordants were prepared in the following ways:

   Mordant beaker A: 1.5 g copper sulfate pentahydrate ($CuSO_4 \cdot 5H_2O$) dissolved in 75 mL of distilled water. (The four strings in this copper mordant will each have a knot in one end of the yarn.)

   Mordant beaker B: 1.5 g alum and 0.75 g cream of tartar dissolved in 75 mL of distilled water. (The four strings in this alum mordant will each have a knot in both ends of the yarn.)

   Mordant beaker C: 0.35 g tin (II) chloride ($SnCl_2$) and 2.00 g cream of tartar dissolved in 75 mL of distilled water. (The four strings in this tin mordant will each have a knot in the center of the yarn.)

   Mordant beaker D: Distilled water. (The four strings in the water without a mordant will have no knot in the yarn.)

3. Use the same group number as in *Part A*. Follow these steps for *Part B*.
   - Use a glass stirring rod to remove a piece of yarn from the mordant beakers indicated in the table.
   - Lay the pieces of yarn on paper towels.
   - Obtain the number of 100-mL beakers indicated. Using beaker tongs, decant (pour) about 75 mL of the dye indicated below into each of these beakers.
   - Place one piece of yarn from each of your mordant beakers into the dye.
   - Place the beakers on the hot plate and allow the solutions to simmer with occasional stirring for about 15 min.
   - Half-fill a 250-mL beaker with warm water. Remove the yarn pieces from the dye baths, and rinse them in the warm water. Lay them according to coded group on a paper towel to dry.

Clean up any spills immediately.

The hot plate will remain hot for a period of time even after it is turned off.

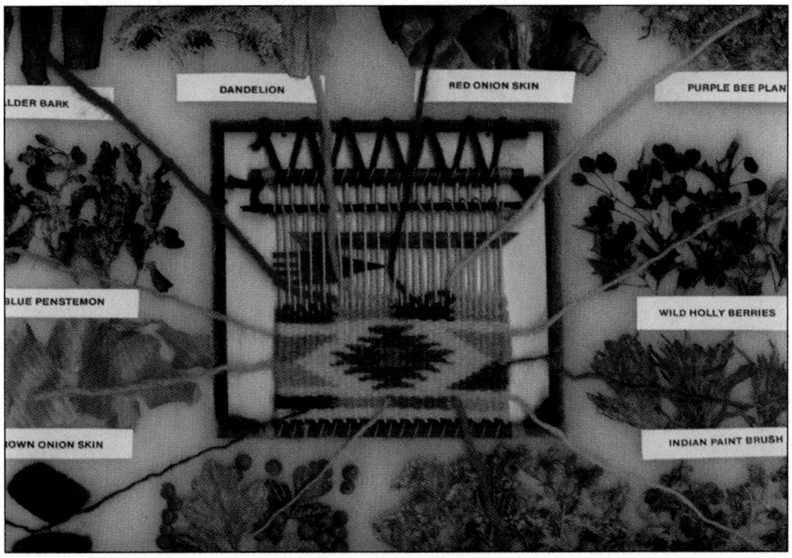
DANDELION
RED ONION SKIN
WILD HOLLY BERRIES
INDIAN PAINT BRUSH

		Mordant Beaker			
		A	B	C	D
Dye Beaker Number	1	Group 1	Group 1	Group 1	Group 2
	2	Group 2	Group 2	Group 3	Group 3
	3	Group 3	Group 4	Group 4	Group 4
	4	Group 5	Group 5	Group 6	Group 6

Wash your hands and arms thoroughly after the activity.

Dye material	Mordant	Color
carrot tops	copper	
	alum	
	tin	
	no mordant	
onion skins	copper	
	alum	
	tin	
	no mordant	
rose hip and hibiscus tea	copper	
	alum	
	tin	
	no mordant	
chamomile	copper	
	alum	
	tin	
	no mordant	

4. When the samples are dry, share your data with other teams.
   a) Complete the data table on the left in your *Active Chemistry* log.
5. Dispose of the materials as directed by your teacher. Clean up your workstation.
6. Answer the following questions in your *Active Chemistry* log.
   a) Did each mordant affect the yarn in the same way?
   b) Did any of the mordants appear to cause a more dramatic change in the dye color?
   c) Which mordant appeared to cause the least change in the dye color?

Chem Talk

Chem Words

dye: typically defined as organic molecules that bond directly to a textile.

DYES

Early Uses of Dyes

The human race has been awed by color since antiquity. Early use of coloring agents was limited to pigments obtained from rocks and salts. **Dyes** are typically defined as organic molecules that bond directly to a textile. Since they are tightly bound to the material, they do not wash out like the early coloring agents did.

The production of dyes has been a human activity since the art of weaving was first developed. Egyptian tombs from around 3500 B.C. contained dyed materials. There is recorded evidence of Chinese dye workshops that existed around 3000 B.C.

In the past, dyes were made from animal, vegetable, and mineral materials. Because the raw materials used for these dyes varied, the

results were often unpredictable. One very famous dye was Tyrian purple. This dye was extracted from the shells of the marine mollusk *Murex brandaris*. The mollusks were crushed and then boiled in seawater for ten days. The material to be dyed was dipped into this solution and then exposed to sunlight. This produced a beautiful purple color. The Roman Empire decreed that only members of the ruling class could wear robes colored with Tyrian purple. Julius Caesar and Cleopatra were among those who dressed in clothing dyed with this expensive dye.

Chemical Features of Dyes

What are the important chemical features of a dye molecule that make it useful as a dye? The **chromophore** is that part of the dye molecule responsible for the color you see. These are groups of atoms within an organic molecule that absorb only certain colors of visible light. The light of the colors not absorbed is reflected to our eyes. White light is the sum of all colors of the spectrum: red, orange, yellow, green, blue, indigo, and violet. (ROY G BIV is a helpful mnemonic to remember the spectrum colors.) The Tyrian purple molecule absorbs red, green, yellow, and blue light from ordinary light. The other colors are reflected and appear purple. Sometimes an **auxochrome** will be present, which will modify the chromophore's ability to absorb light energy.

A dye must also be water soluble so that it can interact with the textile to be colored. Once it has penetrated the fabric, the **mordant** assists in the binding of the dye to the textile.

The color from natural dyes often fades upon repeated washings or from exposure to light. Early in dyeing history, it was discovered that if certain metallic salts were added to wool, the dyeing became less likely to wash out. These metal salts were called mordants (from the French word, *mordre*, "to bite"). It was thought that these salts helped the dye "bite" into the wool and "hold it fast" during washings.

Chem Words

chromophore: the part of the dye molecule responsible for the color.

auxochrome: a functional group attached to a chromophore that enhances the chromophore's ability to absorb light energy. It can alter the wavelength, intensity or both.

mordant: metallic salts added to a dye to make it less likely to wash out.

Aluminum ion (Al^{3+}), chromium (III) ion (Cr^{3+}), copper (II) ion (Cu^{2+}), iron (III) ion (Fe^{3+}), and tin (II) ion (Sn^{2+}) are commonly used as mordants. Generally, the wool is pre-treated with a solution of the metal salt in order to allow the metal ions to attach themselves to the wool before dyeing. When the dye is introduced, it forms an insoluble complex salt, sometimes called a lake, with the metal ion within the fiber. This large, complex molecule is less water soluble than the individual dye molecules. Therefore, the dyed material is less likely to lose its color upon washing. Mordants are also used to increase the range of colors available from a given dye.

While early dyes were obtained from natural sources, today nearly all dyes are produced synthetically. Synthetic dyes provide a wide range of color and reproducibility not found in dyes extracted from natural sources. The latter half of the 20th century has seen a renewed interest in natural dyes. The unpredictability of the results is an attractive feature of dyeing with natural materials; each dye bath provides a "one-of-a-kind" color.

Checking Up

1. In textiles, what property must a dye have in order for it to be used?
2. What is an auxochrome?
3. What is a chromophore?
4. What is a mordant?

What Do You Think Now?

At the beginning of the activity you were asked to:

- **List some desirable properties of a dye.**
- **Identify as many natural sources of dyes as you can.**

From what you learned in this activity, how would you change or improve your answers to these questions? Record these in your *Active Chemistry* log.

Chem Essential Questions

What does it mean?

Chemistry explains a macroscopic phenomenon (what you observe) with a description of what happens at the nanoscopic level (atoms and molecules) using symbolic structures as a way to communicate. Complete the chart below in your *Active Chemistry* log.

MACRO	NANO	SYMBOLIC
When describing the chemistry of dyeing fabric, what is the macroscopic aspect of the process?	*When a fabric is dyed, what is happening at the molecular level?*	*Mordant, chromophore, and auxochrome are terms introduced to help you discuss dyeing. What is the meaning of each of these terms?*

How do you know?

What was the effect of altering the pH of solutions containing different natural dyes?

Why do you believe?

Coloring fabrics is big business these days. There has also been renewed interest in natural dyes. Why do you think this is? What are the advantages of a natural dye versus a synthetic one? What are the disadvantages (if any)?

Why should you care?

Coloring your artwork using natural dyes would add an element of "coolness" to your project. Being able to explain the chemistry behind it would appeal to your audience as well as your teacher. How are you going to be sure that your dye will not be lost after a period of time?

Reflecting on the Activity and the Challenge

In this activity you experimented with natural dyes. This is something artisans have been doing for thousands of years. Beautiful clothing, tapestries, blankets, rugs, and wall hangings often depend upon unique colors to enhance their artistic value. An understanding of the dyeing process might be useful for your museum display. Consider how you might incorporate some of the techniques or the chemistry that you learned from this activity into completing your *Chapter Challenge*.

Chem to Go

1. Indigo dye is one of the oldest known dyes, dating back to over 5000 years ago. Indigo plantations were found in many parts of the world, from India to the United States. Indigo was first synthesized in 1880, and by 1920 synthetic indigo had virtually replaced all natural indigo. It is still one of the most widely used dyes today—think denim.

   Small, family-owned farms are on the verge of economic collapse in the United States. The once lucrative cash crops, like tobacco, are no longer good investments for farmers. Since indigo is fairly easy to grow and grows well in the southern United States, would you recommend it as a potential crop for small farms to replace the use of synthetic indigo? Explain your reasoning.

2. Review your procedure and data on the effects of pH on dyes to assist you with this question. Soap solutions are often very basic in character. What would the effect be of rinsing acid-dyed wool in a soapy solution?

3. After treating wool yarn with various mordants and making observations of it, did you notice any difference in the way some of the yarn felt when compared to yarn in other treatments? Why would one of the mordants be less desirable for wool?

4. Using information from the *Chem Talk* section, make a drawing that shows how a mordant might affect a dye's adhesion to wool yarn. Explain how this might make some dyes more wash-fast and color-fast.

5. What criteria did you and your group use to determine good sources of natural dyes? Did the color of the dye material always resemble the color of the dye? What factors might affect the color of a dye?

6. ***Preparing for the Chapter Challenge***

   Explain how the various chemical groups of a dye might affect its properties. Describe several ways an artist might have to apply knowledge of chemistry in preparing and applying dyes.

Inquiring Further

1. Creating a successful dye

A successful dye must satisfy many conditions, such as range of color, reproducibility, wash-fastness, and colorfastness. The dye industry has many standardized scientific tests for these and other conditions. Consider what you think would be important considerations for dyes used in artwork. Choose one of these considerations and design a test to determine which dye source, mordant, pH, fabric or combination of these factors produces the best dye for your consideration. After running your tests, summarize your findings and your recommendation.

2. Using natural dyes

Determine a procedure for extracting dyes from natural materials and use them to dye pieces of wool. You may wish to develop your own procedure or do research to find proven methods. Natural, unbleached yarn is preferable for dyeing as residual bleach may affect the colors. Distilled water or soft water must always be used when dyeing as the minerals in hard water will interfere with the dye process.

Activity 8 How Does Stained Glass Get Its Color?

What Do You See?

METAL SALT
BORAX

GOALS

In this activity you will:

- Discover what gives different glass their colors.
- Examine the effect of heat on the colors of glass.

What Do You Think?

Stained glass windows adorn churches and other buildings around the world. Tiffany glass in lamp shades is now worth thousands of dollars.

- **What gives colored glass its color?**

Record your ideas about this question in your *Active Chemistry* log. Be prepared to discuss your responses with your group and the class.

Investigate

1. You will need several glass stirring rods or a nichrome wire, a small beaker of water, a Bunsen burner, borax, and several different metal compounds. You will use borax (sodium borate) as a glass substitute. This is because the temperatures needed to melt glass are usually higher than you can get in a science classroom.

   The compounds that you will be testing will all be salts with various metal cations. The anion should be the same for each metal to ensure that the differences observed are due to the metal alone and not the anion. Some cation possibilities include: iron, cobalt, nickel, copper, manganese, strontium, and other transition metals.

Safety goggles and apron must be worn *at all times* in a chemistry lab.

Follow all safety rules for working with open flames.

The borax beads will be very hot—do not touch them.

Do not inhale or ingest borax!

Some anion possibilities include: oxides, nitrates, carbonates, chlorides.

Example: FeO, CoO, NiO, CuO, and MnO

2. Light a Bunsen burner and adjust the flame to get the inner blue cone. Dip one end of a stirring rod into water and then in borax. Heat the borax in the flame just above the inner blue cone. The borax will melt and should form a bead. Dip the stirring rod in the borax again and repeat until you have formed a good bead of borax "glass" on the stirring rod.

3. Once you have a good-sized bead on the stirring rod, flick the rod so that the bead falls off. You may try gently tapping the rod against a block of wood, or use some other technique that your teacher describes. The procedure takes some practice, but you can do it.

4. Repeat the procedure to make enough borax beads to test your metal samples.

   a) Describe the appearance of the borax bead in your *Active Chemistry* log. What color is it? Is it opaque, translucent or transparent?

5. Make a table similar to the one shown below in your *Active Chemistry* log. To test the metal compounds reattach the bead to the glass rod. Reheat the borax bead and quickly dip it in the compound to be tested. Heat just above the inner blue cone. Keep turning the stirring rod while heating, checking to see if the bead is taking up a color as you do so.

   a) Record the compound tested and the color produced in the table. Repeat the procedure with the rest of the compounds.

Compound tested	Color of borax bead

6. Test one or two of the compounds by heating them at the top of the outer flame. It is not as hot and does not have as much oxygen present.

   a) Is there a difference in the colors produced?

   b) How can you be certain that the metals in the compounds caused the colors that were produced?

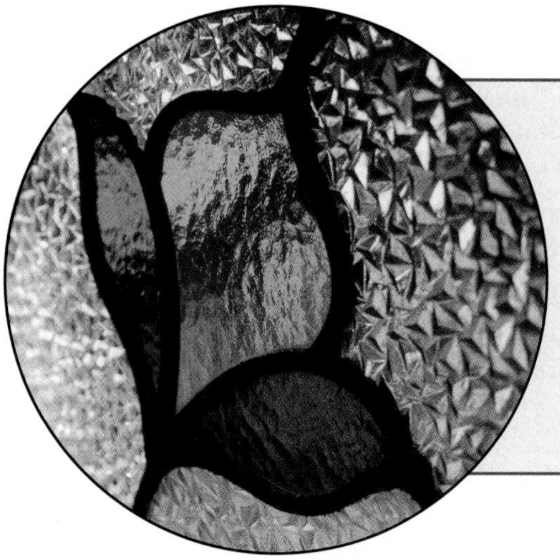

Chem Talk

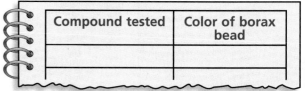

METAL COMPOUNDS AND COLOR IN ART

Glass

Glass is used widely, not only in windows and artwork, but also in fiber optics. Most windows in houses are colorless and transparent; however, many beautiful windows use colored glass.

Ordinary glass is made by heating a mixture of silica (regular sand found on a beach), sodium carbonate, and calcium carbonate until it becomes a liquid and then allowing it to cool. If impurities are present, colors result. In fact, early glass derived its color from the impurities present when the glass was formed. In the 17th century, iron impurities in the sand used to make the glass, and sulfur from the smoke of the burning coal used to melt the glass often caused glass to be dark brown or green. Today, when you look at a cross section of a window, you will see a light green color. This is because of light absorption of the iron contained in the glass as an impurity.

To make different colored glass, metal oxides are added. To get the color blue, cobalt oxide and copper oxide are added, while chromium oxide and iron oxide are added to get the colors green and yellow, respectively. These compounds absorb different colored light from the white light passing through them and transmit the colors that you see.

Another popular red-colored glass is called ruby glass. It was invented in 1679 and contains gold chloride. Some of the elements were named after the colors of their salts, like rhodium, which makes a rose-colored glass (*rhodon* is Greek for rose). The salts of iodine are used in glass to give a purple color. Iodine is named after *Ioeides*, which is Greek for violet.

Ceramics

In ceramics, the chief source of color in glazes is from metallic oxides—iron, cobalt, copper, manganese, chromium, and nickel, to name a few. The colors obtained depend on concentrations, firing temperatures, and conditions of firing. Iron compounds produce amber to dark red, cobalt compounds produce blues, and copper compounds produce greens. Uranium compounds were once used to make a bright orange color (red "Fiesta Ware") for tableware that was available in the 1950s and 1960s. Due to its radioactivity, it is no longer used! Combinations of compounds will produce other colors.

Glazes are suspensions of different clays and minerals in water. These are blended to melt at specific temperatures. Some glazes may contain lead compounds but these are not used when the ceramic object will be in contact with food. Glaze recipes are as varied as the artists who produce them. The firing of the glaze may cause unexpected results too. In addition to providing color to the ceramic objects, glazes also protect the ceramic and help to slow down deterioration.

Checking Up

1. List some metal oxides that are used in glazing.
2. Why are uranium salts no longer used in glazing?
3. Why is it a bad idea to use lead in ceramic objects that are used to serve food?
4. Why did early glass have a green tint to it?

What Do You Think Now?

At the beginning of the activity you were asked:

- **What gives colored glass its color?**

What are the similarities between the compounds that produce pigments and the compounds that produce colors in glass?

Chem Essential Questions

What does it mean?

Chemistry explains a macroscopic phenomenon (what you observe) with a description of what happens at the nanoscopic level (atoms and molecules) using symbolic structures as a way to communicate. Complete the chart below in your *Active Chemistry* log.

MACRO	NANO	SYMBOLIC
Describe some of the colors that were obtained by using different metal compounds.	*At the molecular level, what causes different glass to have different colors?*	*How could you keep track of what combinations of compounds make desirable colors for glass works of art?*

How do you know?

What evidence do you have to support the idea that the metal compounds are responsible for the colors seen?

Why do you believe?

You see colored glass objects around you every day. List several uses of colored glass in artistic work. What are some of the most vibrant colors? Can you suggest metals that might be used to get these colors?

Why should you care?

Using colored beads in your artwork could add beauty. Being able to describe the chemistry of the color would be fascinating.

Reflecting on the Activity and the Challenge

You have seen how color can be introduced into glass. You have learned that the compounds that produce the colors contain metal salts. The metal salts absorb certain colors and reflect others. Symbolically, the formulas of the compounds can be written. Works of art made of glass often include color. Artists are constantly experimenting with different compounds and different firing techniques to produce new colors and varied results. Combining different compounds can produce various colors. Think about how glass can enhance your *Chapter Challenge*.

Chem to Go

1. Glass artists in Colonial Williamsburg used local sand for glassmaking. The glass produced had a pale green color. What does this tell you about the sand that was used?
2. Use the Internet or another source to find out what compounds are used for the red, amber (yellow), and green-colored glass used in older traffic lights.
3. Use the Internet or another source to find the recipe for two different colors of glazes.
4. ***Preparing for the Chapter Challenge***

   Do an Internet search of glazes and find several recipes. List the "ingredients," paying particular attention to the compounds that produce the colors. You will probably also see that glazes are prepared for different "cone" numbers. What does this tell the potter? How are the glazes applied? You might incorporate this information into your museum display.

Chem at Work

Susana Arias

Artist, Ceramist, Sculptor, Santa Cruz, CA

Appreciation for art and a knowledge of chemistry don't always go hand in hand. You can look at a beautiful painting and grasp its meaning without knowing what it is composed of at an atomic level. But it is very difficult to create art without some understanding of chemistry.

Susana Arias is a perfect example of an artist who uses chemistry. She has had a passion for art ever since she was a young girl in Panama. She says, "The passion for art is not something you can control, it is like falling in love. You don't know why it happens."

Susana is a ceramist, which means she uses clay for her sculptures. Clay must be fired for strength. Clay surfaces that are finished without a glaze can get spectacular color from an "organic" firing. These firings coax the iron within the clay to the surface by starving the fire of oxygen. An effective way to starve a fire of oxygen is to add organic material (like bones or manure) to it. The fire draws oxygen from the material and from tiny bubbles in the clay instead of the air. This process also "pulls" the high concentrations of iron from within the clay to the surface, turning the sculpture's finish black. Susana can now predict and control the color of her finished art.

Non-organic materials (such as red iron oxide, and yellow copper carbonate) can be added to the fire itself to alter the color of the sculpture. Susana uses materials like seaweed and fish bones to make her pottery turn red, yellow, and black.

There are many different methods for altering the surface of clay. All methods spark a chemical change in the clay and its surface. Without this change, clay would just be another form of mud.

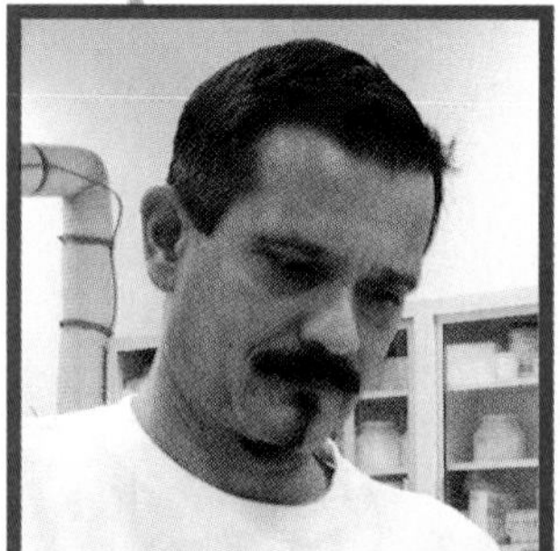

Steve Mellor

Head of Conservation, National Museum of African Art, Washington, DC

Steve Mellor is a conservationist and the head of conservation for the National Museum of African Art in Washington, DC. He uses microscopes, infrared and ultraviolet light, x-ray machines, and chemical solvents to identify the origin of each artifact. Using organic chemical solvents, he can also identify fakes from the real thing.

Tomas Bunk

Illustrator, New Rochelle, NY

Tomas Bunk is a well-known cartoonist. In addition to illustrating *MAD* magazine and *Garbage Pail Kids*, he has applied his talent to illustrating many complex chemistry and physics concepts. He works closely with the authors to learn the concepts before he begins his sketches so that his illustrations are not only funny but also scientifically accurate.

Artist as Chemist Assessment

Your *Chapter Challenge* is to create a work of art that represents you and/or your times using appropriate artistic techniques. In addition to the artwork itself, you will also need to create an informative museum display that includes:

- A demonstration of the techniques involved
- Your original work
- A museum placard or pamphlet explaining the chemistry involved.

Chemistry Content

To begin, you should review all of the activities that you have completed. You can skim through the text and your *Active Chemistry* log to help remind you of the chemistry concepts in each activity.

Activity 1: You discussed art in general and what makes something a piece of art.

Activity 2: You learned about acids, pH and how materials are affected by exposure to acids.

Activity 3: You investigated the chemical behavior of metals and learned how to electroplate a piece of metal.

Activity 4: You studied the physical behavior of metals and alloys.

Activity 5: You observed the effect of heat on hydrates and learned how clay could be part of your artwork. You were also introduced to the mole—the chemistry way of counting.

Activity 6: You investigated the role of solid precipitates and double-replacement reactions in creating paints of many colors.

Activity 7: You learned about dyes and how the use of dyes is dependent on the pH of the chemicals.

Activity 8: You experimented with stained glass and the way in which metal salts are used to create specific colors.

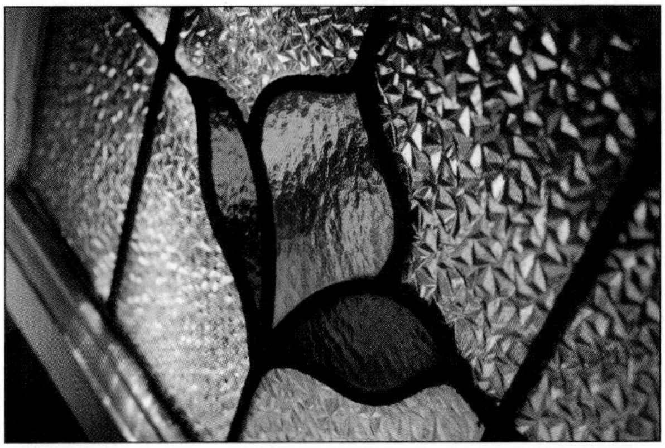

You may want to make a chart that shows the activity number, some chemistry concepts in the activity, and some ideas as to how you can use these concepts as part of your *Artist as Chemist* museum display. Your chart may include whether the concept will be part of the artwork itself or part of the informative pamphlet that will accompany the art. You should pay particular attention to the *Reflecting on the Activity and the Challenge, Chem Essential Questions,* and *Preparing for the Chapter Challenge* sections. You should also compare your list with that given in the *Chem You Learned* summary.

Activity #	Chemistry concepts	How to use concepts

You may decide to do the first activity as a group to ensure that everybody understands how to proceed. After completing the first activity, each team member can be assigned two or three activities. You can then review all of the activities as a group with the activity expert reviewing each summary.

Criteria

You and your team should review the criteria by which you will be graded. Before beginning the chapter, your teacher led a class discussion to get a sense of what criteria should be used to judge the quality of work for this *Artist as Chemist* product and display. It is time to revisit that discussion since you now have considerable understanding of the chemistry concepts that you can include in your artwork and placard or pamphlet. Think about and discuss what would make a piece of art and a unique display. Remember you must also have documentation including chemistry principles and techniques.

How will your art work and display be graded? What qualities should an original piece of art have? How will you represent your culture, your family, your friends or your feelings? How will you engage the viewer? Discuss these issues in small groups and with your class. How many chemical principles are required for an A?

Preparing for the Chapter Challenge

- Choose Your Art Product and Display

Your team's next step would then be to decide on what kind of art you want to create. How will you each have input into the art design and contribute to the nature of the piece? How can you be creative in both the art and in the display that accompanies the art? Will the art be beautiful or puzzling? Will you try to represent something others would recognize or will you create an abstract work? Will you use paints or clay or glass? How will you title your work? What will you say in the museum display so that people will understand the techniques you used and the chemistry behind these techniques?

- Practice Your Presentation

You need to practice your presentation to the class. You will have to show the artwork and describe the techniques and chemistry involved in the creation of the art. You do not have to explain the meaning of the art—that can be left to the viewer, if you desire. You will have to decide who will be responsible for which aspect of the presentation.

- **Chemistry content is necessary, but not sufficient.**

Art is about expression. Chemistry techniques and control of your materials is important. The best chemists in the world are not the best artists. Although artists do know a great deal about the materials they use, their success comes from their creativity and their ability to communicate visually. Whether your art impresses people will have more to do with your thoughts and reflection than it will have to do with your knowledge of chemistry. Chemistry content is required, but creativity is desired.

- Manage Your Time

You have a sense of how you want to proceed and what you want the final product to be. You now have to allocate the work. How much time do you have to complete the project? When is the presentation? How will you get everything done in this timeframe? Who will be working on the artwork and who will be working on the chemistry principle and display and museum placard or pamphlet? How will you ensure that each member's work meets the standard of excellence so that everybody on the team gets an A? Create a time chart for the challenge. Divide the responsibilities. How much time will each take? Some work can be done individually as homework. Leave time to review each other's work.

Planning a project well does not ensure success, but poor planning almost always leads to disappointment.

Engineering/Technology Design

Reflect on the engineering/technology design process. Recall the successes and disappointments from the *mini-challenge*. How can you use the feedback that you received to improve your show? At this point, you are starting the design cycle again.

Now, enjoy expressing yourself through your art and museum display!

Chem You Learned

- The strength of **acids** and **bases** is measured on the **pH scale** from 0 (very acidic) to 14 (very basic). An aqueous solution of a strong acid or base is 100 % ionized. $pH = -\log[H^+]$.
- **Acid-base indicators** are used to visually estimate the pH of a solution by color.
- An **acid** has **properties** of sourness and reactivity with metals, while **bases** are slippery, bitter, and corrosive.
- **Weak acids** are not completely ionized in water, having a **pH less than 7** (7 being neutral). **Weak bases** are also not completely ionized and will have a **pH greater than 7**.
- The **definition** of an acid or a base has evolved in the last century, with major contributors being **Arrhenius, Brønsted and Lowry**, and **G.N.Lewis**.
- The **Brønsted-Lowry** definition states that acids are proton donors while bases are proton acceptors.
- The **Lewis acid-base** concept is the most general and states that acids are electron-pair acceptors and bases are electron-pair donors.
- The **activity series of metals** places the elemental form of each metal in a descending order of reactivity. A metal higher in the series will oxidize and replace a lower metal in a solution of its salt.
- Families of elements in the periodic table either gain or lose electrons in order to fulfill the **octet rule**, with few exceptions.
- Metals typically lose electrons to become **cations,** while many nonmetals will gain electrons to become **anions**.
- Bonding in metals is often described as an **electron-sea model** because the **valence electrons** have the ability to move from one atom to another, allowing electrical **conductivity**.
- Some **physical properties of metals** are conductivity and malleability, although these properties can be altered by the formation of alloys. For example, gold alloys are harder than pure gold.
- Many compounds include specific numbers of loosely bonded water molecules in their formula and are called **hydrates**.

- Chemical reactions are recorded in shorthand by using **chemical formulas** and by **balanced equations** so that matter is neither created nor destroyed.
- A **double-replacement reaction** is a reaction where either a **precipitate** or a gas is formed as a product. A table of **solubility rules** is useful for predicting this type of reaction.
- A **dye** is often a complex **organic molecule** which binds to the fibers of a material like wool. By adjusting the pH, or by using a **mordant**, the binding can be strengthened.
- In the oxidized state, many metal ions exhibit a specific color which can be seen in **bead tests**. For example, Co^{2+} gives a blue color and Fe^{3+} gives a yellow-colored bead.

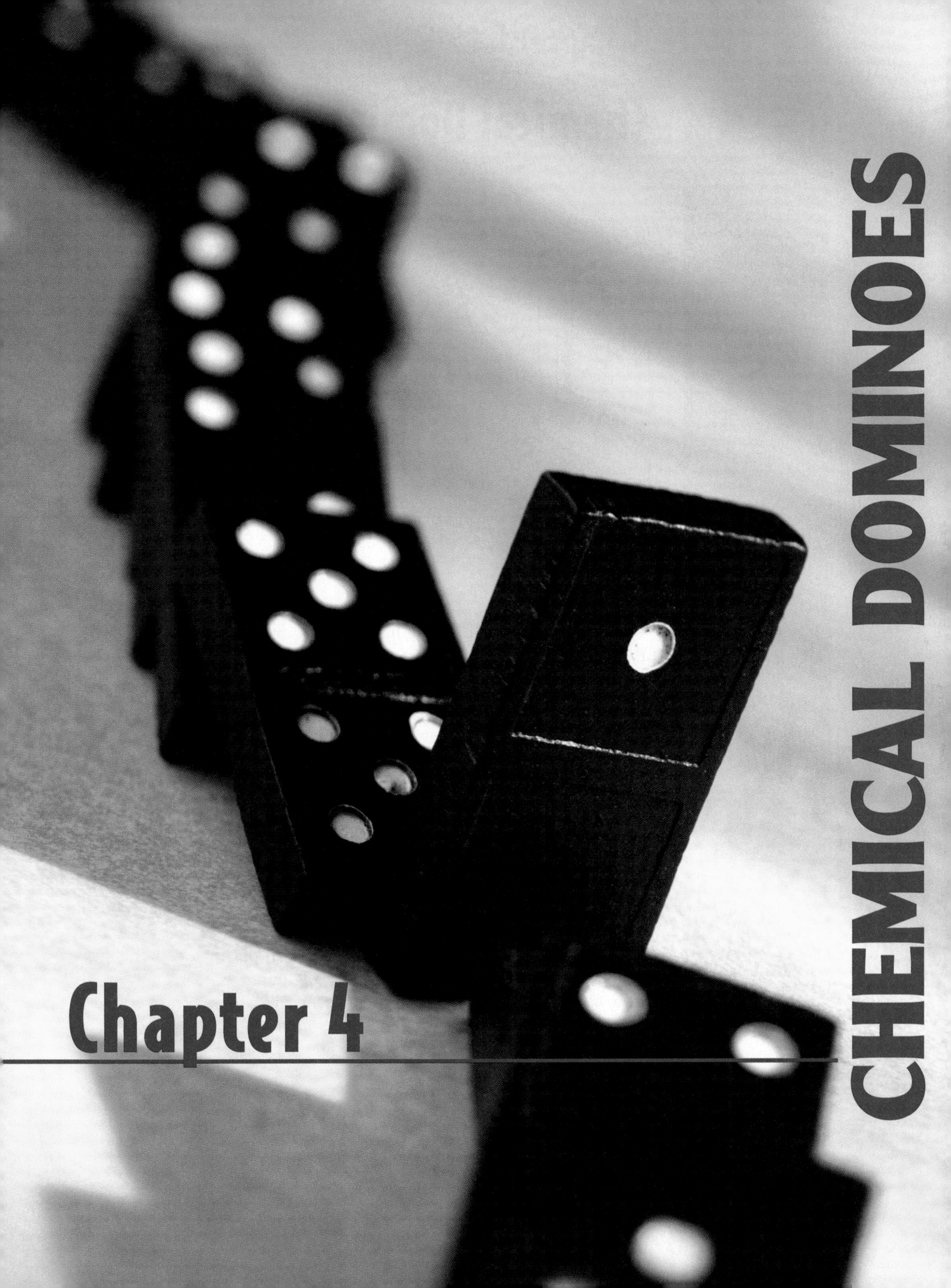

Chapter 4

CHEMICAL DOMINOES

Chapter Challenge

4

Chemical Dominoes

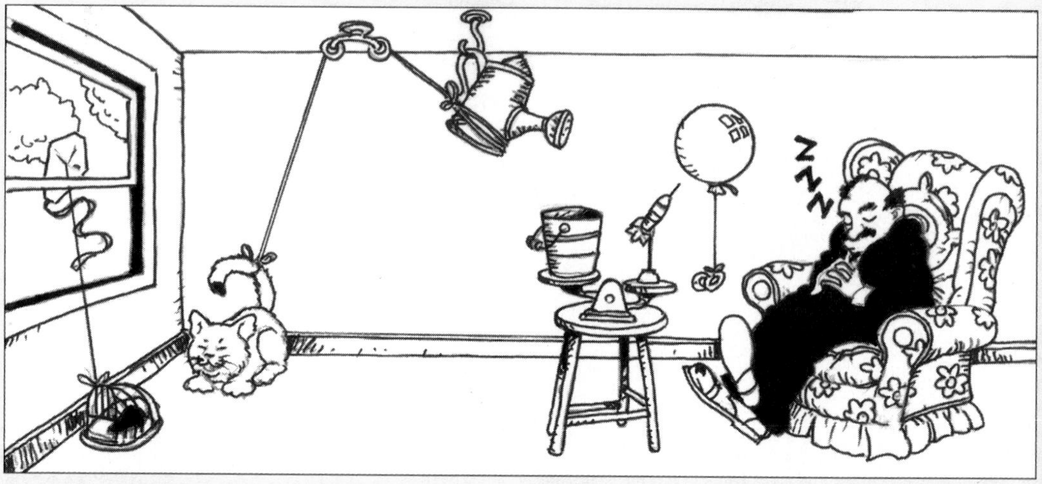

Scenario

You may have seen Rube Goldberg type of drawings like the one shown above. If you look carefully at the drawing as you read the description, you see that each action triggers another action.

This action-reaction sequence is similar to one that you would see if you pushed against the first of a carefully placed row of upright dominoes. Timing and exact locations of objects are very important to the smooth operation of these sequences. Setting up a successful domino-effect display like this takes patience and persistence on the part of the artist.

Chemistry kits are popular toys for young people. They are a great way to have fun while learning about how exciting science can be. A toy company would like to take the idea of the chemistry kit a step further. They would like to market a toy for ages 10 and up that consists of an entertaining sequence of chemical and physical (mechanical) changes. The sequence would eventually light a tiny light bulb, called an LED. The toy must present an appropriate challenge to set up without being too frustrating for the consumer. It should include instructions and a drawing that shows how to arrange the sequence so that the customer could assemble the pieces to create a

"chemical dominoes" effect. Detailed safety precautions should be included with the kit. The components of the kit must be sturdy (not fragile) and the sequence should be able to run more than once. (Some ingredients may need to be replenished before each re-running.) Most important of course for the company is that the kids love it and want to buy it.

Your Challenge

You have been asked to develop a chemical dominoes toy that meets all the requirements set out by the company. The sequence must run successfully if set up properly. This will require testing to make sure the process works reliably. You will demonstrate your final product to an audience of executives at the toy company. At that time, you will present the executives with a prototype of your product and all the accompanying materials required. During your demonstration, you will briefly explain the chemistry behind how each step of the sequence works. You will also provide a written, detailed explanation of how the chemistry behind your *Chemical Dominoes* works.

If the company likes your product and decides to produce it, they will want to patent it. To make this possible, you must keep an extremely complete notebook, carefully recording everything you try in developing this product and the results of each experiment (for every component, not just the whole product all together). This will allow the company to show the lawyers the extent of your investigation into the effects you studied, and document the

ChemCorner

Chemistry in *Chemical Dominoes*

- Atoms
- Single-replacement reactions
- Double-replacement reactions
- Atomic mass
- Compound
- Law of Definite Proportions
- Electrons
- Neutrons
- Protons
- Line spectrums and elements
- Electromagnetic spectrum
- Bohr's Atomic Theory
- Orbits of electrons
- Periodicity of the elements
- Atom's energy level
- Electron configuration
- Valence electrons
- Chemical formulas

BATTERY

failures as well as the successes that went into your invention. Pay particular attention to recording each step you go through in setting up the completed sequence, as well as any troubleshooting you do to make everything work together in a sequence (including any problems that must be solved at the last minute).

Criteria

How will your *Chemical Dominoes* and accompanying materials be evaluated? What characteristics should a quality product have? How good do your explanations of the chemistry need to be? Discuss these issues in small groups and with your class. You may decide that some or all of the following qualities should be graded. You may use what you learn in this chapter of *Active Chemistry* or anything from previous chapters you studied.

For the prototype you create and demonstrate:

- How many chemical reactions or physical changes must you use?
- How well does your prototype work?
- How entertaining is the display? Colorful? Funny? Surprising?
- How many tries should a team get to make the demonstration work for the audience?
- How sturdy is the prototype?
- How can you tell if the prototype is targeted to the appropriate age group?
- How enjoyable will it be for kids to build?

For the written material you submit:

- Have all safety issues been addressed?
- How understandable are the directions and the diagram for assembly?
- How clear and accurate are the explanations of the chemistry?

Your teacher may provide you with a sample rubric to help you get started.

Activity 1 Alternative Pathways

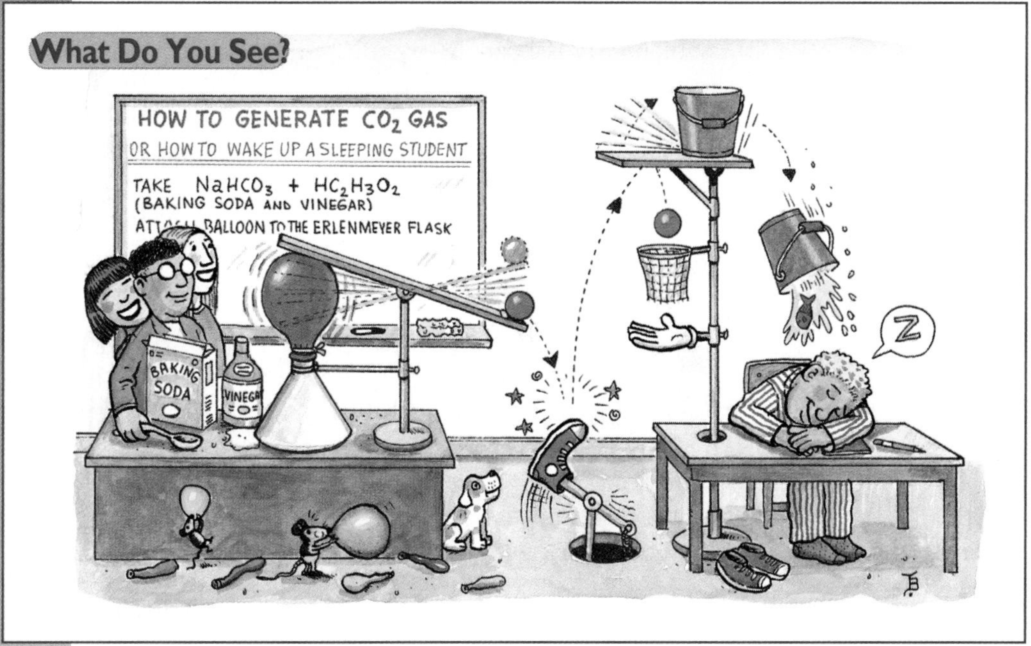

What Do You See?
HOW TO GENERATE CO_2 GAS
OR HOW TO WAKE UP A SLEEPING STUDENT
TAKE $NaHCO_3 + HC_2H_3O_2$
(BAKING SODA AND VINEGAR)
BALLOON TO THE ERLENMEYER FLASK
BAKING SODA
VINEGAR
Z

GOALS

In this activity you will:

- Apply the engineering-design process to scientific and everyday situations.
- Generate evaluation criteria and use those criteria to compare and evaluate various methods to achieving a goal.
- Determine how energy and disorder change during physical and chemical processes.

What Do You Think?

Imagine that you are making chocolate-chip cookies. At the same time, your friend across town is also making chocolate-chip cookies.

- **Suppose some of your ingredients are not the same as those of your friend. Can you and your friend produce identical chocolate-chip cookies? How?**
- **Suppose you and your friend both have identical sets of ingredients. Could you produce chocolate-chip cookies that are completely different from those your friend produces? How?**

The *What Do You Think?* questions are meant to get you thinking about what you already know or think you know. Don't worry about being right or wrong. Discussing what you think you know is an important step in learning.

Record your ideas about these questions in your *Active Chemistry* log. Be prepared to discuss your responses with your small group and the class.

Investigate

Often, there are many ways to achieve a goal. In this activity, you will compare different ways of arriving at a product and learn how you can make decisions about which way is best. Also, you will consider if a change in circumstances might cause you to choose a different method.

Safety goggles and apron must be worn *at all times* in a chemistry lab.

1. Carbon dioxide (CO_2) is a gas at room temperature. You will examine four different methods of generating CO_2 gas. The gas you generate will then have to blow up a balloon that will tip a lever.

2. Your teacher will assign each lab group one method of CO_2 production. Your group has 15 minutes to set up the apparatus and practice making the lever tip by a distance of 2 cm. At the end of 15 minutes, each group will demonstrate their method for the class.

3. As you practice making CO_2 gas using your group's method, make observations about the changes that happen using the CO_2 production method. You will want to record the following:

   a) the time it takes to generate the gas

   b) the volume of gas generated

   c) the mass of the starting materials

   You will also make other observations during the experiment.

   You will need to decide the amount of each substance to use. Make sure you record quantitative data. (These are measurements that involve numbers, such as the size of the balloon and the mass of starting materials necessary.) Record qualitative data as well. (These are observations of what happens.)

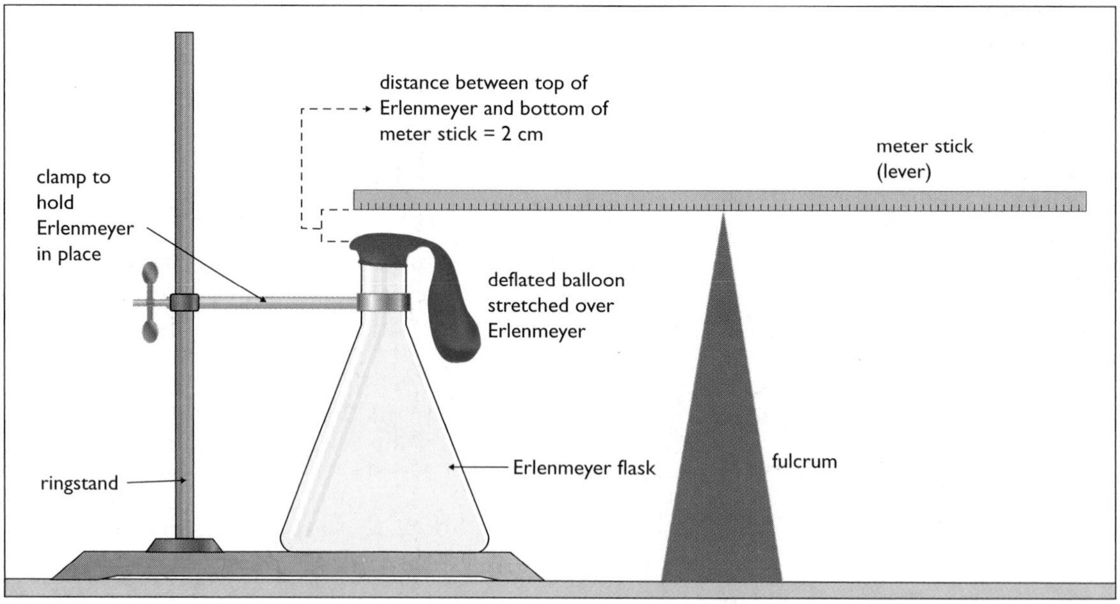

distance between top of Erlenmeyer and bottom of meter stick = 2 cm
meter stick (lever)
clamp to hold Erlenmeyer in place
deflated balloon stretched over Erlenmeyer
Erlenmeyer flask
fulcrum
ringstand

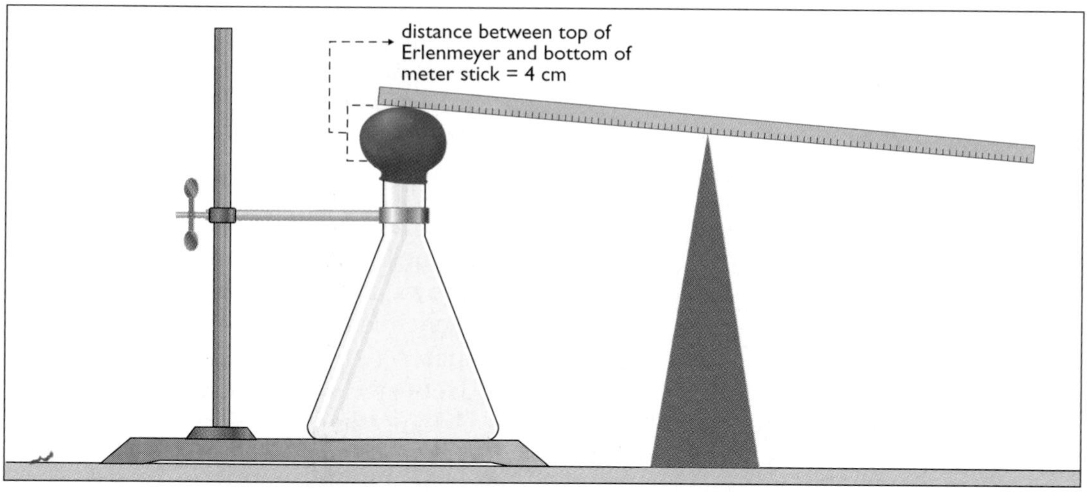
distance between top of
Erlenmeyer and bottom of
meter stick = 4 cm

Method 1

Starting materials: Sodium bicarbonate and acetic acid

Sodium bicarbonate is also known as baking soda. Sodium bicarbonate is represented by the chemical formula $NaHCO_3$. A chemical formula shows how many atoms or ions of an element are needed to combine with the other elements in the compound. The formula for sodium bicarbonate shows that one sodium ion, one hydrogen atom, one carbon atom, and three oxygen atoms bond together to make sodium bicarbonate, $NaHCO_3$. Acetic acid, $HC_2H_3O_2$, is the ingredient that gives vinegar its characteristic odor. Acetic acid is present in vinegar in low concentration, about 5%. The majority of vinegar is water. The reaction that occurs between sodium bicarbonate and acetic acid is:

$$\underset{\text{sodium bicarbonate}}{NaHCO_3(s)} + \underset{\text{acetic acid}}{HC_2H_3O_2(aq)} \rightarrow$$

$$\underset{\text{sodium acetate}}{NaC_2H_3O_2(aq)} + \underset{\text{water}}{H_2O(l)} + \underset{\text{carbon dioxide}}{CO_2(g)}$$

The symbol (g) indicates that the substance is a gas, (s) indicates a solid, and (l) indicates a liquid. The symbol (aq) shows that the substance is dissolved in water. Note that the equation is balanced. The number of each element (Na, H, C, O) is identical before and after the reaction.

Method 2

Starting materials: Calcium carbonate and hydrochloric acid

Calcium carbonate, $CaCO_3$, is the principal component of limestone and chalk. Hydrochloric acid, HCl(aq), is one of the acids in your stomach. Like vinegar, the majority of a hydrochloric acid solution is water. The reaction that occurs between calcium carbonate and hydrochloric acid is:

$$\underset{\text{calcium carbonate}}{CaCO_3(s)} + \underset{\text{hydrochloric acid}}{2\ HCl(aq)} \rightarrow$$

$$\underset{\text{calcium chloride}}{CaCl_2(aq)} + \underset{\text{water}}{H_2O(l)} + \underset{\text{carbon dioxide}}{CO_2(g)}$$

Note that the equation is balanced. The number of each element (Ca, Cl, H, C, O) is identical before and after the reaction.

Avoid getting chemicals on skin. Clean up spills immediately.

Be careful with the heat source. Have your teacher check your procedure before beginning.

Do not eat or drink anything while in the lab.

Wash your hands and arms thoroughly after the activity.

Method 3

Starting material:
Calcium carbonate

When heat energy is added to calcium carbonate, bonds between atoms break and then re-form in a different way. This allows carbon dioxide gas to escape while leaving calcium oxide as a solid:

$CaCO_3(s)$ + energy →
calcium carbonate

$CaO(s) + CO_2(g)$
calcium oxide *carbon dioxide*

Method 4

Starting material:
Carbonated beverage

Note: This method of CO_2 production will be demonstrated by your teacher.

Some beverages, such as naturally occurring mineral water, contain natural carbonation. Carbon dioxide also results from fermentation processes, causing some alcoholic beverages to become carbonated. Other beverages, such as cola and ginger ale, are artificially carbonated. Carbon dioxide is less able to remain dissolved in water at higher temperatures, because at higher temperatures the water molecules move faster. Hence, soda loses its fizz faster when exposed to air at room temperature than when exposed to air inside a refrigerator. You can cause soda to lose carbon dioxide rapidly by placing a hot object in the soda to warm it.

$CO_2(aq)$ + energy →
dissolved carbonation

$H_2O(l) + CO_2(g)$
water *gaseous carbon dioxide*

Notice that the equation above shows a physical change rather than a chemical one. Both the starting materials and ending materials are water and carbon dioxide. Adding the hot object to the soda doesn't change the carbon dioxide and water into other materials. The carbon dioxide and water are merely separated from each other.

4. Present your group's method to the class.
5. Dispose of the materials as directed by your teacher. Clean up your workstation.
6. Decide which CO_2 production method is best for blowing up a balloon to tip a lever. There may not be one "correct" answer.
   a) Once you decide on the best method, record it in your *Active Chemistry* log and describe why you decided that was the best method.
   b) Explain why each of the methods you did not choose was not as good as the one you chose.

Chem Talk

ENERGY AND ENTROPY CHANGES IN CHEMICAL REACTIONS

In this activity, you generated CO_2 gas and used that gas to both blow up a balloon and move a lever. Each production method used different materials and generated a different amount of gas in a different amount of time. There are other ways in which chemists look at the generation of the gas. You will now look at the reactions in terms of energy and entropy.

Does the Generation of the Gas Require Energy Input or Does It Release Energy?

When matter undergoes a change, there is often a change in energy involved. That is, energy will move from being stored in one form or place to another form or place. However, the total amount of energy in the entire universe stays the same. If the matter involved in a change loses energy, then the energy has to go somewhere. It can't just disappear. Likewise, if the matter involved in a change gains energy, the energy must come from somewhere. It doesn't just appear.

One indication of whether energy is entering or exiting matter is heat energy. Is heat energy gained to create a change or is heat energy lost when the change occurs? If heat energy goes in, then the chemicals gain energy. This is shown in the diagram as A.

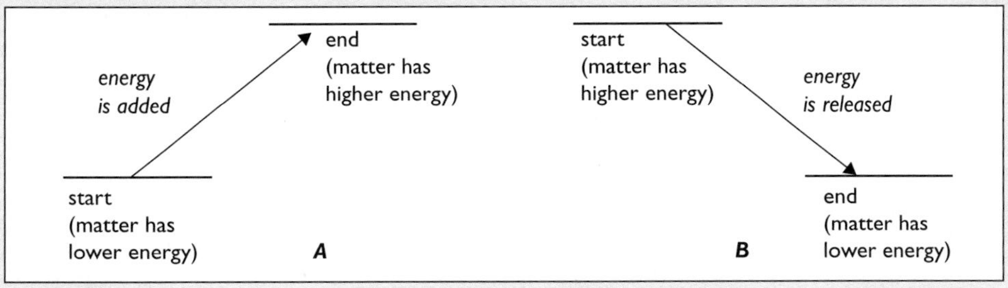
energy
is added
end
(matter has
higher energy)
start
(matter has
lower energy)
A
start
(matter has
higher energy)
energy
is released
end
(matter has
lower energy)
B

Conversely, if heat energy is released and the chemicals lose energy, the change can be represented as B.

Many reactions can be understood in terms of energy change by reflecting on your experience with water. If you place ice cubes on a heated stove, the ice will melt (as it gains more energy), the water will increase its temperature (as it gains energy), and the water will boil and become vapor (as it gains even more energy). On the other hand, changing vapor to water, cooling water, or making ice requires a loss of energy.

Where is the Energy?

When you add heat energy to something, the particles inside it gain the energy. Therefore, the particles have more energy than before the heat energy was added. The additional energy has to go somewhere. One place it can go is into making the particles (atoms or molecules) move faster.

The extra energy could also change the bonds that exist between atoms or molecules.

It is important at this point to make a distinction between *bonds* holding a molecule together and *attractive forces* holding molecules together. *Bonds* exist within molecules. They hold the atoms in an individual molecule together. For example, it takes heat energy input to break bonds between atoms and ions in materials (such as the $CaCO_3$ crystals you heated in *Method 3*). *Attractive forces* exist between molecules in solids and liquids. These attractive forces hold the molecules of solids and liquids together and prevent them from separating to form a gas. For example, it takes heat energy input to break apart the forces that hold water molecules together in ice to turn them into liquid water.

It takes the input of energy to overcome weak intermolecular forces or chemical bonds. Of course, it takes less energy to break the attractive forces holding molecules near each other in the liquid and solid phase. These forces are involved in the phase changes of a substance. On the other hand, chemical bonds are much stronger than the intermolecular forces of attraction so it takes a lot more energy to break bonds. In any chemical reaction, bonds are broken so that new and different molecules can be formed. Whether breaking chemical bonds or intermolecular forces of attraction, it takes an input of energy.

Conversely, when attractions form, energy is given up and heat energy is released to the surroundings. Most processes you will encounter involve both breaking and forming bonds or forces between molecules. In those cases, knowing whether the overall process will absorb or release heat energy requires an answer to the following question: Does it take more heat energy input to break the original bonds or forces, or is more heat energy released when new bonds or forces form?

A Matter of Perspective

Whether an energy change is "positive" or "negative" depends on the perspective from which it is viewed. In chemistry, the perspective is always from that of the reactants. In the previous example of heating the

$CaCO_3$ to form CaO and CO_2, you have to add energy. However, if you consider the chemicals, they gain energy during the change. The energy change from start to end in the chemicals is a positive one. This is called an **endothermic** change, because heat energy goes into the chemicals. If you consider a match that is burning, the matter (wood) is releasing (losing) energy. The ash that remains after burning is complete and has less energy than the unburned match. The change in energy for the match is negative. This kind of energy change is called **exothermic**.

In the four reactions in the activity used to produce CO_2, the two in which heat was added were endothermic reactions. The two reactions which occurred spontaneously were exothermic reactions.

What Happens to the Organization of Particles That Make up the Matter?

Most changes also involve a change in how the particles that make up the matter are organized. Chemists choose to measure, or speak in terms of, disorganization. If the arrangement of particles in the matter gets more disorganized (less organized), the change can be shown as in the diagram.

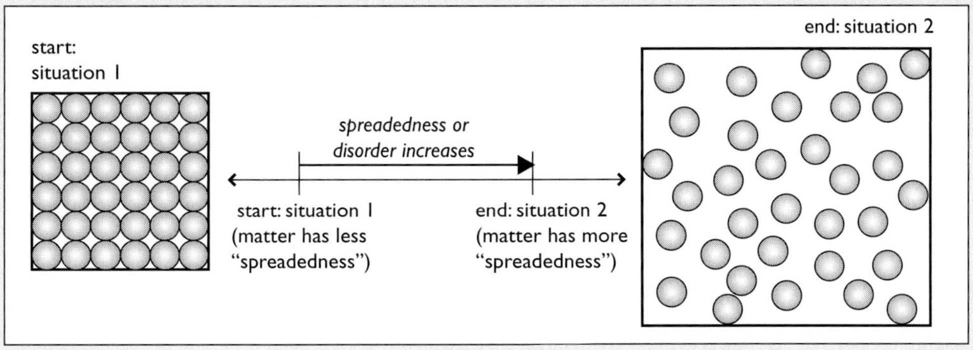
start:
situation 1
spreadedness or
disorder increases
start: situation 1
(matter has less
"spreadedness")
end: situation 2
(matter has more
"spreadedness")
end: situation 2

The way that chemists consider "disorder" is to think about how many arrangements of the particles are possible. You can think of this as the space available for individual particles to move. A better term for this might be "spread out." For example, consider the two situations 1 and 2 in the diagram. In situation 1, the particles are arranged in a regular repeating structure. The particles are tightly packed, so it is not possible for any particle to move to a different location. A particle can only wiggle around within its little space. In situation 2, the same number of particles is shown in an arrangement in which each particle has the ability to move to other locations throughout the entire space. In situation 2, the matter is

Chem Words

endothermic: a process that absorbs heat energy.

exothermic: a process that releases heat energy.

more "spread out." If particles move from situation 1 to situation 2, chemists say that the *disorder increases*. A number line can be used to represent an increase in disorder as shown in the diagram.

On the other hand, if particles move from situation 2 to situation 1, chemists would say that the *disorder decreases*. The arrangement of particles in the matter is less spread out. This kind of change represents an increase in order.

Gases have their molecules very spread out. Reactions that create gases from solids and liquids have an increase in disorder. All of the reactions that were used to generate CO_2 gas increased in disorder. In general, any substance going from solid to liquid to gas is increasing in disorder.

Chemists quantify "spread" or disorder under the name **entropy**, which is given the symbol S. The entropy that a material has is a measure of its amount of disorder. For example, one can look up in standard reference tables the entropies of the three substances in the decomposition of calcium carbonate ($CaCO_3$) into calcium oxide (CaO) and carbon dioxide (CO_2): $CaCO_3(s) + \text{energy} \rightarrow CaO(s) + CO_2(g)$. One mole of calcium carbonate will produce one mole of calcium oxide and one mole of carbon dioxide when it goes to completion. With the entropy values, it can be seen mathematically that the total entropy increases.

Chem Words

entropy (*S*): the disorder of particles in a substance.

Checking Up

1. What is the difference between bonds holding together atoms and forces between molecules?
2. What two things compete to determine whether a particular change releases heat energy overall or absorbs heat energy overall?
3. What is the amount of disorder called?
4. Which has more disorder, a gas or a solid? Why?

What Do You Think Now?

At the beginning of the activity, you were asked:

Imagine that you are making chocolate-chip cookies. At the same time, your friend across town is also making chocolate-chip cookies.

- **Suppose some of your ingredients are not the same as those of your friend. Can you and your friend produce identical chocolate-chip cookies? How?**
- **Suppose you and your friend both have identical sets of ingredients. Could you produce chocolate-chip cookies that are completely different from those your friend produces? How?**

Imagine that this time, you want to make the cookies unique. After looking through the cabinets, you find nuts, cinnamon, chocolate syrup, and marshmallows. Describe criteria you may use to decide on the best recipe. How do the energy and entropy of the matter change when you make cookies with these other ingredients? Support your answer with an explanation.

Chem Essential Questions

What does it mean?

Chemistry explains a macroscopic phenomenon (what you observe) with a description of what happens at the nanoscopic level (atoms and molecules) using symbolic structures as a way to communicate. Complete the chart below in your *Active Chemistry* log.

MACRO	NANO	SYMBOLIC
Describe the observations you might make in each of the following situations: • *Disorder of matter increases* • *Disorder of matter decreases* • *Energy of matter increases* • *Energy of matter decreases*	*Explain how the arrangement of particles changes as disorder changes.* *Explain how the bonding of atoms may be affected by changes in energy.*	*Show how you would represent a decrease in disorder using a drawing and a "number line."* *Show two different methods you would use to illustrate how a change releases energy overall.*

How do you know?

Describe the four methods used to produce carbon dioxide gas and how you could know what type of change(s) occurred in energy and entropy in each case.

Why do you believe?

Changes in energy and entropy are common occurrences in everyday life. Describe the energy and entropy changes that occur in a situation that you have experienced or are aware of. You might choose cooking over an open fire, burning gasoline in a car, or another situation.

Why should you care?

You will be developing a series of physical and/or chemical changes that result in the lighting of a small bulb called an LED. Assume that tipping a lever will be the first step in your apparatus. Brainstorm a list of things that tipping the lever could cause to happen next.

Reflecting on the Activity and the Challenge

There are lots of alternative pathways for arriving at a destination, but one is usually better than all the rest. In this activity, you practiced some of the steps in the engineering-design process. In order to design an apparatus for the *Chapter Challenge*, you will have to complete the entire process, inventing your own pathways and deciding which is best. It will be helpful to establish criteria for judging different possible solutions so that you can evaluate them. You have also learned several methods for producing carbon dioxide gas. You may want to use one of those methods in your toy. One use for producing a gas could be to blow up a balloon. There could be other uses for the gas as well.

Chem to Go

1. Identify each of the following changes as endothermic, exothermic, or not possible to tell. The matter to keep in perspective is in italics in each case. Explain your decision in each case.

   a) When *effervescent antacid* tablets are dropped into water, the tablets slowly disappear and the water becomes fizzy.

   b) On a hot day, *water* vapor condenses out of the air and turns into liquid droplets on the outside of a cold glass of lemonade.

   c) The *copper* on the Statue of Liberty oxidizes and turns blue.

2. Identify each of the changes listed in *Question 1* as disorder (spreadedness) increases, disorder (spreadedness) decreases, or not possible to tell. Explain your decision in each case.

3. Use the following chemical equations to answer parts (a) and (b).
   $4Fe(s) + 3O_2(g) \rightarrow 2Fe_2O_3(s)$ and $2KClO_3(s) \rightarrow 2KCl(s) + 3O_2(g)$

   a) Identify the reactants and products in each chemical equation.

   b) Decide if each change represents an increase in disorder or decrease in disorder. Explain your choice in each case.

4. What occurs when an atom of chlorine and an atom of hydrogen become a molecule of hydrogen chloride?

   a) A chemical bond is broken and energy is released.

   b) A chemical bond is broken and energy is absorbed.

   c) A chemical bond is formed and energy is released.

   d) A chemical bond is formed and energy is absorbed.

5. Given the balanced equation: $KNO_3(s) + 34.89\ J \xrightarrow{H_2O} K^+(aq) + NO_3^-(aq)$
   Which statement best describes this process?

   a) It is endothermic and entropy increases.

   b) It is endothermic and entropy decreases.

   c) It is exothermic and entropy increases.

   d) It is exothermic and entropy decreases.

6 Which of these changes produces the greatest increase in entropy?

   a) $CaCO_3(s) \rightarrow CaO(s) + CO_2(g)$
   b) $2\ Mg(s) + O_2(g) \rightarrow 2\ MgO(s)$
   c) $H_2O(g) \rightarrow H_2O(l)$
   d) $CO_2(g) \rightarrow CO_2(s)$

7. ***Preparing for the Chapter Challenge***

   a) You have just investigated several methods for blowing up a balloon that can tip a lever. Review your *Why should you care?* response. Which method for blowing up the balloon would be most appropriate in each case you listed? Provide reasons for your selections.

   b) Provide at least one situation in which you might want to inflate the balloon slowly. Which method would be best in that case?

Activity 2 Balancing Chemical Equations

What Do You See?

CHEMICAL EQUATIONS
(1C,4H)
(4O)
(1C,2O)
(4H,2O)
REACTANTS
PRODUCTS

GOALS

In this activity you will:

- Explain the purpose of balancing a chemical equation.
- Relate the balancing of an equation to the Law of Conservation of Matter.
- Balance a chemical equation.

What Do You Think?

The word "balance" is used in both literary and scientific contexts. Consider the following statements.

Arthur Wellesley, Duke of Wellington, said:

"It is very true that I have said that I considered Napoleon's presence in the field equal to forty thousand men in the balance."

Plutarch, a Greek biographer who lived from 46-120 A.C.E., wrote:

"Prosperity is no just scale; adversity is the only balance to weigh friends."

- **What is meant by the word "balance" in each of these contexts?**
- **How might this be related to the concept of balanced equations in chemistry?**

Record your ideas about these questions in your *Active Chemistry* log. Be prepared to discuss your responses with your small group and the class.

Investigate

Part A: Is Matter Really Conserved?

1. Look at the following chemical reaction:

   $CaCO_3(s) + 2HCl(aq) \rightarrow CaCl_2(aq) + H_2O(l) + CO_2(g)$

   It is one of the reactions from the previous activity. You will be given the following:

- **calcium carbonate, $CaCO_3$**
- **hydrochloric acid, HCl**
- **balloon**
- **beaker**
- **Erlenmeyer flask**
- **resealable plastic bag**
- **graduated cylinder**
- **rubber bands**
- **balance**

2. Design an experiment to find out if the mass of the starting materials is equal to the mass of the ending materials.

   a) Record your procedure in your *Active Chemistry* log.

   b) Be sure to make a table in which to record your data.

3. Have your procedure approved by your teacher first before beginning.

4. With your teacher's permission, carry out your procedure.

   a) Record your results.

Safety goggles and apron must be worn *at all times* in a chemistry lab.

Be careful with the chemicals used. Clean up any spills immediately.

Wash your hands and arms thoroughly after the activity.

Part B: Visualizing Chemical Formulas and Balancing Reactions

1. It is helpful to be able to visualize the number of elements and their arrangement either in your head or on paper when balancing an equation. To help you begin to visualize atoms and molecules, an example of three molecules of H_2O ($3H_2O$) is shown. Use Bingo markers or other colored circles and blank paper to illustrate each of the molecules below. Be sure to use a different color for each element.

   a) $4Fe_2O_3$ b) $2KNO_3$ c) $6Al_2(SO_4)_3$

2. Next, use the Bingo markers to illustrate each of the chemical equations below. Be sure to use the same color for the same atom on the input and output sides of the equation. It will be helpful to make a key, as shown in the $3H_2O$ example.

Three Water Molecules

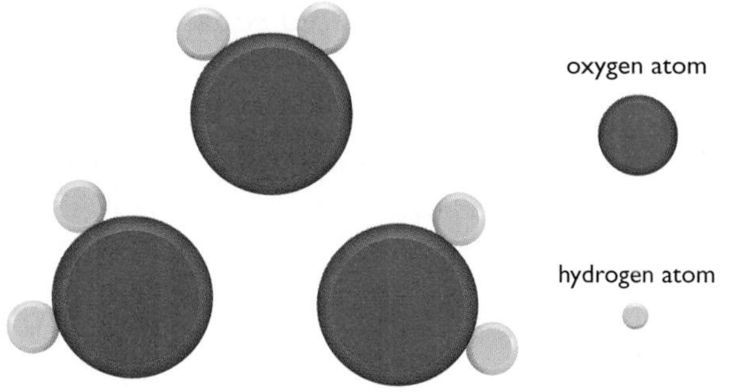
oxygen atom
hydrogen atom

   a) hydrochloric acid + zinc → zinc chloride + hydrogen

   $\_\_ HCl + \_\_ Zn \rightarrow \_\_ ZnCl_2 + \_\_ H_2$

   b) sodium + fluorine → sodium fluoride

   $\_\_ Na + \_\_ F_2 \rightarrow \_\_ NaF$

   c) sodium chlorate → sodium chloride + oxygen

   $\_\_ NaClO_3 \rightarrow \_\_ NaCl + \_\_ O_2$

   d) hydrochloric acid + calcium carbonate → water + carbon dioxide + calcium chloride

   $\_\_ HCl + \_\_ CaCO_3 \rightarrow$
   $\_\_ H_2O + \_\_ CO_2 + \_\_ CaCl_2$

e) lead nitrate + sodium chloride → lead chloride + sodium nitrate

__ $Pb(NO_3)_2$ + __ $NaCl$ → __ $PbCl_2$ + __ $NaNO_3$

Tip #1: NO_3 can be treated as a single item since it's the same on both the left and the right. There are two NO_3 items on the left and one on the right.

f) copper + silver nitrate → copper (II) nitrate + silver

__ Cu + __ $AgNO_3$ → __ $Cu(NO_3)_2$ + __ Ag

g) aluminum sulfate + calcium hydroxide → aluminum hydroxide + calcium sulfate

__ $Al_2(SO_4)_3$ + __ $Ca(OH)_2$ → __ $Al(OH)_3$ + __ $CaSO_4$

Tip #2: Remember to write the parentheses ( ) around an item if there is more than one of it in a chemical. $Al(OH)_3$ and $AlOH_3$ mean different things. The first one means there are 3 of the OH item in the chemical. The second one means there is one O and there are 3 H's. Likewise, write $Al_2(SO_4)_3$, not Al_2SO_{43}.

h) iron + water → iron (II, III) oxide + hydrogen

__ Fe + __ H_2O → __ Fe_3O_4 + __ H_2

i) methane + oxygen → carbon dioxide + water

__ CH_4 + __ O_2 → __ CO_2 + __ H_2O

3. Use the Bingo markers to add the necessary atoms and/or molecules to make the equations balanced. The type and number of each atom of the reactants' side must be identical to the type and number of each atom on the products' side. It is important to use only whole numbers as coefficients since the coefficient represents the number of atoms or molecules present. Once you have each equation balanced, prove that matter is conserved by making sure the input equals the output for each item. Write the balanced equations in your *Active Chemistry* log.

Part C: Using Chemical Symbols to Balance Equations

1. Now that you have mastered the visualization of reactions, you will work in symbolic terms. One way to balance chemical equations is to make a list that compares how many of each atom exist on the reactant (left) and product (right) sides of the arrow.

   When a chemical reaction occurs, the amount of matter that is present before the reaction occurs is still present after the reaction. The atoms have simply rearranged, not changed. You write coefficients in front of each chemical substance to indicate how many of each substance are necessary for the equation to be balanced. (When there is exactly one, the coefficient is assumed to be "1" and is not written.)

   a) What are the coefficients of each of the substances (starting materials and ending materials) in the following chemical equation?

   $CaCO_3$ + $2HCl$ →
   $CaCl_2$ + H_2O + CO_2

2. In understanding equations of chemical reactions, there are three considerations. The first is the chemical formula itself. This tells

you exactly how many atoms of each element are in the compound. This cannot be changed. The second are the subscripts that appear in the formulas. The subscripts tell you exactly how many atoms or groups of atoms are present in one formula unit. This also cannot be changed. (If the subscript is "1" it is not written.) Finally, the third consideration is the coefficient. This tells you how many units of the entire compound take part in the reaction. In "$3H_2O$," the 3 is the coefficient, which tells you there are three water molecules (H_2O). The 2 is a subscript, that tells you that there are two hydrogen atoms in each water molecule. The total number of hydrogen atoms in $3H_2O$ is six. The coefficient is the only number that can be changed in balancing an equation.

Figure out the number of each item in each of the following:

a) How many O's are there in $4Fe_2O_3$?

b) How many NO_3's are there in $2KNO_3$?

c) How many SO_4's are there in $6Al_2(SO_4)_3$?

d) Write down some rules to help you remember how to figure out how many of an item there are.

3. In the reaction:

$$CaCO_3 + 2HCl \rightarrow CaCl_2 + H_2O + CO_2$$

you can list the numbers of each atom on the reactant and product side, as shown on the table below.

Atom/ Ion	Reactant	Product
Ca	1 (in $CaCO_3$)	1 (in $CaCl_2$)
C	1 (in $CaCO_3$)	1 (in CO_2)
O	3 (in $CaCO_3$)	3 (1 in H_2O and 2 in CO_2)
H	2 (in 2HCl)	2 (in H_2O)
Cl	2 (in 2HCl)	2 (in $CaCl_2$)

The number of each atom remains constant. Atoms are recombining in the reaction, but are not themselves changing.

4. The following is a set of unbalanced equations. Your teacher will assign your group one equation. Your task will be to analyze the equation, balance it using chemical symbols, and to write a procedure for balancing equations.

Helpful hints are provided in *Steps 5* and *6*.

Group 1:

$Pb(NO_3)_2$	+	$(NH_4)_2SO_4$	$\rightarrow$	$PbSO_4$	+	NH_4NO_3
lead nitrate	*and*	*ammonium sulfate*	*yield*	*lead (II) sulfate*	*and*	*ammonium nitrate*

Group 2:

$Cu(NO_3)_2$	+	Na_3PO_4	$\rightarrow$	$Cu_3(PO_4)_2$	+	$NaNO_3$
copper (II) nitrate	*and*	*sodium phosphate*	*yield*	*copper (II) phosphate*	*and*	*sodium nitrate*

Group 3:

$Fe(NO_3)_3 + K_2CO_3 \rightarrow Fe_2(CO_3)_3 + KNO_3$

iron (III) nitrate and potassium carbonate yield iron (III) carbonate and potassium nitrate

Group 4:

$AlCl_3 + Pb(NO_3)_2 \rightarrow PbCl_2 + Al(NO_3)_3$

aluminum chloride and lead (II) nitrate yield lead (II) chloride and aluminum nitrate

Group 5:

$Al_2(CO_3)_3 + HCl \rightarrow AlCl_3 + H_2O + CO_2$

aluminum carbonate and hydrogen chloride yield aluminum chloride and water and carbon dioxide

Group 6:

$Al(NO_3)_3 + K_3PO_4 \rightarrow AlPO_4 + KNO_3$

aluminum nitrate and potassium phosphate yield aluminum phosphate and potassium nitrate

Group 7:

$Ba(NO_3)_2 + Cr_2(SO_4)_3 \rightarrow BaSO_4 + Cr(NO_3)_2$

barium nitrate and chromium sulfate yield barium sulfate and chromium nitrate

5. Consider the statement: "The chemical reaction is not balanced." What does this mean?
   a) Write down your answer to this question in your *Active Chemistry* log.
   b) What are the atoms to consider in the equation your group was assigned?
   c) Do the same type and number of atoms exist on both sides of the arrow?
6. Copy the chemical equation you were assigned into your *Active Chemistry* log. Make a table like the following one beneath for your equation:
   a) Fill in the "Atom/Ion" column.

Atom/Ion	Reactant	Product

   b) Look at the reactants (starting materials on the left side of the arrow). Count how many of each element there are and write it in the table.
   c) Next, look at the products (ending materials on the right side of the arrow). Count how many of each element there are and write it in the table.
   d) What's wrong with the balance?
   e) Change the coefficients in a logical way to balance the equation.
   f) Describe what happens when a chemical reaction is balanced.
7. Now that you have practiced balancing equations several times, you have a system in place for how to do it.
   a) With your group, write down a list of step-by-step instructions that you could give to someone to balance equations.

Chem Talk

Chem Words

Law of Conservation of Matter: the amount of matter present before and after a chemical change remains the same.

LAW OF CONSERVATION OF MATTER

Balanced chemical equations are an example of the **Law of Conservation of Matter.** You may already have learned a formal definition for this principle: matter cannot be created or destroyed, but it can change form. In the case of chemical reactions, this means that the same quantity of each element must enter and exit a chemical reaction; however, the elements can be associated with different elements on each side. When chemical equations are written, the quantity of an element on the reactant side must equal the quantity of that element on the product side, although the atoms of the element may be bonded differently.

Historical Background of Ideas about the Conservation of Matter

Scientists haven't always known that matter is conserved. In fact, about 2500 years ago they were struggling with this concept. In Greece, several philosophers, including Democritus, Heraclitus, and Aristotle, were among the first to postulate that there was an "equivalence of matter." Heraclitus (530–470 B.C.) said of the changing forms of water that "Sea is liquefied and measured into the same proportion as it had before it became Earth." Parmenides (born circa 510 B.C.) argued that "Being (that which exists) is conserved, that nothing comes from nothing." Democritus (460–370 B.C.) made up the term "atom" to mean the smallest part of matter that is unchanging and cannot be cut into smaller pieces. Aristotle (384–322 B.C.) laid the foundation for the Western study of science by arguing that there were four "atoms:" fire, earth, water and air.

Very little that is historically documented was added to the understanding of the Law of Conservation of Matter for many centuries. Nasiraddin Tusi (born in A.D.1201 in what is now Iran) wrote that "a body of matter cannot disappear completely. It only changes its form, condition, composition, color, and other properties and turns into a different complex or elementary matter." Western science did not recognize the principle until Antoine-Laurent Lavoisier (1743–1794) in France and Mikhail Lomonosov (1711–1765) in Russia stated it explicitly.

Checking Up

1. State the Law of Conservation of Matter. Then, explain in your own words what it means.
2. What is the smallest particle of matter with unique properties called?

What Do You Think Now?

At the beginning of this activity you were asked what was meant by the word "balance."

In which of the two quotes from the beginning of the activity do you now think the use of the word "balance" is closer to the meaning of the word when it is used to describe chemical equations?

Chem Essential Questions

What does it mean?

Chemistry explains a macroscopic phenomenon (what you observe) with a description of what happens at the nanoscopic level (atoms and molecules) using symbolic structures as a way to communicate. Complete the chart below in your *Active Chemistry* log.

MACRO	NANO	SYMBOLIC
Explain how your observations in this activity provide evidence that supports the Law of Conservation of Matter.	*Explain how you know that the following equation is balanced:* $Pb(NO_3)_2 + 2NaCl \rightarrow$ $PbCl_2 + 2NaNO_3$	*Here are two symbolic ways of depicting a reaction:* $2HCl_{(aq)} + Zn_{(s)} \rightarrow$ $ZnCl_{2(aq)} + H_{2(g)}$ 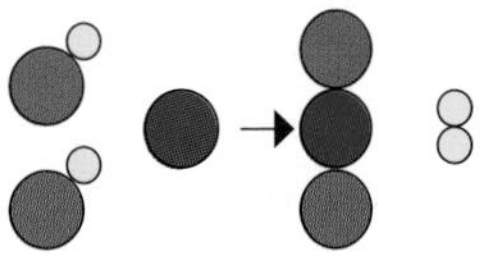 *Make and label a similar drawing for the equation:* $CaCO_3 \rightarrow CaO + CO_2$

How do you know?

Describe how the outcome of your experiment in *Part A* would have been different if balloons and resealable plastic bags had not been provided. Would the Law of Conservation of Matter still have been true?

Why do you believe?

Measuring the mass of an effervescent antacid table and the mass of water before and after the tablet dissolves seems to indicate that mass is not conserved. Explain what is happening to the matter that causes the law to appear to be violated. Describe how you could design an experiment to see if the amount of matter present actually changes.

Why should you care?

Balancing equations indicates the amount of reactants required to yield a specific amount of product. How would this be important if you chose to generate gas for your *Chemical Dominoes* toy?

Reflecting on the Activity and the Challenge

If you are using a chemical reaction to blow up a balloon with a gas that tips a lever (or to accomplish another task in your apparatus), then you will need to know how much of the starting materials to use to get the balloon to blow up to a certain size. As you learned in this activity, starting with a certain number of molecules of a substance does not mean the reaction will produce that number of molecules of a product. You have to consider how many atoms of elements are needed to form the molecules of the reactants and how many atoms are needed to form the molecules of the products.

While the number of atoms of each element will not change, the number of molecules that are formed may be different. It may take two of an input item to make three of an output item, or one of an input item to make two of an output item. These numbers, which are really coefficients, can only be determined by balancing the chemical equation for the reaction. So, if you want to use a particular chemical reaction to accomplish a task in your apparatus, you will have to be able to balance the chemical equation that represents the reaction so you will know how much input (starting materials) to use.

Chem to Go

1. Which of these equations is balanced, and which is not balanced? Explain how you can tell.

   a) $2C_2H_6 + 7O_2 \rightarrow 4CO_2 + 6H_2O$

   b) $2MgCO_3 + H_2SO_4 \rightarrow 2MgSO_4 + H_2O + 2CO_2$

2. The following equation is incorrectly balanced. What mistake was made in balancing it?

   $2AgNO_3 + 3CaCl_2 \rightarrow 3Ca(NO_3)_2 + 2AgCl$

3. What is wrong with the following chemical equation?

   $Na_2SO_4 + BaCl_2 \rightarrow Cl_2 + BaSO_4$

4. The input side of a chemical equation is:

   $KMnO_4 + I_2 \rightarrow$

   What elements must be on the output side?

5. Balance the following equations using the method that works best for you.

   a) $Na + Cl_2 \rightarrow NaCl$

   b) $C_3H_8 + O_2 \rightarrow CO_2 + H_2O$

   c) $MgCO_3 + HBr \rightarrow MgBr_2 + CO_2 + H_2O$

   d) $AgNO_3 + CaCl_2 \rightarrow AgCl + Ca(NO_3)_2$

   e) $KClO_3 \rightarrow KCl + O_2$

   f) $Cu(NO_3)_2 + Fe \rightarrow Fe(NO_3)_3 + Cu$

6. a) What is the difference between $Mg(OH)_2$ and $MgOH_2$?

   b) Does $Mg(OH)_2$ or $MgOH_2$ replace X in the balanced equation below? How can you tell?

   $X + 2HCl \rightarrow 2H_2O + MgCl_2$

7. A white solid is heated in a crucible over a flame. Oxygen gas is released and potassium chloride remains in the crucible. What elements were in the white solid? Explain your reasoning.

8. A metal is added to a solution. Lead chloride crystals precipitate out of solution (form a solid) and hydrogen gas is released. What metal was added to the solution? Explain your reasoning.

9. a) Indicate which of the numbers in the following equation are *coefficients* and which are *subscripts*.

   $3H_2SO_4 + 2Al \rightarrow Al_2(SO_4)_3 + 3H_2$

   b) Which are you allowed to adjust when balancing an equation?

10. Given the incomplete equation:

    $4Fe + 3O_2 \rightarrow 2X$

    Which compound is represented by X?

    a) FeO b) Fe_2O_3 c) Fe_3O_2 d) Fe_3O_4

11. Which equation shows a conservation of mass?

    a) $Na + Cl_2 \rightarrow NaCl$ b) $Al + Br_2 \rightarrow AlBr_3$

    c) $H_2O \rightarrow H_2 + O_2$ d) $PCl_5 \rightarrow PCl_3 + Cl_2$

12. Given the equation:

    $X + Cl_2 \rightarrow C_2H_5Cl + HCl$

    Which molecule is represented by X?

    a) C_2H_4 b) C_2H_6 c) C_3H_6 d) C_3H_8

Activity 3 How Much Gas is Produced?

CHEM POETRY

At the end of the elements' trendiest street
Was a beaker where just getting in was a feat;
One day ol' Tony, an atom of tin,
Went to "Club Atomic" to try and get in.

So to avoid big groups and bottleneck jams,
Of each el'ment we allow only ten grams.
"But wait just a moment," said Tony with care.
"Your admissions policy just isn't fair.

A much better way for you to be doin' it
Is to choose a different sort of unit.
Don't go by mass; instead you should try
To cap the number of atoms let by."

So Tony and all of his friends were admitted;
From their lowly status were they now acquitted.
And all it took was a little defiance
Grounded in fairness and knowledge of science.

–Mala Radhakrishnan

GOALS

In this activity you will:

- Use stoichiometry to determine the amount, mass, or volume of a substance produced or required in a chemical reaction.

What Do You See?

What Do You Think?

Suppose you have decided that you want to inflate a balloon to a volume of 50 mL with carbon dioxide gas as a part of your *Chemical Dominoes* apparatus.

- **What information would you need to predict how much of the reactants you would need?**
- **How could you use that information to determine the final volume of the balloon?**

Record your ideas about these questions in your *Active Chemistry* log. Be prepared to discuss your responses with your small group and the class.

Investigate

Part A: Equivalent Measures — Mass of One Mole

1. Your teacher will give you a bag of pennies, a single penny, and a balance. Without opening the bag of pennies, and without counting the pennies individually, figure out how many pennies are in the bag. (Assume the mass of the bag is so much smaller than a penny that it doesn't matter.)

    a) Write down any data you have to take and calculations you have to do in your *Active Chemistry* log.

b) Explain in writing how to figure out the number of pennies in the bag.

c) If you have a bunch of pennies with a mass of 143 g, how many pennies are there? Show your work or explain how you arrived at your answer.

2. The *Equivalent Measures* game uses dominoes. There is only one rule to this game. By studying the examples below, can you figure out the rule?

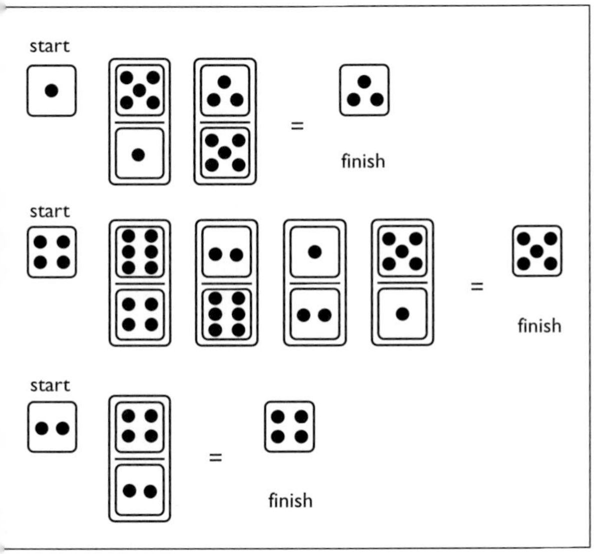
start
=
finish
start
=
finish
start
=
finish

a) What is the rule? Write it down in your *Active Chemistry* log.

3. You will be creating your own dominoes to use when you solve chemistry problems. The dominoes will include both a number and a unit. The top and bottom of each domino must be equivalent. For example, 24 h (hours) is equal to 1 d (day). The numbers 24 and 1 are different but the values are the same because they are just a different way of expressing 1 day. The following are some equivalent dominoes for time measurements.

a) Are the two halves of the time-measure dominoes shown equivalent to each other? Explain your answer.

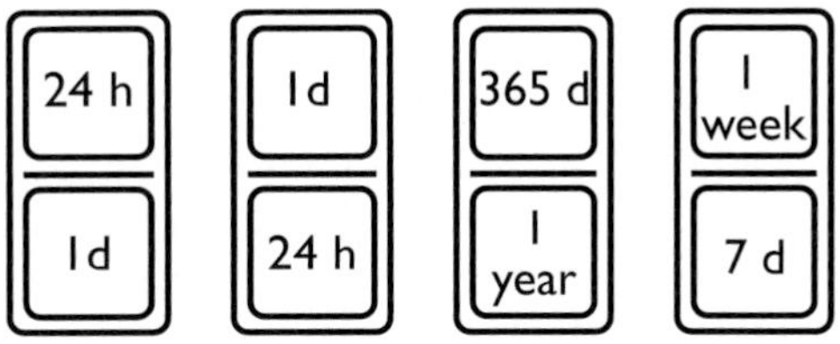
24 h
1 d
1 d
24 h
365 d
1 year
1 week
7 d

4. Complete the dominoes below in your *Active Chemistry* log.

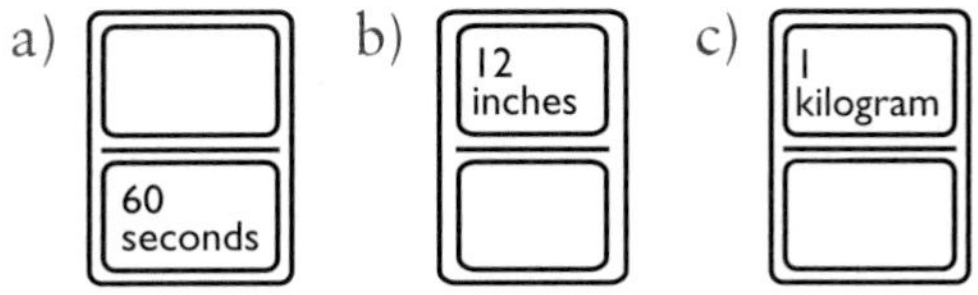
a)
60 seconds
b)
12 inches
c)
1 kilogram

d) Write three equivalent dominoes of your own.

5. When you use equivalent dominoes to solve problems, the "game" is played using the *unit* instead of the number in the domino. To change from one domino to another, the unit in the bottom of the second domino must be the same as the *unit* in the top of the first domino. The numbers in the dominos may differ.

2.50 g of pennies
1 penny

6. Atoms and molecules are like the pennies. All particles of one kind have the same average mass. If you know the mass of one particle, you can figure out the mass of a bunch of particles. But since atoms and molecules are so small, it doesn't make sense to talk about the masses of individual ones. Instead, chemists talk about the mass of a "counting group" of them, called a ***mole***.
A mole is like a dozen. There are always 12 in a dozen, and there is always a specific quantity of atoms or molecules in a mole. If you know the mass of a mole of some chemical, then you can figure out

how many moles of that chemical there are in a sample. This is just like when you figured out how many pennies were in the bag once you knew the mass of one penny.

7. First you have to be able to determine the masses of different elements. This is given on the periodic table. Each element on the periodic table has an ***atomic mass.*** This is the average mass of one atom of the element measured in atomic mass units (amu).

   Conveniently, the mass of one mole of atoms of the element has a mass with the same numerical value but measured in grams. For example, the average mass of a *single* atom of chlorine is 35.45 amu. The mass of a mole of chlorine atoms is 35.45 g. The unit "grams" is the unit you will use to measure mass. An equivalent domino relating mass of Cl and moles of Cl is shown. Answer each of these questions by drawing a domino for the answer.

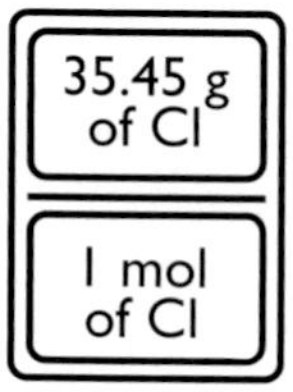
35.45 g of Cl
1 mol of Cl

   What is the mass of 1 mole of:

   a) oxygen? b) magnesium?

   c) carbon? d) hydrogen?

8. Not all of the substances you will encounter exist as single atoms. To determine the mass of one mole of a chemical that is not an individual atom, you need to know how many atoms of each kind are represented by the formula. You use the subscripts present in the formula to do this. How many of each kind of atom are in:

   a) $NaNO_3$? b) $Mg(OH)_2$?

   c) $Al_2(SO_4)_3$? d) $KC_2H_3O_2$?

9. To figure out the mass of one molecule of a chemical, you add up the masses of the atoms inside it.

   What is the mass of one mole of:

   a) CO_2? b) $NaHCO_3$? c) NaCl?

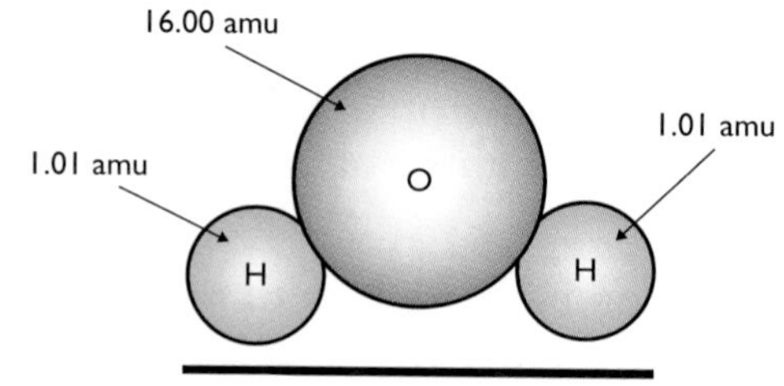
16.00 amu
1.01 amu
1.01 amu
O
H
H

The mass of one molecule of H_2O is 18.02 amu

10. Make dominoes for the following chemicals. Use the example for H_2O.

    a) CO_2 b) $NaHCO_3$ c) NaCl

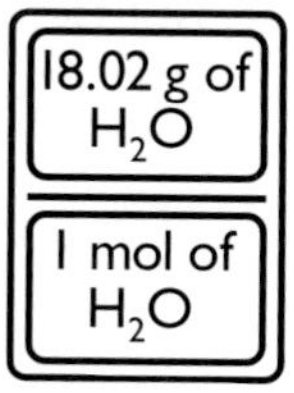
18.02 g of H_2O
1 mol of H_2O

11. Use these dominoes to figure out the answers to the following questions. The first one is done for you as a sample. Remember that it's important to figure out where you're starting and where you're finishing before you do any calculations. (You can use a domino either right-side-up or upside-down to answer a question.)

    a) If you have 36.04 g of water, how many moles of water are there?

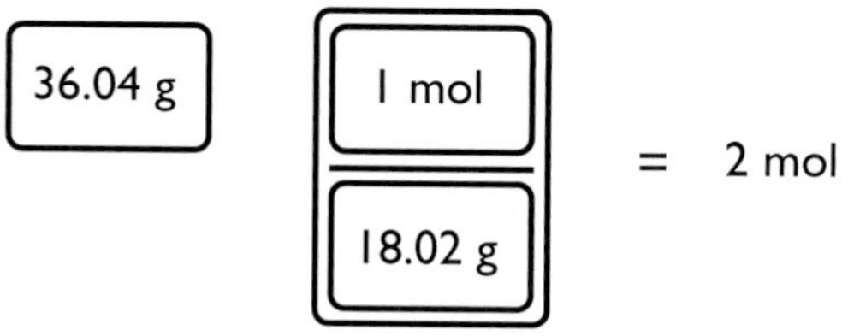
36.04 g
1 mol
18.02 g
= 2 mol

    Note that the "g" in the "numerator" cancels with the "denominator" of the dominoes.

    b) If you have 3.0 mol of NaCl, how many grams of NaCl are there?

    c) How many moles of CO_2 are in 66.0 g of CO_2?

    d) What is the mass of 0.80 mol of $NaHCO_3$?

Part B: Equivalent Measures—Coefficients from a Balanced Chemical Equation

1. A second kind of equivalent measure (domino) comes from balanced chemical equations. You can make equivalent-measure dominoes out of any two substances in a balanced chemical equation. Do the following problems using the equivalent-measures method. This equation $2AgNO_3 + CaCl_2 \rightarrow 2AgCl + Ca(NO_3)_2$ tells you that 1 mol of the reactant $CaCl_2$ produces 2 mol of the product AgCl. (Ignore the other reactants and products.) This domino illustrates this:

2 mol of AgCl
1 mol of $CaCl_2$

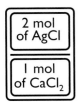

If you begin with 2 mol of $CaCl_2$ you can find the number of moles of AgCl produced:

start			finish
2.0 mol of $CaCl_2$	2 mol of AgCl / 1 mol of $CaCl_2$	=	4.0 mol of AgCl

a) For the following equation, create a domino to show that 2 mol of HCl produce 1 mol of $CaCl_2$.

$Ca(OH)_2 + 2HCl \rightarrow CaCl_2 + 2H_2O$

b) If you want to make 3.0 mol of $CaCl_2$, how many moles of HCl must you use?

c) If you use 7.5 mol of O_2, how many moles of Al_2O_3 will be made?

$4Al + 3O_2 \rightarrow 2Al_2O_3$

d) The following chemical equation is **not** balanced, so you will first have to balance it. If you use 5.0 moles of CH_4, how many moles of O_2 will you need?

$CH_4 + O_2 \rightarrow CO_2 + H_2O$

Part C: Equivalent Measures—Space Occupied by One Mole of Gas

1. Finally, consider a third use for equivalent-measure dominoes. This third use is to change between moles of a gas and volume of that gas. Chemists have found that it is a good approximation to say that the same number of moles of any gas will take up the same space as long as the temperature and pressure are the same. Under standard conditions of temperature and pressure (273 K temperature and 1.0 atm pressure), 1 mol of any gas will fill 22.4 L of space. That's about 11 two-liter soda bottles worth of space. Therefore, the equivalent-measure domino you would use looks like the one shown. For conversions between 1 mol of any gas at standard conditions and the volume of that gas, always use the same domino. Try the following problems using the equivalent measure.

1 mol of any gas at standard conditions
22.4 L of volume occupied

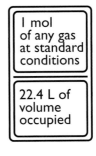

a) How many liters of space will 2.0 mol of O_2 gas fill at standard conditions?

b) If a helium balloon fills 5.6 L of space at standard conditions, how many moles of He are in it?

c) If you wanted to fill a balloon to 0.50 L with CO_2 at standard conditions, how many moles of CO_2 would you need?

2. Back in *Activity 1*, you filled a balloon with gas in order to make a lever tip by 2 cm. To do this, you had to blow up the balloon with gas so that its diameter was 4 cm. You can now determine what volume of gas had to be produced to inflate the balloon. Think of the balloon as a sphere. The volume of the gas you need to produce to do this, then, can be calculated from the volume equation for a sphere that has a radius of 2 cm.

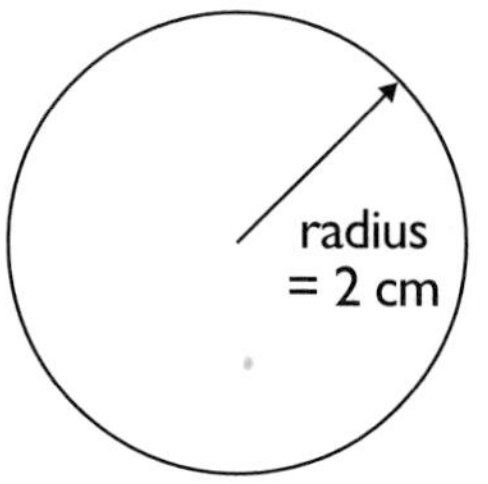
radius
= 2 cm

$$V = \frac{4}{3}\pi r^3$$
$$= \frac{4}{3}(3.1416)(2\text{ cm})^3$$
$$= \frac{4}{3}(3.1416)(8\text{ cm}^3)$$
$$= 33.5\text{ cm}^3$$
$$= 33.5\text{ mL}$$

In the metric system, it is convenient that volume in cm^3 is the same as volume in mL. You can also use an equivalent measure to convert from mL to L, since there are 1000 mL in 1 L.

$$33.5\text{ mL} \times \frac{1\text{ L}}{1000\text{ mL}} =$$
$$0.0335\text{ L of } CO_2 \text{ gas needed}$$

Before you do the next step, review the three ways you can generate equivalent-measure dominoes in chemistry.

3. The balanced equation that describes the reaction between baking soda and acetic acid is

$$\underset{\textit{sodium bicarbonate}}{NaHCO_3} + \underset{\textit{acetic acid}}{HC_2H_3O_2} \rightarrow$$
$$\underset{\textit{sodium acetate}}{NaC_2H_3O_2} + \underset{\textit{water}}{H_2O} + \underset{\textit{carbon dioxide}}{CO_2}$$

If you had 1 mol of sodium bicarbonate and added it to 1 mol of acetic acid, you could produce 1 mol of carbon dioxide. The 1 mol of carbon dioxide would fill a balloon of 22.4 L. That would be a big balloon!

Your balloon only has to be filled to a volume of 33.5 mL or 0.0335 L of gas. You will need much less than 1 mol of baking soda.

Assume that you have plenty of acetic acid available and that you are working at standard conditions.

a) What mass of baking soda would you have to add to the vinegar in order to fill the balloon enough to tip the lever?

4. Look back at your recorded observations from *Method 1* in *Activity 1*.

a) How much baking soda was required to get the balloon to tip the lever by 2 cm? Is your prediction equal to it? Account for any differences between the two amounts.

Chem Talk

STOICHIOMETRY

Moles and Molar Mass

"Dozen" is a counting word you use to count groups of things such as eggs and donuts. One dozen is always the same number. A **mole** is a counting word used to count very large quantities of very small objects (primarily atoms and molecules). 1 mol = 6.022×10^{23}. However, in this activity, the actual number doesn't matter very much. What is more important is that one mole of anything is always the same quantity. Three moles of something is three times as much as one mole.

The next important thing to know about moles is that one mole of any single kind of atom or molecule has a mass equal to its atomic or molecular mass expressed in grams. For example, an oxygen atom has an atomic mass of 16.00 amu (you can find this on the periodic table). One mole of oxygen atoms has a mass of 16.00 g. This is called the **molar mass** of oxygen atoms. An oxygen molecule (O_2) is made of two oxygen atoms. One mole of oxygen molecules has a mass of 32.00 g. This is the molar mass of an oxygen molecule. To find the mass of a compound, you add up the masses of each atom in the compound. The molecular mass of water (H_2O) is 18.02 amu (1.01 amu + 1.01 amu + 16.00 amu). One mole of water has a mass of 18.02 g.

How Balanced Chemical Equations Are Involved

Recall the equation for one method you used to generate carbon dioxide gas.

$$NaHCO_3 + HC_2H_3O_2 \rightarrow NaC_2H_3O_2 + H_2O + CO_2$$

$NaHCO_3$	$HC_2H_3O_2$	$NaC_2H_3O_2$	H_2O	CO_2
sodium bicarbonate	*acetic acid*	*sodium acetate*	*water*	*carbon dioxide*

From the balanced equation you know one mole of baking soda and one mole of vinegar form one mole each of sodium acetate, water, and carbon dioxide. Three moles of baking soda would be enough to produce three moles of carbon dioxide. If you know how many moles of carbon dioxide you need to make, you can calculate the number of moles of baking soda you need. The molar mass of baking soda will let you convert moles of baking soda to grams.

→

Chem Words

mole: 6.022×10^{23} units, the number equal to the number of carbon atoms in exactly 12 g of pure ^{12}C.

molar mass: the mass of one mole of a pure substance.

Chem Words

standard temperature and pressure (STP): standard temperature is 273.15 kelvins and standard pressure is 760 mm Hg.

stoichiometry: the study of the relationships (mass-mole-volume) among substances involved in chemical reactions.

The Molar Volume of a Gas

Another piece of information you have learned in this activity is that one mole of almost any gas at **standard temperature and pressure (STP)** will occupy the same volume (22.4 L). Standard pressure (1 atm or 760 mm Hg) is close to the pressure under which you live. It is a reasonable approximation for the pressure in the laboratory. However, room temperature is likely to be closer to 298 K than 273 K. When the temperature of a gas increases, the volume occupied by the gas increases. So, while one mole of a gas at standard conditions will occupy 22.4 L, one mole of the gas at room temperature will be a bit larger.

Stoichiometric Calculations

In the activity, you calculated the volume of carbon dioxide gas needed to blow up a balloon. You also calculated the number of moles of the reactants needed. This kind of computation is called **stoichiometry**. The heart of a stoichiometric calculation involves calculating the number of moles of one chemical in a reaction based on the number of moles of one of the other chemicals in the balanced chemical equation. The coefficients in the balanced equation set the proportions. These proportions relate the number of moles of any reactant or product in the reaction to the other reactant or product. For example, look at the balanced equation:

$$N_2 + 3H_2 \rightarrow 2NH_3$$

It tells you that nitrogen and hydrogen gases combine to form ammonia. Also, it tells you that one mole of nitrogen molecules and three moles of hydrogen molecules will produce two moles of ammonia molecules. These ratios or proportions never change, because compounds have fixed formulas or proportions.

If you use three times as much of a starting material, that will be enough to make three times as much product. You can use equivalent-measure dominoes to do this calculation.

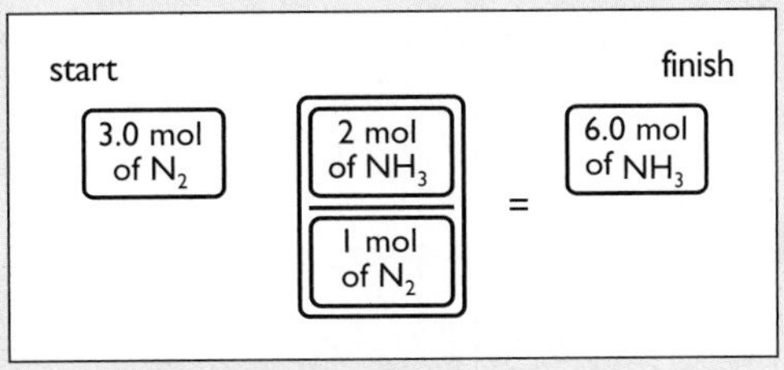
start
finish
3.0 mol of N_2
2 mol of NH_3
1 mol of N_2
=
6.0 mol of NH_3

This can be written mathematically as

$$3 \text{ mol } N_2 \times \frac{2 \text{ mol } NH_3}{1 \text{ mol } N_2} = 6 \text{ mol } NH_3$$

Although the amount of a substance generated or consumed during a chemical reaction is based on the number of moles of particles that interact, there is no equipment that can measure moles directly. Therefore, moles must be converted into something you can actually measure. Two measurements that are easy to make in the lab are mass of a solid or liquid and volume of a gas. That's why chemists work with these measurements in stoichiometry. Using the stoichiometry method, you can convert a known mass of any chemical (or the volume of a gas at STP) into moles, and then convert your answer in moles back into grams (or liters of a gas at STP).

For example, if you begin with 84.0 g of nitrogen gas, you can calculate the volume of ammonia that should be produced at STP. Doing this is a three-step process and involves three dominoes. N_2 has a molar mass of $2 \times 14.01 \text{ g} = 28.02 \text{ g}$ (since each of the two N atoms has an atomic mass of 14.01 amu). This is one domino. One mole of NH_3 occupies 22.4 L of space at STP. This is another domino. The balanced chemical equation provides another domino. One mole of N_2 produces two moles of NH_3.

$$84.0 \text{ g } N_2 \times \frac{1 \text{ mol } N_2}{28.02 \text{ g } N_2} \times \frac{2 \text{ mol } NH_3}{1 \text{ mol } N_2} \times \frac{22.4 \text{ L } NH_3 \text{ at STP}}{1 \text{ mol } NH_3} = 134 \text{ L } NH_3 \text{ at STP}$$

To solve a stoichiometry problem, you have to figure out what measurement you are beginning with and what measurement you want to end with before you do the problem. Then you look at ways you can convert, using dominoes, between one unit and another. There are three kinds of dominoes at your disposal:

1. You can use the molar mass of a substance. The domino will include one mole of the substance and its molar mass. To use this domino, you will need the periodic table.
2. You can use the coefficients from a balanced chemical equation. When using this domino, both units will be moles.

Chem Words

dimensional analysis: a name for "equivalent measures." A method for solving problems that involves canceling units.

3. You can use the volume (amount of space) that one mole of gas takes up. This will always be the same domino: 1 mol of gas at STP is equivalent to 22.4 L of gas.

Dimensional Analysis

Notice that in all these calculations, the units multiply and divide (canceling each other out) to give the proper units for the answer. This is called **dimensional analysis**. It indicates that your method of solution is reasonable. If the procedure you followed to produce an answer was incorrect, it would be unlikely to yield the proper units. One way to think about the mole ratio is that you put the chemical and measure (moles, grams or liters) you're converting *from* on the bottom of the ratio so that it will cancel the chemical and measure on the top of the preceding domino. This leaves only the units from the top half of the ratio (domino), which come from the chemical and measure you are converting *to*.

$$84.0\ \cancel{g\ N_2} \times \frac{1\ \cancel{mol\ N_2}}{28.02\ \cancel{g\ N_2}} \times \frac{2\ \cancel{mol\ NH_3}}{1\ \cancel{mol\ N_2}} \times \frac{22.4\ L\ NH_3\ \text{at STP}}{1\ \cancel{mol\ NH_3}} = 134\ L\ NH_3\ \text{at STP}$$

Stoichiometry in the Real World

Chemical changes produce new substances with new properties. Knowing what new substances and new properties will be produced allows chemists to produce remarkable results: new chemicals that can cure diseases, withstand the most difficult conditions, explode or react with other chemicals, or help you do things that couldn't be done before. In order to control the results and produce the desired effect, you need to be able to predict the amounts of these new chemicals. Stoichiometry allows you to do that. In this case, you were able to inflate a balloon to move a lever by a specific amount. If you were producing a new chemical you would also want to produce just the amount you wanted. Stoichiometry is crucial in calculating the amounts of materials that are needed in a process, without unnecessary waste.

Checking Up

1. a) How many atoms are in 1 mol of atoms?
   b) How many paper clips are in 1 mol of paper clips?
   c) What does a mole mean?
2. a) Where do you find the mass of 1 mol of a particular element's atoms?
   b) What are the units of measurement for that mass?
3. What is stoichiometry?
4. Why is stoichiometry useful in the real world?

What Do You Think Now?

At the beginning of this activity you were asked the following questions about producing a gas to inflate a balloon.

- **What information would you need to predict how much of the reactants you would need?**
- **How could you use that information to determine the final volume of the balloon?**

How would you answer these questions now that you have completed this activity?

Chem Essential Questions

What does it mean?

Chemistry explains a macroscopic phenomenon (what you observe) with a description of what happens at the nanoscopic level (atoms and molecules) using symbolic structures as a way to communicate. Complete the chart below in your *Active Chemistry* log.

MACRO	NANO	SYMBOLIC
In this activity, you developed a method for determining an unknown number of pennies without counting them. Explain how the mole concept is similar to buying a bag of flour without counting the particles of flour.	*On a molecular level, describe what is happening when two substances react to form new products.*	*Describe the information provided in the symbolic notation of a chemical equation. Can you make an equivalent domino with any two units? Explain why or why not.*

How do you know?

At the beginning of this activity you carried out an activity using pennies. Explain how this activity relates to stoichiometry.

Why do you believe?

One example of stoichiometry used in the real world is in recipes. Different amounts of certain ingredients must be combined together to produce a certain amount of a food. Describe another real-life application of stoichiometry.

Why should you care?

Some of the requirements for the *Chapter Challenge* are that the sequence of events be reliable, repeatable, and safe. Describe how stoichiometry will be important in ensuring that these three requirements are met. What might be the consequences of forming too little product? What might be the consequences of forming too much product?

Reflecting on the Activity and the Challenge

If you want to use a chemical reaction to do anything in your *Chemical Dominoes* apparatus, chances are you will have to calculate how much starting materials to use to make the chemical reaction do what you want it to do. It's helpful to use stoichiometry to begin with a prediction. Then you have a place to start and you won't have to waste time and supplies trying to figure out the right amount by trial and error.

Chem to Go

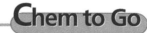

1. The following questions are about the reaction that you used to fill the balloon with gas and tip the lever in *Activity 1*.
   a) What gas filled the balloon?
   b) Where did it come from?
   c) If it comes from only one of the starting materials, is the other one necessary to complete the reaction?
   d) Does it matter how much of the other starting material was available?
2. Prove that mass is conserved in the chemical reaction you used to fill the balloon to tip the lever. That is, prove that the mass of the compounds on the input side of this chemical equation equals the mass of the compounds on the output side.

$$NaHCO_3 + HC_2H_3O_2 \rightarrow NaC_2H_3O_2 + H_2O + CO_2$$

$NaHCO_3$	$HC_2H_3O_2$	$NaC_2H_3O_2$	H_2O	CO_2
sodium bicarbonate	*acetic acid*	*sodium acetate*	*water*	*carbon dioxide*

3. What is the mass of one mole of each of the following substances:
   a) C (graphite in the lead of your pencil)
   b) Al (aluminum foil)
   c) NH_3 (ammonia gas)
   d) $CaCO_3$ (chalk dust)
   e) $NaAl(SO_4)_2$ (sodium aluminum sulfate, an ingredient in baking powder)
4. Use your answers from *Question 3* to do the following calculations. Show your work using equivalent measures.
   a) How many moles of C are in 18.0 g of graphite pencil leads?
   b) What is the mass of 0.50 mol of aluminum foil?
   c) What is the mass of 2.84 mol of ammonia gas?
   d) How many moles of $CaCO_3$ are in 10.0 g of calcium carbonate (chalk dust)?
   e) A container of baking powder has 198 g of baking powder in it. If one-fourth of this (49.5 g) is sodium aluminum sulfate, how many moles of $NaAl(SO_4)_2$ are in the container?

5. The chemical reaction represented by the balanced equation

   $2KClO_3 \rightarrow 2KCl + 3O_2$

   is not a very good method for producing oxygen gas for the purpose of blowing up a balloon to tip a lever, because it requires heating the $KClO_3$. However, it can be used as an illustration of the conservation of mass.

   a) Prove that the moles of each atom in the chemical equation are balanced.

   b) Prove that the mass in the chemical equation is balanced.

   c) How many moles of $KClO_3$ are required to make 22.4 L of O_2 gas at STP?

6. Three balloons are filled to the same volumes of 3.73 L at standard conditions. The first balloon contains CO_2 gas, the second contains H_2 gas, and the third contains He gas.

   a) How many moles of gas are in each balloon?

   b) What is the mass of the CO_2 balloon?

   c) What is the mass of the H_2 balloon?

   d) What is the mass of the He balloon?

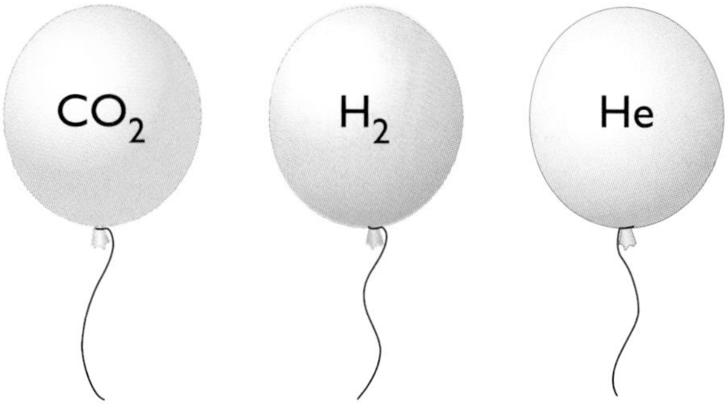
CO2
H2
He

7. The balanced equation

   $Zn + 2HCl \rightarrow ZnCl_2 + H_2$

   describes the production of hydrogen gas from hydrochloric acid and zinc. It is another option for blowing up a balloon that works faster than the one in this activity. However, hydrogen gas is highly flammable, so you'll have to make sure not to have any flames near it.

   a) If you wanted to blow up a balloon to a size of 0.56 L at standard conditions, how many moles of H_2 gas would you need to produce?

   b) A much more realistic size for a balloon to tip a lever is 0.035 L of H_2. How many grams of zinc would this require? Assume standard conditions.

   c) For all the zinc to react, there must be enough HCl that some is left over. To blow up a balloon to 0.035 L as in part (b), what is the minimum amount of moles of HCl that you must use?

8. The balanced equation

   $2C_2H_2 + 5O_2 \rightarrow 4CO_2 + 2H_2O$

   describes the burning of acetylene gas (C_2H_2) in a torch used by welders.

   a) If the tank attached to the torch contains 100 g of acetylene, how many liters of oxygen are used at standard conditions if you burn the entire contents of the tank?

   b) How many liters of CO_2 would be produced at standard conditions?

   c) What is the mass of the CO_2 that would be produced?

9. ***Preparing for the Chapter Challenge***

   If you are going to use a lever tipped by a gas-filled balloon as part of your *Chemical Dominoes* apparatus, you will need to calculate the quantity of starting materials necessary to do this. In your *Active Chemistry* log, write down the equation that represents the reaction you will use to make the gas, and calculate the quantity of starting materials you will need to be able to blow up a balloon enough to tip a lever a distance of 5 cm. You may not decide to tip a lever this distance, but writing down these calculations now will help you later when you return to your notes to prepare for the *Chapter Challenge*.

Inquiring Further

Limiting reagent

The reactant that is used up first in a reaction is called the limiting reagent. In the reaction you used to blow up the balloon and tip a lever (baking soda and vinegar), which reactant is the limiting reagent? To figure this out, you'll need to find out how much acetic acid is in vinegar as well as how much vinegar you used.

Design an experiment to determine whether it matters which of the two starting materials, baking soda or acetic acid, is the limiting reagent.

Distilled White Vinegar
ALL PURPOSE
Baking
SODA
Bicarbonate of Soda

Activity 4 What Can Destroy a Metal?

What Do You See?
BATTERY
LED

GOALS

In this activity you will:

- Use proper materials to light an LED and explain the procedure.
- Use the Metal Activity Series to determine which metal of a given pair of metals is most reactive.

What Do You Think?

Since you have to light an LED as the final step of your *Chapter Challenge*, you will have to build an electrical circuit somewhere in your apparatus.

- **If you wanted to destroy a metal wire in a circuit by pouring a chemical on it, what kind of chemical would you use?**
- **Would all metals be destroyed equally well, or would there be some difference between metals?**

Record your ideas about these questions in your *Active Chemistry* log. Be prepared to discuss your responses with your small group and the class.

Investigate

Part A: Destroy the Circuit and Light the LED

1. You will use the LED (light-emitting diode) that you need to light as part of your *Chemical Dominoes* apparatus in this activity. The first thing you need to figure out is how to get an LED to light.

   For electricity to flow there must be a complete circuit that starts with a power source and ends back at that power source. Efficient circuits use good conductors such as metals. Set up a circuit with a battery, a 100-Ω (ohm) resistor, a 10-Ω resistor, a piece of metal (marked with an X), and the LED as shown on the next page.

Safety goggles and a lab apron must be worn *at all times* in a chemistry lab.

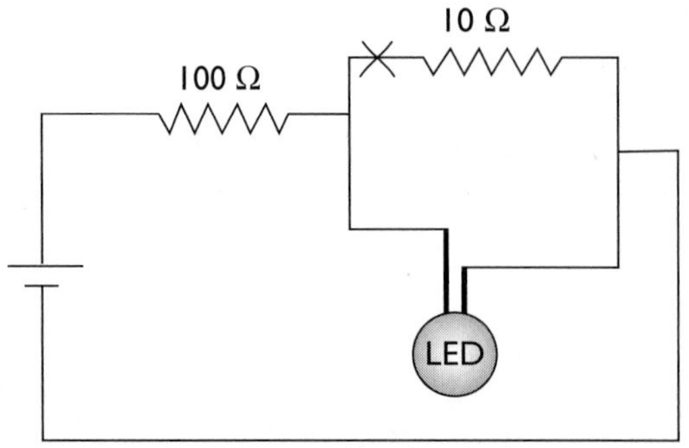
10 Ω
100 Ω
LED

If you have not learned how to read a schematic diagram, the same circuit is repeated with all the wires shown. (Notice that one end of the LED is longer than the other end. LEDs must be in the correct orientation to work properly because they only let electricity pass through in one direction.)

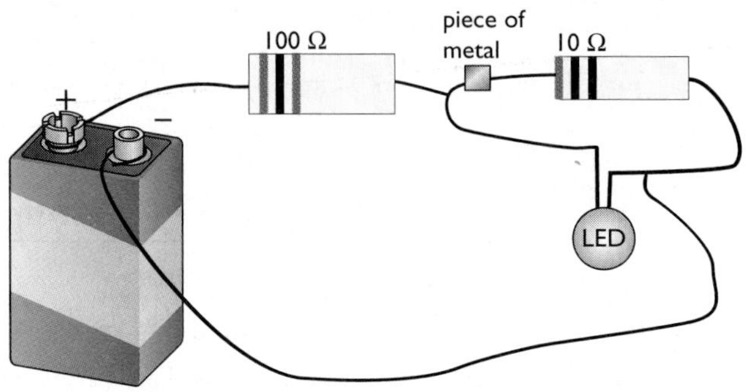
100 Ω
piece of metal
10 Ω
+
–
LED

In this design, there are two circuits. Some of the electricity flows through the 10 Ω resistor and other electricity flows through the LED. By removing the piece of metal, all electricity flows through the LED. This extra electricity effectively "turns the LED on." If your circuit does not behave in this way, you may have hooked up the LED incorrectly. Reverse the LED and try it again.

a) Record your results.

Be careful with the chemicals. Do not get them on your skin.

Do not breathe fumes from the chemicals or the reaction with the aluminum.

Clean up all spills immediately.

Wash your hands and arms thoroughly after the activity.

2. In your *Chemical Dominoes* challenge, you can break the circuit by destroying the piece of metal chemically rather than removing it by hand. To do this, you must investigate metals and their behavior.

Now that you have learned how to create a complete circuit to light an LED, you need to learn how different chemicals affect materials you have used in your circuit. Your teacher will give you three dropper bottles containing "mystery" chemicals 1, 2, and 3. These mystery chemicals will all destroy the magnesium in the circuit.

First, practice dropping some of the mystery chemical on tiny pieces of magnesium on a safe surface.

a) Record all observations that will help you tell the mystery chemicals apart, both in how they look and in how they interact with the magnesium.

b) Next, decide which mystery chemical does the best job of destroying the circuit. Write down what it does, and why it is the best one.

3. Dispose of the materials as directed by your teacher. Clean up your workstation.

Part B: What Kinds of Chemicals Affect Metals?

1. Chemists use a list called the activity series of metals (as shown on the next page) to help them figure out which metals are more reactive with other chemicals and which ones are less reactive. Read the following statements.

- Wires in electrical circuits are usually made of copper.
- Gold, silver, and platinum are considered precious metals and are used for making jewelry.
- When you use an aluminum pot for cooking, it soon gets dull.
- As a cheaper alternative to making pennies, the U.S. government now makes pennies

using a zinc filling that is covered with a copper shell. If they used just zinc, the pennies wouldn't last very long.

2. On the basis of the statements in *Step 1*, in which direction does the "activity" run in the table. Which end is most active and which end is least active?

   a) Record your answer in your log.

3. When a metal atom reacts, it gives up one or more electrons and becomes a positively charged ion. For example, when sodium and chlorine react, an ionic compound is formed, NaCl (table salt). Metals can exist in two forms:

   - as *neutral metal atoms* in a piece of shiny metal
   - as *positively charged metal ions* in salts that can be dissolved in water to form a solution

4. Different metal atoms give up different numbers of electrons.

   a) Copy the Metal Activity Series table into your *Active Chemistry* log and add another column titled, "Changes when atoms give up electrons."

5. The equation that shows how a silver atom gives up electrons and becomes a silver ion is

$$Ag \rightarrow Ag^{+} + 1e^{-}$$

What this means is that when a neutral atom of Ag gives up one electron, the Ag ion has a charge of +1.

The information will be useful as you compare how much one chemical substance can affect another.

You can reverse a chemical equation. The reversed equation shows how a positively charged metal ion gains electrons.

$$Ag^{+} + 1e^{-} \rightarrow Ag$$

Activity Series of Metals

Name	Symbol
lithium	Li
potassium	K
calcium	Ca
sodium	Na
magnesium	Mg
aluminum	Al
zinc	Zn
iron	Fe
tin	Sn
lead	Pb
hydrogen*	H
copper	Cu
mercury	Hg
silver	Ag
platinum	Pt
gold	Au

* Hydrogen is not a metal but it behaves like a metal in some chemical reactions so it is included in the activity series.

6. In order for electrons to be available to be gained by an ion, another atom has to have given up the electrons. Below is an example of how electrons are transferred between silver ions and zinc atoms.

$$Ag^{+} + 1e^{-} \rightarrow Ag$$

$$Zn \rightarrow Zn^{2+} + 2e^{-}$$

   a) How many electrons does each zinc atom give up?

   b) How many electrons does each silver ion accept?

   c) Can one zinc atom transfer its electrons to one silver ion?

   d) If one zinc atom gives up electrons, how many silver ions will have to be present to accept electrons?

7. This change is represented in the chemical equation below. Since the zinc atoms and silver ions interact with each other, the two equations that represent the interaction can be combined. The combined equation (Net Ionic Equation) is shown in the box.

$$(Ag^{+} + 1e^{-} \rightarrow Ag) \times 2 \quad = \quad 2Ag^{+} + 2e^{-} \rightarrow 2Ag$$

$$(Zn \rightarrow Zn^{2+} + 2e^{-}) \times 1 \quad = \quad Zn \rightarrow Zn^{2+} + 2e^{-}$$

$$\boxed{2Ag^{+} + Zn \rightarrow 2Ag + Zn^{2+}}$$

The combined reaction could also be written the other way around as:

$$2Ag + Zn^{2+} \rightarrow 2Ag^{+} + Zn$$

This equation represents the change that occurs when two neutral silver atoms lose one electron each to a zinc ion.

Only one of these two reactions actually occurs in nature. The activity series tells you which one will occur.

a) The activity series shows that some metals (toward the top of the list) react more easily with most metal ion solutions than other metals do. Use the activity series to determine which of the two reactions actually occur in nature. Look at which metal is closer to the top of the activity series.

Be careful with the HCl. Do not get it on your skin.

Do not breathe fumes from the chemicals or the reaction with the aluminum.

Clean up all spills immediately.

8. Now use aluminum and copper as an example.

When Al gives up its electrons:

$$Al \rightarrow Al^{3+} + 3e^-$$

When Cu^{2+} receives the electrons:

$$Cu^{2+} + 2e^- \rightarrow Cu$$

The same number of electrons must be given up as are gained, so you have to use the least common multiple of 2 and 3, which is 6.

If the interaction occurs as represented by the equation below, aluminum atoms would give up electrons to copper ions.

$$(Al \rightarrow Al^{3+} + 3e^-) \times 2 \quad = \quad 2Al \rightarrow 2Al^{3+} + 6e^-$$

$$(Cu^{2+} + 2e^- \rightarrow Cu) \times 3 \quad = \quad 3Cu^{2+} + 6e^- \rightarrow 3Cu$$

$$\boxed{2Al + 3Cu^{2+} \rightarrow 2Al^{3+} + 3Cu}$$

An equation that represents the opposite change is shown below. That equation represents copper atoms giving up electrons to aluminum ions.

$$2Al^{3+} + 3Cu \rightarrow 2Al + 3Cu^{2+}$$

a) As before, only one of these two reactions occurs naturally. Use the activity series to predict which one will occur.

Part C: Investigating the Activity Series of Metals

1. You will receive a set of six neutral metals and solutions of salts that contain metal ions. With this set, you will be able to investigate the activity series of metals. The set should contain most or all of the chemicals listed in the table.

   You will also experiment with hydrogen, to compare to the metals. You will not use neutral hydrogen (which occurs as H_2 gas) in this experiment because it's too dangerous. However, you will be provided with hydrogen ions in solution, made from HCl dissolved in water.

   a) First, list all the possible pairs of metals to try and all possible metals to try out with hydrogen. For example, you will test aluminum metal with copper ions from $CuCl_2$ and you will test copper metal with aluminum ions from $AlCl_3$. There should be 21 possible pairs if you have all the metals on the list, plus hydrogen.

   b) Next, divide up all of the possible pairs among groups in your class, so that each group has about the same number of pairs to test. Record the pairs your group will use.

   c) Write both possible interactions for each pair that your group will test.

   d) Use the activity series to predict which interaction will occur for each pair of metals you will test. For each prediction, explain your reasoning.

2. Pair up with a member of another group and walk that person through what you did for one of the pairs of metals. Include an explanation

of how you predicted which interaction would occur naturally.

3. Return to your group, and test the interactions your group is assigned. For hydrogen, you will only be able to test the interaction in one direction.

   Place about 10 drops of the solution in one well in a 24-well microplate. Then, using forceps, place the piece of metal into the well. Make sure the metal piece breaks the surface of the liquid so that there is opportunity for the metal and the metal ions to interact.

   When observing, sometimes it is helpful to view the wells with different colors of paper underneath. It is also helpful to look at the well from below to look for changes.

   a) Record your observations if a reaction occurred. If nothing happened note that as well.

   b) Compile the entire class's results. Now compare all of the predictions based on the activity series with all of the results that you observed. Do they match?

4. Dispose of the materials as directed by your teacher. Clean up your workstation.

5. Look back at the data you recorded about the mystery chemicals when you tested them on magnesium *(Part A, Step 3)*. Use those observations and results you just collected to figure out what mystery chemicals 1, 2, and 3 were.

   a) Record your findings.

Safety goggles and a lab apron must be worn *at all times* in a chemistry lab.

If you spill any chemicals on your skin, wash your skin with water. Report any spills to your teacher.

Wash your hands and arms thoroughly after the activity.

Neutral metals	Metal ions in solution
aluminum	aluminum ions from $AlCl_3$ crystals that break apart into ions when added to water
copper	copper (II) ions from $CuCl_2$ crystals in water
iron	iron (II) ions from $FeCl_2$ crystals in water
magnesium	magnesium ions from $MgCl_2$ crystals in water
silver	silver ions from $AgNO_3$ crystals that break apart into ions when added to water (AgCl doesn't break apart well enough to give enough Ag^+ ions)
zinc	zinc ions from $ZnCl_2$ crystals in water

Chem Talk

Chem Words

metals: a class of materials that exhibit the properties of conductivity, malleability, reactivity, and ductility. Metallic elements lose electrons more easily than non-metallic elements, so they form positive ions in ionic compounds.

REDOX REACTIONS

What is a Metal?

Metals are shiny (or can be polished to shine). They also have other important properties. They conduct electricity, so they are used in electrical circuits. They conduct heat, so they are used in cookware. Since most metals can withstand high temperatures, they are used to build strong structures. They can be pounded into different shapes with a hammer, and can be made into nails, flat surfaces, or boxes.

Most of the elements in the periodic table are metals. If you draw a diagonal line from boron (B, #5) down to astatine (At, #85), the metals are all the elements to the left of the line, including elements 57–71 and 89–103 at the bottom of the table. Most of these elements don't occur very commonly in nature as pure metals. The majority of metals are more reactive than hydrogen, and are most commonly found in nature in their ionic forms, as positively charged ions involved in solid crystals or dissolved in water.

The Origin of the Activity Series

Chemists have experimented with the activities of metals for many hundreds of years. Much of chemistry grew out of the field of alchemy, which was popular in medieval times. The goal of an alchemist was to create gold out of other metals. You now know that it is not possible to do this by chemical means, because the identity of an atom is specified by how many protons are in its nucleus (the meaning of the *atomic number* on the periodic table). When an atom interacts with another, only the arrangement of electrons is changed.

In the process of experimenting with metals, however, alchemists discovered that some metals react more easily with most metal ion solutions than other metals do. They developed the activity series from their observations. Since then, chemists have measured these more accurately. There are now ways to measure numbers and figure out where a metal (or any other chemical) belongs in the activity series.

Special Reactions between Metals and Metal Ions

The reactions that can occur between neutral metal atoms, such as Zn, and metal ions, such as Cu^{2+}, are part of a special class of reactions called **oxidation-reduction reactions** ("**redox**" for short). **Oxidation** is defined as giving up electrons, so all of the equations you listed in the activity series represented oxidations.

Zinc metal oxidizes: $Zn \rightarrow Zn^{2+} + 2e^-$

Reduction is receiving electrons. An oxidation equation turned backwards represents a reduction.

Copper ions reduce: $Cu^{2+} + 2e^- \rightarrow Cu$

As you found out in the activity, when an oxidation happens, a reduction also occurs. Electrons that are given up have to be received by something. So, oxidation changes and reduction changes are often called *half-reactions* because you need both halves for a reaction to happen.

You can use half-reactions to balance redox equations by making sure the number of electrons lost is equal to the number of electrons gained. For example, when zinc metal oxidizes, copper ions reduce:

Zinc metal oxidizes: $Zn \rightarrow Zn^{2+} + 2e^-$

Copper ions reduce: $Cu^{2+} + 2e^- \rightarrow Cu$

Since the same number of electrons are lost as are gained, the half-reactions can be added as they are, and the electrons will cancel. This gives the redox equation:

$$Zn + Cu^{2+} \rightarrow Zn^{2+} + Cu$$

You learned that although you can write the equation in two directions and you can test both equations, the reaction will occur naturally in only one direction. For example, for the pair of metals Zn and Cu, the two possible equations are as follows:

$$Zn + Cu^{2+} \rightarrow Zn^{2+} + Cu$$

or $$Cu + Zn^{2+} \rightarrow Cu^{2+} + Zn$$

The activity series can be used to predict which equation represents a reaction that will occur. From the activity series you can see

Chem Words

oxidation-reduction (redox) reaction: a chemical reaction (change) in which electrons are transferred from one substance to another.

oxidation: a loss of one or more electrons.

reduction: a gain of one or more electrons.

Checking Up

1. List four properties that define metals. For each property, give one way that metals are used by humans to take advantage of that property.
2. Where are most metals found and in what form?
3. How was the activity series developed?
4. a) Define oxidation.

   b) Define reduction.

   c) How are they related?
5. What is the activity series useful for predicting, in terms of redox reactions?

that zinc is a more reactive metal than copper. That is, copper is less likely to react than zinc. The first reaction on the previous page is zinc metal reacting with copper ions. The second reaction is copper metal reacting with zinc ions. Since zinc is more reactive than copper, the activity series leads you to predict that the first reaction will occur and the second reaction will not. You were able to test for this during the activity.

When Is a Metal Not a Metal?

You may wonder why hydrogen is included in the Metal Activity Series when it is clearly not a metal. Metals, in general, are solid, shiny, ductile, malleable, and conductive of heat and electricity. Hydrogen is none of these since it is a gas. However, hydrogen takes on the positive nature of a metal in its role in strong acids, such as hydrochloric (HCl vs. $NaCl$), sulfuric (H_2SO_4 vs. Na_2SO_4), and nitric (HNO_3 vs. $NaNO_3$) acids.

The most important reason to include hydrogen in the Metal Activity Series is because these acids are simple and convenient reagents which can quickly establish where an unknown metal stands in the series. For example, if a metal reacts with dilute HCl, then it is above hydrogen in the series. If it does not react with dilute HCl, then it lies below hydrogen in the series.

What Do You Think Now?

At the beginning of this activity you were asked:

- **If you wanted to destroy a metal wire in a circuit by pouring a chemical on it, what kind of chemical would you use?**
- **Would all metals be destroyed equally well, or would there be some difference between metals?**

Now that you have studied circuits and the metals that can be used to make them, how would you answer these questions?

Chem Essential Questions

What does it mean?

Chemistry explains a macroscopic phenomenon (what you observe) with a description of what happens at the nanoscopic level (atoms and molecules) using symbolic structures as a way to communicate. Complete the chart below in your *Active Chemistry* log.

MACRO	NANO	SYMBOLIC
In this activity, you tested a variety of combinations of metals, metal ions, and acids to determine reactivity. Describe some of your observations that indicated a reaction had occurred.	*Explain how electrons, atoms, and ions were involved in the chemical reactions you observed in this activity.*	*Show how half-reactions can be represented in equations that show the gain and loss of electrons.*

How do you know?

You learned in this activity that a redox reaction will only occur naturally in one direction. You then tested various combinations of metals and metal ions to compare experimental results with the activity series. How consistent were your results with the activity series?

Why do you believe?

The activity series determines how humans can use a variety of metals. Examples given in the text include using very unreactive metals for wiring, jewelry, building structures, etc. Describe other situations where it would be necessary to use a very reactive metal to achieve a desired result.

Why should you care?

You have learned how to light an LED using a circuit. You have also learned you can make circuits out of aluminum and then destroy them. Lighting the LED is a mandatory part of your challenge. You may also want to destroy a circuit in your apparatus. From what metals other than aluminum could you make circuits? What characteristics should a metal have if it is to be used in a circuit? Do these characteristics change if you plan to destroy the metal, causing electricity to flow through a different circuit? How could you make a circuit that will suddenly begin to operate when you destroy some metal somewhere else in the circuit? Include a diagram of the circuit including the wires, LED, and battery.

Reflecting on the Activity and the Challenge

You have learned how to light an LED using a circuit. You have also learned you can make circuits out of aluminum and then destroy them. The final step of your dominoes apparatus must be the lighting of an LED. At this point, you can choose between completing a circuit or destroying an existing circuit to cause the LED to light. You might make a wire fall into place to complete a circuit that includes the LED and battery. You could also cause one path through an already operating circuit to be destroyed. If you have designed your circuit correctly, that would force the electricity to flow through the path that includes the LED, which would cause it to light. In a later activity, you will learn about how batteries are constructed and how they operate. This will give you additional options for how to light the LED.

Chem to Go

1. Using the periodic table, identify which of the following elements are metals: Na, Cl, Ni, Co, Ar, Sn, Cd, Sr, P.
2. Some metals are more reactive than hydrogen, and others are less reactive. This is explained in greater detail in the *Chem Talk* section.
   a) Based on your experiments in this activity, which metals that your class tested are more reactive than hydrogen?
   b) Which metals that your class tested are less reactive than hydrogen?
3. For each pair below, indicate which metal is more reactive.
   a) Al or Pb b) Au or Fe c) Sn or Al
4. Choose one of the pairs in the previous question and write the balanced redox reaction that should occur naturally. You will need to research how many electrons the metal you haven't worked with gives up. Show your work.
5. Why is it incorrect to say, "When aluminum metal and copper ions were mixed, the aluminum melted?" What is correct to say? Explain why.
6. Many nails and other types of hardware are made out of steel, which contains mostly iron metal. The trouble is that iron rusts, especially when it is exposed to water and air. Galvanized nails contain zinc to prevent the nails from rusting. Explain how this works, using what you know from the activity series and your experiments. (Hint: What happened with your Fe/Zn pair in the lab?)
7. Given the balanced ionic equation:

   $2Al(s) + 3Cu^{2+}(aq) \rightarrow 2Al^{3+}(aq) + 3Cu(s)$

   Compared to the total charge of the reactants, the total charge of the products is

   a) less b) greater c) the same

8. Given the balanced ionic equation:

   $Zn(s) + Cu^{2+}(aq) \rightarrow Zn^{2+}(aq) + Cu(s)$

   Which equation represents the oxidation half-reaction?

   a) $Zn(s) + 2e^- \rightarrow Zn^{2+}(aq)$ b) $Zn(s) \rightarrow Zn^{2+}(aq) + 2e^-$

   c) $Cu^{2+}(aq) \rightarrow Cu(s) + 2e^-$ d) $Cu^{2+}(aq) + 2e^- \rightarrow Cu(s)$

9. When a lithium atom forms an Li^+ ion, the lithium atom

   a) gains a proton b) gains an electron c) loses a proton d) loses an electron

10. Given the redox reaction:

    $Cr^{3+} + Al \rightarrow Cr + Al^{3+}$

    As the reaction takes place, there is a transfer of

    a) electrons from Al to Cr^{3+} b) electrons from Cr^{3+} to Al

    c) protons from Al to Cr^{3+} d) protons from Cr^{3+} to Al

11. Which metal reacts spontaneously with a solution containing zinc ions?

    a) magnesium b) nickel c) copper d) silver

Inquiring Further

Reacting metals with bases

While acids can be defined as chemicals that split into H^+ ions and an anion when dissolved in water, bases can be defined as chemicals that split into a cation and OH^- ions when dissolved in water. You learned in this *Investigate* section that acids react with some metals, including aluminum. Some metals also react with bases. Design an experiment to test which metals react with bases, and whether the activity series can also help predict this. Have your experiment approved by your teacher, and then carry it out. This will give you more options for reactions you can use in your *Chemical Dominoes* apparatus.

Be careful with chemicals.

Clean up spills and wash hands and arms well.

Chapter mini Challenge

HONK
THE BRIDGE

Your challenge for this chapter is to create a prototype of a "chemical dominoes sequence" that can be sold by a toy company to 10-year-olds and up. You will design, build, and test an entertaining sequence of chemical and physical (mechanical) changes that eventually light an LED. You will demonstrate the display to an audience of executives at the toy company that has hired your group as consultants. At that time, you will present the executives with a prototype of your product and all the required accompanying materials. During your demonstration of the product, you will briefly explain the chemistry behind how each step of the sequence works. You will also provide a more detailed written explanation of how the chemistry behind your *Chemical Dominoes* apparatus works.

Having completed four activities, this is a good time to give your *Chemical Dominoes* toy a *first try* by describing what you intend to do and what you intend to explain. Of course, being limited to the chemistry content of four activities will limit your presentation. This *first try*, however, will give you a good sense of what the challenge entails and how you and other teams are going to approach this task.

Chemistry Content

Your team should first review the chemistry content that may be included in your *Chemical Dominoes* toy.

Activity 1: You learned how to produce carbon dioxide gas and used that gas to fill a balloon that could tip a lever.

Activity 2: You used the Law of the Conservation of Matter to balance chemical equations.

Activity 3: You used balanced equations and stoichiometry to determine how much of a reactant is required to produce a given volume of gas.

Activity 4: You investigated circuits and how you could destroy a metal and light an LED.

Criteria

Your team should also review the criteria that you discussed on the first day of this chapter. Your *Chemical Dominoes* toy should have a clear set of directions describing how it will work and be accompanied by an explanation of the chemistry principles that are used. The toy should be creative, fun, and age appropriate. Your written chemistry summary should be accurate, clear, and organized. You should also include a number of chemistry concepts.

Preparing for Your mini Challenge

At this point, you can decide on what your toy prototype will include. How will you light the LED? Will you generate a gas to tip a lever? How will you use a circuit? How will you make it fun and unique? For the *mini-challenge*, you will not have to create the prototype or demonstrate the toy. You will have to show a series of sketches describing what will happen.

The *mini-challenge* is a way to get a sense of what you will be involved with at the end of the chapter when you have more chemistry content to include in your *Chemical Dominoes* toy and its corresponding written summary.

ENGINEERING/TECHNOLOGY DESIGN

The engineering-design process involves a number of distinct steps. In creating a *Chemical Dominoes* toy and related summaries of the chemistry content, you are involved in a design process. Note how your efforts follow the design model described.

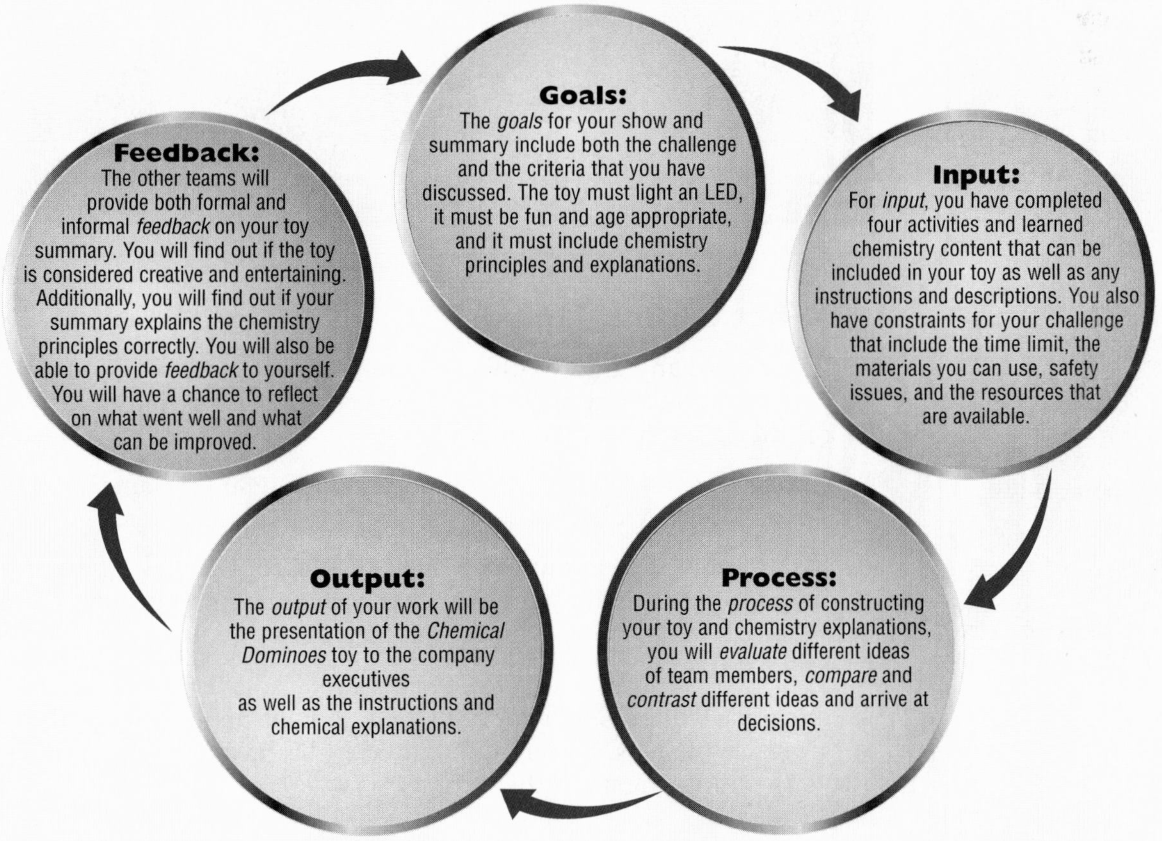
Goals:
The goals for your show and summary include both the challenge and the criteria that you have discussed. The toy must light an LED, it must be fun and age appropriate, and it must include chemistry principles and explanations.
Input:
For input, you have completed four activities and learned chemistry content that can be included in your toy as well as any instructions and descriptions. You also have constraints for your challenge that include the time limit, the materials you can use, safety issues, and the resources that are available.
Process:
During the process of constructing your toy and chemistry explanations, you will evaluate different ideas of team members, compare and contrast different ideas and arrive at decisions.
Output:
The output of your work will be the presentation of the Chemical Dominoes toy to the company executives as well as the instructions and chemical explanations.
Feedback:
The other teams will provide both formal and informal feedback on your toy summary. You will find out if the toy is considered creative and entertaining. Additionally, you will find out if your summary explains the chemistry principles correctly. You will also be able to provide feedback to yourself. You will have a chance to reflect on what went well and what can be improved.

Remember: This is a *first try*. The feedback that you get from the toy description and summary will be extremely valuable when you create your *Chemical Dominoes* toy and the written descriptions. At that point, you will have additional chemistry demonstrations and materials to incorporate in your work. You will begin the entire design cycle again. That's why it is called a cycle—you keep going through it over and over to improve your design or, in this case, your *Chemical Dominoes* toy and written materials.

Activity 5 Producing and Harnessing Light

What Do You See?

GLOW IN THE DARK STARS

GOALS

In this activity you will:

- Describe the relationship between energy, frequency, and wavelength of electromagnetic radiation.
- Explain how atoms are able to produce light of different colors.
- Contrast fluorescence and phosphorescence.

What Do You Think?

If you have any glow-in-the-dark items, such as stars on the ceiling of your bedroom, you know that they keep giving off light after you turn off the lights in your room.

- **How are an LED and a glow-in-the-dark item the same? How are they different?**

Record your idea about these questions in your *Active Chemistry* log. Be prepared to share your thoughts with your small group and the class.

Investigate

For the *Chapter Challenge*, you have to light up an LED at the end of a sequence of steps. Different colors of LEDs have different properties that you will investigate in this activity.

Part A: Examining Colors of Light

1. Examine the light produced by a light-bulb (incandescent) lamp through a diffraction grating.

   a) Use colored pencils to record what you see with the naked eye and through the diffraction grating in your *Active Chemistry* log.

2. You will now investigate the light from at least four LEDs.

   First, view each LED with the naked eye. Then look at it through the diffraction grating.

   a) Record the color of each LED when viewed with the naked eye and when viewed through the diffraction grating.

      If your diffraction grating denotes wavelengths, you should record these as well. If not, use this chart to approximate the wavelengths of the light you see.

Color	Wavelength
	660 nm
	610 nm
	587 nm
	555 nm
	430 nm
	395 nm

   b) Compare and contrast the light from the incandescent bulb and that from the LEDs.

Part B: What Makes a Glow-in-the-Dark Star Glow?

In this part of the activity, you will use the different-colored LEDs as tools to investigate how a glow-in-the-dark star glows.

1. Use a single-hole paper punch to make a hole in the side of a film canister. Place a piece of masking tape over the hole. You will use the canister to isolate a glow-in-the-dark star from the overhead lights. It will allow you to expose the star to only light from the LED. You can remove the masking tape from the hole in the canister to observe the star.

2. Place the star inside the film canister. Keep the lid on the container until the star stops glowing. When you check to see if the star has stopped glowing, make sure that you avoid letting any light into the canister.

3. Once the star has stopped glowing, remove the cap from the canister. Illuminate the star with the LED for one minute. Recap the canister. Remove the masking tape and look at the star.

   In your *Active Chemistry* log, you may wish to use a data table similar to the one shown below to record your data.

   a) Which LEDs cause the star to glow?

4. As you saw in *Part A*, the light bulb produces a light with a variety of colors and specific wavelengths.

   a) Which of these wavelengths are responsible for making the star glow?

Color of LED	Wavelength of LED	Did the star glow (phosphoresce)?	How long did the star glow (phosphoresce)?

Chem Talk

Chem Words

electromagnetic radiation: the energy that travels through space as waves.

wavelength: the distance between two corresponding points on a wave. For instance, from crest to crest or trough to trough.

speed of light: in a vacuum, the speed of light is 3.00×10^8 m/s (meters per second).

frequency: the number of cycles of a wave that occur in a second.

HOW IS LIGHT PRODUCED?

The Nature of Light

In this activity you examined the colors that make up visible light and used LEDs to investigate a glow-in-the-dark star. Light is a form of energy known as **electromagnetic radiation**. Electromagnetic radiation includes X-rays, ultraviolet (UV) rays, microwaves, and radio waves in addition to visible light. The only thing that makes visible light special is that your eyes can detect it. The electromagnetic spectrum (a list of electromagnetic radiation in order of wavelength) is illustrated in the diagram.

Light can be characterized by its wavelength and its energy. The **wavelength** of light is the distance between two corresponding points of a wave, for example, from crest (high point) to crest, or from trough (low point) to trough. Wavelength is measured in nanometers (nm). A nanometer is one-billionth of a meter or 1×10^{-9} m.

Notice that gamma rays have the shortest wavelength and radio waves have the longest wavelength. The wavelength of radio waves is close to 10^9 nm (nanometers) or 1 m. Gamma rays have a wavelength of less than 0.1 nm, which is close to the size of an atom.

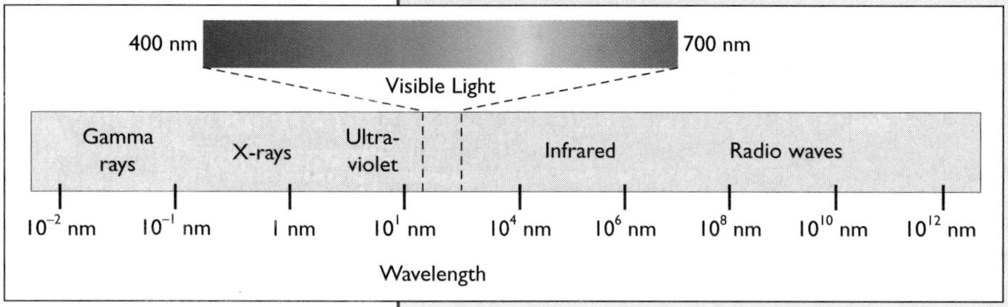

400 nm
700 nm
Visible Light
Gamma rays
X-rays
Ultra-violet
Infrared
Radio waves
10^{-2} nm
10^{-1} nm
1 nm
10^{1} nm
10^{4} nm
10^{6} nm
10^{8} nm
10^{10} nm
10^{12} nm
Wavelength

All waves of light travel at the same speed in a vacuum. This speed is called the **speed of light**. Technically, light travels at the speed of light only in a vacuum (a space where there is nothing, not even air). However, air slows down light waves only a little, so it's a good approximation to say that even in air, all light waves travel at the same speed.

Since you can make the approximation that all waves of light travel at the same speed, you can relate the wavelength to another property of light, called **frequency**. The frequency of light is related to the wavelength of light by the following expression:

$$c = \lambda \times f$$

where c = speed of light = 3.00×10^8 m/s
f = frequency in waves per second
λ = wavelength in meters

Remember that you recorded the wavelengths of light using the unit of nanometers. You must be consistent and convert wavelength to meters if you are using the value of the speed of light in meters per second (m/s).

Waves with long wavelengths have relatively low frequencies. Waves with short wavelengths have relatively high frequencies. This relationship is expressed as "frequency and wavelength are inversely related." This means that as wavelength increases, frequency decreases.

The energy of light is related to the frequency (and wavelength) of the light.

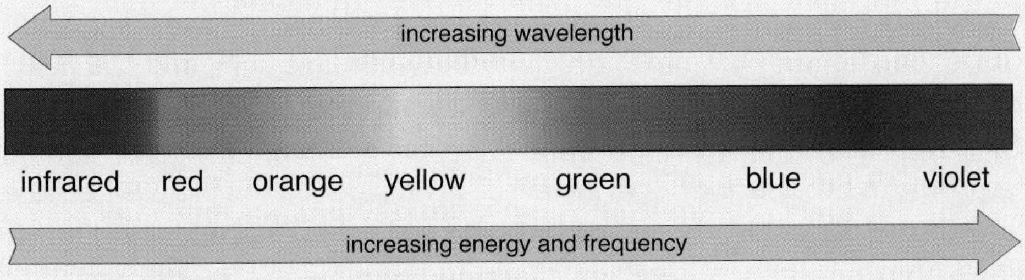
increasing wavelength
infrared
red
orange
yellow
green
blue
violet
increasing energy and frequency

The mathematic expression that relates the two is:

$E = h \times f$ where E = energy measured in joules
h = Planck's constant = 6.63×10^{-34} J·s
f = frequency in s^{-1}

Light that has a long wavelength has less energy than light that has a short wavelength. The wavelengths of visible light range from 700 nm for red to 400 nm for violet. As the wavelength of light becomes shorter, the energy of the light increases. For example, red light has less energy than blue light. This is why the red LED had no effect on the glow-in-the-dark star. The wavelength of light determines if the light has enough energy to interact with the electrons in an atom.

Chem Words

valence electrons: electrons contained in the outermost electron shell of an atom.

excited state: state of an electron of an atom that has absorbed enough energy to be raised to a higher energy sublevel.

ground state: the lowest energy sublevel that an electron of an atom can occupy.

fluorescence: the process by which an electron absorbs energy and moves up an energy level followed by rapid release of part of the energy as visible light when the electron returns to ground state.

phosphorescence: the process by which an electron absorbs energy and moves up an energy level. This is followed by a release of energy as the electron goes back to the lower energy level.

How an Atom Produces Light

The atom is composed of protons, neutrons, and electrons. The protons and neutrons are located in the nucleus of the atom. The electrons exist outside the nucleus in certain allowable states that are called energy levels. The outermost electrons are called the **valence electrons**. These are the electrons that take part in chemical reactions.

The main idea behind spectroscopy (study of spectra) is that energy is conserved. When an electron absorbs energy it can move from a lower energy level to a higher one. However, the energy that the electron absorbs must be equal to the energy difference between the two levels. Think of the energy levels as the rungs of a ladder. If you only give your foot enough energy to make it halfway between one rung and the next, it is not going to reach the next rung. Instead, your foot will remain on the lower rung. If an electron does not receive enough energy, it will not be promoted to a higher energy level. This happened in *Part B* when the glow-in-the-dark star was irradiated with red light. The red light did not have enough energy to have any effect on the glow-in-the-dark star.

When an electron absorbs enough energy to be promoted to a higher state, that state is called an **excited state**, to distinguish it from the **ground state** where the electron began. The energy that an electron absorbs may come from lots of sources of energy, including heat energy, collisions between particles in the material, chemical reactions, visible light, or even other forms of electromagnetic radiation. The electron, however, cannot remain in the excited state forever. It eventually falls to a lower energy state and gives up energy in the process.

Fluorescence and Phosphorescence

A common process by which light is emitted from atoms or molecules is **fluorescence**. The process of fluorescence is illustrated in the diagram.

When the LEDs gave off light, they did so by a process of fluorescence. When the glow-in-the-dark star gave off light, it did so by a slightly more

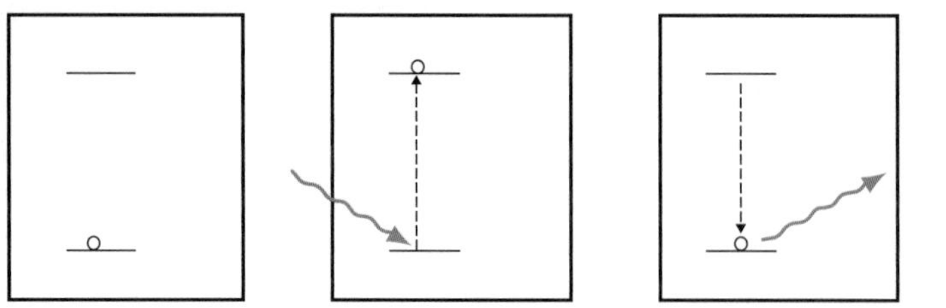
Fluorescence

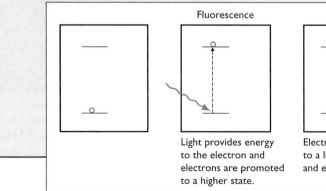

Light provides energy to the electron and electrons are promoted to a higher state.

Electron drops down to a lower energy state and emits light.

complicated process called **phosphorescence**. In phosphorescence, there is another excited state in between where the electron is first promoted and the ground state. Depending on conditions such as temperature, the electron can temporarily get stuck in this intermediate state. As a result, the emission of light in some cases of phosphorescence is delayed over a period of time, ranging from seconds to hours. This delayed emission of light causes the glow-in-the-dark star to continue to glow long after the source of excitation, in this case the UV LED or the blue LED, is removed.

In the activity, a glow-in-the dark star was irradiated with red, orange, yellow, green, blue, UV, and white light. Red, yellow, and green light did not do anything to the star because they did not have enough energy to move electrons from their ground state to an excited states. However, when blue or ultraviolet light was used, electrons were excited and the star emitted a green-yellow light. The white LED also caused the star to glow because a small portion of the light that the white LED emits is in the blue portion of the visible spectrum.

Phosphorescence

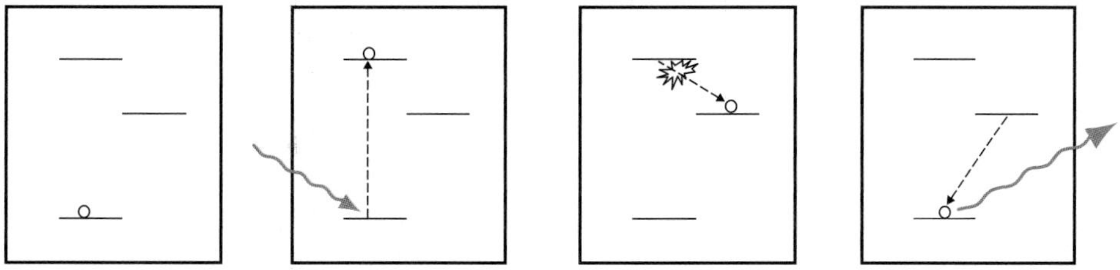

Checking Up

1. Name four kinds of electromagnetic radiation in the electronic spectrum, and order them from shortest wavelength to longest wavelength.
2. What are the colors of visible light, in order from longest wavelength to shortest wavelength?
3. What is the speed of light (in a vacuum)?
4. Are wavelength and frequency directly or indirectly related to each other? Explain.
5. Why did the red LED have no effect on the glow-in-the-dark star, but the blue LED did have an effect?
6. What is the difference between the process of fluorescence and the process of phosphorescence?

What Do You Think Now?

At the beginning of this activity you were asked:

- **How are an LED and a glow-in-the-dark item the same? How are they different?**

Now that you have investigated LEDs that produce different colors of light, review your answer. Why would more energy have to be provided to produce blue light as opposed to red light? Why must a glow-in-the-dark object be exposed to light before it will glow?

Chem Essential Questions

What does it mean?

Chemistry explains a macroscopic phenomenon (what you observe) with a description of what happens at the nanoscopic level (atoms and molecules) using symbolic structures as a way to communicate. Complete the chart below in your *Active Chemistry* log.

MACRO	NANO	SYMBOLIC
Compare and contrast the light given off by a typical light bulb and an LED when observed through a diffraction grating.	*Describe the changes that the atoms undergo when they produce light. Explain what determines the color of light that an atom will produce.*	*Sketch a series of drawings that would illustrate the changes that occur when an atom produces light. Show how you would modify your changes to indicate that light of greater energy is produced.*

How do you know?

The production of light from an LED is different from the production of light in the glow-in-the-dark star. How are they different? How are they similar?

Why do you believe?

When electricity is passed through gaseous samples of different elements, different colors of light are produced. You may have observed this phenomenon in the form of different colored "neon" signs. Use your knowledge from this activity to explain why atoms of different elements would be likely to produce light of different colors.

Why should you care?

In your report to the board executives, you will need to explain the chemistry behind how atoms produce light. Take some time now to write down in your *Active Chemistry* log a rough draft of the explanation you will give in your report.

Reflecting on the Activity and the Challenge

In this activity you learned that light is composed of different wavelengths. Each wavelength has a specific energy associated with it. If the energy of the light is equal to the difference in energy between two energy levels in an atom or a molecule, it can cause a change to take place. These changes include the emission of light in LEDs and phosphorescence in glow-in-the-dark pigments. You have several colors of LEDs to choose from for the end product of your *Chemical Dominoes* apparatus. The color of LED you choose to use may affect how much energy you must supply to the LED. In the next activity, you will learn how to manipulate the amount of energy a battery produces. You may need to take advantage of some of that information to light your LED.

Chem to Go

1. Which color of visible light has a longer wavelength, yellow or green?
2. Which wavelength of visible light is of higher energy: 535 nm or 620 nm? Explain.
3. Calculate the frequency and the energy of light that has a wavelength of 450 nm. Show your work.
4. What evidence is there that the LEDs give off light by a fluorescent process and not a phosphorescent process? Explain.
5. When you exposed the glow-in-the-dark star to blue light, it gave off green light.
   a) Which color of light has less energy, blue or green?
   b) Why was the light given off in the phosphorescent process different in energy than the light that entered originally?
   c) Why is it impossible for an atom to absorb yellow light and give off green light in a phosphorescent process?
6. An electron in an atom moves from the ground state to an excited state when the energy of the electron
   a) decreases b) increases c) remains the same
7. ***Preparing for the Chapter Challenge***

   What will you and your group write about the color of light you decide to use in your *Chemical Dominoes* apparatus? Brainstorm a list of concepts with your group members and choose which are most important to you or your presentation.

Inquiring Further

The spectroscope

Scientists such as Niels Bohr learned much about the atom using a technique called spectroscopy. Research spectroscopy using the Internet or a college-level chemistry textbook. Ask your teacher for a diffraction grating and use the Internet to build a spectroscope. You can also build a spectroscope using an old music CD. The following reference has an excellent set of directions for making a CD spectroscope—*Journal of Chemical Education.* (Wakabayashi, F.; Hamada, K.; Sone, K.; *J. Chem. Educ.* 1998, 75, 1569). Examine different light sources in your home, in the mall, and in a parking lot. Is light being emitted by a fluorescent or phosphorescent process? Draw the spectra you see. Explain why the spectra you see are different from each other.

Activity 6 Electrochemical Cells

What Do You See?
HOW TO MAKE BATTERIES
COPPER NITRATE
ZINC NITRATE
ZINC STRIP
COPPER S
ZINC NITRATE
ANODE CATHODE

GOALS

In this activity you will:

- Determine if a substance will conduct electricity when dissolved in water.
- Construct a galvanic cell and explain the function of its components.
- Describe the effect of adding cells in series.

What Do You Think?

Portable CD players, electronic video games, and watches are just a few of the items that are powered by batteries.

- **How does a battery work?**
- **Why does a battery eventually "die"?**

Record your ideas about these questions in your *Active Chemistry* log. Be prepared to discuss your responses with your small group and the class.

Investigate

In this activity, you will learn how to build batteries that generate voltage in different amounts. To be able to control the amount of voltage produced, you will have to understand how electricity is produced.

Part A: Solutions That Conduct Electricity

1. In *Activity 4*, you learned how electricity flows through metal wires and magnesium strip to produce a complete circuit. Now you are going to investigate how electricity can flow through solutions. To do this, you are going to build a circuit to test the conductivity of solutions. Construct a conductivity tester using a wooden tongue depressor, two wires, a 9-V battery, a resistor, and the red LED, as shown in the diagram.

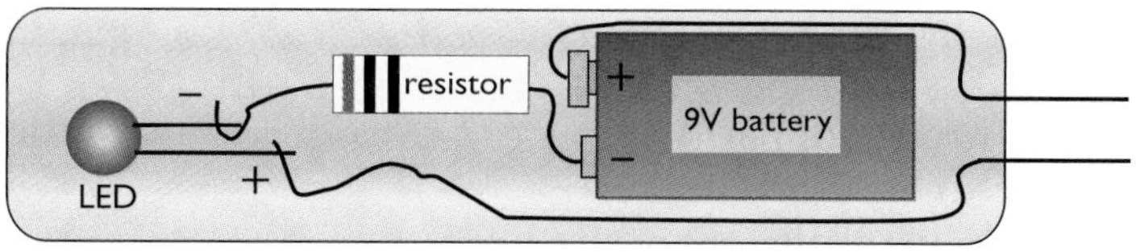
resistor
9V battery
LED
+
−

Touch the two exposed wires together briefly to make sure the LED will light. Your conductivity tester is now ready to use. If the two exposed wires are placed in a solution that conducts electricity, the LED will light.

2. All of the solutions you will test are made of different substances dissolved in distilled water. Add some distilled or de-ionized water to a beaker. Dip the exposed wires of your conductivity tester into the water. Make sure that the exposed parts of both wires are in contact with the water.

   a) Does the LED light? Record what you did and what you saw in your *Active Chemistry* log.

   b) What is the purpose of testing distilled water before beginning the tests of substances dissolved in distilled water?

3. Obtain five clean 100-mL beakers. Label the beakers:

   - distilled water $H_2O(l)$ (control)
   - sodium chloride solution $NaCl(aq)$
   - potassium nitrate solution $KNO_3(aq)$
   - sucrose solution $C_{12}H_{22}O_{11}(aq)$
   - fructose solution $C_6H_{12}O_6(aq)$

4. Fill each beaker with 25 mL of the appropriate solution.

   a) In your *Active Chemistry* log, record the appearance of each solution.

   b) Look at the formula for each substance that is dissolved in distilled water. Based on what you learned in *Activity 4*, predict which substances are likely to create charged ions when dissolved in water. Explain how you arrived at these predictions.

5. Test each solution to see if it conducts electricity. In between each test, wash off the exposed wires and dry them. Then test the distilled water again to make sure there is nothing left on the wires that would contaminate solutions and give you false results for some of your tests.

   a) Organize your observations in a data table in your log.

6. You used distilled water in this investigation as the control. Why didn't you use tap water? Test the conductivity of tap water and explain why it can't be used as the control.

   a) Based on your results, draw pictures in your *Active Chemistry* log to represent the particles in distilled water and the particles in tap water.

7. Dispose of the materials as directed by your teacher. Clean up your workstation.

Part B: Making a Battery

1. Construct a battery. Begin by cleaning a piece of zinc metal and a piece of copper with steel wool. This should get rid of any oxides that have built up on the surface. These pieces of metal are called ***electrodes***.

2. Add 25 mL of 1.0 *M* copper (II) nitrate solution to a 50-mL beaker. Label the beaker. Place the copper electrode into the beaker. This beaker is called a ***half-cell.***

   a) What happens to the copper electrode? Record your observations in your *Active Chemistry* log.

3. Add 25 mL of 1.0 *M* zinc nitrate solution to another 50-mL beaker. Label the beaker. Place the zinc electrode into this beaker. This beaker is also a half-cell, specifically a zinc half-cell.

   a) What happens to the zinc electrode? Record your observations in your *Active Chemistry* log.

   b) Based on your observations, why can't you place the copper in the zinc solution or the zinc in the copper solution in order to construct half-cells to make a battery?

4. In this system, each beaker contains a metal and its salt, forming a half-cell. A half-reaction will occur between zinc atoms and zinc ions in one beaker. In the other beaker, a half-reaction will occur between copper atoms and copper ions.

   a) Write the two half-reactions that show how zinc atoms and copper atoms lose electrons. Refer to *Activity 4* for help.

   b) Combine the two half-reactions into a single oxidation-reduction equation. Use your Metal Activity Series to be sure the equation you have written represents a reaction that will actually occur.

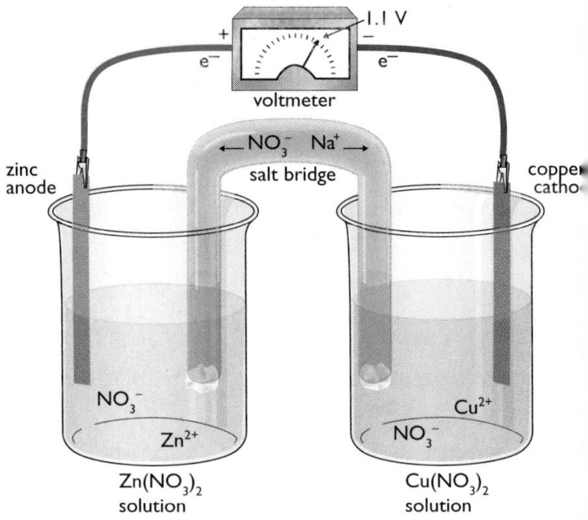

1.1 V
+
−
e⁻
e⁻
voltmeter
NO_3^- Na^+
salt bridge
zinc anode
copper cathode
NO_3^-
Zn^{2+}
Cu^{2+}
NO_3^-
$Zn(NO_3)_2$ solution
$Cu(NO_3)_2$ solution

5. Place the copper half-cell next to the zinc half-cell. Holding a U-shaped tube U-side up, fill the tube with 1.0 *M* sodium nitrate solution to within 1 cm of the open ends of the tube. Place one piece of glass wool into each end to seal it. This tube is called a ***salt bridge.***

6. Place the U-shaped tube into the half-cells so that the U is upside down. One end of the U will be in the copper half-cell and one end in the zinc half-cell. (See the diagram.)

   a) Does any change appear to occur?

7. Attach one wire to each metal electrode.

   a) Draw what your cell looks like in your *Active Chemistry* log. Make sure to label all of the parts.

8. You now have a battery. Place a voltmeter across the anode and cathode.

   a) Record the voltage of the battery and which half-cell is the ***anode*** (–) and which half-cell is the ***cathode*** (+).

9. It is likely that your battery does not produce enough voltage to light the LED on its own. Add a commercial D-cell battery in series (in line) with your copper/zinc battery to increase the amount of voltage that flows through the LED.

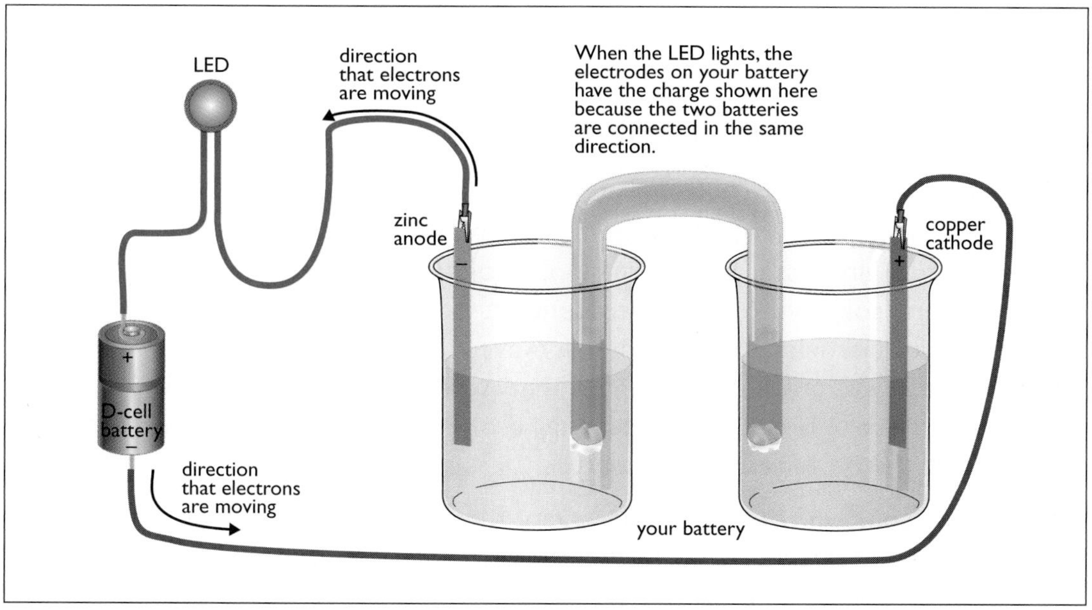
LED
direction that electrons are moving
When the LED lights, the electrodes on your battery have the charge shown here because the two batteries are connected in the same direction.
zinc anode
–
copper cathode
+
+
D-cell battery
–
direction that electrons are moving
your battery

First, connect the longer leg of the LED to the (+) terminal of the D-cell and the shorter leg of the LED to the (–) terminal of the D-cell. Then open the (–) connection from the D-cell battery and connect it to zinc anode. Add a lead from the (–) terminal of the battery to the copper cathode. After adding the copper/zinc battery, the LED should light.

10. Once the LED is connected to your battery and producing light, allow your cell to run for 5–10 min.

    a) After this time period, look at the copper and the zinc electrodes. Record your observations of the electrodes. Where does the copper that appears on the copper electrode come from? Where does the zinc go as the zinc electrode is disappearing?

11. While the LED is lit, remove the salt bridge from the circuit.

    a) Does the LED remain lit?

    b) Put the salt bridge back. Does the LED light up again?

12. Remove the salt bridge from your cell again. Hold the bridge so the "U" is right side up. Remove the glass wool and empty the potassium nitrate solution into a beaker. Rinse the salt bridge three times with distilled water. Fill the salt bridge with distilled water and seal the ends with two new glass wool plugs. Predict if the LED will light up when the salt bridge is put back. Why or why not?

    a) Record your answer and your reasoning in your *Active Chemistry* log.

    b) Put the salt bridge back. Does the LED light up?

13. Dispose of the materials as directed by your teacher. Clean up your workstation.

Wash your hands and arms thoroughly after the activity.

Chem Words

electrolyte: a solute that forms ions in an aqueous (water) solution.

ion: an atom or molecule that has acquired a charge by either gaining (anion) or losing (cation) electron(s).

Chem Talk

SOLUTIONS THAT CONDUCT ELECTRICITY

Substances that dissolve in water to make solutions that conduct electricity are called **electrolytes**. In this activity, you used a conductivity tester to determine if a solution conducted electricity. For any solution to be able to conduct electricity, it must contain charged particles that are able to move. All of the solutions you tested were made of substances that were dissolved in distilled water. But only the substances that broke into charged particles when dissolved were electrolytes.

For a solution to conduct electricity, there are two conditions that must be met. Charged particles must be present and the charged particles must be able to move around. Some compounds dissolve in water to form charged particles called **ions**. Usually, these compounds are made of a positively charged metal ion and a negatively charged ion to balance the charge. For example, regular table salt, sodium chloride (NaCl), is made of sodium ions (Na^+) with charges of +1, and chloride ions (Cl^-) with charges of –1. When some NaCl crystals dissolve in water, sodium ions and chloride ions separate from the crystal and are surrounded by water molecules.

Sodium Chloride Solution

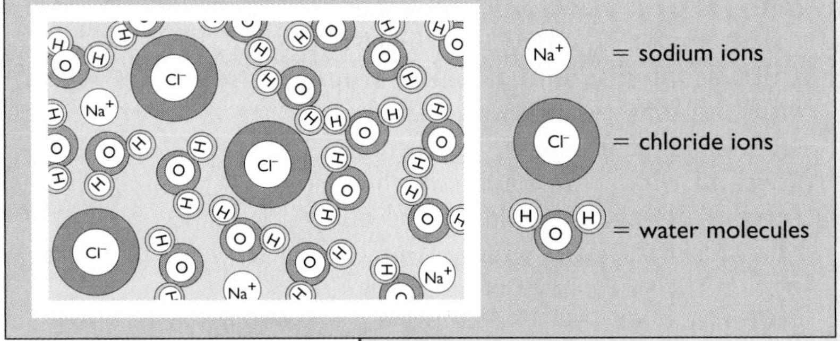
Na+ = sodium ions
Cl- = chloride ions
H O H = water molecules

Since the ions are surrounded by water, they can move about in the water. Since there are charged particles that can move, a solution of sodium chloride is able to conduct electricity.

Molecular compounds do not break up into ions when they dissolve. For example, sugar remains as sugar molecules when it dissolves.

Sugar Solution

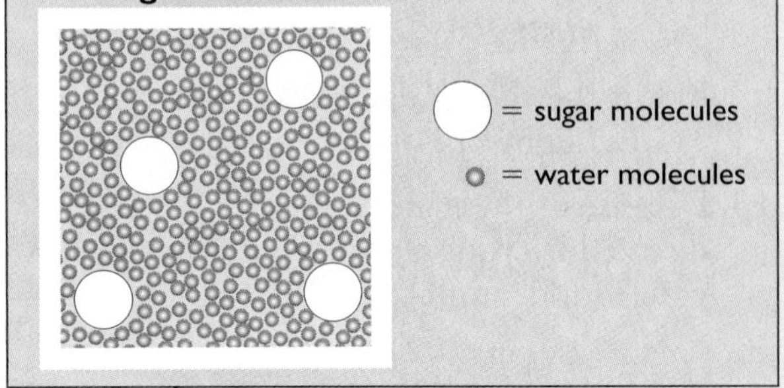
= sugar molecules
= water molecules

Since molecules do not form charged particles in solution, solutions made of molecules dissolved in water do not conduct electricity.

The Path of Electricity in a Battery

In a battery, part of the path of the electricity runs through the solutions. First, electrons are produced by the oxidation half-reaction that occurs.

$$Zn \rightarrow Zn^{2+} + 2e^-$$

While the battery is operating, the zinc metal electrode is slowly undergoing a reaction. Neutral zinc metal atoms (Zn) make two products. Zinc ions (Zn^{2+}) enter the zinc nitrate solution and electrons (e^-) are produced.

These electrons flow through the wire, through anything that's connected to the operating battery, and into the copper metal electrode. When the electrons reach the copper electrode, they enter into the reduction half-reaction:

$$Cu^{2+} + 2e^- \rightarrow Cu$$

In this half-reaction, copper ions from the solution combine with electrons to make neutral copper metal atoms. So, the copper metal electrode increases in mass because copper metal is slowly attaching to it. This was the reddish brown sludge you observed forming on the copper electrode. The blue color of the copper (II) nitrate solution will diminish as the copper ions are used up.

The copper ions are not the only ions in the solution. The solution was originally prepared by dissolving $Cu(NO_3)_2$ crystals in water. When this compound dissolves in water, Cu^{2+} ions and NO_3^- ions (twice as many of the latter) are both surrounded by water molecules. As the positively charged copper ions (Cu^{2+}) in the solution get used up, negatively charged nitrate (NO_3^-) ions get "kicked out" of the solution, because the solution must remain neutral.

The only place for the NO_3^- ions to go is through the salt bridge. On the other side of the bridge, they enter the zinc half-cell. The Zn^{2+} ions are being created in the zinc half-cell as the battery operates. So, there is a need for more negative ions to balance the charge in that solution.

How Does This Relate to the Metal Activity Series?

One very important point here is that the electricity only runs spontaneously in one direction in a battery. This is due to the relative activities of the two metal electrodes used in the half-reactions. In this case, the half-reactions were converting from Zn metal atoms to Zn^{2+} ions in one of the cells, and from Cu^{2+} ions to Cu metal →

Checking Up

1. Why can a solution containing salt, NaCl, conduct electricity but one containing sucrose, $C_{12}H_{22}O_{11}$, cannot?
2. What is the difference between an electrolyte and a non-electrolyte?
3. Describe where the electrons in the zinc-copper battery come from and where they go to.
4. What is the anode of a battery and what happens there?
5. What is the cathode of a battery and what happens there?

atoms in the other cell (see half-reactions on the previous page). If the opposite conversions were happening, then the electricity would run in the other direction. So, why does it happen spontaneously in one direction and not the other?

DO NOT CONNECT IMPROPERLY.
OR DISPOSE OF IN FIRE. BATTERY
EXPLODE OR LEAK
Made in U.S.A.
1.5 VOLTS
BATTERY

The Metal Activity Series provides an answer. Zinc (Zn) metal is more reactive than copper (Cu) metal. Therefore, Zn will react spontaneously with Cu^{2+}, and Cu will not react spontaneously with Zn^{2+}. Recall also from *Activity 4* that not only does the activity series provide predictions of which reactions will and won't occur spontaneously, but also, the farther apart two metals are from each other within the activity series, the more powerful the metal/other metal ion reaction will be.

What Do You Think Now?

At the beginning of this activity you were asked:

- **How does a battery work?**
- **Why does a battery eventually "die"?**

Now that you have investigated batteries and electricity flow, how would you answer these questions? Why do electronic devices not work if you insert the battery backwards?

Chem Essential Questions

What does it mean?

Chemistry explains a macroscopic phenomenon (what you observe) with a description of what happens at the nanoscopic level (atoms and molecules) using symbolic structures as a way to communicate. Complete the chart below in your *Active Chemistry* log.

MACRO	NANO	SYMBOLIC
Describe how you constructed a battery using electrodes, solutions, and wires.	*How do electrons flow through the zinc/copper battery when it is connected in series with the LED?*	*Draw a labeled picture of the battery you built. Show how you would connect the LED to this circuit. Draw arrows on your picture to show the flow of electrons through the battery.*

How do you know?

The battery in your activity does not resemble the battery you use in your CD or MP3 player. How do you know that it is a battery?

Why do you believe?

List five items that use battery power that you use on a regular basis.

Why should you care?

Suppose you decide to build a battery to light the LED in your *Chemical Dominoes* apparatus. List three ways you could change the design of a battery system to make it produce more voltage. Explain why you think these changes increase the voltage of the system.

Reflecting on the Activity and the Challenge

In this activity, you built a conductivity tester and tested whether particular solutions conducted electricity. You may want to use the conductivity tester as part of your *Chemical Dominoes* apparatus. Think about how you could lower it into a solution that would cause the LED to light. Or, if the conductivity tester were already sitting in a container of pure water, perhaps you could add a substance to the water that would make the LED light. In the activity, you also built a galvanic cell, or battery. You experimented with two ways of creating more voltage. If you want to use a battery to light the LED in your dominoes apparatus, you will have to be able to produce enough voltage. This may require you to use the activity series to choose a certain combination of metals. You might also need to connect several batteries in series and use certain concentrations of the solutions in the apparatus.

Chem to Go

1. In *Part A* of the activity, you tested the conductivities of four solutions. Identify which of the solutions were electrolytes and explain how you could tell.

2. Which compounds listed below would you expect to form solutions that conduct electricity when you dissolve the compounds in water? Explain your reasoning.

   a) KF b) C_6H_6 c) CCl_4 d) Na_2SO_4

3. All hair dryers, shavers, and other electrical appliances that are often used in the bathroom come with labels, mandated by the government, saying not to operate the appliance while taking a bath.

   a) Based on what you learned in *Part A* of the activity, explain why it would be dangerous to use an appliance while bathing.

   b) You observed in the experiment that distilled water does not conduct electricity. If you were to take a bath in distilled water, why would it still not be safe to use an electrical appliance while bathing? Explain.

4. You may have seen sports drink advertisements talk about the electrolytes in the sports drink. When you sweat, you lose electrolytes. (Sweat tastes salty, right?) Electrolytes are important in the body because your nerves require electrolytic solutions to transfer electrical impulses.

   a) Would you expect a sports drink to conduct electricity?

   b) Design an experiment to determine which sports drink on the market has the highest concentration of electrolytes. List the equipment and other materials you would need to conduct the experiment, and briefly describe the procedure you would follow.

   c) Would you need a control in this experiment? If so, what would you use and what would you expect the results from testing the control to be?

5. Predict a metal half-cell that you could replace the zinc half-cell with in your battery and produce more voltage. Assume you would use 1.0 *M* metal ion solutions in both half-cells. Explain the reasoning behind your prediction.

6. A student was studying how the voltage generated by a battery can be changed. She prepared five different cells and changed something about each. The changes she tested are shown below. For each change, state if the voltage would increase, decrease, or remain the same. Explain your reasoning in each case.

   a) The salt bridge was removed.

   b) The contents of the salt bridge were replaced with distilled water.

   c) The wire at the anode was disconnected.

   d) The battery was allowed to run for one hour.

7. Given the reaction:

$Ba(OH)_{2(aq)} + H_2SO_{4(aq)} \rightarrow BaSO_{4(s)} + 2H_2O_{(l)} + \text{energy}$

As the barium hydroxide solution is added to the solution of sulfuric acid, the electrical conductivity of the acid solution decreases because the:

a) volume of the reaction mixture increases

b) temperature of the reaction mixture decreases

c) concentration of ions increases

d) concentration of ions decreases

8. Which half-reaction correctly represents reduction?

a) $Ag \rightarrow Ag^+ + e^-$

b) $F_2 \rightarrow 2F^- + 2e^-$

c) $Au^{3+} + 3e^- \rightarrow Au$

d) $Fe^{2+} \rightarrow Fe^{3+} + e^-$

9. In a redox reaction, how does the total number of electrons lost by the oxidized substance compare to the total number of electrons gained by the reduced substance?

a) The number lost is always greater than the number gained.

b) The number lost is always equal to the number gained.

c) The number lost is sometimes equal to the number gained.

d) The number lost is sometimes less than the number gained.

10. ***Preparing for the Chapter Challenge***

Decide with your group on a way that you could use either a battery you make or the conductivity tester (or both) to light the LED in your *Chemical Dominoes* apparatus. From other activities, you already have several other components you may use in the sequence. Describe how you will light the LED using your battery and/or conductivity tester. Include a labeled drawing in your description.

Inquiring Further

Factors affecting voltage generated

Use your knowledge from this activity and the activity series to design an experiment to determine which of the following factors most affects voltage generated:

1. Identity of electrodes
2. Number of cells in series
3. Concentration of cathode and anode cells used

After your teacher approves your procedure, carry out your experiment under supervision.

Activity 7 Reactions that Produce Heat

What Do You See?
POP
MRE
MRE
AC
AC

GOALS

In this activity you will:

- Explain the effect of particle size and use of a catalyst on reaction rate.
- Represent energy changes graphically.
- Explain the role of energy in chemical reactions.

What Do You Think?

You may already know that when American soldiers are in the field and don't have access to stoves, they eat pre-packaged meals called MREs or "Meals, Ready-to-Eat." These meals include a packet of chemicals that allow soldiers to quickly heat their meals without having to build a fire.

- **What is the source of the heat produced by the hot pack?**
- **How is the hot pack able to increase in temperature without an external (added) source of heat?**

Record your ideas about these questions in your *Active Chemistry* log. Be prepared to discuss your responses with your small group and the class.

Investigate

In your *Chemical Dominoes* apparatus, you may want to use a chemical reaction that produces heat to cause something to happen. Perhaps you could melt an ice cube that is tied to a lever. To produce heat by a chemical reaction, you have to know a little about how the heat is produced, so you can have some control over it.

Part A: Working With the MRE Heater

In this part of the activity you will investigate the chemical method that military personnel use to heat their meals when they are in the field and do not have access to stoves.

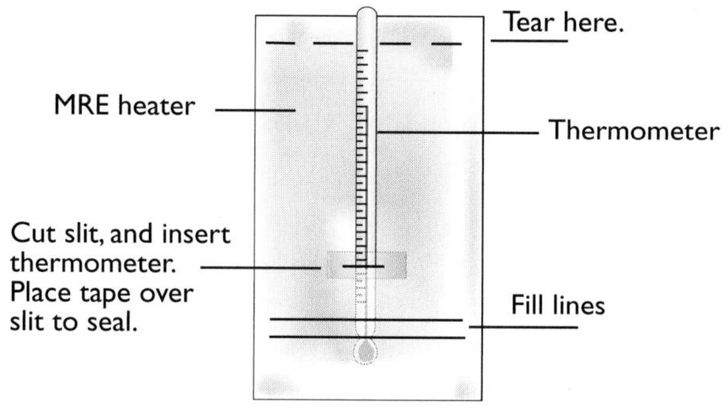
Tear here.
MRE heater
Thermometer
Cut slit, and insert thermometer. Place tape over slit to seal.
Fill lines

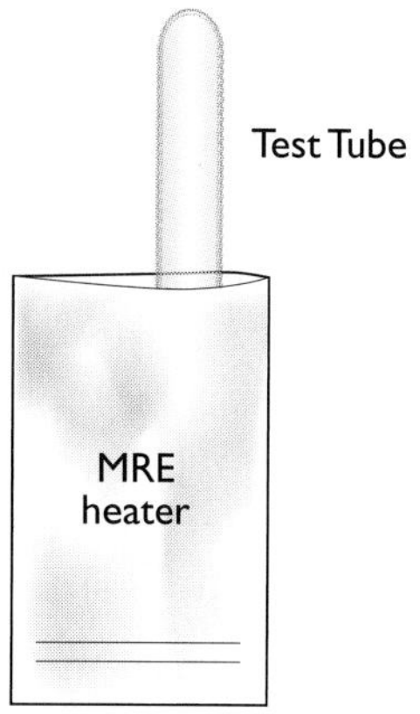
Test Tube
MRE heater

1. Examine an MRE heater carefully.
   a) Record your observations in your *Active Chemistry* log.
2. Open the MRE heater by tearing it open at the top. Look inside the bag.
   a) Record what you see.
3. Fill the MRE heater to the fill line with distilled water.
   a) Record your observations of the reaction as it proceeds for several minutes. From where do you think the heat comes?
4. After five minutes, hold a watch glass over the opening of the bag.
   a) Describe anything you notice forming on the watch glass.
   b) Place a thermometer in the MRE heater. Record the temperature in your log.
5. The chemical reaction that is occurring in the MRE heater produces a gas. Collect the gas escaping from the heater by carefully holding the opening of the bag around the mouth of a test tube. *Caution: The bag and the gases are hot.* Then, in an area designated by your teacher, test the gas. Bring a glowing wood splint to the mouth of the test tube. If the splint is extinguished, the gas might be carbon dioxide or some other non-flammable gas. If the splint glows brighter, the gas in the tube is oxygen. Finally, if there is a pop or barking sound, the gas is likely hydrogen.

   Water vapor is one of the gases produced by the reaction inside the MRE heater, but another gas is also produced.

   a) Based on the results of the wood-splint test, what other gas is produced? Explain how your results support your conclusion.
6. When the reaction is complete, add 20 mL of distilled water to the MRE heater. Then pour the solution from the MRE heater into a test tube. Add a few drops of phenolphthalein to the solution in the test tube. Phenolphthalein is an indicator that will turn the solution pink if a base is present. Is the solution basic?
   a) Record your results and explain how you arrived at your conclusion.
7. Dispose of the MRE heater according to your teacher's directions.
8. The MRE heater produces heat by reacting magnesium metal with water. The balanced chemical equation that represents the reaction that is occurring inside the MRE heater is:

$$\underset{\text{magnesium metal}}{Mg(s)} + \underset{\text{water}}{2HOH(l)} \rightarrow$$

$$\underset{\text{magnesium hydroxide}}{Mg(OH)_2(s)} + \underset{\text{hydrogen gas}}{H_2(g)} + \text{energy}$$

(We use HOH instead of H_2O to make it easier to see where the H_2 and OH come from.)

a) Use the equation for the reaction in the MRE heater to account for your observations. (Example: In *Step 4*, you observed that steam (water vapor), escapes from the heater as it operates. Steam is not one of the products of this chemical reaction. What is the source of the steam?)

Part B: How the MRE Heater Works

1. Your teacher will provide you with three test tubes. One contains magnesium metal pieces. The second one contains small grains of magnesium metal. The third one contains small grains of magnesium and some salt (NaCl). All three test tubes contain the same mass of magnesium.

   a) Record your observations of the contents of the three test tubes in your *Active Chemistry* log. Be sure to include how the contents are similar to and are different from each other. Use a wax marker to label the test tubes so you know the contents of each tube.

2. Obtain a small sample of the contents of the MRE heater from your teacher. Examine it using a magnifying glass. Which test tube or test tubes contain magnesium closest in size to the contents of the MRE heater?

   a) Record your observations.

3. Add 20 mL of distilled water to a small beaker. Add three drops of phenolphthalein solution to the beaker. The water with the phenolphthalein should not change color.

4. Use a graduated cylinder to measure out three 5-mL samples of the water-indicator solution. Add these to the three test tubes *at the same time*. Observe and compare how quickly the reaction occurs in each test tube.

   a) Record your observations. Which sample turns the solution dark pink most quickly?

5. Look over your results and discuss them with your group.

   a) Write a statement that relates particle size to reaction rate.

   b) What do you think the salt in the third test tube did?

6. Carefully feel the sides of the three test tubes.

   a) Do they feel warm? Do all three test tubes feel the same? Explain.

7. Dispose of the magnesium and the solutions by placing them in the waste beaker. Do not put magnesium ribbon, pieces, or powder down the drain or in the garbage because they can generate enough heat to catch fire to paper or to melt plastic pipes. Clean your test tubes when you are done.

Chem Talk

THERMODYNAMICS

"Will it continue to occur?" "How fast will it occur?" Those are two important questions that chemists and engineers need to be able to answer about any chemical reaction they plan to use. In this activity, you explored a chemical reaction that continues to occur on its own once it begins. Chemists call such a reaction **spontaneous**. You also explored some factors that affect how quickly a reaction will occur. In the case of a reaction that produces heat energy (like the reaction that occurs in the MRE heater), controlling the speed of the reaction will let you control how quickly heat is produced. For chemists and engineers to be able to control chemical reactions, they must be able to predict when reactions can occur spontaneously, and also what can be done to speed up or slow down reactions. One set of theories called **thermodynamics** is used to answer the question "Can a reaction occur spontaneously?" A second set of theories called **kinetics** is used to answer the question "How fast can a reaction occur?" Together, thermodynamics and kinetics help chemists and engineers to design reactions and processes that impact everyone's lives.

Thermodynamics and Spontaneity

There are two factors that determine if a change can occur spontaneously. You used these factors in *Activity 1* as criteria with which to compare reactions that produced gas. The first factor that affects spontaneity is if the change gives off heat energy when it occurs or absorbs heat energy when it occurs. The second factor that affects spontaneity is if the change results in particles becoming more disordered (randomly arranged) or less disordered (more organized).

Two commonsense rules apply to these two questions. First, lower energies are more stable than higher energies. So, in the same way that a ball tends to roll downhill, energy changes in chemical reactions tend to occur in ways that allow the substances to end up with lower energy. This means that changes that release energy tend to be favored. Second, everything tends to become more disorganized over time. So, changes in which particles become more disordered (spread out) are favored over those that make particles become more ordered.

The two factors that affect spontaneity can work together. If a change both releases energy and results in an increase in disorder, the change is definitely spontaneous. If a change both absorbs energy and results in a decrease in disorder, the change is definitely not spontaneous. →

Chem Words

spontaneous: a change that, once begun, continues without an input of energy.

thermodynamics: the study of how heat and other forms of energy are involved in chemical and physical reactions.

kinetics: the study of reaction rates and how they can be affected by variables such as concentration, particle size, and temperature.

However, if one factor is favorable and the other is not, whichever is the stronger tendency controls whether the change is spontaneous.

In this activity you explored a change that was spontaneous. Heat energy was given off as the system went from a higher energy to a lower one. This means at least one of the two factors affecting spontaneity is favorable for this reaction. This *Chem Talk* will focus on heat changes.

Heat Energy Changes: Endothermic and Exothermic Reactions

Consider the chemical reaction between magnesium and water that you observed in the activity.

$$\underset{\text{magnesium metal}}{Mg_{(s)}} + \underset{\text{water}}{2HOH_{(l)}} \rightarrow \underset{\text{magnesium hydroxide}}{Mg(OH)_{2(s)}} + \underset{\text{hydrogen gas}}{H_{2(g)}} + \text{energy}$$

The main points here are that:

- When chemical reactions happen, bonds in the reactants (starting materials) break, and new bonds form to make products (ending materials).
- Breaking bonds requires energy input, so bond-breaking is an endothermic change.
- Forming bonds releases energy, so bond-forming is an exothermic change.
- The overall or net change can be endothermic or exothermic, depending on whether the total energy input (required to break bonds in reactants) or the total energy output (given off when bonds form in products) is greater.

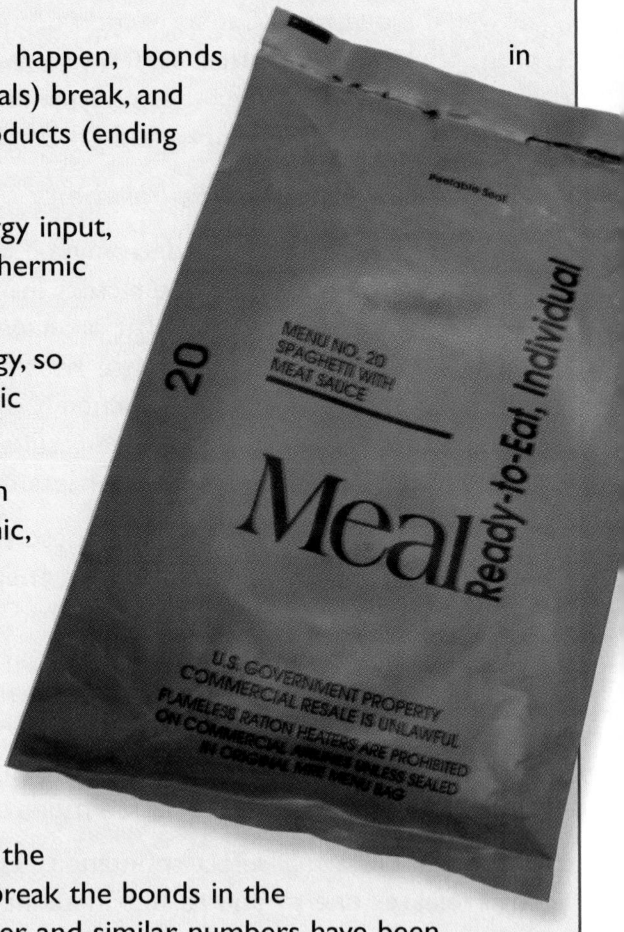
20
MENU NO. 20
SPAGHETTI WITH
MEAT SAUCE
Meal Ready-to-Eat, Individual
U.S. GOVERNMENT PROPERTY
COMMERCIAL RESALE IS UNLAWFUL

In the chemical reaction between magnesium and water, the total energy input required to break the bonds in the reactants is +572 kJ. This number and similar numbers have been measured precisely and can be found in reference books.

(Endothermic changes are positive, because the system gains energy.) When the new bonds form in the products (making magnesium hydroxide and hydrogen gas), the total energy output is –925 kJ. (Exothermic changes are negative, because the system loses energy.) The overall or net change is more exothermic than endothermic. More energy is produced than absorbed.

The reaction in the MRE heater, like most changes (both chemical and physical) studied in chemistry, occurs at constant pressure. Chemists call an energy change that occurs at constant pressure "change in **enthalpy**" and represent it with the symbol ΔH. The Δ (the Greek letter "delta") is frequently used to mean "change." Hess's Law states that, for a given reaction, enthalpy changes are additive. When the Standard Enthalpies of Formation ($\Delta H_f{}^{\circ}$, see Tables) of the reactants are subtracted from the products, the result is the net change in enthalpy for the reaction. A negative ΔH tells that the reaction is exothermic; a positive ΔH tells that the reaction is endothermic. The enthalpy change (ΔH) for the reaction in the MRE heater can be calculated as shown below.

ΔH = –925 kJ (for $Mg(OH)_2$ – 2 × (–286 kJ) (for $2H_2O$) = –353 kJ

ΔH is negative, which tells you that the net change is exothermic (the system loses energy to the surroundings). Therefore, the temperature of the MRE heater increased. You could also compare the energy absorbed and the energy released graphically like we did in *Activity 1*.

The enthalpy change that occurs when a reaction occurs is sometimes included in the chemical equation as shown below.

$$Mg_{(s)} + 2H_2O_{(l)} \rightarrow Mg(OH)_{2(s)} + H_{2(g)} \qquad \Delta H = -353 \text{ kJ}$$

Energy Diagrams

Another way to represent an enthalpy change is to draw an **energy diagram**. An energy diagram shows the progress of the reaction from reactants to products along the horizontal axis. Along the vertical axis, the diagram shows the change in potential energy that occurs as substances progress from reactants to products. An energy diagram provides the following two important pieces of information:

Endothermic or exothermic: The relative locations of the reactant (starting) energy and product (ending) energy indicate whether the overall enthalpy change (ΔH) is endothermic or exothermic. If the starting point (reactants) is higher than the ending point (products), then the system releases heat energy to the surroundings (an exothermic change), and the overall enthalpy change is negative ($\Delta H < 0$). If the energy of the reactants is lower than that of the products, then the system absorbs heat energy from the surroundings (an endothermic change), and the overall enthalpy change is positive ($\Delta H > 0$).

Chem Words

enthalpy change: change in heat energy for a process that occurs at constant pressure; symbolized by ΔH.

energy diagram: a graph showing how energy changes during the course of a reaction.

Chem Words

activation energy (E_a): the energy that must be gained by molecules so they can break existing bonds and undergo a reaction.

activated complex: the intermediate state that is a combination of reactant and product atoms.

catalyst: a substance that provides a lower-energy pathway for a reaction which increases the speed of a reaction; it is not consumed (used up) during the reaction.

Activation energy: Regardless of whether the change is endothermic or exothermic, bonds must always be broken in the reactants (requiring energy input) before new bonds can form in the products (releasing energy). Therefore, some initial amount of energy (always a positive value, since it is added to the system) must be supplied to the system in order for the reaction to begin. This is represented as an activation barrier, or an initial "bump" in the curve, to get from reactants to products. The height of this bump, measured from the reactant energy, is called the **activation energy (E_a)** and it is always positive ($E_a > 0$). The intermediate (in-between) state, between reactants and products, at the top of the barrier is called the **activated complex**.

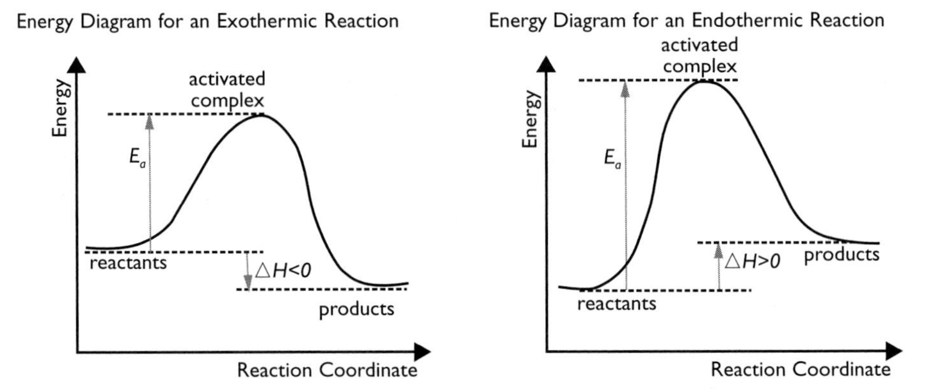
Energy Diagram for an Exothermic Reaction
Energy
activated complex
E_a
reactants
$\Delta H<0$
products
Reaction Coordinate
Energy Diagram for an Endothermic Reaction
Energy
activated complex
E_a
$\Delta H>0$
products
reactants
Reaction Coordinate

More about the Bump

When you compared the reaction of three types of magnesium with water, you observed that the reaction of magnesium pieces with water was very slow (if you could even detect a reaction at all). Magnesium metal reacts easily with oxygen from the air to form a magnesium oxide coating on the metal. This coating makes it difficult for water to get to the magnesium metal. As a result, the reaction is very slow. Although there was more heat produced by the reaction of granular magnesium with water, that reaction was also pretty slow. You know from your observations of the MRE heater that the reaction between magnesium metal and water produces a huge amount of heat energy. But in the first two test tubes, the amount of heat that was produced was not very great. Clearly, providing soldiers with magnesium pieces or granules would not help them heat their food very well.

The scientists and engineers who designed the MRE heater made two modifications to make the reaction produce heat faster. First, the MRE heater uses smaller, ground-up particles of magnesium. The smaller particles give the magnesium a greater surface area. This allows more water molecules to come in contact with the magnesium atoms, which speeds up the reaction. Second, the MRE heater also uses a **catalyst**. A catalyst is a substance that speeds up a chemical reaction without being used up itself. A catalyst works by providing a lower-energy alternative pathway for the reaction to take. In essence, it provides a lower activation energy (a lower energy barrier). As a result, more starting materials at a given temperature have enough energy to get over the energy barrier. This speeds up the reaction.

Remember that when you compared different magnesium samples, the sample containing NaCl reacted much more quickly than the others. However, if you look at the chemical equation that represents the reaction, NaCl is not a reactant. It provides a chloride ion, Cl^-, that acts as a catalyst. This speeds up the rate of the reaction between magnesium and water remarkably, so it produces heat faster.

Energy Diagram for an Exothermic Reaction with a Catalyst Added

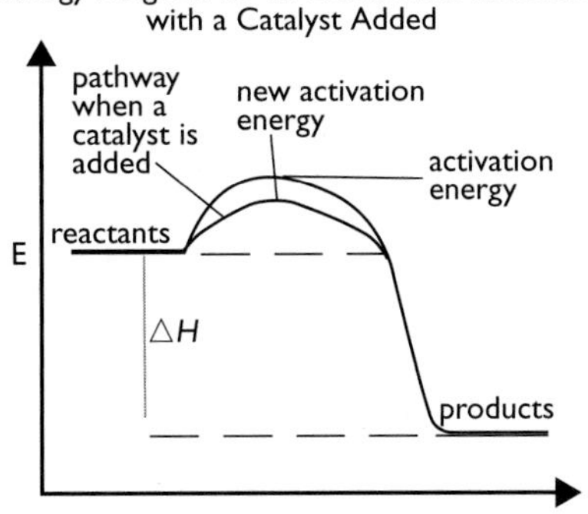
pathway when a catalyst is added
new activation energy
activation energy
reactants
E
ΔH
products

Checking Up

1. What does it mean for a change to occur spontaneously?
2. What two questions must be answered to determine if a change can occur spontaneously?
3. What evidence do you look for to tell if a change is exothermic or endothermic?
4. From where does the energy in an exothermic reaction come?
5. What are two things that chemists or engineers designed into the MRE heater to make the reaction happen faster?
6. What does a catalyst do to speed up a reaction?
7. How does an energy profile graph look for a reaction with a catalyst vs. one without a catalyst? What's different? What's the same?

What Do You Think Now?

At the beginning of this activity you were asked:

- **What is the source of the heat produced by the hot pack?**
- **How is the hot pack able to increase in temperature without an external (added) source of heat?**

Now that you have explored the MRE heater, how would you answer these questions?

Chem Essential Questions

What does it mean?

Chemistry explains a macroscopic phenomenon (what you observe) with a description of what happens at the nanoscopic level (atoms and molecules) using symbolic structures as a way to communicate. Complete the chart below in your *Active Chemistry* log.

MACRO	NANO	SYMBOLIC
Describe observations that would lead you to conclude that a reaction is exothermic. *Describe observations that would lead you to conclude that a reaction is endothermic.*	*Explain whether breaking a bond between atoms is an endothermic process or an exothermic process.* *Describe how a catalyst particle would interact with a molecule of a reactant to speed up the reaction.*	*Draw an energy diagram for both an endothermic and exothermic process. Label the axes, ΔH, E_a, reactants, and products for each diagram. Show how the diagrams are affected by adding a catalyst to the reaction.*

How do you know?

A catalyst lowers the activation energy and speeds up a reaction. What evidence do you have from this activity that this occurs?

Why do you believe?

The use of chemical reactions to release energy for human use is common. Describe some situations in which exothermic reactions are used to produce energy.

Human use of endothermic reactions seems to be much less common than use of exothermic reactions. Why would this be the case? What are some situations where an endothermic change (either chemical or physical) might be useful?

Why should you care?

How might you use a reaction that produces heat as part of your *Chemical Dominoes* apparatus? What would set it off and what would it cause to happen next?

Suppose the reaction you have chosen is not producing enough heat. What would be some ways to change the situation so more heat would be generated?

Reflecting on the Activity and the Challenge

In this activity, you learned how chemical reactions can be used to generate heat. Heat is produced in a reaction when the energy released by the formation of new bonds is greater than the energy used to break the old bonds. You also observed that increasing the surface area of the reactants and the addition of a catalyst will speed up a chemical reaction. You may want to use a chemical reaction that releases heat as a part of your *Chemical Dominoes* apparatus. You could use the heat produced to melt ice, heat a liquid or gas, or cause some other change you design. Knowing how to determine the amount of energy a change will produce is important so you will know how much of the reactants to use. Also, you will need to be able to control how rapidly the heat is produced so that the change happens when you want it to, rather than too soon or too late.

Chem to Go

1. Identify each process as endothermic or exothermic.
   a) Burning wood
   b) Melting ice
   c) Evaporation of sweat
   d) A chemical hand warmer
2. Hydrogen peroxide decomposes to form oxygen gas and water. (Your teacher might have shown you this reaction as a demonstration.)

$2H_2O_2(aq)$	$\rightarrow$	$O_2(g)$	+	$2H_2O(l)$
hydrogen peroxide (dissolved in water)		*oxygen (gas)*		*water (liquid)*

   a) Use the following information to determine the enthalpy change (ΔH) of the reaction.
      - The energy required to break the bonds in 1 mol of H_2O_2 is +188 kJ. (Note: there are 2 mol of H_2O_2 required in this reaction.)
      - The total energy released in forming both 1 mol of oxygen gas and 2 mol of water is –572 kJ.

   b) Is the overall change endothermic or exothermic? How do you know?

   c) Why is it necessary to use a balanced chemical reaction to calculate ΔH?

   d) How much heat would be released if 50.0 g of H_2O_2 decomposed? Show your work.

   e) Sketch what the energy diagram. Label the following on your energy profile: reactants, products, activated complex, total energy change (indicate the sign by the direction of the arrow), activation energy (indicate the sign by the direction of the arrow), the "energy" axis, and the "reaction coordinate" axis.

   f) Sketch a dotted line on your energy diagram to show what it would look like if you added a catalyst.

3. Look back at the description of the reaction in the MRE heater.

   a) What kind of reaction occurs in the MRE heater? You've seen these reactions before in a previous activity in this chapter.

   b) Why does the reaction occur spontaneously?

   c) How does the amount of energy required to break the bonds in the reactants compare to the amount of energy released when the products form?

4. Adding a catalyst to a chemical reaction results in:

   a) a decrease in activation energy and a decrease in the reaction rate

   b) a decrease in activation energy and an increase in the reaction rate

   c) an increase in activation energy and a decrease in the reaction rate

   d) an increase in activation energy and an increase in the reaction rate

5. ***Preparing for the Chapter Challenge***

   One way you might use a heat-producing reaction in your *Chemical Dominoes* apparatus is to cause an ice cube to melt that would tip a lever (as described in the introductory words in the *Investigate* section). Brainstorm with your group to come up with an idea of how you could use a heat-producing chemical reaction to melt an ice cube that tips a lever that causes the LED to light. You may need to review your response to *Preparing for the Chapter Challenge* from *Activity 4*. Draw diagrams and make some notes so that you can return to these ideas when you build your apparatus. If your group has a different idea of how to use a heat-producing reaction, you may draw a diagram and explain that idea instead.

Inquiring Further

Calorimetry

Calorimetry is the quantitative study of heat. Research coffee-cup calorimetry and build a simple calorimeter. Under the supervision of an adult, determine the heat capacity of your calorimeter.

Calcium chloride is a salt used to melt ice on sidewalks. An interesting property of calcium chloride is that it produces a large amount of heat when it dissolves. Under the supervision of an adult, use your coffee-cup calorimeter to calculate how much heat is produced when different amounts of calcium chloride are dissolved in water. Other ionic salts such as ammonium chloride and sodium hydroxide may also be tested.

Activity 8 Rubber Bands and Spontaneity

What Do You See?

RUBBER BANDS
RUBBER BANDS

GOALS

In this activity you will:

- Determine if a change results in an increase or decrease in entropy.
- Determine if a change will be spontaneous by considering change in enthalpy and change in entropy.
- Describe the structure of polymers.

What Do You Think?

Rubber is an example of a polymer. Polymers are long strings of similar small molecules (monomers) joined together in many places by cross-links.

- **Draw what you think the molecules inside a rubber band look like.**
- **Predict what will happen if a rubber band is heated. Explain why you think your prediction is correct.**

Record your ideas about these questions in your *Active Chemistry* log. Be prepared to discuss your responses with your small group and the class.

Investigate

You could use the unusual properties of rubber to make a wheel that turns using heat energy from a lamp. If you are going to use rubber bands as a part of your apparatus, it will be important to understand why rubber has unusual properties.

Part A: Adding or Removing Heat Energy from Rubber

1. In the first part of this activity, you will investigate what happens when a rubber band is heated and cooled. Then you will investigate how a rubber band stretches and contracts. Make a data table similar to the one shown to record your data.

Experiment	Observations	Is heat added ($\Delta H > 0$) or released ($\Delta H < 0$)?
heating rubber band		
cooling rubber band		
rubber band stretching		
rubber band contracting		

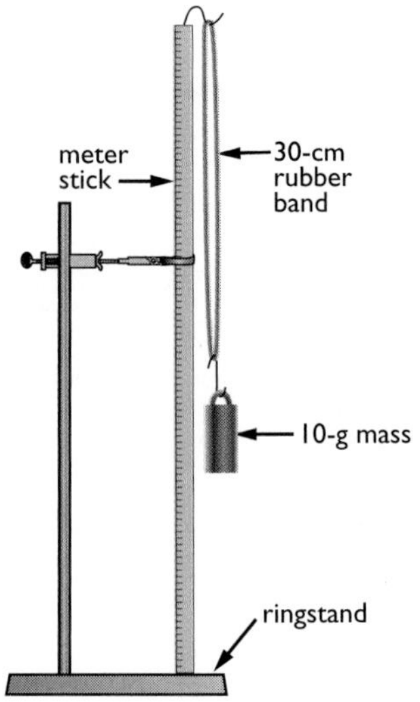
meter stick
30-cm rubber band
10-g mass
ringstand

2. Set up the apparatus as shown in the diagram. You will need a ringstand, a clamp, a meter stick with a hook at one end, a 30-cm rubber band, and a 10-g mass.
3. Place a piece of masking tape just opposite the bottom of the rubber band to mark where it starts.
4. Heat the rubber band with a hair dryer and observe what happens. When the rubber band is heated with the hair dryer, does the rubber band gain heat energy ($\Delta H > 0$) or release heat energy ($\Delta H < 0$)?

   Record your observations of what happened in your data table.
5. Cool the rubber band with ice and observe what happens to the rubber band. When you cool the rubber band, does the rubber band gain heat energy ($\Delta H > 0$) or release heat energy ($\Delta H < 0$)?

   Record your observations of what happened in your data table.
6. Obtain a rubber band that has a wide, flat surface. Hold the flat surface of the unstretched rubber band against your forehead. Make sure you can detect its temperature (warmer or colder than your skin). Try it a couple of times until you are familiar with the temperature of the rubber band. Then, hold the rubber band away from your face and quickly stretch the rubber band as far as you can (but don't break it). Quickly place it back against your forehead and notice the temperature difference. Is it warmer, cooler or the same as before? Try it several times to be sure of your results.

   Record your observations in your data table. As you determine the ΔH for the rubber band, consider if the rubber band is releasing energy to your forehead or absorbing energy from your forehead. If the rubber band is releasing energy, it will feel warmer.
7. Now do the experiment the other way around to find out whether rubber gives off or takes in heat energy as it contracts. Stretch a rubber band and keep it stretched. Allow it a few moments to become room temperature. Then, hold the stretched rubber band against your face and familiarize yourself with its temperature. Next, move the rubber band away from your forehead and quickly allow it to retract. Once it has retracted, hold it against your forehead again and notice the temperature difference. Is it warmer, cooler or the same as before? Try this several times to be sure of your results.

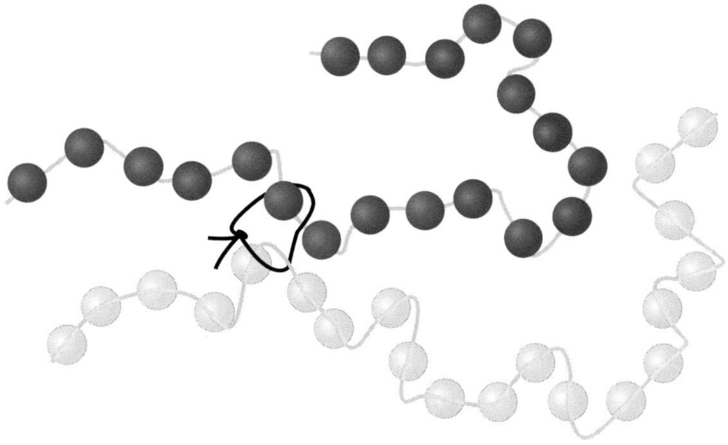

Record your observations in your data table.

a) There should be a relationship between the results from *Steps 4* and *5* and the results from *Steps 6* and *7*. Describe this relationship in your log.

8. Return to the model you drew of rubber molecules in the *What Do You Think?* section.

a) Describe how your model would explain what happened when you heated the rubber band and when you cooled the rubber band. If your model does not explain the evidence you collected about heating and cooling the rubber band, revise your model and use the revised model in your explanation.

Part B: Modeling the Behavior of Rubber Molecules

1. Obtain ten chains of round beads and nine pieces of string. The chains of beads represent polymers. Each bead represents a single part of a polymer, called a monomer.
2. Use nine pieces of string to create a tangled mess of the chains of beads by tying each string around any two chains of beads, as shown. The drawing shows only two chains of beads as an example. You will link together ten chains into one large group. Each string represents a cross-link that binds the polymer chains together to create a network of long-chain molecules. When you have all the strings tied, you should be able to lift the entire tangled mess by grasping any single location in the mess. In other words, no chains should remain unattached.
3. Set the tangled beads down randomly on a rectangular piece of flat rubber. Using masking tape, attach the beads to the rubber in about five different locations, so that the beads will move along with the rubber as you stretch it.

a) Make a drawing of what the chains of beads look like, making sure to indicate the cross-links. Identify one of the chains of beads by shading the beads that you draw, as one of the chains is identified in the drawing above.

4. Now stretch the rubber gently, the long way, but try not to break any strings of beads.

a) While one person holds the rubber stretched, everyone else should sketch what the polymer chains look like now. Try to identify the very same chain of beads as before, by shading the beads.

b) Compare and contrast the two configurations of bead chains (not stretched and stretched). It might be helpful to look at the difference between the shaded chain in your first drawing and the shaded chain in your second drawing. How are the chains arranged differently in each configuration? Which configuration is more ordered (organized) and which is more disordered (disorganized)?

5. The amount of disorder is called entropy and has the symbol *S*. You can think of disorder as the opposite of order. Here are some other synonyms and their opposites to help you think about entropy.

Less "spread"	More "spread"
order	disorder
neat	messy
organized	disorganized
low entropy	high entropy

a) Of the two configurations you drew, contracted, and stretched, which one has the higher entropy and which has the lower entropy?

b) Determine whether a change of configuration that occurs has a positive or negative entropy change. One way to do this is to represent entropy as a number line (look back at the *Chem Talk* section of *Activity 1* for a reminder and example). On a number line in your *Active Chemistry* log, indicate the locations of the contracted rubber band and the stretched rubber band:

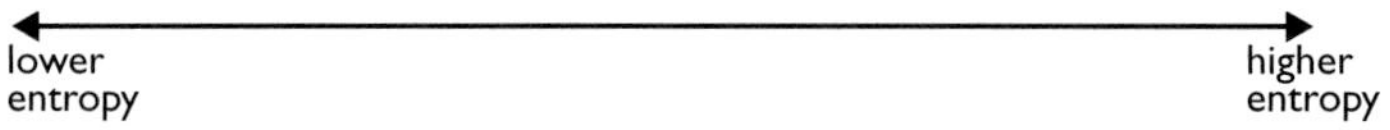
lower entropy
higher entropy

c) As you change from a contracted rubber band to a stretched rubber band, is the change of entropy in the positive or negative direction?

d) The sign of the entropy change (ΔS) is the same as the direction of the change on the number line. Complete the table below to indicate if the entropy change (ΔS) for stretching and contracting the rubber band is positive or negative.

Change	Entropy change
stretching rubber band	ΔS is ?
rubber band contracting	ΔS is ?

e) Now return to the drawings you made at the beginning of the activity or your revision from *Part A*. Describe how your model would explain what happened when you heated the rubber band and when you cooled the rubber band. If your model does not explain the evidence you collected about heating and cooling the rubber band, revise your model and use the revised model in your explanation.

Chem Talk

SPONTANEITY

When speaking of a change, chemists refer to the **system** and the **surroundings**. Together, the system and surroundings make up the universe. You choose the system that you want to investigate. You can imagine drawing a dashed surface around the system, to separate it from the surroundings.

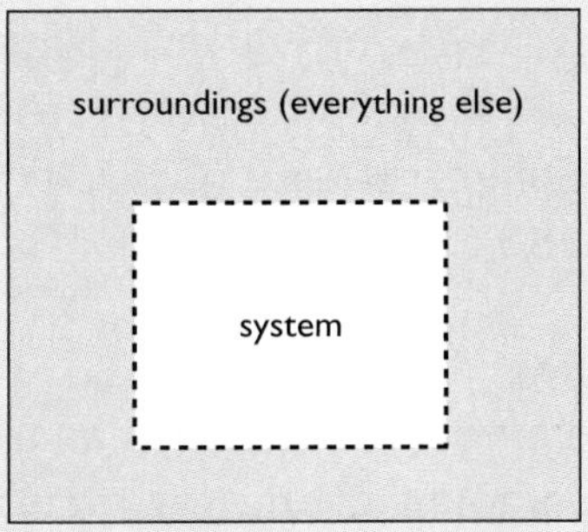
surroundings (everything else)
system

When considering change, you think about what the *system* is doing. Is the enthalpy *of the system* increasing or decreasing? Is the entropy *of the system* increasing or decreasing? For example, when stretching the rubber band, you asked, "Is the rubber band producing heat energy or releasing heat energy?"

Enthalpy Changes

When heat energy is released from the system, the surroundings gain that energy, while the system loses energy. If your hand is resting on the system (but you are part of the surroundings), you feel heat energy coming from the system. When a system loses heat energy, there is a loss in the amount of enthalpy that the system contains. The *change* of enthalpy is negative ($\Delta H < 0$).

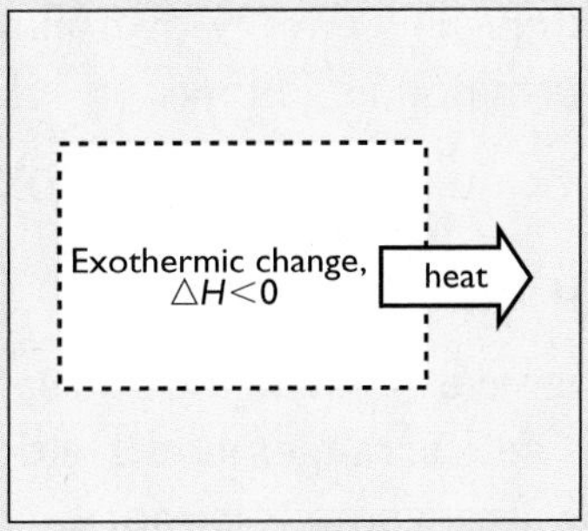
Exothermic change,
ΔH<0
heat

When heat energy is absorbed by a system, the surroundings must give that heat energy to the system. Energy must come from somewhere. The **Law of Conservation of Energy** states that energy cannot be created or destroyed. It can only be transferred from one location to another. If your hand is resting on the system (but you are part of the surroundings), you feel heat energy leaving your hand and going to the system. In other words, your hand feels cold.

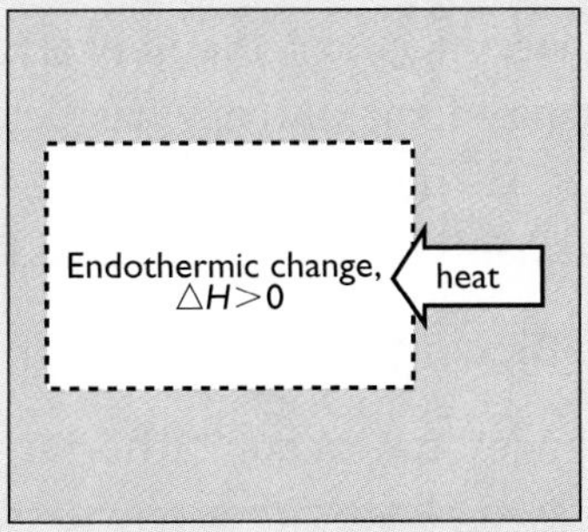
Endothermic change,
ΔH>0
heat

Chem Words

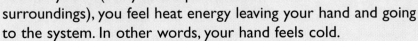

system: the part of the universe under study.

surroundings: all of the universe not under study.

Law of Conservation of Energy: the law that states that energy cannot be created or destroyed; it is merely transferred.

When a system gains energy, there is an increase in the amount of energy the system possesses. The change of enthalpy is positive ($\Delta H > 0$).

Let's review how to calculate enthalpy changes by considering a reaction that you used in *Activity 1* to generate CO_2 gas. In *Method 3*, you heated calcium carbonate ($CaCO_3$) to produce CaO and CO_2. This chemical reaction is symbolized as:

$$CaCO_{3(s)} + \text{energy} \rightarrow CaO_{(s)} + CO_{2(g)}$$

The amount of energy absorbed and released by a reaction depends on the amount of starting materials, as you learned in *Activity 7*. If you begin with a specific amount (1 mol) of $CaCO_3$:

- It takes an input of +1207 kJ (kilojoules) of energy to break apart the bonds in the $CaCO_3$.
- When the CaO and CO_2 form, the energy released is –1029 kJ.

For this change, you have to put more energy in than you get out. Looking at it from the perspective of the matter that is changing, the matter gains energy overall. Mathematically, the enthalpy change is determined as follows:

$$\Delta H = (+1207 \text{ kJ}) + (-1029 \text{ kJ}) = +178 \text{ kJ}$$

Entropy Changes

Whenever a change occurs, particles inside the system are rearranged. The new arrangement is either more or less disorganized. When the new arrangement is more disorganized the entropy has increased. The change in entropy is positive, or $\Delta S > 0$. The final entropy is a larger value than the initial entropy.

Conversely, when the new arrangement is less spread out or more organized, the entropy has decreased. The entropy change is negative, or $\Delta S < 0$. The final entropy is a lower value than the initial entropy. When materials change from gas to liquid or liquid to solid, the entropy decreases.

Predicting Spontaneity in Nature

Changes can occur either spontaneously or not. As you have learned, the two factors that affect spontaneity are changes in enthalpy (ΔH) and changes in entropy (ΔS). Exothermic changes (those with $\Delta H < 0$) drive a process toward spontaneity. This is because substances are produced that have lower energy than the reactants from which they formed. Lower-energy states are favorable. Changes that result in an increase in entropy of the system also drive a process toward spontaneity. This is because nature tends to become more disorganized ($\Delta S > 0$) over time.

If both factors change in the direction that favors spontaneity, the reaction will definitely be spontaneous. If neither factor changes in the direction that favors spontaneity, the reaction will definitely not be spontaneous. If only one change occurs in a favorable direction, the more dominant change will determine if the reaction is spontaneous. This information is summarized below.

Possible combinations of changes in enthalpy and entropy	Signs of ΔH and ΔS	Is the process spontaneous?
Enthalpy decreases (exothermic) Entropy increases (more disorder)	$\Delta H < 0$ $\Delta S > 0$	Yes
Enthalpy increases (endothermic) Entropy decreases (less disorder)	$\Delta H > 0$ $\Delta S < 0$	No
Enthalpy decreases Entropy decreases	$\Delta H < 0$ $\Delta S < 0$	Only if enthalpy change (ΔH) is dominant
Enthalpy increases Entropy increases	$\Delta H > 0$ $\Delta S > 0$	Only if entropy change (ΔS) is dominant

A third factor determines if a process will be spontaneous. Consider the freezing of water to form ice. If the water is left on the counter, freezing is not spontaneous. However, if the water is placed in the freezer, the process becomes spontaneous. The temperature at which a process occurs can affect whether or not a process will be spontaneous. It would be convenient to combine the three quantities that affect spontaneity (ΔH, ΔS, and T) into one value.

An American scientist Josiah Willard Gibbs, 1839–1903, developed a very useful mathematical relationship between ΔH, ΔS, and T. It is called **Gibbs free energy** (named in his honor). It is a measurement that can be used to tell whether a change will occur spontaneously. If the change in Gibbs free energy, ΔG, is negative, the change will occur spontaneously at the given temperature. In other words, the change is favorable. →

Chem Words

Gibbs free energy change: a combination of ΔH, ΔS, and T that is used to determine if a change is spontaneous at a given temperature.

If ΔG is positive, the change cannot occur spontaneously at the given temperature; it is not favorable.

The change in Gibbs free energy can be determined using the following equation:

$$\Delta G = \Delta H - T\Delta S$$

where the temperature (T) is measured in kelvins.

If ΔH is negative and ΔS is positive, then ΔG will be negative no matter what the temperature. This is a situation where the change can occur spontaneously under any circumstances. If ΔH is positive and ΔS is negative, then ΔG will be positive no matter what the temperature. A spontaneous change cannot occur for such a system.

When ΔH and ΔS both have the same sign, ΔG could be positive or negative, depending on whether ΔH or ΔS is more influential in determining the sign of ΔG. Notice that at the higher temperatures, ΔS is more influential on ΔG because ΔS is multiplied by the temperature. Multiplying ΔS by a large temperature would make it a large number. At low temperatures, the product of ΔS and T would be a small number. Therefore, at low temperatures, the ΔH is more influential on ΔG and spontaneity.

Consider when $CaCO_3$ breaks down:

$$CaCO_3 \rightarrow CaO + CO_2$$

The ΔH for the process is +178 kJ. The value is positive, which indicates an endothermic reaction. This would drive the reaction to not be spontaneous. The ΔS is 0.159 kJ/K. This value is also positive, which indicates disorder increases during the change. This would drive the reaction to be spontaneous. So, which factor dominates and determines if the process is spontaneous? This is a place where the Gibbs free energy equation is useful.

At room temperature (298 K), the ΔG would be calculated as shown below.

$$\begin{aligned} \Delta G &= \Delta H - T\Delta S \\ &= +178 \text{ kJ} - (298 \text{ K})(0.159 \text{ kJ/K}) \\ &= +131 \text{ kJ} \end{aligned}$$

Since the value for ΔG is positive, the reaction is not spontaneous at room temperature.

What if the temperature were increased by heating $CaCO_3$, as in *Activity 1*? Assume that the temperature was 373 K.

$$\begin{aligned} \Delta G &= \Delta H - T\Delta S \\ &= +178 \text{ kJ} - (373 \text{ K})(0.159 \text{ kJ/K}) \\ &= +118 \text{ kJ} \end{aligned}$$

Notice that the ΔG is still positive indicating that the process is not spontaneous. In order to make the reaction continue to occur, energy must still be added to the substances. The reaction is not spontaneous at the temperature you used, so once you stopped supplying energy to the reaction, the reaction stopped.

Polymers Have Unusual Properties

Polymers are molecules made of long strings of **monomers** that are attached to each other. This structure causes materials that are made of polymers to exhibit some unusual behaviors. You probably predicted initially that when you heated a rubber band (with the hair dryer) it would get longer. In fact, it spontaneously contracted (got shorter). To understand this, you need to compare the enthalpy and entropy of the two states (stretched and contracted) of the rubber band.

When the rubber band is in a stretched state, the entropy (disorder) is low because the molecules are pulled relatively straight and lined up. You saw this in your bead and string model. The enthalpy is also low when the rubber band is in a stretched state because the aligned molecules are able to experience attractions to each other. You learned in *Activity 1* that oppositely charged ions have less energy (and enthalpy) when they are near each other than when they are separated. Molecules exhibit a similar relationship between distance and energy. Molecules experience relatively weak attractions for each other when they are close together. This means when a molecule is attracted to another, it is at a lower energy (enthalpy) state.

Chem Words

polymer: a very long-chain molecule composed of repeating monomers joined together.

monomer: a small, repeating molecule that composes a polymer.

When the rubber band is in a contracted state, the entropy (disorder) is high because the molecules are tangled around each other. The enthalpy is also high because the molecules are farther apart from other molecules. (This may sound a little strange at first, but think about pulling the rubber with the bead strings attached. More molecules would be closer to one another when the rubber is stretched than when contracted.) When a molecule does not have other nearby molecules to be attracted to, the molecule is at a higher energy (enthalpy). A comparison of the two states of the rubber band is shown in the chart.

State of rubber band	Enthalpy (H)	Entropy (S)
stretched	lower	lower
contracted	higher	higher

Is a rubber band more likely to be stretched or contracted based on the two factors that affect spontaneity? Nature favors changes that result in lower energy (enthalpy). Therefore, the enthalpy factor would favor the rubber band becoming stretched. Nature favors changes that result in higher entropy. The entropy factor would favor the rubber band contracting. Which factor dominates and determines the state of the rubber band? At room temperature, nature favors the contracted state. A rubber band will not spontaneously stretch. Unless you apply force to the rubber band by holding it stretched, it will spontaneously return to its contracted state. So, at room temperature, the change in entropy dominates the change in enthalpy.

Effect of Temperature on Rubber Band

The rubber band stretched when you decreased its temperature by cooling it with ice. This means that at a lower temperature, the stretched state is favored. As you saw, the change in enthalpy drives the rubber band toward a stretched state. Therefore, at a lower temperature, the enthalpy factor becomes dominant over the entropy factor.

Since the rubber band is stretched when cooled with ice and is contracted at room temperature, increasing temperature causes the rubber band to contract. You observed this when you heated the rubber band with the hair dryer. As the temperature is increased, the change in entropy makes the contraction of the rubber band more and more spontaneous. Therefore, the rubber band contracts more than it does at room temperature.

Putting Polymers to Use

Rubber is a polymer. Its elasticity is only one of its unusual properties. Polymeric materials can be designed to have other unusual properties by controlling the composition of the monomers, the number of monomers present, and the degree of cross-linking that joins the polymer molecules. If there is no cross-linking, polymer molecules can slide past each other, just as pieces of cooked spaghetti in water are able to, and the polymer material can flow like latex paint and silicone-plastic "clay." Properties of polymers range from being so sturdy that you can build cars and buildings out of them, to being so elastic that you can make trampolines and bouncy superballs out of them. The fields of polymer chemistry and materials science are exciting and lucrative and employ many chemists.

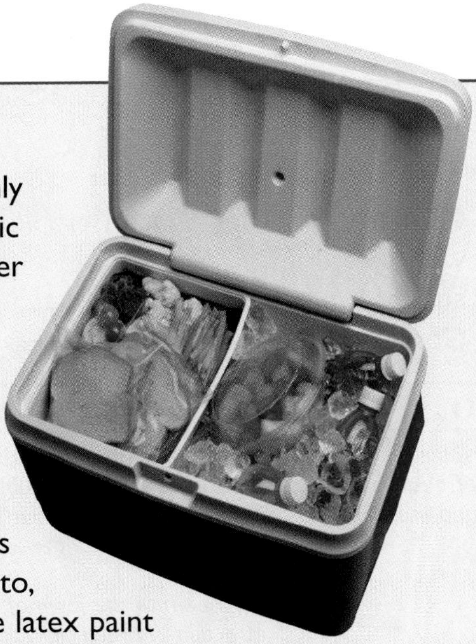

Checking Up

1. What happens to a system during an endothermic change?
2. What happens to the entropy of your room when you go from a neat room to a messy room?
3. What two factors determine whether a change is spontaneous?
4. If a particular change has a negative enthalpy change ($\Delta H < 0$) and also a negative entropy change ($\Delta S < 0$), can the change be spontaneous? If so, what must be true for the change to be spontaneous?
5. Why does a rubber band contract when you heat it?

What Do You Think Now?

At the beginning of this activity you were asked:

- **Draw what you think the molecules inside a rubber band look like.**
- **Predict what will happen if a rubber band is heated. Explain why you think your prediction is correct.**

Based on your study of rubber in this activity, how would you answer the questions now? What makes a rubber band exist in the state that it does at room temperature?

Chem Essential Questions

What does it mean?

Chemistry explains a macroscopic phenomenon (what you observe) with a description of what happens at the nanoscopic level (atoms and molecules) using symbolic structures as a way to communicate. Complete the chart below in your *Active Chemistry* log.

MACRO	NANO	SYMBOLIC
Describe your observations about the behavior of a rubber band when heated and cooled.	*Describe how the organization or particles within the rubber changes when the rubber band is stretched and contracted.* *Describe how the force of attraction between particles within the rubber changes when the rubber band is stretched and contracted.*	*Draw a picture to represent a system with high entropy.* *Draw a picture to represent a system with low entropy.*

How do you know?

Describe how you can tell if a process releases heat or absorbs heat.

Why do you believe?

The equation that represents the reaction that occurred in the MRE heater in *Activity 7* is:

$$Mg_{(s)} + 2H_2O_{(l)} \rightarrow Mg(OH)_{2(s)} + H_{2(g)}.$$

Is the ΔH for this reaction positive or negative? Explain how you can tell based on your observations in *Activity 7*. Is the ΔS for this reaction positive or negative? Explain how you can tell by looking at the phase subscripts provided in the equation. Is the reaction spontaneous at room temperature? Explain how you know.

Why should you care?

Would spontaneity be an important concept to add to your list of important criteria used to evaluate methods of producing CO_2 in *Activity 1*? Why or why not? If you did decide to consider spontaneity, would you prefer a spontaneous or non-spontaneous reaction for your dominoes apparatus? Explain your reasoning.

Reflecting on the Activity and the Challenge

For the *Chapter Challenge*, you must create a series of cascading physical and chemical changes that ultimately light an LED. Once the user starts the series, he or she is not involved again. You must be able to design the process so that energy transfers cause changes to occur. You have learned in this activity how to determine if a chemical reaction or a physical change is spontaneous. If you choose to use a spontaneous reaction in your dominoes apparatus, you will likely have to find some way to supply the initial activation energy to the reactants to get the reaction started. If you choose to use a non-spontaneous reaction, you will have to find a way to supply energy to the reactants for however long you need the reaction to occur. The most common way to supply energy to a reaction is through the use of heat. Some reactions do not require the additional input of heat. The reactants are able to absorb the heat they need from their room temperature surroundings. An example of this would be the reaction that occurred in the MRE heater in *Activity 7*. Once the water and magnesium come in contact, the reaction begins.

Chem to Go

1. Make drawings depicting each change below. Then decide on what you believe the signs of ΔH and ΔS are for each change. Explain your reasoning.

   a) Ice melting   b) A candle burning (the wax burns)

2. Here is a pictorial representation of how crystals of $AgNO_3$ dissolve in water.

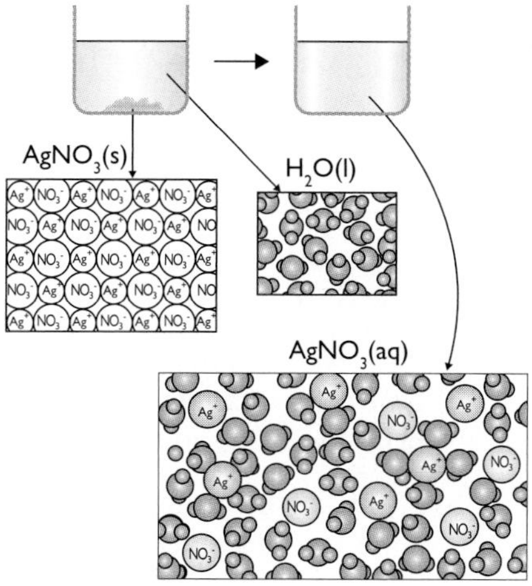
AgNO$_3$(s)
H$_2$O(l)
AgNO$_3$(aq)
Ag$^+$
NO$_3^-$

   a) When $AgNO_3$ dissolves in water, the solution and beaker feel a little cold to the touch. Is dissolving $AgNO_3$ in water endothermic or exothermic? Explain. Which term describes this change: ΔG, ΔH or ΔS? Is the term positive or negative?

   b) Is the change creating more disorder or more order? (Look at the diagram.) Explain how you can tell. Which term describes changes in disorder: ΔG, ΔH or ΔS? Is the term positive or negative?

   c) Which of the two terms needs to be stronger in order for the change to be spontaneous? Support your explanation using the Gibbs free energy equation.

3. For the dissolving of silver nitrate, $AgNO_3$, shown in the diagram, the initial (before) and final (after) information is:

Enthalpy and Entropy Changes	
Energy required to break bonds between Ag^+ and NO_3^- ions, plus open up space between H_2O molecules for those ions to fit between	+124 kJ per mole of $AgNO_3$ (positive because this bond breaking requires energy input)
Energy given off when new attractive forces form between Ag^+ and its surrounding H_2O molecules, and NO_3^- and its surrounding H_2O molecules	−102 kJ per mole of $AgNO_3$ (negative because the forming of attractive forces releases energy)
Entropy (amount of disorder) in the "before" (undissolved) state	0.141 kJ/K per mole of $AgNO_3$
Entropy in the "after" (dissolved) state	0.219 kJ/K per mole of $AgNO_3$

a) What is the system? What are the surroundings?

b) Sketch a bar graph to illustrate the energy change.

c) Based on the numerical information above, what is the change of enthalpy (ΔH) for the system?

d) Does the change in enthalpy drive the process to be spontaneous or non-spontaneous? Explain.

e) Place x's, the words "before" and "after," and an arrow going from before to after on the number line below to illustrate the entropy change. (See examples in *Activity 1*.)

entropy

f) Based on the numerical information above, what is the entropy change (ΔS) for the system?

g) Does the change in entropy drive the process to be spontaneous or non-spontaneous? Explain.

h) At an absolute temperature, T, of 298 K (about room temperature), calculate the Gibbs free energy for this system, using the equation

$$\Delta G = \Delta H - T\Delta S$$

Is ΔG positive or negative? Does this indicate that the change is spontaneous or non-spontaneous?

i) What would be the sign of ΔG for the reverse process (separating the solution into solid $AgNO_3$ and liquid water) at room temperature? Explain your reasoning.

4. At STP, a sample of which element has the highest entropy?

   a) Na(s) b) Hg(l) c) Br_2(l) d) F_2(g)

5. Systems in nature tend to undergo changes toward:

   a) lower energy and lower entropy b) lower energy and higher entropy

   c) higher energy and lower entropy d) higher energy and higher entropy

6. ***Preparing for the Chapter Challenge***

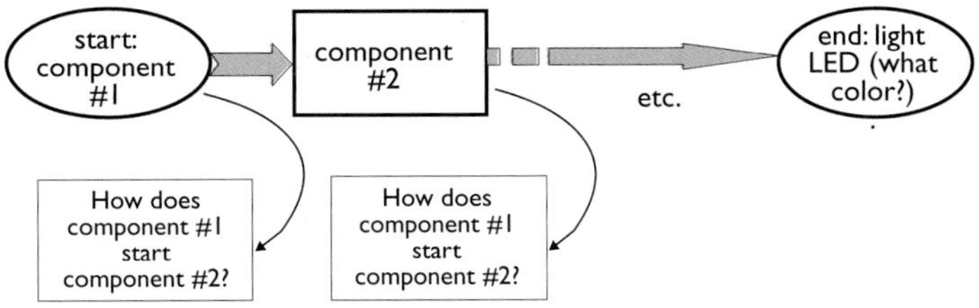

start: component #1
component #2
etc.
end: light LED (what color?)
How does component #1 start component #2?
How does component #1 start component #2?

   It is time for you to compare all the different ideas you have generated throughout this chapter and select the ones that will make the best *Chemical Dominoes* apparatus. In your *Active Chemistry* log, make a list of all the possible components you can build from different ideas you have explored in the activities. Remember that you must light an LED as the final step. List several different possible sequences of components that could be part of your apparatus. In between each component, explain how the previous step sets off the next step. You may use the example flowchart above as a method to organize your ideas.

Inquiring Further

Build a rubber-band engine

You can use what you have learned about enthalpy and entropy to make a rubber-band wheel or "engine" that runs on heat energy from a lamp. An infrared lamp works best.

1. Look at the photograph, and then design and build a rubber-band engine that spins when a lamp is turned on. Think about how rubber behaves when heated to figure out where to place the lamp.
2. The materials you can use include, but are not limited to, the following:
   - **rubber bands**
   - **embroidery hoop**
   - **wooden dowel with a large diameter**
   - **metal eye-hook screws**
   - **infrared lamp (or regular lamp)**
   - **pliers, screwdriver, scissors**

3. Once you have your rubber-band engine working, observe it carefully. What is actually happening to the rubber bands? Do your observations match your predictions that were behind the design of your wheel?
4. Think about how you could use the rubber-band engine in your *Chemical Dominoes* apparatus. Where would it be? Would you have something activate it, or would you turn it on at the beginning? What domino effect might the rubber-band wheel cause?

Chem at Work

Alice Madjani

Participant, Rube Goldberg Machine Contest, West Lafayette, IN

Rube Goldberg was a cartoonist whose drawings depicted machines that made simple tasks extremely complex. His images were designed for people who like to do things the hard way! Many young engineers have become interested in Rube's concept of "exerting maximum effort to accomplish minimal results." For example, designing and building a machine that employs more than 20 steps simply to crush a can or peel an apple can present a challenge. This kind of passion for machine building culminates every year at Purdue University in West Lafayette, Indiana, where students compete to build the "best" Rube Goldberg device.

The commitee selects a simple task, such as shredding paper, to be accomplished by a machine in a minimum of 20 steps. Participants compete in teams to see who can invent and construct the most needlessly complicated device to perform this simple task.

Alice Madjani, who was president of a freshman council of engineers, participated for the first time in 2006. She and her teammates built a device that has a fan blowing a sailboat across water, which then knocks a marble on a string that swings and topples some dominoes which then sets off a mousetrap that pulls a cord sending metal pellets into a funnel, thus completing an electrical circuit that activates a conveyor belt delivering the paper into a shredder. Got it?

Alice's team did not win. (The winning team shredded the paper in 215 steps!) She did, however, benefit. "We got to see everyone else's designs and see that there were so many possibilities. I would advise people to try and accomplish their wildest dreams... Don't limit what you try to do, just go for it." Alice will use what she has learned and try again next year.

Nadia Makar

Chairperson, Project SEED, Union Hill, NJ

Nadia is a high school science teacher who heads the Project SEED program in New York. The program, which is directed by the American Chemical Society, is an internship program for economically disadvantaged high school students. It provides career opportunities in the field of chemical sciences.

Dimitrios Kourouklis

Law Student, Brooklyn, NY

Dimitrios is a student working to earn his degree in patent law. A patent gives legal ownership to an invention or process. Once he becomes a patent lawyer, he will use his background in chemistry to protect new ideas and breakthroughs in science from being stolen or misused.

Chemical Dominoes Assessment

Your *Chapter Challenge* is to design a sequence of changes that will eventually light a tiny bulb called an LED (light-emitting diode). The toy company is interested in marketing this product to an audience of 10-year-olds and up. The company would like you to design a series of entertaining, individual events, with instructions. You also need to provide a drawing that shows how to arrange the sequence so that the customer could assemble the pieces to create a "chemical dominoes sequence."

In developing the prototype of this product for the toy company, it will be important to make sure the product and its components are sturdy (not fragile), and that the sequence can be run more than once (although some ingredients may need to be replenished before each rerun). The toy must present an appropriate challenge to set up without being too frustrating for the consumer.

If the company likes your product and decides to produce it, you and they will want to patent it. To make this possible, you must keep an extremely complete notebook, carefully recording everything you try in developing this product and the results of each experiment (for every component, not just the whole product all together).

Chemistry Content

To begin, you should review all of the activities that you have completed. You can skim through the text and your *Active Chemistry* log to help remind you of the chemistry concepts in each activity.

Activity 1: You learned how to produce carbon dioxide gas and used that gas to fill a balloon that could tip a lever.

Activity 2: You used the Law of Conservation of Matter to balance chemical equations.

Activity 3: You used the balanced equations and stoichiometry to determine how much of a reactant is required to produce a given volume of gas.

Activity 4: You investigated circuits and how you could destroy a metal and light an LED.

Activity 5: You explained how atoms are able to produce light of different colors.

Activity 6: You constructed a galvanic cell and explained the function of its parts.

Activity 7: You examined the role of energy change in reactions. You also observed the effect of particle size and the use of a catalyst on reaction rate.

Activity 8: You predicted whether a change would be spontaneous by looking at change in enthalpy and entropy. You also investigated the structure of polymers.

You may want to make a chart that shows the activity number, some chemistry concepts in the activity, and some ideas as to how you can use these concepts as part of your *Chemical Dominoes* sequence or the written summary. Your chart may include whether any principle will be used more than once in the toy as it sequences to light the LED. You should pay particular attention to the *Reflecting on the Activity and the Challenge, Chem Essential Questions,* and *Preparing for the Chapter Challenge* sections. You should also compare your list with that given in the *Chem You Learned* summary.

Activity #	Chemistry concepts	How to use concepts

You may decide to do the first activity as a group to ensure that everybody understands how to proceed. After completing the first activity, each team member can be assigned two or three activities. You can then review all of the activities as a group with the activity expert reviewing each summary.

Criteria

You and your team should review the criteria by which you will be graded. Before beginning the chapter, your teacher led a class discussion to get a sense of what criteria should be used to judge the quality of work for the *Chemical Dominoes* toy and the written materials. The rubric you developed will assign points to the toy demonstration, and all the written materials. It will also assign points to specific aspects of each major category. This rubric can be a useful tool for your team to check the quality of your work and to ensure that you have included all necessary parts of the project.

Preparing for the Chapter Challenge

• Decide on Your Toy Design

Your team's next step is to decide on the final design of the toy. How will you light the LED? Will you generate gas or heat? Will you destroy a piece of metal? Will you light more than one LED? How can you make your toy both unique and fun?

• Prepare Your Written Materials

Your written materials must include:

- instructions for setting up and running the sequence
- detailed safety precautions

- a drawing of the sequence
- the chemistry principles involved
- the engineer's notebook for the patent attorneys.

Your engineer's notebook should show the lawyers the extent of your investigation into the effects you studied, and document the failures as well as the successes that went into your invention. Pay particular attention to recording each step you go through in setting up the completed sequence, as well as any troubleshooting you do to make everything work together in a sequence (including any problems that must be solved at the last minute).

- **Chemistry content is necessary, but not sufficient.**

All your knowledge of chemistry will be necessary for use in developing the *Chemical Dominoes* toy, but it won't be enough for the success of the toy. You must also create a toy that is both fun and unique. It should be challenging, but not frustrating for 10-year-olds and up to put together. The toy must work the first time and every time. It must be safe and sturdy. Make a list of the materials that you will need to build the toy. Where will you get the materials?

Creating your toy is a creative process. Your entire team should have input and every one on the team should be comfortable with the plan.

- **Manage Your Time**

You have a sense of how you want to proceed and what you want the final product to be. You now have to allocate the work. How much time do you have to complete the project? When is the project due? How will you get everything done in this time frame? Who will be working on the written materials including the instructions? Who will maintain the engineer's notebook during the design process? Who will prepare the chemistry descriptions for the toy executive? Will each team member contribute one chemistry concept? How will you ensure that each team member meets the standard of excellence to ensure that everybody on the team gets an A? Create a time chart showing how much time you have. Allocate responsibilities to everybody, including work that must be done in class and work that can be done individually for homework. Leave time to review each other's work.

Planning a project well does not ensure success, but poor planning almost always leads to disappointment.

- **Do a Practice Run**

You will need to make sure that you have enough time to put all the components together. You have to have the toy, the presentation, and the written materials ready on the due date. You also want to have saved some time for a practice run. You may be able to make some last minute adjustments to your toy based on the results of the practice session.

Engineering/Technology Design

Reflect on the engineering/technology design process. Recall the successes and disappointments from the *mini-challenge*. How can you use the feedback that you received to improve your toy? At this point, you are starting the design cycle all over again. Review the steps of the design process described in the *mini-challenge*.

Have fun with your Chemical Dominoes toy!

Chem You Learned

- **Entropy** is a thermal energy process and is frequently thought to be a measure of disorder in a system. A substance in the gas phase will have more entropy than that substance in the solid phase.
- **Standard temperature and pressure (STP)** are the conditions of 1 atmosphere and 273 kelvin.
- Much of the mathematics in chemistry is found in stoichiometric calculations.
- Using a balanced equation, the quantities of reactants and products can be calculated.
- The **Metal Activity Series** is used in **single-replacement reactions** and in making an **electrochemical cell**.
- **Fluorescence** is the immediate emission of light by an atom as an electron returns from an **excited state** to its **ground state.** The light is of a different wavelength than was absorbed by the atom, taking it from a **ground state** to an **excited state.**
- **Phosphorescence** is a process similar to fluorescence where light is emitted by an atom or molecule but, unlike fluorescence, the light persists after the exciting source is removed.
- An **electrolyte** is an ionic substance which will conduct electricity in solution or when molten.
- The **rate of a chemical reaction** is dependent upon several factors, such as, **temperature**, **surface area**, **concentration**, and, if available, the use of a **catalyst**.
- All chemical reactions have an energy barrier that must be overcome and this is called the **activation energy**.
- The **Law of Conservation of Energy** states that energy cannot be created or destroyed. If the **system** under study gains energy (**endothermic**), then the **surroundings** must lose energy. If the system loses energy (**exothermic**), then the surroundings must gain energy.
- According to the **Gibbs free energy equation**, a reaction will be **spontaneous** if it is exothermic and entropy is increasing. If it is endothermic and entropy is decreasing, it will not be spontaneous. Other combinations of enthalpy and entropy will depend on their values and the temperature.

$$\Delta G = \Delta H - T\Delta S$$

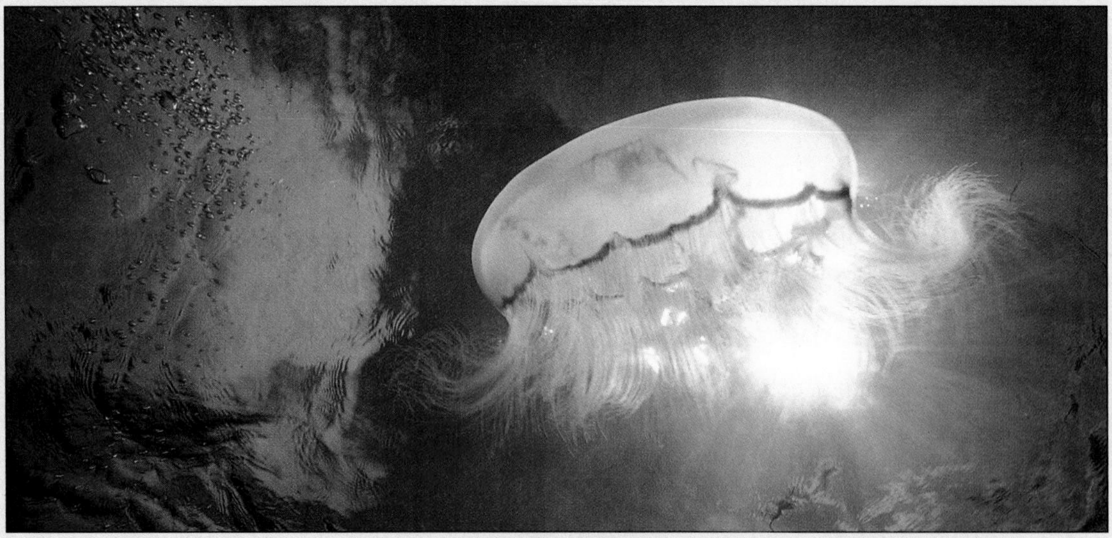

Chapter 5

IDEAL TOY

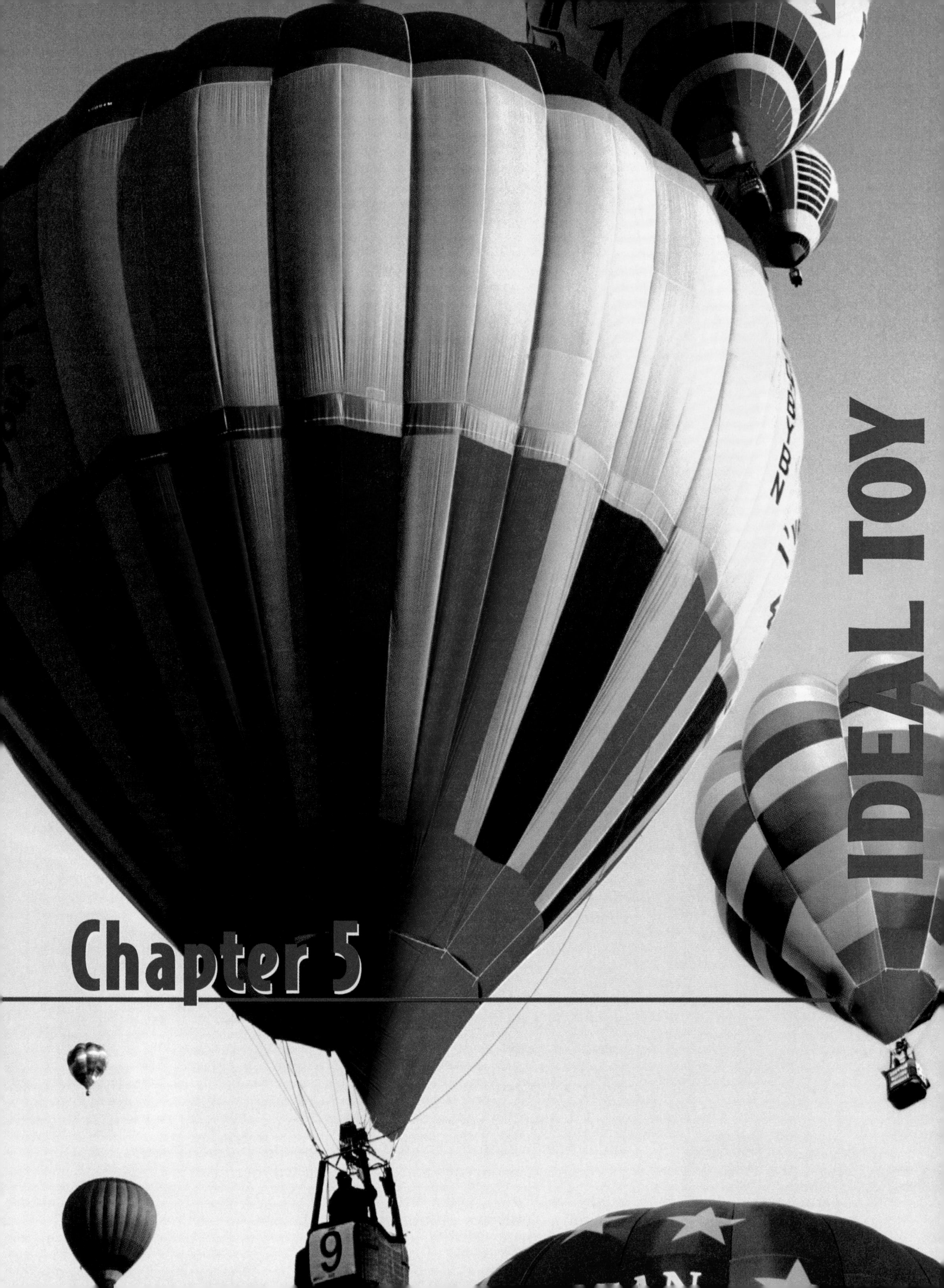

PEAN

Chapter Challenge

5

Ideal Toy

Scenario

What was your favorite toy as a child? A doll? A battery-powered, remote-controlled car? Action figures? Crayons and a coloring book? Everyone in your class can probably name at least one favorite toy. The range of the types of toys would be astounding! Look around the toy section of a store and examine the different types of toys. Different cultures have different toys. Some team members may be able to share toy ideas from places that they have lived or visited. Have you ever wondered who develops the ideas for the toys that are on the market? Perhaps you have even thought that if given a chance, you could develop the next big "gotta get" item.

Well, here's your chance! Your *Active Chemistry* class has been asked to act as a research and development team for a major toy company. For the company to remain competitive, it needs your team to come up with a hot new item for the next season of sales.

Your Challenge

Your challenge is to create a toy that uses various chemical and/or gas principles. The toy should be appealing to a certain age group of your choice. You will need to prepare a presentation for the board of the toy company. Your presentation should include:

- A written proposal, either a detailed drawing or a mock prototype of the toy, any potential hazards or waste-disposal issues, and a cost analysis of the item for manufacturing. Your presentation will be evaluated on the quality of your visual aids or your prototype, the quality of your presentation, the explanation of the chemistry involved, and the quality of your written proposal.
- You will need to complete the following tasks:

- Create a toy targeted for a specific age group.
- Prepare a written proposal about your toy to submit to the board.
- Prepare a three-minute presentation for the board to promote your toy.

ChemCorner

Chemistry in *Ideal Toy*

- Electrochemical cells
- Metal Activity Series
- Oxidation-reduction
- Size and shape of molecules
- Polarity of molecules
- Properties of molecules
- Boyle's Law
- Charles's Law
- Kelvin scale
- Kinetic theory of gases
- Replacement reactions
- Synthesis reactions
- Decomposition reactions
- Ideal Gas Law
- Molar volume of gas
- Graham's Law of Effusion
- Types of plastic

Criteria

How will your toy be graded? What qualities should an effective proposal and presentation have? Discuss these issues in small groups and with your class. You may decide that some or all of the following qualities should be graded:

Presentation

- Visual aid
- Schematic or prototype of toy
- Explanation of how the toy works
- Hazard and waste-disposal issues
- Cost analysis

Quality of Presentation

- Organization
- Audience appeal
- Eye contact
- Time limit
- Clarity of explanation

Chemical Principles

- Variety used
- Explanation of chemistry involved
- Accuracy of explanation

Written Proposal

- Rationale
- Visuals
- Explanation
- Cost analysis

Once you have determined the list of qualities for evaluating the toy, presentation, and proposal, you and your class should also decide how many points should be given for each criterion. How many points should be awarded for the presentation and how many for the proposal? Should more points be awarded if more chemistry is involved? How many different chemical principles should be incorporated into your toy? Determining the grading criteria in advance will help you focus your time and effort on the most important aspects of your work.

Since you will be working with other students in small groups, you will need to determine grading criteria that reward each individual in the group for his or her contribution and also reward the group for the final presentation. What is a fair contribution of each person? How can the group be judged fairly for their toy, presentation, and proposal? Your teacher may provide you with a sample rubric to help you get started.

Activity 1 Batteries

What Do You See?

BATTERIES
RECHARGEABLE CELLS FOR
Pb PLATES
H_2SO_4
Cell Connectors
SUPER BATTERY

GOALS

In this activity you will:

- Make observations about commercial batteries.
- Make an electrochemical cell.
- Understand the chemistry of an electrochemical cell.
- Use an electrochemical cell to power a toy.

What Do You Think?

Many toys use batteries. You pop these small metal containers into a toy and it "comes to life."

- **What is a battery and how does it work?**

The *What Do You Think?* question is provided to get you engaged in the activity. It is meant to grab your attention. It is also used to find out what you already know or think you know. Don't worry about being right or wrong. Discussing what you think you know is an important step in learning.

Record your ideas about this question in your *Active Chemistry* log. Be prepared to discuss your responses with your small group and the class.

Investigate

Part A: Commercial Batteries

1. There are many different batteries available commercially. Your teacher will provide you with some examples.
   a) List all the types of batteries that you can think of (AA, C, D, etc.). Record your observations of the physical properties of the batteries such as size, shape, markings, etc.

Safety goggles and a lab apron must be worn *at all times* in a chemistry lab.

Clean up any spills immediately. Detach the metal electrodes when you are not taking a reading.

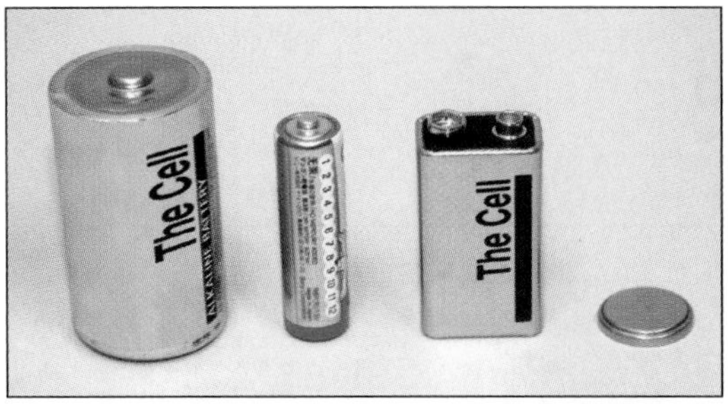
The Cell
The Cell

2. Use a voltmeter to determine the voltage of each type of battery that you were given. Take two wires connected to the terminals of the voltmeter and touch them to the terminals of the battery (plus to plus and negative to negative). If the voltmeter shows a negative reading or if the needle attempts to go to the left of zero, reverse the wires to the battery.

   a) Record your observations.

3. In your group answer the following questions.

   a) What do you think voltage means?

   b) If you were to connect two identical 1.5-V batteries in series (as if they were in a long flashlight), what would be the total voltage?

   c) Try it and record the new voltage.

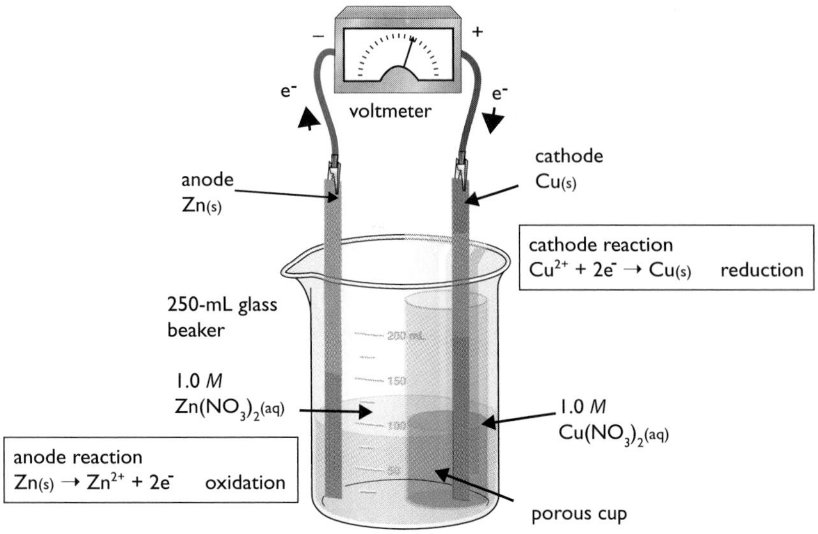
–
+
e^-
e^-
voltmeter
anode
$Zn_{(s)}$
cathode
$Cu_{(s)}$
cathode reaction
$Cu^{2+} + 2e^- \rightarrow Cu_{(s)}$ reduction
250-mL glass beaker
1.0 *M* $Zn(NO_3)_{2(aq)}$
1.0 *M* $Cu(NO_3)_{2(aq)}$
anode reaction
$Zn_{(s)} \rightarrow Zn^{2+} + 2e^-$ oxidation
porous cup

Part B: Electrochemical Cells

1. In this part of the activity you will make an electrochemical cell (a battery) that produces the greatest voltage. An electrochemical cell is prepared by immersing different metals in a solution of its ions. (An ***ion*** is a charged atom or group of atoms.) A porous cup makes it possible for ions to flow between solutions. The porous cup permits the flow of dissolved ions, but prevents too much mixing of the solutions. An example of the setup is shown in the diagram.

2. Pour 75 mL of $Zn(NO_3)_2$ salt solution for the zinc electrode into the 250-mL beaker.

3. Fill the porous cup about $\frac{3}{4}$ full of the $Cu(NO_3)_2$ salt solution for the copper electrode. Be careful not to spill the contents of the porous cup into the beaker solution. Also, make sure that the solution in the beaker does not enter the top of the cup.

4. Attach wire leads to the zinc and copper metal electrodes. The zinc will be placed in the $Zn(NO_3)_2$ and the copper will be placed in the $Cu(NO_3)_2$. The metal electrode is always placed in its own salt solution. Attach one wire lead to the voltmeter. (If the voltmeter has selectable scales, select a scale with an appropriate range of 0 to 2 V.) Very quickly and lightly touch the second wire lead to the other electrode of the voltmeter. If the needle moves in the positive direction (electrons are flowing from the negative terminal through the wire to the positive terminal), secure the wire to the electrode. If the needle moves in the negative direction, detach the first wire lead, reverse the positions of the leads, and attach them to the electrodes.

5. You will now vary the metal strips (electrodes) in your cell to find the combination that produces the greatest voltage. Every time a new metal is used as an electrode, the salt solution must also be changed.

Electrode choices	Salt solutions (1 *M*)
Mg	$Mg(NO_3)_2$
Zn	$Zn(NO_3)_2$
Fe	$Fe(NO_3)_3$
Cu	$Cu(NO_3)_2$

To achieve any voltage, one metal must release electrons and the other metal must capture electrons. The metals you will use in this activity are listed in a specific order (Mg, Zn, Fe, Cu). Magnesium has the greatest tendency to release electrons, while copper has the least tendency to release electrons. This information may guide you in your selection of metals for your battery.

Remember, in this part of the activity you are to create the electrochemical cell with the greatest voltage (electrical potential difference). You will only be permitted to test three electrode combinations, so choose wisely!

6. Determine what information you will need. Construct an appropriate data table in your *Active Chemistry* log.

7. Test your three electrode pairs, making sure to rinse the beaker and the porous cup thoroughly between each test. Check with your teacher about the proper disposal of the liquids.

8. Answer the following questions in your log.

   a) Which electrode pair produced the greatest voltage?

   b) Share your data with the other groups.

   c) Explain the observed order in terms of the activity series of metals (the tendency of metals to release electrons).

   d) Describe any modifications to the setup that you used that might affect the voltage.

Part C: Powering a Toy

1. Bring a battery-powered toy from home. Your teacher may supply you with some examples. Examine the toy that you have chosen.

   a) What voltage does it require to power it? Record this in your *Active Chemistry* log.

2. Determine how many of the electrochemical cells that you tested in *Part B* will be needed in a series to power your toy. The total voltage of batteries in series is equal to the sum of the voltages of each battery. In order to connect batteries in a series, you must connect a wire between the negative terminal of the first battery and the positive terminal of the second battery and then the negative terminal of the second battery to the positive terminal of the third battery, and so on. Then you will have a lead coming off of the positive terminal of the first battery and a negative lead coming off of your last battery.

   A series battery setup is shown in the diagram on the next page.

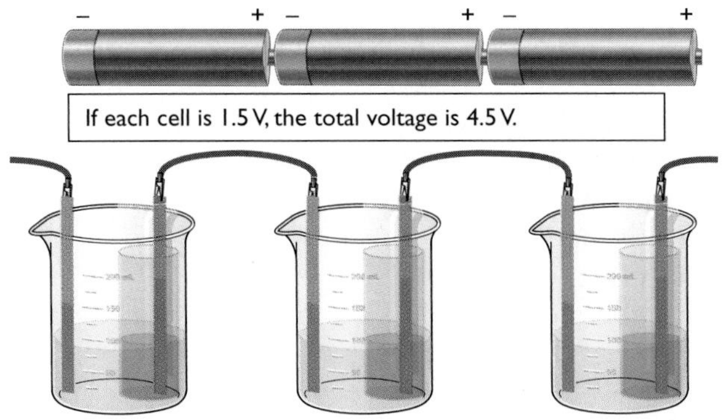
– + – + – +
If each cell is 1.5 V, the total voltage is 4.5 V.

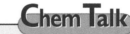

3. Use alligator clips to hook the electrode from one electrochemical cell to the different metal electrode of the next electrochemical cell. Continue in this fashion until you have enough voltage to power your toy. You will have to share your cell with other teams to get enough voltage to run some toys.

4. Compare your setup to the battery arrangement in the toy.

   a) How many electrochemical cells were required?

   b) How long do you think it will take for your battery to die?

Wash your hands and arms thoroughly after the activity.

Chem Talk

OXIDATION-REDUCTION REACTIONS AND ELECTROCHEMICAL CELLS

Electrochemical Cell

An **electrochemical cell** is a cell or a battery that uses chemical reactions to generate electricity. When two metals of differing electron-releasing tendencies are connected, an electrical potential is created between the two metals. The electrical potential (**voltage**) is measured in **volts** (V) and represents the energy that drives electrons through the wire connecting the two metals. A 9-V battery has a larger electrical potential than a 1.5-V battery. **Current** describes the rate of flow of electric charge. Larger batteries can generate larger currents than smaller batteries.

Some metals tend to lose electrons (become oxidized) more readily than other metals. Examine the Metal Activity Series shown on the next page. A metal that is higher in the activity series will "give up," or release, electrons more readily than one that is lower. You can make use of these differing tendencies to convert chemical energy to electrical energy. As you may have found in the activity, metals that are furthest apart in the activity series will produce the largest voltages.

Metal Activity Series

A **battery** is a system that directly converts chemical energy to electrical energy. The Consumer Electronics Association claims that there

Chem Words

electrochemical cell: a cell or a battery that uses chemical reactions to generate electricity.

voltage: a measure of the difference in electrochemical potential between two electrodes.

volts: the electrical potential of an electrochemical cell. They represent the "push" that drives electrons through the wire connecting the two metals.

current: the rate of flow of electric charge.

battery: a system that directly converts chemical energy to electrical energy.

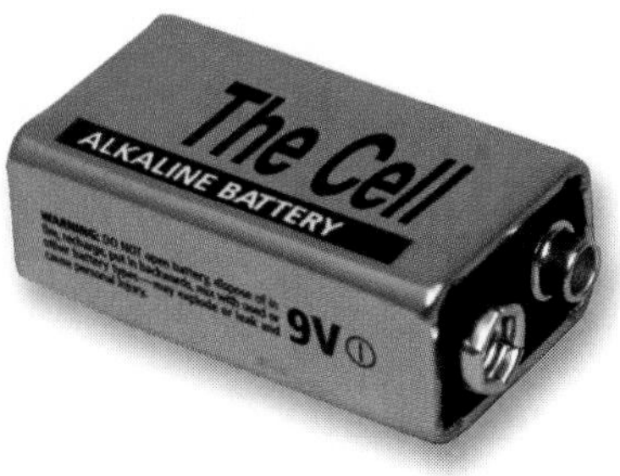
The Cell
ALKALINE BATTERY
9V

decreasing tendency to release electrons

Li
K
Ba
Ca
Na
Mg
Al
Mn
Zn
Cr
Fe
Cd
Co
Ni
Sn
Pb
Cu
Ag
Hg
Au

were over 4.9 billion dollars worth of batteries sold in the U.S. in 2002. The typical batteries used in toys are more correctly called electrochemical cells.

If you examine any commercial battery you will see two terminals. One terminal is marked (+), or positive, while the other is marked (−), or negative. These are typically located at the ends of the battery.

Electrons (which are negative) flow from the negative terminal of the battery. If connected to the positive terminal, the electrons will flow toward the positive. Wires and a **load** provide the path for the electrons. The load may be a motor or a light or something else that runs on electricity (the flow of electrons).

Before considering how your chemical batteries worked, look at a simpler system.

Consider the following reactions:

$$Zn_{(s)} \rightarrow Zn^{2+}{}_{(aq)} + 2e^-$$

In certain situations, neutral zinc (Zn) loses two electrons. When that happens, a Zn **ion** and two free electrons are formed. Since the zinc has lost two electrons, the charge on the Zn ion is +2.

$$Cu^{2+}{}_{(aq)} + 2e^- \rightarrow Cu_{(s)}$$

In certain situations, a copper (Cu^{2+}) ion tends to gain two electrons. When that happens, a neutral copper atom is formed. The Cu ion had a charge of +2 so it needed two electrons to become electronically neutral.

When the neutral zinc and the copper ion interact, as shown by these reactions, the neutral zinc supplies electrons to the copper ion. This flow of electrons is produced by the potential difference (voltage) and the result is a battery.

The zinc reaction of *losing* electrons is called **oxidation.** The copper reaction of *gaining* electrons is **reduction.** Each of the two reactions are called **half-reactions.**

$$Zn_{(s)} \rightarrow Zn^{2+}{}_{(aq)} + 2e^-$$
(loss of electrons = oxidation, occurs at the anode)

$$Cu^{2+}{}_{(aq)} + 2e^- \rightarrow Cu_{(s)}$$
(gain of electrons = reduction, occurs at the cathode)

A mnemonic device to remind you of these two processes is:

LEO the lion says **GER**
Lose **E**lectrons **O**xidation **G**ain **E**lectrons **R**eduction →

Chem Words

load: a motor, light bulb, or other device that runs on electricity (the flow of electric charge).

ion: an atom or molecule that has acquired a charge by either gaining or losing electron(s).

oxidation: the process of a substance losing one or more electrons.

reduction: the process of a substance gaining one or more electrons.

half-reactions: two separated parts of a redox reaction. One part is the oxidation reaction and the other part is the reduction reaction.

oxidized: the acquiring of a positive charge on an atom or molecule by losing electron(s).

reduced: the acquiring of a negative charge on an atom or molecule by gaining electron(s).

oxidation-reduction (redox) reaction: a chemical reaction in which the valence electrons of one substance are transferred to the valence shell of the second substance.

spectator ions: ions that do not chemically react in the overall reaction.

dry cell: an electrochemical cell in which the electrolyte is a paste instead of a solution.

Checking Up

1. Which metal will lose electrons more easily, Ca or Mg?
2. Which combination of metals will produce the greater voltage, Ca and Al or Ca and Cu?
3. What units are used to measure electrical potential?
4. Why is the NO_3^- ion in an electrochemical cell called a spectator ion?
5. Define reduction and oxidation.
6. Another memory "trick" for remembering oxidation and reduction is "OIL RIG." What do the letters in this device stand for?
7. What is the difference between a dry cell and the one you built in this activity?

The pair of reactions occurring at the same time is called an **oxidation-reduction** (often called **redox**) **reaction.**

$$Zn_{(s)} + Cu^{2+}{}_{(aq)} \rightarrow Zn^{2+}{}_{(aq)} + Cu_{(s)}$$

One of the characteristic properties of metals is that they tend to lose or "give up" electrons more easily compared to nonmetal atoms. When an atom has lost electrons, it has been **oxidized**. No atom or particle can be oxidized unless some other particle is simultaneously reduced. An atom is **reduced** when it gains electrons.

In the activity, the Zn metal and the Cu^{2+} ions were kept separated by using a porous barrier. This separation forces the electrons to flow through the wire and the load from the anode (Zn) to reach the cathode (Cu). In this way electricity is produced that can do useful work. The Zn anode is bathed in a solution of $Zn(NO_3^-)_2$ while the Cu cathode sits in a solution of $Cu(NO_3^-)_2$ in the porous cup. Because the nitrate ions (NO_3^-) do not participate in the reaction, they are referred to as **spectator ions**. Typically, they are not written into the equation.

When the wire is connected, the zinc metal is oxidized to Zn^{2+} ions, which dissolve into the solution. The Cu^{2+} ions are converted to neutral copper atoms that come out of the solution as copper metal.

As the reaction takes place, the zinc half-cell becomes positive and the copper half-cell becomes negative. This would slow and eventually stop the reaction unless the two sides can become electrically neutral. The porous cup allows for the negative NO_3^- ions to move from the copper half-cell to the zinc half-cell. This keeps both sides neutral and the reaction continues.

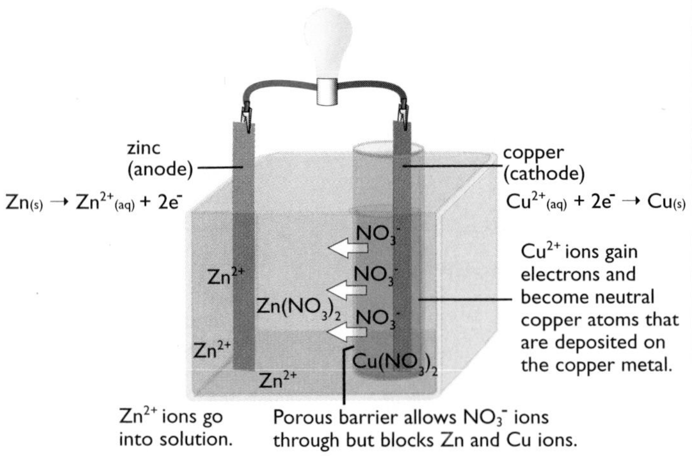
zinc (anode)
$Zn_{(s)} \rightarrow Zn^{2+}{}_{(aq)} + 2e^-$
copper (cathode)
$Cu^{2+}{}_{(aq)} + 2e^- \rightarrow Cu_{(s)}$
NO_3^-
NO_3^-
NO_3^-
Zn^{2+}
$Zn(NO_3)_2$
Zn^{2+}
Zn^{2+}
$Cu(NO_3)_2$
Cu^{2+} ions gain electrons and become neutral copper atoms that are deposited on the copper metal.
Zn^{2+} ions go into solution.
Porous barrier allows NO_3^- ions through but blocks Zn and Cu ions.

Your car battery is a wet cell battery that functions similarly to the electrochemical cells that you created. However, most toy batteries are **dry cell** batteries. They operate on exactly the same principles as your electrochemical cells, but the electrolytic substances are in a paste form.

What Do You Think Now?

At the beginning of this activity you were asked:

- **What is a battery and how does it work?**

Take a look at your original thoughts on the nature of batteries. How have they changed? How would you answer the question now?

Chem Essential Questions

What does it mean?

Chemistry explains a macroscopic phenomenon (what you observe) with a description of what happens at the nanoscopic level (atoms and molecules) using symbolic structures as a way to communicate. Complete the chart below in your *Active Chemistry* log.

MACRO	NANO	SYMBOLIC
How do you know that a battery is working?	*Decribe what is occurring at the nanoscopic level when a cell is producing electrical energy.*	*Make a sketch of a cell. Be sure to label all of the important parts.*

How do you know?

What evidence do you have to support the idea that your battery actually produced electrical energy?

Why do you believe?

Batteries are such an important part of your life. The electronics that are part of the items you use every day are, for the most part, limited only by the batteries that power them. Propose future breakthroughs that could take place as technology continues to improve batteries, making them more powerful, longer lasting, and smaller/lighter.

Why should you care?

Many toys are powered by batteries. Write an explanation of how the battery works as part of your toy explanation. Include a labeled diagram.

Reflecting on the Activity and the Challenge

In this activity, you explored how batteries work. You know that metals tend to give up electrons. If an electrical-charge difference can be created between the electrodes (terminals), then a current can be generated and chemical energy is converted to electrical energy! You were able to witness this using the voltmeter. By connecting batteries in a series more energy is available, thus increasing the electrical potential. You may decide that the new toy product that you propose will require batteries. Your new knowledge of batteries should assist you in the design of your toy.

Chem to Go

1. For the highest electrical potential, should an electrochemical cell's two metals be close together or far apart on the activity series? Explain.
2. Predict whether the electrical potential of cells composed of these metal pairings will be higher or lower than that of the pairs you tested:

   a) Zn and Cr b) Zn and Ag c) Sn and Cu
3. Notice that silver, platinum, and gold have good reduction potential. Why are these elements not generally found in batteries?
4. Predict the direction of electron flow in an electrochemical cell made from each pair of metals in solutions of their ions.

   a) Mg and Cu b) Zn and Cu c) Ag and Mg
5. a) Identify the anode and the cathode for the metal pairs in *Question 4*.

   b) Write the half-reactions for each metal pair in *Question 4*.
6. List some of the pros and cons of batteries. Consider cost, size, and disposal issues, among others.
7. Which half-reaction correctly represents reduction?

   a) $Ag \rightarrow Ag^{+} + e^{-}$ b) $Au^{3+} + 3e^{-} \rightarrow Au$

   c) $F_2 \rightarrow 2F^{-} + 2e^{-}$ d) $Fe^{2+} \rightarrow Fe^{3+} + e^{-}$
8. Which reaction is an example of an oxidation-reduction reaction?

   a) $AgNO_3 + KI \rightarrow AgI + KNO_3$

   b) $Cu + 2AgNO_3 \rightarrow Cu(NO_3)_2 + 2Ag$

   c) $2KOH + H_2SO_4 \rightarrow K_2SO_4 + 2H_2O$

   d) $Ba(OH)_2 + 2HCl \rightarrow BaCl_2 + 2H_2O$
9. Where does oxidation occur in an electrochemical cell?

   a) at the cathode

   b) at the cathode and the anode in the electrolytic cell

   c) at the anode

   d) neither the cathode nor the anode

Inquiring Further

Storing batteries

Design and conduct a test for determining the best way to store batteries in order to extend their life.

Activity 2 Solid, Liquid, or Gas?

What Do You See?
MOLECULES SOAP OPERA
FATAL ATTRACTION
SCRIPT

GOALS

In this activity you will:

- Describe how the size and shape of molecules affect their physical state.
- Classify molecules as polar or non-polar.

What Do You Think?

A number of toys use gases.

- **What makes a gas different from a liquid or a solid?**
- **Why are some substances gases at room temperature, while others are not?**

Record your ideas about these questions in your *Active Chemistry* log. Be prepared to discuss your responses with your small group and the class.

Investigate

Part A: Size and Shape of Molecules

1. Look at the following computer-drawn diagrams of molecules.

Shape and relative size of diatomic halogen molecules

fluorine F_2 | chlorine Cl_2 | bromine Br_2 | iodine I_2

Safety goggles and a lab apron must be worn *at all times* in a chemistry lab.

Wash your hands and arms thoroughly after the activity.

Shape and relative size of CX_4 molecules (where X = H, F, Cl, or Br)

methane CH_4 | carbon tetrafluoride CF_4 | carbon tetrachloride CCl_4 | carbon tetrabromide CBr_4

Shape and relative size of hydrocarbons

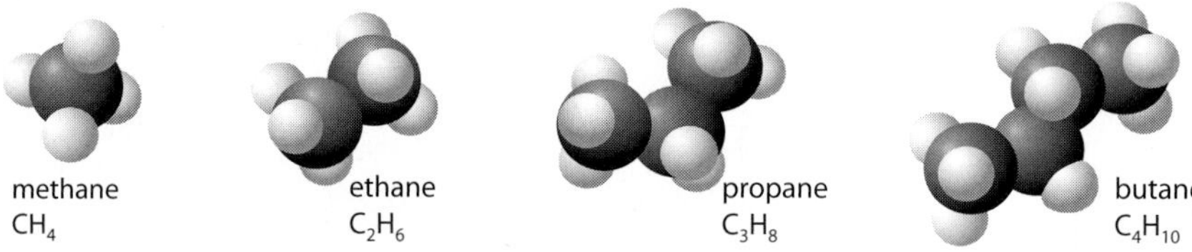

methane CH_4 | ethane C_2H_6 | propane C_3H_8 | butane C_4H_{10}

Shape and relative size of alcohols

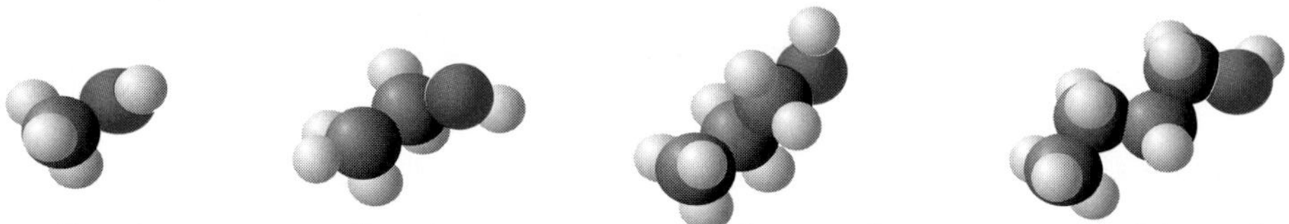

methanol CH_3OH | ethanol C_2H_5OH | 1-propanol C_3H_7OH | 1-butanol C_4H_9OH

2. In your *Active Chemistry* log record your answers to the following questions.

   a) What do you notice about the shape of the diatomic halogen molecules? How do their sizes compare?

   b) What do you notice about the shape of the CX_4 molecules? How do their sizes compare?

   c) The hydrocarbon and alcohol molecules are similar. CH_4 is methane and CH_3OH is methanol. C_2H_6 is ethane and C_2H_5OH is ethanol. The other pairs are propane and 1-propanol, and butane and 1-butanol. What is the difference between each of the pairs of molecules? Look carefully at their shapes. Describe any differences that you notice between the pairs of molecules.

Part B: Boiling and Melting Point of Molecules

Room temperature is about 22°C. If a substance has a boiling point below room temperature, it must be a gas at room temperature. If its boiling point is above 22°C, then it is a liquid (or possibly a solid) at room temperature. If its melting point is above 22°C, then it is a solid at room temperature.

1. Look at the table showing the melting and boiling points of halogens.

Melting and Boiling Points of Halogens (Group 7A)		
Substance	Melting point (°C)	Boiling point (°C)
F_2 (fluorine)	–220	–188
Cl_2 (chlorine)	–101	–34
Br_2 (bromine)	–7	59
I_2 (iodine)	114	185

Answer the following in your *Active Chemistry* log.

a) Fluorine will be a solid at any temperature less than its melting point of –220°C. At –220°C, fluorine melts and becomes a liquid. The liquid then heats up until it reaches the boiling point of –188°C. At that temperature the fluorine becomes a gas and remains a gas for all higher temperatures. Which of the halogens are gases at room temperature of 22°C? Which are liquids? Which are solids?

b) Since all of the halogens have the same shape, what is the difference between those that are gases and the ones that are liquids or solids at room temperature?

2. Look at the table showing the melting and boiling points of CX_4 compounds.

Melting and Boiling Points of CX_4 Compounds		
Substance	Melting point (°C)	Boiling point (°C)
CH_4 (methane)	–183	–161
CF_4 (carbon tetrafluoride)	–184	–128
CCl_4 (carbon tetrachloride)	–23	77
CBr_4 (carbon tetrabromide)	90	190

Answer the following in your *Active Chemistry* log.

a) Of the CX_4 compounds, which are gases, liquids, and solids at room temperature?

b) Since all of the CX_4 compounds have the same shape, what is the difference between those that are gases at room temperature and the ones that are liquids or solids?

3. Hydrocarbons are simply molecules made up of carbon and hydrogen. Alcohols are molecules containing an –OH group. Note the difference between methanol (CH_3OH) and sodium hydroxide (NaOH). Both have an OH in the formula, but the alcohol is a covalently bonded molecule and NaOH is an ionic compound, not a molecule.

Look at the graph showing the boiling points of hydrocarbons and alcohols.

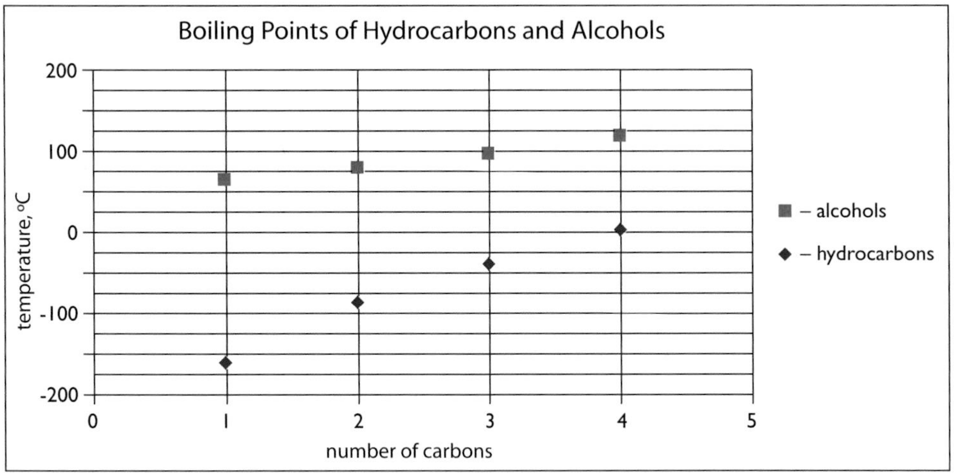
Boiling Points of Hydrocarbons and Alcohols
200
100
0
-100
-200
temperature, °C
0
1
2
3
4
5
number of carbons
– alcohols
– hydrocarbons

Answer the following in your *Active Chemistry* log.

a) Which substances are gases at room temperature? Which are liquids?

b) Examine the boiling points of the series of hydrocarbons. What is the general trend as the number of carbons increases? That is, what happens to the boiling point as the number of carbons (and thus the size of the molecule) increases?

c) Now look at the boiling point differences between the pairs of methane/methanol, ethane/ethanol, propane/1-propanol, and butane/1-butanol. What factor could contribute to the large difference in boiling points for each pair?

4. Based on the information that you have, what two factors can be used to form a general rule to determine if a substance is a solid, a liquid, or a gas at room temperature? Explain the relationship between these factors and the boiling points of the substances.

Chem Talk

INTERMOLECULAR FORCES

Intermolecular Forces in Liquids, Solids, and Gases

Gases are different from liquids and solids. In solids, the molecules or atoms that form the substance are in an orderly crystalline structure. They are locked in place and are not able to move around much because the atoms have a fairly strong attraction for one another. These attractions are electrical in nature, meaning they are related to the number and position of the molecules' electrons. Motion of the atoms of solids consists of vibrating in place. In liquids, the molecules or atoms are still in contact with each other, but they are not locked in place. The particles vibrate and are able to move

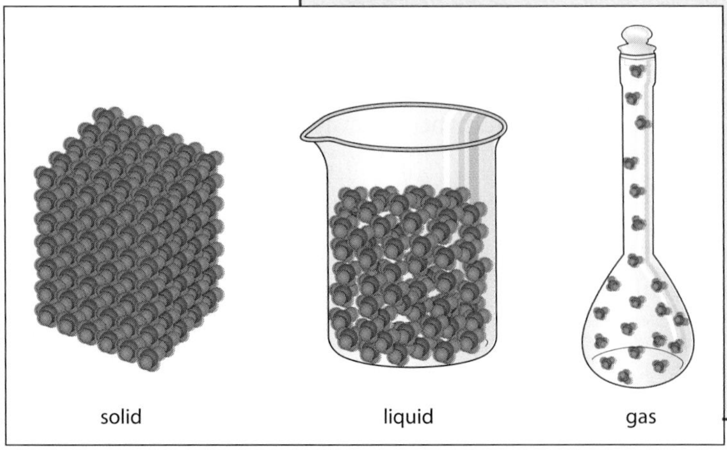
solid
liquid
gas

around each other. The molecules of liquids have less attraction for one another than the molecules of solids. The molecules or atoms of a gas have very little contact with each other because they have very little attraction for one another. All molecules have some attraction but some are very weak. If you take nitrogen gas and slow the molecules down by cooling it, the attractions will become strong enough that the gas will liquefy. If you cool it enough, it will freeze and become a solid. These attractions or forces between molecules are called **intermolecular forces.** The fact that there is a lot of space between the particles of a gas accounts for the reason that it is easy to compress gases.

Non-polar Molecules

Halogens, oxygen, nitrogen, carbon dioxide, and the CX_4 molecules have shapes that are symmetrical. The electrons of these molecules are distributed evenly in such a way that there are no permanent partial electric charges anywhere on the molecules. These molecules are said to be **non-polar.** The symmetrical shapes of non-polar molecules cause them to have very little attraction for each other. Small, non-polar molecules tend to have low boiling points.

As the size of non-polar molecules increases, the attractive forces between molecules also begin to increase. You saw this for the series of hydrocarbon molecules. Larger molecules have more electrons and when there are a greater number of electrons they may, at one instant, be distributed unevenly. One part of the molecule may have, only for the briefest of moments, an increased number of electrons. This distortion of electrons gives rise to a temporary partial negative charge (represented by the Greek letter delta, δ^-). Since one part of the molecule has an overabundance of electrons another part of the molecule must have a deficiency of electrons, creating a partial positive charge (δ^+) on that part of the molecule.

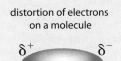

distortion of electrons on a molecule

δ+
δ−

The molecule becomes a temporary dipole (meaning two poles or two charges). This in turn triggers (induces) a similar dipole in neighboring molecules and this process spreads from molecule to molecule. These attractive forces, called **London dispersion forces**, are much weaker than ionic or covalent bonds which hold atoms together. The polarity causes a greater attraction between molecules. The molecules are difficult to separate, which is what takes place when a substance boils. The larger molecules tend to have higher boiling points and can be liquids or solids at room temperature.

Chem Words

intermolecular forces: the attractive forces acting between molecules.

non-polar molecule: a molecule that has small intermolecular forces due to symmetry of charge distribution.

London dispersion forces: weak intermolecular forces that cause the electrons of an atom or a molecule to shift slightly to form a temporary dipole moment. These forces are also called London forces.

Chem Words

electronegativity: the ability of an atom of an element to attract electrons in a chemical bond.

polar bond: the difference in the electronegativity of neighboring atoms causes the electrons to be attracted more to one of the atoms of the bond, making one atom slightly negative and the other slightly positive.

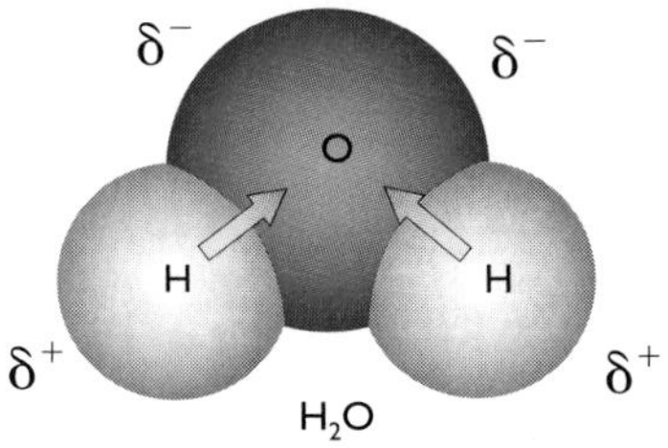
δ⁻
δ⁻
O
H
H
δ⁺
δ⁺
H_2O

Polar Molecules

Other molecules have a permanent polarity due to their shape and/or the types of atoms in the molecule. Some elements have a greater tendency to pull the electrons of a covalent bond toward themselves. This property is called **electronegativity**. Oxygen is more electronegative than hydrogen so the electrons in the O–H bond are pulled closer to the oxygen atom. This creates a partial negative charge on the oxygen and a partial positive charge on the hydrogen atoms. These partial charges are permanent, not fleeting, like the dispersion forces.

Water molecules have two hydrogen atoms attached to the oxygen atom at an angle of about 107.5°. The electronegativity differences and the shape of the molecule cause the molecule to be **polar**.

Even though water molecules are very small, their polarity allows them to attract other water molecules. (You can represent the water molecule as shown in the diagram.)

You can then imagine how the molecules will interact with one another.

δ⁺
δ⁻
δ⁺

While this is a simplified picture of what occurs (the actual three-dimensional orientation of the molecules is more complicated), it gives you an idea of the forces between molecules. These intermolecular forces between water molecules are called hydrogen bonds. When there is a strong attraction between molecules, the substances are probably liquids or solids at room temperature. The alcohols discussed in this activity have an –OH group that makes these molecules polar in nature. Just like in water, this polarity increases the amount of energy needed to separate the molecules, increasing the boiling point of alcohols.

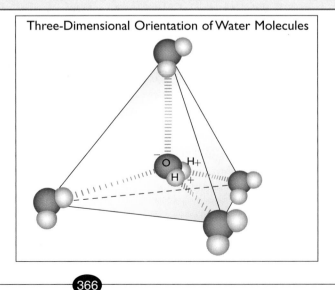

Checking Up

1. What is meant by a molecule's polarity?
2. What are London dispersion forces?
3. Which would have a greater boiling point: C_5H_{12} or C_7H_{16}?

Three-Dimensional Orientation of Water Molecules

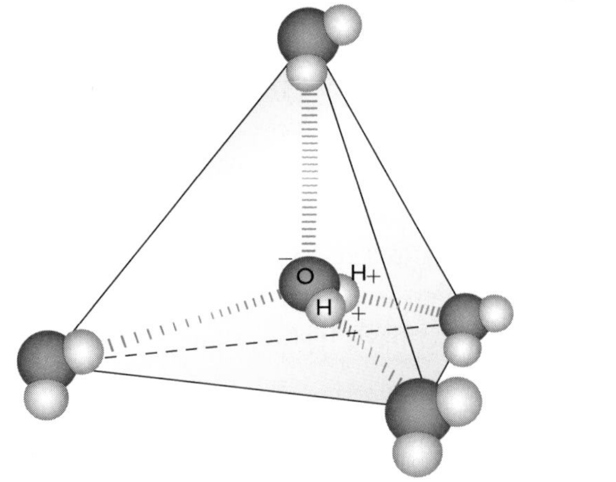
O
H+
H
+

What Do You Think Now?

At the beginning of this activity you were asked:

- **What makes a gas different from a liquid or a solid?**
- **Why are some substances gases at room temperature, while others are not?**

Revisit your initial responses to these questions. Now add to or modify your thoughts in light of what you learned in this activity.

Chem Essential Questions

What does it mean?

Chemistry explains a macroscopic phenomenon (what you observe) with a description of what happens at the nanoscopic level (atoms and molecules) using symbolic structures as a way to communicate. Complete the chart below in your *Active Chemistry* log.

MACRO	NANO	SYMBOLIC
Explain the visible macroscopic features of a solid, a liquid, and a gas.	*Compare and contrast the nanoscopic nature of a solid, a liquid, and a gas.*	*Make sketches of water molecules in the solid state (ice), the liquid state, and the gas state.*

How do you know?

What conclusions can you draw regarding the shape of a molecule and its physical state? Use data from this activity to support your ideas.

Why do you believe?

It is important to have an understanding about the nature of matter in its different states. In this activity there was a discussion of how cooling a gas could cause it to liquefy by slowing the molecules enough to allow them to attract each other. In boiling, the increase in energy allows the molecules to move apart despite their intermolecular attractive forces. Provide a similar discussion of what happens at the molecular level when a chocolate bar melts or how ice forms on a windshield overnight even though it didn't rain. Be sure to include intermolecular forces in your discussion.

Why should you care?

Your toy design may include the use of a gas such as you find in toy rockets, or some high-tech water guns. Explain the nature of gas particles as you would in your toy project, if a gas were involved in your toy.

Reflecting on the Activity and the Challenge

You now understand that the size and shape of molecules determine whether or not the substance is a gas at room temperature. The molecules of most gases at room temperature show very little attraction for one another, and there is a lot of space between the molecules. Because of this, gases are easily compressed, which is something that is not easily done with most liquids and solids. Your toy may take advantage of the compressibility of gases.

Chem to Go

1. Explain why most gases have very little attraction between their molecules.
2. Ignoring the electronegativity values of the atoms, label each molecule as polar or non-polar based on shape alone.

a) 

b) 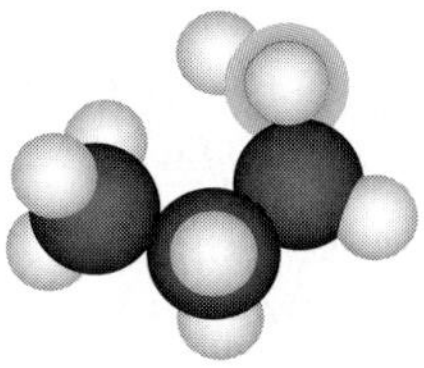

c) 

3. a) Rank the molecules listed in *Question 2* from lowest to highest boiling points.

   b) Only one is a liquid at room temperature. Which one is it?
4. Water is a liquid at room temperature while methane is a gas. Which of the following statements correctly describes the intermolecular forces between these molecules?

   a) Water and methane basically have no intermolecular forces.

   b) The intermolecular forces in water are stronger than those of methane.

   c) The intermolecular forces in methane are stronger than those of water.

   d) More information is needed in order to compare the intermolecular forces.

5. Under which conditions do you think you could dissolve the most gas in a liquid:

   (Hint: Think of a carbonated soda-carbon dioxide dissolved in water.)

   a) low pressure and high temperature c) high pressure and low temperature

   b) low pressure and low temperature d) high pressure and high temperature
6. Draw sketches and compare:

   a) methane and methanol

   b) methane and carbon tetrachloride

   c) fluorine and carbon tetrachloride
7. ***Preparing for the Chapter Challenge***

   Prepare a list of all of the toys you know that use a gas in some manner. List the gases used and the purpose of each gas.

Activity 3 Cartesian Divers

What Do You See?

GOALS

In this activity you will:

- Investigate the relationship between the volume and pressure of gases at constant temperature.
- Quantify changes in volume or pressure with changes in the other.
- Interpret data concerning gas, volume, and pressure.

What Do You Think?

Have you ever had a chance to play with the ever-popular air-powered water gun? The more you pump the water gun, the more water comes out, and the further it goes! Squirting someone on a hot day sounds like a lot of fun.

- **Why do you think pumping the water gun makes the water that comes out of the gun travel further?**

Record your ideas about this question in your *Active Chemistry* log. Be prepared to discuss your responses with your small group and the class.

Investigate

In this activity, you will observe the effect of pressure on the volume of a gas. Then, you will explore this effect further by using a gas-pressure probe to better quantify your observations. As you examine this relationship, consider all the application possibilities for toys.

Safety goggles and a lab apron must be worn *at all times* in a chemistry lab.

Wash your hands and arms thoroughly after the activity.

Part A: Boyle's Toys

1. Observe and explore a syringe.
   a) What happens to the volume of air in the syringe as you depress the plunger?
   b) Hold your finger over the hole in the end of the syringe and depress the plunger again. What did you notice?
   c) What happens to the volume of air when you stop pushing on the plunger?
   d) Think of a toy or invent a toy that could be based on the syringe behavior. Record this in your log.

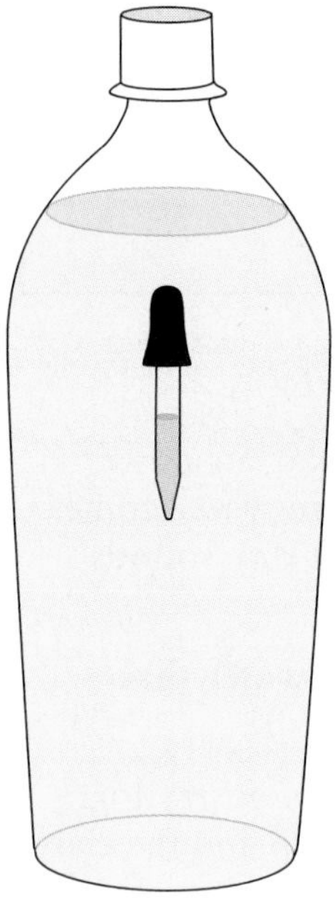

2. Observe and explore a "Cartesian diver." A Cartesian diver is created by placing an eyedropper with some water in it into a 2-L bottle that is filled 7/8 full with water. The dropper should have enough water so that it is submerged in the water as shown in the diagram.
   a) What happens to the dropper (diver) as you squeeze the plastic bottle?
   b) What happens as you release the pressure on the bottle?
   c) What observations can you make about the volume of water and air in the dropper (diver) as you squeeze and release the bottle?
   d) Think of a toy or invent a toy that could be based on the "Cartesian diver."
3. In your *Active Chemistry* log, summarize the observations you made about the effect of pressure on the volume of a gas.

Part B: Pressure–Volume Relationship

In this part of the activity, the gas you use will be air confined in a syringe.

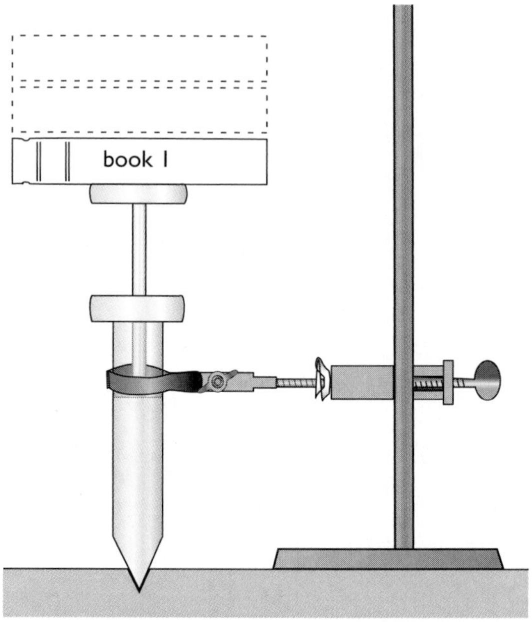
book I

1. Set up a syringe (as shown) that can be placed on a support and on which you can balance several books (or other masses). You can use the weights of the books as a measure of the pressure or you may use a pressure sensor and probeware. (Follow the instructions given with your probeware and associated software.)
   a) For each pressure, record the volume of the gas.
   b) Make a graph of volume versus pressure, or view the graph produced by your probeware.
2. Based on the graph of volume vs. pressure, decide what kind of mathematical relationship you think exists between these two variables, direct or inverse.

(Reminder: In a direct relationship, as the pressure increases, the volume increases. In an inverse relationship as the pressure increases, the volume decreases.)

3. In the experiment, you varied the pressure and recorded volume. You could have changed the volume and measured the pressure required to maintain that volume. This would be equal to the pressure of the gas.

   Record your answers to the following in your *Active Chemistry* log:

   a) If the volume *doubled* from 5.0 mL to 10.0 mL, what does your data show happens to the pressure?

   b) If the volume is *halved* from 20.0 mL to 10.0 mL, what does your data show happens to the pressure?

   c) If the volume is *tripled* from 5.0 mL to 15.0 mL, what does your data show happened to the pressure?

   d) Based on your data, what would you expect the pressure to be if the volume of the syringe was increased to 40.0 mL? Explain or show your work to support your answer.

   e) Based on your data, what would you expect the pressure to be if the volume of the syringe was decreased to 2.5 mL? Explain or show your work to support your answer.

   f) What experimental factors are assumed to be constant in this experiment?

4. One way to determine if a relationship is inverse or direct is to find a proportionality constant, k, from the data. If this relationship is direct, $P = kV$. If it is inverse, $P = k/V$. Based on your data, choose one of these formulas and calculate k for each ordered pair in your data table (divide or multiply the P and V values). Record your answers in your log.

   a) How *constant* were the values for k you obtained? Good data may show some minor variation, but the values for k should be relatively constant.

   b) Using P, V, and k, write an equation representing their relationship. Write a verbal statement that correctly expresses this relationship.

   c) Does this equation support your summary statement from your *Part A* observations? Write a generalization about the effect of the pressure on the volume of a gas at a constant temperature.

Chem Talk

Chem Words

gas: a state of matter in which the molecules are free to move without fewer restrictive forces. A gas has neither definite shape nor definite volume.

natural law: a concise verbal or mathematical statement of a relation that is always the same under the same conditions.

pressure: force applied over a surface area. $P = F/A$

BOYLE'S LAW

Pressure

As you saw in this activity, **gas** is easily compressed. It will fill any container, and mixes completely with other gases.

The observation and study of gases have led to various natural laws. A **natural law** is a summary of observed and measurable behavior. An Irish chemist, Robert Boyle (1627–1691), was one of the scientists whose work played a valuable part in the development of the natural laws of gases. Robert Boyle was the fourteenth child of the first Earl of Cork, Ireland. He wrote *The Sceptical Chymist* in 1661, saying that supposed elements must be tested to see if they were indeed simple. If a substance could be broken down into simpler substances, it was not an element. Boyle is also credited with carrying out the first quantitative experiments on gases. He presented to the scientific community a law that relates the pressure and the volume of gases.

One familiar property of gases is that they exert **pressure** on their container. When you blow up a balloon, the air molecules inside the balloon collide with the sides of the balloon, exerting pressure to keep it inflated.

Pressure is defined as the force exerted per unit of surface area:

$$\text{Pressure } (P) = \frac{\text{force } (F)}{\text{area } (A)}$$

As you pushed on the syringe to compress the gas, you could feel the pressure of the gas on your finger.

Enough air for many minutes of breathing can be compressed into a tank.

Pressure can be measured by using devices like a barometer, as shown in the diagram.

A glass tube is filled with mercury and inverted into a pool of mercury that is open to the air. The mercury in the tube falls, but only a short distance. The air is exerting pressure on the pool of mercury and keeps the mercury in the tube. Under normal conditions, the pressure of the air pushes the mercury to a height of 760 mm. The units of measurement for pressure are **atmospheres** (atm) or **mm Hg** (millimeters of mercury). The relationship between the two is:

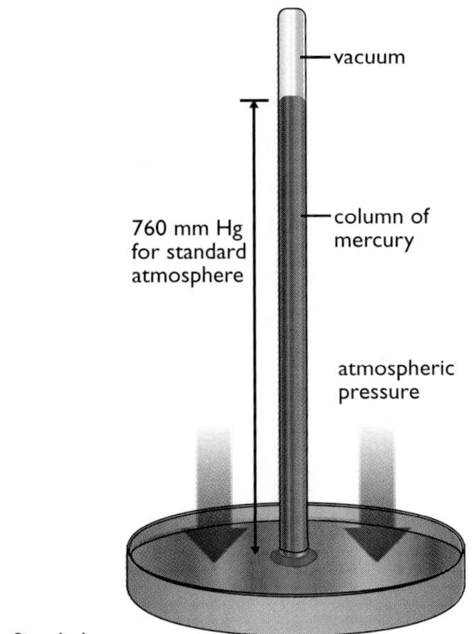
vacuum
760 mm Hg for standard atmosphere
column of mercury
atmospheric pressure
Simple barometer

$$1 \text{ atm} = 760 \text{ mm Hg}$$

In SI, which stands for *Système International d'Unités,* a modern, international version of the metric system, the unit used for pressure is kilopascals (kPa).

$$1 \text{ atm} = 101.325 \text{ kPa}$$

Relationship between the Pressure and the Volume of a Gas

Boyle studied the relationship between the pressure and the volume of a gas trapped in a tube. He described what is now called **Boyle's Law.** *For a given amount of a gas at a constant temperature, the volume of the gas varies inversely with its pressure.* That simply means that when the pressure increases, the volume decreases; when the volume increases, the pressure decreases.

Imagine a group of 15 students. They are all running in straight lines in the classroom at top speed, hitting and bouncing off the walls. The additional pressure on one classroom wall will be determined by the speeds of the students and how often the students hit that wall. If the same 15 students now moved to the gymnasium and ran in straight lines at top speed, the number hitting one wall in a given time would be less than in the classroom. This is because the walls are larger and also because it takes a longer time for the students to get from one wall to the opposite wall.

The **Kinetic Theory of Matter** provides a way to understand what is happening to gases at the nano or molecular level. The particles of →

Chem Words

atmosphere: a measurement of the pressure being exerted on a surface. One atmosphere will support a column of mercury 760 mm high.

mm Hg: a unit commonly used in barometers to measure the height of a mercury column that the atmospheric pressure will support.

Boyle's Law: a gas law that states that for a given amount of a gas at a constant temperature, the volume of the gas varies inversely with its pressure. $P \times V = k$, where k is a constant.

Kinetic Theory of Matter: states that the particles that make up matter (atoms and molecules) are always in constant motion.

Chem Words

constant: a mathematical value that does not change under controlled conditions.

a gas are moving about with a range of speeds and corresponding kinetic energy. These particles can collide with the walls of the container. These collisions create the pressure, or force per area, on the walls of the container. When you increase the volume (the size of the container), the number of gas particles hitting any section of the wall in a given time decreases and the pressure then decreases. It's similar to the students going from the classroom (small volume) to the gym (large volume). When you decrease the volume (make the container smaller), the gas particles have less distance to go before they hit the walls and so the particles will strike the container walls more often and create a greater pressure.

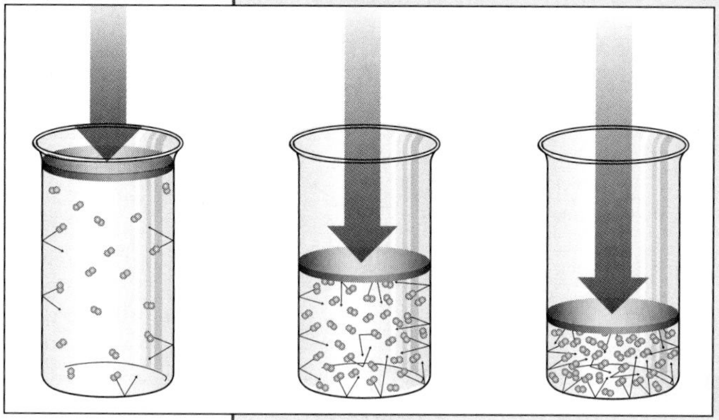

This behavior can be represented mathematically as:

$$\text{pressure} \times \text{volume} = \text{a constant}$$

or

$$PV = k$$

where k is a **constant** for a given sample of air at a constant temperature. It can also be represented graphically as shown. The pressure × volume of each point on the graph is identical.

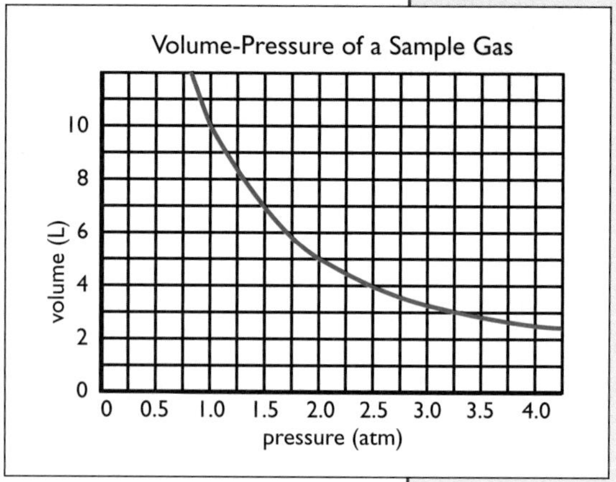
Volume-Pressure of a Sample Gas
volume (L)
0
2
4
6
8
10
0 0.5 1.0 1.5 2.0 2.5 3.0 3.5 4.0
pressure (atm)

In this activity you started with a fixed amount of air in a syringe. When you pushed the plunger in, you squeezed the air into a smaller volume. The molecules of air inside the syringe were then colliding with the sides of the syringe more often and the pressure increased. You felt that pressure on your finger. You measured the additional pressure with the number of books that could be supported by the gas.

You can use the following equation to calculate the new volume of a gas when the pressure has been changed, or the new pressure of a gas when the volume has undergone a change. The equation compares the initial and final pressures and volumes.

$$P_1V_1 = P_2V_2$$

P_1 and V_1 are the initial pressure and volume, and P_2 and V_2 are the final pressure and volume at constant temperature.

Example:

Suppose you have a 1.0 L sample of oxygen gas at a pressure of 1.0 atm. If the pressure were increased to 2.0 atm, what would be the resulting volume?

$$P_1 = 1.0 \text{ atm} \qquad P_2 = 2.0 \text{ atm}$$

$$V_1 = 1.0 \text{ L} \qquad V_2 = ?$$

Rearrange Boyle's Law equation to solve for V_2.

$$V_2 = \frac{P_1V_1}{P_2}$$

$$V_2 = \frac{(1.0 \text{ atm})(1.0 \text{ L})}{(2.0 \text{ atm})}$$

$$V_2 = 0.50 \text{ L}$$

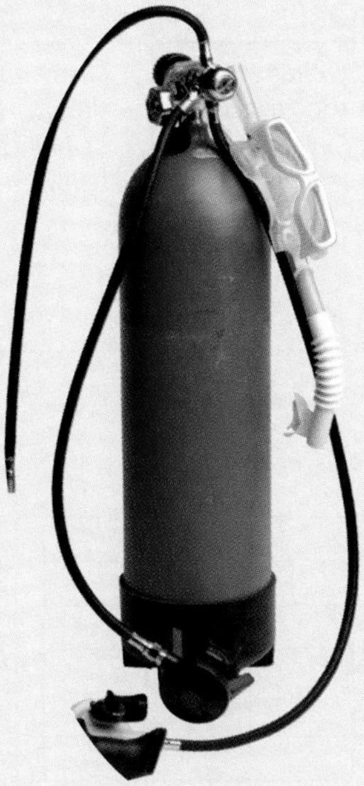

The final volume would be 0.50 L. This is the volume you would predict. The pressure was doubled, so the volume was decreased by one-half.

The Cartesian diver toy can also be explained using Boyle's Law. When you squeeze the container, the volume of the air decreases, causing an increase in the pressure of the air. This increased pressure drives the diver down into the water. If the diver is an eyedropper, you can see how the extra pressure on the water drives more water into the eyedropper. This increases the density of the eyedropper and it sinks.

Pressurized airplane cabins, tennis balls, and SCUBA diving are some of the applications of this pressure-volume law.

Checking Up

1. Define pressure.
2. What units are used to measure pressure?
3. What units are usually used to measure the volume of a gas?
4. State Boyle's Law.
5. Determine the change in pressure if 1.0 L of gas at 1.0 atm was reduced to 0.25 L.
6. Give two practical applications of Boyle's Law.

What Do You Think Now?

At the beginning of this activity you were asked:

- **Why do you think pumping the water gun makes the water that comes out of the gun travel further?**

Diagram and explain the pressure-volume changes in a water gun. How does the change in pressure affect the volume of the gas and how the toy operates? Compare this response to your ideas at the beginning of the activity.

Chem Essential Questions

What does it mean?

Chemistry explains a macroscopic phenomenon (what you observe) with a description of what happens at the nanoscopic level (atoms and molecules) using symbolic structures as a way to communicate. Complete the chart below in your *Active Chemistry* log.

MACRO	NANO	SYMBOLIC
How did the pressure changes in the syringe affect the volume of gas in the syringe?	*Draw and label a picture of the gas particles in the syringe at points A and B on the graph below.*	*The graph is one way to represent the observations that you made symbolically. An equation for that graph is another representation of the relationship. Write the mathematical equation that describes this relationship.*

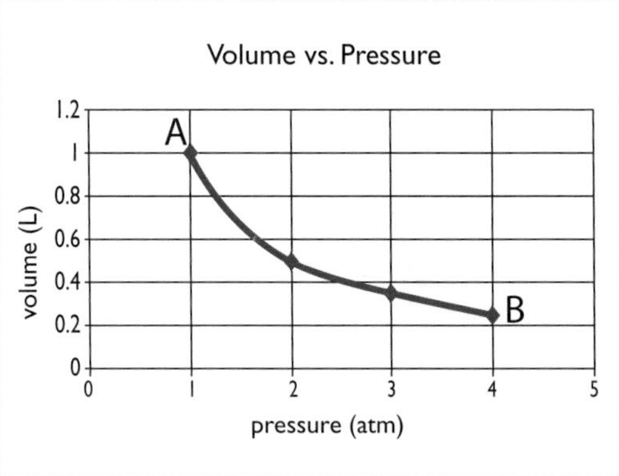
Volume vs. Pressure
volume (L)
1.2
1
0.8
0.6
0.4
0.2
0
A
B
0
1
2
3
4
5
pressure (atm)

How do you know?

What observations did you make and what data did you collect that allowed you to determine the relationship between pressure and volume in a closed system?

Why do you believe?

Describe one experience you have had that illustrates the relationship between pressure and volume in a closed system.

Why should you care?

List two toys that illustrate the pressure-volume relationship. How might you use Boyle's Law to explain your toy design?

Reflecting on the Activity and the Challenge

In this activity, you determined the relationship between pressure and volume for a confined gas under a constant temperature. For a relationship between variables to be considered a law in science, it must have predictive powers. You found that you could predict volume or pressure changes fairly accurately using the relationship that you derived.

Consider applications of this relationship for toy possibilities. Sporting goods, such as balls and some tennis shoes, and tires are just some examples of putting this relationship to work. Realizing that increased pressure decreases the volume of a gas might even improve your on-court performance or help you become the best air-powered water gun shot in your neighborhood. Using the understanding of the effect of pressure on volume may be an important concept in the toy that you are designing.

Chem to Go

1. a) Sketch a graph that shows a direct relationship between two variables.

   b) Sketch a graph that shows an inverse relationship between two variables.

   c) Which of your graphs best depicts the relationship between pressure and volume? Explain.

2. What is the mathematical relationship for pressure and volume of a confined gas at constant temperature?

3. What pressure would be required to decrease the volume of a balloon from 1200 cm^3 to 750 cm^3 if the original pressure was 1 atm?

4. A tire gauge actually expresses the difference in pressure between air inside the tire and the atmospheric pressure. Therefore, if a tire gauge reads 30 lb/in^2 on a day when the atmospheric pressure is 14 lb/in^2, the total tire pressure is 44 lb/in^2. Determine the volume of atmospheric air (at 14 lb/in^2) needed to fill your bike tires (assuming it holds 500 mL of air) to the pressure recommended by the manufacturer (70 lb/in^2).

5. If the pressure of a gas in a 1 liter system was increased fourfold (4 times), the volume of the gas would:

   a) increase 4 times b) increase 2 times c) decrease by $\frac{1}{4}$ d) decrease by $\frac{1}{2}$

6. Describe how a tennis ball bounces by commenting on the pressure and volume changes during the bounce.

7. Which pressure change would cause the volume of a sample of gas to double when the temperature stays the same?

   a) from 1 atm to 2 atm b) from 2 atm to 1 atm

   c) from 4 atm to 1 atm d) from 1 atm to 4 atm

8. ***Preparing for the Chapter Challenge***

   Select a toy that applies Boyle's Law. Draw the specs (specifications) for the toy and include any changes in volume that might result due to pressure changes.

Inquiring Further

1. SCUBA diving and the bends

Research SCUBA diving and a condition known as the bends. Explain how pressure changes while descending and then ascending in the ocean affect your lungs.

2. Mars Rover

Research the Mars Rover. It deployed a unique landing tactic. What did NASA engineers have to take into account in order for this landing to succeed?

3. Crushing a soda can

Do this activity only with adult supervision. Never use a hot plate without adult supervision.

Follow these steps to crush a soda can without exerting any physical force on your part!

Step 1: Place about 10 mL of water in an empty soda can.

Step 2: Heat the can on a hot plate until water is steaming out of the can.

Step 3: When steam is seen coming out of the can, use beaker tongs to quickly invert the can into a tub of cold water.

Use Boyle's Law to explain what happens.

Activity 4 Hot-Air Balloons

What Do You See?

GOALS

In this activity you will:

- Investigate the relationship between temperature and volume of a gas.
- Understand why the Kelvin scale is used for temperature relationships.
- Apply Charles's Law to launch a hot-air balloon.

Safety goggles and a lab apron must be worn *at all times* in a chemistry lab.

What Do You Think?

A young child takes a helium-filled balloon outside the store on a cold, wintry day and the balloon seems to deflate.

- **How might a decrease in temperature affect an inflated balloon?**

Record your ideas about this question in your *Active Chemistry* log. Be prepared to discuss your responses with your small group and the class.

Investigate

In this activity, you will explore the effects of temperature on a gas's volume under constant pressure. You will then invent a toy that can be based on this relationship.

Part A: Volume and Temperature of a Gas

1. Completely fill an empty pipette with water.
2. Count and record the number of drops it takes to empty the pipette.
   a) This number represents the volume of the pipette. It also represents the volume of gas at room temperature in the empty pipette in this activity. Record this as the volume of the empty pipette.
3. Half-fill a 600 mL-beaker with H_2O (approximately 20°C).

4. Half-fill a second 600 mL-beaker with water and place it on a hot plate. Place a thermometer in the beaker. Do not allow the thermometer to rest on the bottom of the beaker. Do not turn the hot plate on until the entire setup is ready to go. (Your teacher may supply you with pre-heated water instead of the hot plate.)
5. Turn the hot plate on and begin heating. Continue heating until the water reaches the temperature assigned to your group by your teacher.
6. Use tongs to hold the bulb of the pipette under water in the beaker being heated. The stem of the pipette should be above the water level. Keep the pipette immersed for 2 minutes. After 2 minutes, squeeze and seal the tip of the pipette with tweezers. Then lift the pipette out of the water. This traps the hot air in the pipette. Quickly transfer the pipette to your room temperature water bath and, removing the tweezers, completely submerge the pipette bulb and stem. Hold it in place with your tongs.

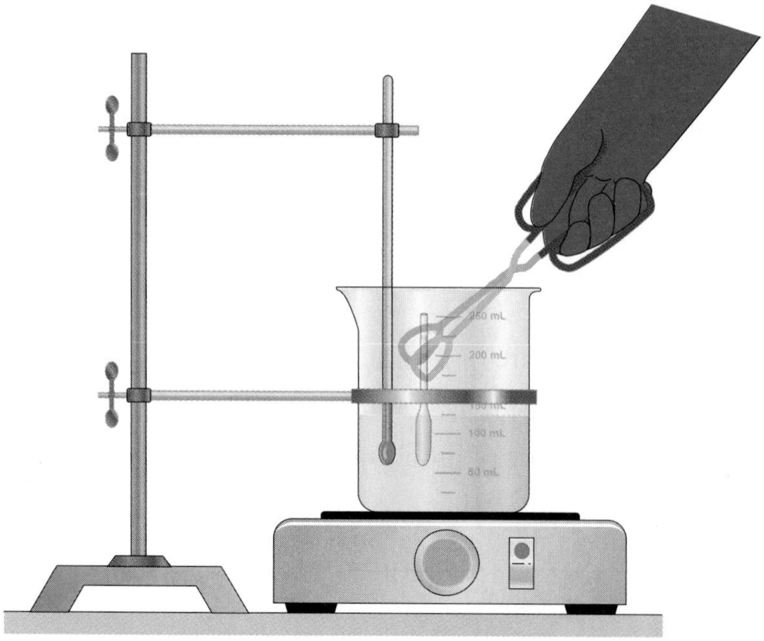
250 mL
200 mL
100 mL
50 mL

7. Notice that water is entering the pipette. Keep the pipette submerged until no further changes are noted (about 1 minute).
8. Remove the pipette from the water and dry the outside. Count the number of drops of water that were drawn into the pipette. This number allows you to calculate the volume of the air in the pipette when the pipette is at room temperature (20°C). Subtracting the number of drops of water from the total volume of the pipette (found in *Step* 2) gives you the volume of the air at 20°C.
   a) Complete this calculation and record the volume of the 20°C air in the pipette in your log.
   b) When the hot air in the pipette cooled in the room temperature (20°C) water, it took up less space and water got sucked into the pipette. Write a statement summarizing this observation using the terms temperature and volume.
9. Repeat these measurements three times.
   a) Calculate and record the average.
   b) Your class will now share the data and complete the first three columns of the following data chart:

Temperature of hot air (equal to the temperature of the heated water bath)	**Volume of hot air (equal to the total volume of the pipette from *Step 2*)**	**Volume of room temperature 20°C air**	**Ratio of volumes (hot air to room temperature 20°C air)**	**Volume of hot air corresponding to 100 drops of room temperature 20°C air**

c) What is the relationship between the volume of hot air and the volume of room temperature 20°C air for different temperatures of hot air?

d) It would be very helpful to compare the volume of hot air if each group had an identical amount of room temperature 20°C air. This is not possible with one size pipette and your procedure. However, a bit of math can help you. You can calculate what the volume of hot air would have been for any volume of room temperature 20°C air. For example, if your volume of hot air was 200 drops and your volume of room temperature 20°C air were 80 drops, you can see that the volume of hot air is 200/80 or 2.5 times larger than the volume of room temperature air.

Calculate the ratio of your hot air to room temperature 20°C air and place this in the class data chart.

e) Use the ratio to calculate what the volume of hot air would be if the volume of room temperature 20°C air was 100 drops. Record this in the class data chart.

10. Prepare a graph of your class data, with temperature (in degrees Celsius) on the horizontal axis (x-axis) and the volume of hot air corresponding to 100 drops of room temperature 20°C air on the vertical axis (y-axis). Although your temperature data goes from 0°C to 100°C, the x-axis should be numbered from –350°C to 150°C for reasons that will be clear soon. Draw the line with the best fit through all the data points. Answer the following questions in your *Active Chemistry* log:

a) What is the relationship between the volume and the Celsius temperature as shown on your graph?

b) Based on the graph, at what temperature would the volume be zero? What would a zero volume look like?

c) Your temperature estimate was probably close to –273°C. If you created a new temperature scale where the volume becomes zero at a temperature of zero, what would 0°C be on this new scale? This presumes that both temperature scales have the same scale units.

11. You are now going to graph your class data on the Kelvin temperature scale where the lowest possible temperature is 0 K (called absolute zero). To do so, you need to add 273 to your Celsius temperatures.

$$K = °C + 273$$

a) Set up a graph in your *Active Chemistry* log with volume on the *y*-axis and temperature (in K) on the *x*-axis from 0 to 400 K. Draw the line with the best fit for the class data points.

b) Determine the slope of the line, making sure to include the units on the slope value. The slope intercept form of a straight line is:

$$y = mx + b,$$

where b is the y-intercept and m is the slope.

You can use this form of the equation to calculate the slope:

$$m = \frac{\Delta y}{\Delta x} = \frac{y - b}{x - 0} = \frac{y - b}{x}$$

c) In your graph, the *y*-values are volume and the *x*-values are temperature. Using the Kelvin scale, the *y*-intercept or "*b*" in the equation is 0. The equation for your straight line is $V = mT$. This relationship is identical to the one expressed in ***Charles's Law***.

Part B: Hot-Air Balloon Challenge

In this part of the investigation, you will apply your understanding of the relationship between temperature and volume by constructing a "hot-air balloon," and competing to find the balloon that can lift the most mass.

1. Construct your hot-air balloon using a plastic dry-cleaning bag. Tape the hole across the top with clear postal tape. Next, gather the ends of the bag from the open end around a 2.5 cm wide (about one inch) paper collar. Tape the paper collar to the bag. The diameter of the opening formed by the collar should be about 10 cm.
2. Inflate your hot-air balloon with a hair dryer.

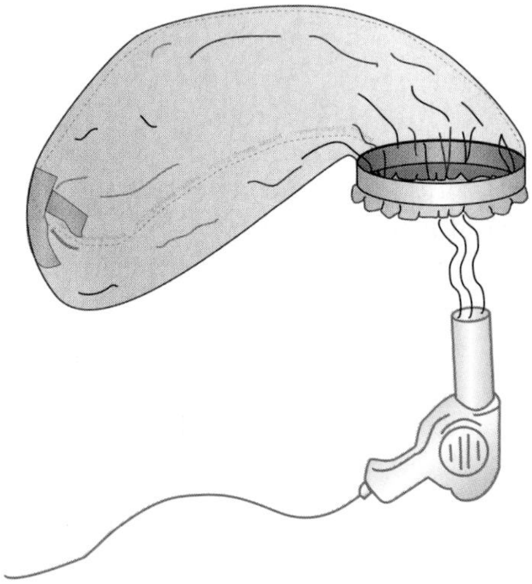

3. Add large paper clips to the paper collar and see which group can get lift off with the greatest mass attached.

a) In your *Active Chemistry* log, use the change in volume of air with respect to temperature, to explain how your balloon worked.

b) What variables affected your balloon?

Chem Talk

CHARLES'S LAW

Charles's Experiment Was Similar to Boyle's

In France, in the early 1800s, there were many advances made in the understanding of gases and their behavior. Hot-air balloons were becoming popular at that time and scientists were challenged to improve the performance of these balloons. A French scientist, Jacques Charles, made many observations and measurements on how the volume of a gas was affected by changes in temperature. Charles discovered that a quantity of gas kept at a constant pressure expands as it warms and contracts as it cools. The equipment used by Charles was very similar to that employed by Boyle. A quantity of gas was trapped in a glass tube that was sealed at one end. This tube was immersed in a water bath. By changing the temperature of the water, Charles was able to observe the change in volume of the gas. The pressure was held constant by adjusting the height of mercury so that the two columns of mercury had equal height, and so the pressure was always equal to the atmospheric pressure. This allowed Charles to examine the effect of only one variable, temperature, on the volume of a gas. Through repeated experimentation with many different gases, Charles found that there was a relationship between the volume of a gas and the temperature of that gas. Your class's graph from the activity demonstrated this direct relationship.

N. CHARLES P. DE PHYSIQUE

Jacques Charles

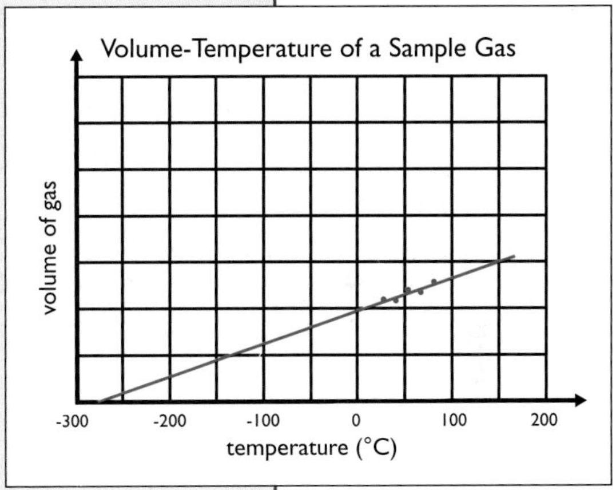

Volume-Temperature of a Sample Gas
volume of gas
-300
-200
-100
0
100
200
temperature (°C)

Relationship between the Temperature and the Volume of a Gas

Charles's Law states: *the volume of a gas varies directly with the temperature (measured in kelvins) for a given amount of gas at a constant pressure.*

$$\text{volume} = \text{a constant} \times \text{temperature}$$

$$\frac{\text{volume}}{\text{temperature}} = \text{a constant}$$

Expressed mathematically:

$$V = kT \text{ or}$$

$$\frac{V}{T} = k, \text{ where } k \text{ is a constant}$$

Chem Words

Charles's Law: a gas law that states that for a given amount of gas at a constant pressure, the volume of the gas varies directly with the temperature.

$V = kT$

Chem Words

absolute zero: a theoretical temperature at which molecular motion is minimal. 0 K, or –273°C

You can compare the volumes of the same gas at two different temperatures:

$$\frac{V_1}{T_1} = \frac{V_2}{T_2}$$

Kinetic Theory of Matter and Charles's Law

A mass weighing 10 N (newtons), approximately 2 lb, is supported by a column of air in a piston. The air must be supplying a force of 10 N to keep the mass from falling down. When the air is heated to a higher temperature, the mass rises due to the increase in volume of the air. The piston stops moving when once again, the air is supplying a force of 10 N to keep the mass from falling.

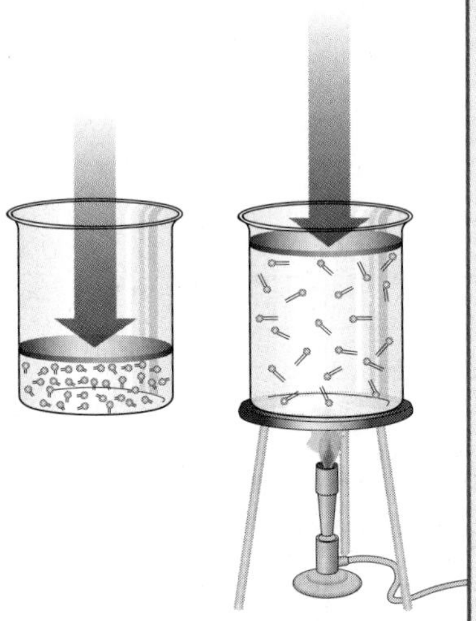

The Kinetic Theory of Matter provides a way to understand this relationship between the temperature and the volume of a gas at the nanoscopic or molecular level. The particles of a gas are moving about with a range of speeds and corresponding kinetic energy. These particles can collide with the walls and the moveable piston. These collisions create the pressure, or force per area, on the piston. The particles hit the piston so that the average force on the piston is 10 N. When you increase the temperature of the air, you are increasing the speed and kinetic energy of the air molecules. These molecules hit the piston more often and with a greater force. If the average increased force is 12 N, then the mass will move up. When the piston moves up, it increases the volume. As the volume increases, these energetic air particles don't hit the piston as often because of the extra distance they must travel. The average force of the energetic particles once again becomes 10 N and the piston remains in its elevated position. When the air cools, the particles have a decrease in their kinetic energies. They hit the piston less often and the average force is now less than 10 N and the mass descends again.

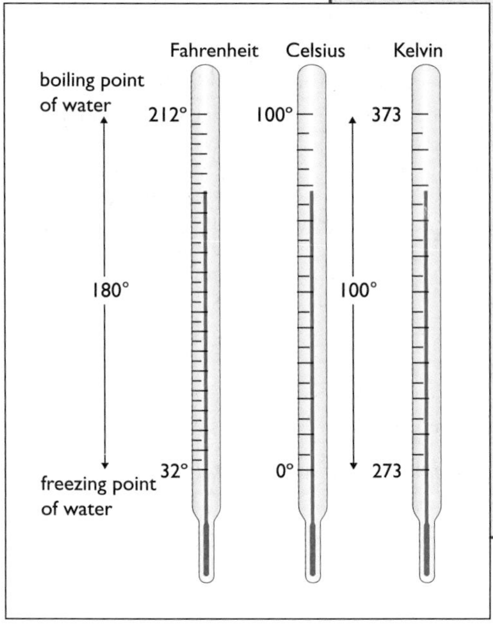
Fahrenheit
Celsius
Kelvin
boiling point of water
212°
100°
373
180°
100°
freezing point of water
32°
0°
273

Absolute Zero and the Kelvin Temperature Scale

If a decrease in temperature results in a decrease in volume, what happens if the temperature is lowered to a point where the volume drops to zero? A negative volume is impossible, so the temperature at which the volume drops to zero must be the lowest temperature that can be achieved. This temperature is called absolute zero. **Absolute zero** is the lowest possible temperature. It is 0 K, or –273°C. Whenever determining the effect of a temperature change on the volume of a gas, you must first convert from the

Celsius temperature to the Kelvin temperature. You do this by adding 273 to the Celsius temperature.

$$K = °C + 273$$

Applying Charles's Law

The mass of your plastic hot-air balloon is the mass of the plastic plus the mass of the air. To get the balloon to fly, you have to decrease the mass of the air in the balloon. In the hot-air balloon activity that you conducted, you found that the hot air takes up more volume than the cool air. Filling your plastic balloon required less hot air than cool air. With less air in the balloon, the balloon had a smaller total mass and it could fly.

Example:

A balloon is in a room at 25°C. The volume of the balloon is 2.0 L. Suppose that the balloon is taken outside at a temperature of –5°C. What will be the new volume of the balloon?

Charles's Law lets you predict what the volume of the balloon will be.

$$\frac{V_1}{T_1} = \frac{V_2}{T_2}$$

$V_1 = 2.0$ L $\qquad V_2 = ?$

$T_1 = 25°C$ (298 K) $\qquad T_2 = -5°C$ (268 K)

Notice that temperature in kelvin must be used to solve problems with Charles's Law.

Rearrange Charles's Law equation to solve for V_2.

$$V_2 = \frac{V_1 T_2}{T_1}$$

$$= \frac{2.0 \text{ L } (268 \text{ K})}{298 \text{ K}}$$

$$= 1.8 \text{ L}$$

Checking Up

1. What is the relationship between the temperature and the pressure of a gas?
2. What is absolute zero on the Kelvin and Celsius temperature scale?
3. What problems would you encounter in your calculations if you did not convert the Celsius temperature to the Kelvin scale?
4. How might the temperature in the gym affect the volume of a basketball and thus its bounce?
5. Determine the effect on the volume of a basketball if the initial volume is 6.4 L at 20°C and the ball is taken outside to a temperature of 27°C.

What Do You Think Now?

At the beginning of this activity you were asked:

- **How might a decrease in temperature affect an inflated balloon?**

Now that you have investigated Charles's Law, how would you answer this question? How would an increase in temperature affect the balloon?

Chem Essential Questions

What does it mean?

Chemistry explains a macroscopic phenomenon (what you observe) with a description of what happens at the nanoscopic level (atoms and molecules) using symbolic structures as a way to communicate. Complete the chart below in your *Active Chemistry* log.

MACRO	NANO	SYMBOLIC
What variables were you measuring during the investigation? What variables did you assume would remain constant?	*Describe what happens with the particles of a gas when you heat it up while holding the pressure constant.*	*What equation can express the relationship between the volume of a gas as the temperature of the gas changes?*

How do you know?

Does a change in temperature have a predictable effect on the volume of a gas? Use your data to support your answer. Why must the pressure be held constant to make this prediction?

Why do you believe?

On a very cold day, you notice that your bicycle tires appear under-inflated. You add air to the tires to fully inflate them. Why is there a danger of the tires bursting if you ride long distances and the tires warm up?

Why should you care?

You are expected to utilize several chemical principles to develop an exciting new toy to market. How could you use your knowledge of the effects of temperature on a gas's volume in your proposed toy?

Reflecting on the Activity and the Challenge

In this activity, you determined the relationship between temperature and volume in a gas. The volume of a gas is proportional to temperature (Charles's Law). This relationship is represented by the Charles's Law equation. You then applied that understanding by launching a hot-air balloon. Consider all the examples of this relationship you encounter every day — hot air rising in a room, the effect of temperature on inflated tires, and wind patterns, to name a few. You might be able to use this relationship in your proposal for a toy and for your presentation.

Chem to Go

1. If you could install only one thermostat in a two-story toy factory, should it be placed on the first or second floor? Explain.
2. Predict the effect of hot temperatures on car tires. Will they appear fuller or flatter? Predict the effect of cold temperatures on car tires. How will their appearance change? Explain your answer.
3. Why must the temperature measurements used in Charles's Law be in kelvin? Show an example that supports your reasoning.
4. Using Charles's Law, what would the volume of a gas be if 2.8 L at 25°C were heated to 75°C?
5. If 5.5 L of a gas at 78°C were cooled to 25°C, what would the resulting volume be?
6. To what temperature would you need to heat 750 mL of a gas at 25°C in order to increase its volume to 2500 mL?
7. In a hot-air balloon, the balloonist may have to light the propane torch for a few minutes. Using Charles's Law, explain why he might need to do this.
8. As the temperature of a given sample of gas decreases at constant pressure, the volume of the gas:

   a) decreases b) increases c) remains the same
9. ***Preparing for the Chapter Challenge***

   Think of a toy or a sporting goods product that uses or is affected by the relationship between volume and temperature. Explain how Charles's Law is applied and how temperature changes in the environment could affect the product. Brainstorm ways the designer could minimize the effect of temperature on this product.

Inquiring Further

1. The motorists' guide to temperature and volume

Write a short, practical guide for motorists explaining changes in their automobile tire volume during different seasons. Provide them with tips on how to prolong the life of their tires by keeping them properly inflated. Explain to them why these changes in volume occur. Your article could be publishable as "consumer help" for your local paper.

2. Balloon storage

The prom committee has decided to use lots of balloons in this year's décor. Write a memo to the committee suggesting how the inflated balloons should be stored in order to minimize deflation prior to the prom. They're a hard committee to convince, so back up your suggestions with calculations.

Chapter mini Challenge

THE BRIDGE
HONK

Your challenge is to create a toy that uses various chemical and/or gas principles. The toy should appeal to a certain age group. You will need to prepare a presentation for the board of the Ideal Toy Company. Your presentation should include a written proposal, either a detailed drawing or a mock prototype of the toy, any potential hazards or waste-disposal issues, and a cost analysis of the item for manufacturing. Your presentation will be evaluated on the quality of your visual aids/prototype, your presentation, the explanation of the chemistry involved, and your written proposal.

Having completed four activities, this is a good time to give your *Ideal Toy* a first try. It's time to describe what you intend to do and what you intend to explain. This *first try* will give you a good sense of what the challenge entails and how you and other teams are going to approach this task.

Chemistry Content

Review the chemistry content that may be included in your *Ideal Toy* presentation for the board.

Activity 1: You learned about battery construction and created your own electrochemical cell. Your battery investigation helped you learn about the Metal Activity Series and redox reactions.

Activity 2: You investigated the differences between solids, liquids, and gases and compared the boiling points of hydrocarbons and alcohols.

Activity 3: You constructed a Cartesian diver toy and gained knowledge about Boyle's Law and the relation between pressure and volume of a gas.

Activity 4: You studied the relationship between the volume and temperature of a gas and the representation of that relationship in Charles's Law. You also constructed a hot-air balloon.

Criteria

Your *Ideal Toy* should be creative, safe, and age appropriate. Your written chemistry presentation to the board should be accurate, clear, and organized. You should also include a number of chemistry concepts.

At this point, you can decide on what you will present to the toy company board of directors. What age group will you target for your toy? Will you have a single toy that uses more than one chemical principle? Will your toy be based on a product that you have seen or played with? What are the safety considerations surrounding your toy?

Preparing for Your mini Challenge

Sharing your *Ideal Toy* sketch and board presentation with your class will help you learn about what works and doesn't work. You will be able to provide feedback to other teams and they will provide feedback to you. You will not be given much preparation time for the creation of this trial *Ideal Toy* and presentation. The *mini-challenge* is a way to get a sense of what you will be involved with at the end of the chapter when you have more chemistry content to include in your actual toy and its corresponding corporate presentation.

Engineering/Technology Design

The engineering design process involves a number of distinct steps. In creating an *Ideal Toy* and the related presentation to the company board, you are involved in a design process. Note how your efforts follow the design model described.

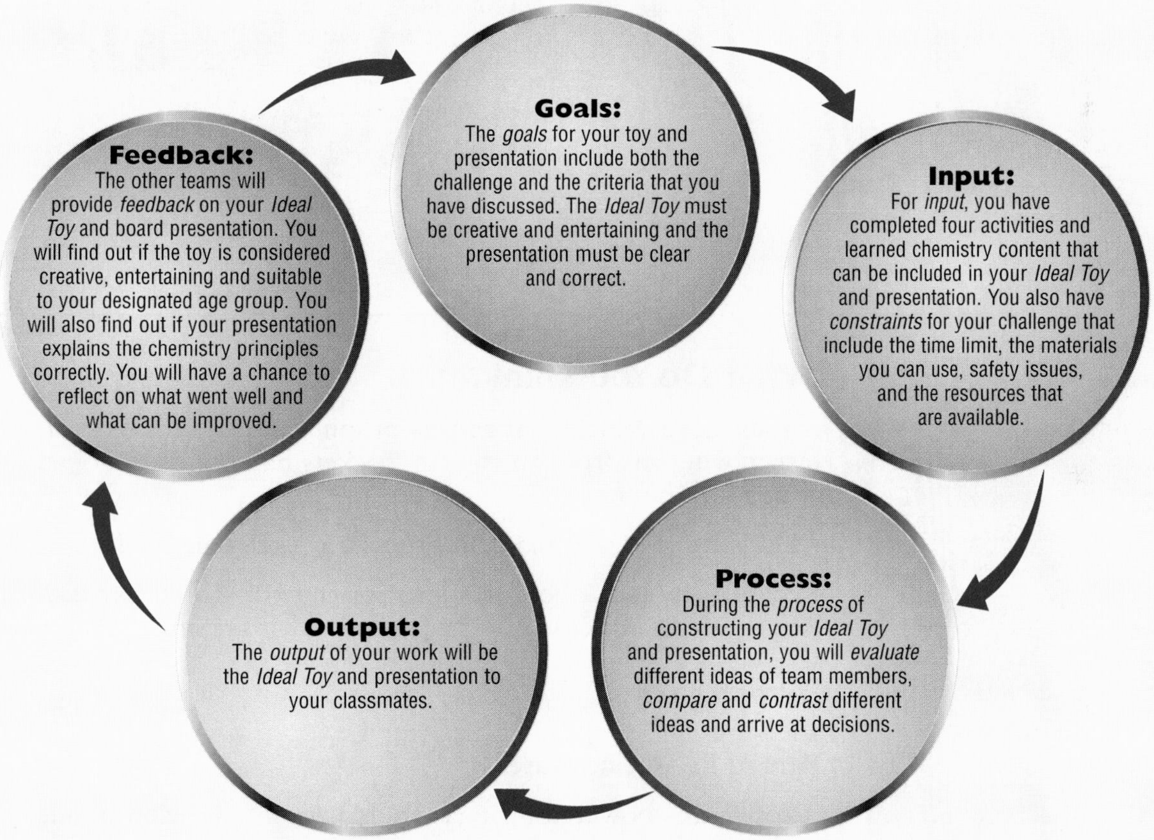

Goals:
The goals for your toy and presentation include both the challenge and the criteria that you have discussed. The Ideal Toy must be creative and entertaining and the presentation must be clear and correct.
Input:
For input, you have completed four activities and learned chemistry content that can be included in your Ideal Toy and presentation. You also have constraints for your challenge that include the time limit, the materials you can use, safety issues, and the resources that are available.
Process:
During the process of constructing your Ideal Toy and presentation, you will evaluate different ideas of team members, compare and contrast different ideas and arrive at decisions.
Output:
The output of your work will be the Ideal Toy and presentation to your classmates.
Feedback:
The other teams will provide feedback on your Ideal Toy and board presentation. You will find out if the toy is considered creative, entertaining and suitable to your designated age group. You will also find out if your presentation explains the chemistry principles correctly. You will have a chance to reflect on what went well and what can be improved.

Remember: This is a *first try*. The feedback that you get from the toy and presentation will be extremely valuable when you create your *Ideal Toy* and the written presentation. At that point, you will have additional chemistry demonstrations and materials to incorporate in your work. You will begin the entire design cycle again. That's why it is called a cycle — you keep going through it over and over to improve your design or, in this case, your *Ideal Toy* and presentation to the board of directors.

Activity 5 How Are Gases Produced?

What Do You See?

GAS
HYDRO GAS
CARBON DIOXIDE

GOALS

In this activity you will:

- Produce and test for three different gases.
- Use chemical reactions to make gases to use as a rocket fuel.
- Investigate four types of chemical reactions.

What Do You Think?

A rocket is a vehicle that gets its propulsion from the discharge of a fast-moving gas from an engine. Rockets have helped to open the frontier of space to humankind.

- **How are the gases that can propel a rocket generated?**

Record your ideas about this question in your *Active Chemistry* log. Be prepared to discuss your responses with your small group and the class.

Investigate

Part A: Producing Gases

A toy that is powered by a gas could certainly be entertaining. Let's take a look at how various gases can be produced.

Safety goggles and a lab apron must be worn *at all times* in a chemistry lab.

Hydrochloric acid is caustic.

1. ***Producing and testing hydrogen gas*** Obtain two test tubes. Fill one test tube about a third of the way with hydrochloric acid (1 *M* HCl). Add a piece of zinc and invert the second test tube over the first one. After a few minutes, use rubber stoppers to cap the test tubes. Have your lab partner light a match. With the test tube still inverted carefully bring the mouth of the test tube to the match. Remove the stopper and see what happens.

   a) Record what happened in your *Active Chemistry* log.

2. ***Producing and testing oxygen gas*** Oxygen gas can be obtained by decomposing hydrogen peroxide. Fill a test tube about one-third full with 3% aqueous hydrogen peroxide. Add a small scoop of manganese (IV) dioxide (MnO_2) to the test tube. When a gas is being produced, light a wooden splint and blow out the flame. Quickly insert the glowing splint into the test tube.

   a) Record what happens in your *Active Chemistry* log.

3. ***Producing and testing of carbon dioxide gas*** Carbon dioxide gas can be produced by the double-replacement reaction of an acid with baking soda (sodium hydrogen carbonate). Put two scoops of sodium hydrogen carbonate in a 250-mL beaker. Add 10 mL of hydrochloric acid (1*M* HCl) and cover the beaker with a watch glass. Test the gas by lighting a splint and then quickly inserting it into the mouth of the beaker (after removing the watch glass).

   a) Record what happens in your *Active Chemistry* log.

4. Answer the following in your *Active Chemistry* log.

   a) Describe how each gas behaved in the presence of a lit or glowing splint.

   b) Summarize the positive test for determining if an unknown gas is H_2, O_2, or CO_2.

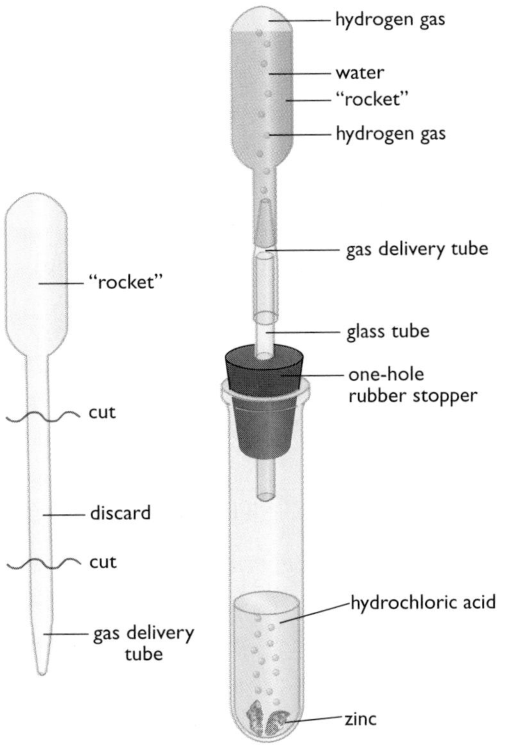
hydrogen gas
water
"rocket"
hydrogen gas
gas delivery tube
"rocket"
glass tube
one-hole rubber stopper
cut
discard
cut
hydrochloric acid
gas delivery tube
zinc

Part B: Gas-Powered Rockets

In this part of the activity, you will use two of the gases that you produced to provide the propellant for a small rocket. You will use hydrogen and oxygen gases as the fuel for your rocket.

Safety goggles and a lab apron must be worn *at all times* in a chemistry lab.

1. For your rocket, you will use the bulb end of a Beral pipette. Fill the pipette (rocket) completely with water by immersing it in a beaker of water.

2. To make hydrogen gas, fill one test tube one-third full with 1*M* HCl. Build the gas collection system shown in the diagram above. Add two pieces of zinc and place the stopper in the test tube. Fill a half of the rocket with hydrogen.

3. To make oxygen gas, fill the other test tube one-third full with 3% aqueous hydrogen peroxide. Add a small scoop of MnO_2 and cover the tube with a stopper and nozzle. Fill a half of the rocket with oxygen gas.

4. Place the rocket on a nail. The rocket should contain equal amounts of the two gases. Leave a water plug in the neck of the rocket and bring it to the launch pad, open end down.

5. Place the Beral pipette on a nail and use the Tesla Coil (a device that produces an electrical spark) to jump a spark through the plastic to the tip of the nail. Record the results in your *Active Chemistry* log.

Rocket Launching Setup

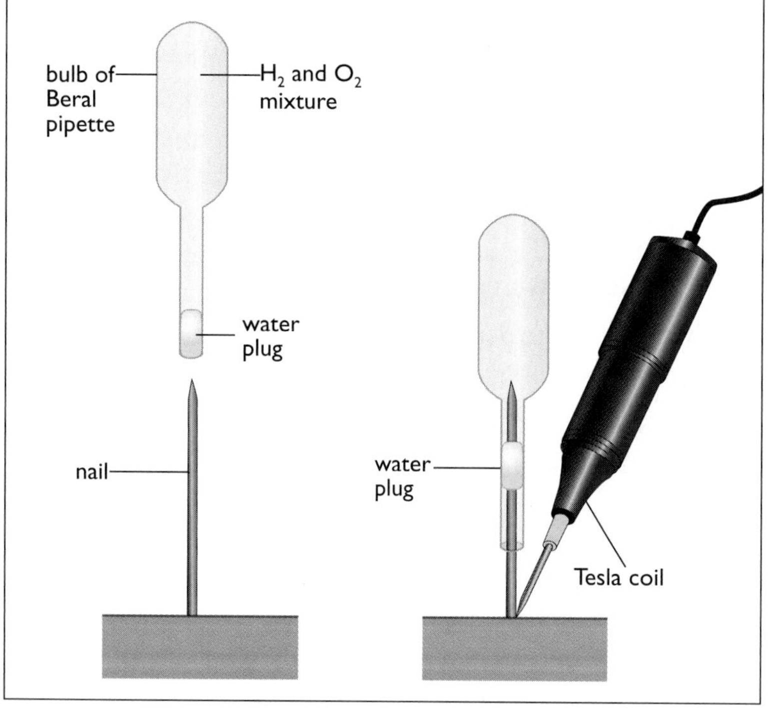
bulb of Beral pipette
H_2 and O_2 mixture
water plug
nail
water plug
Tesla coil

Wash your hands and arms thoroughly after the activity.

6. Now that you know the proper procedure, you can perform an inquiry activity to determine the optimum hydrogen-to-oxygen gas ratio for a successful rocket. Should there be one part hydrogen to one part oxygen as you first tried? Should there be more hydrogen or more oxygen?

   a) Collect the two gases in the rocket, noting the relative amounts of each gas in your *Active Chemistry* log. Leave a water plug in the neck of the rocket and bring it to the launch pad, open end down.

   b) Launch your rocket and compare this launch to the first trial.

   Repeat the procedure as often as time allows.

7. Answer the following in your *Active Chemistry* log.

   a) Were both gases necessary in order for the rocket to launch? Explain your answer.

   b) Was there a combination of gases that worked best? What was the ratio?

   c) The reaction in the rocket was a synthesis reaction. In a synthesis reaction, one product is made from two simpler reactants. In this case, the reactants were hydrogen and oxygen. What was the product? Write a word equation and a balanced chemical equation for the reaction in the rocket.

8. Dispose of the materials as directed by your teacher. Clean up your workstation.

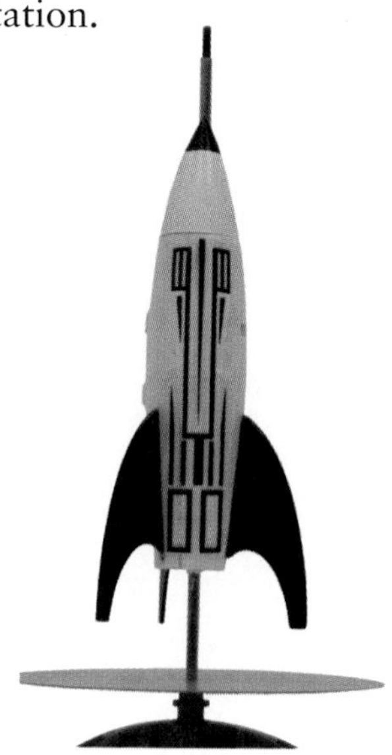

Chem Talk

KINDS OF CHEMICAL REACTIONS

Single-Replacement Reactions

The reaction in this activity that produces hydrogen gas was a **single-replacement reaction**. In this type of reaction, substances are rearranged and one element takes the place of another in a compound. The result is two new products. The general equation for this type of reaction can be written as follows:

$$A + BC \rightarrow B + AC$$

reactants *products*

The reaction you carried out to produce hydrogen gas was:

zinc + hydrochloric acid → hydrogen + zinc chloride

You can see how it fits the pattern in the general equation. The zinc replaced the hydrogen. It can be written as a formula equation as follows:

$$Zn_{(s)} + HCl_{(aq)} \rightarrow H_{2(g)} + ZnCl_{2(aq)}$$

Using models, the equation would look like this:

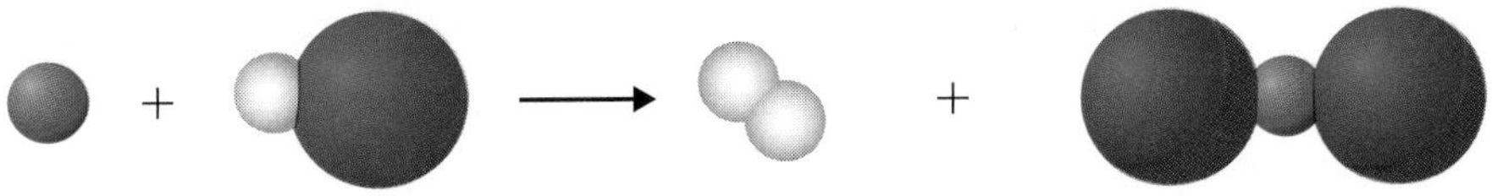

$Zn_{(s)}$ $HCl_{(aq)}$ $H_{2(g)}$ $ZnCl_{2(aq)}$

You probably noticed that there is something wrong with the equation and drawing. When writing chemical equations representing reactions, it is important that the numbers of atoms on both sides of the equation are equal because mass cannot be created or destroyed in a chemical reaction. In the above reaction as written, you see that there are two atoms of hydrogen on the right side of the equation, while there is only one on the left. You must adjust the proportions of the reactants and products to satisfy the **Law of Conservation of Mass**. Remember, in a chemical reaction, atoms are rearranged to form different compounds when bonds are broken and new bonds are formed. The atoms are not changed or destroyed. They are simply rearranged. Therefore, you must balance the equation.

Chem Words

single-replacement reaction: a reaction in which an element displaces or replaces another element in a compound.

Law of Conservation of Mass: the law that states that the total mass of the products of a chemical reaction is the same as the total mass of the reactants entering into the reaction.

Chem Words

mole: the number equal to the number of carbon atoms in exactly 12 g of pure ^{12}C. It is represented by Avogadro's number, 6.022×10^{23}.

You can do this by placing numeral coefficients in front of the different reactants and products. In this reaction, you could place a two in front of the HCl. That would give two hydrogen atoms on each side of the equation. There are also equal numbers of atoms of zinc and chlorine on both sides of the equation. The balanced equation is represented as:

$$Zn(s) + 2HCl(aq) \rightarrow H_2(g) + ZnCl_2(aq)$$

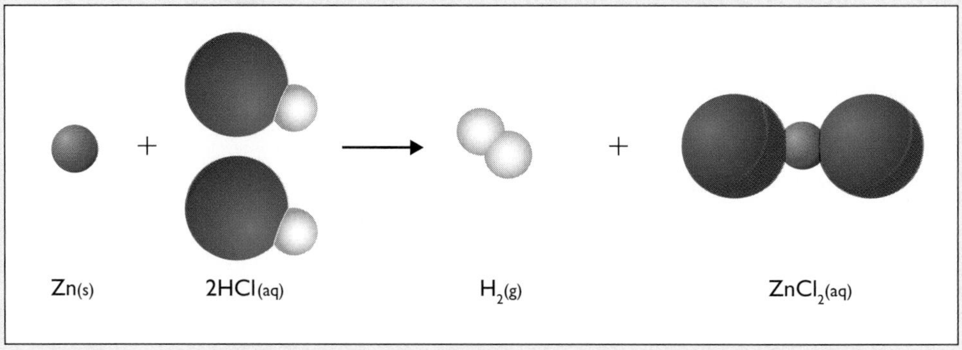
Zn(s)
2HCl(aq)
H2(g)
ZnCl2(aq)

This tells you that one atom of zinc reacts with two molecules of hydrochloric acid to yield one molecule of hydrogen gas and one unit of zinc chloride (zinc chloride is an ionic compound so it cannot be called a molecule). It should be noted that you balance equations *only* by placing coefficients in front of the reactants and products. You cannot change the subscripts in the molecular formulas. The subscripts cannot change, because then you would change the compound you were representing. If there is only one chemical unit in the balanced equation, then you do not write the numeral one as a coefficient. The coefficient is understood.

Since single molecules are so small, chemists use a larger quantity when referring to chemical reactions. Chemists use **moles** to represent large quantities of small particles. A mole of molecules (or anything, for that matter), is equal to 6.022×10^{23} of those molecules. Since the number of particles in a mole is constant, the ratio in the balanced equation does not change. The equation can now be read as:

One mole of zinc reacts with two moles of hydrochloric acid to produce one mole of hydrogen gas and one mole of zinc chloride.

This is a much larger quantity than individual molecules and is one that can be easily measured in the laboratory. You will find out more about this in the next activity.

Decomposition Reactions

The reaction in this activity that produced oxygen gas was a **decomposition reaction**. In a decomposition reaction, a more complex compound breaks down into simpler substances. The general equation for a decomposition reaction is:

$$\underset{\textit{reactants}}{AB} \rightarrow \underset{\textit{products}}{A + B}$$

The products of decomposition reactions may be two elements, an element and a compound, or two compounds. In any case, they will be simpler than the reactant.

The reaction you used to produce oxygen gas was the decomposition of hydrogen peroxide. It was catalyzed (sped up) by adding manganese dioxide. Since the manganese dioxide is a catalyst and not a reactant, it is shown above the arrow in the equation.

The word equation is:

$$\text{hydrogen peroxide} \xrightarrow{MnO_2} \text{oxygen} + \text{water}$$

and the chemical equation is:

$$H_2O_{2(aq)} \xrightarrow{MnO_2} O_{2(g)} + H_2O_{(l)}$$

This equation is not balanced. Placing a two in front of H_2O changes the odd number of oxygen atoms to an even number. This now gives a total of four oxygen atoms in the products. If a two is placed in front of the H_2O_2 on the reactant side, it too will now have four oxygen atoms. Checking the number of hydrogen atoms indicates that there are four on each side. The equation is now balanced and shows the correct coefficients for the reactants and the products.

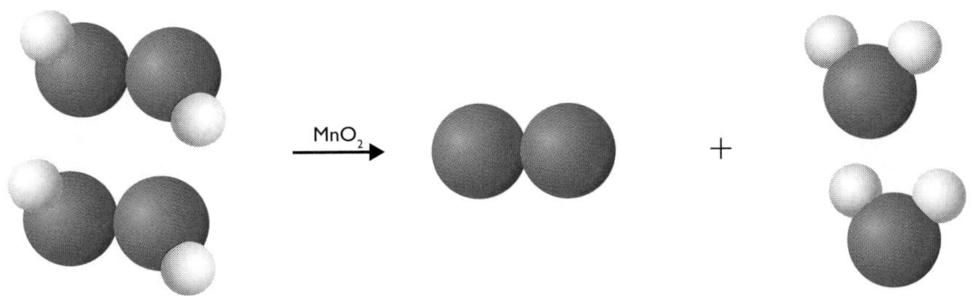
MnO2
+

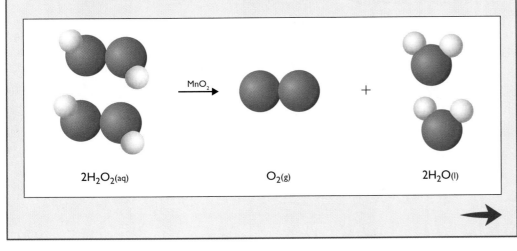

$2H_2O_{2(aq)}$ $O_{2(g)}$ $2H_2O_{(l)}$

Chem Words

decomposition reaction: a chemical reaction in which a single compound breaks down into two or more products.

Checking Up

1. Why do chemists use moles to describe quantities involved in chemical reactions?
2. Distinguish between a single- and a double-replacement reaction.
3. Give an example of a decomposition reaction.
4. The reaction in the rocket was a synthesis reaction. In a synthesis reaction, one product is made from two simpler reactants. In this case, the reactants were hydrogen and oxygen. What was the product? Write a word equation for the reaction in the rocket.
5. Identify each reaction as a synthesis, decomposition, single-replacement, or double-replacement reaction. What information from the reaction did you use to help you categorize them?
   a) $NaOH(aq) + AgNO_3(aq) \rightarrow AgOH(s) + NaNO_3(aq)$
   b) $Mg(s) + CuBr_2(aq) \rightarrow Cu(s) + MgBr_2(aq)$
   c) $NH_4OH(aq) + HBr(aq) \rightarrow H_2O(l) + NH_4Br(aq)$
   d) $Pb(s) + O_2(g) \rightarrow PbO_2(s)$
   e) $Na_2CO_3(s) \rightarrow Na_2O(s) + CO_2(g)$

It can now be read as "Two moles of hydrogen peroxide decompose to produce one mole of oxygen and two moles of water."

Double-Replacement Reactions

Carbon dioxide gas was produced by a **double-replacement reaction**. In a double-replacement reaction, parts of two compounds in solution switch places with each other. The general equation for a double-replacement reaction is:

$$\underbrace{AB + CD}_{\text{reactants}} \rightarrow \underbrace{AD + CB}_{\text{products}}$$

The word equation for the reaction that you did is:

hydrochloric acid + sodium hydrogen carbonate →
sodium chloride + carbonic acid

The carbonic acid decomposed into water and carbon dioxide, so the entire equation would be:

hydrochloric acid + sodium hydrogen carbonate →
sodium chloride + water + carbon dioxide

Note: If you are talking about the gas then HCl is called hydrogen chloride, but if the gas is dissolved in water then HCl is called hydrochloric acid (HCl(aq)).

The chemical equation would be:

$$HCl(aq) + NaHCO_3(aq) \rightarrow NaCl(aq) + H_2O(l) + CO_2(g)$$

By counting the number of H, Cl, Na, C, and O atoms of the reactants and products, you can see that the equation is balanced.

Synthesis Reactions

In the rocket, a mixture of hydrogen and oxygen was made to react. The reaction was a **synthesis reaction** in which two simple substances combine to form a more complex substance. The general equation for a synthesis reaction is:

$$\underbrace{A + B}_{\text{reactants}} \rightarrow \underbrace{AB}_{\text{product}}$$

The word equation for the reaction in the rocket is:

hydrogen + oxygen → water

The balanced chemical equation is:

$$2H_{2(g)} + O_{2(g)} \rightarrow 2H_2O_{(l)}$$

The ratio of hydrogen to oxygen is 2 mol to 1 mol in the balanced equation. You might have noticed as you were testing your rockets that more hydrogen than oxygen was needed for the rocket to work well. The balanced equation gives you a clue as to why.

Chem Words

double-replacement reaction: a chemical reaction in which two ionic compounds "exchange" cations to produce two new compounds, one of which is a precipitate or a gas.

synthesis reaction: a chemical reaction in which two or more substances combine to form a compound.

What Do You Think Now?

At the beginning of this activity you were asked:

- **How are the gases that can propel a rocket generated?**

Now that you have completed this activity, how would you answer this question?

Chem Essential Questions

What does it mean?

Chemistry explains a macroscopic phenomenon (what you observe) with a description of what happens at the nanoscopic level (atoms and molecules) using symbolic structures as a way to communicate. Complete the chart below in your *Active Chemistry* log.

MACRO	NANO	SYMBOLIC
What observations did you make that indicated a gas was being generated in each of the reactions in Part A?	*Explain what was happening on the nanoscopic level to generate the gases.*	*How do chemical equations represent what is happening at a nanoscopic level? Why must the equation be "balanced"?*

How do you know?

Identification of unknown substances requires that known properties are used and compared to the unknown's properties in order to identify a substance. What properties of oxygen, hydrogen, and carbon dioxide gases were used to determine which gas was being generated in *Part A* of the *Investigate* section?

Why do you believe?

Could you have used any combination of gases to power your rockets in *Part B* of the activity? Why or why not? What evidence did you have from *Part B* that reacting proportions are important considerations for chemical reactions?

Why should you care?

If you were manufacturing a toy rocket that required the combination of compounds to produce a chemical reaction that would propel your rocket, would it be more cost-effective to include a surplus of each reactant or specific ratios of each compound to ensure liftoff? Explain.

Reflecting on the Activity and the Challenge

You have investigated how to form different gases. You saw the bubbles of gas form and the launching of a rocket. Gases may be formed by the rearrangement of reactant molecules and the formation of new product molecules. You can represent these reactions using chemical equations.

You now know how to predict the products of reactions and how to balance equations. If your toy involves the generation of some gas, this information will be useful in determining the optimum amount of materials needed for each product.

Chem to Go

1. Using the reaction of Zn reacting with HCl as an example, predict the products of the following reactions.

   a) magnesium + hydrochloric acid →

   b) magnesium + dihydrogen sulfate (sulfuric acid) →

2. Balance the following equations.

   a) $Mg(s) + CH_3COOH(aq) \rightarrow H_2(g) + Mg(CH_3COO)_2(aq)$
   magnesium + hydrogen acetate (acetic acid)) →
   hydrogen + magnesium acetate

   b) $Zn(s) + H_2SO_4(aq) \rightarrow H_2(g) + ZnSO_4(aq)$
   zinc + sulfuric acid → hydrogen + zinc sulfate

   c) $Al(s) + HCl(aq) \rightarrow H_2(g) + AlCl_3(aq)$
   aluminum + hydrochloric acid → hydrogen + aluminum chloride

3. Write the balanced chemical equation of each reaction in *Question 1*.

4. For the following, identify the type of reaction and tell what the products are.
   a) aqueous sodium chloride + aqueous silver nitrate →
   b) magnesium solid + fluorine gas →
   c) lithium solid + aqueous aluminum chloride →
   d) calcium hydroxide solid + aqueous hydrochloric acid →
5. Write the balanced chemical equation of each reaction in *Question 4*.
6. $Pb(NO_3)_2(aq) + 2NaI(aq) \rightarrow PbI_2(s) + 2NaNO_3(g)$ is a:
   a) synthesis reaction
   b) decomposition reaction
   c) single-replacement reaction
   d) double-replacement reaction
7. $CaCO_3(s) \rightarrow CaO(s) + CO_2(g)$ is a:
   a) synthesis reaction
   b) decomposition reaction
   c) single-replacement reaction
   d) double-replacement reaction
8. $2ZnS(s) + O_2(g) \rightarrow 2ZnO(s) + 2S(s)$ is a:
   a) synthesis reaction
   b) decomposition reaction
   c) single-replacement reaction
   d) double-replacement reaction
9. $SO_3(g) + H_2O(l) \rightarrow H_2SO_4(l)$ is a:
   a) synthesis reaction
   b) decomposition reaction
   c) single-replacement reaction
   d) double-replacement reaction
10. In a correctly written chemical equation, all of the following are true ***except***:
   a) the number of atoms of the reactants equals the number of atoms of the product.
   b) the coefficients indicate the proportions of the reactants and the products.
   c) the subscripts represent the proportions of the reactants and the products.
   d) the mass of the reactants is equal to the mass of the products.
11. Given the unbalanced equation:

   $\_\_\_\_Al(s) + \_\_\_\_O_2(g) \rightarrow \_\_\_\_Al_2O_3(s)$

   When this equation is correctly balanced using *smallest* whole numbers, what is the coefficient of $O_2(g)$?

   a) 6 b) 2 c) 3 d) 4

12. ***Preparing for the Chapter Challenge***

    Your toy design may require the production of a gas from a chemical reaction. The reaction you carried out in this activity had you use HCl(aq) (hydrochloric acid) for the production of hydrogen gas. Propose a reaction that generates carbon dioxide gas using a common household acid, one that would be less dangerous than hydrochloric acid for storage in a toy. Make a sketch of a toy that might use this chemical reaction.

Inquiring Further

History of rockets

Explore the different types of propellants that have been used throughout history. (The Chinese are credited with creating the first rockets hundreds of years ago for fireworks and as weapons.) What are some commonalities of these propellants? What are some differences? What are some of the newest propellants being tested currently? Select two or three different types of commercial toy-rocket propellants. Design a test to determine which propellant is the best. Write up a short article detailing your findings that might be of interest to local rocket clubs and other rocket enthusiasts.

Activity 6 Ideal Gas Law for the Ideal Toy

What Do You See?

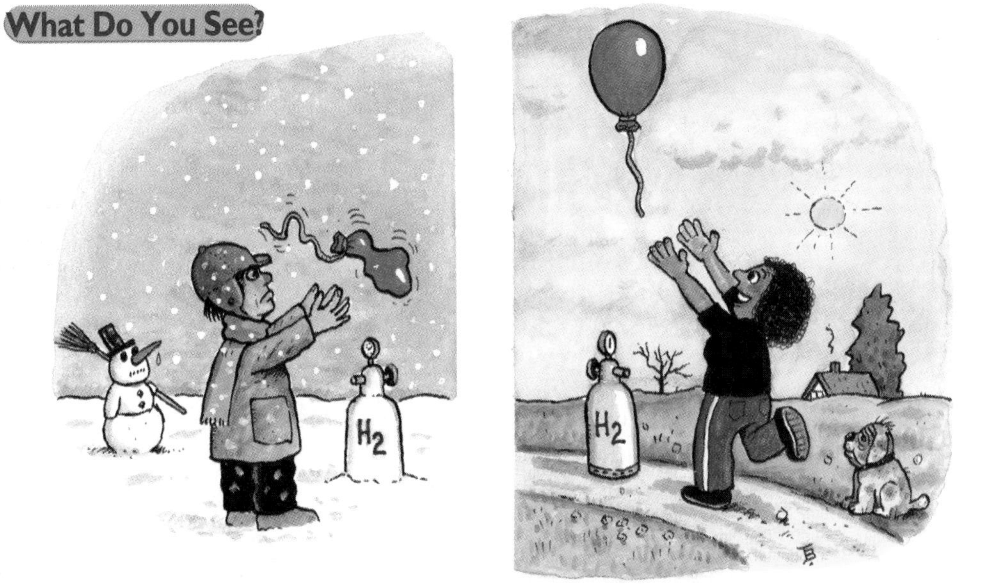
H2
H2

CHEM POETRY

My name is Ned,
a magnificent Neon,
Been bouncing about
in this box for an eon.
A long time ago,
we used to roam
In a luxury test tube –
she was our home.

But anyway, there we were,
living our lives
When a girl with a
Bunsen burner arrived.
See, the heat flowed into
that test tube and
Our gas wasn't given the
right to expand.

The "T" was increased, and
to maintain the equation,
The "V" couldn't change,
so the "P" saw inflation.
CRACK! We pushed on the
glass 'til it burst.
That day will live on in my
mind as the worst.

To imagine the graphic
events makes me wince,
And alas, I've been bitter
ever since.
The lesson my friends is a
real no-brainer:
Don't ever heat a sealed
container!

–Mala Radhakrishnan

GOALS

In this activity you will:

- Determine the volume of one mole of a gas.
- Calculate the gas-law constant "*R*."
- Derive the Ideal Gas Law equation.

What Do You Think?

A toy dart gun uses a CO_2 cartridge to shoot darts.

- **How does a toy company know how many times a CO_2 cartridge can be used to shoot the darts in a dart gun before it runs out?**

Record your ideas about this question in your *Active Chemistry* log. Be prepared to discuss your responses with your group and the class.

Investigate

From previous activities, you know that pressure and temperature affect gas volumes. In this activity you will investigate another variable that influences the behavior of gases, the number of particles. Then you will combine the relationships from all of these variables in order to derive an equation that allows you to more accurately predict changes in a gaseous system.

1. Measure the mass of 100 cm of polished magnesium ribbon. Your teacher may provide you with this mass.

   a) Record this mass in your *Active Chemistry* log.

2. Obtain a small piece of polished magnesium ribbon (approximately 2.5 cm) and carefully measure its length to the nearest 0.05 cm.

   a) Record the length of your piece of magnesium.

3. Set up a ratio to determine the mass of your small piece of

Safety goggles and a lab apron must be worn *at all times* in a chemistry lab.

The 6 *M* hydrochloric acid is very caustic and you should use caution when handling.

Use caution when adding the water to the acid in the tube because of the heat generated.

magnesium ribbon to three significant digits.

$$\frac{\text{mass of 100 cm Mg}}{\text{100 cm}} = \frac{\text{mass of small piece of Mg}}{\text{length of small piece of Mg}}$$

a) Calculate the mass of your small piece of magnesium in grams.

b) Convert this mass in grams to moles. From the periodic table, you can see that 1 mol of magnesium has a mass of 24.3 g. (One mole of any element is equal to its gram atomic weight.)

$$\text{mols of Mg} = \frac{\text{mass of small piece of Mg}}{\text{24.3 g/mol}}$$

Your teacher will provide you with a graduated gas-collecting tube fitted with a one-hole stopper. The stopper has a piece of copper wire threaded through it. Using the copper wire, you will make a cage that will hold the piece of magnesium in place while the reaction occurs in the gas tube.

You are now ready to begin the reaction.

4. Fill a 1000-mL beaker to about 2 cm from the top with water.

5. Carefully pour 10 mL of 3 *M* hydrochloric acid into the gas-collecting tube. Then, carefully and slowly fill the rest of the tube with water by pouring the water down a slightly tilted test tube. (The hydrochloric acid is denser than water and will remain at the bottom of the tube.)

6. Wrap the copper wire around the piece of magnesium to make a cage and place the stopper in the gas tube.

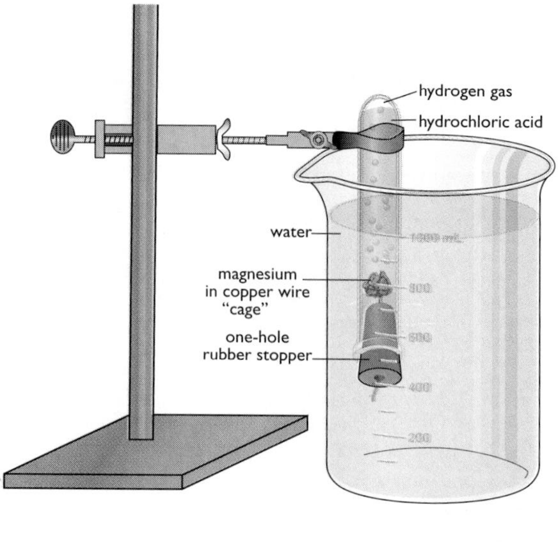
hydrogen gas
hydrochloric acid
water
magnesium in copper wire "cage"
one-hole rubber stopper

Place your finger over the hole in the stopper and invert the gas tube into the 1000-mL beaker of water. The glass tube should be clamped to a ringstand. Remove your finger and watch as the hydrochloric acid falls toward the magnesium. As the reaction concludes, tap the gas tube in the beaker to dislodge any bubbles. When the reaction is complete, adjust the height of the tube so the height of the water in the tube is level with the water in the beaker. This way the pressure exerted externally equals the pressure in the gas tube.

a) Record the air pressure in the room and the volume of gas that was collected in the gas-collecting tube.

7. Rinse out the gas tube and dispose of the water in the beaker as directed by your teacher.

8. Carry out the calculations as outlined in this step.

The equation for the reaction you carried out in this activity is:

magnesium + hydrochloric acid → hydrogen + magnesium chloride

$$Mg(s) + 2HCl(aq) \rightarrow H_2(g) + MgCl_2(aq)$$

The balanced equation shows that one mole of magnesium reacts with two moles of hydrochloric acid to produce one mole of hydrogen gas and one mole of magnesium chloride.

a) The balanced equation also shows that one mole of magnesium will produce one mole of hydrogen gas. The number of moles of magnesium you used is therefore equal to the number of moles of hydrogen gas that forms.

$$\_\_ \text{ mol Mg } \frac{1 \text{ mol } H_2}{1 \text{ mol Mg}} = \_\_ \text{ mol } H_2$$

b) From the volume of gas collected and the number of moles of hydrogen gas, calculate the volume of one mole of hydrogen gas.

$$\frac{\_\_ \text{ L of } H_2}{\_\_ \text{ mol of } H_2} = \_\_ \frac{\text{L}}{\text{mol}}$$

This is the number of liters in a mole of hydrogen gas at the present conditions of room temperature and pressure.

9. You can use a combination of Boyle's and Charles's Laws to determine the volume at any given temperature and pressure.

You learned in earlier activities that the pressure and volume of gases are inversely related and the volume and temperature are directly related (as long as the number of particles remains constant).

By combining the two equations you get:

$$\frac{\text{(pressure) (volume)}}{\text{(temperature)}} = \text{constant}$$

For the same gas, if temperature and pressure conditions are changed, you can calculate the expected change in volume using this ***Combined Gas Law***.

$$\frac{P_1 V_1}{T_1} = \frac{P_2 V_2}{T_2}$$

This states that the pressure × volume/temperature of a gas at any one time is equal to the pressure × volume/temperature of that gas under any other conditions.

Using this equation, you can calculate the molar volume of hydrogen under the conditions of standard temperature (0°C or 273 K) and standard pressure (1 atm or 760 mm Hg), also called STP conditions.

a) Record the room temperature and pressure as provided by your teacher.

b) Convert the temperature to kelvins by adding 273 to the Celsius degrees.

	In your lab	At STP
P		760 mm Hg
V		
T		273 K

Using the above equation, you know the pressure, volume, and temperature for the hydrogen gas you collected. You also know the temperature and pressure at STP.

Using this information, calculate the molar volume of hydrogen at STP.

$$V_2 = \frac{P_1 V_1 T_2}{P_2 T_1}$$

Where P_1 is room pressure, T_1 is room temperature, V_1 is your calculated volume of hydrogen, P_2 is standard pressure (1.0 atm) and T_2 is standard temperature (0°C). Remember to change Celsius degrees to kelvins.

Wash your hands and arms thoroughly after the activity.

c) Record the molar volume at STP in your *Active Chemistry* log.

d) The accepted value for the molar volume of *any* gas at STP is 22.4 L/mol. How close was your value?

e) Find your percent error by finding the difference between your value and 22.4 and then dividing by 22.4. Multiply by 100 to get a percent. Record this information in your *Active Chemistry* log.

f) What are some factors that may account for your percent error?

10. You now have all the information you need to compare changes in pressure, temperature, and volume for gases. The Combined Gas Law allows you to look at changes in these three variables that affect gases. The fourth variable is the number of particles—the number of moles of gas involved. How does it fit into the equation?

You know the Combined Gas Law:

$$\frac{\text{(pressure) (volume)}}{\text{(temperature)}} = \text{constant}$$

or more simply: $\frac{PV}{T} = k$

Using the conditions of STP, you can add the number of particles to the equation. The unit for molar volume is liters per mole, so the number of moles will go into the denominator in the equation. Using n for the number of moles you get:

$$\frac{PV}{Tn} = k$$

Substituting the conditions for STP into the equation you get:

$$\frac{\text{(1 atm) (22.4 L)}}{\text{(273 K) (1 mole)}} = R$$

By convention, "R" is called the ***Ideal Gas Law constant.***

a) What is the value and unit of "R"? Record this in your *Active Chemistry* log.

b) What would be the value and unit for "R" if the pressure were measured in 760 mm Hg? Calculate and record this in your *Active Chemistry* log.

Chem Talk

IDEAL GAS LAW

Temperature, pressure, and the number of particles must be considered when talking about a gas. An **ideal gas** is defined as one in which all collisions between atoms or molecules are perfectly elastic and in which there are no **intermolecular** attractive **forces.** The molecules/atoms of an ideal gas have no volume. You can picture the ideal gas as a number of perfectly hard spheres that collide but that otherwise do not interact with each other. Many common gases exhibit behavior very close to that of an ideal gas at high temperature and low pressure.

In spite of their different masses, all ideal gases have similar characteristics, as shown in the table.

Chem Words

ideal gas: a gas in which all collisions between atoms or molecules are perfectly elastic and in which there are no intermolecular attractive forces.

intermolecular forces: the attractive forces acting between molecules.

Gas	Number of moles	Volume (L)	Number of particles	Mass (g)
hydrogen (H_2)	1	22.4	6.02×10^{23}	2
oxygen (O_2)	1	22.4	6.02×10^{23}	32
krypton (Kr)	1	22.4	6.02×10^{23}	84

Note: Molar volumes of real gases vary a little, but they are close to the molar volume shown in the table. As examples, a mole of chlorine gas (22.1 L) and carbon dioxide gas (22.3 L) are a little less than the volume of an ideal gas (22.4 L). You can think of a real gas as being close to an ideal gas under standard conditions. This is due to attractive forces,

The **Ideal Gas Law** relates the pressure, temperature, volume, and number of moles of an ideal gas. The Ideal Gas Law was originally derived from the experimentally measured Charles's Law, Boyle's Law, and Avogadro's Law.

The Ideal Gas Law states:

$$PV = nRT$$

where P = pressure in atmospheres
n = the number of moles of gas
R = the **universal gas constant** (62.4 L·mm Hg/mol·K, or 0.0821 L·atm/mol·K)
T = temperature in kelvins

(Notice that the R values differ depending upon the units of pressure, volume, temperature, and mass of the gas. However, the preferred and most convenient units are liter, atmosphere, moles, and kelvins in which R has the value of 0.0821 L·atm/mol·K.)

Example:

The Ideal Gas Law can be used to make predictions about the pressure, temperature, volume, and number of particles of a gas. For example, you might want to find the pressure of 2.5 mol of hydrogen gas at 25.0°C if its volume is 8.55 L.

Using $PV = nRT$, rearrange the equation to solve for pressure:

$$P = \frac{nRT}{V}$$

Substituting values into the equation:

$$P = \frac{(2.5\ \text{mol})(0.0821\ \text{L} \cdot \text{atm/mol} \cdot \text{K})(298\ \text{K})}{8.55\ \text{L}}$$

$$P = 7.2\ \text{atm}$$

By using the Ideal Gas Law, you are able to make predictions about the behavior of a gas based upon the data you have measured.

Chem Words

Ideal Gas Law: a law relating the pressure, temperature, and volume of an ideal gas. $PV = nRT$.

universal gas constant: a constant factor in the ideal gas equation. R = 0.0821 L·atm/mol·K

Checking Up

1. Explain how pressure, temperature, and the number of particles affect the behavior of a gas.
2. What are the differences between an ideal gas and most common gases under normal room conditions? Why do we distinguish between ideal and non-ideal gases?
3. What is the volume of 6.5 moles of oxygen gas if the temperature is 40.0°C and the pressure is 6.2 atm?

What Do You Think Now?

At the beginning of this activity you were asked:

- **How does a toy company know how many times a CO_2 cartridge can be used to shoot the darts in a dart gun before it runs out?**

Do toy companies just guess as to how many times a cartridge can be used to shoot darts before it runs out? Do they just test several cartridges and use an average to manufacture the rest of their cartridges? Or is there a better, more predictable method to determine how much CO_2 to put in their cartridges? Explain.

Chem Essential Questions

What does it mean?

Chemistry explains a macroscopic phenomenon (what you observe) with a description of what happens at the nanoscopic level (atoms and molecules) using symbolic structures as a way to communicate. Complete the chart below in your *Active Chemistry* log.

MACRO	NANO	SYMBOLIC
What determined the volume of hydrogen gas collected in the investigation?	*How did the number of magnesium atoms impact the number of molecules of hydrogen produced?*	*Write the formula equation for the reaction between Mg and HCl. Would you expect to get the same value for R under the same room conditions for another gas, e.g., O_2 from the decomposition of H_2O_2? Explain.*

How do you know?

What does your experimental data suggest about the behavior of gases?

Why do you believe?

What does the Ideal Gas Law suggest about the predictability of gas behavior?

Why should you care?

You will be creating a toy for your challenge in this unit. You have seen that many toys are designed to use gases in some way. It could be as simple as inflating the tires to something more complicated, like generating a propellant. Write a short explanation for how determining the amounts of materials to include as a gas propellant can be determined.

Reflecting on the Activity and the Challenge

You have now discovered a way to relate the pressure, volume, amount, and temperature of a gas. You saw the formation of hydrogen gas in this activity. You know that when the magnesium reacted with the acid, H_2 gas formed. You are able to symbolically represent the reaction with a balanced chemical equation.

If your toy was designed to employ a CO_2 gas cartridge to inflate a balloon, propel a car, or blast a rocket, you should include information telling the consumer how many times the toy can be used with one CO_2 cylinder.

Chem to Go

1. A sample of dry gas weighing 1.05 g is found to occupy 1.43 L at 23.5°C and 0.951 atm. How many moles of the gas are present?
2. What is the mass of one mole of the gas in *Question 1*?
3. Let's say that you are designing a toy that requires the generation of 1.0 L of oxygen gas to operate it. What reagents would you use, and how many moles would be required if the gas was being produced at 1.0 atm and 20°C? (See *Activity 5* for help.)
4. Many gases are stored in their compressed form (under pressure). Calculate the mass of N_2 that could be stored at 22°C and 125 atm in a cylinder with a volume of 45.0 liters. The molecular mass of N_2 is 28.0 g/mole.
5. Calculate the mass in grams of the air in a hot-air balloon that has a volume of 4.0×10^5 L when the temperature of the gas is 90.0°C and the pressure is 750 mm Hg. Assume that the average molecular mass of air is 30.0 g/mole.
6. A 2.0 L soda bottle is used as a water rocket. If 0.30 L of water is in the bottle and it is pumped with air to a pressure of 3.8 atm at a temperature of 25°C, how many moles of air are in the rocket?
7. Explain how you could determine the identity of an unknown gas by using the Ideal Gas Law.
8. A balloon is to be filled with 30.0 kg of helium gas. What volume can be filled to a pressure of 1.15 atm if the temperature is 20.0°C?
9. You want to send chlorine gas, Cl_2, safely across your state. Chlorine gas is very poisonous and corrosive. You have a 5000 L truck cylinder that will withstand a pressure of 100 atm. The cylinder will be kept at 2°C throughout the trip. How many moles of chlorine gas can you safely ship?
10. ***Preparing for the Chapter Challenge***

    Discuss with your group how you might use a gas in your toy. Try to decide how much gas will need to be generated, how you will generate this gas, and the quantity of reactants that will be required to produce the desired amount of gas. Keep in mind that you will probably be forming the gas under normal atmospheric conditions and room temperatures.

Activity 7 Moving Molecules

What Do You See?

GAS
A
GAS
B

GOALS

In this activity you will:

- Determine the effect of molecular size on molecular motion.
- Predict quantities of gas produced in chemical reactions.

What Do You Think?

Party balloons are often filled with air or helium.

- **Predict which balloons — ones filled with air or ones filled with helium — will stay inflated longer. Explain why you predicted this.**

Record your ideas about this question in your *Active Chemistry* log. Be prepared to discuss your responses with your small group and the class.

Investigate

1. If your teacher were to open a bottle containing a substance with a strong perfume odor at the front of the class, estimate how much time it would take before you could smell it. Have your teacher tally the estimates at the board.

   a) Explain why you think the time for someone in the front of the class would or would not be different from someone in the back of the class.

2. Your teacher will now open the bottle. Raise your hand when you smell the odor so that the entire class can observe how the odor is traveling.

   a) Measure and record the time that elapses before you can smell the odor.

3. Dry air is composed of 79% nitrogen, 20% oxygen, 1% argon, 0.3% carbon dioxide, and trace amounts of other elements.

   a) Draw pictures of the internal views of two latex balloons. One balloon is filled with pure helium (He) and one is filled with air from your breath. Your pictures should show the size of the molecules as well as arrows depicting the speed and direction of the particles. The greater speeds will be represented by the longer arrows.

4. You are going to examine two gases under identical conditions to help you understand what might be happening in the balloons. You will use sandwich-sized plastic bags to represent the balloons. Before beginning, you must determine the amounts of chemicals required to fill the plastic bags with gas.

5. In one plastic bag, you will generate H_2 by reacting Zn with HCl (hydrochloric acid).

   a) In your *Active Chemistry* notebook, write down the balanced equation for reacting Zn and HCl.

   $$Zn(s) + 2HCl(aq) \rightarrow ZnCl_2(aq) + H_2(g)$$

   b) Show that this equation is balanced.

   c) If you wish to fill the plastic bag with 0.85 L of H_2 gas, you will need to calculate the amount of zinc that will be necessary to do this. (Too much gas could burst the bag.) Since 1 mol of H_2 fills a volume of 22.4 L, calculate how many moles of H_2 will be required to fill a volume of 0.85 L.

   d) Since the mole ratio in the reaction shows that 1 mol of Zn produces 1 mol of H_2, write down the number of moles of Zn that will be required to create the number of moles of H_2 that will fill the volume of 0.85 L.

   e) Since 1 mol of zinc is 65.4 g (see the atomic mass on the periodic table), determine the mass of zinc to add to the HCl to produce the volume of 0.85 L of gas. You can also determine the required mass of HCl, but that is not necessary. If you have extra HCl, then the reaction will be limited by the amount of zinc. Zinc is called the limiting reactant.

6. In the other plastic bag, you will generate CO_2 by reacting $NaHCO_3$ (baking soda) with CH_3COOH (vinegar).

   a) In your *Active Chemistry* notebook, write down the balanced equation for reacting $NaHCO_3$ and vinegar (CH_3COOH).

   $$NaHCO_3(s) + CH_3COOH(aq) \rightarrow CO_2(g) + H_2O(l) + NaC_2H_3O_2(aq)$$

   b) Show that the equation is balanced.

   c) Since you wish to fill the plastic bag with 0.85 L of CO_2 gas, calculate the amount of baking soda that will be necessary to do this.

7. Have your teacher approve your calculations. Set up your labeled plastic bags, and generate the different gases in each. Then measure the circumference of each bag.

   a) Record the circumference in your lab notebook.

8. Dispose of the materials as directed by your teacher. Clean up your workstation.

Safety goggles and a lab apron must be worn *at all times* in a chemistry lab.

Wash your hands and arms thoroughly after the activity.

Hydrogen gas is very flammable. Keep the bag away from sparks or a flame.

9. Allow the bags to sit for several days.
   a) Record your observations and new circumference measurements in your *Active Chemistry* log each day.
10. Your teacher may have generated the gases in the balloons a few days earlier so that you can compare the volume of the balloons after several days. A pair of balloons is shown in the diagram, so that you can complete this activity rather than halt everything for the days it may take for your balloons to change.
    a) Describe the differences between the gases you generated that might account for the differences you observe in the two models.
    b) How could these differences explain your observations?

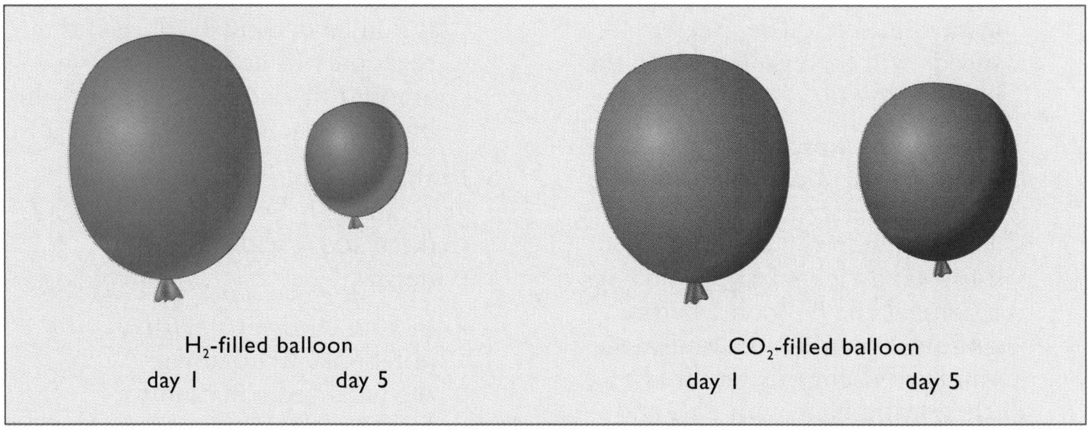
H_2-filled balloon
day 1
day 5
CO_2-filled balloon
day 1
day 5

Chem Talk

MOLECULAR SIZE AND MOLECULAR MOTION OF GASES

Small-particle Model of Gases

Scientists have adopted the following model for gases:

- Gases consist of tiny particles (atoms or molecules) which are separated by relatively large distances. For water, the particles are about 1000 times further apart in the gas phase as in the liquid phase.
- Gas molecules are in constant, random motion, and travel in a straight line between collisions. They do collide frequently with other gas molecules and with the walls of their container. Gas pressure is related to the sum of all of these collisions with the walls during a given time.

- At any given temperature (Kelvin scale), the average kinetic energy of all the molecules of gas is directly proportional to that temperature. However, some of the molecules will be moving faster than the average, some slower.
- At the same temperature, all gases have the same average kinetic energy in their molecules. As the temperature increases, so do the average velocities and kinetic energies of the molecules.

Diffusion

When the perfume or other odors left the bottle and traveled about the room, you observed that the students closest to the teacher smelled the perfume first. **Diffusion** is the spontaneous mixing of one gas (or liquid) with another that occurs because of the random movement of the molecules. This occurs with perfumes because the fragrant gaseous molecules move freely through the widely spaced air molecules to reach your nose. (In typical classrooms, with radiators, air conditioners, open windows, students moving around, etc., convection currents are much more important in distributing gases than diffusion.) The process of diffusion is complete when the molecules of the gases are evenly spread within the room. Diffusion is purely a physical phenomenon. The rate of diffusion has to do with the speed of the gas molecules. All gases at the same temperature have the same average kinetic energy. However, gases with a large molar mass have slow speeds while gases with small molar mass have fast speeds. The velocity (v) of a gas molecule is related to its kinetic energy (KE):

$$KE = \frac{1}{2}mv^2$$

where m is the mass of the molecule.

Since two gases have the same kinetic energy, you can derive the relationship from the equation above. Assume that you have a gas with a large mass, m_L and one with a small mass, m_S. Since their kinetic energies are equal:

$$\frac{1}{2}m_L v^2_L = \frac{1}{2}m_S v^2_S$$

$$\frac{v_L}{v_S} = \sqrt{\frac{m_S}{m_L}}$$

The velocity of large-mass gases is smaller than the velocity of small-mass gases and its diffusion is also slower. For example, if the ratio of the masses of the gases is 1:9, then the ratio of speeds will be 1:3. If you make the mass of the particles nine times larger, the speed decreases by a factor of 3.

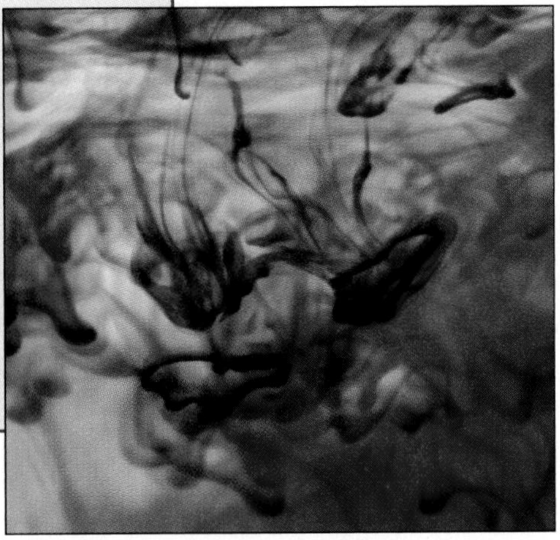

Chem Words

diffusion: the spontaneous mixing of one gas (or liquid) with another that occurs because of the random movement of the molecules.

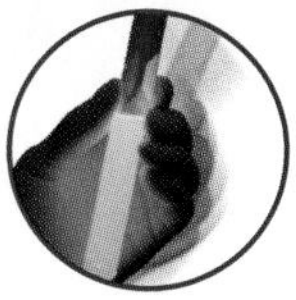

Chem Words

effusion: the movement of a gas through an extremely tiny opening into a region of lower pressure.

Graham's Law of Effusion: a law that states that the rate of escape of a gas from a container through a pinhole (effusion) is inversely proportional to the square root of the molar mass of the gas.

Effusion

When the balloon deflated over time, it was due to the leaking of the gas through tiny openings in the latex of the balloon. These holes in the material are much, much smaller than a puncture. The **effusion** of a gas is its movement through an extremely tiny opening into a region of lower pressure. In the *Investigate* section, you observed the effusion to be much greater for the hydrogen gas than for the carbon dioxide gas. You might think that the smaller hydrogen molecules are able to fit through the tiny holes and therefore escape faster. However, since the larger carbon dioxide molecules can also fit through the holes, the difference in the rate of effusion must be dependent on another property of the gases.

A Scottish scientist, Thomas Graham (1805–1869), studied the rates at which various gases effuse. He found that the more dense the gas is, the slower it effuses. The exact relationship between rate and gas density, *d*, is called **Graham's Law of Effusion**.

Graham's law states that the rate of effusion of a gas is inversely proportional to the square root of the density of the gas. Since equal volumes of gas at the same temperature and pressure contain equal numbers of gas molecules, the rate of effusion is also inversely proportional to the square root of the molar mass of the gas. The gas with the lowest molar mass effuses the fastest.

Once again, since the kinetic energies are identical:

$$\frac{1}{2}m_L v^2_L = \frac{1}{2}m_S v^2_S$$

$$\frac{v_L}{v_S} = \sqrt{\frac{m_S}{m_L}}$$

Look at the velocities of the two gases in the activity—hydrogen and carbon dioxide. The molar mass of hydrogen is 2.0 g/mole. The molar mass of carbon dioxide is 44.0 g/mole.

What is the rate of effusion of hydrogen to carbon dioxide?

$$\frac{v_{H_2}}{v_{CO_2}} = \sqrt{\frac{44.0}{2.0}} = 4.7$$

Solving the equation gives a ratio of 4.7:1. This tells you that at the same temperature, hydrogen molecules have a velocity 4.7 times greater than carbon dioxide molecules. It was the higher velocity that allowed the hydrogen to leave the latex balloon faster than the carbon dioxide.

Diffusion and effusion have the same mathematical relationship. They also sound very much the same. They also both deal with gases. This certainly leads to confusion. Diffusion has to do with the random motion of the gases across space. Effusion has to do with the random motion of the gases through the tiny openings.

Checking Up

1. Explain diffusion of a gas in your own words.
2. What is meant by the effusion of a gas?
3. Two equal-sized boxes with identical small openings contain different gases. One contains carbon dioxide (CO_2) and the other contains helium (He). Which gas will effuse faster?
4. How is the average kinetic energy of gas particles related to temperature?

What Do You Think Now?

At the beginning of this activity you were asked:

- **Predict which balloons — ones filled with air or ones filled with helium — will stay inflated longer. Explain why you predicted this.**

How would you answer this question now that you have completed this activity?

Chem Essential Questions

What does it mean?

Chemistry explains a macroscopic phenomenon (what you observe) with a description of what happens at the nanoscopic level (atoms and molecules) using symbolic structures as a way to communicate. Complete the chart below in your *Active Chemistry* log.

MACRO	NANO	SYMBOLIC
What visual evidence do you have that supports Graham's Law of Effusion?	*Describe what is happening at the nanoscopic level when two gases of different masses are escaping from tiny holes in their containers.*	*Use an equation to represent Graham's Law of Effusion.*

→

How do you know?

Using the molar mass of H_2 of 2.0 g and an approximation of the molar mass of air to be 28.6 g, what is the rate of effusion of H_2 to air? From this information, what would you predict for the "leak rate" of air-filled and hydrogen-filled balloons?

Why do you believe?

A tennis ball contains a mixture of gases. Why does a tennis ball lose its bounce over time?

Why should you care?

If your toy uses a gas to propel or otherwise support the way it is used, what considerations will you need to keep in mind as you design it? If the toy must contain a constant amount of some gas, will choosing the heaviest gas available always be the best decision? Explain your answer using examples to support your thoughts.

Reflecting on the Activity and the Challenge

In this activity you explored the effect of gas size on effusion rates. You found that the more massive the gas, the slower its rate of effusion. For example, H_2 has a molar mass of 2; He has a molar mass of 4; and N_2 has a molar mass of 28. Using Graham's Law, you would predict that H_2 would effuse at a faster rate than helium or nitrogen.

You have probably seen the effect of mass on effusion with party balloons lots of times but had never really tested what might be occurring. You might apply your new knowledge of what is occurring to the toy model your team is proposing. Your proposal will have to explain the advantages and disadvantages of using one particular gas over another. The use of different gases might impact the behavior of your toy. Consider how you could make that knowledge work to your advantage in the toy design.

Chem to Go

1. If latex balloons are filled with the following gases and allowed to sit for two days, which balloon will have the most volume? Which would have the least volume? Rank them all in order of smallest to largest volume. Explain your reasoning.

   a) H_2 (molar mass = 2.0 g/mol)   b) He (molar mass = 4.0 g/mol)

   c) O_2 (molar mass = 32.0 g/mol)   d) N_2 (molar mass = 28.0 g/mol)

   e) CO_2 (molar mass = 44.0 g/mol)

2. Two cotton plugs are placed simultaneously in each end of a glass tube, 12 cm in length. On one end the cotton is soaked with aqueous NH_3 and on the other end the cotton is soaked with aqueous HCl. Within minutes a white ring of NH_4Cl appears about 4 cm from the HCl side. NH_4Cl has formed as the HCl reacted with the NH_3. Explain why the reaction occurred much closer to the HCl than to the NH_3 side.

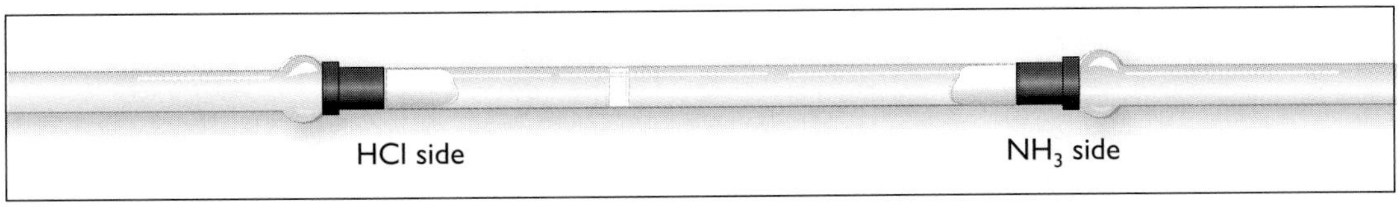
HCl side
NH_3 side

3. Which of the following gases would most likely keep automobile tires inflated the longest: CO_2, air (average molar mass 29 g/mol), or He? Why?

4. Given the molar mass of carbon dioxide (44.0 g/mol) and oxygen (32.0 g/mol), determine the rate of effusion of the CO_2 to O_2.

5. The rate of effusion of Gas A to Gas B is 1:2. Which gas has the higher molecular mass?

6. ***Preparing for the Chapter Challenge***

   Different gases could be used in the toy that you are proposing. Based on your toy's design, certain criteria will determine what the best gas to use will be. List the key criteria to consider and tests that would need to be carried out on the gases to be used in a toy proposal.

Inquiring Further

The cost factor

If you wanted to generate as much carbon dioxide gas as possible, but had only $1 to spend, how much baking soda and vinegar would you purchase? Assume that the cost of baking soda is 5¢ per gram and the price of vinegar is 3¢ per gram.

Activity 8 Plastics

What Do You See?

OPEN
PURE PLASTIC
JUST ADD WATER

GOALS

In this activity you will:

- Distinguish between thermoset and thermoplastic plastics
- Test materials for product design.

What Do You Think?

In 1909, Leo Baekeland developed the polymer, Bakelite. The polymer industry hasn't stopped growing since! The term "plastics" was introduced in the 1920s to describe these new materials that were being introduced. Here is a *partial* list of common items that contain polymers.

- 2-L soda bottles
- balloons
- carpet
- caulking
- cellophane tape
- coffee stirrers
- combs
- computers
- contact lenses
- credit cards
- disposable razors
- epoxy glue
- erasers
- foam cups
- foam rubber
- food wrap
- football helmet
- garbage bags
- guitar strings
- hairspray
- hockey puck
- insulation
- margarine tubs
- milk jugs
- paint
- pantyhose
- raincoat
- rubber bands
- sandwich bags
- shampoo bottles
- shoe laces
- slime
- snorkle and swim fins
- sunglasses
- teflon coating
- tennis ball
- thread
- tires
- toothbrush
- umbrella
- velcro
- vinyl car top

- **What properties of plastics have made their use so widespread?**

Record your ideas about this question in your *Active Chemistry* log. Be prepared to discuss your responses with your small group and the class.

Investigate

Part A: Thermoplastic Activity

1. Pour about 300 mL tap water into a 400 mL-beaker. Place the beaker on a hot plate. Turn on the hot plate and bring the water to a boil. Then turn off the hot plate.
2. Wearing gloves, hold one end of a strip of thermoplastic modeling material, and dip the other end into the hot water until it softens. Keep it away from the sides of the beaker. Remove it from the water. With *wet* gloved fingers, grasp the softened end. Dip the other end in the water until it is also softened.
3. Remove the strip from the water bath, and quickly mold the thermoplastic modeling material into a design of your own choosing. *Do not mold it on yourself as a bracelet or a ring as the final product could be difficult to remove!* You might mold it into some component of the toy model your group is going to propose. If the polymer becomes too hard, dip it in hot water to soften it.

4. Let the material cool on the countertop.
5. Clean up your workstation and return all equipment as directed.

Part B: Thermoset Activity

1. Get a 2 cm piece of epoxy putty. Note that it is composed of two colored components.
2. Knead the putty until the two components are thoroughly mixed.
3. Quickly shape the putty into a design of your choosing. Again, you might want to shape it into something that you could use in your toy model.
4. Let the putty harden on a paper towel or piece of plastic bag. Do *not* let the putty harden on the countertop; it may be difficult to remove.
5. As the putty is hardening, test its temperature with your fingertips.

   a) Does the sample change temperature? Describe what you observe.

   b) Describe the difference between the thermoplastic and thermoset polymers.

   c) In what applications would a thermoset polymer be most desirable? Thermoplastic? Explain your reasoning.
6. Clean up your workstation.

Safety goggles and a lab apron must be worn *at all times* in a chemistry lab.

Wash your hands and arms thoroughly after the activity.

Part C: Testing Plastics to Determine Product Use

1. Think carefully about the plastics that may be a part of your toy model. How will it be used, and what type of wear and tear could be expected on each part? How strong will the parts need to be? What type of impact might the parts be subjected to? How bendable will the parts need to be? What other conditions will be important in considering the durability and the quality of your toy? Brainstorm these questions with members of your group.

   a) Record your thoughts in your *Active Chemistry* log.

2. Identify two important criteria that will need to be considered for your toy model. Now, determine a way to test the types of plastic that you are considering, so that you can justify that choice on more than availability and costs. For example:

- If strength of the plastic is important, then you will need to design a method to determine the strength of the material by measuring how large a constant force the plastic can withstand without breaking.
- If resistance to impact is important, then you will need to design a method to determine the amount of impact force the plastic you will be using can take.
- Perhaps your plastic will need to withstand lots of flexing, bending, stretching, compressing, and twisting. Design a valid method to determine the fatigue resistance of your plastic.

3. Design the procedure of the tests you will conduct. Use good experimental design. Collect both quantitative and qualitative data.

   a) Record your procedure in your *Active Chemistry* log.

4. When your teacher has approved your procedure, carry out the tests.

   a) Based on your results, justify the best plastic(s) to use in your toy model. (Use your data.)

5. Share your results with other groups. What else did you learn about some of the materials you were considering using?

Chem Talk

POLYMERS

Polymers Are Long Chains of Monomers

Often referred to as **macromolecules**, **polymers** are enormously long molecules made up of many repeating smaller molecules. The smaller molecules that make up a polymer are called **monomers** (from the Greek *mono*, meaning one). Polymers may be made of tens of thousands of repeating monomer units with molecular weights reaching to millions of daltons (one dalton is equal to one atomic mass unit). Monomers are the building blocks of polymers; the links that make up the polymer chains. These molecular chains may be branched or unbranched, interconnected at various points, or interconnected at a great many points so that they form rigid solids. At the molecular level, they may be long chains, or sheets, or even a complicated three-dimensional lattice.

Plastics

A plastic is simply a substance that can be molded into various shapes that then harden. All of the plastics that you come into contact with today are polymers. Not all polymers are plastic however, as starches, cellulose, proteins, and DNA (natural polymers) are not considered plastic.

The first *synthetic* polymer was created in response to a call for a synthetic substitute for ivory. In 1909 Leo Baekeland received a patent for the first fully synthetic polymer he called Bakelite. Bakelite is a three-dimensional resin network made from the polymerization of phenol and formaldehyde. This polymer is a hard, non-conducting material that *cannot be melted and remolded*. Such a polymer is called a **thermoset polymer** — one that is soft enough to be molded when first prepared, but once it is hard, it stays hard. **Thermoplastic polymers**, on the other hand, are those that can be softened by heat and then remolded.

Polyethylene is a thermoplastic polymer. It is the simplest and least expensive synthetic polymer. It is made from ethylene ($CH_2{=}CH_2$). Over 20 million tons of polyethylene are produced in the United States each year.

There are two principal types of polyethylene, **high-density polyethylene** (HDPE) and **low-density polyethylene** (LDPE). Trash bags, food wrapping, electrical wire insulation and garment bags are but

Chem Words

macromolecules (polymers): very large molecules made up of smaller repeating units (called monomers).

monomers: the smallest repeating unit of a polymer.

thermoset polymer: a polymer that is a hard, non-conducting material that *cannot be melted and remolded.*

thermoplastic polymer: a polymer that can be softened by heat and then remolded.

polyethylene: a thermoplastic polymer of the monomer ethene (ethylene).

high-density polyethylene (HDPE): molecules made of linear chains of polyethylene with very little branching. They are more rigid and have a higher melting point than LDPE.

low-density polyethylene (LDPE): molecules of polyethylene that contain a large amount of branching. They are more flexible and have a lower melting point than HDPE.

a few examples of products made of LDPE. The sturdier HDPE is used for toys, milk jugs, CD boxes, containers for oils and chemicals, and many, many more items. The difference between the two types is that LDPE has a great deal of side chains branching off the polymer chains. The branching of the LDPE prevents the molecules from being packed closely together (resulting in low density), so they tend to be very flexible. HDPE is made of mostly linear chains. HDPE molecules, without the branching side chains, can pack together well (high density), so this material is more rigid and has a higher melting point than LDPE.

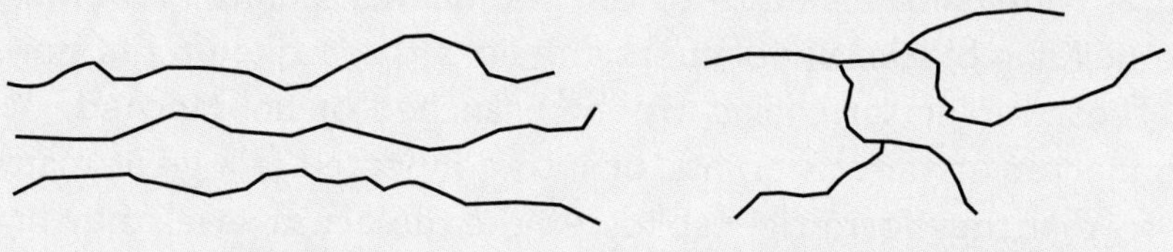

HDPE — LDPE (branching)

Checking Up

1. What is meant by the term "macromolecule"?
2. How does a thermoset polymer differ from a thermoplastic polymer?
3. Explain the difference between a branched-chain and a linear-chain molecule.

What Do You Think Now?

At the beginning of this activity you were asked:

- **What properties of plastics have made their use so widespread?**

How have your ideas about the properties of polymers changed after having completed this activity? List three important properties of polymers that you did not have in your original list.

Chem Essential Questions

What does it mean?

Chemistry explains a macroscopic phenomenon (what you observe) with a description of what happens at the nanoscopic level (atoms and molecules) using symbolic structures as a way to communicate. Complete the chart below in your *Active Chemistry* log.

MACRO	NANO	SYMBOLIC
What important properties of polymers did you observe in this activity?	*Take two of the properties from the macro box and describe how the structure of the polymers gives rise to these properties.*	*Show symbolically how LDPE and HDPE differ. Then draw two polymer chains with cross-linkers that reduce the mobility of a polymer.*

How do you know?

Explain how your tests for two properties of a polymer related to the structure of the polymer.

Why do you believe?

Plastics are a large part of everyday life; Americans use an astounding amount of polymers each year. Most of these materials are derived from petroleum, a limited natural resource. The polymers are made mostly of carbon as well as other elements. Propose an alternative source of carbon for the creation of future polymers.

Why should you care?

It seems reasonable to assume that your toy design may include the use of some plastic. Understanding the nature of and being able to clearly explain your choice of polymer will improve your toy design.

Reflecting on the Activity and the Challenge

In this activity, you compared two types of plastics, thermoplastic and thermoset. You found that they had very different properties, which would help determine which type of plastic to use for different design purposes. Thermoplastics can be recycled as long as the polymer chain remains intact. On the other hand, thermoset plastics cannot be recycled. After examining these two types of plastics, you conducted some material tests, much like those that would be done in an industrial setting, to help you determine which plastic would be best for your toy model. Now, you can use your plastic test results to help you complete your toy model and determine a cost analysis for your product.

Chem to Go

1. Let's consider the first part of this activity where you compared two types of plastics.

   Thermoplastics

   a) Why was it necessary to heat the thermoplastic modeling material in order to shape it?

   b) Was this an exothermic or endothermic change?

   c) Was this a chemical or physical change or both?

   d) How could thermoplastics be used?

   Thermosets

   e) Why are the two epoxy putty components separated?

   f) As the epoxy putty sets, did it feel hot or cold?

   g) Was this an exothermic or endothermic reaction?

   h) Was this a chemical or physical change or both?

   i) Could you remold the material if you did not like the first thing you made? Explain.

   j) How could thermoset plastics be used?

2. Draw pictures of what was occurring at the molecular level as you worked with the thermoplastic modeling material and the epoxy putty.

3. Are all polymers products of chemical industries? Explain.

4. What are the advantages and disadvantages of using plastic rather than other materials in your toy model?

5. Speculate as to why so many products today are made of polymers.

6. ***Preparing for the Chapter Challenge***

   Consider how you might use plastics in your toy model. Draw a scale model of your toy and label the components and the materials that it is made of. Determine how much of each material will be required to manufacture one of your toys, and develop a cost analysis sheet for your toy that could be included in your final presentation.

Inquiring Further

1. The cost of toys

Investigate toys at a local store. Determine the percentages that are made mostly of plastics. Compile a list of the other materials in the toys. Estimate the cost of manufacturing each item based on the materials and compare that to the retail cost. Discuss the markup that toy products have and what other costs are involved in their manufacturing.

2. Exploring other plastics

Make Slime

Mix 20 mL of a 4% polyvinyl alcohol (PVA) solution with 5 mL of 4% borax solution in a small disposable cup. Stir with a wooden stirring stick. Test its properties (i.e., density, viscosity, malleability, resistance to pressure). Determine how this might be used in a toy product.

Do not inhale or ingest borax!

Make Gluep

Mix 15 mL each of white glue and water in a small disposable cup. Add food coloring if desired. Add 10 mL of 4% borax solution and stir vigorously with a wooden stirring stick. Knead the gluep and observe its properties and compare them to the properties of slime. Determine how gluep might be used in a toy product.

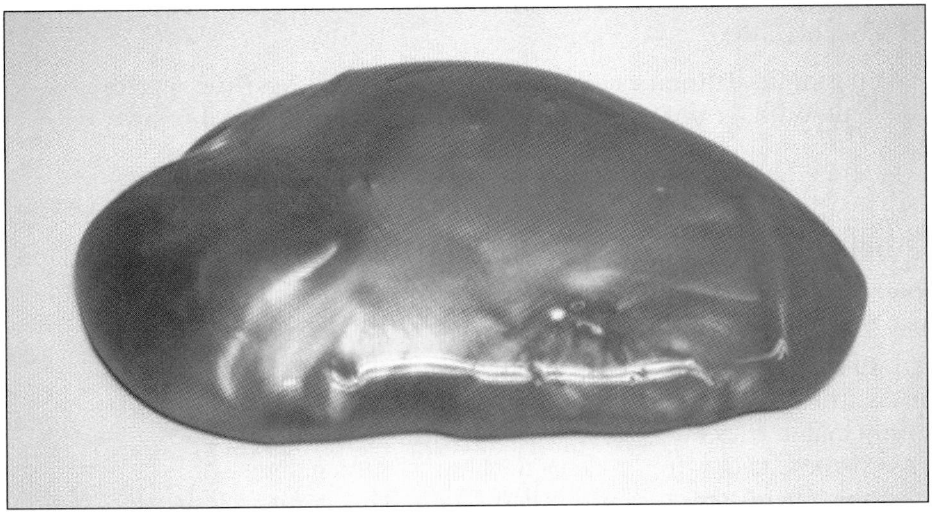

Chem at Work

Susan Stamats

Hot-Air Balloon Pilot, Cedar Rapids, IA

When Susan Stamats saw her first hot-air balloon, she was captivated. The vision of the beautiful, multi-colored ball floating overhead filled her with excitement and she knew instantly that hot-air balloons would become part of her life.

She got a job with a balloon crew and learned about the mechanics of ballooning. Without even realizing it, she was learning a lot of science! Eventually, she worked her way up to becoming pilot of a hot-air balloon.

Over the past two decades, Susan has flown over 1,600 hours. "It's magical," she says. "Every time you fly is different—the conditions always change... It's great for me... I get bored easily!"

Now, Susan is an instructor, teaching other balloon pilots. Pilots have to learn to use complicated equipment, including altimeters, variometers, and thermisters, (heat sensors.) The sensors measure the temperature at the top of the envelope, which is what the balloon is called. Heat is a key factor in balloon piloting because it is what causes the balloon to rise. Heat also controls the altitude.

There are many principles of chemistry that apply to the flight of a hot-air balloon. The fuel is combusting propane and the envelope is made out of nylon (a polymer) with a polymer heat-seal on the inside. Although she hasn't taken chemistry since she was in high school, Susan is very aware of the important part it plays in every flight she takes.

Susan enjoys participating in balloon races and competitions all over the world. So far, she and her balloon have soared high above Mexico, France, Zimbabwe and South Africa.

Kay Gonzales

Owner, Costume and Magic Store, Orlando FL

Kay Gonzales owns a Florida store where you can buy magic tricks. Many of these tricks are just simple chemistry experiments. "Flash paper," for example, is made by altering the hydroxyl groups in papers' natural cellulose to act as an oxidizing agent. Like magic, the paper burns up completely in seconds.

Ron Bonnstetter

Video Game Developer, Lincoln, NE

Teacher and scientist, Ron Bonnstetter worked with students to develop a video game called *Nano*. This game features a laser-toting microscopic robot who patrols the inside of the human respiratory system. It incorporates the fun of blasting "bad guys" with the chemistry and biology used in fighting cancer.

Ideal Toy Assessment

Your *Chapter Challenge* is to create a toy that uses various chemical and/or gas principles. The toy should be appealing to a certain age group of your choice. You will need to prepare a presentation for the board of the toy company. Your presentation should include a written proposal, either a detailed drawing or mock prototype of the toy, any potential hazards or waste-disposal issues, and a cost analysis of the item for manufacturing. Your presentation will be evaluated on the quality of your visual aids or your prototype, the quality of your presentation, the explanation of the chemistry involved, and the quality of your written proposal.

Chemistry Content

To begin, you should review all of the activities that you have completed. You can skim through the text and your *Active Chemistry* log to help remind you of the chemistry concepts in each activity.

Activity 1: You learned about battery construction and created your own electrochemical cell. Your battery investigation helped you learn about the Metal Activity Series and redox reactions.

Activity 2: You investigated the differences between solids, liquids, and gases and compared the boiling points of hydrocarbons and alcohols.

Activity 3: You constructed a Cartesian diver toy and gained knowledge about Boyle's Law and the relation between pressure and volume of a gas.

Activity 4: You studied the relationship between the volume and temperature of a gas and the representation of that relationship in Charles's Law. You also constructed a hot-air balloon.

Activity 5: You produced and tested three different gases. You then used two of these gases to power a toy rocket.

Activity 6: You determined the volume of one mole of gas. You then developed the Ideal Gas Law relating the pressure, temperature, and volume of gas.

Activity 7: You predicted the quantities of gas produced in a chemical reaction.

Activity 8: You investigated the differences between thermoset and thermoplastic plastics.

You may want to make a chart that shows the activity number, some chemistry concepts in the activity, and some ideas as to how you can use these concepts as part of your chemical dominoes sequence or the written summary. Your chart may include how to plan to generate and use the gas for the toy. You should pay particular attention to the *Reflecting on the Activity and the Challenge, Chem Essential Questions,* and *Preparing for the Chapter Challenge* sections. You should also compare your list with that given in the *Chem You Learned* summary.

Activity #	Chemistry concepts	How to use concepts

You may decide to do the first activity as a group to ensure that everybody understands how to proceed. After completing the first activity, each team member can be assigned two or three activities. You can then review all of the activities as a group with the activity expert reviewing each summary.

Criteria

You and your team should review the criteria by which you will be graded. Before beginning the chapter, your teacher led a class discussion to get a sense of what criteria should be used to judge the quality of work for this *Ideal Toy* and the related written summary. It is now time to revisit that discussion since you now have considerable understanding of chemistry concepts that you can include in your presentation. Think about and discuss what would make a great ideal toy and presentation to the corporate board. How will you create a great toy and apply the chemistry concepts of the chapter?

The rubric will assign points to the diagram of prototype of the toy (or mock-up prototype), the quality of the presentation, the accuracy and variety of the chemical principles explained, the written proposal, as well as the cost analysis. You must decide how many points will be assigned to each category and how many diagrams or chemical principles will be required for the top grade. This rubric can be a useful tool for your team to check the quality of your work and to ensure that you have included all necessary parts of the project.

Preparing for the Chapter Challenge

- Decide on the *Ideal Toy*

Your team's next step is to decide on the *Ideal Toy*. For which age group will your toy be targeted? Will your toy use a battery? How will it use a gas and how will that gas be generated? What will be the focus of your presentation to the corporate board of the toy company? How will you ensure that your toy is safe?

• **Prepare Your Written Materials**

Your written materials must include:

- detailed drawing (or mock prototype) of the toy
- explanation of the chemistry principles used
- any potential hazards or waste-disposal issues
- cost analysis of the item for manufacturing

• **Chemistry content is necessary, but not sufficient.**

All your knowledge of chemistry will be necessary for the *Ideal Toy* but it won't be sufficient for the success of the toy and board presentation. You must also find an entertaining and effective way of presenting the content. If you decide to build a prototype of your toy, you will also need to obtain the materials beforehand. Where will these come from?

Creating your toy, presentation, and written description is a creative process. Your entire team should have input and everyone on the team should be comfortable with the plan.

• **Manage Your Time**

You will need to make sure that you have enough time to put all the components together. You have to have both the presentation and the written script ready on the due date. You have a sense of how you want to proceed and what you want the final product to be. You now have to allocate the work. How much time do you have to complete the project? When is the due date? How will you get everything done in this time frame? Who will be working on the written script including the description of chemistry concepts? Will each team member contribute one chemistry concept? How will you ensure that everybody's work meets the standard of excellence so that everybody on the team gets an A?

Planning a project well does not ensure success, but poor planning almost always leads to disappointment. Create a time chart showing how much time you have. Allocate responsibilities to everybody including work that must be done in class and work that can be done individually for homework. Leave time to review each other's work.

• **Rehearse Your Presentation**

You should rehearse your presentation to the board. You may choose to have one team member demonstrate the toy or present the sketches of the toy. Another team member can be explaining the chemistry concepts. You should decide if your presentation would be strengthened by having some of the chemistry concepts described prior to the presentation of the toy or if the explanation should follow the toy presentation.

At that practice session, you will find out if you have conformed to the time limitations. You will also then be able to make some last-minute corrections based on the results of the practice session.

Engineering/Technology Design

Reflect on the engineering/technology design process. Recall the successes and disappointments from the *mini-challenge*. How can you build upon what went right and what could have been improved? At this point, you are starting the design cycle all over again. Review the steps of the design process described in the *mini-challenge*.

Have fun with your Ideal Toy!

Chem You Learned

- **Electrochemical cells** (batteries) produce **voltage** based on the relative **metal activities** of the **electrodes**.
- The **half-reactions** that are taking place at the **anode** and **cathode** can be explained in terms of **oxidation** and **reduction**.
- **Oxidation** is the loss of electrons in a reaction; **reduction** is the gain of electrons. **LEO** the lion says **GER**rrrr is a helpful pneumonic device.
- The size and shape of a molecule depends on what atoms are contained in the molecule.
- **London dispersion forces** are the weak **intermolecular forces** in **non-polar** molecules, such as the **hydrocarbons**.
- In **polar covalent** molecules the strength of the intermolecular forces depend on the **electronegativity** of the atoms and their intramolecular orientation.
- Some **physical properties**, like **melting point** and **boiling point**, increase regularly as the molecular size of a family of compounds becomes larger.
- **Boyle's Law** states that the product of the pressure and volume of a sample of gas will equal a constant when the temperature is constant. $P_1V_1 = P_2V_2$
- **Charles's Law** states that the volume of a sample of gas is directly related to the temperature (**kelvins**) when the pressure is constant. $\frac{V_1}{T_1} = \frac{V_2}{T_2}$
- Producing rocket fuels requires an understanding of the following type of reactions: **synthesis**, **single-** and **double-replacement**, and **decomposition**.
- Using Avogadro's gas law with Charles's and Boyle's Laws allows for the development of the **Combined Gas Law**: $\frac{P_1V_1}{T_1} = \frac{P_2V_2}{T_2}$
- From the **Combined Gas Law** the **Ideal Gas Equation** can be developed: $PV = nRT$. This equation allows the determination of any one of the variables (P, V, T, n) when the other three are known.
- At the same temperature, all gases have the same **kinetic energy**. $KE = \frac{1}{2}mv^2$. It follows that a heavier gas moves more slowly than a lighter gas.
- **Graham's Law of Effusion** states that the rate of **effusion** is inversely proportional to the square root of the density of the gas. In comparing the effusion rate of two gases, note that since the volume is constant, then molecular mass values can be used instead of density. $\frac{v_1}{v_2} = \sqrt{\frac{m_2}{m_1}}$
- **Thermoset** plastics are rigid and cannot be remolded after they set.
- **Thermoplastics** differ from the thermoset plastics since they can be reheated and reformed to different shapes.
- Plastics are **polymers** and built from **monomers**. An example is **polyethylene** which contains ethylene monomers.

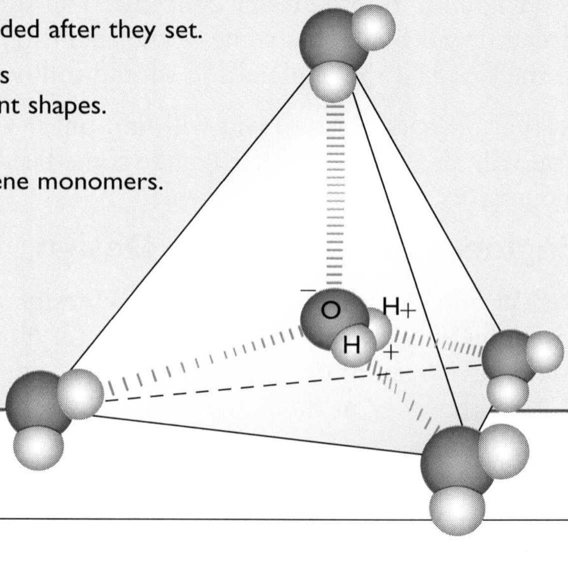
O
H
H

1000 mL
±5%
900
700
600

Chapter 6

COOL CHEMISTRY SHOW

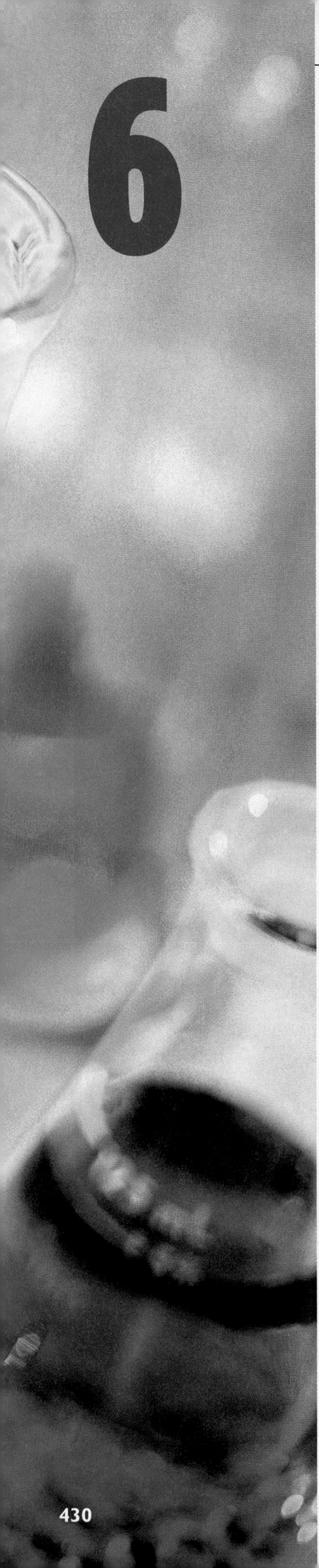

Chapter Challenge

6

Cool Chemistry Show

Scenario

The fourth- and fifth-grade students at a local elementary school have been studying chemistry in their classes. Because of the students' overwhelming interest, their teachers have asked your class to present a chemistry science show to their students. The elementary teachers have requested that the show be both interesting and informative. For the chemistry science show, the fourth-grade teachers are asking your class to include demonstrations and explanations about chemical and physical properties. The fifth-grade teacher wants the students to learn more about acids and bases, and about chemical reactions that involve color changes.

Your Challenge

You and your classmates are being challenged to present an entertaining and informative chemistry science show to fourth- and fifth-grade students.

- The content of the show should meet the needs and interest of your audience. Keep in mind that you will need to tailor your shows to address the specific needs of both the fourth- and fifth-grade teachers' requests.Your class may choose to add other presentations to enhance the show.
- All presentations must include a demonstration and an audience-appropriate explanation of the chemistry concepts involved.
- You must provide the teachers with a written summary including directions for your chemistry show with explanations of the chemistry. Although you are giving a presentation to elementary students, your understanding of your chosen demonstrations should be appropriate for high-school students.
- As always, safety is a top priority. You and your classmates will wear safety gear, including safety goggles, appropriate to the presentation being conducted. Presentations including flammable or explosive reactions are not appropriate for the elementary audience and may not be included in the show.

The class, as a whole, is responsible for putting on this *Cool Chemistry Show*. You will need to coordinate your selection of presentations to provide a show that addresses a variety of chemistry concepts in an entertaining and informative manner.

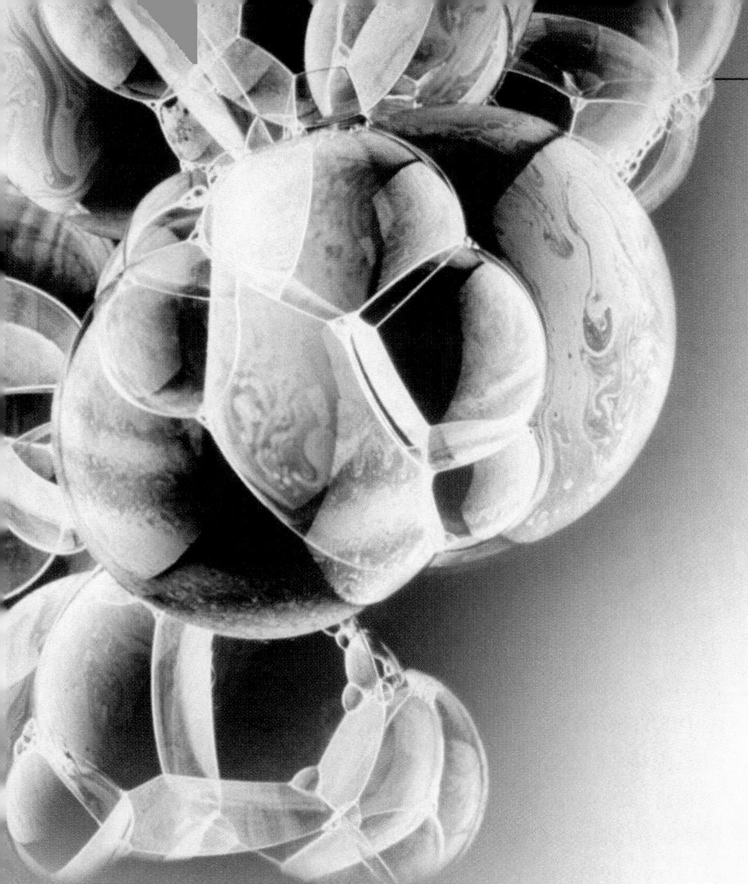

ChemCorner

Chemistry in *Cool Chemistry Show*

- Physical properties
- Chemical properties
- Concentrations of solutions
- Chemical tests
- Chemical names
- Chemical formulas
- Valence electrons
- Ionic compounds
- Polyatomic ions
- Covalent and ionic bonds
- Chemical equations
- Single-replacement reactions
- Double-replacement reactions
- Exothermic and endothermic reactions
- Chemical kinetics
- Acids, bases, indicators
- Acid/base definitions
- Oxidation-reduction reactions

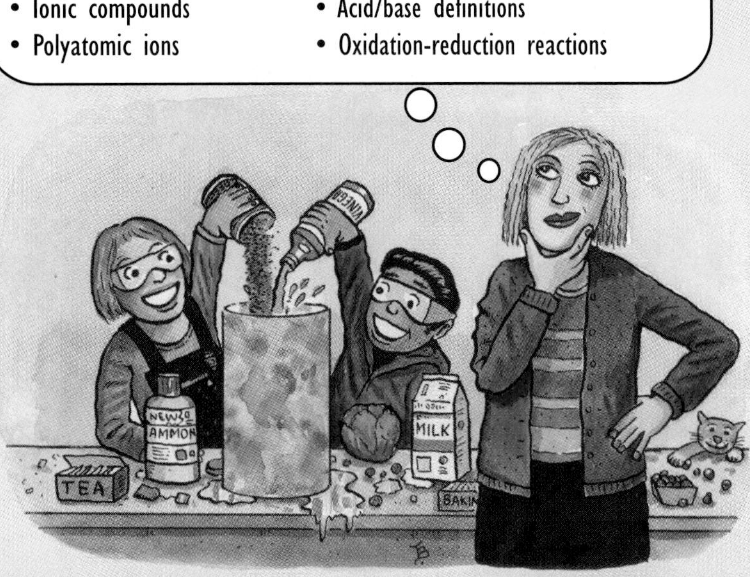
AMMON
MILK
TEA
BAKIN

Criteria

How will your involvement in the *Cool Chemistry Show* be graded? What qualities should a good presentation have? Discuss these issues in small groups and with your class. You may decide that some or all of the following qualities of your presentation should be graded:

- Knowledge of chemistry content beyond what is presented
- accuracy
- meets teacher needs (fourth or fifth grade)
- number of concepts addressed

Demonstration

- carefully planned
- safety
- explanation (age-appropriate)
- adherence to assigned time limits
- showmanship
- creativity
- clarity
- organization
- appeal
- written summary
- directions for experiment
- explanation of chemistry
- appropriateness for an elementary school teacher with limited chemistry background
- statements concerning safety needs

Once your class has determined the list of criteria for judging the presentations, you should also decide how many points should be given for each criterion. Determining grading criteria in advance will help you focus your time and effort on the various aspects of the presentation. How many points should be assigned to the content and how many should be assigned to the actual presentation? Will each high-school student be involved in only one presentation, or more? For each criterion, you should decide on how excellence is defined and how it compares to a satisfactory effort.

Since you will be working with other students in small groups, you will need to determine grading criteria that reward each individual in the group for his or her contribution and also reward the group for the final presentation. You should discuss different strategies and choose the one that is best suited to your situation. Your teacher may provide you with a sample rubric to help you get started.

Activity 1 Chemical and Physical Changes

What Do You See?
MYSTERY CHEMISTRY

GOALS

In this activity you will:

- Learn to differentiate between chemical and physical changes.
- Make observations and cite evidence to identify changes as chemical or physical.
- Give examples of chemical and physical changes you encounter in everyday life.
- Explore the new properties exhibited when new materials are made from combinations of two or more original materials as a result of a chemical change.
- Design an experiment to test properties of different combinations of materials.

What Do You Think?

Chemistry is the study of matter and how matter changes. Changes in matter are described as physical changes and chemical changes. Consider two wooden matches. One is broken in half and the other is lit on fire by striking it along the side of the matchbox. In both of these instances matter has changed.

- **Which match has undergone a chemical change? Which has undergone a physical change? Give specific reasons to support your answer. How did you make your decision?**

The *What Do You Think?* questions are meant to get you thinking about what you already know or think you know. Don't worry about being right or wrong. Discussing what you think you know is an important step in learning.

Record your ideas about these questions in your *Active Chemistry* log. Be prepared to discuss your responses with your group and the class.

Investigate

1. Here are 15 opportunities for you to observe changes in matter. Your teacher may choose to do some or all of these as a demonstration or set up stations for you to visit. Notice that the directions call for small amounts of substances.

Safety goggles and a lab apron must be worn *at all times* in a chemistry lab.

Before you begin the activity, make a data table to organize your observations. You will want to record what was done and detailed observations for changes that take place.

a) Heat an ice cube in a beaker until it melts. Continue heating the ice cube after it melts.

b) Boil a small amount of water.

c) Melt a small amount of candle wax. Allow the wax to cool.

d) Break a wooden splint into several pieces.

e) Hold a wooden splint in a flame.

f) Add a few drops of lemon juice to a small amount of milk.

g) Add a few drops of vinegar to a small amount of baking soda ($NaHCO_3$).

h) Add a small amount of table salt to water. Stir. Consider what would happen if you allowed the water to evaporate from this mixture.

i) Add several drops of iodine solution to a small amount of starch.

j) Add a small piece of polished zinc to a small amount of hydrochloric acid (0.1 *M* HCl).

k) Add a drop of phenolphthalein indicator solution to a solution of sodium hydroxide (0.1 *M* NaOH).

l) Add two drops of sodium carbonate (0.1 *M* Na_2CO_3) to two drops of sodium hydrogen sulfate (0.1 *M* $NaHSO_4$).

m) Add a few drops of household ammonia to a small amount of a copper (II) sulfate (0.1 *M* $CuSO_4$) solution.

n) Add a few drops of vinegar to a small piece of chalk or marble chips.

o) Sharpen a pencil and collect the shavings.

Dispose of the materials as directed by your teacher. Clean up your workstation.

2. Look at your observation notes in your data table.

   a) Prepare and complete a chart table that organizes your observations into separate columns. Create a separate column for each type of observation made, such as color changes observed, the formation of precipitates (sometimes visible as a cloudy solution), gas formation (fizz), and any other changes. Use one column to note where no visible change occurred.

3. A physical change involves changes in the appearance of the material, but does not involve creation of new substances. A chemical change involves the formation of new substances. Chemical reactions are characterized by a number of changes, including color changes and the formation of precipitates or gases.

   a) Which of the interactions you observed were chemical changes? Write the words "chemical change" next to each of these interactions. Explain your answer.

   b) Which of the interactions you observed were physical changes? Write the words "physical change" next to each of these interactions. Explain your answer.

   c) When you placed the wooden splint into a flame, what other evidence (besides the color change) indicated that a chemical change took place?

d) Imagine a situation where two colorless solutions are mixed together. There is no color change, no precipitate is formed, and no gas is released. However, heat is released as the solutions are mixed. Even though dissolving is a physical process, it very often results in a change in temperature, which can be either positive or negative, depending on the solute and solvent. Is this an example of a chemical or physical change? Explain your choice.

4. Each group will be given some material used in disposable diapers. Place the piece in a beaker.

800
700
600
500
400
300
200
100 mL

a) Predict how much liquid the diaper material will be able to hold. Record your prediction in your log.

b) Design an investigation to measure the amount of liquid that the diaper material can absorb. Record your procedure in your log.

c) With the approval of your teacher, carry out your investigation. Record your results.

d) Explain how your prediction compared with your observations.

e) The diapers contain a material called sodium polyacrylate. When it absorbs water, is this a physical or chemical change? Explain your answer.

5. Your teacher will show you a solution of sodium acetate in a 250-mL flask. Observe the solution carefully.

a) Record your observations in your *Active Chemistry* log.

Your teacher will then add one crystal of sodium acetate to the flask.

b) What happens? Record your observations in your log.

c) Was this a chemical or physical change?

6. In a large throwaway glass jar, mix 150 mL of sodium silicate (sometimes called water-glass solution) and 400 mL of water. Carefully drop solid-colored crystal compounds of cobalt, copper, nickel, iron, and/or manganese in different locations inside the jar.

a) Is there evidence of a change immediately? In several minutes? In several hours? In several days? In your *Active Chemistry* log, describe the results.

b) Is the phenomenon you see the result of a physical or a chemical change? Explain your answer.

Wash your hands and arms thoroughly after the activity.

Chem Talk

CHANGES IN MATTER

Physical and Chemical Changes

In this activity, you observed a number of situations that involved changes in matter, both physical and chemical. A **physical change** involves changes in the appearance of the material but does not involve creation of new materials. A change of a solid to a liquid is a physical change. When the candle wax melted it may have appeared different, but it was still wax. After it solidified, it had a similar appearance to the initial product. When the ice cube melted it may have appeared different, but it was still water. Dissolving is also a physical change. When you added the salt to the water, the salt crystals seemed to disappear as they dissolved in the water. However, they had only spread out into a solution. A **solution** is a **homogeneous** mixture of at least two different materials. The materials forming a solution are called the **solute** and **solvent**. The material usually present in the largest amount is called the solvent. When the solvent (water) evaporated away, the solute (salt crystals) remained the same as it was originally.

A **chemical change** involves the formation of new materials. The new materials are called **products** and the starting materials are called **reactants**. The process that brings about a chemical change is called a **chemical reaction**. Chemical reactions are characterized by a number of changes, including color changes, the formation of a **precipitate** or gas, and in many cases a release of heat or light. Chemical changes are usually not easy to reverse. When you burned the wooden splint you could not put the charcoal and gases back together to form the original splint as you could when you simply broke the splint into pieces.

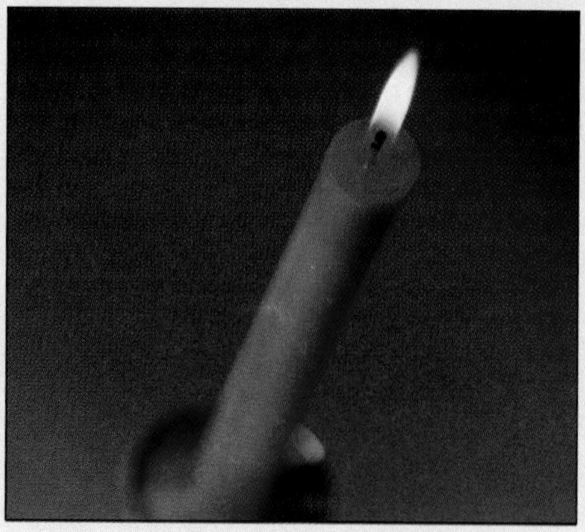

Chem Words

physical change: a change that involves changes in the state or form of a substance but does not cause any change in chemical composition.

solution: a homogeneous mixture of two or more substances.

homogeneous: a word used to describe a substance which appears to contain only one type of matter.

solute: the substance that interacts with a solvent to form a solution.

solvent: a substance present in a larger amount that interacts with the solute to make a solution.

chemical change: a change that converts the chemical composition of a substance into different substance(s) with different chemical composition.

product: a substance formed by a chemical reaction.

reactant: a starting substance in a chemical reaction.

chemical reaction: a process in which new substance(s) are formed from starting substance(s).

precipitate: an insoluble solid formed in a liquid solution as a result of a chemical reaction.

concentration: a measure of the composition of a solution, often given in terms of moles of solute per liter of solution.

Saturated and Supersaturated Solutions

The solution your teacher used in the demonstration was a supersaturated solution of sodium acetate. Solutions are commonly described in terms of **concentration**. The concentration of a solution is the ratio of the quantity of solute to the quantity of solution. The concentration is often expressed as **molarity**, which is the number of **moles** of solute dissolved in one liter of solution. It is represented by the symbol *M*. A dilute solution has fewer solute molecules per volume than a concentrated solution. If you add more solute to a solution and it does not dissolve, the solution is saturated. If the solute does dissolve, the solution is unsaturated.

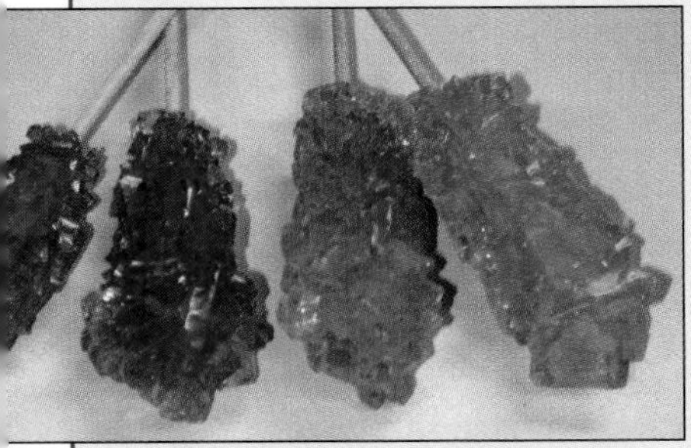

You probably recognize the term "saturated." When something is saturated, it is full. A saturated sponge is full of water; it can't hold any more. A **saturated solution** is one in which no more solute will dissolve under the given conditions. To say that the sodium acetate solution is supersaturated means that it is "over full." A **supersaturated solution** contains more solute particles than it normally would under the given conditions. A supersaturated solution can be made using some solutes. If a saturated solution at a high temperature is allowed to cool undisturbed, all the solute may remain dissolved at the lower temperature. The solution is then supersaturated. As you observed in the activity, such solutions are unstable. By introducing a "seed" crystal the extra solute particles "joined" the crystal and came out of the solution.

Polymers

The chemical material that you were working with when you investigated the absorbency of the diaper was sodium polyacrylate. It is a chemical compound called a **polymer**. It is made up of many (poly) repeating units of a smaller group of elements (the monomer called acrylate). This particular polymer has a unique property. It will absorb more than 800 times its own mass in distilled water. The fascinating ability of this polymer (sodium polyacrylate) to absorb large amounts of water has led to its use in a number of commercial endeavors.

Chem Words

molarity: a measure of the concentration of a solution in moles of solute per liter of solution.

mole: the number equal to the number of carbon atoms in exactly 12 g of pure ^{12}C. It is represented by Avogadro's number, 6.022×10^{23}.

saturated solution: a solution that has the maximum amount of solute that can be dissolved at a given temperature and pressure.

supersaturated solution: a solution that contains more solute particles than it normally would under the given conditions.

polymer: a substance that is a macromolecule consisting of many similar small molecules (monomers) linked together in long chains.

Checking Up

1. What is a physical change? Provide two examples.
2. Explain the meaning of a solution, a solute, and a solvent.
3. What is a chemical change? Provide two examples.
4. What "clues" can you look for to determine if a chemical change has occurred?
5. How do you describe the concentration of a solution?
6. Explain the difference between a saturated and a supersaturated solution.

What Do You Think Now?

At the beginning of this activity you were asked to consider a match broken in half and one lit on fire.

- **Which match has undergone a chemical change? Which has undergone a physical change? Give specific reasons to support your answer. How did you make your decision?**

Did you have difficulty at the beginning of this activity in telling the difference between physical and chemical changes?

A match is lit. Is this an example of a chemical or physical change? An egg is fried. Is this an example of a chemical or physical change?

Chem Essential Questions

What does it mean?

Chemistry explains a macroscopic phenomenon (what you observe) with a description of what happens at the nanoscopic level (atoms and molecules) using symbolic structures as a way to communicate. Complete the chart below in your *Active Chemistry* log.

MACRO	NANO	SYMBOLIC
What does it mean when substances undergo physical change?	*What happens at the atomic level during a chemical change?*	*Determine which equation is representing a chemical change and which is representing a physical change:* $H_2O(l) \rightarrow H_2O(g)$ $2H_2O(l) \rightarrow 2H_2(g) + O_2(g)$

How do you know?

Refer to the data collected from this activity and pick a "best example" for a physical change and a "best example" for a chemical change.

Why do you believe?

Water is a substance that you use in many different ways. When you use water in your daily life, are you changing it chemically? Explain.

Why should you care?

Giving a demonstration of chemistry in your *Cool Chemistry Show* will probably include both physical and chemical changes. How will you explain the difference between a physical change and a chemical change to your audience?

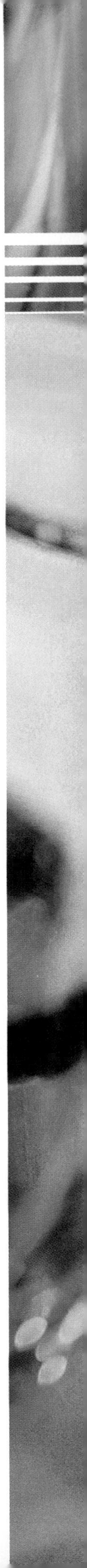

Reflecting on the Activity and the Challenge

In this activity, you investigated the two types of changes in matter. A physical change is a change in the appearance of the material without creating a new substance. The result is the creation of a solution or homogenous mixture. You also learned that solutions are commonly described in terms of concentration, which is the ratio of the quantity of solute to the quantity of solution expressed in molarity (M).The difference between a saturated and supersaturated solution is discussed. A chemical change, on the other hand, does involve the creation of new products from reactants. Chemical reactions are characterized by a color change or the formation of a precipitate or gas. You further investigated a type of physical reaction by testing the absorbency of a diaper made of sodium polyacrylate, a type of polymer. You can now use this knowledge of chemical and physical changes to amaze the fourth- and fifth-grade students.

Chem to Go

1. Which of the following are chemical changes and why?
   a) Toast turns black after being in the toaster too long.
   b) Water condenses on the outside of a glass of iced tea.
   c) Green leaves turn orange, yellow, and red in the fall.
   d) Green bananas become yellow.
   e) Milk becomes sour if left at room temperature.
   f) Butter melts on a hot summer day.
2. Think back to a recent lunch or dinner. Describe two physical and two chemical changes that were involved in preparing and consuming the meal and explain why you think each was a physical or chemical change.
3. Write a paragraph describing the process of making a cake or driving a car. Indicate the physical changes and chemical changes taking place within the activity.
4. The following information is obtained for the element aluminum. Identify which are physical and which are chemical properties.

   Aluminum is a shiny silver metal and melts at 660°C. When a strip of aluminum is placed in hydrochloric acid, hydrogen gas is released. The density of aluminum is 2.70 g/cm^3. When polished aluminum is exposed to oxygen over a period of time it forms aluminum oxide (Al_2O_3) on the surface of the metal.
5. How would you determine whether a clear liquid in a beaker is saturated sugar water or just water? Remember, you do not taste samples in the laboratory.
6. The decomposition of water is shown in the following equation:

   $$2H_2O(l) + \text{energy} \rightarrow 2H_2(g) + O_2(g)$$

   What type of process is this, physical or chemical? Explain!
7. ***Preparing for the Chapter Challenge***

   Describe how you would demonstrate the difference between a physical and a chemical change in a "cool" way.

Inquiring Further

Factors affecting solubility and the rate of dissolving

Understanding the factors that affect how quickly a solute dissolves in a solvent is important in many practical applications in manufacturing. Design an investigation to determine the factors that affect solubility. Consider the following:

- **nature of the solute and solvent**
- **temperature**
- **agitation (stirring or shaking)**
- **surface area (for example, try using a sugar cube, granulated sugar, and icing sugar)**
- **pressure of gases.**

Remember that your investigation must be controlled, if your results are to be reliable. What will be your independent (manipulated) variables and what will be your dependent (responding) variables?

Activity 2 More Chemical Changes

What Do You See?

CuSO4

GOALS

In this activity you will:

- Observe several typical examples of evidence that a chemical change is occurring.
- Make generalizations about the combinations of materials that result in the same evidence.
- Make generalizations about materials that tend to react with everything and materials that tend not to react with anything.
- Practice careful laboratory techniques, such as avoiding contamination of reactants, to ensure that results observed are repeatable and unambiguous.

What Do You Think?

Read the following sets of instructions for two different processes:

a) Mix 1 cup flour, 1/3 cup sugar, 1 teaspoon of baking powder with a cup of milk and 1 egg, well-beaten. Place the mixture in an oven for 30 minutes.

b) Add two drops of sodium carbonate (0.1 *M* Na_2CO_3) to two drops of sodium hydrogen sulfate (0.1 *M* $NaHSO_4$).

- **Which of the instructions above involve chemistry? Explain your answer.**
- **Describe one similarity and one difference in the above instructions.**

Record your ideas about these questions in your *Active Chemistry* log. Be prepared to discuss your responses with your group and the class.

Investigate

1. The following eight solid materials have been dissolved in distilled water to make solutions. You will combine the solutions (one to one) with each other in an organized manner in order to observe their interactions.
   - barium nitrate ($Ba(NO_3)_2$)

Safety goggles and a lab apron must be worn *at all times* in a chemistry lab.

Silver nitrate will stain skin and clothing. Handle with care.

Wash your hands and arms thoroughly after the activity.

- sodium hydroxide (NaOH)
- sodium hydrogen carbonate ($NaHCO_3$)
- copper (II) sulfate ($CuSO_4$)
- potassium iodide (KI)
- silver nitrate ($AgNO_3$)
- iron (III) nitrate ($Fe(NO_3)_3$)
- hydrochloric acid ($HCl_{(aq)}$)

a) Begin by making a chart to record your data. Your chart will require an entire page of your notebook. Allow plenty of room to record your observations. A sample chart has been provided. You will have to replace the numbers with the names of the other chemicals. Notice that some of the blocks in this chart are marked with an X, indicating there is no need to mix those particular chemicals. Why do you suppose those particular blocks have an X?

2. Now it is time to mix the solutions.

Begin with barium nitrate. Add three drops of the barium nitrate solution to each of seven wells of a well plate. Add three drops of sodium hydroxide solution to the first well. After mixing the two solutions, make notes on your chart of any changes you observe. Don't overlook any color changes, the formation of a precipitate (sometimes observed as a cloudy solution), the formation of a gas (fizzing or bubbles), or a change in temperature. Using another dropper, continue by adding three drops of the sodium hydrogen carbonate to the second well. It is important that you do not allow the tip of the dropper of one solution to come in contact with another solution. Your attention to this detail will prevent contamination of the solutions. Continue by adding copper (II) sulfate to the third well, and so on.

a) After mixing the pairs of solutions, make note on your chart of any changes you observe.

You have now completed the first row of your chart. Next, you should begin the second row. Continue by putting three drops of sodium hydroxide into each of seven wells and adding the other solutions.

You may have noticed that adding barium nitrate to the sodium hydroxide (in the second row of the chart) produced the same result as adding sodium hydroxide to the barium nitrate (in the first row of the chart).

	$Ba(NO_3)_2$	NaOH	$NaHCO_3$	4	5	6	7	8
$Ba(NO_3)_2$	x							
NaOH		x						
$NaHCO_3$			x					
4				x				
5					x			
6						x		
7							x	
8								x

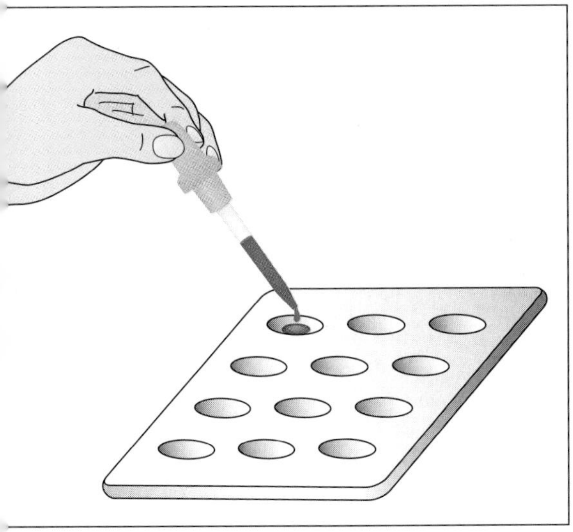

If you can explain why this is so, you can shorten the time needed for your investigation by not repeating other mixtures. After completing your *entire* chart in this fashion and mixing all possible one-to-one combinations of solutions, clean up your workstation. Your teacher will provide disposal information.

3. Use your chart to answer the following questions:

   a) Which combination of reactants seems to produce no reaction when mixed together?

   b) Which combination of reactants forms a gas? Can you guess which gas is formed? Try to deduce this from the reactants' names and chemical formulas.

   c) Which combination of reactants produces a color change when mixed together?

   d) Which combination of reactants forms precipitates quickly? Slowly?

   e) Which combination of reactants forms a yellow precipitate? A muddy brown precipitate? A white precipitate? A blue precipitate?

   f) Which combination of reactants produces heat? How could you tell?

   g) What evidence indicates that a chemical change is occurring?

4. Place the following chemicals in a quart-size resealable plastic bag with a zipper seal:

   One teaspoon (scoop) of calcium chloride ($CaCl_2$)

   One teaspoon (scoop) of baking soda ($NaHCO_3$)

   Seal the bag and mix the powders.

   a) Record your observations in your *Active Chemistry* log. Did a chemical reaction occur? Pour 10 mL of phenol red indicator solution into the bag and seal quickly. Make sure the solids come in contact with the indicator solution.

   b) Observe the reaction and, in your *Active Chemistry* log, describe what you see.

   c) Did a chemical reaction occur in the plastic bag? If so, identify all of the evidence of the chemical change.

   d) For this particular reaction, calcium chloride and sodium hydrogen carbonate combined to produce an aqueous solution of sodium chloride and calcium carbonate in addition to the carbon dioxide, water, and heat. The balanced equation is:

   $$CaCl_2(aq) + 2NaHCO_3(aq) \rightarrow 2NaCl(aq) + CaCO_3(s) + H_2O(l) + CO_2(g)$$

   What do you think are the names of the reactants? What do you think are the names of the products?

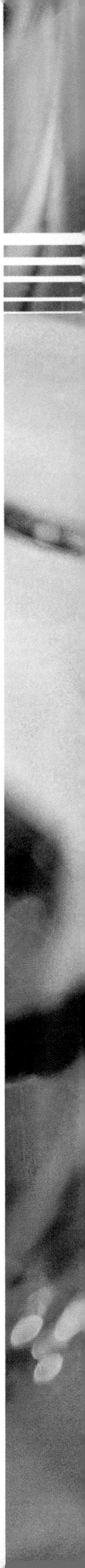

Wash your hands and arms thoroughly after the activity.

5. Your teacher will provide you with a small amount (~25 mL) of limewater, a solution of calcium hydroxide ($Ca(OH)_2$), in a test tube. One end of a straw should be submerged in the solution.

   Gently blow through the straw into the solution for a minute or so. *Caution! Blow gently, and be careful to only blow out through the straw. Avoid ingesting any of the solution.* You are actually bubbling some carbon dioxide through the solution.

   a) Did a chemical reaction occur? What is the evidence?

6. Clean up your workstation and dispose of the chemicals as directed by your teacher.

Chem Talk

Chem Words

chemical test: a procedure or chemical reaction used to identify a substance.

TESTS FOR CHEMICALS

Chemical Tests for Gases

In this activity, you focused on chemical reactions, those processes that result in the formation of new products. You also tested for the presence of some of the new materials. You used **chemical tests** to identify the unknown substances. A chemical test is a form of a diagnostic test. To test for the presence of oxygen, you introduce a glowing splint into a test tube with a small amount of gas. If the splint bursts into a flame, you then know that the gas is oxygen. When you introduce a burning splint into a test tube and hear a loud pop, you assume the gas present to be hydrogen. In this activity you tested for the presence of carbon dioxide. Since carbon dioxide does not burn or support burning, by using a glowing or burning splint, you could not tell if a gas was carbon dioxide. (If the splint is extinguished you can say that the gas is neither oxygen nor hydrogen and therefore could be carbon dioxide.)

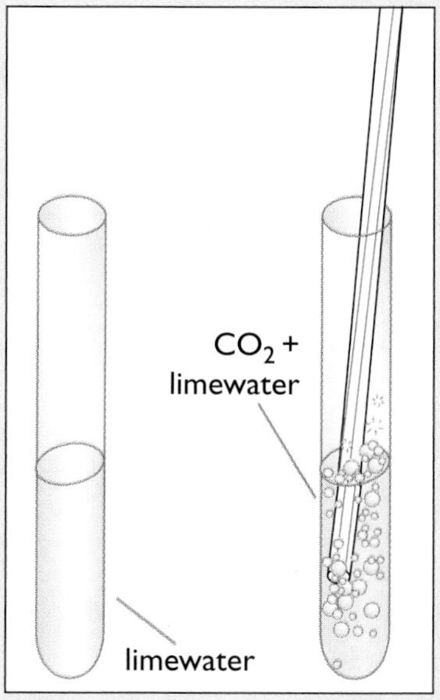
CO_2 +
limewater
limewater

The test for carbon dioxide uses limewater, a clear, colorless solution of calcium hydroxide in water. When you blew bubbles into the test tube you were actually blowing some carbon dioxide from your lungs into the limewater. The carbon dioxide reacted with the calcium hydroxide forming a precipitate. The precipitate caused the limewater to turn cloudy in appearance.

Indicators for Acids and Bases

When acids and bases are involved in a chemical reaction the appearance of the products is often very similar to the appearance of the reactants. (You will learn more about acids and bases in a later activity.) Therefore, indicators are used to determine the presence of an acid or base. Substances that change color when they react with an acid or a base are called **acid-base indicators**. In this activity you used phenol red, an acid-base indicator that turns yellow in the presence of an acid. Chemists use a great variety of acid-base indicators. You may also have used litmus in previous science classes. It is a very common indicator used in school laboratories.

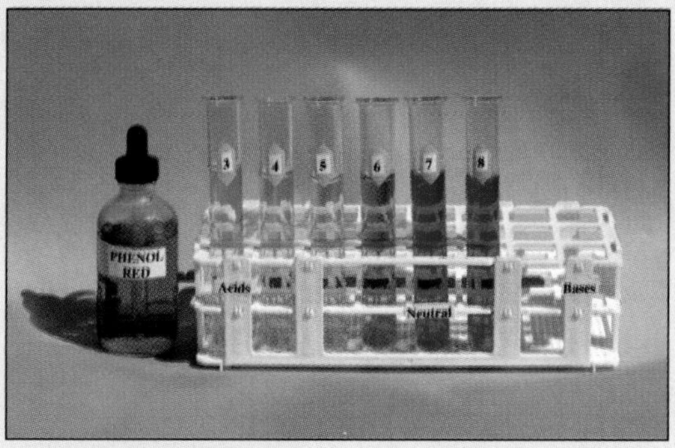
PHENOL RED
Acids
Neutral
Bases

Chem Words

acid-base indicator: a substance that changes color when exposed to either an acid or a base.

Checking Up

1. What is a chemical test?
2. Describe how you can use a burning or glowing splint to test for hydrogen or oxygen.
3. Why is a glowing splint extinguished with carbon dioxide?
4. What test is used to identify the presence of carbon dioxide?
5. What is a precipitate?
6. What are acid-base indicators and how are they useful?

What Do You Think Now?

At the beginning of this activity you were given two procedures and asked which ones involve a chemical reaction and/or chemistry.

Look back at your answers and compare them to what you think now. Are chemical changes usually carried out in a laboratory? What is the most common evidence that a chemical change is taking place?

Chem Essential Questions

What does it mean?

Chemistry explains a macroscopic phenomenon (what you observe) with a description of what happens at the nanoscopic level (atoms and molecules) using symbolic structures as a way to communicate. Complete the chart below in your *Active Chemistry* log.

MACRO	NANO	SYMBOLIC
What evidence do you see that reactants have undergone a chemical change? What happens to substances as they undergo chemical change?	*One evidence of chemical change is the production of a gas. Where did the gas come from in the reaction of calcium chloride and sodium hydrogen carbonate? How is the formation of this gas different from the boiling of water to make vapor? How is a gas different from a liquid at the atomic level?*	*In the following chemical equation, indicate the symbolic representation for carbon dioxide gas being produced.* $NaHCO_3(aq) + HCl(aq) \rightarrow$ $NaCl(aq) + H_2CO_3(aq) \rightarrow$ $NaCl(aq) + CO_2(g) + H_2O(l)$

How do you know?

Refer to your *Active Chemistry* log and develop a list of the evidence revealed in this activity that indicates that a chemical reaction has taken place.

Why do you believe?

Give an example of a chemical reaction you have personally witnessed recently. It can involve cooking food. List the evidences of a chemical reaction for your example.

Why should you care?

Chemical changes are often exciting! Your *Cool Chemistry Show* will probably involve some kind of chemical reaction. How can you make your chemistry show more interesting by utilizing the evidences of chemical change?

Reflecting on the Activity and the Challenge

Recall that the fourth-grade teacher has specifically requested that your chemistry show addresses chemical and physical properties. You are right on track for the fourth graders. The fifth-grade teacher wants the students to learn more about chemical reactions that involve color changes. You have seen a few of those, too. If you had to conduct the show based on your experiences so far, which activity would you use? What additional information would you need to be able to explain the chemistry to fourth- and fifth-grade students?

Chem to Go

1. In both *Activity 1* and *Activity 2*, you gathered evidence for chemical changes. However, this evidence does not always indicate a chemical change. For instance, a change in color can be evidence of a chemical change. However, when you add water to a powdered drink mix, the color often changes, but a chemical change has not taken place.

   In each of the following situations indicate whether the evidence suggests a chemical change or not. Include the evidence that you used to make your decision:

   a) An acid is dissolved in water and heat is released.

   b) A burning match produces light.

   c) A "seed" crystal is placed in a supersaturated solution and the extra solute particles "join" the crystal and come out of the solution.

   d) The glowing filament of a light bulb produces light.

   e) A small piece of metal is placed into an acid and hydrogen is released.

   f) Solutions of sodium hydroxide and copper (II) sulfate are mixed and a blue precipitate appears.

2. Anhydrous copper (II) sulfate ($CuSO_4$) is a white solid. When it is dissolved in water, the solution becomes blue. Is this a chemical change? Give an explanation to defend your answer.

3. If a glass of carbonated soda drink is allowed to sit out for a period of time, you will find that the drink seems to be flat. Discuss this observation in terms of whether this is a physical or chemical change.

4. ***Preparing for the Chapter Challenge***

   Select one of the reactions you observed in this activity that you thought was pretty cool. Describe how you might incorporate it into a possible event in the *Cool Chemistry Show* you are designing. Would it meet the needs of the fourth-grade teacher, the fifth-grade teacher, or both? What additional information would you need to be able to explain the chemistry to the audience?

Activity 3 Chemical Names and Formulas

What Do You See?

SHOWING NOW:
THE
COOL
CHEMISTRY
SHOW

GOALS

In this activity you will:

- Predict the charges of ions of some elements.
- Determine the formulas of ionic compounds.
- Write the conventional names of ionic compounds.
- Make observations to determine whether there is evidence that chemical changes occur when combining two ionic compounds.

What Do You Think?

Your ability to understand chemistry is determined by how well you can understand and write the language of chemistry. Just as there are only 26 letters in the English alphabet and thousands of words, there are only 92 elements found in nature and hundreds of thousands of materials. These elements and their symbols make up the language of chemistry. To make it easier to communicate, the elements are assigned symbols and the symbols are organized into the periodic table of elements.

- **How is water represented in the language of chemistry?**
- **How are symbols useful when communicating?**

Record your ideas about these questions in your *Active Chemistry* log. Be prepared to discuss your responses with your small group and the class.

Investigate

1. The periodic table lists the elements in order of their atomic number. The atomic number is the number of protons (positively charged particles) in the nucleus of one atom of that element. For a neutral atom, the number of protons also equals the number of electrons (negatively charged particles).

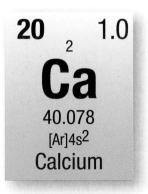

20 1.0
2
Ca
40.078
[Ar]$4s^2$
Calcium

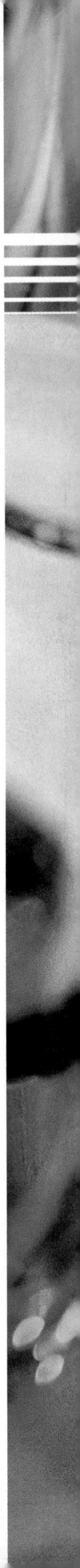

Electrons are found outside the nucleus. A helium atom, with an atomic number of 2, has 2 protons in its nucleus and 2 electrons surrounding the nucleus.

For each of the following elements, write the symbol for the element and indicate the number of protons and electrons an atom of that element would have. (Refer to the periodic table.)

a) copper b) sulfur

c) zinc d) gold

e) oxygen f) carbon

g) silver h) chlorine

i) nitrogen j) hydrogen

k) magnesium l) iodine

m) iron n) calcium

o) aluminum p) sodium

q) potassium r) lead

2. Elements can combine to form compounds. A compound results when two or more different elements bond. Some compounds are comprised of positive and negative ions that are bound by their mutual attraction. An ion is an atom that has lost or gained electrons, and therefore is charged because its protons and electrons no longer balance and cancel each other. For example, when a chlorine atom gains 1 electron, it becomes a chloride ion with a charge of –1 (remember electrons have negative charge). When a sodium atom loses 1 electron, it becomes a sodium ion with a charge of +1 (because now there is one more proton than the number of electrons). The resulting compound is sodium chloride (NaCl), which you know as table salt and it is an ionic compound.

a) The chemical formula for the compound of potassium and bromine is KBr. Look at where potassium is located on the periodic table (Group 1) and also where bromine is located (Group 17). Each of these has an ionic charge of 1. Potassium is +1, and bromine is –1.

List four other compounds that are created from elements in Group 1 combining with elements in Group 17.

b) Magnesium forms an ion with a charge of +2 and oxygen forms an oxide ion with a –2 charge. The chemical formula for magnesium oxide is MgO.

List four other compounds that are created from elements in Group 2 combining with elements in Group 16.

3. The charges for the positive ions in a compound must equal the charges of the negative ions in that compound. If the values of the charge on a positive ion and a negative ion are the same, the formula of the resulting compound is simply the chemical symbols of each element (NaCl, MgO). If the values of the charge on a positive ion and a negative ion are not the same, subscripts can be used to balance them. For example, aluminum loses 3 electrons to become an ion with a charge of +3. An iodine atom gains only 1 electron to form an ion with a charge of –1. It takes 3 iodine atoms to accept the 3 electrons given up by aluminum. This is reflected in the formula AlI_3. (Note where the 3 is placed for the 3 iodine atoms.) Another example is $CaCl_2$, where 2 chloride ions (each gaining 1 electron) and 1 calcium ion (having lost 2 electrons) combine.

Write the chemical formula and name for the compound formed when the following pairs of elements are combined:

a) calcium and oxygen

b) aluminum and fluorine

c) boron and oxygen

d) strontium and nitrogen

e) barium and selenium

4. Some compounds, like baking soda and sodium hydrogen carbonate ($NaHCO_3$), incorporate polyatomic ions. Polyatomic ions are made up of several elements joined together. In the case of baking soda, the sodium (Na^+) ion has a charge of +1 and the hydrogen carbonate ion (the polyatomic ion HCO_3^-) has a charge of −1. (Note: hydrogen carbonate ion is also called bicarbonate ion.)

   Write the chemical formula for each compound below.

   a) potassium nitrate (nitrate: NO_3^-)

   b) barium sulfate (sulfate: SO_4^{2-})

   c) potassium sulfate

   d) sodium acetate (acetate: $C_2H_3O_2^-$)

   Write the name for each compound below.

   e) $(NH_4)_2SO_4$ (ammonium: NH_4^+)

   f) $Al_2(CO_3)_3$

   g) $LiHCO_3$

5. You have learned about ionic compounds that are made from positive and negative ions. In another class of compounds, called molecules, the atoms are bound by electrons being mutually attracted to the protons in adjacent atoms. These bonds are called covalent bonds, because atoms are sharing electrons. It is often useful to imagine, however, that the atoms inside of molecules are charged. These "imagined charges" are called oxidation numbers.

   a) The formula for carbon dioxide is CO_2. If you pretend this is an ionic compound, what is the charge (oxidation number) of carbon?

   b) Carbon monoxide is CO. What is the oxidation number of carbon now?

   c) Explain how you arrived at your answers

6. Find out if chemical changes occur every time reactants are mixed. Let's find out. Read the directions for this step so you can prepare a data table to record and describe all that you observe.

   Put equal amounts of baking soda, crushed effervescent antacid tablet, and baking powder into three separate test tubes respectively. Be sure to label the test tubes!

   Add equal amounts of water to each.

   a) Record your observations. (You should now know the chemical formula for baking soda is $NaHCO_3$.)

   b) Light a wooden splint and blow it out to greate a glowing splint. Place the glowing splint into the top of each test tube. Make note of what happens. A glowing splint bursts into flames in the presence of oxygen. A glowing splint is extinguished in the presence of carbon dioxide. Which gases were most likely given off for each reaction?

Safety goggles and a lab apron must be worn *at all times* in a chemistry lab.

Hold the splint with tongs or wear a heatproof glove. Be sure the mouth of the test tube is pointed away from everyone.

7. When the reactions have stopped completely, your teacher will put three of the test tubes in a beaker of boiling water. Observe what happens.

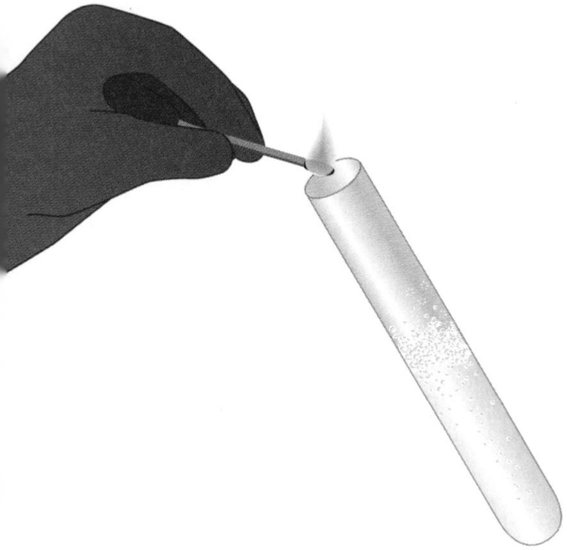

   a) Make a note of the results in your *Active Chemistry* log.

8. Repeat *Step 6* using clean test tubes, fresh reagents, and instead of water add:
   - vinegar
   - ammonia

9. As an inquiry activity, your teacher will give you a small amount of a white powdered substance that is either baking soda, crushed effervescent antacid tablet, or baking powder.

   a) Write down the number of your unknown powder and determine which of the three substances it is. Provide evidence to support your conclusion.

10. Clean all equipment and the laboratory bench when you are finished. Dispose of all chemicals as directed by your teacher.

Wash your hands and arms thoroughly after the activity.

Chem Talk

FORMING COMPOUNDS

Ionic Compounds

There are certainly more than 100 physically different materials in this world. With approximately 100 elements, how is it possible to have such a variety of materials? How is it possible to invent new materials for clothing, building, and food? Elements can combine to form compounds. A **compound** results when two or more different elements bond.

marcasite (above)
hematite (right)

Chem Words

compound: a material composed of two or more kinds of atoms combined in a definite proportion.

Chem Words

ion: an electrically charged atom or a group of atoms that has acquired a net charge, either negative or positive.

anion: a negatively charged ion.

cation: a positively charged ion.

ionic compound: a compound consisting of positive and negative ions.

polyatomic ion: an ion that consists of two or more atoms that are covalently bonded and has either a positive or negative charge.

molecular compound: two or more atoms bonded together by sharing electrons (covalent bond).

covalent bond: a bond formed when two atoms combine by sharing their paired electrons with each other.

oxidation number: a number assigned to an element in a compound designating the number of electrons the element has lost, gained, or shared in forming that compound.

Some compounds are comprised of positive and negative **ions** that are bound by their mutual attraction. An ion is an atom that has lost or gained electrons, and therefore is charged because its protons and electrons no longer balance and cancel each other. For example, when an iodine atom gains one electron, it becomes an iodide ion with a charge of –1 (remember electrons have negative charge). A negatively charged ion is called an **anion.** When a potassium atom loses one electron, it becomes a potassium ion with a charge of +1 (because now there is one more proton than the number of electrons). A positively charged ion is called a **cation.** The resulting **ionic compound** is potassium iodide (KI). Potassium iodide is added to most of the table salt you use as a dietary supplement. Table salt (NaCl) is another example of an ionic compound.

If you refer to the periodic table you will notice that elements that form positive ions are on the left side of the table and elements that form negative ions are on the right side. Metals combine with nonmetals to form ionic compounds. Also, when two elements combine, the name given to the negative ion will end with -ide, and the compound is named with the metal or positive ion first. This is true for binary compounds, for example: sodium chloride, potassium bromide, and magnesium oxide. When they are dissolved in water, you would find that ionic compounds conduct electricity. In this activity you also investigated some compounds formed with **polyatomic ions.** Polyatomic ions are made up of several elements joined together. For example, some antacids incorporate the hydroxide ion (OH^-) with the magnesium ion (Mg^{2+}) to form magnesium hydroxide, $Mg(OH)_2$. The following table lists some polyatomic ions and their charges.

Polyatomic Ions		
nitrate	NO_3^-	negative one, –1
sulfate	SO_4^{2-}	negative two, 2–
hydroxide	OH^-	negative one, –1
carbonate	CO_3^{2-}	negative two, 2–
hydrogen carbonate	HCO_3^-	negative one, –1
acetate	$C_2H_3O_2^-$	negative one, –1
ammonium	NH_4^+	positive one, +1

Molecular Compounds

You also learned about **molecular compounds** in this activity. When molecular compounds form, two elemental atoms come together, neither atom gains nor loses an electron. Instead, the bonding electrons are shared between the two atoms. The mutual attraction of two nuclei for a shared pair of bonding electrons is called a **covalent bond.** Molecular compounds are usually formed by nonmetal-nonmetal combinations. You would find that when dissolved in water, molecular compounds do not conduct electricity. The property of non-conduction is typical of molecular compounds and separates them from ionic compounds.

With covalent bonds you also found that it is often useful to imagine that the atoms inside of molecules are charged. These "imagined charges" are used as a type of bookkeeping and are called **oxidation numbers**. In both ionic compounds and molecular compounds the atoms achieve a stable state, similar to the noble gases.

Checking Up

1. If there are only about 100 elements in this world, why are there so many different materials?
2. What is an ion?
3. How are ionic compounds formed?
4. What is a polyatomic ion? Provide an example of a compound formed with a polyatomic ion.
5. How are molecular compounds formed?
6. Distinguish between an ionic and a covalent bond.

What Do You Think Now?

At the beginning of the activity you were asked:

- **How is water represented in the language of chemistry?**
- **How are symbols useful when communicating?**

Your answers may not have changed much since the beginning of this activity. However, think about how you felt when you first looked at chemical formulas. Are you more at ease about chemical formulas now that you have learned some of the rules that apply to chemical formulas? Do you think that the language of chemistry will get more familiar as you use it more?

Chem Essential Questions

What does it mean?

Chemistry explains a macroscopic phenomenon (what you observe) with a description of what happens at the nanoscopic level (atoms and molecules) using symbolic structures as a way to communicate. Complete the chart below in your *Active Chemistry* log.

MACRO	NANO	SYMBOLIC
How is learning chemistry similar to learning a new language? Describe a chemical reaction that you observed in this activity.	*How do the particles called atoms differ from the particles called ions? How do atoms differ from molecules?*	*You will see subscripts used frequently in the symbolic representation of substances (as in H_2O). What do these subscripts indicate about a compound?*

How do you know?

What experimental evidence from *Step 6* in this activity can you give that baking powder contains carbon and oxygen?

Why do you believe?

Most people can tell you what H_2O is, but they may not know that water is made from two atoms of hydrogen and one atom of oxygen. List two substances for which you know either the chemical formula or at least what elements they contain.

Why should you care?

As you further develop your knowledge of chemistry, you'll gain more confidence in being able to speak and write the language of chemistry. In your *Cool Chemistry Show,* you'll want to dazzle people with your ability to communicate what you are demonstrating. What would happen if you included too much of the language of chemistry in your demonstration?

Reflecting on the Activity and the Challenge

In this activity you have learned how to write the formulas for many compounds and how to name some compounds. You have also investigated both ionic and molecular compounds. As you prepare your presentation for your *Cool Chemistry Show,* you will want to include your knowledge of formulas, the names of compounds, and the different kinds of compounds. Remember that you will be providing the teacher with an explanation of why you included certain demonstrations, and you will also want to include explanations that are grade appropriate. Think about how much information you will need to provide for each demonstration.

Chem to Go

1. Write the chemical formula and name for the compound formed when the following pairs of elements are combined:

   a) sodium and bromine
   b) potassium and sulfur
   c) magnesium and chlorine
   d) cesium and iodine

2. Write the chemical formula for each of the following:

   a) nitric acid (hydrogen nitrate)
   b) ammonium hydroxide
   c) calcium carbonate
   d) acetic acid (hydrogen acetate)

3. a) Write the chemical formula for copper (II) sulfate. The (II) indicates that this copper ion has a +2 charge.

   b) Oxygen ions usually have –2 charge. How would formulas for iron (II) oxide differ from iron (III) oxide?

4. You may have noticed that all the elements in the first column of the periodic table, the alkali metals, have a +1 charge when they combine with negative ions. Another group of positive ions are the alkaline earth metals located in the second column of the periodic table. What charge is typical for ions of the alkaline earth metals?

5. The formula for sodium phosphate is Na_3PO_4. What is the charge on the polyatomic phosphate ion? What information did you use to arrive at your answer?

6. When you write the formula for sodium hydroxide, you do not have to put parentheses around the hydroxide polyatomic ion. However, when writing the formula for aluminum hydroxide, you must put parentheses around the hydroxide polyatomic ion.

   a) Write each formula.

   b) Explain why the parentheses are necessary for aluminum hydroxide.

7. a) If the chemical formula for iron (III) chloride is $FeCl_3$, what is the chemical formula for iron (III) nitrate?

   b) If the chemical formula for lead (II) oxide is PbO, what is the chemical formula for lead (II) sulfate?

   c) If the chemical formula for silver chloride is AgCl, what is the chemical formula for silver nitrate?

8. In *Activity 2*, you tested various compounds for chemical changes. (Barium nitrate, sodium hydroxide, sodium hydrogen carbonate, copper (II) sulfate, potassium iodide, silver nitrate, iron (III) nitrate, and hydrochloric acid.) Write the chemical formulas for each of the reactants.

9. ***Preparing for the Chapter Challenge***

   Review any chemical reactions you will be including in your *Cool Chemistry Show.* Write the formulas of any compounds that you plan to use.

Activity 4 Chemical Equations

What Do You See?

AMMON HYDROXI
PHENOL-PHTHALEIN SOLUTION

GOALS

In this activity you will:

- Represent chemical changes using word equations and chemical equations.
- Distinguish between different classes of chemical reactions.
- Predict the possible products of single-replacement and double-replacement reactions.
- Determine whether a reaction has occurred based on evidence observed.
- Use the Law of Conservation of Matter to balance chemical reactions.

What Do You Think?

When people communicate with each other, they often like to do so in a compact way. Below are a few examples. Can you interpret these?

From the Internet: CUl8r Wat RU ^ 2? TMI LOL

License plates: 14U2C 10SNE1 EDUC8R

- **What are some situations (other than the examples given) when language is compressed or abbreviated?**

Record your ideas about this question in your *Active Chemistry* log. Be prepared to discuss your responses with your small group and the class.

Investigate

1. Watch closely as your teacher shows you some cool chemistry.

   a) Record your observations in your *Active Chemistry* log.

2. Here's how the cool chemistry was done. Into each of three beakers that appeared empty, your teacher added about 45 mL of 2.0 *M* ammonium hydroxide solution.

   Before beginning the demonstration, your teacher had also added the following to each beaker:

   Beaker One — 20 drops of the indicator phenolphthalein solution;

Beaker Two—15 drops of 1 *M* magnesium sulfate solution;

Beaker Three—15 drops of 1 *M* copper (II) sulfate solution.

a) Did a chemical reaction take place in each beaker? What evidence do you have to justify your answer?

3. A chemical reaction occurs when substances change to form new substances. There are many chemical reactions that can occur. You have already observed some of them. One way chemists group reactions is into the following four categories.

- synthesis reactions;
- decomposition reactions;
- single-replacement reactions;
- double-replacement reactions.

a) What do the words synthesis and decomposition mean?

4. In a ***synthesis*** reaction, two or more chemicals combine to form a compound.

$A + B \rightarrow AB$

Here is an example of a synthesis reaction. When magnesium and oxygen react, a white solid, magnesium oxide, is formed.

This can be written as a word equation:

Magnesium (solid) and oxygen (gas) produce magnesium oxide (solid).

This can also be written using a chemical equation:

$Mg + O_2 \rightarrow MgO$

(The subscript tells you the number of atoms in one molecule. Oxygen is diatomic. It exists as a molecule made up of two atoms.)

a) What do you think are the advantages of writing a reaction using chemical symbols?

Any equation in chemistry must follow scientific laws or principles. The number of atoms of each element must be equal before and after the reaction.

b) In the equation to the left, how many atoms of oxygen are in the reactants (before the reaction)?

c) How many oxygen atoms are in the product (after the reaction)?

d) What is the problem with the equation?

Write a two in front of the MgO.

$Mg + O_2 \rightarrow 2MgO$

(The number in front of a chemical formula, called a coefficient, communicates the number of molecules or formula units that are involved in the reaction. In this equation there are two molecules of magnesium oxide represented. That is, there is a total of two magnesium atoms and two oxygen atoms.)

e) How many magnesium atoms are now represented in the product?

f) How many reactant atoms of magnesium are shown?

g) What is the problem with the equation?

Write a two in front of the Mg.

$2Mg + O_2 \rightarrow 2MgO$

h) The chemical equation above is now balanced. (The number of magnesium and oxygen atoms in the product is equal to the number in the reactant.) In your own words, explain the meaning of a balanced equation. How does the chemical equation communicate what happened in the reaction, and how does it follow the Law of Conservation of Matter?

When writing a chemical equation the states of the reactants and products are also given. The following symbols are used:

- (s) for solid
- (l) for liquid
- (g) for gas
- (aq) for aqueous, meaning in a water solution.

The complete balanced chemical equation for the reaction of magnesium and oxygen is:

$2Mg_{(s)} + O_{2(g)} \rightarrow 2MgO_{(s)}$

5. Write a word equation and a balanced chemical equation for each of the following synthesis reactions. Note that there are eight elements that are diatomic, which means that they exist as a molecule comprised of two atoms. They are hydrogen (H_2), nitrogen (N_2), oxygen (O_2), fluorine (F_2), chlorine (Cl_2), bromine (Br_2), iodine (I_2), and astatine (At_2). If you need to include any of these elements in an uncombined state in a chemical equation, don't forget the 2 as a subscript.

   a) Solid carbon (C) burns in air (oxygen gas) to form carbon dioxide gas (CO_2).

   b) Hydrogen gas reacts with oxygen gas to form liquid water (H_2O).

   c) A piece of solid iron (Fe) over time will react with oxygen to form iron (III) oxide (Fe_2O_3).

   d) A piece of solid sodium (Na) is dropped into a container of chlorine gas to produce solid sodium chloride (NaCl).

6. Water can be separated into its elements with an input of energy. The equation for this reaction is:

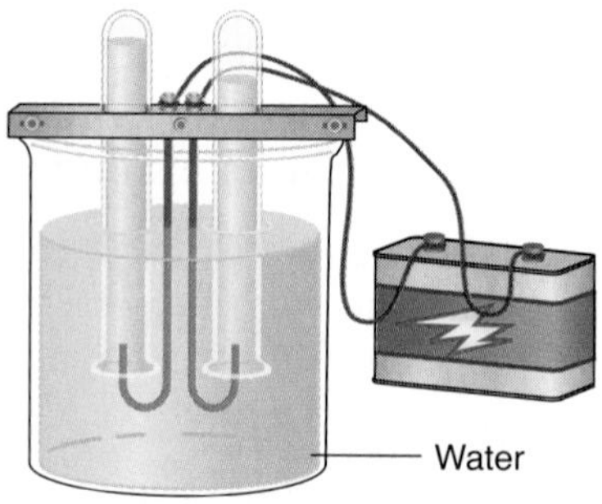
Water

Decomposition of water into $H_{2(g)}$ and $O_{2(g)}$ by electrolysis

Water (liquid) and energy produces hydrogen (gas) and oxygen (gas).

$2H_2O_{(l)} + \text{energy} \rightarrow 2H_{2(g)} + O_{2(g)}$

   a) Is the equation properly balanced? How did you check?

   When a substance breaks down into its component parts, the process is called a ***decomposition*** reaction.

   $AB \rightarrow A + B$

   Write word and balanced chemical equations for the following decomposition reactions.

   (Remember that some elements are diatomic — H_2, N_2, etc.)

   b) sodium chloride solid ($NaCl_{(s)}$)

   c) potassium iodide solid ($KI_{(s)}$)

   d) magnesium bromide solid ($MgBr_{2(s)}$).

7. The reactions mentioned above involve elements combining to form compounds or compounds breaking up to form elements.

   There are other reactions that involve elements reacting with compounds to form products. Such was the case when solid zinc was dropped into hydrochloric acid in *Activity 1*, forming hydrogen gas and aqueous zinc chloride solution.

The equation for this reaction is:

Zinc (solid) and hydrochloric acid (aqueous) produces hydrogen (gas) and zinc chloride (solution).

$Zn(s) + 2HCl(aq) \rightarrow H_2(g) + ZnCl_2(aq)$

a) Check to ensure that the chemical equation is properly balanced by completing the table in your log.

	Number of Atoms		
	Before	After	Balanced
Zn	1	1	yes
H	2		
Cl			

The reaction with zinc and hydrochloric acid is called a ***single-replacement*** reaction because zinc replaces the hydrogen in the acid.

$A + BC \rightarrow B + AC$

Write word and chemical equations for the following:

b) A piece of iron (Fe) metal is added to an aqueous solution of copper (II) sulfate ($CuSO_4$) and produces iron (II) sulfate ($FeSO_4$) and copper metal.

c) Solid lead (Pb) metal is added to an aqueous solution of silver nitrate ($AgNO_3$) and produces lead (II) nitrate ($Pb(NO_3)_2$) and silver metal.

d) Aluminum foil (Al) is placed in a beaker of aqueous copper (II) hydroxide ($Cu(OH)_2$) and produces aluminum hydroxide ($Al(OH)_3$) and copper metal. Balance each of the equations, if you have not done so.

You can use a chart similar to the one above, as you did before.

8. Another type of reaction is a ***double-replacement*** reaction.

$AB + CD \rightarrow CB + AD$

You may have already done double-replacement reactions in a previous chapter. You will soon try some more with your group. Use the chart below to guide your work. The compounds are in water solution.

a) Record your observations of the reactants before you mix them. For example, record your observations of potassium carbonate and silver nitrate before you mix them.

b) Create a chart in your log to record your observations after you mix the reactants. You may wish to use a chart similar to the one shown below.

Safety goggles and a lab apron must be worn *at all times* in a chemistry lab.

	Silver nitrate ($AgNO_3$)	Copper (II) sulfate ($CuSO_4$)	Magnesium sulfate ($MgSO_4$)	Sodium hydroxide (NaOH)
potassium carbonate (K_2CO_3)	1.	2.	3.	4.
sodium hydroxide (NaOH)	5.	6.	7.	8.
potassium iodide (KI)	9.	10.	11.	12.
iron (III) chloride ($FeCl_3$)	13.	14.	15.	16.

Safety goggles and a lab apron must be worn *at all times* in a chemistry lab.

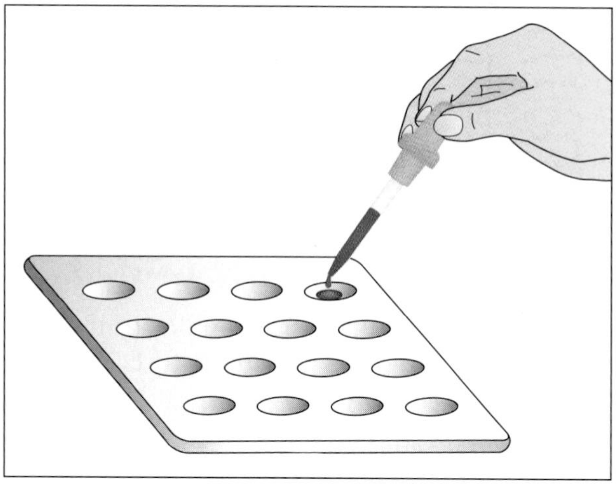

9. Mix three drops of one solution (i.e., potassium carbonate) with three drops of another solution (i.e., silver nitrate), as indicated by the first box on the chart. You can mix these solutions in a well of a well-plate or on a plastic surface. Do not allow the tip of the dropper of one solution to come in contact with another solution. This is important to prevent contamination of solutions.
   a) In the chart in your log, record your observations after mixing the reactants. Continue with the other reactants (i.e., potassium carbonate with copper (II) sulfate; then potassium carbonate with magnesium sulfate; and so on).
   b) Record all your observations in your *Active Chemistry* log.
10. Clean all equipment and the laboratory bench when you are finished. Dispose of all chemicals as directed by your teacher. Wash your hands.
11. Look at the data from the double-replacement reactions that you observed.
    a) Do you think a chemical reaction took place in each case? Explain your answer.
    b) Are you able to predict or identify any of the products that were formed? If so, which ones?
    c) Write word equations and balanced chemical equations for each reaction that you observed.

    In all cases, assume only two reactants are used and only two products are formed. Use the following formulas to help you write your equations:

copper (II) carbonate ($CuCO_{3(s)}$)
*copper (II) iodide ($CuI_{2(s)}$)
iron (III) hydroxide ($Fe(OH)_{3(s)}$)
silver carbonate ($Ag_2CO_{3(s)}$)
*silver hydroxide ($AgOH_{(s)}$)
potassium sulfate ($K_2SO_{4(aq)}$)
silver iodide ($AgI_{(s)}$)
sodium nitrate ($NaNO_{3(aq)}$)
copper (II) hydroxide ($Cu(OH)_{2(s)}$)
iron (III) nitrate ($Fe(NO_3)_{3(aq)}$)
magnesium carbonate ($MgCO_{3(s)}$)
silver chloride ($AgCl_{(s)}$)
potassium nitrate ($KNO_{3(aq)}$)
magnesium hydroxide ($Mg(OH)_{2(s)}$)
sodium chloride ($NaCl_{(aq)}$)
sodium sulfate ($Na_2SO_{4(aq)}$)

*These are more complex than indicated above.

Chem Talk

CHEMICAL REACTIONS

Kinds of Chemical Reactions

A chemical reaction takes place when starting materials (reactants) change to new materials (products). Synthesis, decomposition, single-replacement, and double-replacement reactions are some common kinds of chemical reactions.

Synthesis and Decomposition Reactions

Synthesis means "putting together." In a **synthesis reaction** two or more substances (elements or compounds) combine to form one or more compounds. In this activity you investigated the reaction of magnesium in oxygen to form magnesium oxide. The opposite kind of reaction is a **decomposition reaction**. In chemical decomposition a compound is separated into its elements. Electricity can be used to decompose water into hydrogen and oxygen.

Single-replacement Reactions

A **single-replacement reaction** is one in which an element reacts with a compound to produce a new element and an ionic compound. For example, a single-replacement reaction occurs when you put a strip of zinc into hydrochloric acid. Hydrogen gas and aqueous zinc chloride are formed, as you observed in *Activity 1*.

Activity Series

A single-replacement reaction occurs when you put a strip of zinc in a copper (II) sulfate solution. The zinc metal exchanges places with the copper cations.

If you put copper metal in a zinc sulfate solution you would find that no reaction would take place, as expected. Zinc atoms exchange places with copper ions, but copper atoms will not exchange places with zinc ions. You have learned something about a property of copper and zinc. Zinc is more reactive than copper. If you were to experiment with different metals and metallic solutions, you should be able to create an activity series of metals. The activity series of metals can be put into a table that you can use to predict if a reaction will take place.

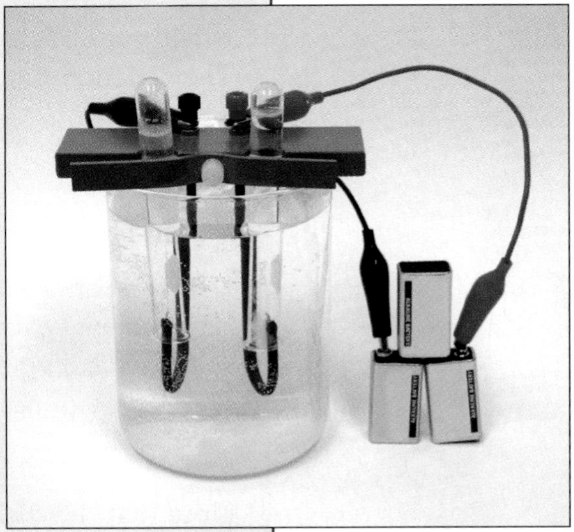

Chem Words

synthesis reaction: a chemical reaction in which two or more substances combine to form a compound.

decomposition reaction: a chemical reaction in which a single compound reacts to give two or more products.

single-replacement reaction: a reaction in which an element displaces or replaces an ion of another element in a compound.

Chem Words

double-replacement reaction: a chemical reaction in which two ionic compounds "exchange" cations to produce two new compounds.

Activity Series of Metals (Most Active to Least Active)
lithium ($Li \rightarrow Li^+ + e^-$)
potassium ($K \rightarrow K^+ + e^-$)
calcium ($Ca \rightarrow Ca^{2+} + 2e^-$)
sodium ($Na \rightarrow Na^+ + 1e^-$)
magnesium ($Mg \rightarrow Mg^{2+} + 2e^-$)
aluminum ($Al \rightarrow Al^{3+} + 3e^-$)
zinc ($Zn \rightarrow Zn^{2+} + 2e^-$)
iron ($Fe \rightarrow Fe^{2+} + 2e^-$)
lead ($Pb \rightarrow Pb^{2+} + 2e^-$)
hydrogen ($H_2(g) \rightarrow 2H^+ + 2e^-$)
copper ($Cu \rightarrow Cu^{2+} + 2e^-$)
mercury ($Hg \rightarrow Hg^{2+} + 2e^-$)
silver ($Ag \rightarrow Ag^+ + e^-$)
gold ($Au \rightarrow Au^{3+} + 3e^-$)

The table looks like the one on this page. The table permits you to determine how a metal will react in a metal solution. A metal that is more active than another will dissolve into the metal solution and plate out the less active metal. Zinc replaced the copper in the copper (II) sulfate solution and the copper plated the zinc. For example, let's say that you place a strip of copper in a silver nitrate solution. According to the table, the copper will dissolve into copper ions (Cu^{2+}) and the silver ions in the silver nitrate solution will plate out on the copper as silver.

In addition to metals, you will notice that hydrogen gas is also listed in the activity series. You read above that metals can replace less active metals in metal salt solutions. Metals that are more active than hydrogen can replace the hydrogen from water to form metal hydroxides. As an example, if you were to react potassium metal with water, you would get hydrogen gas and potassium hydroxide solution. The equation is:

$$2K(s) + 2HOH(l) \rightarrow H_2(g) + 2KOH(aq)$$

(Note: Water, H_2O is written as HOH.)

Double-replacement Reactions

Double-replacement reactions are different from single-replacement reactions, in that you start with two aqueous phase solutions and when they are mixed they "switch partners." An example of this type of reaction is:

$$Ba(NO_3)_2(aq) + Na_2SO_4(aq) \rightarrow 2NaNO_3(aq) + BaSO_4(s)$$

Note that the cation of the one compound (Ba^{2+}) exchanged places with the cation (Na^+) of the other compound. The solid $BaSO_4$ is a precipitate. When examining double-replacement reactions, you know that a reaction has taken place if you see:

- a precipitate
- a gas

Solubility Rules

A precipitate will form if the compound is not soluble in water. In the example above, barium sulfate was not soluble in water. This was noted in the equation by referring to it as a solid (s). Chemists have created a set of solubility rules for **salts**. Salts are classified as ionic compounds having both cations and anions.

In the example above, barium sulfate formed as a precipitate. Since barium sulfate is insoluble, this agrees with the solubility rules. If you mixed silver nitrate with sodium chloride, would you expect to get a precipitate? The two products that would form are silver chloride and sodium nitrate. Solubility rule #2 tells you that silver chloride is insoluble (a precipitate will form) and solubility rule #3 tells you that sodium nitrate is soluble and stays in solution. Using these rules, you can now predict whether a mixture will produce a precipitate or not.

Solubility Rules	
1.	All salts (defined as ionic compounds) of the alkali metals (Group I on the periodic table) and the ammonium ion are soluble in water.
2.	All chlorides, bromides, and iodides are soluble with the exception of silver, lead, and mercury halides.
3.	All nitrate, chlorate, perchlorate, and acetate salts are soluble.
4.	All sulfates are soluble with the exception of calcium, barium, strontium, and lead.
5.	All carbonates, phosphates, chromates, hydroxides, and sulfides are insoluble except when they are combined with alkali metals or the ammonium ion.

Chem Words

salts: ionic compounds that contain a combination of cation(s) and anion(s).

Checking Up

1. What is a synthesis reaction? Provide an example.
2. What is a decomposition reaction? Provide an example.
3. Distinguish between a single- and a double-replacement reaction.
4. What evidence would you look for to determine if a double-replacement reaction has occurred?
5. Will hydrochloric acid react with a clean strip of copper? Explain your answer.
6. Is calcium sulfate soluble in water? Justify your answer.

What Do You Think Now?

At the beginning of the activity you were asked:

- **What are some situations (other than the examples given) when language is compressed or abbreviated?**

As a student chemist, you know that an obvious answer to this question is chemistry. Do you think the use of chemical equations simplifies the communication of chemical change? Explain. Do you think you understand the basic format for how chemical change is communicated in a compact way?

Chem Essential Questions

What does it mean?

Chemistry explains a macroscopic phenomenon (what you observe) with a description of what happens at the nanoscopic level (atoms and molecules) using symbolic structures as a way to communicate. Complete the chart below in your *Active Chemistry* log.

MACRO	NANO	SYMBOLIC
If you add silver nitrate solution to sodium chloride solution, what will you observe that convinces you that a chemical reaction has taken place?	*Why do chemical equations have to be "balanced"? Explain what occurs on the atomic level when potassium iodide reacts with silver nitrate.*	*How can you represent the reaction of silver nitrate solution with potassium iodide solution using chemical symbols?*

How do you know?

Water can be decomposed to form two products: hydrogen and oxygen. What evidence was given in this activity for the chemical composition of water?

Why do you believe?

In mathematics, the = symbol is used to represent "sides" of an equation. In chemistry the symbol $\rightarrow$ is used in chemical equations. Why do you believe this symbol is better for chemistry than the = symbol?

Why should you care?

Being able to represent chemical changes in a compact way simplifies chemistry. When you perform your chemistry show, how might you use chemical equations to make it easier for your audience to understand the chemical changes that you are demonstrating?

Reflecting on the Activity and the Challenge

In this activity you have learned about a number of different types of reactions: synthesis, decomposition, single-replacement and double-replacement reactions. Knowing these types of reactions can help you predict the products of some chemical reactions. You'll need to decide if you want the audience for the *Cool Chemistry Show* to learn about these reaction types. You also learned how to write balanced equations for some of the reactions you observed. Think about a creative way of showing how you can explain balancing chemical equations to your elementary school audience.

Chem to Go

1. Baking soda ($NaHCO_3$) has been used in several reactions in previous activities. When heat is applied to baking soda, three compounds are produced. Two of the compounds are gases and the other is a solid. If the two gases are water and carbon dioxide, what is the third product? Explain how you arrived at your answer.
2. When solutions of sodium hydroxide and potassium carbonate are mixed together, no apparent reaction takes place. The same is true when you mix sodium hydroxide and potassium iodide together. Explain this observation.
3. If you mix sodium sulfate and barium nitrate solutions together, you get a white precipitate. What is the precipitate that formed? What information did you use to arrive at your answer?
4. Use the solubility rules to explain why these reactions do not form precipitates.

   a) $K_2CO_3(aq) + NaOH(aq) \rightarrow$

   b) $KI(aq) + MgSO_4(aq) \rightarrow$

   c) $KI(aq) + NaOH(aq) \rightarrow$

   d) $FeCl_3(aq) + CuSO_4(aq) \rightarrow$

   e) $FeCl_3(aq) + MgSO_4(aq) \rightarrow$

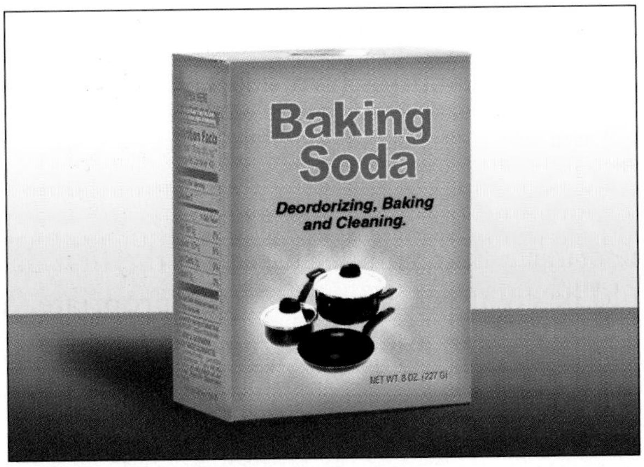
Baking Soda
Deordorizing, Baking and Cleaning.

Chapter mini Challenge

THE BRIDGE
HONK

Your challenge for this chapter is to present an entertaining and informative chemistry science show to fourth- and fifth-grade students. The content of the show should meet the needs and interests of your audience. You must also provide the teachers with a written summary including directions for your chemistry show with explanations of the chemistry.

Having completed four activities, this is a good time to give your *Cool Chemistry Show* a *first try*. It's time to describe what you intend to do and what you intend to explain. Of course, being limited to the chemistry content of four activities will limit your presentation. This *first try*, however will give you a good sense of what the challenge entails and how you and other teams are going to approach this task.

Chemistry Content

Your team should first review the chemistry content that may be included in this *Cool Chemistry Show* and related summaries for the teacher.

Activity 1: You discussed chemical and physical changes.

Activity 2: You learned about more chemical changes including tests for gases and indicator tests for acids and bases.

Activity 3: You studied how to use chemical names and formulas properly as well as the difference between ionic and molecular compounds.

Activity 4: You investigated four types of reactions (synthesis, decomposition, single-replacement, and double-replacement).

Criteria

Your team should also review the criteria that you discussed on the first day of this chapter. Your *Cool Chemistry Show* should be creative, safe, and age-appropriate. Your written chemistry summary should be accurate, clear, and organized. You should also include a number of chemistry concepts.

Preparing for Your mini Challenge

At this point, you can decide on what you will present to the fourth and fifth graders. Will you have a series of separate demonstrations or will you try to weave them into a story? How will you engage the students in the chemistry? Will the chemistry summary you present to the teacher include the chemistry content as well as safety concerns? How much time will the show take? For the *mini-challenge*, you will not have to present the actual demonstration. You will present a description of what you may do as part of your final show at the end of the chapter.

You will not be given much preparation time for the creation of this trial show. The *mini-challenge* is a way to get a sense of what you will be involved with at the end of the chapter when you have more chemistry content to include in your full show and its written summary.

Engineering/Technology Design

The engineering-design process involves a number of distinct steps. In creating a demonstration show and related summaries of the chemistry content, you are involved in a design process. Note how your efforts follow the design model described.

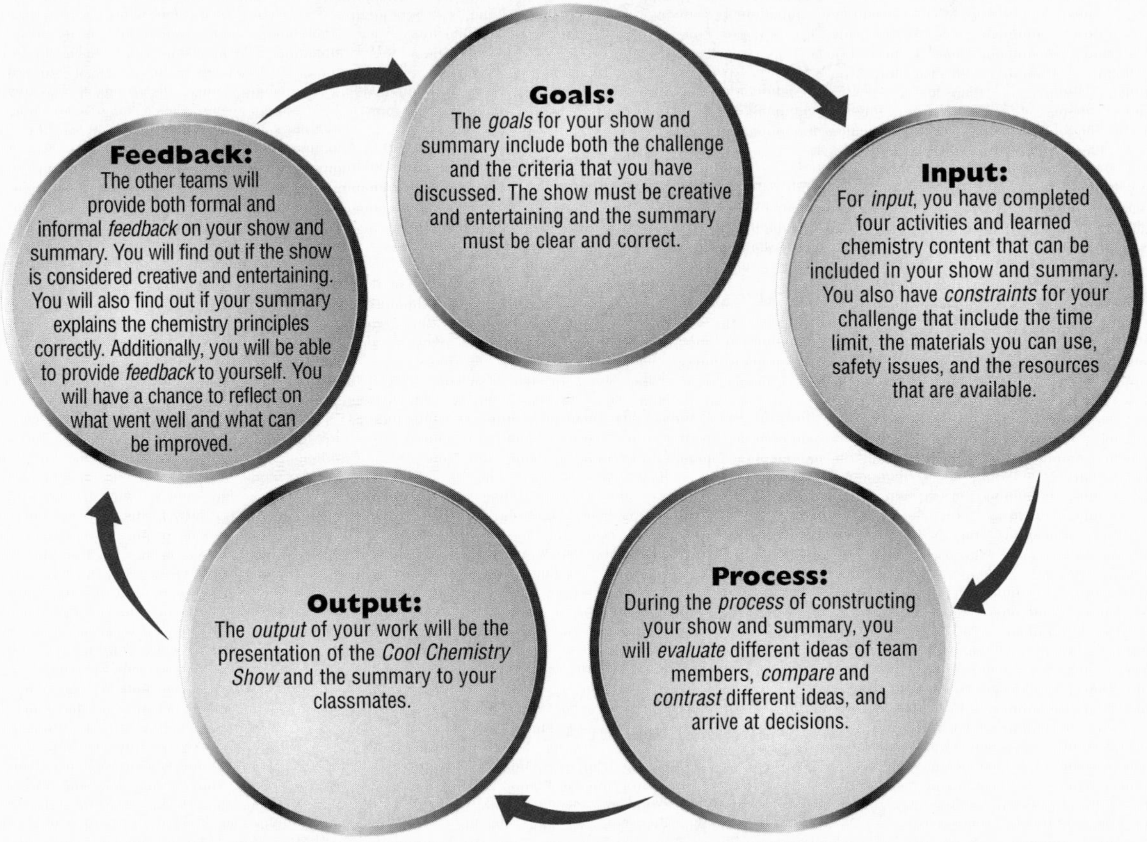

Goals:
The goals for your show and summary include both the challenge and the criteria that you have discussed. The show must be creative and entertaining and the summary must be clear and correct.
Input:
For input, you have completed four activities and learned chemistry content that can be included in your show and summary. You also have constraints for your challenge that include the time limit, the materials you can use, safety issues, and the resources that are available.
Process:
During the process of constructing your show and summary, you will evaluate different ideas of team members, compare and contrast different ideas, and arrive at decisions.
Output:
The output of your work will be the presentation of the Cool Chemistry Show and the summary to your classmates.
Feedback:
The other teams will provide both formal and informal feedback on your show and summary. You will find out if the show is considered creative and entertaining. You will also find out if your summary explains the chemistry principles correctly. Additionally, you will be able to provide feedback to yourself. You will have a chance to reflect on what went well and what can be improved.

Remember: This is a *first try*. The feedback that you get from the show and summary will be extremely valuable when you create your *Cool Chemistry Show* and the written summary. At that point, you will have additional chemistry demonstrations and materials to incorporate into your work. You will begin the entire design cycle again. That's why it is called a cycle—you keep going through it over and over to improve your design or, in this case, your *Cool Chemistry Show* and written summary.

Activity 5 Chemical Energy

What Do You See?
HOT & COLD PACKS

GOALS

In this activity you will:

- Make hot packs and cold packs.
- Observe energy changes when matter undergoes a change.
- Determine whether energy changes are endothermic or exothermic from a particular point of reference.

What Do You Think?

Injury seems to be part of professional sports. Athletic trainers have large kits with first-aid items to treat athletes during a game. One item they use is a cold pack.

- **Do the instant ice packs found in first-aid kits require refrigeration?**
- **How do the cold packs work?**

Record your ideas about these questions in your *Active Chemistry* log. Be prepared to discuss your responses with your small group and the class.

Investigate

1. To make a cold pack, place 10 g of ammonium nitrate in a quart-size, resealable plastic bag. Add 20 mL of water to the bag and seal.

   a) Record your observations.

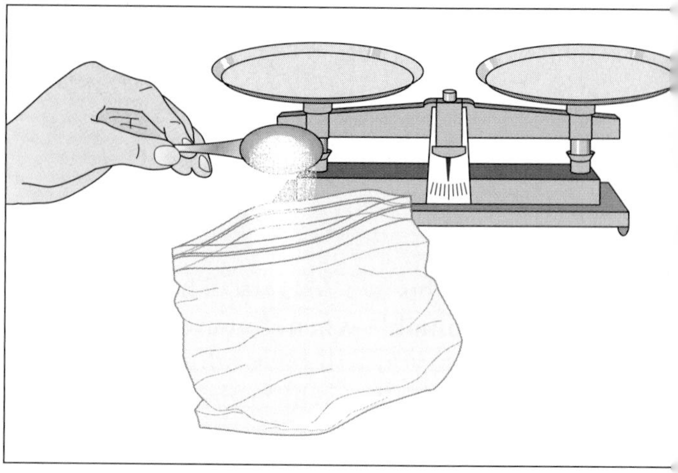

In an endothermic chemical reaction, energy in the form of heat is absorbed in the process. In an exothermic chemical reaction, energy in the form of heat is given off in the process.

b) Was the cold pack an example of an exothermic or endothermic chemical reaction?

2. Make a hot pack by placing 20 g of sodium carbonate (or calcium chloride) in a quart-size, resealable plastic bag. Add 20 mL of water to the bag and seal.

   a) Record your observations.

   b) Was the reaction exothermic (heat generating) or endothermic (heat absorbing)?

3. Your teacher will perform the following demonstration.

   To a flask containing 16 g of ammonium thiocyanate, 32 g of barium hydroxide is added. A rubber stopper is placed in the mouth of the flask. The flask is shaken vigorously.

   The stoppered flask is placed on a wood board that has been wet down so that there are puddles of water.

   a) Record your observations. Cool chemistry!

   b) Was the reaction exothermic (heat generating) or endothermic (heat absorbing)?

4. Using a chemical scoop, transfer a few pellets of sodium hydroxide to a test tube half-full of water. Carefully feel the side of the test tube.

   a) Record your observations.

   b) Was the reaction exothermic (heat generating) or endothermic (heat absorbing)?

5. Dispose of the materials as directed by your teacher. Clean up your workstation.

Safety goggles and a lab apron must be worn *at all times* in a chemistry lab.

Be careful when working with the sodium hydroxide pellets. Wear rubber gloves and eye protection. If you should accidentally drop a pellet, do not try to pick it up with your bare hands as it may burn them. Use gloved hands to retrieve the pellets.

Wash your hands and arms thoroughly after the activity.

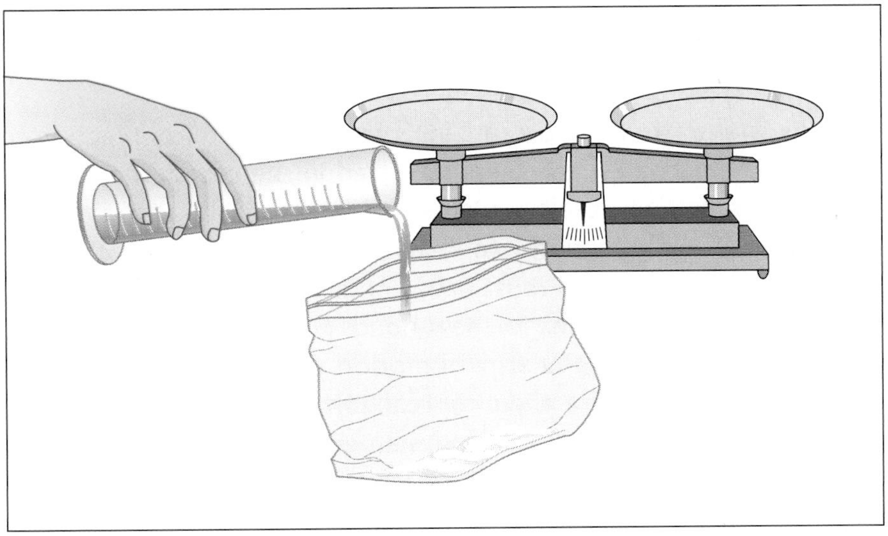

Chem Talk

Chem Words

endothermic change (reaction): a change in which energy in the form of heat is absorbed from the surrounding environment resulting in an increase in the internal energy of the system.

exothermic change (reaction): a change in which energy in the form of heat is released from a system resulting in a decrease in the internal energy of the system.

activation energy: the minimum energy required for a chemical reaction.

kinetic energy: the energy of motion.

$KE = \frac{1}{2}mv^2$

ENDOTHERMIC AND EXOTHERMIC PROCESSES

Reactions That Absorb and Release Heat Energy

A process is described as **endothermic** when heat energy is absorbed, increasing the internal energy of the system. The cold pack you made with ammonium nitrate is an example of an endothermic reaction. Another example is the decomposition of potassium chlorate. In this reaction, energy must be added to the system in order to cause the decomposition of the potassium chlorate to form the products of oxygen gas and potassium chloride. If you touch a container that holds a spontaneous endothermic process, it will feel cool to the touch.

An **exothermic** process results when heat energy is released, decreasing the internal energy of the system. If you touch a container that holds an exothermic process, it will feel warm or hot to the touch. The hot pack you made with sodium carbonate is an example of an exothermic reaction. Another example is the combining of sodium hydroxide solution with hydrochloric acid. This reaction produces sodium chloride and water and releases energy to the environment. The terms endothermic and exothermic can be used when describing both physical and chemical changes.

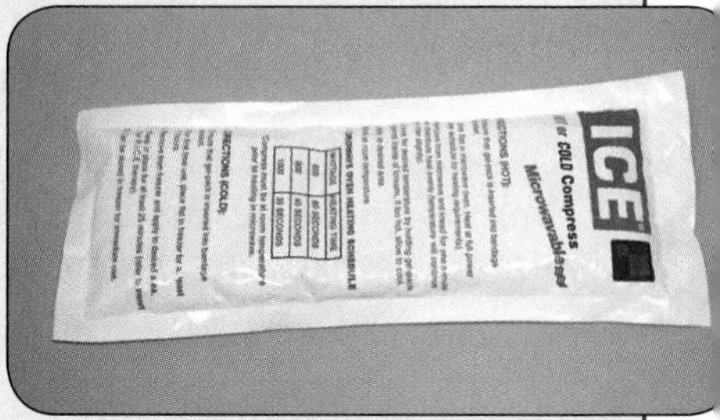
ICE

Importance of Energy

Why is energy so important? In order for a chemical reaction to take place, the particles (reactants) involved in the reaction must interact. Not all collisions result in a chemical reaction. The particles involved must have enough energy to enable them to react with each other. The colliding particles must have enough **kinetic energy** to break the existing bonds in order for new bonds to be formed. (Physics reminder: Kinetic energy is the energy of motion. $KE = \frac{1}{2}mv^2$) The minimum energy required for a chemical reaction is called the **activation energy** for the reaction. Bond breaking is an endothermic process and requires an addition of energy. Bond formation is an exothermic process and is accompanied by a release of energy.

As products form, energy is released as new bonds are created. If this released energy is greater than the energy needed to break the bonds of the reactants (bond-forming > bond-breaking), the reaction is exothermic, as shown in the graph. The prefix *exo* means "leaving" and *thermo* means heat energy and so, heat energy is leaving. The products have less energy than the reactants. For example, the cells in your body use glucose to get energy for cellular functions. Glucose plus oxygen (from breathing) provides you with energy.

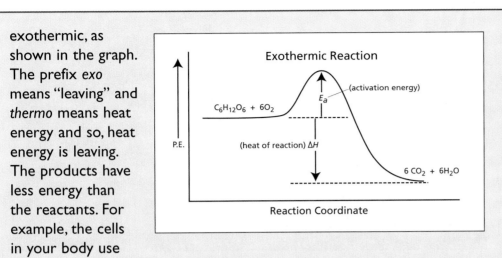

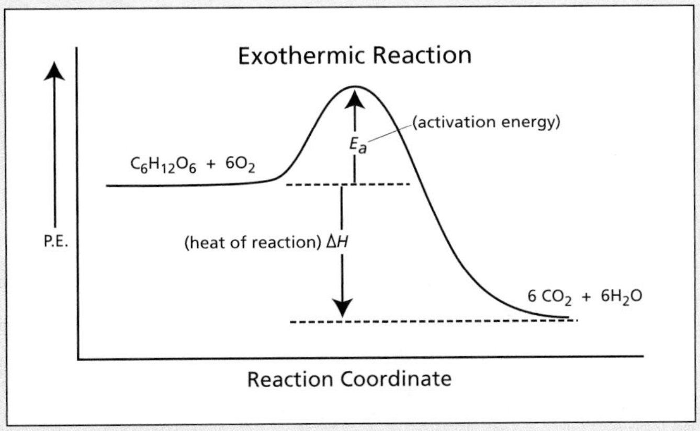
Exothermic Reaction
(activation energy)
E_a
$C_6H_{12}O_6$ + $6O_2$
P.E.
(heat of reaction) ΔH
6 CO_2 + $6H_2O$
Reaction Coordinate

$$\underbrace{C_6H_{12}O_6 + 6O_2}_{\textit{Reactants}} \rightarrow \underbrace{6CO_2 + 6H_2O + \text{energy}}_{\textit{Products}}$$

This energy is used by the body. When the released energy from bond formation is less than the energy needed to break the bonds of the reactants (bond-forming < bond-breaking), the reaction is called endothermic, as shown in the second graph. The prefix *endo* means "taking in" and so the products have more energy than the reactants. The reverse reaction, which is performed by plants during photosynthesis, requires energy and is endothermic.

$$12H_2O + 6CO_2 + \text{energy (sunlight)} \rightarrow C_6H_{12}O_6 + 6O_2 + 6H_2O$$

Plants produce glucose for their own growth and release oxygen for living things (including the plants) to breathe.

In the process of photosynthesis, plants use energy from light to break the bonds of carbon dioxide and water in order to form the products, glucose and oxygen.

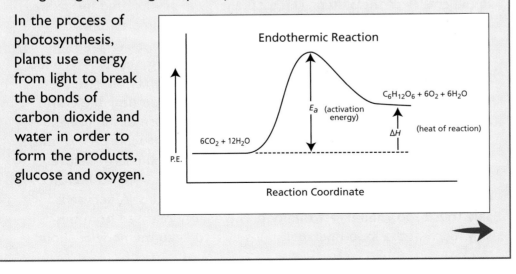

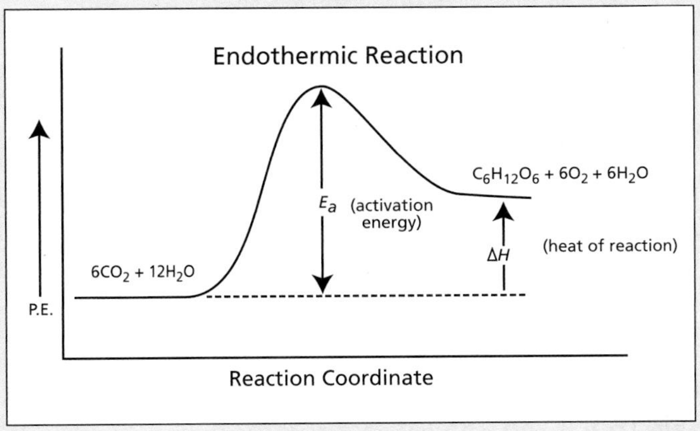
Endothermic Reaction
$C_6H_{12}O_6$ + $6O_2$ + $6H_2O$
E_a (activation energy)
ΔH
(heat of reaction)
$6CO_2$ + $12H_2O$
P.E.
Reaction Coordinate

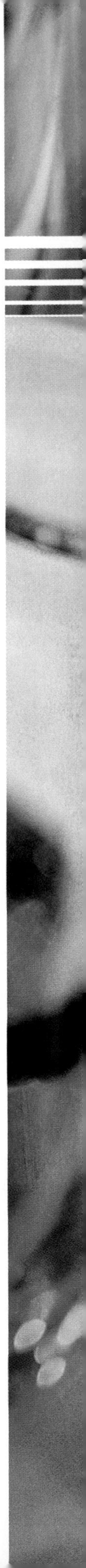

Conservation of Energy

Energy transfer is an important feature in all chemical changes. Energy is transferred whether the chemical reaction takes place in the human body, like the metabolism of carbohydrates, or in a car, like the combustion of gasoline. In both of these cases energy is released into the surroundings. The photosynthesis that occurs in living plants and the decomposition of water into hydrogen and oxygen both require energy from the surroundings. Energy is the great organizing principle of all science. The conservation of energy allows you to better understand the world around you.

Energy exists as light energy, heat energy, sound energy, nuclear energy, kinetic energy, and chemical energy, as well as other forms. According to the **Law of Conservation of Energy**, the energy absorbed from the surroundings or released to the surroundings is equal to the change in the energy of the system. The total energy in any isolated (perfectly insulated), closed system remains the same. In the simplest physical systems, it is quite easy to describe the energy changes. When a bowling ball falls, its original **gravitational potential energy** becomes kinetic energy as the ball increases its speed. After the ball hits the ground, this kinetic energy is converted to sound energy (you hear the crash) and heat energy (you can measure a temperature rise of the ball and ground) and the compression and vibration of the ground. Each of these can be measured and it is always found that the total energy before an event is equal to the total energy after the event. When a human being is involved, you notice other energy interactions. A person is able to eat food and digest the food. The energy released from this slow-burn of the food (metabolism) is able to keep the body at about

Chem Words

Law of Conservation of Energy: states that the energy absorbed from the surroundings or released to the soundings is equal to the change in the energy of the system.

gravitational potential energy: is a stored energy determined by an object's position in a gravitational field.

37°C. As all non-living things in a room cool down to room temperature, humans are able to stay warm in the 22°C room environment. People also use the food energy that they ingest for moving muscles, keeping the heart pumping, and operating all human functions. Living organisms are superb energy conversion systems.

Heat and Temperature

Both **heat** and **temperature** have been mentioned in this activity. It is important to note that heat and temperature are not the same, although they are related. Heat is one form of energy. When two materials of different temperatures interact, they exchange heat energy until they arrive at the same temperature. Temperature is a number associated with how hot or cold something is. On a molecular level, temperature is related to the average kinetic energy of the atoms in the material. All particles in a material are in a constant state of motion. The temperature of the material is a measurement of this molecular motion. If the kinetic energy of the particles increases, the temperature increases.

A thermometer is an instrument that measures temperature. Heat is the transfer of energy, which often results in a change in the kinetic energy of particles. That is, it results in a change in the temperature of the system.

Chem Words

heat: a form of energy that results from the motion of atoms and molecules.

temperature: a measure proportional to the average kinetic energy of all the particles of a material.

Checking Up

1. Describe an endothermic reaction.
2. Describe an exothermic reaction.
3. Explain whether each of the following is endothermic or exothermic:
   a) bond breaking
   b) bond forming
4. Distinguish between heat and temperature.

What Do You Think Now?

At the beginning of the activity you were asked:

- **Do the instant cold packs found in first-aid kits require refrigeration?**
- **How do the cold packs work?**

How would you answer these questions now that you have completed this activity?

Chem Essential Questions

What does it mean?

Chemistry explains the macroscopic phenomenon (what you observe) with an explanation of what happens at the nanoscopic level (atoms and molecules) using symbolic structures (formulas and measurements) as a way to communicate. Complete the chart below in your *Active Chemistry* log:

MACRO	NANO	SYMBOLIC
What do you observe when heat energy is absorbed during a chemical reaction? What do you observe when heat energy is released during a chemical reaction?	*What happens to atoms and molecules as they become heated?*	*How can you graphically depict an exothermic reaction and the activation energy required for the reaction to take place?*

How do you know?

In the activity, what chemical reaction did you observe that was an exothermic reaction? What evidence did you have that the process was exothermic?

Why do you believe?

Consider the chemical reactions that you encounter in daily life. Which are more common, endothermic reactions or exothermic reactions? Hand and feet warmers are used in the winter. Why do you think that hand and feet coolers are not used in the summer?

Why should you care?

Experiences that involve more than one sense (as in sight, sound, etc.) add interest to a presentation. Consider and explain how the concept of chemical energy can safely incorporate the sense of touch in your chemistry show.

Reflecting on the Activity and the Challenge

Energy is involved in any process that requires the breaking or making of bonds. The process may be a chemical or physical change. Sometimes energy changes are not noticed or measured, but other times an energy change is significant enough to be detected. In this activity you explored both endothermic and exothermic processes. As you select activities to include in the *Cool Chemistry Show*, you must be aware of any heat energy released or absorbed. The audience may be interested to learn about the energy changes that accompany chemical processes. In addition, your awareness will ensure that the presentations are safe for both the presenters and the audience.

Chem to Go

1. Identify the following changes as endothermic or exothermic. (Ask yourself whether the reaction requires the addition of heat energy to occur or does it release energy in the form of heat.)

   a) Melting ice
   b) Lighting a match
   c) Dry ice subliming into carbon dioxide gas
   d) Frying an egg
   e) Burning gasoline
   f) Explosion of hydrogen gas when it reacts with oxygen gas

2. The water in a teapot is heated on a stovetop. The temperature of the water increases. Is this an endothermic or exothermic process?

3. If a red-hot piece of iron is dropped into a bucket of water, what type of heat change takes place in reference to the water? What type of heat change takes place in reference to the iron? Use the conservation of energy to describe the event.

4. Explain in terms of energy flow how a cold pack works on a sprained ankle.

5. If a sample of ice is at –20°C and you set a beaker of the ice on a warm hot plate, explain why the ice does not appear to start melting immediately.

6. Given the reaction:

   $S(s) + O_2(g) \rightarrow SO_2(g) + \text{energy}$

   Which diagram best represents the potential energy changes for this reaction?

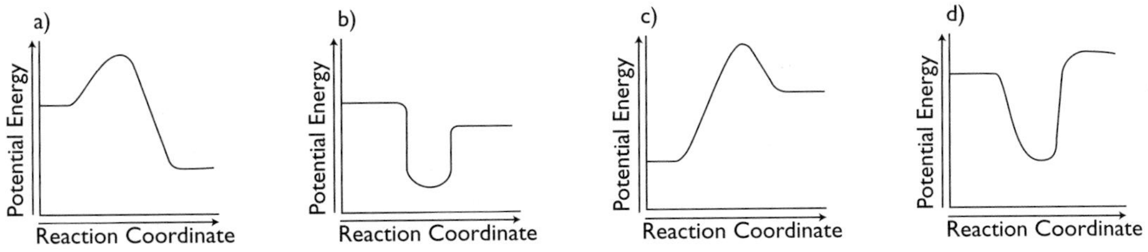
a)
b)
c)
d)
Potential Energy
Reaction Coordinate

7. Rumor has it that a leading cola producer is preparing a new can of cola that does not need refrigeration! That's right, you simply take the can right out of the cupboard, open the can, and after waiting for five minutes you're able to enjoy an ice-cold can of your favorite soda!

   a) Do you think this "instant cold" is possible? Give an explanation for your answer.

   b) How much would you be willing to pay for such a feature (in addition to the cost of a regular can of soda)?

8. ***Preparing for the Chapter Challenge***

   Review the chemical reactions that you have so far planned to feature in your *Cool Chemistry Show*. Have you included both endothermic and exothermic reactions? In a paragraph describe the difference between the two types of reactions. Be sure to mention why energy transfers are important.

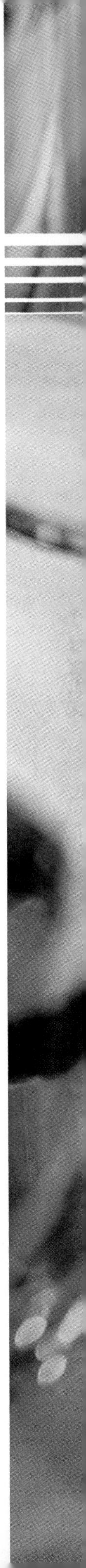

Inquiring Further

1. Commercial cold and hot packs

Research several cold and hot packs. What materials are used in the packs, and how is the chemical reaction activated? You should be aware that there are a variety of commercially available hot and cold packs. Some are reusable and some are not. Those that are not reusable are typically chemical reactions. Those that are reusable are typically physical changes. Design a process to make a cold pack, using your research. Have your teacher approve your design before you actually try it out.

2. One colligative property of a solvent

A salt solution will depress the freezing point of water. This is commonly known as the colligative property of a solution. When you add anti-freeze (ethylene glycol) to water, you find that the freezing point of the solution is lowered, which prevents the water in the car radiator from freezing at 0°C. It also elevates the boiling point of the solution, which will prevent the water solution from boiling at 100°C. Design an experiment to demonstrate the colligative property of a solvent. With the approval of your teacher carry out your experiment.

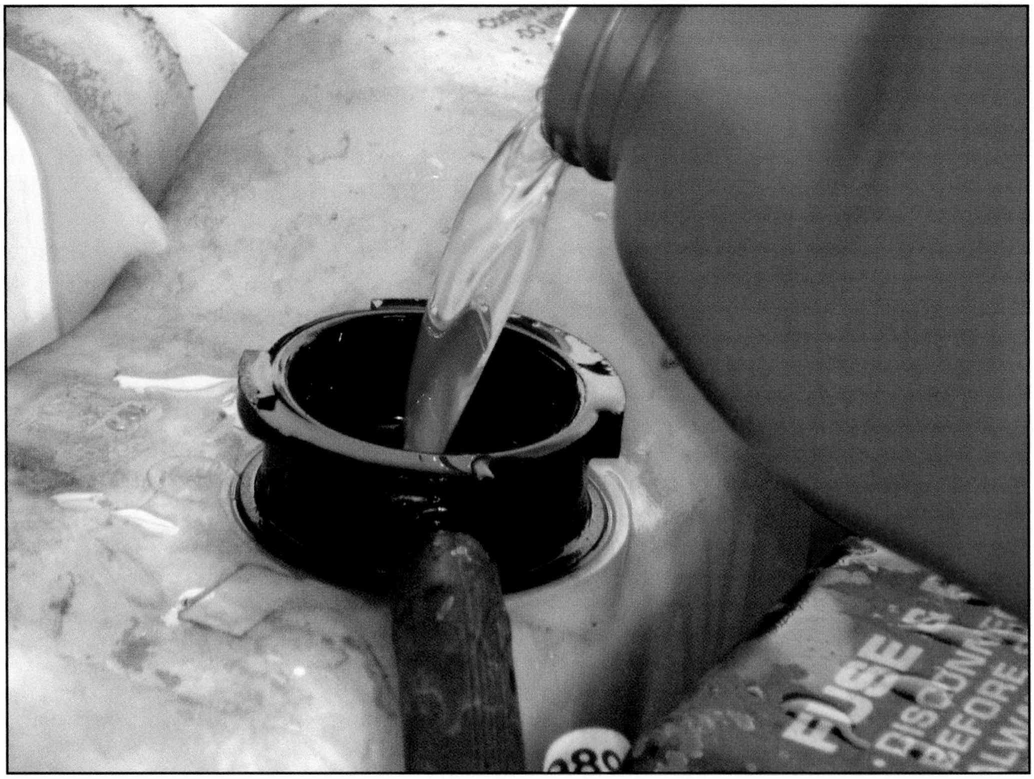

Activity 6 Reaction Rates

What Do You See?

REACTION RATE COMPETITION
Z
DISSOLVING OF ANTACID TABLET
SPOILING OF MILK

GOALS

In this activity you will:

- Discover conditions that make a reaction proceed faster or slower.
- Discuss explanations for why this happens at the molecular level.

What Do You Think?

Have you ever wondered why some chemical reactions, like the burning of a match, take place at a fast rate, while others, like the spoiling of milk, take place slowly? The rate of a chemical reaction is the speed at which the reactants are converted to products.

- **What are some factors that influence the rate of a reaction?**
- **How could you make a reaction take place at a faster rate?**
- **How could you slow a reaction down?**

Record your ideas about these questions in your *Active Chemistry* log. Be prepared to discuss your responses with your group and the class.

Investigate

1. Predict how the concentration (strength) of vinegar will affect how fast it will react with magnesium. One way to study the rate of a reaction is to time the reaction with a stopwatch. Try this!

   Place 20 mL of vinegar into a large test tube.

   To a second test tube, add 10 mL of vinegar and 10 mL of water. Mix well using a stirring rod.

   In a third test tube, add 5 mL of vinegar to 15 mL of water. Mix.

Safety goggles and a lab apron must be worn *at all times* in a chemistry lab

Prepare three equal-sized pieces of polished magnesium ribbon. Set your stopwatch so that it is ready to start immediately.

Add a piece of polished magnesium ribbon to the first test tube, keeping track of the time the reaction takes.

Be careful with the HCl. Do not get it on your skin.

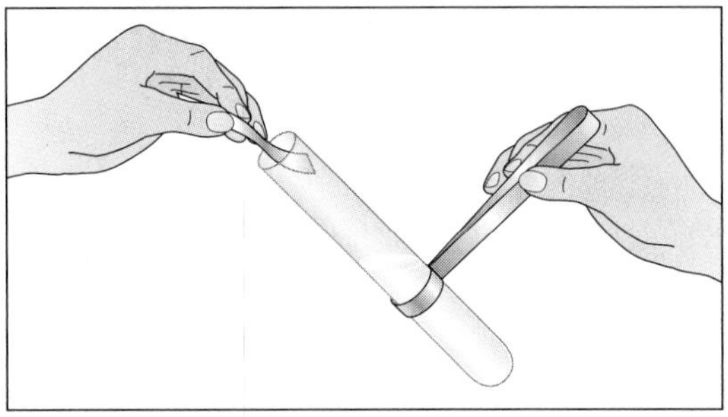

a) Record your observations and the reaction time on a data table. Repeat for the other two test tubes.

b) In this step, you changed the concentration of one of the reactants (the vinegar). The vinegar was less concentrated (more dilute) in each successive test tube. Did this impact the reaction rate? If so, describe the relationship between the concentration of the vinegar and the resulting reaction rate.

c) Compare your experimental results to the prediction you made before conducting the experiment.

2. Using the same reaction above, design a small-scale experiment using a well-plate and smaller amounts of reagents.

a) Record your design. Include the equipment you will need, the amount of reactants, and any safety procedures.

b) With the approval of your teacher, carry out the procedure. Record your data and results.

c) How do the results compare with the reaction in *Step 1*?

3. Place 10 drops of 0.1 *M* HCl (weak concentration) into a small test tube and 10 drops of 1.0 *M* HCl (strong concentration) into a second test tube. Drop a small piece of polished zinc (equal size) into each test tube containing HCl.

a) Record your observations.

b) How do these results compare to your earlier results? Do these results support or refute the relationship you stated in *Step 1 (c)*?

4. Hydrogen peroxide (H_2O_2) is sold over the counter in pharmacies to be used as a disinfectant for minor injuries. Because hydrogen peroxide decomposes slowly to form oxygen and water, it is also a source of oxygen gas.

$$2H_2O_{2(aq)} + \text{light energy} \rightarrow O_{2(g)} + 2H_2O_{(l)}$$

Pour a small amount of hydrogen peroxide into each of two test tubes. Add a small amount of manganese dioxide to one of the test tubes.

a) Record your observations.

The manganese dioxide did not actually react with the hydrogen peroxide; it simply acted as a catalyst for the decomposition of the hydrogen peroxide. A catalyst is a material that speeds up a reaction without being permanently changed itself. The chemical equation for this reaction is:

$$2H_2O_{2(l)} \xrightarrow{MnO_2} O_{2(g)} + 2H_2O_{(l)}$$

5. As an inquiry activity, design an investigation to prove that the manganese dioxide did not get used up in the reaction. Record your design. Include the equipment you will need, the amount of reagents, and any safety procedures.

a) Record your procedure in your *Active Chemistry* log.

b) With the approval of your teacher, carry out the experiment.

c) Record your data and results.

d) Describe the relationship between the use of a catalyst and the rate of a reaction.

6. Pour 200 mL hot water into one beaker and 200 mL ice water into another beaker. Add a tea bag to each.

a) Record your results.

b) Repeat the procedure using an effervescent antacid tablet in place of the tea bag. Record your observations.

c) Describe the relationship between temperature and the rate of reaction, based on the two situations you studied.

7. Prepare two beakers, each containing equal amounts (about 200 mL) of room temperature water. Obtain two effervescent antacid tablets. Crush one and leave the other whole. Simultaneously add the crushed tablet to one beaker and the whole tablet to the other beaker.

a) Record your observations. What factor was being studied in *Step 7*?

b) Describe the relationship between that factor and the rate of reaction.

8. Use the results of this activity to answer the following:

a) Describe how you could increase the rate of reaction by altering:
- concentration
- catalyst
- temperature
- surface area

Wash your hands and arms thoroughly after the activity.

9. Dispose of all chemicals as directed by your teacher. Clean and put away any equipment as instructed. Clean up your workstation.

10. Chemical systems that highlight reaction rates can be very interesting. Because time is a factor, these systems are often called clock reactions. Your teacher may do the following reaction as a demonstration. Your teacher will use the following solutions:

Solution A = 0.1 *M* potassium iodate (KIO_3)

Solution B = 1% starch solution

Solution C = 0.25 *M* sodium hydrogen sulfite ($NaHSO_3$)

Two rows of five beakers (all the same size!) will be arranged. The front row is shown here.

100 mL of solution A, 50 mL of solution B, and 100 mL of distilled water.
95 mL of solution A, 50 mL of solution B, and 105 mL of distilled water.
90 mL of solution A, 50 mL of solution B, and 110 mL of distilled water.
85 mL of solution A, 50 mL of solution B, and 115 mL of distilled water.
80 mL of solution A, 50 mL of solution B, and 120 mL of distilled water.

Each beaker in the back row contains 20 mL of solution C and 130 mL of water. Your teacher will add the contents of one beaker from the back row to the contents of one of the beakers in the front row. Use a stopwatch and stop when a color change occurs. Your teacher will then combine the next set of beakers as you again use the stopwatch. She or he will continue down the row.

a) Record the time and your observations about the change in each case.

Chem Talk

Chem Words

rate of reaction: the decrease in the concentration of reactants with a corresponding increase in products over time.

surface area: the physical property of a solid which measures its surface in square units. For example, a 1 cm sugar cube has a surface area of 6 cm^2.

FACTORS AFFECTING THE RATE OF A REACTION

In this activity you investigated several common factors that influence reaction rate. The **rate of reaction** is the decrease in the concentration of reactants over time. This leads to a corresponding increase in products over time. The factors you investigated included surface area, concentration of reactants, temperature, and catalysts. On a molecular level, these factors either increase or decrease the collision frequency of the particles of the materials involved in the reaction or they lower the activation energy of the reaction.

Consider **surface area**. In water, a sugar cube dissolves at a much slower rate than if the same cube is first crushed. The crushed cube has a greater surface area. More parts of the sugar are in contact with the water. In a fireplace, wood chips burn faster than a pile of logs. In your activity, the crushed effervescent antacid tablet probably reacted faster. In all of these cases, the smaller pieces, with their increased surface area, allow the particles that are reacting to come in contact with each other more often. This increases the collision frequency.

Another factor that influences reaction rate is the *concentration* of the reactants. You investigated increases of concentration with vinegar and with hydrochloric acid. An increase in concentration means an increase in the number of particles in the reaction. This results in an increase in the collision frequency. If a chemist wants to increase the rate of a reaction, an increase in the concentration of one or more of the reactants will do the trick.

Altering collision frequency and efficiency can also be accomplished through *temperature* changes. According to the kinetic theory, particles move faster at higher temperatures and slower at lower temperatures. The faster motion of the particles increases the energy of the particles and increases the probability that particles will collide. In addition, increasing the temperature of the reactants increases the number of particles that have an energy that equals or exceeds the activation energy required for the reaction to take place. You probably noticed an increase in the reaction rate when you compared tea bags in hot and cold water. As a result of adding heat, the reaction rate increased.

Catalysts play an important role in many chemical reactions. A catalyst is a substance that speeds up a reaction without being permanently changed or consumed itself. The catalyst lowers the activation energy of the reaction. In the activity, you used manganese dioxide as a catalyst in the decomposition of hydrogen peroxide.

$$\underset{\textit{hydrogen peroxide}}{2H_2O_2(l)} \xrightarrow{MnO_2} \underset{\textit{oxygen}}{O_2(g)} + \underset{\textit{water}}{2H_2O(l)}$$

Many commercial reactions make use of catalysts, because the catalysts can be recovered and reused. You are probably familiar with the term catalytic converter. This is a device used in automobiles to convert the pollutants CO and NO into CO_2 and N_2. This lessens the environmental impact of the combustion products. The catalyst in this converter is platinum.

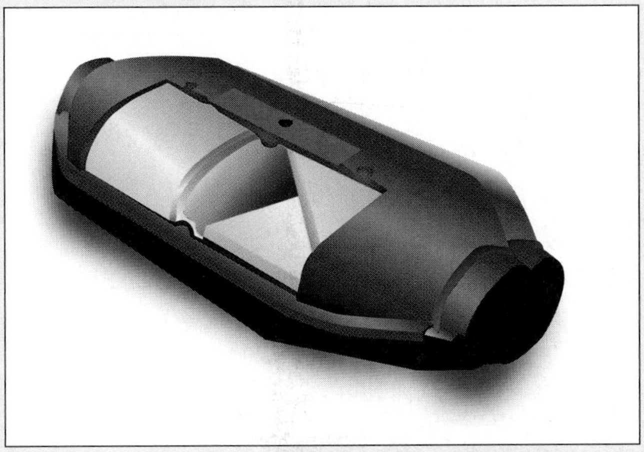

Chem Words

catalyst: a substance that speeds up a chemical reaction without being permanently changed or consumed itself.

Checking Up

1. List four factors that influence the rate of a reaction.
2. For each of the factors you listed above, describe how the factor increases the collision frequency of efficiency of the particles of the materials involved in the reaction.
3. How is a catalyst different from the reactants and products of a chemical reaction?

What Do You Think Now?

At the beginning of the activity you were asked:

- **What are some factors that influence the rate of a reaction?**
- **How could you make a reaction take place at a faster rate?**
- **How could you slow a reaction down?**

How would you answer these questions now that you have completed this activity?

Now think about these questions:

- **Why do you think it takes a long time for a nail to rust?**
- **In what form are the reactants prepared in fireworks?**
- **Why do you think that food spoilage (chemical change) takes place more slowly in the refrigerator?**

Record your answers in your *Active Chemistry* log.

Chem Essential Questions

What does it mean?

Chemistry explains a macroscopic phenomenon (what you observe) with a description of what happens at the nanoscopic level (atoms and molecules) using symbolic structures as a way to communicate. Complete the chart below in your *Active Chemistry* log.

MACRO	NANO	SYMBOLIC
Explain what you observed when you changed different factors of the reaction, such as temperature, concentration, surface area, and catalyst.	*How does collision theory help to explain that chemical reactions usually take place faster when hot reactants are used instead of cold reactants?*	*When hydrogen peroxide is decomposed in the presence of the catalyst manganese dioxide, oxygen gas and water are produced. Write a chemical equation for this reaction.*

How do you know?

A pad of steel wool rusts out much faster than the hull of a steel ship. Why?

Why do you believe?

The process of digesting food is a chemical process. You sometimes hear that food must be chewed a certain number of times before being swallowed. Give a chemical explanation for why increasing your chewing aids in digestion.

Why should you care?

In your chemistry show, the goal is to entertain the audience at some level. Therefore, the reactions presented should actually take place during the show! (Hint: Try to avoid using the slow rusting of nails as a demonstration during the show!) You want to be able to control the reaction somehow to get the best effect. If a reaction is slow, what might you do to speed it up? If it takes place too fast, what might you do to slow it down?

Reflecting on the Activity and the Challenge

In this activity you have observed how different factors affect the rate of a reaction. This knowledge can be applied to the presentations you will make in the *Cool Chemistry Show*. If you need to cause a reaction to happen faster or slower, you now know what changes you can make. Of course, it is important for you to check with your teacher before making adjustments to any procedure you might be considering.

Chem to Go

1. Explain each of the following in terms of the factors that influence reaction rate:
   a) Which will bake faster: cookies at 50°C or at 150°C?
   b) Bears (and many other animals) hibernate during the winter months. Scientists claim that low body temperature slows down the animal's metabolism. Explain.
   c) Why does a sugar cube dissolve slower than the same amount of sugar in granulated form?
   d) Antacid tablets are used to neutralize acid in the stomach. Explain why two tablets are faster than one tablet in neutralizing the acid.
   e) If you tried to burn a sugar cube with a match, you would find it very difficult to get the sugar to burn. However, if you put some cigarette ash on the cube, the cube would then burn when you put a flame to it. Explain the purpose of the cigarette ash in changing the burning of the sugar cube.
   f) Why does powdered aspirin dissolve faster than an aspirin tablet in water?
   g) Sugar dissolves more readily in hot tea than in iced tea. Explain.
2. In most cases, if you increase the temperature, the reaction rate increases. Explain this in terms of the collision theory.
3. Imagine that you purchase a light-stick necklace or wristband at a social event and want to make it last as long as possible. What would you do? Why would it help?
4. Explain why the effervescent antacid tablet did not seem to react as fast when it was put in a more dilute solution of vinegar.
5. Explain in terms of the reaction-rate factors that you have studied why it is possible for a person who has been submerged in very cold ice water to survive. However, individuals who have been submerged in warmer water for the same length of time may not survive.
6. Grain elevators have been known to have explosions because of the production of fine grain powders. Explain in terms of the reaction-rate factors that you have studied as to why this could happen.
7. In each of the four beakers shown below, a 2.0-cm strip of magnesium ribbon reacts with 100 mL of $HCl(aq)$ under the conditions shown. In which beaker will the reaction occur at the fastest rate?

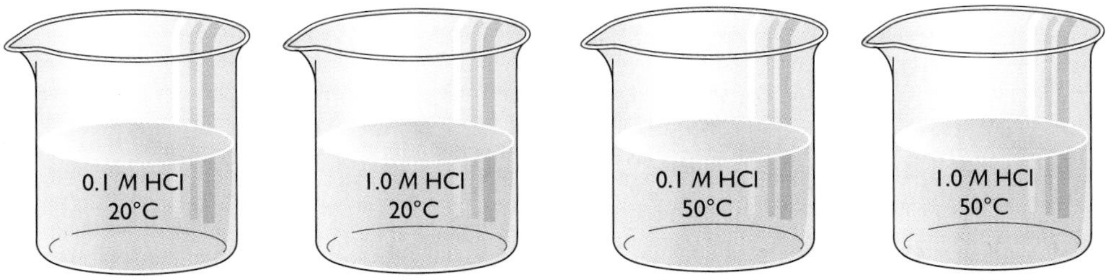
0.1 M HCl
20°C
1.0 M HCl
20°C
0.1 M HCl
50°C
1.0 M HCl
50°C
Beaker A   Beaker B   Beaker C   Beaker D

8. ***Preparing for the Chapter Challenge***

   The factors affecting a reaction can be varied to achieve different reaction rates. How could you use this information in developing a presentation for the *Cool Chemistry Show*? Describe one possible scenario.

Inquiring Further

Quantifying the relationship between temperature and reaction rate

You have seen that temperature is a factor that influences the rate of reaction. In general, if the temperature increases, the reaction rate increases. When the temperature decreases, the reaction rate decreases. Can this relationship be quantified? Is there a mathematical relationship between temperature and reaction time? To answer these questions, explore the reaction between magnesium ($Mg_{(s)}$) and vinegar ($CH_3COOH_{(aq)}$).

Design and conduct an investigation that will use this reaction to show the relationship between temperature and reaction time in a quantitative way. Have your teacher approve your design before you begin. Remember—the point of the investigation is to see if the relationship between temperature and reaction time is quantifiable. You'll need to monitor both the temperature and the time carefully. Plot your data on a graph to make the relationship explicit. In your notes, include the chemical equation for this reaction.

150
100

Activity 7 Acids, Bases, and Indicators—Colorful Chemistry

What Do You See?

CABBAGE JUICE INDICATOR CHART
BASE
AMMONIA
SOAP
VINEGAR
BAKING SODA
MILK
SODA
TEA
COFFEE

GOALS

In this activity you will:

- Identify common household acids and bases.
- Identify characteristic properties of acids and bases and learn to tell the difference between acids and bases.
- See how strong acids and bases behave differently from weak acids and bases.
- Determine the pH of various solutions using indicators.
- Categorize solutions based on the pH scale.
- Use the mathematical definition of pH.

What Do You Think?

If you add red cabbage to boiling water a special bluish colored solution is made. Vinegar, a common acid, will turn the solution red. Ammonia, a common base, will turn the solution green.

- **What are some other properties of acids and bases you know about?**
- **How can you tell the difference between an acid and a base?**

Record your ideas about these questions in your *Active Chemistry* log. Be prepared to discuss your responses with your group and the class.

Investigate

1. Your teacher will provide you with samples of some of the materials listed below. Place a small amount of each solution in a separate well of a well plate. Add a small piece of polished zinc (or magnesium) to each of the solutions.

   - hydrochloric acid ($HCl(aq)$)
   - lemon or orange juice (citric acid)
   - vinegar (acetic acid, $CH_3COOH(aq)$)
   - sulfuric acid ($H_2SO_4(aq)$)

Safety goggles and a lab apron must be worn *at all times* in a chemistry lab.

Be careful with the NaOH. Do not get it on your skin!

- mineral water or carbonated beverage (contains $H_2CO_{3(aq)}$)
- milk
- dishwashing solution
- sodium hydroxide ($NaOH_{(aq)}$)
- magnesium hydroxide (contains $Mg(OH)_{2(aq)}$)
- apple juice (malic acid)
- potassium hydroxide ($KOH_{(aq)}$)
- calcium hydroxide ($Ca(OH)_{2(aq)}$)
- household ammonia ($NH_{3(aq)}$)

a) Make a data table to record your observations.

b) Which substances reacted with the metal? How could you tell? What do these substances have in common? (Consider the chemical formulas listed for some of the substances.)

c) Which substances did not react with the metal? What do these substances have in common? (Consider the chemical formulas listed for some of the substances.)

2. Place small amounts of each solution you used in *Step 1* in a separate well of a well plate. Test the solutions with one or more common laboratory indicators. (Your teacher will provide acid-base indicators like blue litmus paper, red litmus paper, phenolphthalein, bromothymol blue, and methyl red.) Indicator papers are activated simply by dipping a small piece of the paper into the solution and noting any color change. If the indicator is a solution, add a drop or two to the substance being tested and note any color change. You will need to use fresh test solutions if you want to test with more than one indicator solution.

   a) Make a chart and record your observations.

3. Use your observations as well as previous experiences to answer the following:

   a) Make a list of some of the observable properties for acids and bases. For example:

   - How do substances containing acids or bases taste? You should never taste substances in a lab, but you have probably had the opportunity to taste vinegar or lemon juice at home, or you may have accidentally gotten soap in your mouth.

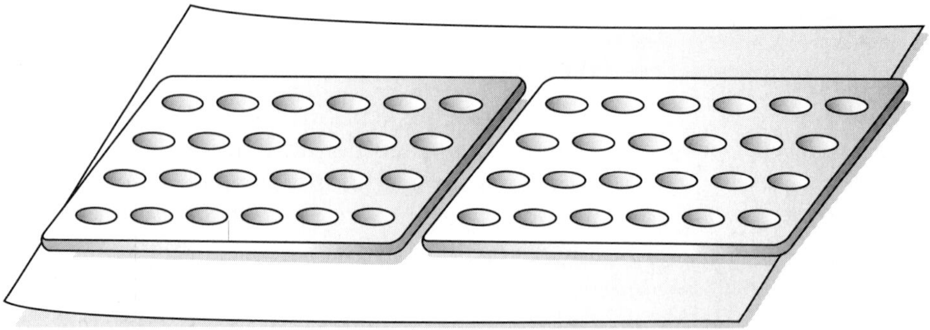

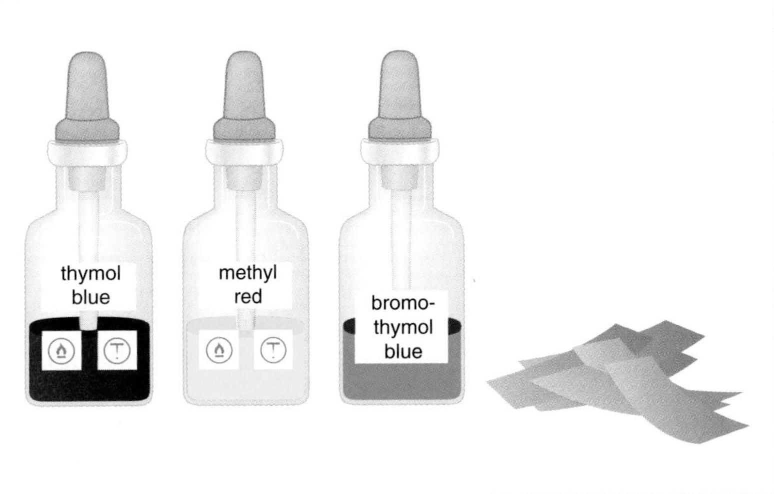
thymol blue
methyl red
bromo-thymol blue

- How do acids and bases feel? You must be very cautious when handling chemicals both at home and in the lab. However, you've probably had the experience of touching cleaning materials, such as soaps or floor cleaners. Think about vinegar or citrus fruits. How do they feel on a cut on your skin or a canker sore in your mouth?

4. The pH scale can also be used to describe acids and bases. This number scale ranges from 0 to 14. Acid solutions have a pH less than 7. The more acidic a solution is, the lower the pH. Base solutions have a pH greater than 7. The more basic a solution is, the higher the pH. Neutral solutions have a pH of 7. There are a number of ways to measure pH. You will use pH paper and/or a universal indicator solution. Determine the pH of some of the substances you used in *Step 1.*

   a) Make a data table that includes the name of the substance, the pH test, and whether the substance is an acid, a base, or a neutral substance.

   b) You may have used both pH paper and universal indicator solution to measure pH. Both are made from a combination of indicators to produce a range of colors throughout the pH scale.

   Universal indicator solution contains four separate indicators, including the following: Thymol blue is a chemical that changes color twice. Between a pH of 1.2 and 2.8, it changes from red to yellow. Between a pH of 8.0 and 9.6, it changes from yellow to blue. Methyl red is another indicator but it changes from red to yellow in the pH range of 4.8 to 6.0. Bromothymol blue is a third component which changes color from yellow to blue in the pH range 6.0 to 7.6.

   How could these three chemicals be used to create an indicator scale? What are the limitations of the pH scale if only these three chemicals are used?

Wash your hands and arms thoroughly after the activity.

5. Use the pH paper to test additional common household substances in order to determine which are acids and which are bases. (Hint: Try carbonated beverages, tea, coffee, baking powder, mayonnaise, power drinks, pickle juice, window cleaner, and stain removers.) Your teacher may give you some pH paper to take home with you.

   a) Make a list of common acids and bases found in your school or home. When possible, include both the name and formula for each substance you test.

6. Dispose of all chemicals as directed by your teacher. Clean and put away any equipment as instructed. Clean up your workstation.

Caution must be used with these sprays, because they can cause eye damage if they get into the eyes.

7. Here are two activities that display the characteristics of acids and bases in a colorful way. Your teacher may show you these as demonstrations.
   - Paint a message on a large sheet of paper or poster board using phenolphthalein indicator solution. (How about painting a message announcing your *Cool Chemistry Show*?) Allow the message to dry completely and hang the paper/poster board where everyone can see it. Use a window glass cleaner that contains ammonia water and when you are ready to reveal the message, lightly spray the design with the basic solution. (The secret message can also be revealed with a dilute ammonia solution. As the ammonia evaporates, the secret message that has been revealed will disappear again.)
   - Rinse a small beaker with a strong acid and label it "A." Rinse another small beaker with a strong base and label it "B." Let both beakers air dry. In another beaker (label it "I") add 20 drops of phenolphthalein indicator solution to about 50 mL of distilled water. When you are ready, pour some of the solution from beaker "I" into beaker "A." Then pour the solution from beaker "A" into beaker "B."

   a) Record your observations.

   b) Account for the observations in each case.

Chem Talk

ACIDS AND BASES

Arrhenius's Definition of Acids and Bases

Acids and **bases** were first classified according to their characteristic properties. As you've experienced, acids and bases have different, distinct interactions with indicators (substances that change color with changes in the acidic or basic nature of another material). Some acids react with metals, while bases do not. Bases have a characteristic bitter taste and slippery feel, while acids have a characteristic sour taste. In fact, the term acid comes from the Latin word *acidus*, which means sour. Acids and bases are also good conductors of electricity.

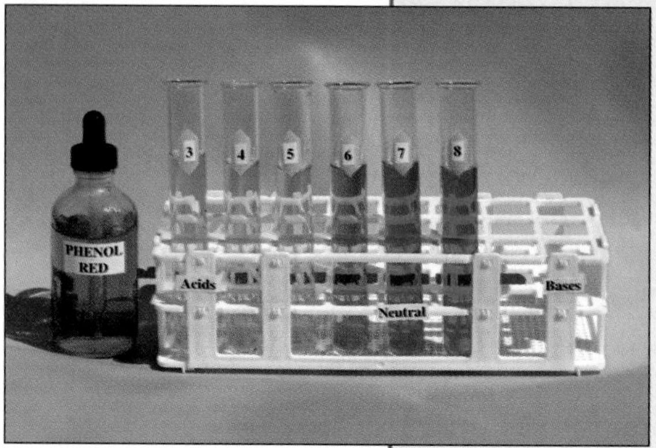
PHENOL RED
3
4
5
6
7
8
Acids
Neutral
Bases

In the 19th century a chemist named Svante Arrhenius attributed the characteristic properties of acids to their ability to produce hydrogen ions when dissolved in water. If you look at the formulas for many common acids (HCl, H_2CO_3, H_2SO_4), you'll notice that they all have H as a common element. When these acids are added to water, a hydrogen atom can be drawn off into the water solution. The hydrogen atom leaves an electron behind, forming a positive hydrogen ion (H^+) and a negative ion. Consider the action of hydrogen chloride in aqueous solution:

$$HCl(g) \xrightarrow{water} H^+(aq) + Cl^-(aq)$$

The chemical equation shown above is valuable because of its simplicity. However, in reality, the hydrogen ion (H^+) is simply a proton and readily attaches itself to a water molecule. The result is called a hydronium ion (H_3O^+).

$$\underset{\textit{hydrogen ion}}{H^+(aq)} + \underset{\textit{water}}{H_2O(l)} \rightarrow \underset{\textit{hydronium ion}}{H_3O^+(aq)}$$

To be more complete, the chemical equation above could be written as shown below. (Your teacher may allow you to use the simpler form of the equation—using the hydrogen ion as opposed to the hydronium ion.)

$$HCl(g) + H_2O(l) \rightarrow H_3O^+(aq) + Cl^-(aq)$$

Arrhenius also addressed bases and their characteristic properties. He defined a base as a substance that produces hydroxide ions (OH^-) when dissolved in water. Let's look at a base using Arrhenius's definition. When solid sodium hydroxide is dissolved in water, both sodium ions and hydroxide ions are produced, as shown in the chemical equation below:

$$NaOH(s) \xrightarrow{water} Na^+(aq) + OH^-(aq)$$

Over time, scientists have extended their definition of acids and bases beyond Arrhenius's definition to be more inclusive. These include the contributions of scientists like Johannes Brønsted of Denmark, Thomas Lowry of England, and Gilbert Lewis of the United States described in the *Artist as Chemist* chapter.

Neutralizing Acids and Bases

When acids and bases react together in solution, the hydrogen ions and hydroxide ions react in a one-to-one ratio to produce water. The remaining ions can join to form a salt. The process of an acid and base reacting to form water and a salt is called **neutralization**. Because the hydrogen ions and hydroxide ions have formed water, the solution is said to be neutral. The process of neutralization is shown in the chemical equations on the next page. The chemical formula for water is actually H_2O. In the equations on the next page the formula is written as HOH, so that you can see where the hydrogen and hydroxide ions end up.

Chem Words

acid: a substance that produces hydrogen ions in water, or is a proton donor.

base: a substance that releases hydroxide ions (OH^-) in water, or is a proton acceptor.

neutralization: the process of an acid and base reacting to form water and salt.

Chem Words

titration: a procedure for determining the concentration of an unknown chemical by having it react with measured amounts of a second chemical of known concentration.

endpoint: the point at which the indicator changes color.

buffer: a solution containing a weak acid (or weak base) and the salt of the weak acid (or base). A buffer solution will resist large changes in pH when small amounts of acid or base are added to the solution.

$H^+(aq)$	$+$	$OH^-(aq)$	$\rightarrow$	$HOH(aq)$		
hydrogen ion		*hydroxide ion*		*water*		
$HCl(aq)$	$+$	$NaOH(aq)$	$\rightarrow$	$HOH(aq)$	$+$	$NaCl(aq)$
acid		*base*		*water*		*salt*

If a suitable indicator is added to the reaction system, it will change colors when neutralization occurs. The point at which the indicator changes color is called the **endpoint**.

Consider the reaction of a strong acid (HCl) and a strong base (NaOH), as shown in the equation above. These substances are described as "strong" because they ionize completely in solution. For every HCl molecule, one hydrogen ion is released. For every NaOH molecule, one hydroxide ion is released. These two ions then combine in a one-to-one ratio to form a neutral water molecule.

Titration

Chemists take advantage of the neutralization process to help determine the concentration of solutions of acids or bases. Suppose you wanted to determine the concentration of an acid solution. You would add measured amounts of a base to the acid until the solution became neutral (pH = 7). The name of this experimental procedure is **titration**. The actual titration technique requires you to know the concentration of the base. It also requires an indicator, such as phenolphthalein, or a pH meter to determine when the solution reaches pH 7. The neutralization point or endpoint of a strong acid titrated with a strong base is at a pH of 7 as shown in graph for hydrochloric acid vs. sodium hydroxide.

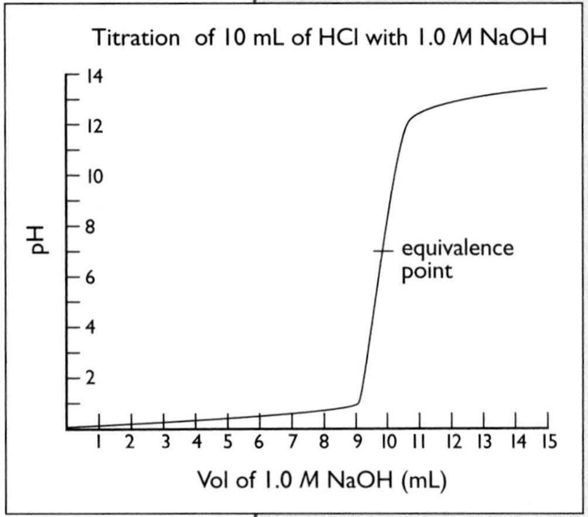
Titration of 10 mL of HCl with 1.0 M NaOH
pH
14
12
10
8
6
4
2
equivalence point
1 2 3 4 5 6 7 8 9 10 11 12 13 14 15
Vol of 1.0 M NaOH (mL)

Buffers

A **buffer** is a solution that resists changes in pH when a small amount of acid or base is added. Because of this buffering effect, titration of a solution of a weak acid with a strong base is slightly different than the titration of a strong acid. When a weak acid such as acetic acid is titrated with a strong base like NaOH, the endpoint or equivalence point is not pH = 7. Also, the endpoint does not occur as suddenly as with a strong acid. As you neutralize some of the weak acid, some of the acid's conjugate base is formed. In the case of acetic acid, the conjugate base is the acetate ion. The acetate ion is a weak base itself and a buffer solution is created which contains both the weak acid and its conjugate base. The solution now resists a change in pH as more of the strong base is added. The increase in pH is more gradual and the end point will be shifted to the basic side. The equivalence point or endpoint of acetic acid titrated with a strong base is 8.72, not 7.00.

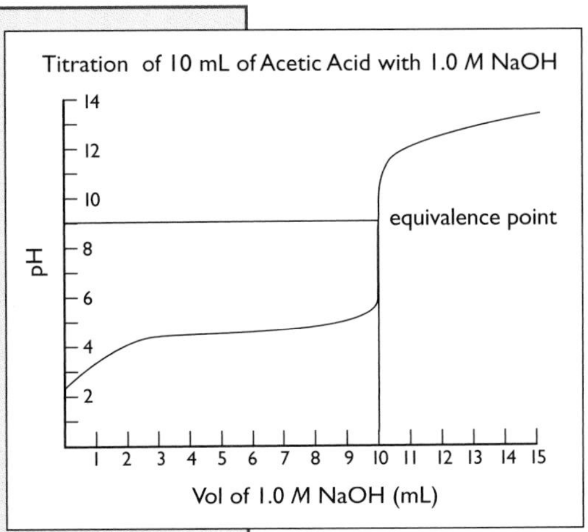

Titration of 10 mL of Acetic Acid with 1.0 M NaOH
pH
14
12
10
8
6
4
2
equivalence point
1 2 3 4 5 6 7 8 9 10 11 12 13 14 15
Vol of 1.0 M NaOH (mL)

$$CH_3COOH + OH^- \leftrightarrows CH_3COO^- + H_2O$$

acetic acid *base* *acetic ion* *water*

The titration of a weak base such as ammonia (NH_3) with a strong acid will also show these characteristics. The pH will decrease more slowly and the endpoint will be shifted to a pH less than 7.00.

Buffers are frequently used intentionally in situations where the chemist wants to avoid large changes in pH. Your blood is a natural buffer based upon the carbon dioxide-carbonic acid-bicarbonate system which maintains the pH at 7.4.

In all cases, a good buffer will absorb small quantities of acid or base with little change in pH. Any acid added to the system reacts with the conjugate base to maintain a constant pH.

$$CH_3COOH + CH_3COO^- + H_3O^+ \leftrightarrows CH_3COOH + CH_3COOH + H_2O$$

If a strong base is added to the buffer system, it reacts with the weak acid to maintain a constant pH.

$$CH_3COOH + CH_3COO^- + OH^- \leftrightarrows CH_3COO^- + CH_3COO^- + H_2O$$

The pH Scale

In this activity you observed that one way of describing acids and bases is by examining their effects on indicators. Scientists also use the pH scale to express how acidic or basic a solution is. This number scale ranges from 0 to 14. Acid solutions have a pH less than seven. The more acidic a solution is, the lower the pH. Base solutions have a pH greater than seven. The more basic a solution is, the higher the pH. Neutral solutions have a pH of seven. The pH of a

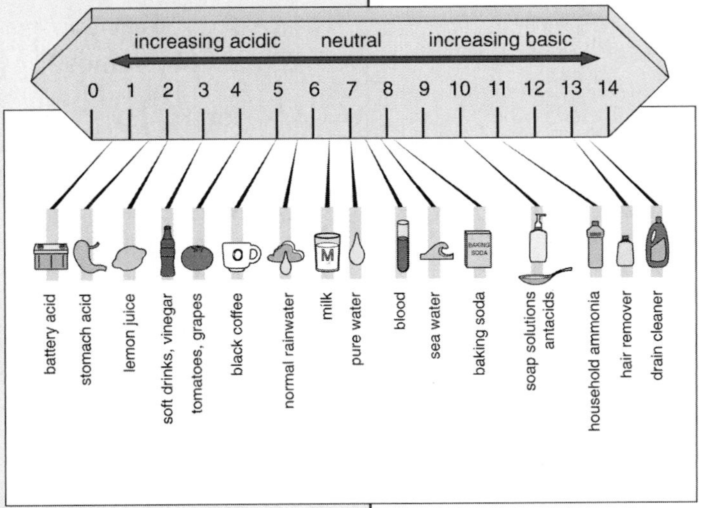

increasing acidic
neutral
increasing basic
0 1 2 3 4 5 6 7 8 9 10 11 12 13 14
battery acid
stomach acid
lemon juice
soft drinks, vinegar
tomatoes, grapes
black coffee
normal rainwater
milk
pure water
blood
sea water
baking soda
soap solutions antacids
household ammonia
hair remover
drain cleaner

Chem Words

pH: a quantity used to represent the acidity of a solution based on the concentration of hydrogen ions ($pH = -\log[H^+]$).

Common Laboratory Acid–Base Indicators		
Indicator	**Color change**	**pH Range**
methyl violet	yellow to blue	0.0 to 1.6
thymol blue	red to yellow	1.2 to 2.8
methyl orange	red to yellow	3.2 to 4.4
bromocresol green	yellow to blue	3.8 to 5.4
methyl red	red to yellow	4.8 to 6.0
litmus paper	red to blue	5.5 to 8.0
bromothymol blue	yellow to blue	6.0 to 7.6
thymol blue	yellow to blue	8.0 to 9.6
phenolphthalein	colorless to pink	8.2 to 10.0
thymolphthalein	colorless to blue	9.4 to 10.6

substance can be measured using methods like a pH meter or probe, pH paper, or universal indicator solution.

Acid and base indicators are compounds that are sensitive to pH. The color of the indicator changes as the pH of the solution changes. Most indicators are weak acids or weak bases that typically exhibit two different colors under varying pH conditions. The table above shows some common laboratory indicators and the colors they display under different pH conditions.

The pH scale ranges from 0 to 14 and is used to express the concentration of the hydrogen (H^+) or hydronium ion (H_3O^+) of a solution at 25°C. Mathematically, it is defined as the negative logarithm of the hydrogen ion concentration in moles per liter (*M*). The term **pH** stands for **p**ower of **H**ydrogen ion. It can be written as:

$pH = -\log[H+]$

where the brackets [ ] stand for "concentration of" (hydrogen ions in solution). Because pH is a logarithmic scale, the concentration of the hydrogen ion $[H^+]$ actually increases or decreases tenfold for each unit on the scale. An acid with a pH of 2 has a $[H^+]$ that is 10 times greater than an acid with a pH of 3 and 100 times the concentration of an acid with pH 4. A base with a pH of 10 has a $[H^+]$ that is 10 times less than a base with a pH of 9.

Checking Up

1. Use a chart to compare the properties of acids and bases. Be sure to include headings like taste, feel, pH, and reaction with metals.
2. What characteristic property did Arrhenius attribute to acids and bases?
3. Describe the process that occurs when an acid reacts with a base.
4. Why are litmus paper and phenolphthalein particularly useful indicators for distinguishing between acids and bases?
5. What does pH stand for?
6. How much more acidic is a solution of pH 3 than one of pH 5?

What Do You Think Now?

At the beginning of the activity you were asked:

- **What are some other properties of acids and bases you know about?**
- **How can you tell the difference between an acid and a base?**

Have your answers changed now that you have completed this activity? Think about the following questions:

- **Is it accurate to describe a mixture of an acid and a base as in "conflict"?**
- **What happens when equal amounts of acid are added to equal amounts of a base?**
- **How would you know how strong an acid is or how strong a base is?**

Chem Essential Questions

What does it mean?

Chemistry explains a macroscopic phenomenon (what you observe) with a description of what happens at the nanoscopic level (atoms and molecules) using symbolic structures as a way to communicate. Complete the chart below in your *Active Chemistry* log.

MACRO	NANO	SYMBOLIC
Explain what you saw when you used an indicator to identify if a solution was an acid or a base.	*What characteristic of a solution makes it an acid? A base?*	*How does the pH scale help to describe whether a substance is an acid, a base, or neutral?*

How do you know?

Make specific reference to your data and give experimental evidence that some substances are acids, some are bases, and some are neutral.

Why do you believe?

List some experiences you have had with acids, bases, and neutralization in your everyday life (foods, personal care products, cleaning products, etc.). Are indicators or tests involving a color change ever used in everyday life? Give examples.

Why should you care?

As your group prepares for the *Cool Chemistry Show*, consider how you might include some acid/base chemistry in your part of the show. How could you present acids and bases in an interesting way? Be prepared to share your thoughts with the rest of the class.

Reflecting on the Activity and the Challenge

In this activity you expanded your knowledge about acids and bases by becoming familiar with many of their characteristics. You learned about Arrhenius's definition of acids and bases. You also learned a bit about pH, another way of expressing the acid or base nature of substances. This information will all come in handy as you plan your presentation for the *Cool Chemistry Show*. Remember that the fifth-grade teacher has specifically asked that your class includes presentations and information about acids and bases.

Chem to Go

1. Identify which of the following characteristics relate to acids and which relate to bases:

   a) taste sour
   b) release hydroxide ions (OH^-) when dissolved in water
   c) feel slippery
   d) release hydrogen ions (H^+) when dissolved in water
   e) turn pink in the presence of phenolphthalein
   f) react with metals to produce hydrogen gas
   g) taste bitter
   h) turn red cabbage juice indicator green

2. Use Arrhenius's definition of an acid to help you write a chemical equation that shows the acidic nature of the following:

   a) sulfuric acid (H_2SO_4)
   b) carbonic acid (H_2CO_3)

3. Use Arrhenius's definition of a base to help you write a chemical equation that shows the basic nature of the following:

   a) potassium hydroxide (KOH)
   b) calcium hydroxide ($Ca(OH)_2$)

4. If you prepared the same concentration of two strong acids, sulfuric and hydrochloric, why would the pH of the sulfuric acid be lower than the pH of the hydrochloric acid?

5. Distilled water should have a neutral pH of 7, but water often has a pH less than 7. Suggest a reason for this lowering of the pH.

6. If you bubbled carbon dioxide through water, what would the new pH of the solution be?

7. Lemon juice, curdled milk, and vinegar all taste sour. What other properties would you expect them to have in common?

8. Which statement correctly describes a solution with a pH of 9?

   a) It has a higher concentration of H_3O^+ than OH^- and causes litmus to turn blue.
   b) It has a higher concentration of OH^- than H_3O^+ and causes litmus to turn blue.
   c) It has a higher concentration of H_3O^+ than OH^- and causes litmus to turn red.
   d) It has a higher concentration of OH^- than H_3O^+ and causes litmus to turn red.

9. Which pH change represents a hundredfold increase in the concentration of H_3O^+?

   a) pH 5 to pH 7 c) pH 3 to pH 1

   b) pH 13 to pH 14 d) pH 4 to pH 3

10. ***Preparing for the Chapter Challenge***

    You have seen a number of interesting color changes using acids, bases, and indicators. Choose one or two different cool activities to demonstrate in your show. Describe the procedure you will use and explain the chemistry involved. You may also wish to include an interesting scenario to accompany your "presto-change-o" demonstrations.

Inquiring Further

1. Titration

Titration is a procedure for determining the concentration of one chemical by having it react with measured amounts of a second chemical. An acid is titrated with a base; a base is titrated with an acid. Research how chemists perform a titration and the importance of indicators. With your teacher's permission, demonstrate titration to your class.

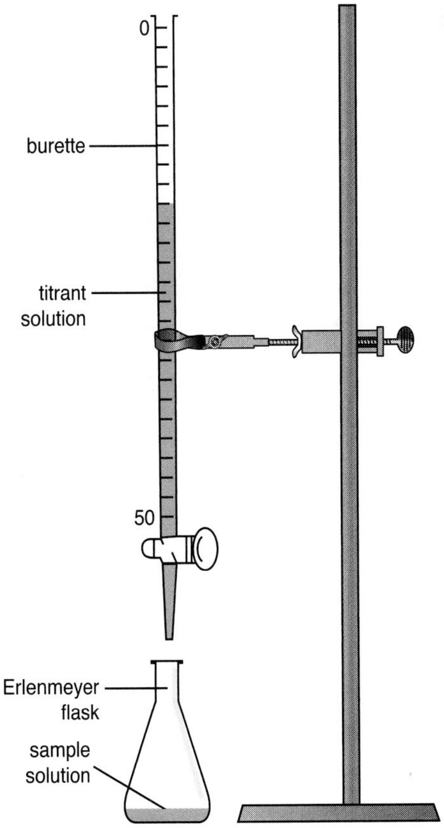
0
burette
titrant solution
50
Erlenmeyer flask
sample solution

2. The changing definition of an acid and base

The definition of acids and bases has changed through time. You are familiar with the earliest definitions that defined acids and bases in terms of their characteristic properties. The traditional definition has been expanded a number of times to include other substances that behave like acids and bases, but don't fit the traditional definition. Review (from *Artist as Chemist*) and further research the expansion through time of the definition of acids and bases. Identify the scientists involved and the changes that were made. Consider researching chemists such as Johannes Brønsted of Denmark, Thomas Lowry of England, or the American chemist Gilbert Lewis.

3. Is it pH balanced?

You may have heard the term "pH balanced" used to describe a shampoo or a deodorant. What does this term mean? What is the pH of most shampoos? Deodorants? Is it important for a shampoo or deodorant to be "pH balanced"? Conduct some research, both in and out of lab, to get answers to these questions. Focus just on shampoos or just on deodorants.

Activity 8 Color Reactions that Involve the Transfer of Electrons

What Do You See?

GOALS

In this activity you will:

- Cause different metals to rust by oxidation-reduction (redox) reactions.
- Determine what materials can react with metals, causing the metals to corrode.
- Write the word equations and chemical equations for redox reactions.
- Identify the materials that react, and the materials that are simply spectators, in a redox reaction.
- Learn how to impede corrosion.

What Do You Think?

A scratch on a car that is not repaired will rust. The same thing will happen to metal barbecue tools that get left out in the rain for a few weeks.

- **What is rust and what causes it?**

Record your ideas about these questions in your *Active Chemistry* log. Be prepared to discuss your responses with your group and the class.

Investigate

1. Half-fill a test tube with copper (II) sulfate solution ($CuSO_{4(aq)}$). Add a small amount of zinc powder to the test tube. Stopper the test tube, and shake carefully. Then remove the stopper.

   a) Record your observations. Dispose of the products as directed by your teacher.

   b) The reaction you just observed was a single-replacement reaction. The zinc replaced the copper. Use this information and your observations to complete the following equations:

   zinc + copper (II) sulfate → _______ + _______

c) Write the word equation as a sentence. Also, explain why this would be classified as a single-replacement reaction. (Refer back to *Activity 4*.)

d) Write the equation using the chemical formulas of the products.

$Zn(s) + CuSO_4(aq) \rightarrow$ ____ + ____

Because the sulfate ion shows on both sides of the equation, it is considered a spectator ion and the equation can be written as shown below:

$Zn(s) + Cu^{2+}(aq) \rightarrow$
$Cu(s) + Zn^{2+}(aq)$

e) Write a sentence or two describing what happened in the test tube in terms of the zinc and copper.

2. Cut a design or a strip of aluminum from a pie plate or tray. If you cut a strip of aluminum, twist it into an interesting shape.

Place the aluminum in a solution that contains copper (II) ions ($Cu^{2+}(aq)$). Possible solutions include: copper (II) nitrate ($Cu(NO_3)_2(aq)$) or copper (II) chloride ($CuCl_2(aq)$).

a) Observe and record your results. Dispose of the products as directed by your teacher.

b) What evidence do you have that a chemical reaction occurs? What changes have taken place with the aluminum? With the copper ions?

c) Complete this equation:

$Al(s) + Cu^{2+}(aq) \rightarrow$
______ + ______

3. Repeat *Step 2* using a different metal such as zinc.

a) Record your observations.

b) Write a chemical equation for the reaction that takes place.

4. Repeat *Step 2* again, this time using a strip of copper in a solution of aluminum nitrate ($Al(NO_3)_3(aq)$).

a) Record your observations.

b) Write a chemical equation for the reaction that takes place.

5. Dispose of the materials as directed by your teacher. Clean up your workstation.

Safety goggles and a lab apron must be worn *at all times* in a chemistry lab.

Wash your hands and arms thoroughly after the activity.

Chem Talk

Chem Words

oxidation: the process of a substance losing one or more electrons.

reduction: the process of a substance gaining one or more electrons.

redox reaction: a chemical reaction where both oxidation and reduction occur simultaneously.

REDOX REACTIONS

When zinc solid reacts with copper ions in solution, a change occurs. Atoms of zinc lose electrons to form zinc ions (Zn^{2+}) that dissolve in the solution. Copper ions (Cu^{2+}) gain the electrons from the zinc atoms to form copper atoms that plate out as a solid. Whenever an atom or ion becomes more positively charged in a chemical reaction, as in the case of zinc atoms forming positive zinc ions, the process is called **oxidation**. Oxidation is the process of losing electrons. Whenever an atom or ion becomes less positively charged in a chemical reaction, as in the case of the copper ions forming copper atoms, the process is called **reduction**. Reduction involves a gain of electrons. The processes of oxidation and reduction happen together and as such are commonly referred to as **"redox" reactions**. An easy way to remember which is oxidation and which is reduction is by remembering "LEO the lion says GERrr,"—Lose Electrons Oxidation; Gain Electrons Reduction.

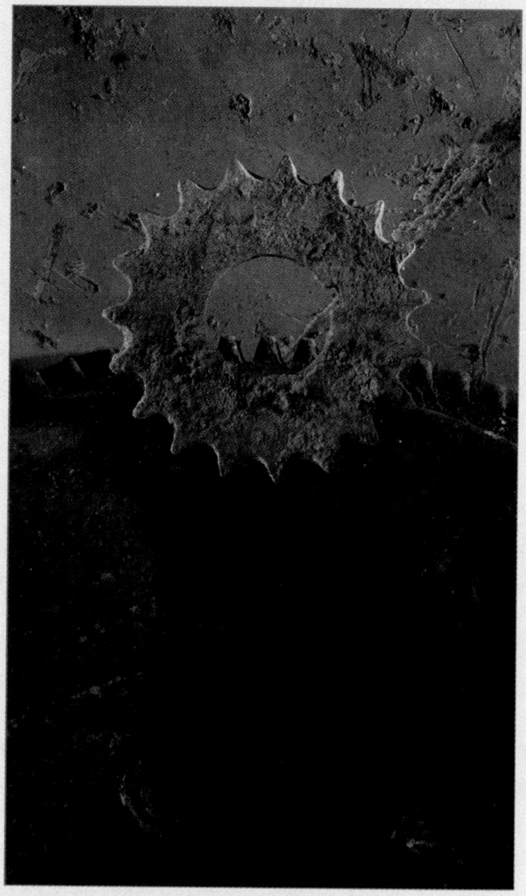

The formation of rust is a redox process. Water and oxygen are necessary for the iron metal to corrode (rust). Iron atoms lose electrons to form mostly Fe^{3+} ions with the help of the moisture in the air and the heat of the Sun. Because the atoms have given up electrons to become more positively charged, oxidation of iron has taken place. Molecules of oxygen gain electrons to form O^{2-} ions. The oxygen has accepted electrons and is said to have been reduced. Corrosion can be prevented by painting a surface of iron to prevent moisture and air from coming in contact with the metal. Let's summarize what you have learned about atoms and ions:

The term atom means that the element is neutral; this means that it has the same number of protons and electrons.

Ions mean that the atom (or ion) has gained or lost electron(s). When an atom gains or loses one or more electrons, an ion results.

Examples are:

$Na \rightarrow Na^{+} + e^{-}$ (Sodium atom loses one electron and now has a net charge of +1.)

$Cl_2 + 2\ e^{-} \rightarrow 2Cl^{-}$ (The two chlorine atoms gain one electron each and the net charge is −1 for each chloride ion.)

Polyatomic ions like the sulfate ion ($SO_4{}^{2-}$) imply that there are two more electrons than protons in the entire structure.

In some cases you will find that an ion can gain or lose an electron and form a new ion. An example of this type is: $Fe^{2+} \rightarrow Fe^{3+} + e^{-}$ (The iron in the +2 state loses 1 more electron and now will be in a +3 state.)

Checking Up

1. What charge does an ion have when it is oxidized?
2. What charge does an ion have when it is reduced?
3. Explain what happens in a redox reaction.

What Do You Think Now?

At the beginning of this activity you were asked:

- **What is rust and what causes it?**

How has your understanding of rusting changed from when you first answered this question?

How do you think you could slow down the oxidation process involved in the corrosion and destruction of things made from metal?

Chem Essential Questions

What does it mean?

Chemistry explains a macroscopic phenomenon (what you observe) with a description of what happens at the nanoscopic level (atoms and molecules) using symbolic structures as a way to communicate. Complete the chart below in your *Active Chemistry* log.

MACRO	NANO	SYMBOLIC
What evidence did you see to indicate that an oxidation-reduction reaction had taken place?	*How does oxidation differ from reduction? Describe how the flow (loss or gain) of electrons indicates oxidation or reduction.*	*Copy the following equations into your Active Chemistry log. Determine which equations represent oxidation and which equations represent reduction.* $Na \rightarrow Na^{+} + e^{-}$ $Cl + e^{-} \rightarrow Cl^{-}$ $4Fe + 3O_2 \rightarrow 2Fe_2O_3$ $2Al_2O_3 \rightarrow 4Al + 3O_2$

How do you know?

What evidence can you give that metals are often oxidized? Are nonmetal elements usually oxidized?

Why do you believe?

Describe a situation in your everyday life in which oxidation occurs.

Why should you care?

Oxidation often produces interesting and surprising effects. Give an example of something that happened in the activity today that produced an interesting effect and could be used during your *Cool Chemistry Show.*

Reflecting on the Activity and the Challenge

Although many colorful chemical reactions involve the use of acids and bases with indicators, there is an entire group of chemical reactions that produce colorful results through the transfer of electrons. In this activity you became familiar with some of the simple concepts behind redox reactions, and you saw several examples of the color changes they can produce. You and/or your classmates may decide to include some redox reactions in the *Cool Chemistry Show.*

Chem to Go

1. Aluminum metal can react to form an ion with a charge of +3. Does the aluminum atom gain or lose electrons to form the Al^{3+} ion?
2. A copper ion with a charge of +2 can react to form an atom of copper. Does the copper ion have to gain or lose electrons in this reaction?
3. The element iron can form two different ions. The iron (II) ion (Fe^{2+}) is commonly called a ferrous ion while the iron (III) ion (Fe^{3+}) is called a ferric ion. When ferrous ions undergo a chemical change to become ferric ions, what process has taken place, oxidation or reduction? Explain your answer.
4. In the reaction you did with zinc metal reacting with copper ions, which substance gains electrons? Which loses electrons?
5. What must take place for copper metal to be oxidized?
6. Galvanized iron nails are used to fasten materials that will be exposed to the outdoors. A galvanized nail is a regular iron nail that is coated with zinc.
   a) Why would a zinc coating be an advantage here? What do you think is the purpose of the zinc?
   b) What two reactants could you use to test this in the laboratory? What results would you expect if you were right about the purpose of the zinc?
7. When a zinc metal strip is placed in a blue copper (II) nitrate solution we observe that the blue solution disappears. Explain why this is happening.
8. Which reaction is an example of an oxidation-reduction reaction?
   a) $AgNO_3 + KI \rightarrow AgI + KNO_3$
   b) $Cu + 2AgNO_3 \rightarrow Cu(NO_3)_2 + 2Ag$
   c) $2KOH + H_2SO_4 \rightarrow K_2SO_4 + 2H_2O$
   d) $Ba(OH)_2 + 2HCl \rightarrow BaCl_2 + 2H_2O$

Inquiring Further

The Statue of Liberty

In the 1980s the Statue of Liberty in New York harbor underwent extensive renovation. Research the involvement of oxidation-reduction reactions in this renovation. Identify what the problem was and its solution.

Chem at Work

Dr. Bassam Shakhashiri

Professor of Chemistry–University of Wisconsin-Madison, Chairman for the Wisconsin Idea

"Science is Fun" reads the T-shirt of Dr. Bassam Shakhashiri. It appears fun when he works with Bucky Badger, the 6-foot tall mascot of the University of Wisconsin, at his annual Christmas science show. But if you talk to Dr. Shakhashiri candidly, he will probably tell you that demonstrating science is all about preparation and hard work (in spite of his T-shirt).

Over the last 35 years, Dr. Shakhashiri has demonstrated science to over 1,100 audiences worldwide. On several occasions his shows have been nationally televised. He has put on large public demonstrations at the National Academy of Sciences, the Smithsonian Museum in Washington, and Boston's Museum of Science.

He is an educator for all ages. People from age 5 to 85 enjoy his displays. On stage, the principles of chemistry come to life through smoking beakers and chemiluminescence. "Young kids are especially curious. They see changing colors and bubbles and they want to know 'why is that?' They are seeking explanations."

Careful planning is at the heart of every show. "When I do a demonstration, I follow a carefully designed plan. I remember my professor who failed in a demonstration in front of a hundred students. I don't want that to happen to me." It's that memory that fuels the doctor's need for careful planning.

He doesn't have a secret. He is not overly dramatic or flamboyant. Dr. Shakhashiri is an educator. He goes on stage armed with science knowledge and genuine enthusiasm. These are the powerful tools he uses to reach an audience. His audiences react in kind. "I feed off the expressions on their faces. I tell them I wish I could take their picture."

Cathy Culver

Chemist, Tarrytown, NY

Cathy Culver, a chemist, is the resident expert on drink colors at the Pepsi Cola Corporation. One of Cathy's favorite activities is to give color demonstrations to students. The students help her create new flavors of soda (like peanut butter and jelly, buttered popcorn, mint chocolate-chip and bubble gum) and then use chemistry to color them accordingly.

Ken Furstoss

Event Coordinator, Pyrotecnico, New Castle, PA

Ken Furstoss is trained as a jet pilot, not a chemist. However, his current job is all about oxidation reactions. Ken is a salesperson and a producer at Pyrotecnico, Inc. The company produces some of the biggest and best fireworks displays in the country, including the fireworks at the Philadelphia Eagles home games.

Cool Chemistry Show Assessment

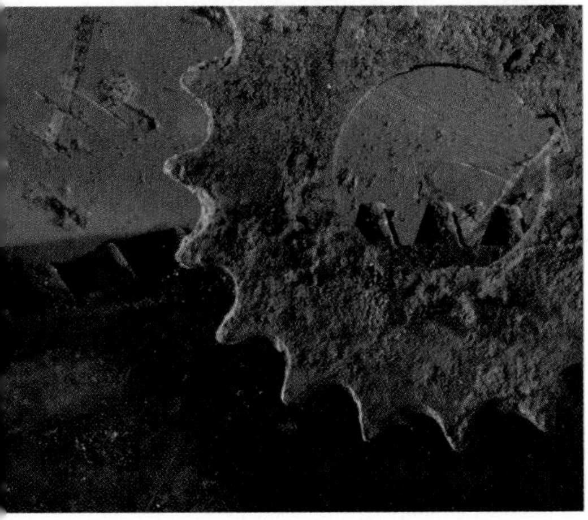

Your *Chapter Challenge* is to present an entertaining and informative chemistry-science show to fourth- and fifth-grade students. The show for fourth graders should address chemical and physical properties. The show for fifth graders should help students learn about acids and bases, and about chemical reactions that involve color changes. All presentations must include a demonstration. Along with the demonstration, you will need to explain the chemistry to the students in a way that they can understand. Finally, the teachers of the fourth- and fifth-grade students need written directions for your chemistry show. The explanation of the chemistry concepts for the teacher must be at a high-school level.

Chemistry Content

To begin, you should review all of the activities that you have completed. You can skim through the text and your *Active Chemistry* log to help remind you of the chemistry concepts in each activity.

Activity 1: You discussed chemical and physical changes.

Activity 2: You learned about more chemical changes including tests for gases and indicator tests for acids and bases.

Activity 3: You studied how to use chemical names and formulas properly as well as the difference between ionic and molecular compounds.

Activity 4: You investigated four types of reactions (synthesis, decomposition, single-replacement and double-replacement).

Activity 5: You observed energy changes when matter changed and identified the change as either exothermic or endothermic.

Activity 6: You discovered conditions that make a reaction proceed faster or slower and explained this at the molecular level.

Activity 7: You investigated acids and bases, read about different definitions of acids, and categorized acids and bases using the pH scale.

Activity 8: You demonstrated oxidation-reduction reactions and wrote word and chemical equations for redox reactions.

You may want to make a chart that shows the activity number, some chemistry concepts in the activity, and some ideas as to how you can use these concepts as part of your *Cool Chemistry Show* or the written summary. Your chart may include whether these demonstrations would be most appropriate for the fourth or fifth grade show. You should pay particular attention to the *Reflecting on the Activity and the Challenge, Chem Essential Questions,* and *Preparing for the Chapter Challenge* sections. You should also compare your list with that given in the *Chem You Learned* summary.

Activity #	Chemistry concepts	How to use concepts

You may decide to do the first activity as a group to ensure that everybody understands how to proceed. After completing the first activity, each team member can be assigned two or three activities. You can then review all of the activities as a group with the activity expert reviewing each summary.

Criteria

You and your team should review the criteria by which you will be graded. Before beginning the chapter, your teacher led a class discussion to get a sense of what criteria should be used to judge the quality of work for this *Cool Chemistry Show* and the related written summary. It is time to revisit that discussion since you now have considerable understanding of the chemistry concepts that you can include in your presentation. Think about and discuss what would make a great *Cool Chemistry Show*. How will you both entertain and teach concepts at the same time?

The rubric should assign points to the demonstration, the chemistry content, and the written summary. It will also assign points to specific aspects of each major category. For instance, how many points will be given for additional concepts introduced in the demonstration? How many points will be assigned for creativity, showmanship, and timing of the demonstration? Safety is also an important consideration. How many points will you assign to safety? This rubric can be a useful tool for your team to check the quality of your work and to ensure that you have included all necessary parts of the project.

Preparing for the Chapter Challenge

- **Choose Your Demonstrations**

Your team's next step is to decide on which demonstrations are best suited to your interests and will be the most interesting, informative, creative, and entertaining for the elementary students. Your teacher may wish you to share your decision with the class as a whole so that the full cool chemistry program of the entire class is not repetitious.

- **Write Your Explanations**

Each demonstration must also be accompanied with an explanation of chemistry concepts. Remember that the students must be able to understand the explanation.

You also need to provide detailed instructions to the fourth- and fifth-grade teachers so that the teachers can repeat the demonstration. This will require a list of materials, step-by-step directions, notes on what should be happening, and safety considerations. You must also provide a written explanation of the chemistry concepts. Your chemistry concepts should be more thorough than the oral presentation during the show. Your explanation of chemistry concepts is now targeted to teachers rather than elementary students. You can include more formulas, more background, and provide additional experiments that clarify the chemistry concepts.

- **Chemistry content is necessary, but not sufficient.**

You must also find an entertaining and effective way of presenting the content. Remember also, that you are teaching the students about the chemistry concepts. Teachers use models that help promote learning. One model is the 7E instructional model. In the 7E model, you begin by *engaging* the students as well as *eliciting* their prior knowledge. This means that you use a way to find out what they already know so that you can be more aware of this during the teaching and learning process. This is then followed by an *explore phase* where students are involved in finding out about something and experiencing some phenomenon. Following explore, your students and *you can explain* what they experienced. You can then *elaborate* on the concepts and describe where else they may observe similar events. You then end with an *extend* where you give the students something to think about that is beyond what you have introduced. The last of the 7E model is *evaluate*. The evaluation of what the students are learning and what they are understanding takes place throughout the cycle—through the *engage, elicit, explore, explain, elaborate, extend.*

- **Manage Your Time**

You have a sense of how you want to proceed and what you want the final product to be. You now have to allocate the work. How much time do you have to complete the project? When is the presentation? How will you get everything done in this time frame? Who will be working on the written script, including the description of chemistry concepts? How will you ensure that each member's work meets the standard of excellence so that everybody on the team gets an A? Create a time chart for the challenge. Divide the responsibilities. How much time will each take? Some work can be done individually as homework. Leave time to review each other's work.

Planning a project well does not ensure success, but poor planning almost always leads to disappointment.

- **Practice Your Cool Chemistry Show**

You need to practice your chemistry demonstrations so that your show runs smoothly. This will include thinking about how you will set up and do the demonstration. You should also rehearse your explanation so that it complements the demonstration itself. You may choose to have one team member producing the demonstration, another team member explaining what is happening and focusing the audience's attention on specific observations, and a third team member explaining the chemistry concepts. You should decide if your presentation would be strengthened by having some of the chemistry concepts described prior to the demonstration or if the explanation should follow the demonstration.

Engineering/Technology Design

Reflect on the engineering/technology design process. Recall the successes and disappointments from the *mini-challenge*. How can you use the feedback that you received to improve your show? At this point, you are starting the design cycle again.

Enjoy your Cool Chemistry Show!

Chem You Learned

- In general, a **physical change** is a process where a substance's chemical properties have not changed.
- A **chemical change** occurs when new substances or materials are produced that have different chemical properties from the reactants.
- **Chemical tests** are used to identify substances and also to confirm that a chemical reaction has taken place.
- A typical **single-replacement reaction** occurs when an active metal reacts with a strong acid to produce hydrogen gas.
- Formation of a **precipitate** is commonly seen in **double-replacement reactions** and is a method to identify the presence of specific ions in a solution.
- Using **acid-base indicators** is a simple, quick method to determine the **pH** of a solution.
- The periodic table aids in writing **chemical formulas** by organizing the symbols for elements, as well as providing information about **oxidation states**.
- **Polyatomic ions**, such as **carbonate** (CO_3^{2-}), carry an overall **ionic** charge but internally the atoms are **covalently bonded**.
- **Chemical equations** are a shorthand method of writing the **reactants** and **products** of a reaction. **The Law of Conservation of Mass** requires that the equation be **balanced**.
- **Endothermic** and **exothermic** reactions are commercially used in cold and hot packs.
- **Chemical kinetics** or **chemical rates of reactions** are dependent on several factors: **surface area** of reactants, **temperature**, **concentration**, and presence of a **catalyst**.
- **Strong acids** and **strong bases** are 100% ionized while **weak acids** and **weak bases** are partially ionized.
- **pH** is used to determine the concentration of **hydrogen ions** (**hydronium ions**) of a solution.

$$\mathbf{pH = -\log[H]}$$

- When several indicators covering the entire **pH** range are mixed together they form a **universal indicator** solution.
- The definition of acid and base has evolved from that of **Arrhenius** who defined an acid as a compound that releases hydrogen ions and a base as releasing hydroxide ions.
- **Brønsted-Lowry** defined acids as proton donors and bases as proton acceptors.
- Finally, **Lewis** provided the most general definition, stating that acids are electron pair acceptors and bases are electron pair donors.
- **Oxidation-reduction** or **redox reactions** involve the equal transfer of electrons between the elements. If iron is in the presence of oxygen and moisture it will **oxidize** (commonly called rust) while the oxygen is correspondingly **reduced**.
- A **single-replacement reaction** is another example of an oxidation-reduction reaction.

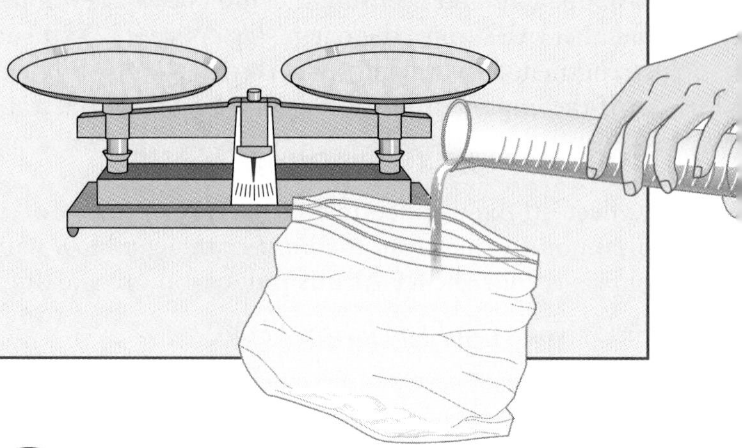

Chapter 7

COOKIN' CHEM

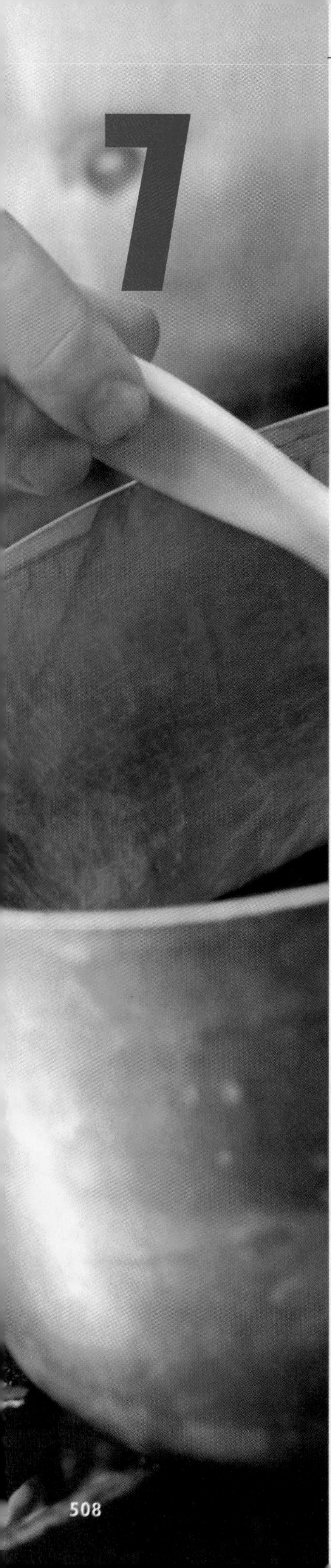

7

Chapter Challenge

Cookin' Chem

Scenario

Everyone enjoys good food! That is probably why cooking shows are so very popular. However, if you want to know why you can cook hard-boiled eggs or which pan to use, don't turn to your cookbook. Pick up your chemistry book instead. The Cooking Science Foundation knows this. That is why the Foundation wants to add a chemistry segment to a cooking show. One of the goals of the Foundation is to make the public aware of the chemistry involved in cooking. Your *Active Chemistry* class has been asked to help by creating a chemistry segment for a cooking show.

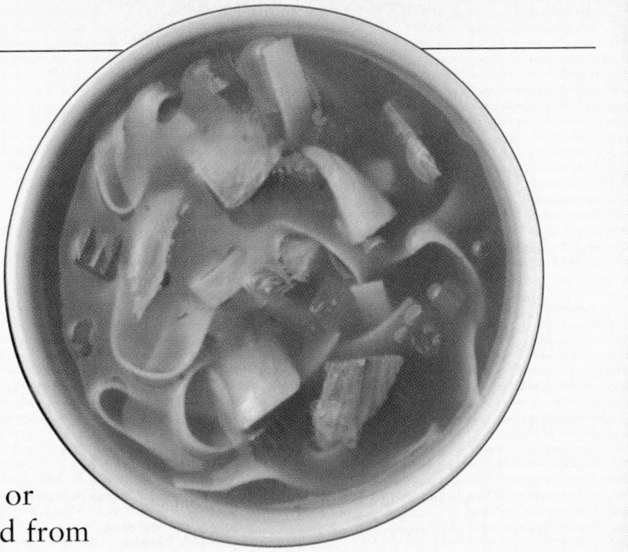

Your Challenge

Your challenge is to create a five-minute chemistry segment for a cooking show. The segment should provide the audience with a detailed explanation of the chemistry involved. Your presentation could be live action, a videotape, or even a voice-over of an actual show.

You can bring your cultural heritage into play by focusing on ethnic food. Your show might be humorous or serious. It could deal with cafeteria food or gourmet food from a five-star restaurant. The show should be interesting and entertaining. It must include correct chemistry content. In addition to the presentation, you will submit a script for the show that includes a discussion of the chemistry involved.

This challenge has an almost unlimited number of possibilities because there is so much chemistry that goes on in the kitchen. You may find it difficult to limit the number of chemical principles that you discuss!

Think of all the possibilities!

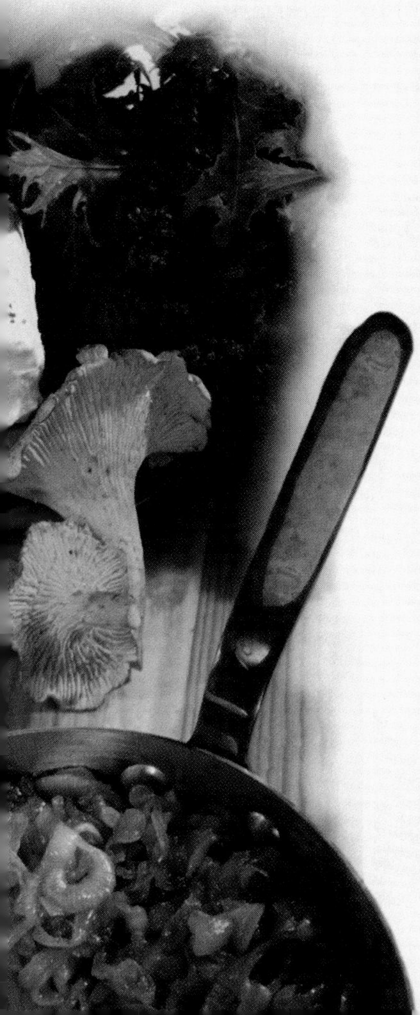

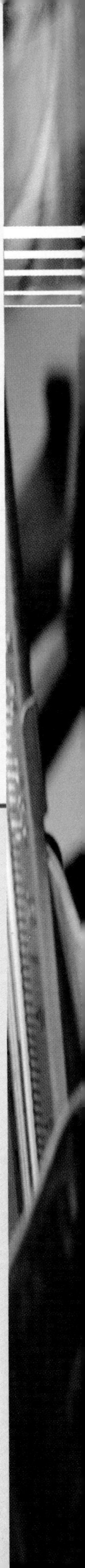

ChemCorner

Chemistry in *Cookin' Chem*

- Heat transfer
- Combustion reaction
- Balanced equations
- Quantitative analysis
- Qualitative analysis
- Heat energy of fuels
- Thermochemistry
- Boiling point
- States of matter
- Heating curve
- Freezing point
- Heat of fusion
- Alloys
- Amino acids
- Protein structure
- Denaturation
- Boyle's Law

SALT
OLIVE OIL
SUGAR
VINEGAR
MILK

Criteria

How will you present your cooking-show segment? Will it be performed live in your classroom, video taped, or will you create a voice-over of an existing show? Has everybody in the class seen at least one cooking show on TV? Discuss the types of shows with which you are familiar. Your teacher may show you video clips from one or two shows. Discuss with your classmates the attributes of a successful segment and how your cooking-show segment might be graded. You may want to consider some or all of the following in your discussion:

Visual Presentation

- Multiple chemical principles explained
- Accuracy of explanation
- Creative, engaging, fun
- Overall quality of presentation
- All group members contribute

Written Script

- Multiple chemical principles explained and highlighted
- Accuracy of explanation
- Mechanically correct
- All group members contribute
- Script matches presentation

Once you have determined the list of qualities for evaluating the cooking-show segments, you and your class should also decide how many points should be given for each criterion. Should creativity of the presentation be awarded more points than the clarity and accuracy of the script? How many different chemical principles should be addressed in the segment? How many points should be given for each chemical principle? For each criterion you should decide how excellence is defined and how it compares with a satisfactory effort. Determining grading criteria in advance will help you focus your time and effort on the important parts of the challenge.

Activity 1 What is Heat?

What Do You See?

AC

GOALS

In this activity you will:

- Demonstrate the three ways that heat energy is transferred.
- Distinguish between heat energy and temperature.

What Do You Think?

When you think of cooking, you think of heat. Good cooks have an understanding of how heat interacts with food (matter).

- **What is heat?**
- **What is the difference between heat and temperature?**

The *What Do You Think?* questions are meant to get you thinking about what you already know or think you know. Don't worry about being right or wrong. Discussing what you think you know is an important step in learning.

Record your ideas about these questions in your *Active Chemistry* log. Be prepared to discuss your responses with your group and the class.

Investigate

To help you understand how heat interacts with food (matter), you will investigate the heat from a light bulb. Heat energy can be transferred in several distinct ways. Each way has its own characteristics, and all are used in cooking.

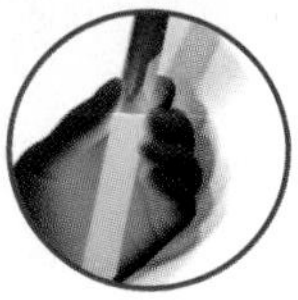

Goggles and apron must be worn *at all times* in the laboratory.

Part A: Transferring Heat Energy

1. The first investigation is probably the most dangerous. Screw a 25-W incandescent light bulb into a bulb holder. Turn on the light. After 2 min, touch the bulb quickly.

   a) Can you feel the heat?

   Unplug the bulb and let it cool. You have just investigated one way heat energy is transferred—through touching. This form of heat-energy transfer is also called **conduction**.

   b) Conduction is often used in cooking by placing food in contact with a hot frying pan. List three foods that can be cooked by conduction. Which of these is your favorite?

2. After the 25-W bulb has cooled, replace it with the 75-W bulb. Turn on the light. After a few minutes, put your hand as close to the side of the bulb as you can without touching it.

   a) Can you feel the heat from the bulb without touching the bulb?

You have just investigated a second way heat energy is transferred—by **radiation**. The heat energy from the bulb radiated out from the bulb and came in touch with your finger. Radiation is often used in restaurants by placing heat lamps above food to keep it warm.

3. Construct the pinwheel "cap" for your light bulb using a pattern and a piece of aluminum foil provided by your teacher.

   Cut on the diagonal from each corner to about 2.5 cm from the center point. Starting with one corner, fold every other corner to the center.

   Push a straight pin through the center, making sure to catch every corner. Secure the pinwheel to the rubber end of a pencil.

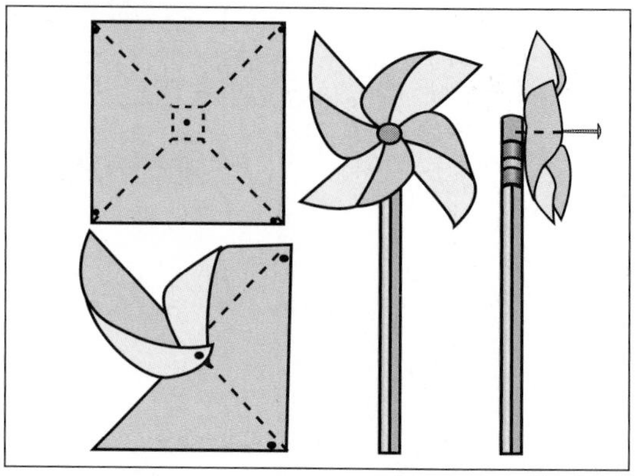

The pinwheel should spin freely.

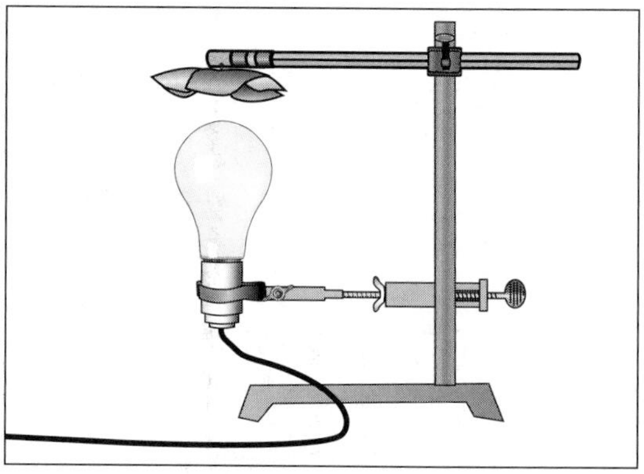

Set up your light-bulb heat-energy model as shown in the diagram. Test to see if the pinwheel turns freely by blowing air across it.

   a) Turn on the light. When this works well, you should be able to observe the pinwheel rotate. What is causing the pinwheel to move? Write down your hypothesis in your *Active Chemistry* log.

   b) You know that the air above the light bulb gets warm by radiation. This hot air rises and cool air from the sides takes its place. Draw a diagram that can show the movement of air around the heated light bulb and the pinwheel that can cause the pinwheel to rotate.

The movement of heated air is called **convection**. The convection currents of hot air can also be used to cook food. Some ovens work by convection currents. It is a third way of cooking food.

4. Cooking peas in boiling water seems simple enough. Peas are placed in a pot of water. The pot is placed above a flame or hot coils. The pot gets heated. The water is in contact with the pot and the water gets heated. The hot water at the bottom of the pot begins to rise and cooler water takes its place at the bottom of the pan. The peas begin to cook.
   a) Rewrite the description of cooking peas to include the correct use of the new vocabulary words—radiation, conduction, and convection.

Part B: Observing the Transfer of Heat Energy

1. Potatoes are very useful models for observing how heat energy is transferred when cooking food. When you heat a potato to 60°C (or higher), there is a change in its appearance. The potato changes from an opaque, white texture and becomes translucent.

   If you put some potatoes into boiling water for various lengths of time, and then remove them and cut them open, you will see the increase in size of a ring of translucent material. (Note: It is easier to see the ring of translucent material if you do not peel the potato.)

   Design an experiment using five different potatoes and boiling water. Use time as the independent variable and the growth of the translucent ring of cooked potato as your dependent variable. Have your teacher approve your experiment before you begin.

2. Construct a data table for recording the width of the ring in millimeters and the cooking time in minutes. Graph the data.
   a) Include your data table and graph in your *Active Chemistry* log.
   b) What conclusions can you draw about cooking time and heat-energy transfer?
   c) How is this kind of data useful for developing recipes?
3. All three types of heat-energy transfer occur when you are boiling the potatoes in your experiment.
   a) Diagram and label the three types of heat-energy transfer (include a hot plate, beaker, water, and potatoes).

Use extreme caution around boiling water. It can cause very serious burns.

The potatoes will be very hot. Remove them very carefully using tongs.

Wash hands and arms thoroughly before leaving the lab area.

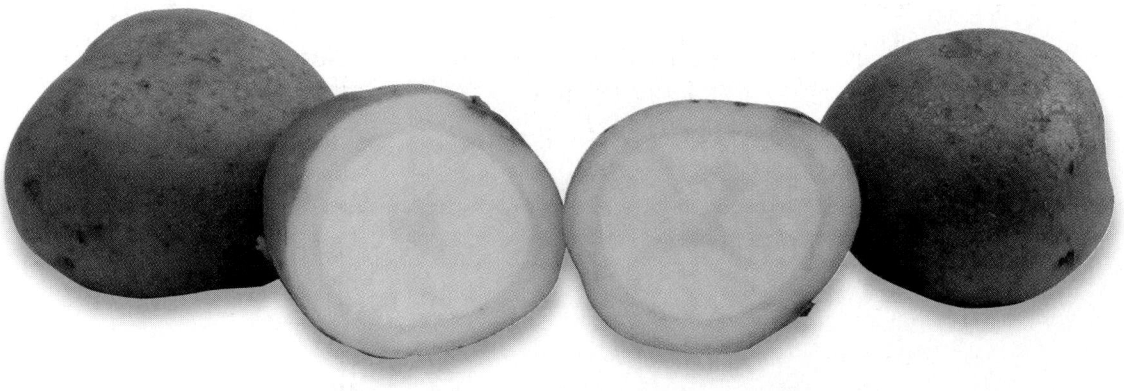

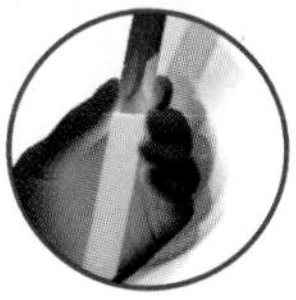

Chem Talk

Chem Words

conduction: the transfer of heat energy from particle to particle between substances through contact or within a substance.

convection: the transfer of heat through the movement of air or liquid currents.

radiation (of heat): transfer of heat energy by emission of electromagnetic radiation in all directions.

HEAT ENERGY

How Heat Energy Is Transferred

Heat energy is transferred to matter (food) in three ways. One way is conduction. **Conduction** is the movement of heat energy through matter by the transfer of vibrational energy between atoms and molecules that are in contact with each other. The transfer of heat energy inside of any solid occurs by conduction. You experienced this when you touched the light bulb. Another example of conduction is an egg cooking in a frying pan. The key to conduction is contact.

Another method of heat-energy transfer is convection. **Convection** is the transfer of heat energy by the physical motion of masses of fluid. (A fluid can be a liquid or a gas.) Convection describes a movement of heat energy through the transfer of a fluid medium from one place to another. When peas are boiling in a pot of water, thermal energy is being transferred by convection. As hot water is heated at the bottom of the pot on the stove, the hot water circulates around the pot, heating the peas.

Finally, there is radiation. **Radiation** is the transfer of heat energy by electromagnetic radiation. This is the only form of heat-energy transfer that does not require atoms or molecules. All bodies, when hot, radiate heat energy. The most important source of radiation is the Sun.

When you held your hand close to the light bulb, the heat you felt was due (in part) to radiation and (in part) to convection. In this case, the convecting substance was air. When you touched the light bulb, the heat you felt was due to conduction.

Difference between Heat Energy and Temperature

What is heat? **Heat** is a form of energy that results from the motion of atoms and molecules. (Random motion means that the atoms and molecules are moving in no specific pattern.) Moving particles have kinetic energy. This kinetic energy is transferred to other particles through collisions on the atomic or nanoscopic scale. In this way, heat energy is transferred.

It is not uncommon for people to confuse heat and temperature. **Temperature** is a property of matter that is measured with a thermometer. You can use your sense of touch to judge temperature. However, a thermometer is a more accurate and precise tool. At the molecular or nanoscopic level, temperature is a measure of the average kinetic energy (energy of motion) of an object's molecules. Temperature is a measure of how much kinetic energy individual molecules have, or how fast they are moving about. Faster-moving, more energetic molecules, will have a higher temperature than slower, less energetic molecules. When you watch the temperature on a meat thermometer inside a roast increase steadily as the roast cooks, you know that the molecules of the meat are absorbing heat energy and, as a result, these molecules are vibrating faster.

Heat energy is a measure of both the amount of matter and the temperature of that matter. A cup of coffee at 90°C is very hot. A swimming pool at 25°C is quite cool by comparison. The coffee has a higher temperature. The swimming pool has more heat energy. That is because of the enormous amount of water present. Think about how much heat energy would be required to raise the temperature of the coffee by 1°C and the amount of heat energy required to raise the temperature of the entire swimming pool by 1°C. Think about what would happen if the hot coffee in a closed container were thrown into the pool. The coffee would cool off and its temperature would drop to 25°C. The swimming pool's temperature would rise only the tiniest amount. The swimming pool has much more heat energy, even though it is at a cooler temperature.

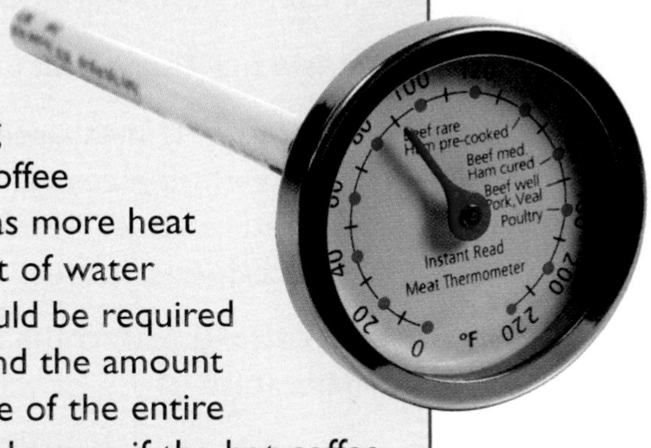
Beef med
Ham cured
Beef well
Pork, Veal
Poultry
Instant Read
Meat Thermometer
°F

Temperature determines the exchange of heat energy. Heat energy is transferred as a result of a temperature difference between bodies that are in contact. Heat energy always travels from a hotter to a colder body. A colder body always gets warmer when placed in contact with

Chem Words

heat: a form of energy that results from the motion of atoms and molecules.

temperature: a measure of how much kinetic energy individual molecules have, or how fast they are moving.

Chem Words

thermal conductivity: the ability of an object to move heat energy from one part of itself to another.

calorie: the amount of heat energy required to raise the temperature of 1 g of water 1°C.

joule: a measurement of heat energy.
1 J (joule) = 1 cal ÷ 4.184

absolute zero: 0 K or –273°C. Molecular motion is minimum.

a hotter body. The fast-moving molecules of the hotter substance collide with the slow-moving molecules of the cooler substance and both substances reach an intermediate temperature.

When a molecule vibrates it transfers some of its energy to neighboring molecules and they begin to vibrate more vigorously. As their motion starts to increase the first molecule now vibrates a little less because some of its energy has been passed on. This is how heat energy spread through your potatoes as they were cooked. The physical property known as **thermal conductivity** is the ability of an object to move heat energy from one part of itself to another. Metals are used in cookware because they spread heat energy very quickly.

Measuring Temperature

Temperature is measured in units called degrees. You are probably familiar with degrees Fahrenheit or Celsius. There is also a kelvin temperature scale. Heat energy, on the other hand, is measured in units such as calories, **joules**.

One **calorie** (cal) is the amount of heat energy required to raise the temperature of 1 g of water 1 degree Celsius.

$$1000 \text{ cal} = 1 \text{ kcal (kilocalorie)}$$
$$1 \text{ cal} = 4.184 \text{ J (joules)}$$

Celsius is a metric temperature scale based on water freezing at 0°C and boiling at 100°C. Kelvin is another metric scale. It is also called the absolute temperature scale. When a temperature is 0 K (kelvin), this is called **absolute zero**. This is the temperature at which molecular motion is brought to a minimum. (Note: temperatures on this scale are called kelvins, not degrees kelvin.)

The size of a Celsius degree is equal to the size of a kelvin. The only difference is where the zero point is set. Absolute zero on the kelvin scale is equal to –273°C.

To convert from Celsius degrees to kelvins, add 273. To convert from kelvins to Celsius degrees, simply subtract 273.

Although there are equations for converting from Fahrenheit to Celsius and vice versa, it is more important to be able to approximate temperatures in both units. To do this, it's useful to know some common temperatures in each scale. It is also useful to know that one-degree change in Celsius is almost a two-degree change in Fahrenheit.

Event	Celsius temperature (°C)	Fahrenheit temperature (°F)
water freezes	0	32
room temperature	20	68
body temperature	37	99
water boils	100	212

If you have reason for a precise conversion, you can refer to a table showing sets of both temperatures, create a spreadsheet, or use the algebraic equations given below.

To convert Fahrenheit to Celsius use: $°C = \frac{5}{9}(°F - 32)$

To convert Celsius to Fahrenheit use the following: $°F = \frac{9}{5}°C + 32$

Cooking Food in a Microwave Oven

How does a microwave oven work? A microwave oven emits electromagnetic waves of a frequency identical to the frequency that causes water molecules to vibrate and rotate. The microwaves enter the food and the water molecules within the food move and vibrate against one another at the rate of over a billion times a second. The heat from the vibrating molecules moves throughout the food by conduction.

Summary of Heat-Energy Transfer

Conduction is the transfer of heat energy throughout a material or through contact between different materials. When you cook pancakes in a frying pan, the flame never touches the pancake batter. The frying pan gets hot because part of it is in contact with the flame or the hot electric coils. The molecules of the pan that are in direct contact with the coils or flame begin vibrating and this heat energy is transferred to neighboring molecules through collisions. Before too long, the entire pan is hot. This movement of the heat energy throughout the metal pan is conduction.

Convection is the transfer of heat energy through the movement of air or liquid currents. Hot air rises because it is less dense than cool air. When the hot air rises, other air must come in from the sides to take up the space of the rising hot air. This sets up a flow of air that is called convection. The currents of moving air are called convection currents. The shape of a candle flame gives you a sense of the convection currents. The hot air rises and cool air comes in from the sides. Similar convection currents are set up when you have a pot of water on the stove. The hot water at the bottom of the pot begins to rise and cooler water takes its place. This creates a convection current and gradually all the liquid heats up.

Radiation is the transfer of heat energy by emission of electromagnetic radiation in all directions. The Sun is a source of electromagnetic radiation. This includes visible light, infrared rays, ultraviolet rays, and radio waves. Your eyes detect the visible light. Your skin detects the infrared radiation. You call it "heat." These electromagnetic waves are able to travel through empty space as well as through air and other materials. When a heat lamp is used to keep foods warm, the expectation is that the food will gain the energy from the infrared radiation (heat energy).

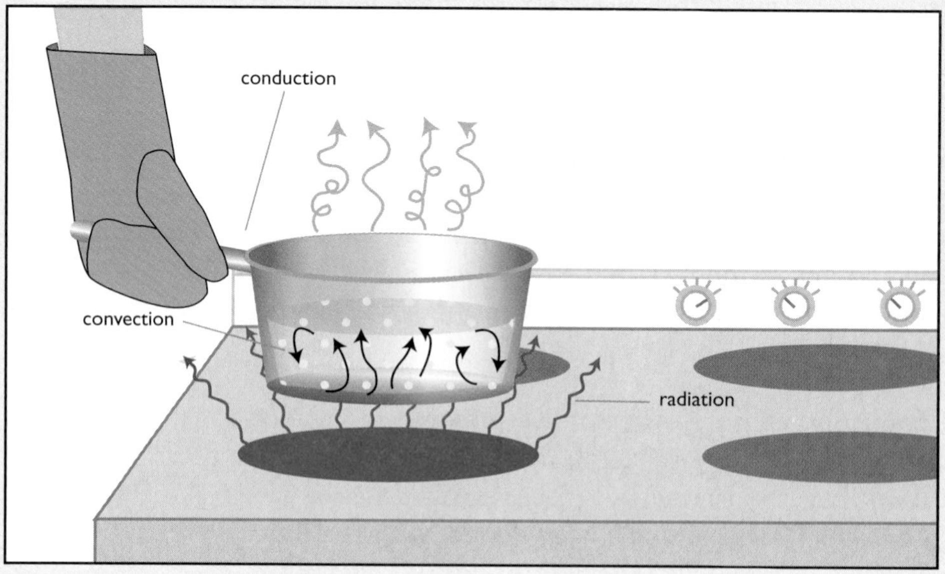
conduction
convection
radiation

Checking Up

1. Explain three ways that heat energy can be transferred.
2. Give an example for each method of heat-energy transfer as it relates to cooking.
3. What is the difference between heat energy and temperature?
4. Define thermal conductivity.
5. How is temperature measured? Identify the three temperature scales used.
6. What units can be used to measure heat energy?
7. At which approximate temperatures would you do the following activities? Give the temperatures in degrees Fahrenheit and degrees Celsius.
   a) go swimming
   b) go ice skating

What Do You Think Now?

At the beginning of the activity you were asked:

- **What is heat?**
- **What is the difference between heat and temperature?**

Now that you have completed this activity on heat-energy transfer, how would you explain the difference between heat and temperature?

Chem Essential Questions

What does it mean?

Chemistry explains a macroscopic phenomenon (what you observe) with a description of what happens at the nanoscopic level (atoms and molecules) using symbolic structures as a way to communicate. Complete the chart below in your *Active Chemistry* log.

MACRO	NANO	SYMBOLIC
Describe how to take measurements using a thermometer. In this activity, how did you observe temperature changes due to radiation, conduction, and convection?	*Explain what is happening to the particles (or molecules) in the object that causes the temperature to rise.*	*In convection, the movement of the air is invisible. Draw a picture showing how the air moves.*

How do you know?

What evidence do you have that heat energy can be used to cook a potato? Describe what was happening to your potatoes as they cooked–include the method(s) of heat transfer, and evidence that thermal energy was absorbed.

Why do you believe?

You can cook hot dogs by frying them, boiling them, barbecuing them, or microwaving them. Describe where in each of these methods there is conduction, convection, and/or radiation.

Why should you care?

It is very likely that you will want to discuss conduction, convection, and radiation as you cook foods or choose typical kitchen equipment in your cooking show. Suggest one food preparation that you may use in your cooking show.

Reflecting on the Activity and the Challenge

In this activity, you explored heat-energy transfer in matter as it applies to cooking. The next time you cook or eat a meal, you may wish to identify as many ways that you can remember that illustrate heat transfer. You might decide to incorporate an understanding of heat transfer into your cooking-show segment. Consider how you will explain what is happening at the nanoscopic level (in such a way that the general public can understand), and that successful cooking is related to understanding energy transfer in matter.

Chem to Go

1. Choose from the words *conduction*, *radiation*, and *convection* to complete the following:
   a) The transfer of heat energy by the motion of a heated liquid or a gas is ____ .
   b) The transfer of heat energy between particles in a solid is ______________ .
   c) The transfer of heat energy from a substance through empty space is ______ .
2. How are the particles of objects affected when their heat energy is increased?
3. What is absolute zero? What happens at this temperature?
4. How does the ring "grow" in the potato as it is heated in *Part B*?
5. How might inserting an iron skewer (spike) into a potato affect the baking time? Would it be quicker, slower, or the same?
6. The temperature of a sample of pudding is a measure of the ________ of the particles that make up the pudding.
   a) activation energy
   b) potential energy
   c) kinetic energy
   d) ionization energy
7. What temperature on the kelvin scale is equal to 25°C?
   a) 248 K
   b) 298 K
   c) 100 K
   d) 200 K
8. As ice cools from 273 K to 263 K, the kinetic energy of its molecules will
   a) decrease
   b) increase
   c) remain the same

9. Solid X is placed in contact with solid Y. Heat energy will flow spontaneously from X to Y when
   a) X is 20°C and Y is 20°C
   b) X is 10°C and Y is 5°C
   c) X is −25°C and Y is −10°C
   d) X is 25°C and Y is 30°C
10. How many joules are equivalent to 35 kJ?
    a) 0.035 J
    b) 0.35 J
    c) 3500 J
    d) 35,000 J
11. ***Preparing for the Chapter Challenge***

In a paragraph, explain how heat is transferred from the time you turn the oven on until you remove your cooked turkey for Thanksgiving dinner. Make sure you describe what is happening at the molecular level and include what you have learned about temperature.

Inquiring Further

1. Cooking times for potatoes

Using your data from *Part B*, determine an equation that could help you predict cooking times for potatoes. Would you expect a similar relationship for boiling eggs? Explain your reasoning.

2. Comparing cooking appliances

Create a pamphlet that you might find in the cooking appliance section of a store that compares how microwave ovens, conventional ovens, and convection ovens work.

3. Grilling instructions

Grilling is a popular and tasty way of preparing food. Create a pamphlet that could be included in the instruction booklet for a new grill explaining how food is cooked on a grill. Include tips for getting the best results from the heat transfers that occur.

Activity 2 Safety and Types of Fires

CHEM POETRY

Oliver learned all those
"Don't"s and "Do"s,
The ones that get passed
down through moles of O_2's;
Each new generation did soon
learn to trust
That its purpose on Earth was
to make things combust.

The highest honor an O_2 could
earn
Came from causing organic
matter to burn.
A kamikaze maneuver, this
game,
The O_2 destroyed in creating
the flame.

One day, while diffusing out
in the park,
He saw an object that started
to spark.
'Twas no matter what caused
this electrical prank;
It had gone and ignited a
propane tank!

Though prospects for honor
had started to tire,
'Twas his turn now to add fuel
to the fire:
"I just need to get close, to
come into their view,
And then we'll make water
and CO_2!"

–Mala Radhakrishnan

GOALS

In this activity you will:

- Discover what a combustion reaction is and what the products of a combustion reaction are.
- Generate carbon dioxide and oxygen gases.
- Practice balancing chemical equations.

What Do You See?

OXYGEN
BAKING SODA
VINEGAR
CARBON DIOXIDE

What Do You Think?

Humans have been using fire to cook food for thousands of years.

- **What is necessary for a fire?**
- **What can be used to put out an unwanted fire in a kitchen?**

Record your ideas about these questions in your *Active Chemistry* log. Be prepared to discuss your responses with your group and the class.

Investigate

Many of the activities of science involve making *observations* with your senses, mainly sight, but to a lesser extent smell, touch, and sound. Observations can be either qualitative or quantitative. *Qualitative observations* are descriptions of what is occurring. *Quantitative observations* involve the use of measurements. *Interpretations* are based on your observations. They are an explanation of the observations.

In this lab activity, you will make qualitative and quantitative observations about a candle before, during, and after it is lit. You will then interpret several of your observations. This will give you information that could be used as a part of your cooking show.

For each step in the procedure, write a brief description of what you are doing, followed by your observations in your *Active Chemistry* log. Leave room for interpretations (three or four lines), but do not attempt to make interpretations yet.

1. Obtain a ruler, a candle, and a foil-covered cardboard square. Place the candle in a holder on the square, or fix it to the square using putty. Make between six and ten observations about the *unlit* candle.

   a) Record your observations in your *Active Chemistry* log.

2. Light the candle. Make an additional six to ten observations. Be sure to make observations about the flame.

   a) Record your observations.

3. Light a match. Blow out the candle and quickly bring the lit match into the smoke. Repeat once or twice and make observations.

   a) Record your observations.

   b) Leave room in your log for the interpretations that you will make later.

4. Light the candle and then invert a clean, dry 250-mL beaker over the flame. Slowly lower the beaker over the flame. Repeat once or twice and make observations. Be sure to look carefully into the beaker too. Note: The beaker will become hot over time!

   a) Record your observations.

   b) Leave room for your interpretations.

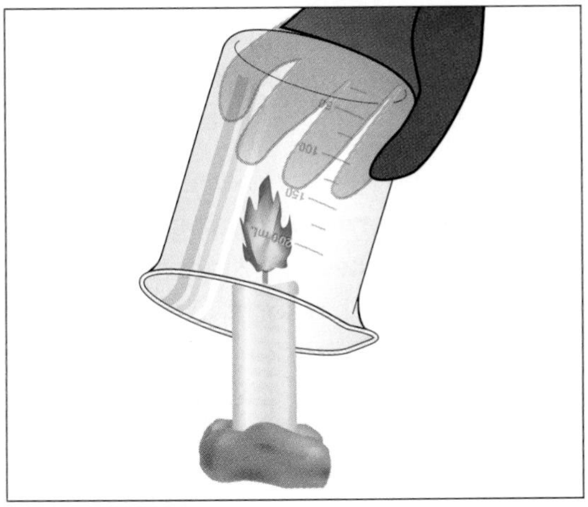

5. Hold a piece of string with forceps over the table. Light the string.

   a) Record your observations.

   b) Leave room for your interpretations.

6. Place a foil collar around the wick of the candle. Light the candle.

   a) Record your observations.

   b) Leave room for your interpretations.

Safety goggles and a lab apron must be worn *at all times* in a chemistry lab.

7. The reaction between vinegar and baking soda releases carbon dioxide gas. Place a small scoop of baking soda with about 50 mL of vinegar in a 250-mL beaker. Observe the reaction. Carefully 'pour' the gas (but not the liquid) over the flame of the candle.

   a) Record your observations.

   b) Leave room for your interpretations.

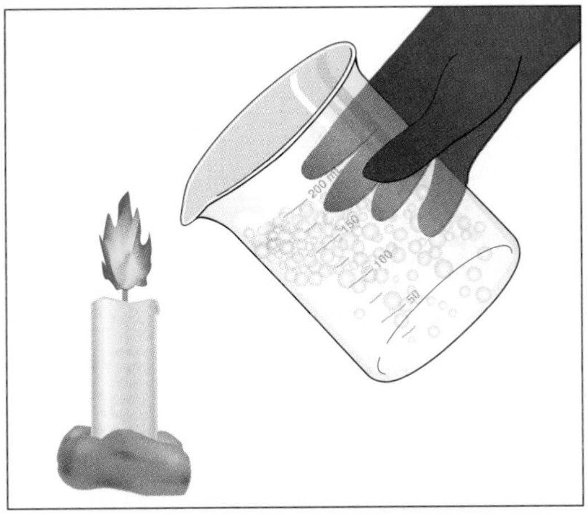

8. The decomposition of hydrogen peroxide releases oxygen gas. The reaction is catalyzed (sped up) by the addition of manganese dioxide to the hydrogen peroxide. Fill a test tube one-third of the way with hydrogen peroxide. Add a small amount of manganese dioxide to the test tube. Test the resulting gas by lighting a splint and blowing it out.

The end should be glowing. Quickly insert and remove the glowing splint into the mouth of the test tube.

a) Record your observations.

b) Leave room for your interpretations.

9. For *Steps 3* through *8*, write a sentence to interpret your observations. These should be an explanation of what you observed. Why do you think each observation occurred? How can you explain what you saw?

Wash hands and arms thoroughly before leaving the lab area.

10. There are three things necessary for combustion—fuel, oxygen, and a source of heat. The fuel in this case is the candle, which is made of wax and a string. The source of heat was from the match. The oxygen is found in the air. Answer the following questions in your *Active Chemistry* log, based upon your observations and interpretations.

a) What are two methods that you used to put out the fire? Explain how each one worked in terms of the three necessities for combustion.

b) What is the actual fuel for the combustion of the burning candle? What are the functions of the wax and the string? What evidence do you have to support your response?

c) Suppose you were to let the candle burn until the wick was completely gone. Describe what would be left and how it would compare to the original candle. What happened to the wax? Could you make a new candle from what remained?

Chem Talk

THE COMBUSTION REACTION

The Equation for Combustion

Food is all about eating! Cooking food is all about heat. Fire is one way of producing heat. Creating a flame was certainly one of the great advances in the history of humankind. The first fire may have been from lightning, but some human decided to maintain the flame and use it to begin other fires. Eventually, someone invented a means to create a spark and start fires at will.

When a substance burns in the presence of oxygen, a chemical change takes place. In a **chemical change**, new substances are produced. The substances you start with are called **reactants**, and the substances that form are called **products**. The key part of a chemical reaction is that the products are different substances from the reactants.

When a **hydrocarbon** (a compound composed of hydrogen and carbon) reacts with oxygen (O_2), a **combustion reaction** occurs. The products of a complete combustion reaction are carbon dioxide (CO_2) and water (H_2O). There are lots of materials you can burn. Candles, wood, gasoline, and natural gas are some. Candle wax is made of relatively long-chain hydrocarbons ($C_{20}H_{42}$ and larger). Other hydrocarbon fuels that you might be familiar with are methane (CH_4, the chief component of natural gas), propane (C_3H_8), butane (C_4H_{10}), and octane (C_8H_{18}, a component of gasoline). When any of these compounds are burned in the presence of sufficient oxygen, the products are CO_2 and H_2O.

Consider the complete combustion of propane gas:

C_3H_8	+	O_2	$\rightarrow$	CO_2	+	H_2O
propane		*oxygen*		*carbon dioxide*		*water*
	reactants				*products*	
(total of 3 C atoms, 8 H atoms, 2 O atoms)				(total of 1 C atom, 2 H atoms, and 3 O atoms)		

The propane gas and the oxygen reacts to produce carbon dioxide and water.

The chemical equation is one way you can describe the reaction. Another symbolic representation (ball-and-stick models) is shown in the diagram. The products are carbon dioxide and water.

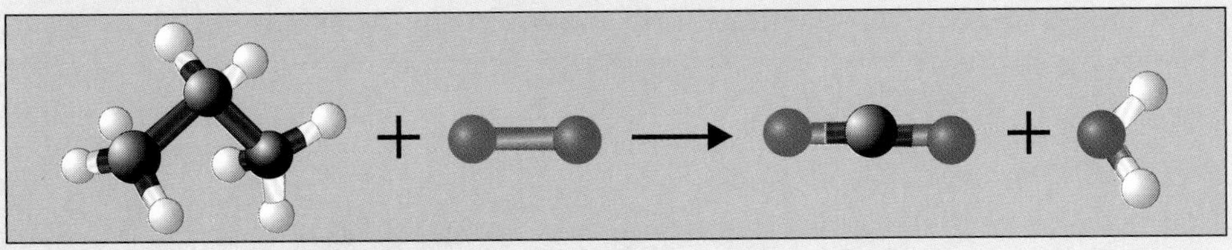

Balancing the Combustion Equation

Look closely at the chemical equation for the combustion of propane. You can see that there are different numbers of atoms on both sides of the equation. On the reactant side, there are 3 carbon atoms (shown in black), 8 hydrogen atoms (shown in white), and 2 oxygen atoms (shown in red). On the product side of the equation, there is only 1 carbon atom, 2 hydrogen atoms, and 3 oxygen atoms. This violates the **Law of Conservation of Mass**. The law states that the total mass of the products of a chemical reaction is the same as the total mass of the reactants entering into the reaction. Since there are different numbers of atoms before and after the reaction, the total mass of atoms involved is not equal. To fix this, you need to **balance** the equation.

Chem Words

chemical change: a process in which new materials with different properties are formed.

reactants: the materials that you initially start with in a chemical reaction.

products: the materials that are produced in a chemical reaction.

hydrocarbon: an organic compound that contains hydrogen and carbon atoms.

combustion reaction: a chemical reaction that involves the burning of a hydrocarbon in presence of oxygen.

Law of Conservation of Mass: a law that states that the total mass of the products of a chemical reaction is the same as the total mass of the reactants entering into the reaction.

balanced chemical equation: an equation in which the number and kind of atoms of the reactants equals the same number and kind of atoms of the products.

Atoms are rearranged during a chemical reaction. This is the nature of a chemical change. It is *not* required that both sides of an equation contain the same number of molecules. It *is* required that they have the same number of atoms though.

You can balance this equation by adding appropriate coefficients (numbers) in front of the molecular formulas of the reactants and products. *It is important that you change only coefficients, not the molecular formulas.* If you were to change the molecular formulas, you would no longer be working with the same chemical reaction. If you place a 3 in front of the CO_2 product, you will now have 3 carbon atoms on both sides of the equation. Placing a 4 in front of the H_2O product will bring the total number of H atoms on both sides to 8. However, this now makes a total number of 10 oxygen atoms on the right side of the equation. If you place a 5 in front of the reactant O_2, this will make the total number of oxygen atoms on both sides equal.

You now have a balanced equation that is represented as:

$$C_3H_{8(g)} \quad + \quad 5O_{2(g)} \quad \rightarrow \quad 3CO_{2(g)} \quad + \quad 4H_2O_{(g)}$$

3 carbon atoms	3 carbon atoms
8 hydrogen atoms	8 hydrogen atoms
10 oxygen atoms	10 oxygen atoms

The ball-and-stick representation is shown in the diagram.

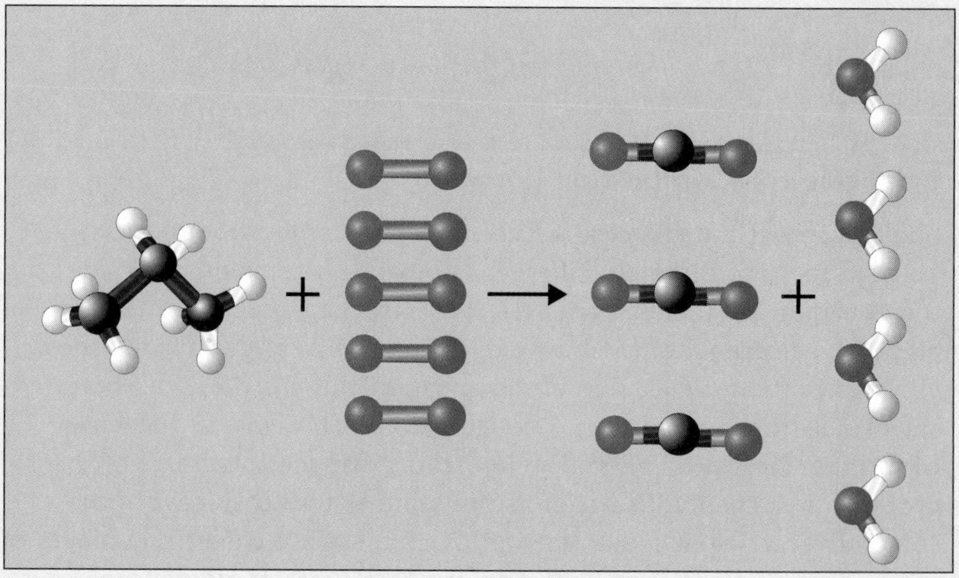

This states that 1 molecule of propane reacts with 5 molecules of oxygen to yield 3 molecules of carbon dioxide and 4 molecules of water.

There are two important understandings for balancing equations that you should have:

- You need to understand that you can balance equations because mass is conserved during a chemical reaction. The mass before the reaction must be identical to the mass after the reaction.
- You need to understand that you can balance equations because atoms are conserved during a chemical reaction. For example, the oxygen atoms entering the reaction must be the same oxygen atoms after the reaction.

There are two skills concerning balancing equations that you should also develop:

- You should be able to recognize whether a chemical equation is balanced by checking if the numbers of each atom are identical in the product and reactant sides of the equation.
- You should be able to balance the equations so the numbers of each atom are identical in the product and reactant sides of the equation. This skill has more to do with solving a "math puzzle" than the essence of chemistry and chemical principles.

All chemists understand why equations must be balanced. They can check to see if an equation is balanced. Some chemists enjoy balancing equations, while others do not.

The Role of Oxygen and Carbon Dioxide in Combustion

In *Step 4* of this activity, you placed a beaker over the candle flame. This reduced the amount of O_2 entering into the reaction. Without a source of O_2, the combustion reaction eventually stops.

In addition to the requirement that oxygen be present for fuel to burn, energy must be provided in order to start the reaction. In lighting a candle, a burning match provides the energy required to initiate the reaction.

In *Step 7*, you prepared CO_2 gas by reacting vinegar with baking soda. This happens in two steps. Vinegar contains acetic acid. This acetic acid reacts with baking soda (sodium hydrogen carbonate), and produces carbonic acid and sodium acetate. The carbonic acid is an unstable compound. It decomposes into CO_2 and H_2O.

→

Chem Words

catalyst: a substance that lowers the amount of energy needed to start a reaction by providing an alternate reaction pathway but is itself not changed in the reaction.

qualitative observation: an observation of features that do not involve measurement.

quantitative observation: an observation of features that involve the use of measurements.

$$\underset{\text{acetic acid}}{HC_2H_3O_{2(aq)}} + \underset{\text{sodium hydrogen carbonate}}{NaHCO_{3(s)}} \rightarrow \underset{\text{carbonic acid}}{H_2CO_{3(aq)}} + \underset{\text{sodium acetate}}{NaC_2H_3O_{2(aq)}}$$

$$\underset{\text{carbonic acid}}{H_2CO_{3(aq)}} \rightarrow \underset{\text{carbon dioxide}}{CO_{2(g)}} + \underset{\text{water}}{H_2O_{(l)}}$$

In the activity, the CO_2 produced was poured over the flame and extinguished it.

The formation of O_2 from the decomposition of hydrogen peroxide (H_2O_2) is represented by the following chemical equation:

$$\underset{\text{hydrogen peroxide}}{2H_2O_{2(aq)}} \xrightarrow{MnO_2} \underset{\text{oxygen}}{O_{2(g)}} + \underset{\text{water}}{2H_2O_{(l)}}$$

The rate of this reaction was sped up by adding manganese dioxide (MnO_2) to act as a catalyst. A **catalyst** is something that lowers the amount of energy needed to start and maintain a reaction by providing an alternate reaction pathway. True catalysts are regenerated (not used up) in a reaction.

In the activity, the O_2 produced was able to light a glowing splint.

In *Step 4* of this activity, you placed a beaker over the candle flame. Before the reaction stopped completely, however, an interesting thing took place. Smoke was produced and black soot was deposited on the beaker. This was carbon, which was released from the wax due to incomplete combustion. The other product of incomplete combustion is carbon monoxide (CO). You would not have been able to see or smell the carbon monoxide.

$$\underset{\text{carbon}}{C_{(s)}} + \underset{\text{oxygen}}{O_{2(g)}} \rightarrow \underset{\text{carbon monoxide}}{CO_{(g)}}$$

Carbon monoxide is a poison. It is one reason why incomplete combustion can be dangerous.

At this point you will probably notice that the equation above is not balanced. To fix this, you must place a 2 in front of the CO on the right and a two in front of the C on the left:

$$2C_{(s)} + O_{2(g)} \rightarrow 2CO_{(g)}$$

Checking Up

1. What is the difference between a quantitative and a qualitative observation?
2. Define a chemical change.
3. In a combustion reaction, what are the reactants and what are the products?
4. Name three hydrocarbons with which you are familiar.
5. Explain how the Law of Conservation of Mass helps you balance an equation.
6. Is the following a balanced equation? Justify your answer.
   $CH_4 + 2O_2 \rightarrow CO_2 + 2H_2O$
7. What is a catalyst?

What Do You Think Now?

At the beginning of the activity you were asked:

- **What is necessary for a fire?**
- **What can be used to put out an unwanted fire in a kitchen?**

Now that you have completed this activity on heat-energy transfer, what are the three things required for a fire? Once a fire has started, what should you remove in order to put the fire out?

Chem Essential Questions

What does it mean?

Chemistry explains a macroscopic phenomenon (what you observe) with a description of what happens at the nanoscopic level (atoms and molecules) using symbolic structures as a way to communicate. Complete the chart below in your *Active Chemistry* log.

MACRO	NANO	SYMBOLIC
List three observations that you made about the burning candle.	*In a combustion reaction, describe why the equation must be balanced.*	*Use chemical formulas in a balanced chemical equation to represent the combustion of propane.*

How do you know?

In an incomplete combustion reaction, carbon (soot) is formed. Where did you observe this in the activity?

Why do you believe?

Fires need to be controlled or extinguished. These include campfires, fires in the kitchen, and large-scale fires in the burners of an electrical power plant. Explain the importance of controlling the fire in each of these cases.

Why should you care?

You may choose to use fire in your cooking-show segment. Allowing the fire to rage out of control might not go over well with the TV executives. Being able to explain the chemical reaction responsible for the fire might be of interest to your viewers.

Reflecting on the Activity and the Challenge

In this activity, you learned about the combustion of fuels and what is required to keep the fuel burning. In a kitchen, natural gas (which is mostly methane) is often used as a source of fire for cooking. You may want to discuss the combustion of methane (natural gas) that allows you to cook during the segment. You may find a creative way of describing the need for balancing the equations that describe the combustion. You may also consider some other possible sources of combustion that might be found in a kitchen or used in cooking. There are many precautions that a cook should take when working in the kitchen. You might also want to include some fire safety issues in your cooking-show segment.

Chem to Go

1. Locate the fire extinguisher in your lab or in some other location at your school.
   a) What substances are in the extinguisher?
   b) How do they put out a fire?
2. Prove to yourself that the following equation is balanced by determining the total number of atoms on both sides of the equation:

   $$2C_8H_{18} + 25O_2 \rightarrow 16CO_2 + 18H_2O$$

   (Remember that $25O_2$ means that there are 25 molecules of oxygen. Each molecule of O_2 has two oxygen atoms.)

   How many carbon atoms on the reactant side? How many carbon atoms on the product side?

   Repeat for the H and O atoms.
3. Balance the following reactions:
   a) ___H_2 + ___$O_2 \rightarrow$ ___H_2O
   b) ___C_3H_8 + ___$O_2 \rightarrow$ ___ CO_2 + ___ H_2O
4. Show whether the following reactions are balanced.
   a) $2C_3H_8 + 7O_2 \rightarrow CO_2 + 4CO + 8H_2O + C$
   b) $2CH_3CH_2OH + 7O_2 \rightarrow 4CO_2 + 6H_2O$
5. The products of the balanced equation for the complete combustion of butane ($2C_4H_{10} + 13O_2$) are:
   a) $4CO_2 + 10H_2O$
   b) $4CO + 10H_2O$
   c) $8CO_2 + 10H_2O$
   d) $8CO_2 + 5H_2O$

6. Which of the following must be the same before and after a chemical reaction?
   a) The sum of the masses of all substances involved.
   b) The number of molecules of all substances involved.
   c) The number of atoms of each type involved.
   d) Both (a) and (c) must be the same.
7. Describe the combustion process to someone who has not studied chemistry.
8. Balance the following equations with whole-number coefficients:
   a) $CH_3OH + O_2 \rightarrow CO_2 + H_2O$
   b) $CH_4 + O_2 \rightarrow CO_2 + H_2O$
   c) $HCl + NaOH \rightarrow NaCl + H_2O$
   d) $C_5H_{12} + O_2 \rightarrow CO_2 + H_2O$
9. Determine which of the following equations are balanced.
   a) $NaHCO_3 + HCl \rightarrow NaCl + H_2O + CO_2$
   b) $Al + S \rightarrow Al_2S_3$
   c) $CH_3COOH + NaOH \rightarrow CH_3COONa + H_2O$
   d) $CH_2CH_2 + 6O_2 \rightarrow 2CO_2 + 2H_2O$
10. ***Preparing for the Chapter Challenge***

In your cooking show, how might you include a segment about fire safety? Other than the stove and oven, what are some other possible sources of combustion (expected and unexpected) in the kitchen? How can you make this segment both entertaining and informative?

Inquiring Further

Generic balanced chemical equation

Devise a generic balanced chemical equation for the combustion of those hydrocarbons that have the general formula C_nH_{2n+2}.

Activity 3 Cooking Fuels

What Do You See?

CHAR COAL

GOALS

In this activity you will:

- Make quantitative observations about different fuels.
- Understand where the energy comes from when a fuel is burned.
- Understand the relationship between heat and temperature change.
- Determine the amount of heat released from the combustion of various fuels.

What Do You Think?

Cooks use different fuels for different reasons.

- **Which fuel do you think will cook foods the fastest?**
- **Where does the energy in the fire come from?**

Record your ideas about these questions in your *Active Chemistry* log. Be prepared to discuss your responses with your group and the class.

Investigate

In this investigation, you will compare the energy content of various fuels. Fuels that you may be testing may include methanol, ethanol, kerosene, lamp oil, butanol, paraffin (candle wax), and jellied petroleum.

Part A: Designing Your Own Investigation

1. A common characteristic of most fuels is that they are compounds made of carbon and hydrogen (hydrocarbons) or carbon, hydrogen, and oxygen (alcohols). The amount of energy that a fuel releases has to do with how much and how completely the fuel is burned. But where do you think this energy comes from? You discussed this with your class in the *What Do You Think?* section.

2. To determine the amount of energy released from the combustion of a fuel, you will heat some water. By measuring the amount of fuel used and the change in temperature of the water, you will be able to make conclusions about the energy of each fuel.

   Consider the fuels that your teacher will be asking you to test. Predict which fuel will have the best heating ability.

   a) Record your prediction in your *Active Chemistry* log.

3. Using this strategy, design an experiment that can be conducted to determine the amount of energy released from the combustion of a fuel.

   Include in your design:

   - What apparatus and supplies you will need.
   - What measurements you will make.
   - What data you will record.
   - How you will analyze the data.
   - How you will draw a conclusion based on the data.

4. If your teacher has the materials in your design and approves your design, then you may proceed to carry out your investigation. Your teacher may decide to give you credit for your design and ask you to use the steps outlined in *Part B*.

Part B: Energy Content of Various Fuels

If your teacher does not have the supplies you need to do the investigation you designed, follow this procedure. In this procedure, you will use a soda can as a container for the water. While the soda can will not provide completely accurate results (some heat energy will be lost to the surroundings), it will give you some idea of the energy content of fuels. A cook will want to choose the right fuel for the job.

1. Your teacher will provide you with a soda can that has two holes at the top. Set up a ringstand and ring. Place a glass stirring rod through the holes in the can. Set the can and stirring rod on the ring, as shown in the diagram.

Safety goggles and a lab apron must be worn *at all times* in a chemistry lab.

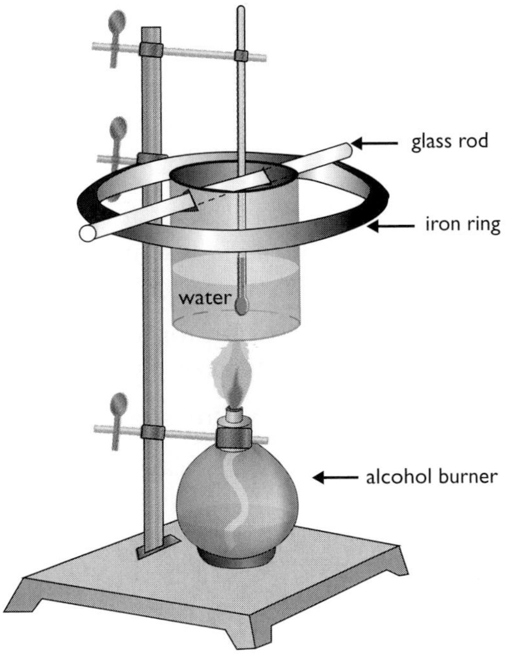
glass rod
iron ring
water
alcohol burner

2. Carefully, measure a specific amount of water (somewhere between 100 mL and 150 mL) in a graduated cylinder. Pour it into the can, being careful not to spill any.

   a) Record the amount of water you use in your log.

   b) Record the starting temperature of the water.

Be sure that the burner setup is secure.

Follow all precautions required around an open flame.

Be aware of the location of the fire extinguisher.

Wash hands and arms thoroughly before leaving the lab area.

3. Obtain an alcohol burner. Measure the mass of the burner and fuel.

   a) Record the type of fuel in the burner.

   b) Record the total mass of the burner and fuel as "mass before."

4. Set the burner under the can of water. Adjust the height of the ring so the flame will hit the bottom of the can. This should be about 2–3 cm from the wick.

5. Light the burner and readjust the height of the can, if necessary. Let the fuel burn for four minutes. Blow out the flame. Measure the temperature of the water using a thermometer or temperature probe.

   a) Record the color of the flame.

   b) Record the highest temperature of the water.

6. Let the burner cool for a while and then measure its mass again.

   a) Record this as "mass after."

7. Now that you have learned the techniques, you can complete the activity. Design an experiment, using the apparatus available, to compare three fuels and their heating ability.

   Each group will now work with one fuel and then the class will share data.

   You may want to prepare a table similar to the one below in your *Active Chemistry* log. Record your measurements for each fuel in the table.

   Note: If you use a candle, record the mass of the candle and foil-covered square base. For the jellied petroleum, record the mass of the open can.

Part C: Analyzing Your Data

1. The thermal energy required to change the temperature of a given amount of water by 1°C is the specific heat capacity. The specific heat capacity of water is one calorie per one gram per one degree Celsius. It is written as:

$$\frac{1\,\text{cal}}{\text{g}\cdot{}^{\circ}\text{C}} \quad \text{or} \quad 1\ \text{cal g}^{-1}\ {}^{\circ}\text{C}^{-1}$$

In other words, it takes one calorie of heat energy to raise the temperature of one gram of water by one degree Celsius.

If you know the amount of water and the change in temperature through which it goes, the specific heat capacity allows you to determine how much heat energy the water absorbs.

The equation to determine heat energy is:

Heat = (mass of water) × (specific heat capacity of water) × (temperature change of water)

Using mathematical symbols, this equation can be written as:

$$Q = mc\Delta T$$

Where Q = the change in heat
m = the mass of water (in grams)
c = the specific heat capacity of water
ΔT = the change in temperature ($T_{\text{final}} - T_{\text{initial}}$)

Fuel and flame color	Amount of water (mL)	Temp. before (°C)	Temp. after (°C)	Mass before (g)	Mass after (g)

Fuel	Mass of water (g)	Temp. change of water (°C)	Heat absorbed by water (cal)	Mass of fuel burned (g)	Heat per gram of fuel burned (cal/g)

2. For each fuel you tested, you will need to complete the calculations shown below. Prepare a table, similar to the one shown above, to display your results in your *Active Chemistry* log.

   a) Mass of water: Since the density of water is 1 g/mL, you simply change the volume of water to mass by changing the units of milliliters to grams. Mass of 150 mL of water = 1 g/mL × 150 mL = 150 g

   b) Temperature change of water: Subtract to find the temperature change.

   c) Heat absorbed by water (lost by the fuel): Use the equation ($Q = mc\Delta T$) to find heat.

   d) Mass of fuel burned: Subtract to find how much of the fuel you burned.

   e) Heat per gram of fuel burned: Divide the heat absorbed by the mass of fuel burned.

3. What conclusions can you draw from your investigation? Record the following in your *Active Chemistry* log:

   a) Compare your results to those of other groups. Which category is best for comparison purposes? Why?

   b) Which fuel did you find produced the most heat per gram? The least?

   c) Rank the fuels and compare the ranking to your prediction.

   d) Look at the flame colors and the amount of heat produced per gram of fuel. Is there any correlation between them? If so, what is it?

Chem Talk

THERMOCHEMISTRY

Specific Heat Capacity

When a fuel is burned, the energy released can be put to good use. In this activity, you used the energy to heat water and raise its temperature. As you learned previously, temperature and heat are related, but they do not measure the same thing. Temperature measures the kinetic energy or motion of molecules in a system. When you added heat energy to the water in the soda can, the water molecules began moving faster. As a result, the temperature went up. Heat is a measure of the total energy in a system. It is measured with a unit called a calorie or a joule.

Chem Words

specific heat capacity: the heat energy required to raise the temperature of 1 g of a substance by 1°C.

thermochemistry: the study of heat effects that accompany chemical reactions.

A calorie is the amount of heat needed to raise the temperature of one gram of water by one degree Celsius. You are probably familiar with the term Calorie as it relates to foods. A food Calorie (note the capital C) is equal to 1000 cal (calories) or 1 kcal (kilocalorie). It is also a measure of the energy available from the food. The joule is also used as the unit of energy.

In chemistry, as in all science, the international community has agreed to use joules as a unit of energy. However, in this activity, you used calories in your calculations. This is because in the USA, the energy content of foods is still given in kilocalories (kcal or C). A food that is 100 C (Calories) has an energy content of 100,000 cal (calories). Since 1 cal is equal to 4.184 J (joules), 100 C food has an energy content of 418,400 J.

To calculate the heat per gram of fuel consumed you needed to use the energy required to raise the temperature of 1 g of water by 1°C. This is the specific heat capacity of water. The specific heat capacity of water is one calorie per one gram per one degree Celsius. It is written as:

$$\frac{1\ \text{cal}}{\text{g}\cdot{}^\circ\text{C}} \quad \text{or} \quad 1\ \text{cal g}^{-1}\ {}^\circ\text{C}^{-1}$$

In other words, it takes one calorie of heat to raise the temperature of one gram of water by one degree Celsius.

In the activity, you measured the amount of water and the change in temperature of the water. Then, using specific heat capacity, you determined how much heat energy the water absorbed using the following equation:

Heat = (mass of water) × (specific heat capacity of water) × (temperature change of water)

Using mathematical symbols, this equation can be written as:

$$Q = mc\Delta T$$

Where Q = the change in heat

m = the mass of water (in grams)

c = the specific heat capacity of water

ΔT = the change in temperature ($T_{final} - T_{initial}$)

Terms Used in Thermochemistry

Thermochemistry is the study of heat effects that accompany chemical reactions. When you measure the quantities of heat gained or lost in chemical reactions, you are investigating the thermochemistry of those reactions. In studying thermochemistry, you use the term **system** to describe the reactants, solvent, and products of a reaction. You use the word **surroundings** to indicate everything outside of the chemical reaction: the can, the room, building, and so on, out into the universe.

When energy is released from the system to the surroundings, it is called an **exothermic reaction**. An **endothermic reaction** is one where energy is absorbed by the system from the surroundings. In the activity, energy was released as the fuel burned in an exothermic reaction.

When energy is released in an exothermic reaction, where does the energy come from? To understand exothermic reactions, you have to look at the same events from the viewpoint of the molecules and atoms. In *Active Chemistry*, we refer to this as the nanoscopic scale. That is because one nanometer is the size of some molecules. The energy in exothermic and endothermic reactions relates to the chemical bonds of the reactants. It takes energy to break a chemical bond. Consequently, when a chemical bond is formed, energy is released to the surroundings. Energy *in* to break a bond. Energy *out* to create a bond.

When your fuel was burned in the presence of oxygen, it underwent a combustion reaction. Combustion of any hydrocarbon is an exothermic process, which produces carbon dioxide and water. The combustion of candle wax you observed earlier was the same exothermic reaction.

Methane is the chief component of natural gas used in kitchens for cooking. Methane undergoes combustion according to the following balanced equation:

$$CH_{4(g)} + 2O_{2(g)} \rightarrow CO_{2(g)} + 2H_2O_{(g)} + \text{energy}$$

You see that + energy has been added to this reaction. It indicates that this is an exothermic process. The energy that is released from this reaction comes from the stored energy in the molecular bonds. The energy to break the bonds of the reactants is less than the energy released to create the bonds in the products. The extra energy is released to the surroundings in this exothermic process.

All molecules have potential energy resulting from the bonds that hold the atoms together. In this reaction, if 1 mol of CH_4 were used, the potential energy of the reactants is equal to 3450 kJ. The total potential energy of the products is equal to 2642 kJ. The heat energy that is released from this reaction is the difference between the potential energies of the reactants and products:

$$2642 \text{ kJ} - 3450 \text{ kJ} = -808 \text{ kJ}$$

These 808 kJ of heat energy are released in this exothermic reaction.

Chem Words

system: the reactants, solvent, and products of a reaction.

surroundings: everything outside of a chemical reaction.

exothermic reaction: a reaction in which energy is released from the system to the surroundings.

endothermic reaction: a reaction in which energy is absorbed by the system from the surroundings.

Checking Up

1. Explain again the difference between heat energy and temperature.
2. What two units can be used to measure heat energy?
3. Define the specific heat capacity of a substance.
4. What is the specific heat capacity of water?
5. What does thermochemistry study?
6. Explain the difference between an exothermic and an endothermic reaction.
7. From where does the energy released in an exothermic reaction come?
8. In the exothermic reaction, is the potential energy of the products *lower* or *higher* than that for the reactants?
9. In the endothermic reaction, is the potential energy of the products *lower* or *higher* than that for the reactants?
10. What type of reaction occurs when the weaker bonds of the reactants are broken and stronger bonds in the products are formed?
11. What is activation energy?
12. What is the difference between methane and methanol?

Energy Change in Exothermic and Endothermic Reactions

One way to graphically represent the energy changes of a reaction is with an **energy diagram.** Typical energy diagrams for both an exothermic reaction and an endothermic reaction are shown below.

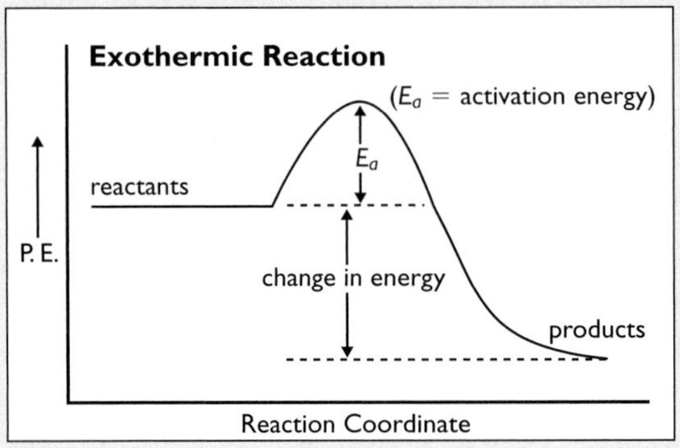

Exothermic Reaction
(E_a = activation energy)
E_a
reactants
P. E.
change in energy
products
Reaction Coordinate

In the exothermic reaction, the potential energy (P.E.) of the products is *lower* than that for the reactants. The energy difference (in the form of heat energy, or *Q*) is negative because it leaves the system and is given off to the surroundings.

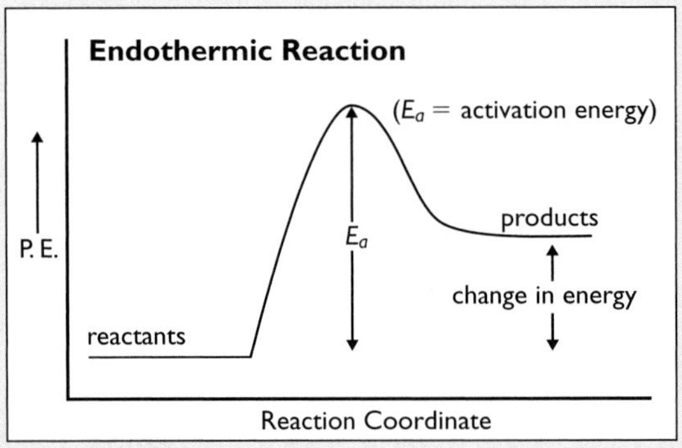

Endothermic Reaction
(E_a = activation energy)
products
P. E.
E_a
change in energy
reactants
Reaction Coordinate

In the endothermic reaction, the P.E. of the products is *higher* than that of the reactants. Energy must be supplied to the reaction to make it occur. The energy difference is positive because it is provided to the system from the surroundings.

When weaker bonds (less stable, higher energy) of the reactants are broken and stronger bonds (more stable, lower in energy) in the products are formed, energy is released to the surroundings in an exothermic reaction. This is because the potential energy of the system (the substances involved in the reaction) has been lowered.
A chemical reaction where stronger bonds of the reactants are broken and weaker bonds are formed in the products is an endothermic reaction that requires energy in order to take place.

In both cases, there is an energy that must be supplied in order for the reactants to have the proper collision energy for the reaction to occur. This is called the **activation energy** (E_a). When you light the propane burner of a camp stove, a spark is needed to start the reaction, supplying the activation energy. Even though the combustion of propane gas is an exothermic reaction, the spark must be supplied before the reaction will proceed. An exothermic reaction can be sustained by the heat liberated by the reaction.

Alcohol Fuels

Alcohol fuels contain the hydroxyl group (–OH). If you replace one of the hydrogens of methane with a hydroxyl group, you will now have a compound that is called an **alcohol**. In this case, the alcohol is called methanol or methyl alcohol. Methane is CH_4 and methanol is CH_3OH.

The combustion of methanol is shown as:

$$2CH_3OH_{(l)} + 3O_{2(g)} \rightarrow 2CO_{2(g)} + 4H_2O_{(g)}$$

As in the combustion of methane, energy is released as the strong carbon-oxygen bonds are formed in CO_2. As a general rule, the fewer carbon-oxygen bonds in the reactants, the more energy released. Larger hydrocarbon compounds with no oxygen present should release more heat on burning than smaller, partially oxygenated hydrocarbons.

Here are the formulas of some possible fuels:

Name	Molecular formula	Condensed structural formula
methanol	CH_4O	CH_3OH
ethanol	C_2H_6O	CH_3CH_2OH
1-propanol	C_3H_8O	$CH_3CH_2CH_2OH$
2-propanol (isopropyl alcohol)	C_3H_8O	$CH_3CH(OH)CH_3$
n-butanol	$C_4H_{10}O$	$CH_3CH_2CH_2CH_2OH$
kerosene	A mixture averaging $C_{10}H_{22}$	
lamp oil	A mixture of paraffin and kerosene	
candle wax (paraffin)	A mixture of $C_{20}H_{42}$ and larger	

Balanced equations show relationships in molar quantities. A **mole** is a specific number of particles (6.022×10^{23} particles). The combustion of methanol shown in equation above can also be described in words as:

> Two moles of methanol react with three moles of oxygen to produce two moles of carbon dioxide and four moles of water, with a certain amount of energy released.

In the investigation, you determined the amount of heat per gram of fuel. In the equation just described, the heat released would be per mole(s) of fuel burned.

Chem Words

energy diagram: a way to represent graphically the energy changes of a reaction.

activation energy: the energy that must be supplied in order for the reactants to have the proper collision energy for the reaction to occur.

alcohol: a hydrocarbon in which a hydrogen atom is replaced with a hydroxyl group (—OH).

mole: a specific number of particles (6.022×10^{23} particles).

What Do You Think Now?

At the beginning of the activity you were asked:

- **Which fuel do you think will cook foods the fastest?**
- **Where does the energy in the fire come from?**

Now that you have completed this activity, where does the energy released in the exothermic process of burning fuels come from?

Chem Essential Questions

What does it mean?

Chemistry explains a macroscopic phenomenon (what you observe) with a description of what happens at the nanoscopic level (atoms and molecules) using symbolic structures as a way to communicate. Complete the chart below in your *Active Chemistry* log.

MACRO	NANO	SYMBOLIC
What did you observe in this activity that led you to believe that the combustion of a fuel is an exothermic reaction?	*When a fuel burns, compare the bonds of the molecules on the product and reactant sides.*	*Use an energy diagram as a symbolic structure to describe what happens during an exothermic reaction.*

How do you know?

Take a look at the class data for the energy content of the different fuels used. In the *Chem Talk* section, you read the hypothesis that partially oxygenated fuels (those with some carbon-oxygen bonds present) will release less heat than similar hydrocarbons without oxygen. Does the class data support this hypothesis?

Why do you believe?

Your everyday experiences make it easy to accept that when a fuel is burned, it is an exothermic process. What examples of fires would you use to explain to someone that fires require fuel?

Why should you care?

Consider some of the fuels that are sources of heat for cooking. You cannot always use fuels with the highest heat output per gram. Consider why not in terms of cost, convenience, and safety.

Reflecting on the Activity and the Challenge

Think about the advantages of gas and electric stoves in terms of the control of the amount of heat, the response to the change in heat, and safety. You may want to describe these as well as the combustion reaction of the gas stove in your show. Making the discussion entertaining is one of the tougher parts of your cooking show because it requires creativity.

Chem to Go

1. How would your data be different if you used only 50 mL of water instead of 150 mL in this experiment?
2. Write balanced chemical equations for the fuels that you tested.
3. a) Explain the difference between an endothermic and an exothermic reaction.

   b) List some technologies that use endothermic and some that use exothermic reactions.
4. Convert the following heat quantities recalling 1 cal = 4.184 J:

   a) 350 cal to joules   b) 515 J to calories   c) 1.6 kcal to joules
5. Suppose you have two containers of water. One contains 150 mL at 80°C and the other has 75 mL at 60°C. Is the heat content of both containers equivalent? If not, which has the lesser heat content?
6. How much heat is required to change the temperature of 150 g of water by 20°C?
7. How much heat will be given off when 1500 g of water cools down by 20°C?
8. Which statement describes the characteristics of an *endothermic* reaction?

   a) The sign of Q is negative, and the products have less potential energy than the reactants.

   b) The sign of Q is positive, and the products have less potential energy than the reactants.

   c) The sign of Q is negative, and the products have more potential energy than the reactants.

   d) The sign of Q is positive, and the products have more potential energy than the reactants.
9. What is the total number of joules of heat energy absorbed by 15 g of water when it is heated from 30°C to 40°C?

   a) 10   b) 63   c) 150   d) 630
10. Whenever bonds between atoms are broken and rearranged:

    a) Energy is involved.

    b) An exothermic reaction has taken place.

    c) Melting has occurred.

    d) Energy is supplied to the system.
11. ***Preparing for the Chapter Challenge***

    In preparing for your *Chapter Challenge*, you may want to explain what source of heat is used for cooking and why it is used. Make a list of possible sources in your *Active Chemistry* log.

Inquiring Further

Cost of fuels and energy content

Investigate whether the cost of fuels is related to the energy content of the fuels.

Chapter mini Challenge

HONK
THE BRIDGE

Your challenge for this chapter is to create an entertaining and informative five-minute segment of a cooking show that gives a detailed explanation of the chemistry involved. Having completed three activities, this is a good time to give your cooking segment a *first try*. It's time to create a one-minute cooking show. Of course, being limited to the chemistry content of three activities will limit the extent of the show. This *first try* though, will give you a good sense of what the challenge entails and how you and other teams are going to approach your media task.

Your *mini-challenge* is to create a one-minute segment of a cooking show. Sharing your one-minute segment with your class will help you learn about what works and doesn't work in a cooking show segment. You will be able to provide feedback to other teams and they will provide feedback to you. You will not be given much preparation time for your *mini-challenge*. It is a way to get a sense of what you will be involved with at the end of the chapter when you have more chemistry content to include in your five-minute segment.

Chemistry Content

Your team should first review the chemistry content that may be included in this cooking segment.

Activity 1: You learned about convection, conduction, and radiation as ways of heating food.

Activity 2: You learned about fires, fire safety, and the chemical reactions in combustion. This included writing balanced chemical equations for combustion.

Activity 3: You extended your knowledge of combustion to compare cooking fuels and calculate the energy released when hydrocarbons or alcohols burn.

Criteria

Your team should also review the criteria that you discussed on the first day of this chapter. Your cooking-show segment should be creative, fun, engaging, as well as having accurate chemistry explanations.

Preparing for Your mini Challenge

Your team should probably discuss how your cooking-show segment would be similar or different from other cooking shows that you may have seen on TV, discussed in class, or found out about on the Internet. What kind of personality will your cooking-show chef or commentator have? Will the chef be humorous or a bit strange? Will the commentator be more exciting than the chef or be a serious, "just the facts," kind of personality?

Your team should also discuss what food you want to feature in the cooking show. With the chemistry content being about heating foods and fuel choices, you can choose ethnic foods, foods from a country that you visited or in which your family lived, healthy foods, gourmet foods, or anything else. Your choice of foods may be the ingredient that makes your show entertaining.

Engineering/Technology Design

The engineering-design process involves a number of distinct steps. In creating a cooking-show segment, you are involved in a design process. Note how your efforts follow the design model described below.

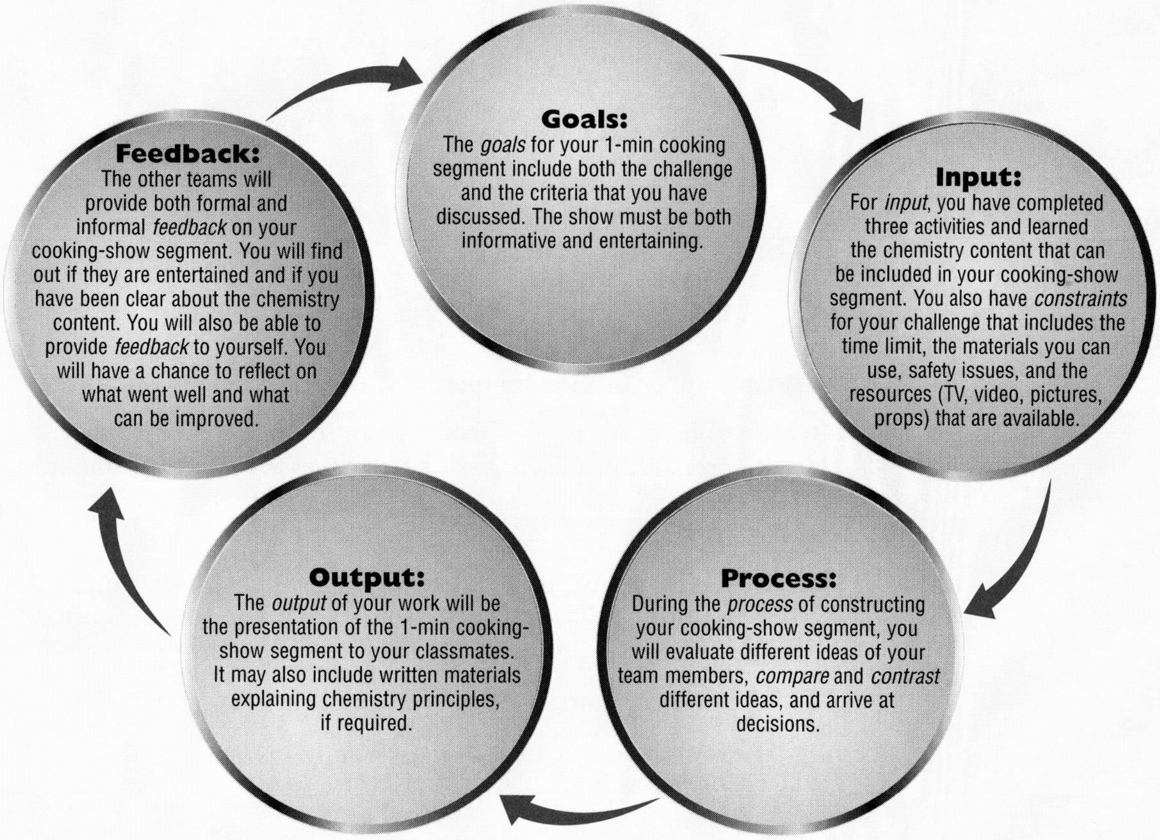

Goals:
The *goals* for your 1-min cooking segment include both the challenge and the criteria that you have discussed. The show must be both informative and entertaining.
Input:
For *input*, you have completed three activities and learned the chemistry content that can be included in your cooking-show segment. You also have *constraints* for your challenge that includes the time limit, the materials you can use, safety issues, and the resources (TV, video, pictures, props) that are available.
Process:
During the *process* of constructing your cooking-show segment, you will evaluate different ideas of your team members, *compare* and *contrast* different ideas, and arrive at decisions.
Output:
The *output* of your work will be the presentation of the 1-min cooking-show segment to your classmates. It may also include written materials explaining chemistry principles, if required.
Feedback:
The other teams will provide both formal and informal *feedback* on your cooking-show segment. You will find out if they are entertained and if you have been clear about the chemistry content. You will also be able to provide *feedback* to yourself. You will have a chance to reflect on what went well and what can be improved.

Remember: This is a *first try*. The feedback that you get from the 1-min show will be extremely valuable when you prepare for the 5-min cooking-show segment at the end of the chapter. At that point, you will begin the entire design cycle again. That's why it is called a cycle. You keep going through it over and over to improve your design or, in this case, your cooking-show segment.

Activity 4 Boiling Water

What Do You See?

GOALS

In this activity you will:

- Determine the boiling point of water.
- Show graphically what happens to the temperature as water is heated to boiling and while the water is boiling.

What Do You Think?

Millions of barrels of oil are used to heat water for coffee and tea. Boiling water is an example of a physical change.

- **What happens to the temperature of water when you boil it?**

Record your ideas about this question in your *Active Chemistry* log. Be prepared to discuss your responses with your group and the class.

Investigate

1. Measure 100 mL of water in a graduated cylinder. Pour the water into a 250-mL beaker. Place a wire gauze mat on the hot plate. Then place the 250-mL beaker of water on the wire gauze mat.
2. Measure the starting temperature of the water.
   a) Record the starting temperature in a table in your *Active Chemistry* log.

Safety goggles and a lab apron must be worn *at all times* in a chemistry lab.

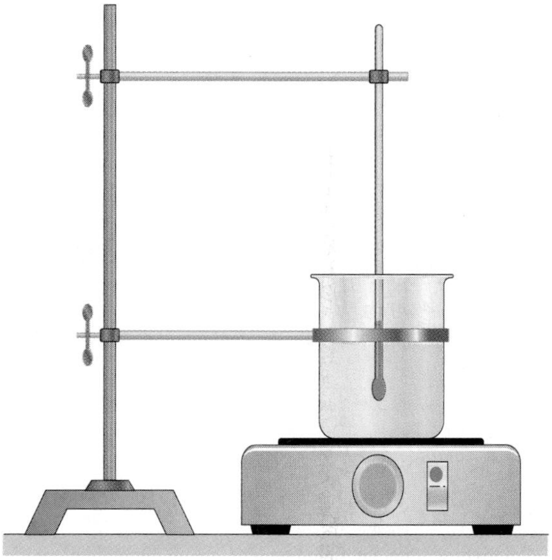

3. Turn on the hot plate to the highest setting to heat the water. Measure the temperature of the water every 30 s. Try to heat the water to 120°C and then stop. You may need to stop heating the water when your teacher instructs you to do so.
   a) Record the temperature of the water every 30 s.
   b) Note the temperature when the water begins to boil.
4. Graph the temperature versus time in your *Active Chemistry* log. Plot time on the x-axis and temperature on the y-axis. With good planning, your lab group may be able to complete the graph as you record the data.

   Alternatively, you may use a temperature probe and software in *Steps 2* and *3*. In this case, the graph will be generated for you.
   a) Place a copy of the graph in your *Active Chemistry* log.
5. Answer the following questions in your *Active Chemistry* log.
   a) Describe the graph of the boiling water. How many sections are present?

      The x-axis of the graph is time. Since you were heating the water at a constant rate, you can also refer to the x-axis as heat energy.
   b) The water gained heat energy the entire time to get it to boil. What happened to the temperature while the water gained heat energy?
   c) Which section of the graph shows where the water is actually boiling? What happens to the temperature while the water is boiling?
   d) Describe the relationship between heat and temperature as water boils.
   e) The instructions were to heat the water to 120°C. Were you able to do this? Why do you think that the water could not be heated beyond 100°C?
   f) Draw three pictures showing the water molecules in the cool water, the hot water, and the steam.

Make certain that the ringstand, ring, beaker, and burner are secure.

Wash hands and arms thoroughly before leaving the lab area.

Chem Talk

HEAT ENERGY AND THE CHANGES OF STATE: BOILING AND CONDENSATION

The States of Matter

Solids, liquids, and gases are three of the states, or phases, of matter. The fourth state of matter is plasma, but this will not be discussed here. The following definitions will help you to identify a substance's state of matter and to describe the changes from one state to another.

Solids have a definite shape and volume. True solids retain their shape and take up a definite volume for a given amount of mass. The particles are close together in solids. They are locked into a fixed position. For the most part, they cannot be compressed and they are unable to flow. All materials become solid if their temperatures are reduced enough or the pressure exerted on them becomes high enough. Many people will mistakenly believe that the particles of a solid are not moving. They do move. They vibrate slightly around a fixed position. The solid state of H_2O (water) is ice. You will study ice in the next activity.

Liquids do not have a definite shape and will flow to take the shape of the container they are in. The particles are close together in liquids. Liquids do have a definite volume for a given mass. All liquids are not easily compressed. There is less attraction between the particles of a liquid than those of a solid. Therefore, they are able to move more than the particles of a solid. They are able to slip and slide over and around one another. The liquid state of H_2O is water.

Gases have no definite shape or volume of their own. Therefore, if the volume of container they are in changes, so does the volume of the gas. The particles are very far apart in a gas. Individual molecules do not change size when they are vaporized (or undergo any phase change). Gases are also easily compressed. All of these characteristics of gases are due to the fact that the particles of a gas have almost no attraction for one another. The gas state of H_2O is vapor.

Change of State: A Physical Change

In this activity, you investigated **boiling**, also called **vaporization**. Boiling is a change from a liquid to a gas phase. The temperature at which this occurs for a given substance is the **boiling point**.

Condensation is the change from a gas to a liquid. The temperature at which this occurs for a given substance is the **condensation point**. The condensation point and the boiling point are the same.

When water boils or steam condenses, a **physical change** takes place. A physical change is one that involves changes in the state or phase of a material. It does not involve the creation of new materials. The water boils and turns to water vapor (steam) and water vapor condenses to form liquid water. However, there is no change to the molecular structure or size of the water. It is still H_2O. The phase change does involve changes in heat though. **Endothermic changes** occur when heat is absorbed. **Exothermic changes** occur when heat is removed. Vaporization is endothermic and condensation is exothermic. You can remember this by recalling the activity you completed. To boil water, the water must gain heat energy. Boiling is therefore an endothermic process. A phase change can also take place with a change in pressure.

Heat of Vaporization and Condensation

When you added heat energy to water, at first, the water's temperature increased. As you supplied more heat energy, the water got hotter and hotter. At a certain point, the water no longer got hotter. At 100°C, the liquid water began to become a gas of water vapor. The molecules of water were no longer bound to the other water molecules and were able to move about the room. You can try to get water in an *uncovered* pot to reach temperatures higher than 100°C, but you cannot do it!

Chem Words

physical change: a process that involves changes in the state or phase of a material.

boiling (vaporization): a change from a liquid to a gas phase.

boiling point: the temperature at which vaporization occurs for a given substance.

condensation: a change from a gas to a liquid.

condensation point: the temperature at which condensation occurs for a given substance.

endothermic change: a change that occurs when heat is absorbed by a system.

exothermic change: a change that occurs when heat is released from a system.

Chem Words

heat of vaporization: the amount of heat gained in changing 1 g of liquid to 1 g of vapor.

heat of condensation: the amount of heat lost in changing 1 g of vapor to 1 g of liquid.

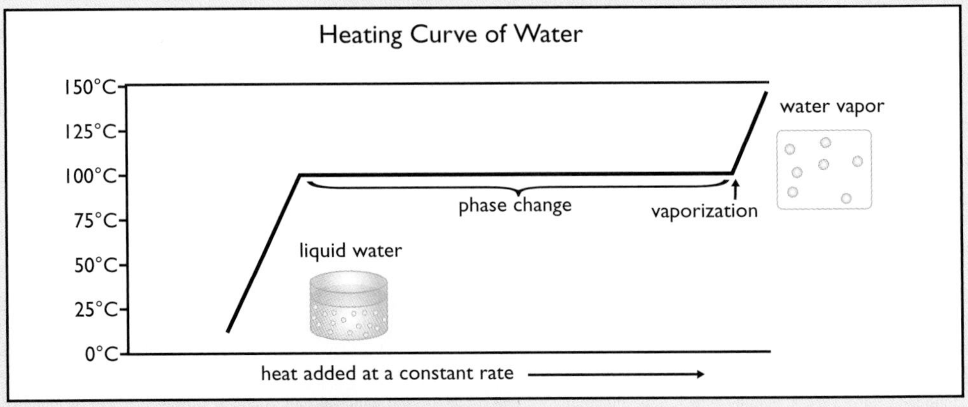
Heating Curve of Water
150°C
125°C
100°C
75°C
50°C
25°C
0°C
water vapor
phase change
vaporization
liquid water
heat added at a constant rate

How much energy is required to boil water? Carefully conducted measurements have shown that each gram of water at 100°C requires 540 cal of energy to become a gram of water vapor at 100°C. This is called the **heat of vaporization** of water. There is an equation that allows you to calculate the required energy for 2 g of water, 50 g of water, or any mass (*m*) of water.

$$Q = mH_v$$

Where Q is the energy, m is the mass of liquid, and H_v is the heat of vaporization. This equation will work for all materials undergoing a phase change from liquid to gas. Each material has its own heat of vaporization.

For example, the heat of vaporization of ethyl alcohol is 200 cal/g at the normal boiling point of 78°C. Peanut oil will boil at a higher temperature. However, it is not safe to try to determine its heat of vaporization, since if the conditions are right it could explode at 238°C. This temperature is still below its boiling point. So, if you are planning to cook with vegetable oil, you must be careful in avoiding these conditions.

Water vapor can become a liquid again. This is referred to as condensation. You may see some condensation of water on a mirror after a hot shower. Since energy had to be added when you boiled water, then energy must be released when water vapor condenses. The heat of vaporization also indicates how much energy is released when water vapor becomes liquid water. Once again, the energy involved is 540 cal/g. The energy required for this phase change is called the **heat of condensation**. Note that vaporization is endothermic and condensation is exothermic. Heats of vaporization and condensation are equal in magnitude, but opposite in sign.

Checking Up

1. Compare and contrast solids, liquids, and gases. Use shape, volume, compressibility, attraction of particles, and movement of particles in your answer.
2. What is boiling and what is condensation?
3. What is the difference between an endothermic and an exothermic change?
4. Explain heat of vaporization and heat of condensation. How are they the same? How are they different?

What Do You Think Now?

At the beginning of the activity you were asked:

- **What happens to the temperature of water when you boil it?**

Now that you have completed this activity, how would you answer the question?

Chem Essential Questions

What does it mean?

Chemistry explains a macroscopic phenomenon (what you observe) with a description of what happens at the nanoscopic level (atoms and molecules) using symbolic structures as a way to communicate. Complete the chart below in your *Active Chemistry* log.

MACRO	NANO	SYMBOLIC
In Step 3, as you continued to apply heat to the water sample, describe what happened to the temperature of the water.	*Describe in words what was happening at the molecular level as more and more heat was applied to the water. Include both the increase in temperature of the water and the change of phase.*	*An equation can be used to describe the changes in the water as energy is supplied. It has to do with the change in the temperature of the water. Write down each equation and explain what each variable represents.*

How do you know?

Describe how you know that the temperature of water does not rise above 100°C. What happens to the water as you continue to heat it when it reaches 100°C?

Why do you believe?

Foods are often cooked in boiling water or hot oil. Steam is also used to cook many foods. List a cooking example for each one of these processes.

Why should you care?

A description of any phase changes occurring during the preparation of food in a cooking-show segment will enhance your audiences' appreciation of the chemistry involved. How can you describe the cooking of pasta or heating milk for hot chocolate in an entertaining and informative way?

Reflecting on the Activity and the Challenge

In this activity, you learned that energy is required to change a liquid into a gas and that a gas must lose heat energy in order for it to condense into a liquid. Boiling water is used to cook different foods. Vegetables, potatoes, and eggs are all examples that can be cooked in boiling water. If you include cooking in boiling water in your segment it will be informative for your audience.

Chem to Go

1. You have a pot of water boiling on the stove. What will happen to the temperature of the water if you increase the heat?
2. Determine the amount of heat needed to vaporize 500 g of water at 100°C.
3. Determine the amount of heat needed to vaporize 250 g of water starting at 80°C.
4. How much heat must be removed from 400 g of steam at 100°C to bring it down to 50°C?
5. Draw a heating curve (temperature versus time) for 100 mL of water where heat is added at 50 cal/min. Start at 0°C and continue to the boiling point.
6. Draw a heating curve (temperature versus time) for 500 mL of water where heat is added at 50 cal/min. Start at 0°C and continue to the boiling point.
7. Draw a heating curve (temperature versus time) for 100 mL of ethyl alcohol where heat is added at 50 cal/min. The heat of vaporization of ethyl alcohol is 200 cal/g. The boiling point of ethyl alcohol is 78°C. Start at 78°C and continue until evaporation is complete.
8. ***Preparing for the Chapter Challenge***

   List three instances where there are condensation/evaporation phase changes occurring in everyday cooking. Describe the processes as either endothermic or exothermic.

Activity 5 Freezing Water

What Do You See?

GOALS

In this activity you will:

- Determine the freezing point of water.
- Show graphically what happens to the temperature as water is cooled to freezing and while it is freezing.

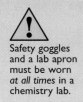

Safety goggles and a lab apron must be worn *at all times* in a chemistry lab.

What Do You Think?

Fast freezing rates promote the formation of many small ice crystals. Slow freezing permits large ice crystals to form. This is important when freezing delicate foods or when making ice cream.

- **What happens to the temperature of water as it freezes?**

Record your ideas about this question in your *Active Chemistry* log. Be prepared to discuss your responses with your group and the class.

Investigate

Part A: Freezing Water

1. Half-fill a test tube with water. Place the test tube in a polystyrene cup containing an ice and salt mixture.
2. Measure the starting temperature of the water in the test tube.
   a) Record the starting temperature in a table in your *Active Chemistry* log.

3. Measure the temperature of the water in the test tube every 30 s as it freezes. Continue until you reach a temperature of –5°C.
   a) Record the temperature of the water every 30 s.
   b) Note the temperature at which freezing begins.
4. Graph the temperature versus time in your *Active Chemistry* log. Plot time on the *x*-axis and temperature on the *y*-axis. With good planning, your lab group may be able to complete the graph as you record the data.

   Alternatively, you may use a temperature probe and software in *Steps 2* and *3*. In this case, the graph will be generated for you.
   a) Place a copy of the graph in your *Active Chemistry* log.
5. Answer the following questions in your *Active Chemistry* log.
   a) Describe the graph of the temperature of water as it cools and freezes. How many sections are present?
   b) The water loses heat energy the entire time it is freezing. What happened to the temperature during this time?
   c) Which section of the graph shows where the water is actually freezing? What happens to the temperature while the water is freezing?
   d) Describe the relationship between heat and temperature as water freezes.
   e) Draw three pictures showing the water molecules in the cool water, the colder water, and the frozen water.
6. From the results of the previous activity and *Part A* of this activity, you can see that temperature remains constant during a phase change. The temperature of a solid, liquid, or gas changes as it gains or loses heat energy. Using the graph you created as a guide, sketch a new temperature versus time graph if ice at –5°C were heated on a hot plate until it boils.
   a) Label the portion of the graph that shows a solid, liquid, and a gas.
   b) Label the portion of the graph that shows melting, freezing, boiling, and condensing.
   c) Draw two arrows and label each arrow as exothermic or endothermic.

Part B: Heat of Fusion

In this part of the investigation, you will determine the amount of heat energy that is added to a certain quantity of ice as it melts. This is called the **heat of fusion** of ice.

The strategy for the experiment is to calculate the heat energy loss of the water from its initial temperature to 0°C. This will be the equivalent of the heat energy gain that was required to melt some ice. By measuring the mass of the melted ice, you can then determine the heat of fusion of ice (the energy required to melt one gram of ice).

1. Prepare a table in your *Active Chemistry* log similar to the one shown below to record your data.
2. Use a hot plate to heat about 200 mL of water in a beaker. When the water reaches about 80°C, turn off the hot plate.

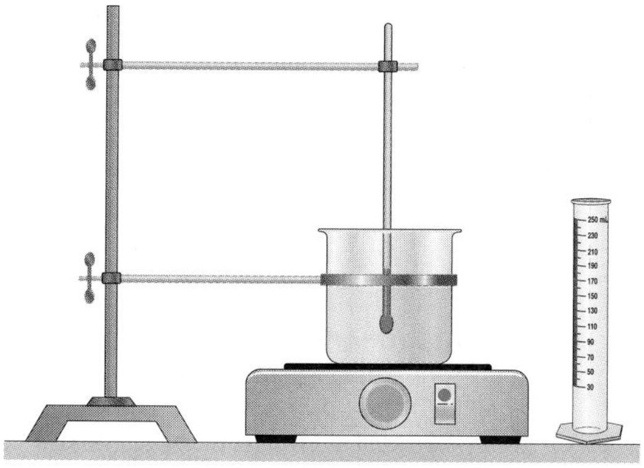

Heating/Cooling Curve of Water

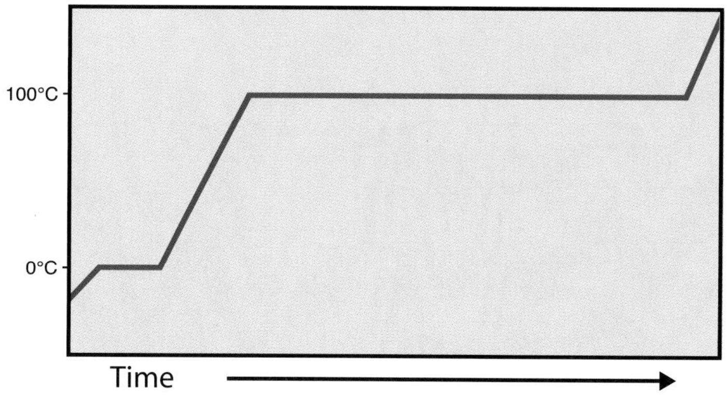
100°C
0°C
Time

3. Using hot pads or paper towels, measure out 150 mL of the hot water. Carefully pour the hot water into a large foam cup.

You may also use rubber gloves to transfer the hot water.

4. Fill a second foam cup about two-thirds full with ice.
5. Measure the starting temperature of the hot water in the cup.

   a) Record the starting temperature.

6. Quickly add several pieces of ice to the hot water. Stir gently. Continue adding ice as it melts. Be sure to keep ice in the hot water at all times. Continue until the temperature of the water stabilizes at 0°C.
7. When the temperature is 0°C, remove the remaining ice. Carefully measure the volume of water that is in the cup now.

Volume of hot water before (mL)	Volume of cold water after (mL)	Volume of ice melted (mL)	Temp. before (°C)	Temp. after (°C)	Temp. change (°C)	Total heat lost (cal)	Heat per gram of ice (heat of fusion) (cal/g)

8. Calculate the heat of fusion using the following steps. Show all your calculations in your *Active Chemistry* log.

   a) Determine the volume of water from ice that melted.

   b) Find the temperature change of the hot to cold water.

   c) Determine how much heat the hot water lost by using the heat equation. Remember that the volume of hot water is also the mass of hot water (density of water = 1g/mL).

   $$\Delta Q = mc\Delta T$$

   d) Since the hot water lost heat energy, the ice gained the same amount of heat energy (assuming no loss to the surroundings). This is a statement of the conservation of energy. The volume of water from melted ice is equal to the mass of ice that melted. (Recall the density of water again.) Determine the heat of fusion of ice by dividing the total heat the ice absorbed by the mass of ice that melted. The unit will be cal/g.

   $$\text{Heat of Fusion} = \frac{\text{total heat}}{\text{mass of ice melted}}$$

9. Prepare a class data table in your *Active Chemistry* log.

   a) Record the heat of fusion of ice from the other groups.

   b) Find the average for the class.

10. You stopped the investigation when the temperature stabilized.

    a) Why do you think you stopped the investigation at this point?

    b) Would the ice continue to melt?

    c) Where would the ice be getting the heat from?

11. When experiments similar to the one that you have done are completed with extreme care and many, many times, chemists publish their work and arrive at a value for the heat of fusion of ice. The accepted heat of fusion of ice is 79.6 cal/g. This means that it takes 79.6 cal of heat to melt one gram of ice.

    a) How close to the accepted value was your heat of fusion of ice?

    b) How close was the class average?

Wash hands and arms thoroughly before leaving the lab area.

Chem Talk

CHANGES OF STATE

Melting and Freezing

In the previous activity, you investigated boiling and condensation. Recall that boiling was also called vaporization. It is the change of state from a liquid to a gas. Condensation is the change of state from a gas to a liquid. Boiling is an endothermic change because water had to gain heat energy in order to boil. Condensation is an exothermic change.

In this activity, you investigated freezing and melting. **Melting** is the change from a solid to a liquid phase. Melting is also called **fusion**. The temperature at which this occurs for a given substance is the **melting point**. At the melting point there is enough kinetic energy to cause particles in the crystal structure to break free from the forces holding them together in the crystal structure. This required energy for a given mass is the **heat of fusion**.

Freezing is the change from a liquid to a solid phase. Freezing is also called crystallization. The temperature at which this occurs for a given substance is the **freezing point**. The freezing point occurs at the same temperature as the melting point. The energy lost when a substance freezes is the **heat of crystallization**. Fusion (melting) is endothermic and crystallization (freezing) is exothermic. The heats of fusion and crystallization are equal in magnitude, but opposite in sign.

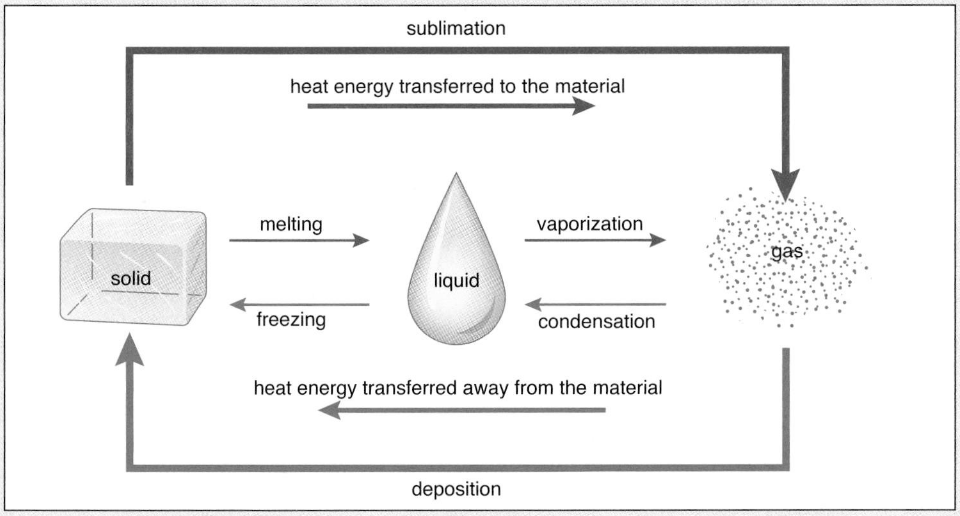
sublimation
heat energy transferred to the material
solid
melting
freezing
liquid
vaporization
condensation
gas
heat energy transferred away from the material
deposition

Recall also, that changes of state are physical changes. If you apply heat to the bottom of a candle, the wax will melt. As it cools, the wax will harden again. This is an example of a physical change. In *Activity 2*, →

Chem Words

melting (fusion): the change from a solid to a liquid phase.

melting point: the temperature at which a solid changes to a liquid.

heat of fusion: the amount of energy that a substance must gain in order for a solid to change to a liquid.

freezing: the change from a liquid to a solid phase.

freezing point: the temperature at which a liquid changes to a solid.

heat of crystallization: the energy released when a substance freezes.

you lit the wick of a candle and the atoms in the hydrocarbons in the wax rearranged as they reacted with oxygen. They underwent a combustion reaction to form carbon dioxide and water. This is a chemical change. In a physical change, no new materials are created. In this activity, when the ice melted or the water froze there was no change in the molecular structure of the water. It was still H_2O.

Heat Energy and the Changes of State

Changes of phase always occur with a change of heat energy. The material either gains (endothermic) or loses (exothermic) heat energy during a phase change. The amount of heat gained or lost during a phase change depends on which phase change is taking place. Although the heat content of the material changes during a phase change, the temperature does not. Since the temperature does not change, the kinetic energy of the particles that make up the material does not change either.

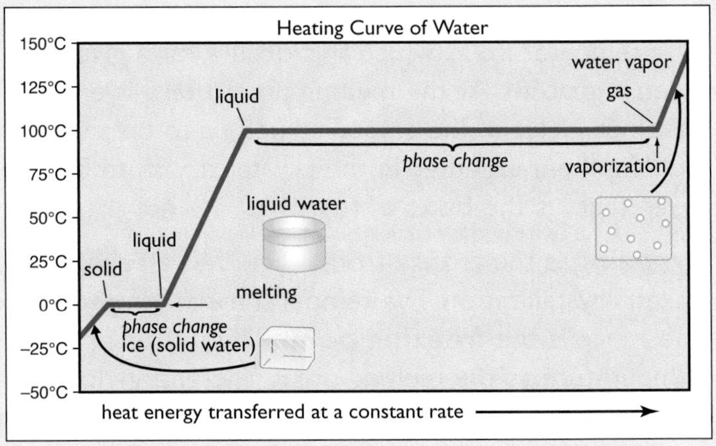
Heating Curve of Water
150°C
125°C
100°C
75°C
50°C
25°C
0°C
–25°C
–50°C
water vapor
gas
liquid
phase change
vaporization
liquid water
liquid
solid
melting
phase change
ice (solid water)
heat energy transferred at a constant rate

If continuing to add (or remove) heat energy to (or from) the material does not change its temperature, what is it doing? The particles of a solid material are held together tightly, liquids less so, and for gases, the bonding energies are negligible. The energy that is absorbed by a material during an endothermic phase change like melting is used to overcome these bonding energies between the particles. The energy that is released during an exothermic phase change like freezing is due to the formation of interactions between the particles. During melting, adding heat energy is breaking the bonds between adjoining water molecules and the solid ice is becoming liquid water.

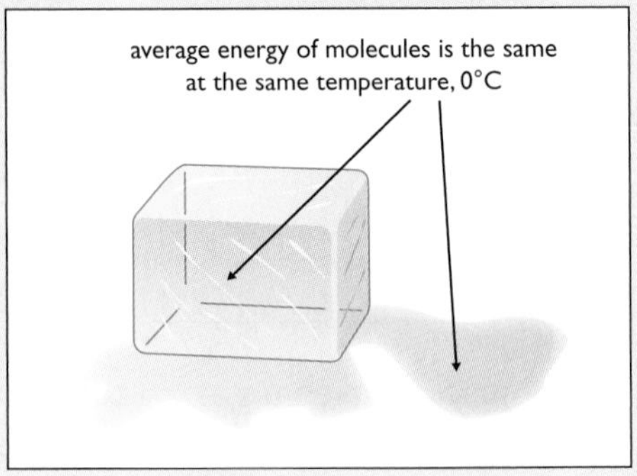
average energy of molecules is the same
at the same temperature, 0°C

Checking Up

1. Compare the following pairs of processes. How are they alike? How are they different?
   a) melting/freezing
   b) vaporization/condensation
   c) sublimation/deposition
2. What happens to the temperature of a material during a phase change?
3. What does the heat energy do during a phase change?

What Do You Think Now?

At the beginning of the activity you were asked:

- **What happens to the temperature of water when it freezes?**

Now that you have completed this activity, how would you answer this question?

Chem Essential Questions

What does it mean?

Chemistry explains a macroscopic phenomenon (what you observe) with a description of what happens at the nanoscopic level (atoms and molecules) using symbolic structures as a way to communicate. Complete the chart below in your *Active Chemistry* log.

MACRO	NANO	SYMBOLIC
What did you observe when hot water was mixed with ice water?	*When ice melts, the solid H_2O becomes liquid H_2O. Explain the relationship between the addition of heat to the solid ice and the change in the way the molecules move relative to one another.*	*You can represent the melting of ice, the heating of the water, and the creation of vapor with a graph to better illustrate what is happening. Draw a temperature vs. time graph for these phase changes of H_2O.*

How do you know?

How do you know that the amount of heat required to melt a quantity of ice is 80 calories per gram of ice? Describe the experiment that can determine this heat of fusion.

Why do you believe?

Foods are frozen and then defrosted. Estimate the time to defrost a specific food from your freezer. List one food that can turn from a solid to a liquid when defrosting and one food that remains a solid after defrosting.

Why should you care?

Adding ice to a warm drink can be a part of your cooking show. How would you describe this in an entertaining way for a 10-second part of your cooking-show segment?

Reflecting on the Activity and the Challenge

You have now learned that heat energy is gained or lost as a solid, liquid, or gas changes temperature. You have also learned that during a phase change, energy is gained or lost, but the temperature remains the same. Freezing foods is an important process that is used in food preparation. It is primarily used to preserve foods but it also can be used to make special desserts and salads. Including descriptions of phase changes in your cooking segment will be informative for your audience.

Chem to Go

1. If you put water in the freezer to make ice, would you set your freezer thermostat at zero Celsius or at a temperature below zero Celsius? Explain why.
2. Use the information on the Heating and Cooling Curve to answer the following questions:

Heating and Cooling Curve of Water

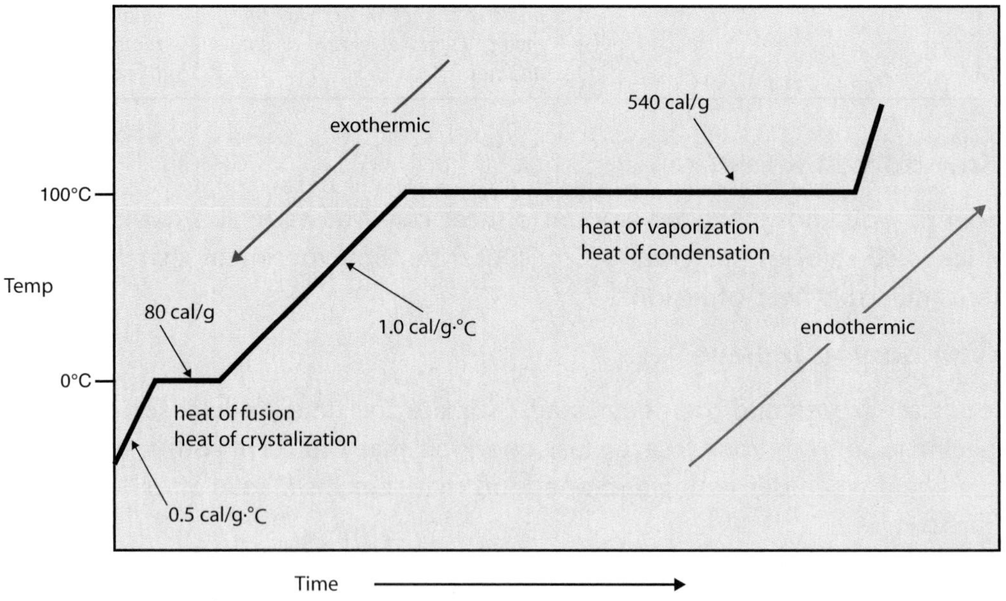
exothermic
540 cal/g
100°C
heat of vaporization
heat of condensation
Temp
80 cal/g
1.0 cal/g·°C
endothermic
0°C
heat of fusion
heat of crystalization
0.5 cal/g·°C
Time

Compare the amount of heat needed to:

a) melt 100 g of ice or freeze 100 g of water if both are at 0°C.

b) change the temperature of 50 g of ice and 50 g of water by 20°C.

3. Compare the amount of heat in:

   a) water at 100°C or water vapor (steam) at 100°C.

   b) 100 g of ice and 100 g of water at 0°C.

4. Determine the amount of heat needed to melt 50 g of ice at 0°C.

5. Determine the amount of heat needed to vaporize 500 g of water at 100°C.

6. Determine the amount of heat needed to raise the temperature of 350 g of water from 20°C to 100°C.

7. How much heat must be removed from 600 g of water at 80°C to bring it down to 0°C?

8. This question will require several steps. Determine the total amount of heat needed to take 200 g of ice at –25°C to water vapor at 100°C.

9. ***Preparing for the Chapter Challenge***

   Prepare a list of three instances where there are melting/freezing phase changes occurring in everyday cooking. Describe the processes as either endothermic or exothermic.

Activity 6 How Do You Choose Cookware?

What Do You See?
METAL SAUNA
METAL SAUNA

GOALS

In this activity you will:

- Explore the concept of specific heat capacity.
- Experimentally determine the specific heat capacity of various substances.
- Distinguish between materials used in cookware.

What Do You Think?

You want to fry some eggs. There are many choices for cookware. Pots and pans can cost anywhere from a few dollars to hundreds of dollars. Some frying pans are steel with a copper bottom, some are steel with a steel bottom, and some are iron.

- **Which cookware would you choose to fry an egg and why?**

Record your ideas about this question in your *Active Chemistry* log. Be prepared to discuss your responses with your group and the class.

Investigate

In this activity, you will investigate and measure the heating ability of different materials, and decide which ones are suitable for cookware.

For each material to be tested, the general procedure involves taking a hot object and placing it in cold water. You then measure the final temperature of the object and water. Recognizing that the heat energy gained by the water is equal to the heat energy lost by the object, you can calculate the specific heat of the object. You want to investigate whether all materials will bring the water to the same final temperature.

1. Before proceeding, make a list of what measurements you will have to record in the experiment.
2. Your teacher will have a large container of boiling water with the different metal samples submerged and sitting on a screen support.
   a) Record the temperature of the boiling water. This will be the starting temperature of the substance.
3. Carefully measure 200 mL of water and pour it into a double foam cup.
   a) Record the beginning temperature of the water in the cup.
4. Using crucible tongs, quickly lift a metal sample out of the boiling water and transfer it to the double foam cup. Try not to transfer any of the hot water. Gently agitate the cup to distribute heat.
   a) Record the highest temperature that the water reaches.
5. Remove the metal sample from the foam cup and after drying it off, determine the mass of the sample.
   a) Record the mass of the metal sample in your *Active Chemistry* log.
6. Now that you know a procedure, you can create an investigation for the other samples. You may want to use a data chart similar to the one shown below to keep track of all the measurements.
7. The Law of Conservation of Energy states that the energy gained by the cold water must be equal to the energy lost by the hot sample. You know how to calculate the energy change by using the equation:

$$Q = mc\Delta T$$

   You can calculate this Q gain for cold water because you know the mass of the cold water, the specific heat of water (1 cal/g·°C), and the change in temperature. You also know the mass of the sample and the change in temperature of the sample. The unknown is the specific heat c of the sample. Knowing all other values, you can solve for this unknown.
   a) If you are confident with your algebra skills, calculate and record the specific heat of each sample. Skip *Step 8*.

Safety goggles and a lab apron must be worn *at all times* in a chemistry lab.

Use extreme caution handling the hot metal.

Wash hands and arms thoroughly before leaving the lab area.

Substance	Mass (g)	Start temp. of substance (°C)	Start temp. of cold water (°C)	End temp. of substance and water (°C)

Temp. change of water (°C)	Heat absorbed by water (lost by substance) (cal)	Substance tested	Mass of substance (g)	Temperature change of substance (°C)	Specific heat capacity of substance (cal/g·°C)

8. If you need more assistance, continue with the steps shown below.

   a) Make a table similar to the one shown above to record your calculations.

   b) Determine the temperature change of the water in the polystyrene cup and record it in the chart.

   c) Use the heat equation to determine the amount of heat the water absorbed from the hot object used.

   heat = (mass of water) (specific heat of water) (temperature change of water)

   or

   $$Q = mc\Delta T$$

   Specific heat of water is 1 cal/g·°C.

   d) Since the heat energy from the hot metal was gained by the water, the quantity of heat energy lost is identical to the amount gained.

Safety goggles and a lab apron must be worn *at all times* in a chemistry lab.

   Knowing the quantity of heat the material lost, the mass of the material, and the temperature change it underwent, the specific heat of the material can be calculated:

   $$c = \frac{Q}{m\Delta T}$$

   The temperature change of the material is from the boiling water temperature to the high temperature of the cold water after the hot substance has been transferred to it.

   The units for your specific heat will be in cal/g·°C or cal $g^{-1}\cdot°C^{-1}$

9. Answer the following questions in your *Active Chemistry* log.

   a) Which substance had the lowest specific heat capacity? Which had the highest?

   b) Explain why you would prefer a substance with a higher or lower specific heat capacity for cookware.

Chem Talk

SPECIFIC HEAT CAPACITY AND COOKWARE

When you reheat pizza that has been wrapped in aluminum foil and remove the food from the oven, the aluminum foil cools quickly while the pizza stays hot. It is the low heat capacity of aluminum that allows it to cool rapidly. Once you have the pizza out of the foil and are holding the slice by the crust, you might think it is safe to go ahead and bite into it. But when you do—yow! It's hot! How can the tomato sauce be so much hotter than the crust if they were in the same oven together? The sauce has a lot of water in it and water has a higher heat capacity than the materials in the crust. So the sauce continued to hold the heat energy while the crust was releasing the heat energy more rapidly.

The **specific heat capacity** (or specific heat) of a material is a measure of the amount of heat energy that is required to change the temperature of a given amount of substance by 1°C. In this activity, you heated different materials to a known temperature and then used the materials to heat up some water. This process allowed you to determine the specific heat of the material using the heat equation:

$$Q = mc\Delta T$$

When a cook selects a pot to use, the most important consideration (besides the size of the pot) would be the material that the pot is made of. Some of the properties that might be considered are durability, cost, how well it holds heat (heat capacity), how evenly it is heated (thermal conductivity), and rust resistance. In this activity, you looked at the specific heat capacity of various materials.

Silver has a low specific heat but would make a rather expensive and non-durable pot or pan. Copper also has a low specific heat and conducts heat well, so some pots have a copper base to allow a uniform temperature when heating. This is a desirable property as most stoves either use a circular flame (like gas ranges) or a spiraling heating element (like electric ranges), which deliver the heat in a non-uniform manner. →

Chem Words

specific heat capacity: the amount of heat necessary to raise the temperature of one gram of a substance by one degree Celsius.

Chem Words

alloy: a mixture of two or more metals.

Aluminum is known for its heat conduction properties. Also, the process by which it is made makes the aluminum up to 30% harder than stainless steel. This process results in an extremely smooth gray surface, which although it is not non-stick, is very easy to clean. On the other hand, the U.S. Consumer Product Safety Commission (CPSC) warns that placing aluminum cookware (or stainless cookware with an aluminum core) on high heat may cause it to melt. When aluminum cookware that is empty (or nearly empty) is placed on high heat, it can "boil dry." If a consumer picks up aluminum cookware that has "boiled dry," the molten aluminum can drip onto the consumer's arms, hands, legs, or feet causing severe burns.

The oldest known metal for cooking is iron, which is never used in its pure form but mixed with other compounds to yield the alloys cast iron and stainless steel. An **alloy** is simply a mixture of two or more metals.

Cast iron has a carbon content of greater than 2%. It takes a long time to heat up, but then it will stay hot for a long time. Foods that require high heat are best cooked in cast iron. Because iron is a reactive metal, one disadvantage of its use is that acidic foods should not be cooked in an iron pot for long periods of time. Aluminum would have this problem as well.

Stainless steel is a strong alloy of iron that contains carbon and also chromium or sometimes nickel. The advantages of stainless steel are that it is rust resistant, and it is quick to heat up. It can withstand high temperatures, but does not distribute heat well. In the oven, food cooks more quickly in steel pans.

Checking Up

1. Why does aluminum foil cool down faster than a piece of pizza?
2. Suppose you take a piece of pizza out of the oven. Will the crust and the sauce on top stay at the same temperature?
3. Why is copper used in cookware?

What Do You Think Now?

At the beginning of the activity you were asked:

- **Which cookware would you choose to fry an egg and why?**

Would you change your original choice of frying pan material for cooking an egg? If so, on what basis would you make the change?

Chem Essential Questions

What does it mean?

Chemistry explains a macroscopic phenomenon (what you observe) with a description of what happens at the nanoscopic level (atoms and molecules) using symbolic structures as a way to communicate. Complete the chart below in your *Active Chemistry* log.

MACRO	NANO	SYMBOLIC
In the activity, a hot object was placed in cool water. Describe the temperature changes of the object and the water.	*When objects change temperature, the average kinetic energy of their molecules change. Describe how collisions of fast-moving molecules of one substance and slow-moving molecules of another substance can lead to a common final temperature.*	*What equations can be used to calculate specific heat?*

How do you know?

How were you able to calculate the specific heat of an object? How was conservation of energy used in your strategy?

Why do you believe?

Any kitchen will have various utensils that are made of different materials for different uses. Items with a low heat capacity include certain metal pots and pans, or glass baking dishes. Why might a stainless steel pan have a copper bottom?

Why should you care?

Providing your audience with the chemistry behind a chef's choice of cookware will certainly add to the cooking show. You may also choose to discuss why some foods cool quickly while others remain hot for some time. How could this be creatively described in your show?

Reflecting on the Activity and the Challenge

Knowing how well a material conducts heat is the first step in making a cookware choice. Heat conductivity is most important for pots and skillets used on the stovetop, where uniform heating helps to prevent hot spots that burn food before it's completely cooked. The low specific heat capacity of metals means that it does not take much heat to increase the temperature of the metal. Consider how information such as this might be used in your cooking-show segment. For instance, you could describe why a chef might choose a copper-coated steel pan over an iron skillet for frying eggs. Your cooking show may also point out how some materials from the oven quickly cool to room temperature while others stay hot. A good restaurant must ensure that all foods are the right temperature when the food is served. This may be something that you want to highlight in your cooking show.

Chem to Go

1. If you had pans (of identical mass) made of each of the following metals—Al, Cu, and Fe—which would be the hottest after sitting on a burner for 1 min? Explain your answer.

Material	Specific heat (J/g·°C)
copper	0.390
iron	0.470
aluminum	0.900
glass	0.840
stainless steel	0.500
water	4.18

2. a) If you had a 1000.0 g copper pot, how many calories of heat energy would it take to raise its temperature by 60.0°C?

   b) How many calories of heat energy would it take to raise an iron pot with the same mass by 60.0°C?

3. Why do confectioners use marble slabs to prepare candies and fudge?

4. When you pour hot water into a china cup, why should you have a spoon in the cup?

5. If you had water in either of the pots in *Question 2*, would the same amount of heat need to be supplied in order to bring about the same temperature change?

6. The heat capacity of a substance depends on:

   a) temperature only

   b) mass only

   c) temperature and mass

   d) mass and specific heat

7. Consider the graph of temperature (°C) vs. time (minutes) showing the cooling curves of metals A and B. If 100 g of metal A loses 840 J of heat in the first 6 min, the specific heat capacity of metal A is about ______ J/g·°C.

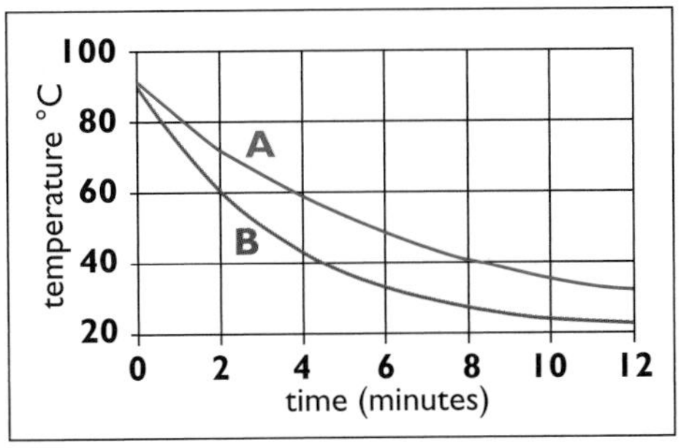
100
80
60
40
20
temperature °C
A
B
0
2
4
6
8
10
12
time (minutes)

   a) 0.21

   b) 0.84

   c) 2.1

   d) 8.4

8. If the temperature of a certain mass of an aluminum alloy (which has a specific heat capacity of 0.8 J/g·°C) is lowered by 10°C and the heat lost is 80 J, then the mass of the aluminum alloy is:

   a) 8 g

   b) 80 g

   c) 100 g

   d) 10 g

9. What properties would you want to see in your pots and pans that would make them good for cooking. Include a list of different materials that are used for cookware and rank the usefulness or suitability of these based on the properties that you listed.

10. ***Preparing for the Chapter Challenge***

    You have investigated the specific heat capacity of various materials and *Activity 1* led you to an understanding of conduction. You should now have some idea why certain materials are selected for use in cookware (and other kitchen utensils) due to their ability to hold different quantities of heat. Prepare a listing of kitchen utensils that have (a) high specific heat capacities; and (b) low specific heat capacities. Include the functions of the pots and pans in the list. Discuss with your group how this might be incorporated into your cooking segment.

Activity 7 How Do Proteins in Foods React?

What Do You See?

TODAY'S
SPECIAL
EGGS
SUNNY
SIDE UP
RESTAURANT

GOALS

In this activity you will:

- Gain an understanding of proteins and what happens to them upon denaturation.
- Observe the effect of temperature on egg proteins.
- Observe the effect of changing pH on egg proteins.

What Do You Think?

In a movie called *Cool Hand Luke*, the main character eats 50 hard-boiled eggs in one hour as a bet. In the movie *Rocky*, the main character eats raw eggs for breakfast.

- **How does an egg change when cooked?**

Record your ideas about this question in your *Active Chemistry* log. Be prepared to discuss your responses with your group and the class.

Investigate

1. Your body is mainly composed of the elements: C, H, N, and O. The sources for these elements are carbohydrates, proteins, and fats with some trace elements being supplied by vitamins and minerals in the foods you eat. If you examine the food label on the next page, you'll notice important dietary information contains the amount of these molecules as well as Na, Ca, and vitamins. But what happens to these major bio-molecules (proteins, fats, and carbohydrates) as they are cooked?

Hard-Cooked Egg
Serving Size 1 egg (50 g)

Amount Per Serving	
Calories 77	Calories from Fat 45
	% Daily Value*
Total Fat 5g	**8%**
saturated fat 2 g	**10%**
Cholesterol 213 mg	**71%**
Sodium 62 mg	**3%**
Total Carbohydrate 1 g	**0%**
Protein 6 g	12%
Vitamin A	6%
Calcium	3%
Iron	3%
Thiamin	2%
Riboflavin	15%

Not a significant source of vitamin C and niacin. Values are not available for fiber and sugars.

*Percent Daily Values are based on a 2,000 calorie diet

a) From the food label, record the total mass of the egg and the calories that are in one egg.

b) Calculate the percentage of total fat in the egg. (This is not the same as the % Daily Value given on the label.)

c) Calculate the percentage of the egg that is protein.

d) Calculate the percentage of carbohydrate in the egg.

e) The protein, fat, and carbohydrates together do not total 100% of the egg's mass. What material do you think makes up most of the mass of the egg?

2. You will now investigate what happens when you cook eggs.

   a) List at least two ways to cook eggs.

3. You will either cook eggs in class or be given a cooked egg and a raw egg that your teacher has supplied. You cannot eat either of these eggs. (Eating in a chemistry room can be extremely dangerous.)

   a) Record at least five differences between a cooked egg and a raw egg.

4. Some people believe that a cooked egg hardens because water was driven off after heating.

   a) Design an experiment to test this hypothesis.

   After teacher approval, conduct your experiment and determine if the "water is driven off" hypothesis is backed up by data.

5. Some people believe that a cooked egg hardens because of a chemical change. The heat changes something on the molecular level. Soaking an egg in hydrochloric acid can also produce a chemical change. Your teacher will provide you with an egg that has been soaked in hydrochloric acid (HCl) for two hours.

   a) Record at least five differences between the acid-soaked egg and a raw egg.

   b) How does the cooked egg differ from the acid-soaked egg?

Safety goggles and a lab apron must be worn *at all times* in a chemistry lab.

Never eat anything in a chemistry lab.

Wash hands and arms thoroughly before leaving the lab area.

Chem Talk

Chem Words

protein: an organic substance made of long chains of amino acids.

molecular formula: a description of the number and types of atoms in a molecule, but not how they are connected.

structural formula: a description of the way the atoms in a molecule are connected.

amino acid: an organic molecule that has both the carboxylic acid and amine functional groups.

functional group: an atom or group of atoms that gives a molecule its characteristic properties.

PROTEINS

Amino Acids Form Proteins

Proteins play extremely important roles in almost every biological process. Their structures are related to their functions and they display a wide range of functions. **Proteins** are made of long chains of amino acids.

Consider the amino acid glycine. It is the simplest amino acid and has the molecular formula $C_2H_5NO_2$. The **molecular formula** gives you a description of the number and types of atoms in this molecule, but does not tell you how they are connected. The **structural formula** of glycine shows the connectivity of the atoms and is shown below.

You can see that there are two hydrogen atoms attached to the nitrogen, two hydrogen atoms attached to the middle carbon, and another carbon that has two oxygen atoms attached to it. One of these oxygen atoms has a double bond to the carbon, and one of them has a hydrogen atom attached.

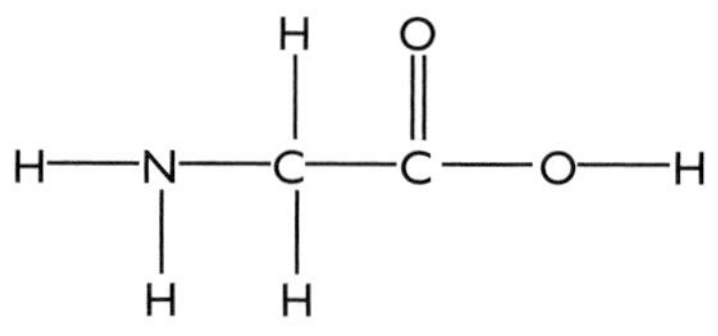

glycine

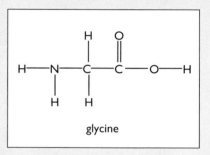

How do these features make glycine an amino acid? A generic structural formula for an amino acid is shown below. An **amino acid** is an organic molecule (carbon and hydrogen) that has both the carboxylic acid and amine functional groups. An organic **functional group** is an atom or group of atoms that gives a molecule its characteristic properties.

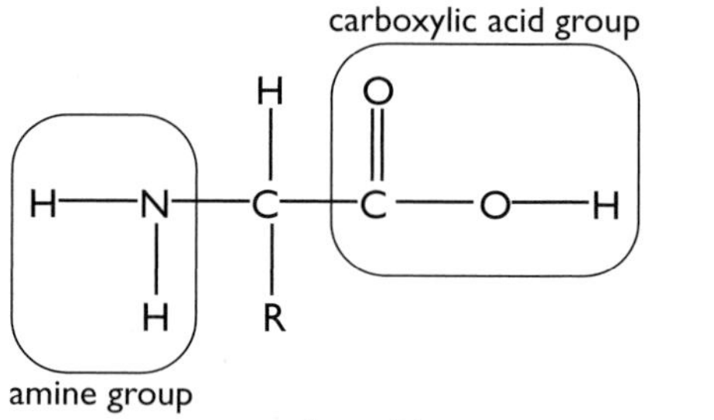
carboxylic acid group
amine group

amino acid

In glycine the "R" is a hydrogen.

What makes one amino acid different from another are their different "R" groups. The "R" designation is a shorthand way to represent various groups of atoms. For the three amino acids shown on the next page (phenylalanine, serine, and cysteine), the "R" groups are circled. There are 20 naturally occurring amino acids with different "R" groups that combine to form proteins.

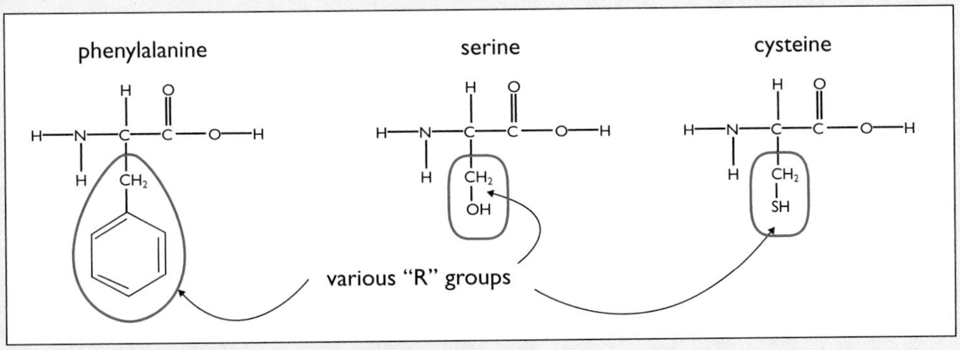
phenylalanine
serine
cysteine
various "R" groups

Structure of Proteins and Function

The different amino acids can combine to form proteins. When they combine they form long chains of amino acids. There are also other bonds that can make the proteins twist and turn.

As you might suspect, the structure of the protein (that is, its shape) determines the function of the protein.

Environmental changes (like temperature or placing the egg in acid) may affect the shape of the protein by affecting the bonding that is responsible for the protein's shape. Any change in the environment will force the protein to adopt a new structure. **Denaturation** is the name of the process when a change in a protein's shape occurs as it unravels and expands outward, still keeping its primary structure. The most common causes of protein denaturation in cooking are heating, adding salt, or adding acid (pickling). When a protein gains heat

The Three Levels of Protein Structure

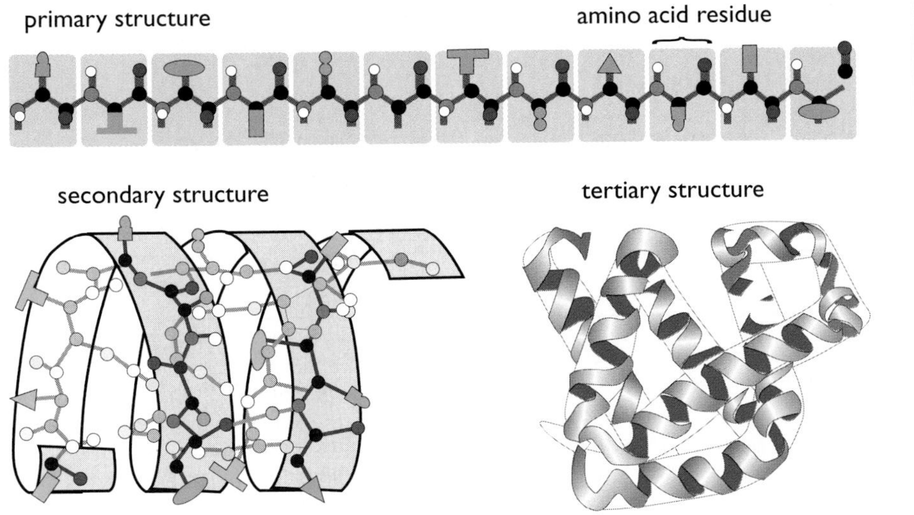
primary structure
amino acid residue
secondary structure
tertiary structure

Chem Words

denaturation: the name of the process during which a change in a protein's shape occurs as it unravels and expands outward, still keeping its primary structure, but changing its function.

Checking Up

1. What are proteins made up of?
2. How are a molecular formula and a structural formula similar? How are they different?
3. What is an amino acid?
4. Define a functional group of a molecule.
5. What determines the function of a protein?
6. Describe the process of denaturation.
7. Give two ways in which proteins are denatured in cooking.

energy, the bonds contributing to its secondary and tertiary structure are broken. However, the sequence of the amino acids in the primary structure is unchanged. Those bonds are stronger and not broken. Denaturation is not a change in composition, only a change in structure. But since structure determines function, denatured proteins behave quite differently from their original or un-denatured form.

Proteins are denatured at temperatures of 40°C. At higher temperatures, they may begin to break up or bond with each other and form clumps. Your clear egg white became firm and opaque when the temperature was raised and more denaturation took place. Changing the pH also disrupts the bonds that give proteins their shapes.

When meat is cooked and the proteins in it are denatured, the proteins are extended and more vulnerable to attack by enzymes that aid in the digestion of your dinner.

What Do You Think Now?

At the beginning of the activity you were asked:

- **How does an egg change when cooked?**

Look back at your answer at the beginning of the activity. How would you change your original answer?

Chem Essential Questions

What does it mean?

Chemistry explains a macroscopic phenomenon (what you observe) with a description of what happens at the nanoscopic level (atoms and molecules) using symbolic structures as a way to communicate. Complete the chart below in your *Active Chemistry* log.

MACRO	NANO	SYMBOLIC
What changes do you see when you cook an egg?	*Describe the denaturation of an egg white at the molecular level. Remember that structure determines function.*	*You can use drawings of protein secondary structures as one way to represent this physical change. What symbolic structure do you use to describe amino acids?*

How do you know?

The change in an egg during cooking is not due to a loss of water, but rather it is due to a chemical change. What evidence do you have for this?

Why do you believe?

Personal experiences tell you that raw foods are different from cooked foods in appearance, texture, and taste. Give examples of how other proteins such as meat change (denature) with cooking.

Why should you care?

Explaining the nanoscopic changes that occur during cooking foods containing proteins would be an exciting addition to your cooking show.

Reflecting on the Activity and the Challenge

In this activity, you designed a way of examining what happens to egg proteins when they are cooked. Since your challenge is to create a segment of a cooking show and provide a detailed explanation of the chemistry that is occurring, consider how you might use the knowledge gained from this activity in your segment. Think about all of the information you would need to explain protein denaturation to your viewers. Consider how you would explain at the molecular level what happens when an egg cooks or when meat is cooked.

Chem to Go

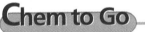

1. What are some indicators that protein denaturation is occurring during cooking?
2. Although boiling an egg is often seen as a measure of minimal competence for a cook, there are actually many things to consider in producing a good hard-boiled egg. Based on your tests and the tests of your classmates, what advice could you give a cook about temperature and cooking conditions for boiling an egg? Provide a recipe for the best way to boil the perfect egg.
3. In one recipe for great, Southern pecan pie, the directions state: *Combine butter, sugar, and corn syrup; cook over low heat, stirring constantly, until the sugar is dissolved. Cool. Add eggs, vanilla, and salt; mix well...*
   a) Why is the cook directed to allow the butter-sugar solution to cool before adding the beaten eggs?
   b) What might be the results if eggs are added before the solution cools?
4. Is protein denaturation a chemical or a physical change? Explain your reasoning.

5. *Preparing for the Chapter Challenge*

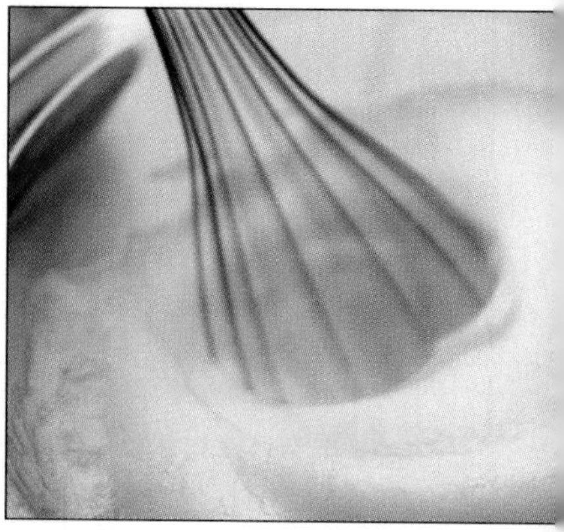

The main bio-molecules found in foods and required by the body are carbohydrates, fats, and proteins. In this activity, you examined the behavior of proteins in eggs when cooked. Design and create a model that can be used to explain what happens to proteins as they are cooked. You might consider using a pipe-cleaner and bead model, or a cut-out "puzzle" model. Perhaps, you can use your computer skills and create a video or claymation that depicts protein denaturation. Use your imagination and be creative but clear in illustrating the process of cooking proteins. Work with your group to determine how you will model protein cooking and then create your model complete with an explanation of what is happening.

Inquiring Further

1. Egg white's foaming ability

Egg whites make excellent foams, however foams can be tricky to produce. Research what foams are and explain how egg whites can form foams. Humidity, dirty or greasy bowls, pH, and the age of the egg can affect egg white's foaming ability. Design a test to determine how one of these factors influences an egg white's foaming ability.

2. Maillard reaction

Most of meat's flavor develops when it is cooked. The amount of fat in meat influences its flavor, as does a process called the Maillard reaction. The Maillard reaction occurs when the denatured proteins on the surface of the meat recombine with the sugars present. The combination creates the "meaty" flavor and changes the color. Find out more information about the Maillard reaction. Explain how the same reaction could account for providing a meaty flavor in meats, browning meat, caramelizing, and even providing the flavor of toast.

3. Green egg yolks

Sometimes when boiling eggs, a greenish-gray discoloration appears on the surface of the yolk of an egg. This discoloration has been identified as iron sulfide. As the egg is heated, some of the sulfur atoms found in the egg white (albumen) are liberated and react with hydrogen ions in the albumen to form hydrogen sulfide (H_2S). In minute quantities, this gas is responsible for the characteristic and pleasant odor of cooked eggs and meat, but in larger quantities it is the odor associated with rotten eggs. As the gas diffuses, some of it reaches the yolk, where it encounters iron contained in the yolk. The hydrogen sulfide then reacts with the iron to form iron sulfide, which is a greenish-gray color. Design and conduct a test to determine the best way to reduce the formation of FeS in a hard-boiled egg. Write a recipe for making the best hard-boiled eggs and include tips for cooks so that they can avoid having green yolks.

Activity 8 How Does the Home Canning Process Work?

What Do You See?

SUGAR
JAM
JAM

GOALS

In this activity you will:

- Compare and explain what happens to two aluminum soda cans after being heated and then plunged into an ice bath.
- "Can" a small balloon in a glass canning jar using a boiling bath.
- Determine the approximate pressure inside a canning jar, using Boyle's Law.

What Do You Think?

In most areas, your great-great-great grandparents could not get fresh tomatoes or peaches in February. The best they could do was to have canned tomatoes and peaches. When the growing season was over they had to preserve their produce.

- **What is canning?**
- **How does it preserve foods?**

Record your ideas about these questions in your *Active Chemistry* log. Be prepared to discuss your responses with your group and the class.

Investigate

Part A: Demonstration Using Heated Soda Cans

1. Your teacher will perform a demonstration that involves heating two soda cans on a hot plate. Your teacher will not speak during the demonstration. You will have to observe carefully and quietly.

   a) Write your observations in your *Active Chemistry* log.

   b) Propose an explanation for what occurred.

Safety goggles and a lab apron must be worn *at all times* in a chemistry lab.

Use extreme caution around boiling water. It can cause very serious burns.

Wash hands and arms thoroughly before leaving the lab area.

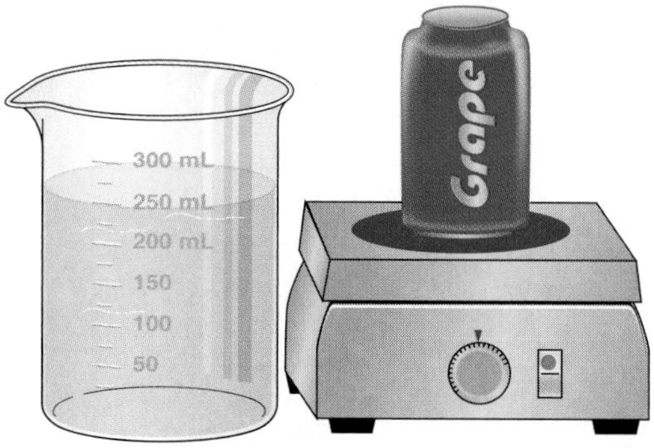
300 mL
250 mL
200 mL
150
100
50
Grape

200 mL
150
100
50

Part B: "Canning" Balloons

1. Prepare a large container of boiling water. The water must be deep enough so that a canning jar resting on the bottom will be covered with the boiling water.
2. Inflate two small spherical balloons to 1/3 the volume of the canning jar and tie a knot in each. Check that the balloons have been blown up to the correct size by placing one of them into the canning jar. It should not occupy more than about a third of the volume of the jar. Check to see that the two balloons are not leaking air.
   a) Measure and record the approximate diameter of each balloon.
   b) Calculate the approximate volume of each balloon. Volume of a sphere $= 4/3\ \pi r^3$
   c) Record the barometric pressure in the room in torr (1 torr = 1 mm of Hg). If you are at sea level, the barometric pressure is probably close to 760 torr.
3. Place one of the balloons into the canning jar. Add about 25 mL of water to the jar. Because it is not loaded with food, the jar will float. A simple way to overcome this is to add weights to the jar. This will ensure that it stays submerged. Place the lid and the sealing ring on the jar. Tighten down the ring until it is only "finger-tight."
4. Submerge the jar in the container of boiling water. *Be careful* of the hot water and steam coming out of the container. (Use tongs!)
5. Leave the jar in the boiling water for about ten minutes.
6. Carefully remove the jar with the tongs or a hot pad and place the jar on the table. *Let it cool.*
   a) What do you observe about the balloon?
   b) Compare it to the other balloon. Did it behave the way you thought it would?
   c) Write in your *Active Chemistry* log what you think accounts for the behavior of the balloon.

Part C: Finding the Pressure in the Jar after Canning

1. If the sealing lid worked right in *Part B*, your canning jar should be sealed tight now. You can see this by looking for an indentation in the lid where the atmospheric pressure pushed it in.

   a) How can you find out what pressure is inside the jar?

   b) Do you think the pressure inside is less than, greater than, or equal to what it was when you put the balloon in the jar? Explain your reasoning in your *Active Chemistry* log.

2. Approximate the new volume of the balloon in the jar. One simple way to do this is by taking another balloon and inflating it to be the same approximate size as the balloon in the jar.

   a) Measure and record the approximate diameter of this second balloon.

   b) Calculate the approximate volume of the balloon the same way as you did in *Step 2* of *Part B*.

3. You now have collected the information about the balloon to fill in the boxes in the following table, except the pressure in jar after canning.

   a) Fill in the boxes that you can in your *Active Chemistry* log.

   Boyle's Law gives a quantitative relationship between pressure and volume if the temperature remains constant.

   $$PV_{\text{(before canning)}} = PV_{\text{(after canning)}}$$

   Use Boyle's Law to calculate the pressure inside the jar after canning when the jar has cooled to room temperature.

4. Predict what will happen if you remove the canning lid from the jar.

   a) Record your prediction.

   b) Write an explanation of your prediction.

5. Remove the lid and observe carefully what does happen.

   a) Record what happens.

   b) What do you think this tells you about the pressure inside the jar before the lid was removed?

Safety goggles and a lab apron must be worn *at all times* in a chemistry lab.

	Before canning	After canning
Volume of balloon		
Pressure in jar		

Chem Talk

CANNING FOOD AND BOYLE'S LAW

Canning and History

Napoleon offered a prize for a means of preserving food for his armies. The winner was Nicolas Appert, who in 1810 showed that foods could be preserved by placing them in glass containers, heating them, and then sealing the containers. This procedure is the basis of the "home-canning industry" today. Just like the commercial food-processing factory, home canning can create an environment that locks the food and the flavor in and keeps the microorganisms that cause spoilage out.

The method employed by many home canners is the boiling-water bath method, in which jars filled with various kinds of food are processed in a kettle of boiling water. There is another method used, requiring a pressure cooker, to can certain foods with low acid content. Because of their low acidity these foods need to be heated to a temperature even higher than 100°C to ensure that all the bacteria are killed.

While in the boiling-water bath, gases in the food and in the jar expand and escape from the jar. When the jar is removed from the boiling-water bath, the remaining gases cool and contract. The pressure that they are able to exert is now lower. Because the outside atmospheric pressure is greater, it pushes the lid down against the mouth of the jar and creates an airtight, and germ-proof seal. You also observed this in the teacher demonstration with the soda can. Quickly cooling condensed the gas in the can and lowered the pressure. The greater outside pressure then collapsed the can.

Understanding Boyle's Law

Robert Boyle

How much lower is the pressure inside the jar? To find out you can use a relationship discovered almost 350 years ago by Robert Boyle. Today it is known as Boyle's Law. He was interested in how the pressure of a gas and the volume of the gas were related if the temperature did not change.

In the activity, when you inflated the balloon, you were blowing oxygen, nitrogen, and carbon dioxide into it. As these molecules move around, they collide with the inside surface of the balloon. Collisions of air molecules inside

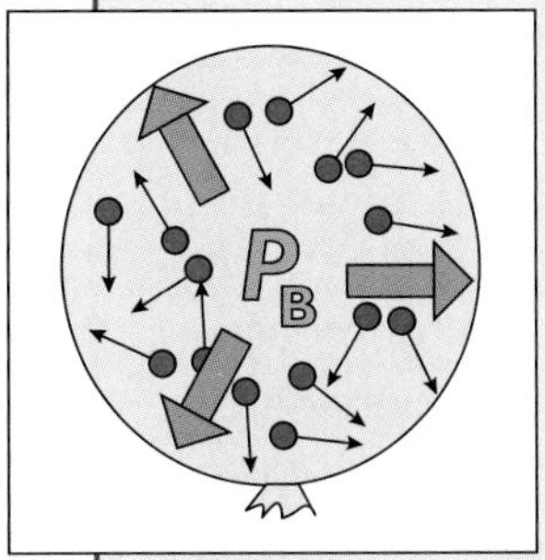
PB

the balloon exert pressure (P_B) on the interior walls of the balloon.

When you tied off the balloon, the volume of the balloon did not change. There was no change even though all those molecules are banging around inside the balloon. The reason is that the air molecules in the room are bombarding the outside of the balloon. Collisions of air molecules outside of the balloon exert pressure (P_A) on the exterior walls of the balloon.

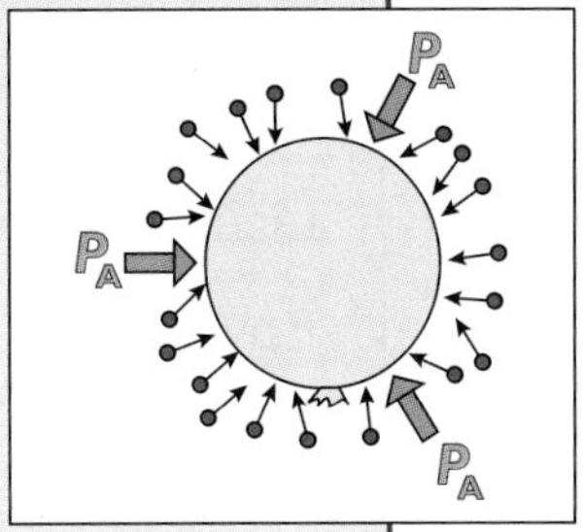
PA
PA
PA

The volume of the balloon does not change because the pressure exerted by the molecules inside the balloon is just equal to the atmospheric pressure being exerted on the outside of the balloon ($P_A = P_B$). There is a "standoff."

How then can the volume of a balloon change? If you suddenly *reduce* the number of collisions of molecules on the outside of the balloon (lowering the external pressure), the pressure on the inside is greater so the balloon volume expands ($P_A < P_B$). Once the volume has increased, the gas molecules have farther to travel before they can hit the inside surface of the balloon. They will impact the container walls less often per unit time. This means the **gas pressure** inside the balloon will decrease because there are fewer molecule impacts per unit time. In other words, the pressure will go down. When it once again equals the pressure on the outside of the balloon, the volume quits expanding.

What if you *increased* the number of collisions on the outside of the balloon ($P_A > P_B$)? When the pressure outside is greater than the pressure inside the balloon, the volume of the balloon decreases. This is because the molecules inside the balloon now have a shorter distance to go before colliding with the wall of the balloon. Consequently, they strike the wall more often per unit time and the internal pressure increases. The pressure will continue to increase until it once again equals the pressure on the outside of the balloon. Then a new "standoff" involving the pressures is created, and the volume stops decreasing.

Imagine inflating a balloon to a volume of 1.0 L. The pressure of the gas in the balloon is equal to the atmospheric pressure outside the balloon ($P_A = P_B$). What would happen to the volume if you took the balloon to the top of Mt. Everest? The air has a very low density up there, meaning that there are not very many molecules to bombard the outside

Chem Words

gas pressure: the number of molecules striking the surfaces of the container.

surface of the balloon so $P_A < P_B$. Under these conditions, the volume of the balloon would expand.

Now take the balloon to Death Valley in California. This is the place in the United States that is farthest below sea level. The air is much more denser down there ($P_A > P_B$). The volume of the balloon will decrease this time because there are more molecules bombarding the outside of the balloon.

Using Boyle's Law to Calculate Pressure

Boyle investigated gases experimentally *to determine how much* the volume changed when the pressure changed at a constant temperature. He found that, for any gas, if he multiplied the initial pressure (P_1) by the initial volume (V_1), that value would be equal to the product of the final pressure (P_2) times the final volume (V_2).

$$P_1 V_1 = P_2 V_2$$

Suppose you are standing next to a lake and the volume of your lungs is 4.0 L and the atmospheric pressure is 760 torr. Then you hold your breath and dive into the lake to a depth of 10 m where the pressure is about 1520 torr. What will be the new volume (V_2) of your lungs? (For this example, disregard the different temperatures of water at the two locations in the lake.)

$$(760 \text{ torr})\ (4.0 \text{ L}) = (1520 \text{ torr})\ (V_2)$$

$$V_2 = \frac{(760 \text{ torr})(4 \text{ L})}{1520 \text{ torr}}$$

Note that 1 atm = 760 torr = 760 mm Hg.

Solving this equation, the new volume turns out to be 2.0 L. In other words, as the pressure doubled, the volume was cut in half. This is called an **inverse proportion**. Mathematically, this means that as one quantity goes up the other one will go down proportionally. **Boyle's Law** gives us a good way to study pressure and volume and to quickly solve for an unknown pressure or volume if we know the other three quantities.

What pressure is required to compress 188.0 cm^3 of gas at constant temperature to a volume of 24.0 cm^3 if the initial pressure is 444 torr?

$$P_1 V_1 = P_2 V_2$$

$$(444 \text{ torr})\ (188.0 \text{ cm}^3) = (P_2)\ (24.0 \text{ cm}^3)$$

Solving this equation, the pressure turns out to be 3480 torr.

Chem Words

inverse proportion: mathematically, a proportion in which if one quantity goes up the other one will go down.

Boyle's Law: a law that states that if the amount and temperature of a gas are constant, then the product of the pressure and volume equals a constant.

Checking Up

1. Why must the water be heated to at least boiling when home-canning foods?
2. How did the pressure inside the canning jar become lower than the pressure outside the canning jar?
3. What is one acceptable unit for measuring the pressure exerted by a gas?
4. What does Boyle's Law describe?
5. Why is the air pressure on top of a high mountain less than the air pressure at sea level?

What Do You Think Now?

At the beginning of the activity you were asked:

- **What is canning?**
- **How does it preserve foods?**

Now that you have completed this activity, how would you explain to someone who had never done any home canning what is happening during the process?

Chem Essential Questions

What does it mean?

Chemistry explains a macroscopic phenomenon (what you observe) with a description of what happens at the nanoscopic level (atoms and molecules) using symbolic structures as a way to communicate. Complete the chart below in your *Active Chemistry* log.

MACRO	NANO	SYMBOLIC
Think back to the demonstration given in Part A of this activity. After cooling, the soda can was crushed by the pressure exerted by air molecules. Describe the event.	*Explain in words what occurred inside of the soda can from the perspective of the atoms and molecules.*	*A way of representing the relation between pressure and volume is through Boyle's Law. Describe this mathematically.*

How do you know?

What evidence do you have that increasing the pressure exerted on a gas decreases its volume?

Why do you believe?

There are kitchen appliances like the popcorn popper that make use of Boyle's Law. Would popcorn kernels popped in New York City (1.0 atm, 760 torr) be larger or smaller than identical kernels popped at higher altitude in Denver (0.83 atm, 630 torr)? Explain your answer.

Why should you care?

Explaining the use of a kitchen appliance that makes use of Boyle's Law will make your cooking show more interesting.

Reflecting on the Activity and the Challenge

In this activity, you saw the dramatic implosion (inward collapse) of a soda can due to the decrease in pressure inside the can. This demonstration provides an opportunity for a very interesting explanation of what happened in microscopic terms. When the molecules of the surrounding air bang against the can with a pressure greater than that of the molecules inside the can—wham! The can collapses.

The canning process is based on Boyle's Law, though many cooks might not know it by that name. Your show might include a process where a volume/pressure relationship is shown. You could use a pressure cooker to can some jam. If a description of what happened at the molecular level is explained in simple terms, and with creativity and humor, the audience will be fascinated.

Chem to Go

1. The pressure on the inside of an inflated balloon equals the pressure on the outside of the balloon.

   a) What is causing the pressure of the gas inside the balloon?

   b) What is causing the pressure on the outside of the balloon?

2. Suppose a balloon inflated at sea level is taken to the top of Mt. Everest.

   a) What happens to the pressure on the outside of the balloon?

   b) What happens to the pressure on the inside of the balloon?

3. When the soda can containing a small amount of water was heated, the can became full of steam. When this can of steam was cooled rapidly, the steam condensed.

   a) What happened to the volume of steam upon cooling?

   b) What happened to the pressure inside the can?

   c) How did the atmospheric pressure outside the can compare to the pressure inside the can when the steam condensed?

   d) As a result of this, what happened to the can?

4. Initially, the balloon in the canning jar expanded because it was being heated. When the jar was taken out of the hot water and cooled, the temperature of the balloon went back to room temperature. Did the volume of the balloon go back to what it was initially at room temperature? How do you explain this?

5. What would be wrong in a student's thinking if she or he opened the cooled canning jar and removed the balloon to measure its volume?

6. The pressure on the inside of a balloon equals the outside atmospheric pressure which is 740 torr. The balloon at the foot of the mountain has a volume of 3.0 L. What will be the pressure inside of the balloon at the top of the mountain where the volume of the balloon has expanded to 4.0 L? Remember the pressure inside the balloon will be the same as the outside of the balloon when you are standing on top of the mountain.

7. A cylinder with a piston contains 10.0 L of gas at 1.00 atm of pressure. The piston is pushed into the cylinder to make the pressure 5.00 atm. What is the new volume of the gas?

8. While driving up a high mountain in Montana, Dr. P heard a loud pop from the rear of the car. There was a burst bag of potato chips in the back of his SUV. Explain what happened to cause the sealed bag to burst.

9. A classmate of yours has proposed that he can inflate the balloon in the jar by sucking on the tube, not blowing into it.

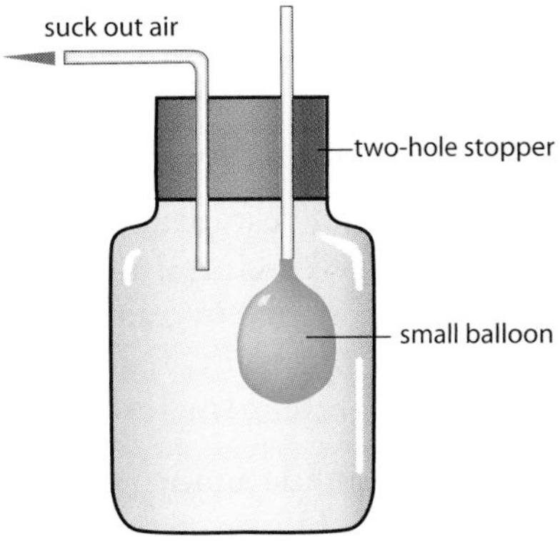
suck out air
two-hole stopper
small balloon

   a) Is this possible? Explain your reasoning.

   b) Does this have any similarity to the collapsing can demo that you saw at the beginning of this activity? If so, explain.

10. ***Preparing for the Chapter Challenge***

    Part of the beauty of science is being able to predict outcomes of events. These outcomes can be macroscopic (like a soda can collapsing) or nanoscopic (foretelling the pressure that molecules will exert after the volume they occupy changes). Since your challenge is to create a cooking-show segment, you will want to describe your cookin' chemistry in a way that is entertaining to an audience. In order to give yourself some practice, write a paragraph or two using exciting and interesting language that explains how you can predict the volume change that results when the pressure of a gas is doubled.

Inquiring Further

1. Researching Robert Boyle

Robert Boyle is credited with discovering Boyle's Law in 1662. They did not have flexible rubber balloons to collect gases for study back in those days. What type of gas-storing vessel did he use in his studies? What was the identity of the gas that he frequently used in his studies?

2. Cartesian diver

Research the idea of the Cartesian diver. Given a 1-L plastic bottle and an eye dropper, build a Cartesian diver and explain why it works.

Chem at Work

René Fernandez

Chef/ Restaurateur, San Antonio, TX

Most chefs use heat to prepare meat, poultry, and fish. Direct or indirect heat fuels a chemical process resulting in the denaturization of the protein. The result is sizzling meat that is ready to eat. But heat isn't the only way to cook protein. Protein can be "cooked" in another way—using acid.

Rene Fernandez is a chef and restaurateur. One of his specialties is a dish called "ceviche" (pronounced say-vee-chay). It is a traditional dish in many Latin American, Mexican, and Caribbean cultures. Ceviche uses the acid from citrus fruits to cook fresh fish into a spicy, fish stew. Usually served cold, it makes a juicy and refreshing meal perfect for lunch on a hot tropical beach.

The fish is placed in a marinade made of lime juice, which has a high concentration of citric acid. Spices and vegetables are added for flavor. Within hours, the acid breaks down the peptide bonds in the raw fish meat, just like heat would. Acid cooks the meat! Chef Rene says, "The concentration of acid in lime (or límones) is just right for cooking. I have tried to make ceviche using other fruit juices like pineapple and lemon, but the concentration is either too weak or too strong. Acid can overcook, just like when using heat."

The fish is marinated with spices and vegetables in addition to the lime. When the time is right for the acid to stop cooking, he drains the marinade or adds a neutralizer. Water dilutes the acid enough to stop the stew from overcooking. More marinade is added for flavor and it is ready to serve.

Chef Rene developed his many ceviche recipes while he was traveling through the Caribbean and South America. He has worked for resort hotels in Puerto Rico, Brazil, Aruba, Guatemala, and all over Mexico. He varies the ingredients and flavors, but each dish is an example of chemical cooking.

Chef

Katricia Kelly

Caterer, Las Vegas, NV

Kat Kelly's dinner parties were a local legend in Las Vegas, NV. She parlayed that skill into a successful business, Top Kat Katering. She couldn't do her job without chemistry. "You can see it on the grill," she says, "when a steak turns from red to brown. Whatever you cook, a chemical change is going to take place."

Sarah Johnston

Executive Director, NOFA, Fultonville, NY

Pesticides are widely used by farmers around the world. Sarah Johnston, the Executive Director of the Northeast Organic Farmers Association (NOFA), is an advocate for farmers and consumers. She lobbies for more government research to investigate the harmful side effects of spraying crops with chemicals.

Cookin' Chem Assessment

Your *Chapter Challenge* is to create an entertaining and informative five-minute segment of a cooking show that gives a detailed explanation of the chemistry involved. Your segment can be live action, a video tape, or even a voice-over of an actual show. You can bring your cultural heritage into view by focusing on ethnic food. Your show might be humorous or serious. It could deal with cafeteria food or gourmet food from a five-star restaurant. The show should be interesting and entertaining. It must include correct chemistry content. In addition to the presentation, you have to submit a script for the show that includes a discussion of the chemistry involved.

Chemistry Content

To begin, you should review all of the activities that you have completed. You can skim through the text and your *Active Chemistry* log to help remind you of the chemistry concepts in each activity.

Activity 1: You learned about convection, conduction, and radiation as ways of heating food.

Activity 2: You learned about fires, fire safety, and the chemical reactions in combustion. This included writing balanced chemical equations for combustion.

Activity 3: You extended your knowledge of combustion to compare cooking fuels and calculate the energy released when hydrocarbons or alcohols burn.

Activity 4: You investigated the change in temperature as water is heated to its boiling point and again while the water is boiling.

Activity 5: You investigated the change in temperature as water is cooled to its freezing point and again while the water is freezing.

Activity 6: You explored the concept of specific heat capacity and how it relates to materials used in cookware.

Activity 7: You investigated the effect of temperature and pH on egg protein. This gave you an understanding of proteins and denaturation.

Activity 8: You applied Boyle's Law to the process of canning.

You may want to make a chart that shows the activity number, some chemistry concepts in the activity, and some ideas as to how you can use these concepts as part of your cooking segment. Your chart may include whether you will apply the principle to the food, the cookware, or the fuel. You should pay particular attention to the *Reflecting on the Activity and the Challenge, Chem Essential Questions,* and *Preparing for the Chapter Challenge* sections. You should also compare your list with that given in the *Chem You Learned* summary.

Activity #	Chemistry concepts	How to use concepts

You may decide to do the first activity as a group to ensure that everybody understands how to proceed. After completing the first activity, each team member can be assigned two or three activities. You can then review all of the activities as a group with the activity expert reviewing each summary.

Criteria

You and your team should review the criteria by which you will be graded. Before beginning the chapter, your teacher led a class discussion to get a sense of what criteria should be used to judge the quality of work for this cooking segment. It is time to revisit that discussion since you now have considerable understanding of chemistry concepts that you can include in your presentation.

The rubric should assign points to the cooking-show segment, the chemistry content, and the script. It should also assign points to specific aspects of each major category. For instance, how many points will be given for additional concepts introduced in the segment? How many points will be assigned for creativity? Safety is also an important consideration. How many points will you assign to safety? This rubric can be a useful tool for your team to check the quality of your work and to ensure that you have included all necessary parts of the project. Determining grading criteria in advance will help you focus your time and effort on the important parts of the challenge.

Preparing for the Chapter Challenge

- **Decide on the Type of Cooking-Show Segment**

You probably have some ideas about how you are going to present your cooking-show segment. What kind of presentation are you going to use? Will it be a live show, a video tape, or a voice-over? Are you planning of focusing on ethnic food? Will you be preparing cafeteria food or gourmet food? Now is the time to make your final decisions.

• Write Your Script

As part of your *Chapter Challenge*, you must submit a script for the show. The script should include a discussion of the chemistry involved. The tone of the script will also give the cooking segment its character. Be ready with some jokes if you are making your segment humorous. If you are cooking ethnic food, you might want to include some information about the country and people of origin.

• **Chemistry content is necessary, but not sufficient.**

All your knowledge of chemistry will be necessary for the cooking segment but it won't be sufficient. You must also find an entertaining way of presenting the content. You have to decide if your segment will be serious or silly. Will it include humor through dialog or outrageous personalities? Will one person be narrating while another acts or will everybody be involved in a skit? What foods will your show highlight? With the chemistry content being about heating foods and fuel choices, you can choose ethnic foods, healthy foods, gourmet food or anything else. Your choice of foods may be the ingredient that makes your show entertaining. Your cooking segment may require props and other materials. Where will you get these? If you are producing a video, you will need to make arrangements to use a video camera.

These are all decisions that only your team can make. When coming up with ideas, listen to one another carefully. Do not reject ideas too quickly. This is a creative process. Your entire team should have input and everyone on the team should be comfortable with your plan.

• Manage Your Time

You have a sense of how you want to proceed and what you want the final product to be. You now have to allocate the work. How much time do you have to complete the project? When is the presentation? How will you get everything done in this time frame? Who will be working on the written script, including the description of chemistry concepts? Will each team member contribute one chemistry concept? How will you ensure that everybody's work meets the standard of excellence to ensure that everybody on the team gets an A? Allocate responsibilities to everybody including work that must be done in class and work that can be done individually for homework. Leave time to review each other's work. Planning a project well does not ensure success, but poor planning almost always leads to disappointment.

• Practice Your Segment or Complete Your Video

If you are doing a live presentation, you will need to make sure that you have enough time to set up the stage. You will want to do a practice run. You may be able to make some last minute adjustments at this time.

If you are making a video, you have some built-in opportunity for adjustments as you tape and edit the show. However, you still will need to make sure that all your materials are in place when you are ready to film.

Engineering/Technology Design

Reflect on the engineering/technology design process. Recall the successes and disappointments from the *mini-challenge*. How can you use the feedback that you received to improve your show? At this point, you are starting the design cycle all over again. Review the steps of the design process described in the *mini-challenge*.

Have fun with your Cookin' Chem show!

Chem You Learned

- There are three ways in which heat energy is transferred: **conduction**, **convection**, and **radiation**. In real situations, these often occur in combination.
- Fuels undergo oxidation during a **combustion reaction**. The complete combustion of **hydrocarbons** results in two products: water and CO_2.
- In the combustion of a hydrocarbon, the reaction equation is **balanced** when there are the same number of C, H, and O atoms in the **reactants** and in the **products**.
- In a **quantitative analysis**, measurements are required. In a **qualitative analysis**, observations are sufficient.
- The **specific heat capacity** of a substance is the amount of heat energy required to raise 1 g of that substance by 1°C. For water this value is 1 cal/g·°C.
- The study of the **heat energy** contained in the chemical bonds of a fuel is called **thermochemistry**.
- When a substance is changing state, the temperature remains constant. This includes the processes of boiling and **condensation**, as well as **freezing** and **fusion** (**melting**).
- A **heating-curve diagram** can be generated by graphing the temperature data vs. the time of heating, assuming the heat input to be constant.
- The **heat of fusion** of a substance is the heat energy required to change 1 gram from solid to liquid at constant temperature. For water, the value is 80 cal/g.
- An **alloy** is a solution of one or more substances in a metal to produce a hybrid substance with improved properties. Chromium in steel makes it more resistant to rust.
- **Amino acids** are organic compounds with at least two **functional groups**, the amine group and the carboxylic acid group. The 20 natural amino acids are the building blocks of the enormous biomolecules, **proteins**.
- The structure of proteins is described at three levels. The **primary structure** shows the sequence in which the amino acids are chemically bonded to form the protein. The **secondary structure** shows the coils and folds of the protein's segments. The **tertiary structure** shows the distinct three-dimensional structure of the protein.
- As the term relates to cooking, **denaturation** refers to changes in the secondary and tertiary structures, but not to the primary structure. This usually leads to a loss in solubility, as well as chemical and biological properties.

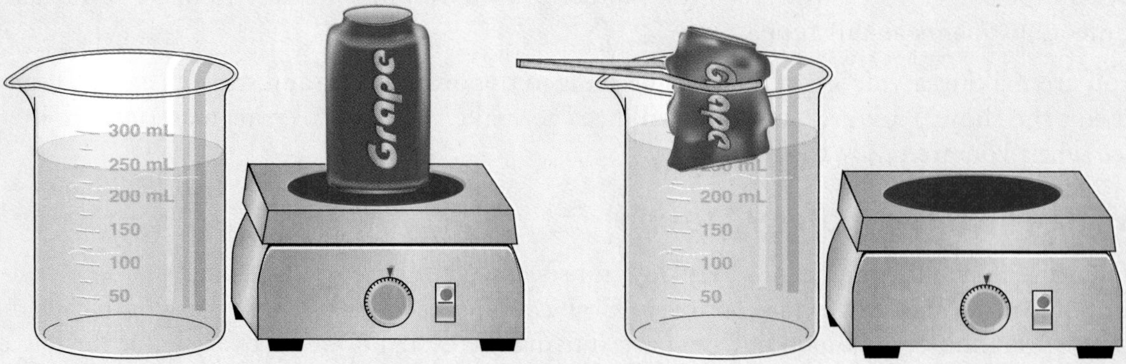
300 mL
250 mL
200 mL
150
100
50
Grape
200 mL
150
100
50
Grape

Chapter 8

CSI CHEMISTRY

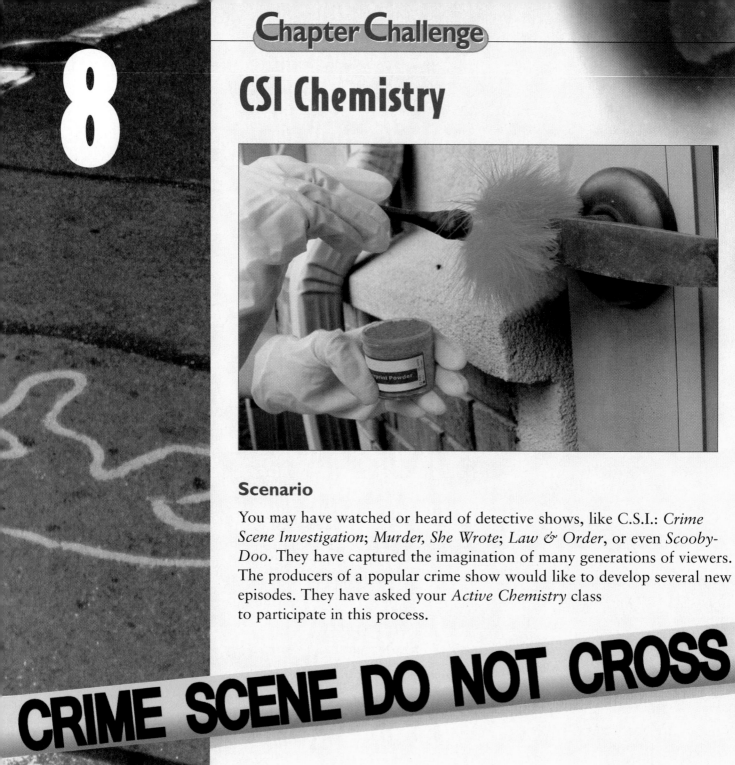

Chapter Challenge

8 CSI Chemistry

Scenario

You may have watched or heard of detective shows, like C.S.I.: *Crime Scene Investigation*; *Murder, She Wrote*; *Law & Order*, or even *Scooby-Doo*. They have captured the imagination of many generations of viewers. The producers of a popular crime show would like to develop several new episodes. They have asked your *Active Chemistry* class to participate in this process.

CRIME SCENE DO NOT CROSS

To put together an exciting and interesting show, the producers begin with a set of evidence that can be analyzed to solve the mystery. Then they introduce a creative story line and bring in intriguing characters. Every piece of evidence is a potential clue that can lead to solving the crime. However, to keep the plot interesting, writers often include dead ends and puzzles along the way to solving the crime. The fact that evidence can lead you in multiple directions makes for some of the great drama in detective stories! Also, multiple pieces of evidence are usually needed to indicate whether a suspect is guilty. Conclusions are more convincing when supported by multiple lines of reasoning and evidence.

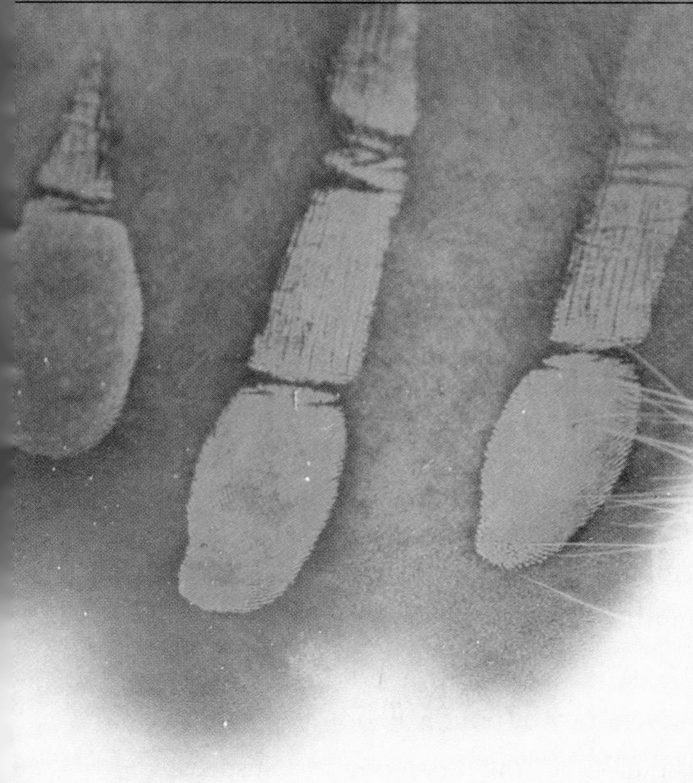

Your Challenge

Your challenge is to create a crime scene and prepare evidence that requires the use of at least three forensic chemistry techniques learned in this chapter in order to solve the crime. Before you develop your story for the crime-show episode, you will need to analyze the evidence you create in the laboratory. Then, determine which pieces the star detectives in the show would use to figure out which suspect is guilty. Finally, based on the evidence, develop the crime story. Your crime story should include a police report, description of the crime, a diagram of the crime scene, a list of all the evidence found at the scene, and anything else that will make the story come to life.

Next, you will create dossiers (descriptions) for at least four different suspects. Each dossier will include personal information about the subject,

RIME SCEN

ChemCorner

Chemistry in *CSI Chemistry*

- Deductive reasoning
- Intensive property
- Extensive property
- Density
- Chemiluminescence
- Ground state
- Excited state
- Qualitative analysis
- Latent fingerprints
- Crystalline structure
- Oxidation number
- Ductile and malleable
- Etching
- Chromatography
- Stationary phase
- Mobile phase
- R_f
- Acid and base

WANTED
SILVER NITRATE

such as a mug shot, fingerprint of right index finger, the suspect's name, occupation, clothing worn on the day of the crime and any other information that will be needed to link the suspect to the crime or eliminate him or her as a suspect. You may be as creative as you'd like with your characters (they are characters after all), but using names or lives of students is not allowed. It is very important that you develop the story and the characters of the suspects so that the evidence you were given logically points to a single guilty suspect. However, you may also want to include a piece of evidence that implicates more than one suspect so that the audience of the crime show cannot immediately guess who the guilty party is right away.

As a way of testing whether your story is solvable by forensic chemists in a crime show, you will present your police report, story of the crime, dossiers of four suspects, and evidence to another group of students, who will act as forensic chemists and try to solve the crime. You will write down the solution to the crime (which suspect is guilty), including a flowchart illustrating the expected outcomes of the analysis of evidence. Your solution should also address the chemical principles used within the crime by explaining the macroscopic, nanoscopic, and symbolic perspectives of each principle used in your crime scene. All of the solution material should be sealed in an envelope. Once the students testing your package have analyzed the evidence and presented their case, they will open the envelope and compare what they decided to what you intended. They will also take a look at your chemistry reflection and provide you with feedback on your explanations.

Criteria

How will your crime scene and investigations of another group's crime scene be evaluated? What qualities should a good crime scene have? What types of information need to be provided in the dossiers? How detailed does your analysis of the evidence need to be? Discuss these issues in small groups and with your class. You may decide that some or all of the following qualities should be graded:

- number of techniques used
- creativity of the story
- authenticity of police report
- originality of the dossiers of the suspects
- number of chemistry principles included
- accuracy of chemistry principles
- solvability of the crime
- logic of the crime story

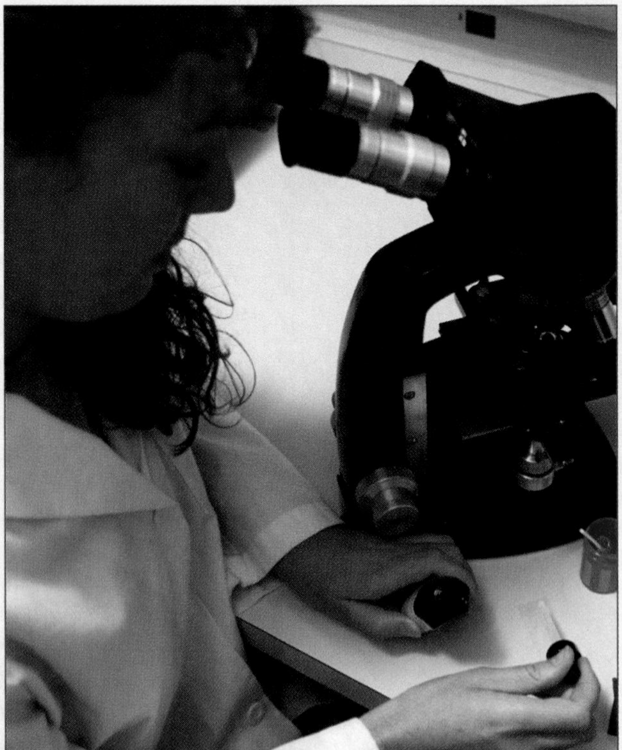

Activity 1 Clue Me In

What Do You See?

RANSOM LETTER
SPECIAL AC UNIT
FORENSIC KIT
CRIME SCENE-DO NOT CROSS

GOALS

In this activity you will:

- Use deductive reasoning to arrive at a conclusion.
- Know and apply different ways in which the elements are classified and organized.
- Use references, including the periodic table, to learn more about individual elements.

What Do You Think?

Pretend you are a detective in a crime lab. You are given a piece of material and you must figure out which of the 114 elements on the periodic table the material is.

- **What information would you need to identify a material?**
- **How would you decide which element the material is?**

The *What Do You Think?* questions are provided to get you engaged in the activity. They are meant to grab your attention. They are also used to find out what you already know or think you know. Don't worry about being right or wrong. Discussing what you think you know is an important step in learning.

Record your ideas about these questions in your *Active Chemistry* log. Be prepared to discuss your responses with your small group and the class.

Investigate

The Elements of Mystery

1. Get two mystery element cards and a periodic table from your teacher for each group of students.
2. Read through the properties listed on the card.

3. You will play a game with other groups in your class.

   The rules of the game: When it is your group's turn, you will tell the other groups one of the properties of your mystery element. The leader of any group can then raise his or her hand and attempt to guess the element on the basis of the first property. If the group guesses correctly, it scores one point. If it guesses incorrectly, that group is out of this round.

   Your goal is to give clues in such an order that nobody is able to identify your element until the last clue is given. You receive 1 point for every clue that you recite. If a team identifies your element after the first clue, you only get 1 point. If the first team to correctly identify your element requires 4 clues, then you score 4 points.

   Each team gets a chance to provide clues to the first mystery element. After one round, each team gets to go again with their second element.

   a) At the conclusion of the game, describe the properties that helped the teams identify your material.

   b) Which properties did not help the team identify the element? Why?

Chem Words

deductive reasoning: organizing, analyzing, and determining the relationships between different pieces of information to construct a solution to the situation being investigated.

Chem Talk

DEDUCTIVE REASONING

Imagine you get up out of your seat to sharpen your pencil. You leave a candy bar on your desk. (Of course, you are not in the lab!) When you return, you notice the candy bar is missing and you wonder, "Where did it go?" Your partner, who sits next to you in class, has chocolate all over his face and an identical wrapper sticking out of his book bag. What do you conclude? Your partner took the candy bar and ate it!

The process you used to assemble and analyze clues that helped you answer the question is called **deductive reasoning**. So, in this case, you *deduced* that your partner ate your candy bar. You based this on the evidence at the scene (the chocolate on his face and the wrapper in his bag). In this activity, you used deductive reasoning skills and a variety of reference materials to identify the mystery element's identity.

Often, investigators and forensic chemists are faced with a jumble of facts and evidence that seem to be unconnected. It is the job of the investigator or forensic chemist to organize, analyze, and determine the relationships between different pieces of evidence to reconstruct

and solve the crime. They are also using deductive reasoning. Some techniques used to analyze information include making lists, making charts, and using the process of elimination.

The Elements and the Periodic Table

The chair you are sitting on, the clothes you are wearing, the air you are breathing, and you, yourself—everything around you is made of **matter**. All matter is made of elements or combinations of different elements. **Elements** are the basic building blocks of matter. They cannot be broken down into simpler substances by physical or chemical means. Currently, there are 114 known elements, each represented by a symbol. These symbols, or more specifically **atomic symbols**, are either one or more letters. The first letter is always capitalized, and the second or third letter, if there is one, is always lowercase. For example, the first element on the table, hydrogen, is represented by the atomic symbol H, and the second element on the table, helium, has the symbol He.

Long ago, data on the individual elements was presented to scientists in a jumble. Chemists sought out a way to organize this information. The result is one of the most marvelous references in science, the **periodic table**. Using the atomic number of each of the elements, scientists have organized the elements on the Periodic Table of the Elements into 18 **groups** (up-down columns) and seven **periods** (across rows).

Elements in the same group have similar chemical and physical properties. Because of this, they are often referred to as families. Some of the families have names. The two groups on the far left and the six groups on the far right are known as the **representative** or **main-group** elements.

Periodic Table of the Elements

Alkali Metals	Alkaline Earth Metals														Chalcogens	Halogens	Noble Gases
1 H 1																	2 He 4
3 Li 7	4 Be 9											5 B 10	6 C 12	7 N 14	8 O 16	9 F 19	10 Ne 20
11 Na 23	12 Mg 24											13 Al 27	14 Si 26	15 P 31	16 S 32	17 Cl 35	18 Ar 40
19 K 39	20 Ca 40	21 Sc 45	22 Ti 48	23 V 51	24 Cr 52	25 Mn 55	26 Fe 56	27 Co 59	28 Ni 59	29 Cu 64	30 Zn 65	31 Ga 70	32 Ge 73	33 As 75	34 Se 79	35 Br 80	36 Kr 84
37 Rb 85	38 Sr 86	39 Y 89	40 Zr 91	41 Nb 93	42 Mo 96	43 Tc 98	44 Ru 101	45 Rh 103	46 Pd 106	47 Ag 108	48 Cd 112	49 In 115	50 Sn 119	51 Sb 122	52 Te 126	53 I 127	54 Xe 131
55 Cs 133	56 Ba 137	57 *La 139	72 Hf 178	73 Ta 181	74 W 184	75 Re 186	76 Os 190	77 Ir 192	78 Pt 195	79 Au 197	80 Hg 201	81 Tl 204	82 Pb 207	83 Bi 209	84 Po 209	85 At 210	86 Rn 222
87 Fr 223	88 Ra 226	89 **Ac 227	104 Rf 263	105 Db 266	106 Sg 266	107 Bh 272	108 Hs 277	109 Mt 276	110 Uun 281	111 Uuu 280	112 Uub 285	113 Uut 284	114 Uuq 289	115	116	117	118

Gases at room temperature
Liquids at room temperature
Solids at room temperature
Metals
Metalloids
Nonmetals
← Transition Metals →

* Lanthanide series **Actinide series

Chem Words

matter: anything that has mass.

element: any material that cannot be broken down into simpler materials.

atomic symbols: one or more letters that represent an element in the periodic table.

group: a column of elements or family of elements in the periodic table. Example: alkali metals are Group 1A.

period: a row of the periodic table. Example: the second period starts with the element lithium and ends with neon.

representative or main-group elements: the elements of the periodic table in which the final electron is placed in either an *s* or *p* orbital. Example: all of the elements of the second period are representative elements.

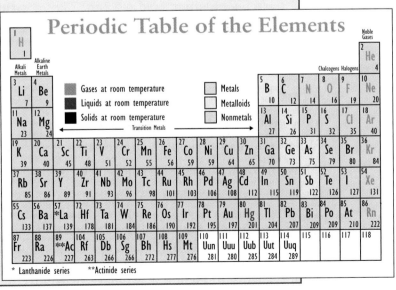

Chem Words

transition metals: the elements between the representative elements in which the final electrons are contained in the *d* orbital.

inner transition metals: elements that contain *f* orbital electrons and are called the lanthanides and actinides series.

metalloid: an element that possesses both metal and nonmetal characteristics. Silicon, arsenic, and germanium are examples of metalloids.

The groups are:

Group 1: alkali metals, which include lithium

Group 2: alkaline earth metals, which include beryllium

Group 13: no common name, which include boron

Group 14: no common name, which include carbon

Group 15: pnictogens, which include nitrogen

Group 16: chalcogens, which include oxygen

Group 17: halogens, which include fluorine

Group 18: noble gases, which include helium

Groups 3-12 are located in between the representative elements and are called the **transition metals.** The groups that lie below the others on the periodic table are called the **inner transition metals.**

Elements can also be classified as metals, nonmetals, and **metalloids.** The metallic elements are located to the left of the stair-step line that starts between aluminum (Al) and silicon (Si) and ends between tin (Sn) and tellurium (Te). Metals are shiny, can be pounded into sheets (malleable), drawn into wires (ductile), and are good conductors of heat and electricity. Nonmetals are located to the right of the stair-step line. Nonmetals tend to be gases or brittle solids at room temperature. They are also poor conductors of heat and electricity. The elements located around the "stair-step" line on the periodic table are called metalloids. Metalloid elements have both metallic and nonmetallic properties. For example, the metalloid element silicon is shiny like a metal but brittle like a nonmetal.

Checking Up

1. Give an example of deductive reasoning.
2. What is the difference between a group and a period on the periodic table?
3. Describe three physical properties of:
   a) metals
   b) nonmetals
4. Where on the periodic table are the metalloids located?

What Do You Think Now?

At the beginning of this activity, you were asked:

- **What information would you need to identify a material?**
- **How would you decide which element the material is?**

Review your thoughts in the *What Do You Think?* section of your *Active Chemistry* log. Now that you have worked specifically with deductive reasoning and have learned more about the properties of elements, create a simple flowchart or concept map of specific questions. Come up with questions about the material that will help you deduce the identity of an unknown element. Be sure your questions have a logical sequence to them that would lead you to the identity of an element.

Chem Essential Questions

What does it mean?

Chemistry explains a macroscopic phenomenon (what you observe) with a description of what happens at the nanoscopic level (atoms and molecules) using symbolic structures as a way to communicate. Complete the chart below in your *Active Chemistry* log.

MACRO	NANO	SYMBOLIC
Which properties of the element cards referred to observable properties that you could identify with your senses?	*The elements in the periodic table are organized in families which exhibit similar chemical properties. At the Nano level, fluorine, bromine, and iodine are described as "diatomic," meaning that these elements have two bonded atoms as elements. Do you think another member of the same family, chlorine, is also diatomic? Explain your reasoning.*	*Rather than write out the names of elements, chemists use symbols. Write down both the names and the symbols for at least three elements.*

How do you know?

What did you do in this activity that led you to a better understanding of deductive reasoning and matter?

Why do you believe?

Explain a situation where you have used deductive reasoning in your life, outside of the classroom. Write a short paragraph explaining the scenario and the outcome of your reasoning.

Why should you care?

Give an example of how you could use the properties of the elements in your crime scene for the *Chapter Challenge*. Be specific, referencing a particular element you could use.

Reflecting on the Activity and the Challenge

Part of your task for the *Chapter Challenge* is creating a crime story for the crime scene you will design. Also, you must make sure that all of the evidence leads to the identification of the correct suspect and that the clues are not too easy or too difficult to follow. Think about how you can use your deductive reasoning skills to design a crime scene that meets all of these requirements.

Chem to Go

You will need to use the periodic table to help answer many of the questions below.

1. What element is in group 17 and period 3?
2. What is the name of the group that contains potassium?
3. Which of the following sets of elements contains all transition elements?

   a) vanadium, strontium, aluminum, titanium

   b) tungsten, gold, chromium, ruthenium

   c) tellurium, nickel, phosphorus, magnesium

   d) zinc, scandium, iron, silver

4. Which of the following sets of elements are all members of the same group?

   a) cobalt, rhodium, iridium, tin

   b) silicon, germanium, lead

   c) iodine, xenon, antimony, indium

   d) barium, calcium, radium, beryllium

5. Identify the metals and the nonmetals in the following list.

   I, Lu, V, C, Ho, Co, La, Te

6. Select an element from the periodic table that interests you. Create a mystery element card for it. Describe how a fellow student would use the clues you have listed to identify the element.
7. ***Preparing for the Chapter Challenge***

   Flip through the entire *CSI Chemistry* chapter of your *Active Chemistry* book. Pay particular attention to the titles and goals of each section. Also, review your *Active Chemistry* log to identify any possible concepts from previous chapters you feel at this point may be useful in creating crime-scene evidence. In your log, prepare a list of possible evidence that you see you'll learn more about in this chapter. If possible, add to that list any topics you have already studied in previous chapters. For topics from other chapters, briefly write down your thoughts on why they may be useful in the crime-scene challenge.

Inquiring Further

Timeline in the development of the periodic table

In developing the Periodic Table of Elements, as more knowledge was acquired about each of the elements, scientists began to ask, "Is there a pattern?" Between 1829 and 1934, chemists attempted to use deductive reasoning to answer this question. Research this period of time in chemistry and create a timeline explaining the history and evolution of the current model of the periodic table. Be sure to cite specific scientists and how they used reasoning skills to organize the elements into the current pattern.

Activity 2 Distinguishing Glass Fragments

What Do You See?

GLASS
PROPERTIES
REFLECTIVE
The
BROKEN GLASS
MYSTERY

GOALS

In this activity you will:

- Experimentally determine the density of a solid without a definite shape.
- Understand the difference between *intensive* and *extensive properties.*
- Use an *intensive property* of matter to identify an unknown substance.

Safety goggles and a lab apron must be worn *at all times* in a chemistry lab.

What Do You Think?

A good detective must be able to apply what he or she knows in any situation. In a well-known movie, *Raiders of the Lost Ark*, the hero replaces a gold statue with a bag of sand.

- **How would the hero of the movie know how much sand to put in the bag to replace the gold statue?**

Record your ideas about this question in your *Active Chemistry* log. Be prepared to discuss your responses with your group and the class.

Investigate

Many crimes result in broken glass fragments. Breaking a window, shattering a bottle, crashing through a glass table—the possibilities are endless because so many products are made of glass. In this activity you are going to learn one way a forensic detective matches a piece of glass from the crime scene.

Part A: Collecting the Data

1. Obtain two samples of glass, labeled A and B, from your teacher. Be careful not to mix the two samples. Examine each sample through a hand lens or stereomicroscope.

   a) Record your observations in your *Active Chemistry* log.

Trial	Mass of sample (g)	Initial volume (mL)	Final volume (mL)	Volume of sample (mL)
1 (20 pieces of glass)				
2 (25 pieces)				
3 (30 pieces)				
4 (35 pieces)				

2. Physical examination may not be enough evidence to distinguish one piece of glass from another. A second method is to compare the masses and volumes of each piece of glass. Your teacher will assign you one of the two glass samples.

   a) You may want to use a data table like the one shown to record your data in your *Active Chemistry* log.

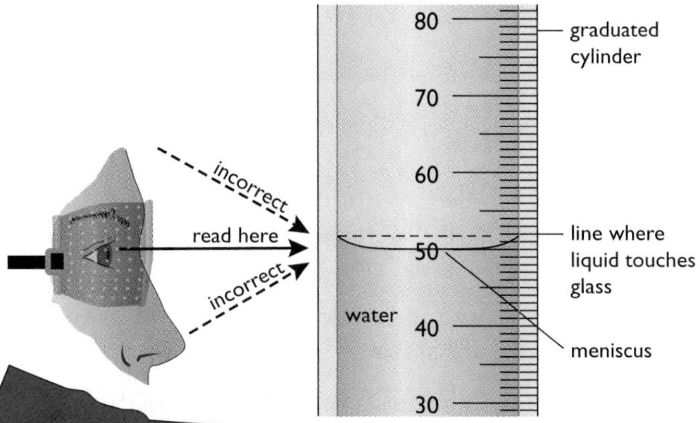
graduated cylinder
80
70
60
50
40
30
incorrect
read here
incorrect
line where liquid touches glass
water
meniscus

3. Using tweezers, obtain approximately 20 pieces of glass from your sample to use in Trial 1. Find the mass of this set of glass to the nearest 0.01 g.

   a) Record the value in your data table.

4. Fill a 100-mL graduated cylinder to the 50-mL mark with water.

   a) Record this volume to the nearest 0.1 mL in the initial volume column of your data table. This will be the initial volume for all four trials. A diagram illustrating the proper way to read a graduated cylinder is shown.

5. Using tweezers, carefully place 20 pieces of glass into the graduated cylinder. Tilt the cylinder so that the glass does not cause a splash. Record the new volume in the final volume column for Trial 1. This method of measuring volume is called water displacement. The diagram illustrates this method.

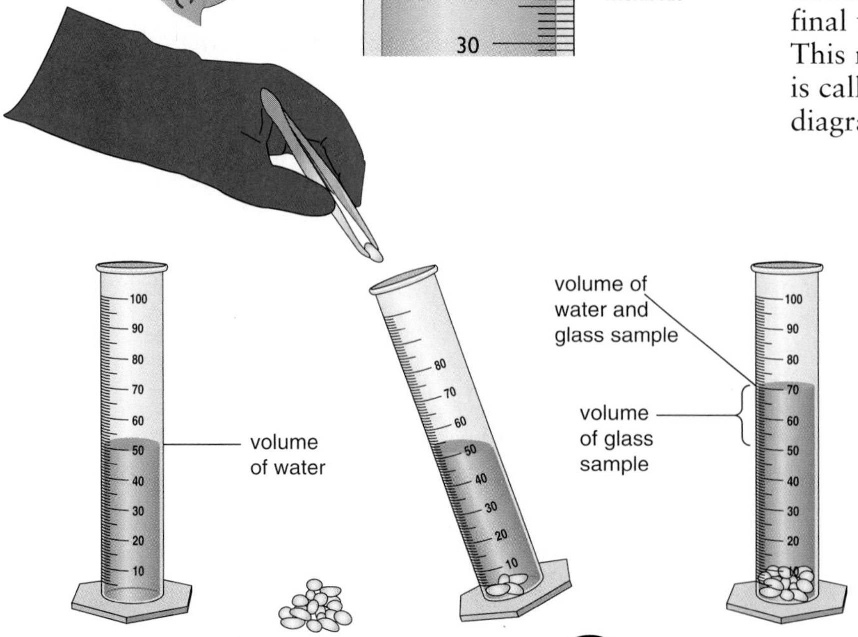
volume of water
volume of water and glass sample
volume of glass sample

6. To calculate the total volume of the sample of 20 pieces of glass, subtract the initial volume from the final volume.

   a) Record the volume of the Trial 1 sample in your *Active Chemistry* log.

7. Find the mass of five more pieces of glass using your laboratory balance. Add this mass to the mass of the 20 pieces from the previous trial.

   a) Record the sum as the total mass for Trial 2.

8. Using tweezers, place the five new pieces into the cylinder containing the original 20 pieces.

   a) Record the final volume for Trial 2.

   b) Subtract the initial volume from the final volume of Trial 2 and record your answer in the column labeled "Volume of sample." This volume should be greater than the final volume for Trial 1, because there are now 25 pieces of glass in the cylinder instead of 20 pieces of glass.

9. Repeat *Steps 7* and *8* for two more trials. The glass sample in each trial will contain five more pieces.

10. When you are done, empty the graduated cylinder and pour the glass pieces onto a paper towel. Dry the cylinder and put it away. Your instructor may have you put the glass in a beaker and place it in a drying oven so it will be dry for the next class. Clean up your workstation.

11. Find a group that collected the same data for the other glass sample.

    a) Record their information in your *Active Chemistry* log in a new data table.

Part B: Analyzing the Data

1. You will now graph the data you collected. Before you do, examine the following graphs to determine which graph represents the best-fit line. A best-fit line has two characteristics: It is a straight line and it is close to as many points as possible (as many points are above and below the line).

Graph 1

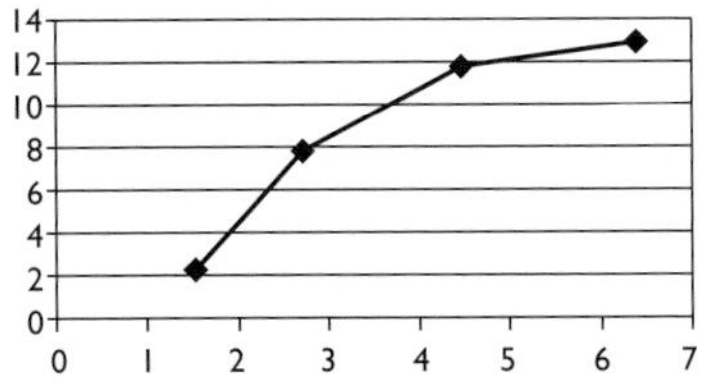
14
12
10
8
6
4
2
0
0
1
2
3
4
5
6
7

Graph 2

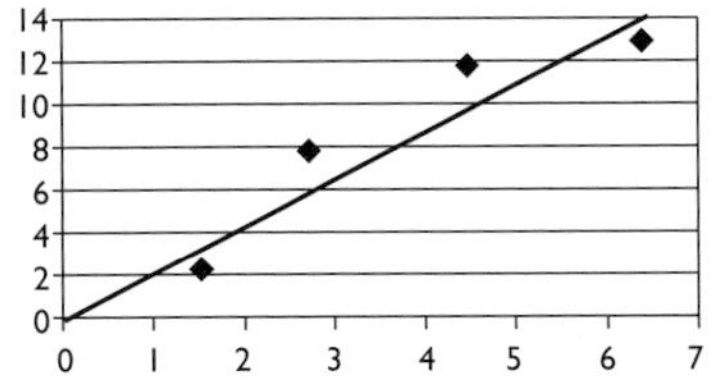
14
12
10
8
6
4
2
0
0
1
2
3
4
5
6
7

Graph 3

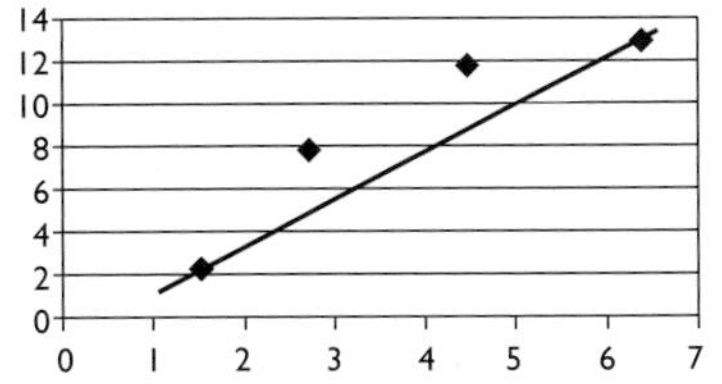
14
12
10
8
6
4
2
0
0
1
2
3
4
5
6
7

   a) Which graph shows a best-fit line? Write your answer and reason in your *Active Chemistry* log.

2. Discuss your choice of graph and your reasoning with a member of your group. Be prepared to discuss your ideas with the class.

3. Graph the data from both glass samples on the same set of graph paper, using different marks or colors for glass sample A and glass sample B. Place volume on the horizontal axis and mass on the vertical axis. The range for the volume axis should be from zero milliliters up to just a few milliliters more than the greatest volume in all your tables. The range for the mass

Report sharp edges on the glass and/or broken glass to your teacher. Do not handle broken or sharp glass with your bare hands.

Wash your hands and arms thoroughly after the activity.

axis should be from zero grams up to just a few grams more than the mass in Trial 4.

a) For each sample, use a ruler to draw a straight line that best fits the five points you graphed.

b) Calculate the slope of each of the lines and record it in your *Active Chemistry* log. Slope $= \frac{y_2 - y_1}{x_2 - x_1}$.

The slope of the line will be measured in g/mL. Since 1.0 mL is equal to 1.0 cm^3, the slope could also have the units g/cm^3. This is the density of the glass.

4. Graphing the data from two samples of glass has provided you with a second way to distinguish between the two samples. Review the table of glass densities provided by your teacher. Using the table of glass densities, identify each sample of glass.

a) Write and justify your conclusions in your *Active Chemistry* log. If there are samples that cannot be identified, write what additional information you would need in order to match your sample of glass to a type of glass on the list.

5. You now have two related techniques to use to match glass samples from a crime scene. Given an unknown piece of glass, you can measure its density mathematically ($D = m/V$) or graphically by finding the slope of the mass vs. volume graph of multiple pieces of the same glass. You can then match the density of the unknown glass with other glass samples that you have investigated.

Chem Words

physical property: a property of matter that can be measured without causing chemical change or a change in the composition of the material. Density is a physical property of a substance.

Chem Talk

PROPERTIES OF MATTER

Physical and Chemical Properties

Forensic detectives use properties of matter to identify an unknown object found at a crime scene. This chapter will focus on using properties of matter and deductive reasoning to construct and solve a crime scene. Size, color, flammability, mass, stability, and temperature are all examples of properties (characteristics) you can use to describe matter. Properties fall into two categories: physical and chemical.

Physical properties are characteristics of matter that can be observed without changing the chemical identity of the substance. Examples of physical properties include luster, color, mass, volume, and odor. Glass is brittle, hard, odorless, and has a high melting point. It may also be transparent or opaque, colored or uncolored. These are just some of the physical properties of glass.

Chemical properties describe how the substance reacts with other materials. Rusting is a chemical property of iron. It describes what happens to iron when in the presence of oxygen and moisture. Firefighters' suits are flame retardant; this is a chemical property. Glass is a fairly unreactive material. However, glass does react with hydrofluoric acid. Reactivity with hydrofluoric acid is a chemical property of glass. Forensic chemists often use a combination of physical and chemical properties to identify materials. In this chapter, you will always reflect on the chemical and physical properties of evidence in order to determine or confirm the identity of the matter.

Intensive and Extensive Properties of Materials

Glass fragments found at the crime scene or on a suspect can be large enough to be pieced back together into the original object, such as a broken glass vase. Then this can be examined for additional evidence such as fingerprints. Could you imagine trying to put the pieces you used today back together! It would probably be a hopeless task because the pieces are so small! In these cases, the properties of the glass itself must be used for identification. Since glass is a fairly unreactive material, scientists rely on the physical properties of glass fragments to match to a crime scene or a suspect. However, not all physical properties are equally useful. A physical property used in identifying a material must not depend on the quantity of the material. In other words, the property must have the same measurement no matter what amount of material is tested, as long as it is the same material. This kind of physical property is called an **intensive property.** You can think of an intensive property as one that doesn't change regardless of how small or how large the sample of a particular substance is. In fact, intensive properties are often called characteristic properties, because they can be used to characterize a material. Examples of intensive properties include melting point and freezing point. Length and mass are not intensive properties of a material because they depend on the amount of substance in a given sample. Properties like length and mass, which vary depending on the amount of material present, are called **extensive properties**. Extensive properties are not used to identify or match matter at a crime scene.

→

Chem Words

chemical property: a property that is displayed when matter undergoes a change in composition (it undergoes a chemical reaction). The burning of wood is a chemical property.

intensive property: a physical property that does not change (has the same measurement) no matter how much of the material is present.

extensive property: a physical property that varies depending on the amount of material present.

Chem Words

mass: a measure of the amount of matter an object contains.

volume: a measure of the space occupied by matter.

density: the mass of a substance per unit volume.

Density

In this experiment, you determined the mass and the volume of four samples of the same glass. Each sample was a different size. **Mass** is a measure of the amount of matter an object contains. It does not depend on gravity (like weight) and will be the same regardless of where it is measured. Since mass depends on the amount of matter present, it is an extensive property. Likewise, **volume**, the amount of space occupied by matter, is also an extensive property. But, you may have noticed that when the mass of the glass sample was plotted against its volume, there was a linear (straight-line) relationship. The ratio of the mass to the volume was constant and did not depend on the sample size. Therefore, the relationship between the mass of a substance and its volume is an intensive property. And since it is an intensive property, you can use the mass versus volume relationship to identify a substance. The relationship between the mass of an object and its volume is called the object's **density.**

Density is defined as the mass per unit volume. Density can be calculated using the equation:

$$\text{Density} = \frac{\text{mass (g)}}{\text{volume (mL or cm}^3\text{)}}$$

Density is reported in units of g/cm^3 or g/mL. For example, if the mass of a solid object is 15.0 g and its volume is 25.3 cm^3, the density of the object is equal to:

$$\text{Density} = \frac{m}{V} = \frac{15.0\text{ g}}{25.3\text{ cm}^3} = 0.593\ \frac{\text{g}}{\text{cm}^3} \text{ or } 0.593\text{ g/mL}$$

Calculating Density from a Mass and Volume Data Set

The density of a substance can be found with a single calculation or by graphing a data set of mass versus volume. In this activity, you used a graph to determine the density of your glass sample. Using this procedure for a sample "X," a data table below was created.

Sample X

Mass (g)	Volume (cm^3)
3.01	5.08
7.01	11.8
11.0	18.5
15.0	25.3

The next step is to plot the mass versus the volume for all four samples on a graph. After plotting the data, a straight-line fit for the data is drawn. This line may not go through all of the data points. The slope of this line will be equal to the density of the substance. That's because the slope is equivalent to

Checking Up

1. Give two physical and two chemical properties of glass.
2. In your own words, describe the difference between an intensive and extensive property.
3. What equation can be used to calculate the density of a material?
4. What does the slope of a mass versus volume graph represent?
5. If two unknown materials have exactly the same density, can you deduce that the two materials are the same?
6. If the density of glass fragments found on a suspect matches the glass fragments at the scene of a crime, can you prove without a doubt that the suspect was at the scene of the crime?

the mass divided by the volume, which is the definition of density. The slope of a line is found by choosing two different points that fall on the best-fit straight line. The points should be widely spaced apart on the graph. The difference between the y-values of the two points chosen is divided by the difference between the x-values of those two points. The result is the slope of the line. The graph with the best-fit straight line and the slope calculations for the sample data are shown.

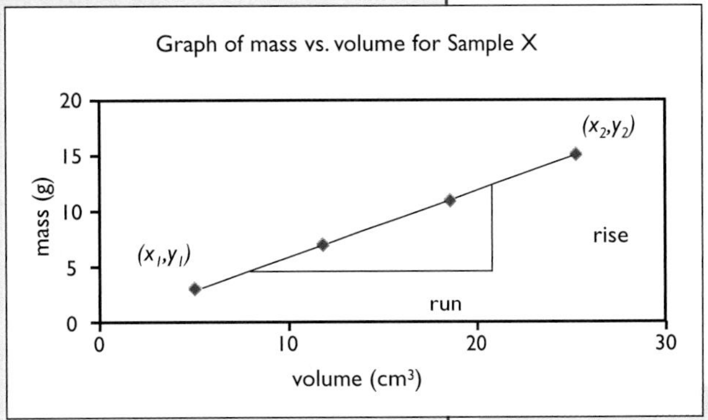

Graph of mass vs. volume for Sample X
mass (g)
volume (cm³)
(x₁,y₁)
(x₂,y₂)
rise
run
0
5
10
15
20
0
10
20
30

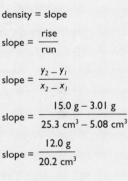

density = slope

$$\text{slope} = \frac{\text{rise}}{\text{run}}$$

$$\text{slope} = \frac{y_2 - y_1}{x_2 - x_1}$$

$$\text{slope} = \frac{15.0\text{ g} - 3.01\text{ g}}{25.3\text{ cm}^3 - 5.08\text{ cm}^3}$$

$$\text{slope} = \frac{12.0\text{ g}}{20.2\text{ cm}^3}$$

$$\text{slope} = 0.594\text{ g/cm}^3$$

Once the density of an unknown substance is determined, the calculated density can be compared to the known densities of substances. The known densities can be found in a number of reference materials, including the table provided by your teacher. If the unknown substance's density is close to one of the known densities, it provides evidence of the unknown substance's identity. Density is not only used to identify glass samples, but also metals and other materials whose density can be calculated. In the case of forensic analysis of glass fragments, the density of the fragments found on a suspect can be compared to the glass fragments left at the scene. If the densities are identical, then there is a strong chance that the suspect was at the scene. However, a scientist must be very careful when drawing conclusions based on data. For example, if the glass in question is automobile glass from a particular make of vehicle, the forensic scientist should keep in mind that there are thousands of these vehicles on the road in this country. There may be hundreds in the area of the crime scene. Therefore, if a suspect has glass fragments that match the glass of the given vehicle with a broken window at a crime scene, that is valuable evidence against the suspect. However, that alone is not enough to prove that the suspect was definitely at the scene.

What Do You Think Now?

At the beginning of this activity you were asked:

- **How would the hero of the movie know how much sand to put in the bag to replace the gold statue?**

The density of sand may be 2.3 g/cm^3, while the density of gold is 19.31 g/cm^3. If the volume of the sand and the gold statue were identical, would that mean that the masses were also equal?

Chem Essential Questions

What does it mean?

Chemistry explains a macroscopic phenomenon (what you observe) with a description of what happens at the nanoscopic level (atoms and molecules) using symbolic structures as a way to communicate. Complete the chart below in your *Active Chemistry* log.

MACRO	NANO	SYMBOLIC
How did increases in the mass of the glass affect the volume and the density of the glass?	*In two separate diagrams, represent the densities of two different elements at the nanoscopic (molecular) level. Make one element lead, a very dense element, and the other aluminum, a less dense element.*	*What are the units you use to represent density? What is the equation you use to define density?*

How do you know?

Making specific reference to your data, explain how a person can distinguish two types of glass.

Why do you believe?

Solid gold and gold-plated jewelry may look identical. How can density measurements be used to determine if a piece of jewelry is real gold or just gold-plated?

Why should you care?

You will be creating and solving a crime scene for your challenge in this unit. Write a short scene using glass fragments to clear one suspect of suspicion and indicate another suspect. In your short scene, explain how the glass fragments were found, analyzed, and interpreted.

Reflecting on the Activity and the Challenge

You have learned how to experimentally determine the density of a glass sample. Because density is an intensive (or characteristic) property, this measurement can help determine the identity of a material that looks like glass found at the crime scene or on a suspect. If glass fragments remain as evidence of a crime, then you may need to measure the density of the glass to determine if the fragment is from the scene of the crime or if it is unconnected to the crime.

Chem to Go

1. Identify the following as physical or chemical properties.

   a) height b) flammability c) tarnishing d) hardness

2. Calculate the density for an object that has a mass of 2.53 g and a volume of 4.54 cm^3.

3. Give another example of an intensive physical property. Explain your choice.

4. A collection of glass fragments was found in the car of the prime suspect, Bob. The glass found at the crime scene was from a crystal goblet made of leaded glass. Using the data obtained by the forensic chemists and the graph-slope method, determine if the glass in Bob's car could be from the crime scene.

Glass Data from Bob's Car		
Set	Mass (g)	Volume (cm^3)
0	0.0	0.0
1	2.0	0.71
2	4.2	1.5
3	6.5	2.1
4	7.9	2.8

Type of glass	Density (g/cm^3)
quartz glass	2.2
borosilicate glass	2.3
soft glass	2.6
leaded glass	2.8

5. If different glass manufacturers use different window glass formulations, density measurements can be used to help identify the manufacturer of a particular glass fragment. How? Explain.

6. ***Preparing for the Chapter Challenge***

   You will want your data used in the challenge's crime scene to be realistic. Look at the four types of glass presented in *Question 4*. Using any resource you choose, find an example of how each of these types of glass may be present at a typical crime scene, such as a kitchen, office, or bedroom. In your *Active Chemistry* log, create a table to organize your findings, including columns for type of glass, density, uses, and examples of crime scenes where you may find that type of glass.

Inquiring Further

Glass used by car manufacturers

Research the density of the glass used by three different automakers. Obtain and test a windshield sample from a local glass shop or car impound lot under the supervision of a responsible adult. Share this information with your classmates by creating a detailed profile document of each of the windshield types, including comparing your experimental results to the known data you researched.

Activity 3

Presumptive Blood Testing: The Luminol Reaction

What Do You See?

THE
BLUE
BLOOD
MYSTERY

GOALS

In this activity you will:

- Gain a basic understanding of atomic structure and its connection to the production of light.
- Define and explain chemiluminescence as it relates to luminol.
- Be able to apply a presumptive test to your crime scene.

What Do You Think?

Every good episode of a crime show has some dealings with blood—what would a good murder be without it? In many episodes of murder mysteries, you can watch the investigators "spray for blood."

- **What do detectives spray when they are spraying for blood?**
- **How do they know blood is present at the scene after spraying?**

Record your ideas about these questions in your *Active Chemistry* log. Be prepared to discuss your responses with your small group and the class.

Investigate

Although it may sound like science fiction, the spraying of a chemical on blood can create light and make the invisible blood "glow." In this activity, you will investigate how the light is produced and whether other materials besides blood can produce the light.

Part A: Experiencing Chemiluminescence

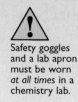

Safety goggles and a lab apron must be worn *at all times* in a chemistry lab.

1. The luminol reaction you'll use in the lab today has quite a bit in common with the typical crack-n-glow lightstick you may have played with. Take a look at an *uncracked* lightstick and complete the following questions.

a) Make some initial observations of the *uncracked* lightstick. Write or draw these in your *Active Chemistry* log.

b) Crack and shake the lightstick. Write what you observe happening. These are observations on the macroscopic level.

c) Describe in words what you think is happening at the nanoscopic level (to the atoms and molecules).

Part B: Using Luminol to Test for Blood

1. Obtain a spray bottle containing some luminol reagent. The luminol reagent contains both luminol and hydrogen peroxide. Add 100 mL of *distilled* water to the spray bottle, then cap and mix. Allow it to sit for five minutes while occasionally stirring it. This solution will be good for one day.

2. While someone in your group is making the solution, have another group member obtain a small pipette of bovine hemoglobin solution. Bovine hemoglobin solution is made from the blood of cows. The red blood cells, which contain hemoglobin, are separated from the rest of the cow's blood, and then they are sterilized and crystallized. Make sure you wash your hands and clean your pipettes and beakers with a dilute bleach solution when you are done.

   a) Record your observations of the hemoglobin solution in your *Active Chemistry* log.

3. Obtain a piece of wax paper and two medium circles of filter paper. Label one circle "blood solution: experimental group" and one circle "distilled water: control group."

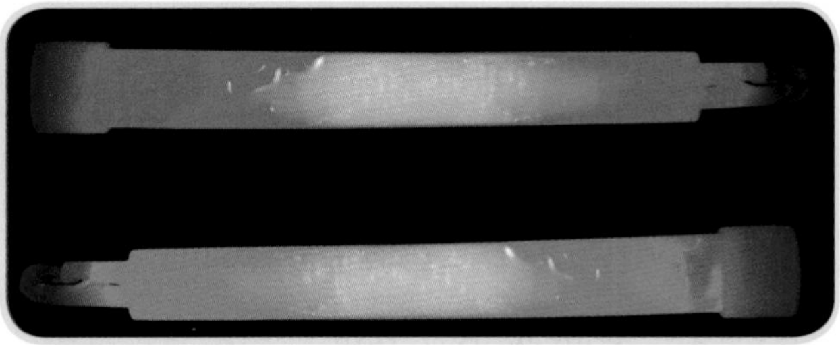

   Place the filter paper circles on the piece of wax paper at your lab bench.

4. Place 10 drops of bovine hemoglobin solution into the circle labeled "blood solution." Place 10 drops of distilled water in the second circle.

   a) Once the circles are dry, record your observations.

   b) Why does this experiment need a control? Record your answer in your *Active Chemistry* log.

5. Turn off the lights in the room and allow your eyes one minute to adjust to the dark. Alternatively, you can place the sample in a box.

6. In a dark room, or inside the box spray the luminol solution onto the test paper over each circle and observe. It will take 5-10 minutes to develop. While you are waiting, discuss your crime-scene story and how blood can be a creative element in your plot.

   a) Record your observations in your *Active Chemistry* log.

   b) What evidence is there that the hemoglobin causes the luminol to glow and not the paper or the distilled water? Record your answer after the lights are back on.

   c) Compare the light produced by the lightstick to the light produced by the luminol-blood mixture. How are they alike? How are they different? Record your answers in your *Active Chemistry* log.

If any solution comes in contact with your skin, wash the area with soap and water immediately. Report all accidents to your teacher.

Avoid breathing dust from the bovine hemoglobin.

7. Rinse the paper with the bovine solution in a small amount of dilute bleach solution before throwing it out. Dispose of the materials as directed by your teacher. Clean up your workstation.

Part C: The Luminol Reaction

As you have seen, in the presence of blood, luminol reacts to produce light. Can something other than blood produce a similar reaction?

1. Obtain a piece of wax paper, and a sheet of white paper with circles on it, similar to the one shown. Label each circle with one of the following labels: 0.1 *M* Fe^{2+}, 0.1 *M* Fe^{3+}, bleach, ketchup, horseradish, a rusty iron nail, hemoglobin mixed with food coloring, and plain food coloring.

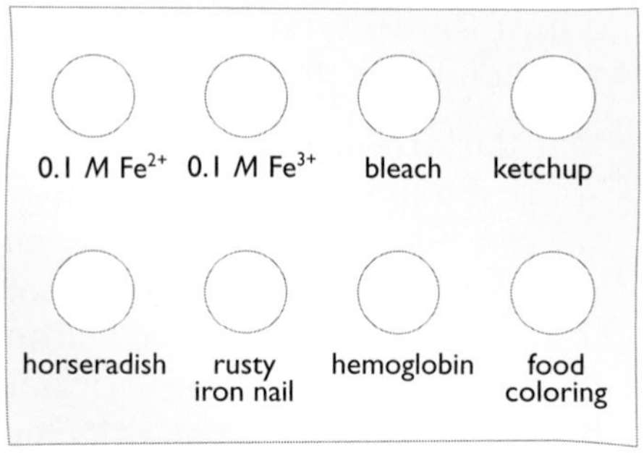

0.1 M Fe2+
0.1 M Fe3+
bleach
ketchup
horseradish
rusty iron nail
hemoglobin
food coloring

Wash your hands and arms thoroughly after the activity.

2. In this activity you will be observing how the luminol solution reacts with these different substances. You may want to record your observations in a table like the one shown.

3. Place three drops of each solution on the appropriately labeled circle. To save time, you may want to share pipettes with another group. Excess solutions should be disposed of as directed by your instructor. The hemoglobin pipette needs to be rinsed with a dilute solution of bleach before it is thrown away. All other pipettes may be rinsed with water and thrown out. The horseradish and iron nail can be placed directly on top of their circles.

4. In a dark room or inside a box, spray each circle with the luminol solution.

   a) Record your observations in your data table in your *Active Chemistry* log.

   b) Compare the results of tests on the different substances. Is the luminol test specific to blood? Explain.

   c) Based on your results, describe what is meant by the statement that the luminol test is a presumptive test for blood.

5. Rinse the hemoglobin circle with a small amount of bleach solution before you throw the circle away.

Substance	Color of paper before treatment	Does it glow?	Brightness of glow	Duration of glow

Chem Talk

HOW ATOMS PRODUCE LIGHT

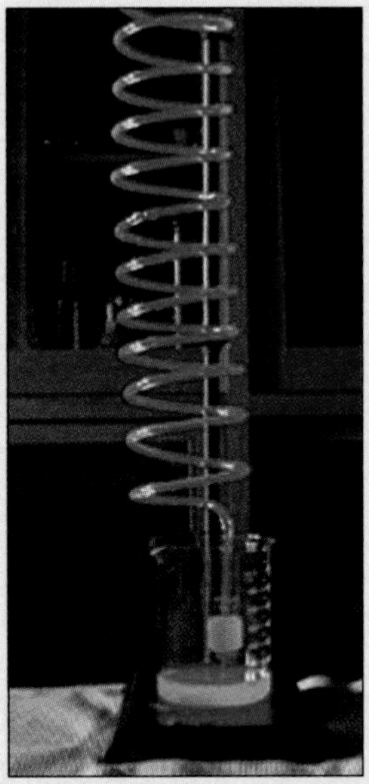

There are many techniques investigators use to find evidence at a crime scene. One of the methods popularized by many of today's crime shows and movies uses a light-producing chemical reaction to visualize hidden bloodstains. As you observed in this activity, when the light-producing molecules of luminol and hydrogen peroxide are sprayed on areas contaminated with blood, a blue glow is produced. Due to the sensitivity of this technique, even invisible blood splatters that have been supposedly "cleaned" off the surface will appear. To learn how the luminol test works, you need to understand the structure of an atom.

Structure of the Atom

The atom is composed of **protons**, **neutrons**, and **electrons**. The protons and neutrons are located in the center of the atom, known as the **nucleus.** Neutrons, n^0, are neutral particles located in the nucleus of the atom. Protons, p^+, are positively charged particles also located in the nucleus. Atoms of the same element contain the same number of protons. For example, every atom of iron has 26 protons. However, every atom of the element copper has 29 protons. The number of protons in a single atom of an element is equal to the element's **atomic number**. The atomic number is found above an element's symbol on the periodic table.

Electrons, e^-, are negatively charged particles located outside the nucleus. The electrons exist outside the nucleus in certain allowable states called **energy levels**. If an atom has an equal number of electrons and protons, then the atom is neutral. For example, a neutral iron atom has 26 protons and 26 electrons. The positive charge of the protons is equal to the negative charge of the electrons. A neutral carbon atom contains 6 protons and 6 electrons.

Atoms Lose or Gain Electrons to Form Ions

Electrons, e^-, can be lost or gained in chemical reactions. If an atom loses an electron, the number of protons is larger than the number of electrons and the atom becomes positively charged. The atom has →

Chem Words

proton: the positively charged subatomic particle contained in the nucleus of an atom. Proton mass is 1.672623×10^{-24} g.

neutron: a neutral particle located in the nucleus of an atom. Neutron mass is 1.674929×10^{-24} g.

electron: the negatively charged subatomic particle of an atom located outside the nucleus. Electron mass is 9.109389×10^{-28} g.

nucleus: the very small dense region in the center of an atom that contains all the positive charge and most of the atom's mass.

energy level: the specific amount of energy that an electron possesses in an atom. The ground state energy level of the hydrogen electron is -2.18×10^{-18} J/atom.

26 ← Atomic Number = # of protons
Fe
55.85

Chem Words

ion: an atom or molecule that has acquired a charge by either gaining or losing electron(s).

one positive charge for every electron it loses. If an iron atom loses 2 electrons it will have a (+2) charge. If an iron atom loses 3 electrons it will have a (+3) charge. The charges are written in the upper right corner above the element's symbol.

Fe	$\rightarrow$ $Fe^{3+} + 3e^-$	Fe	$\rightarrow$ $Fe^{2+} + 2e^-$
26 protons(+)	26 protons(+)	26 protons(+)	26 protons(+)
26 electrons(−)	23 electrons(−)	26 electrons(−)	24 electrons(−)
no charge	+3 charge	no charge	+2 charge

In both examples given, only the number of electrons changes. The number of protons in each atom always remains the same. Atoms that have lost or gained electrons are called **ions**. Atoms of most elements can form ions. Metal elements, like iron, lose electrons when they form ions, so they become positively charged. Nonmetal atoms form ions, too, but when they do, they gain electrons. Thus, they become negatively charged because they have more electrons than they do protons. If a chlorine atom gains an electron it will have a (−1) charge (shown as Cl^-). If sulfur gains 2 electrons it will have a (−2) charge.

$Cl + 1e^-$	$\rightarrow$ Cl^-	$S + 2e^-$	$\rightarrow$ S^{2-}
17 protons(+)	17 protons(+)	16 protons(+)	16 protons(+)
17 electrons(−)	18 electrons(−)	16 electrons(−)	18 electrons(−)
no charge	−1 charge	no charge	−2 charge

Ions have very different properties than the neutral atoms they are formed from. For example, Fe atoms are very different from Fe^{2+} ions. Atoms of some elements, like iron, can form more than one type of ion, because atoms of those elements can lose varying numbers of electrons. Those different ions of the same element, such as Fe^{2+} and Fe^{3+}, not only have different properties from their neutral atoms, but they also are very distinct from each other. You observed one significant difference between Fe^{2+} and Fe^{3+}, that they have different effects on some chemical reactions. In this activity, Fe^{2+} ions speed up the reaction between luminol and hydrogen peroxide, but Fe^{3+} ions do not.

How Substances Produce Light: The Nanoscopic Perspective

Electrons exist outside the nucleus in certain allowable states called energy levels. When an electron gains energy, it can move from a lower energy level to a higher level. However, the energy that the electron gains must be equal to the energy difference between the two levels. Think of the energy levels as the rungs of a ladder. If you only give your foot enough energy to make it halfway between one rung and the next, it is not going to reach the next rung. Instead, it will remain on the lower rung. If an electron does not gain enough energy, it will not be promoted to a higher energy level. When an electron gains enough energy to move to a higher state it is in an **excited state**. This excited state has a higher energy level than the **ground state** where the electron began. The energy the electron gains may come from heat, collisions, chemical reactions, light, or other forms of electromagnetic radiation.

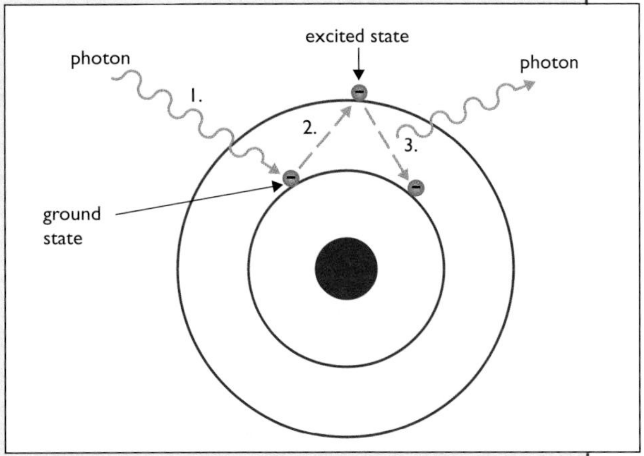
excited state
photon
photon
1.
2.
3.
ground state

The electron does not remain in the excited state for very long. It quickly falls to a lower energy state and in the process loses the energy it gained. The energy lost from the electron's return to the ground state is emitted as light energy and so the atom gives off light. With this basic understanding of how some atoms are able to produce light, you can now make sense of the luminol reaction.

Production of Light with the Luminol Mixture

The glowstick reaction and the luminol reaction are examples of **chemiluminescence**. As you observed in this activity with the lightstick, chemiluminescence is the production of light without heat through a chemical reaction. In chemiluminescence, the starting substances (**reactants**) react and their atoms rearrange themselves to form new substance (**products**) and light. In the luminol blood test, luminol reacts with hydrogen peroxide to form a new compound (called 3-aminopthalate). The energy released in this reaction excites some of the electrons in the new compound. When the electrons in the new compound return to the ground state, blue light is released.

However, at room temperature, luminol and hydrogen peroxide molecules do not react at a significant rate. Some light may be emitted but not enough to easily observe. A **catalyst** is needed in order to speed up the reaction so that more light will be produced in a given time and the light can be more easily observed. A catalyst is a substance that speeds up a chemical reaction without being changed itself.

Chem Words

excited state: a condition where an electron of an atom or molecule has absorbed energy so that the electron is now at a higher energy level than its ground state.

ground state: the lowest energy level that the electron of an atom or molecule can occupy.

chemiluminescence: a chemical reaction that releases energy as light or electromagnetic radiation.

reactants: the starting materials in a chemical reaction that are transformed into products during chemical reactions.

products: the substances formed from reactants as a result of a chemical reaction.

catalyst: a substance that speeds up a reaction without being consumed in the overall reaction.

Chem Words

enzyme: a special type of protein that speeds up chemical reactions occurring in living things.

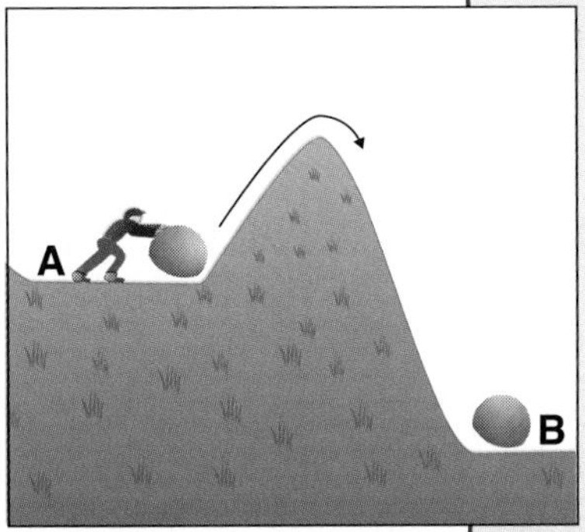
A
B

In every chemical reaction, an energy barrier must be overcome for the reactants to be converted into products. You can picture that energy barrier like a hill, as shown in the diagram. Point A represents the energy level of the reactants and Point B represents the products at the end of the reaction. For the luminol reaction, this energy barrier is high enough that the reaction does not take place at any visible extent at room temperature. This explains why the luminol solution that you made does not glow in the spray bottle, before it comes in contact with a catalyst. A catalyst works by lowering the energy barrier. The iron in the blood, Fe^{2+}, is the catalyst for the luminol and water reaction.

When the luminol-peroxide mixture comes into contact with blood, the Fe^{2+} ions that are in the center of the hemoglobin molecules catalyze the reaction. A visible blue glow is produced. You can picture this as lowering the hill in the diagram, making it a faster process to get the reaction from Point A to Point B.

Why Is the Test Presumptive?

You found other substances also catalyze the reaction and cause the solution to glow. The luminol test is not specific for blood. Examples of other ions that catalyze this reaction include Cu^{2+} and Co^{2+} ions. Different plant materials such as horseradish can catalyze the luminol reaction as well. These materials contain **enzymes**. Enzymes are molecules that catalyze specific reactions in living things. Some enzymes also happen to catalyze the luminol reaction. Because the luminol test is not specific for blood, it is called a presumptive test. A positive result, glowing, indicates that blood *may* be present. A negative result, though, does indicate that no blood or blood residue is present.

Other tests need to be performed on the sample to confirm that the substance is blood. You may have also noticed, however, that each substance speeds up the reaction to a different degree. For example, bleach causes the reaction to glow intensely for a few seconds whereas hemoglobin causes the reaction to glow more uniformly, more dimly, and for a longer period of time. An experienced forensic chemist will have a good idea whether or not the glow is caused by blood. However, no matter how experienced the investigator, a sample will have to be taken back to the lab to determine if the substance is actually blood.

Checking Up

1. What does the atomic number of an element tell you?
2. How is an ion different from a neutral atom?
3. Which is at a higher energy level: an electron at ground state or an electron in an excited state? Explain.
4. What is chemiluminescence?
5. How are an enzyme and a catalyst different? How are they similar?
6. Why is the luminol test for blood called a presumptive test?

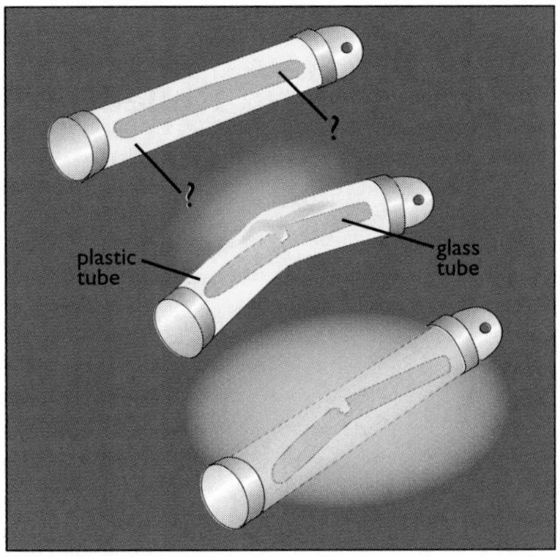
?
?
plastic tube
glass tube

What Do You Think Now?

At the beginning of this activity you were asked:

- **What do detectives spray when they are spraying for blood?**
- **How do they know blood is present at the scene after spraying?**

You investigated the answers to these questions during the activity. Now, think about the lightstick you looked at in *Part A*. The diagram shows how a lightstick works. Assume luminol is causing the glow of this lightstick. (There are other possibilities besides luminol.) What substances could be in the glass and plastic tubes?

Chem Essential Questions

What does it mean?

Chemistry explains a macroscopic phenomenon (what you observe) with a description of what happens at the nanoscopic level (atoms and molecules) using symbolic structures as a way to communicate. Complete the chart below in your *Active Chemistry* log.

MACRO	NANO	SYMBOLIC
What are the observable changes when the luminol is sprayed onto blood?	*Describe how light can be produced by an atom.*	*Graphically and symbolically, how can you represent the reaction you observed both before you sprayed (what is happening in the bottle) and after you sprayed the reaction mixture on your sample?*

How do you know?

Making specific reference to your data and using terms from the *Chem Talk* section, explain why the luminol test is called a *presumptive test* for the presence of blood.

Why do you believe?

A neon sign is nothing more than electrodes, powered through the electrical socket of your house, in atoms of a gas, like neon. When you turn a neon sign on, electrical energy is gained and lost by the gas atoms, and the sign glows. When you stop the electricity, it doesn't glow. How does this relate to the luminol reaction studied in this activity? How is it different?

Why should you care?

How could you use the idea that luminol is a *presumptive test* in your story? Give a specific example.

Reflecting on the Activity and the Challenge

The powdered luminol reagent you used contains both luminol and hydrogen peroxide. The luminol reacts with the hydrogen peroxide once the reagent is dissolved in water, producing light. However, this reaction does not occur fast enough to produce enough light for your eyes to detect it until the hemoglobin comes in contact with the luminol and hydrogen peroxide. The hemoglobin in the blood contains a particular form of iron, and that iron speeds up the reaction. When that happens, the reacting luminol produces enough light for you to see a blue glow. The more blood present, the faster the reaction takes place and the brighter the glow is.

Part of the problem you are facing in creating a crime scene is how to observe something that is not initially visible. In this activity you focused on how the chemiluminescence of luminol could be used to detect the presence of blood. You also examined other substances that caused the luminol to glow. A positive luminol test does not mean the substance is definitely blood. Think how this may mislead you when you are examining a crime scene. Finally, you can now use the concepts that you have learned to describe the chemistry behind this technique, another important element of the *Chapter Challenge*.

Chem to Go

1. Why are the two chemicals in a lightstick separated by glass?
2. Why do lightsticks eventually stop producing light?
3. What prevents the hydrogen peroxide and the luminol from glowing in the spray bottle?
4. What is the symbol for the element that has 16 protons?
5. Identify each as an atom or ion.

   a) 15 protons and 15 electrons

   b) 7 protons and 10 electrons

   c) 3 protons and 2 electrons
6. Write the symbol for the element that has 16 protons and 18 electrons.
7. Examine Group 1 and Group 2 below.

   Group 1: Ti^{2+} Na^{+} Mg^{2+} Al^{3+}

   Group 2: P^{3-} F^{-} As^{3-} O^{2-}

   Which group was formed when electrons were lost?

   Which group was formed when electrons were gained?

8. ***Preparing for the Chapter Challenge***

   Using density to identify glass and using luminol to indicate blood, are two ways that can lead to a false identification of a suspect. In your *Active Chemistry* log, write two scenes; one that uses the properties in the last two activities to correctly identify a suspect as the criminal and one that uses both properties to *falsely* identify a suspect as the criminal. In the false statement, give an explanation as to how it was a false identification. Use this process and your teacher's feedback to start thinking about how you'll make your crime scene have possible twists for the future investigators.

Inquiring Further

1. Other luminol reaction catalysts

Research the luminol blood test. Design an experiment to determine if other household chemicals will catalyze the luminol reaction. Under the supervision of your teacher perform your investigation.

Conduct the experiment you design only under adult supervision.

2. Sensitivity of the luminol test

Design an experiment to determine the sensitivity of the luminol test. Before designing your experiment research the concepts of solution, dilution and concentration. Under the supervision of your teacher perform your experiment and present your results to the class.

3. Other presumptive blood tests

There are many other types of presumptive blood tests. One of the more popular alternatives to the luminol test is the Kastle-Meyer test. In the Kastle-Meyer test, the reagent turns pink in the presence of blood. Research the Kastle-Meyer test. Under the supervision of your teacher, investigate the sensitivity and specificity of this test. Compare your results to the luminol test.

Activity 4 Identification of White Powders

What Do You See?

WANTED
WHITE POWDER
A
B
C
D
The WHITE POWDER MYSTERY
SUGAR
BAKING SODA
SALT
FLOUR

GOALS

In this activity you will:

- Create and use a flowchart to identify an unknown entity.
- Identify an unknown ionic compound based on an understanding of its chemical and physical properties.
- Identify limitations to white powder tests.

What Do You Think?

Forensic scientists and detectives often find traces of white powders at a crime scene.

- **What information would you need to tell different white powders apart?**
- **Can you think of any methods you could use to identify what they are?**

Record your ideas about these questions in your *Active Chemistry* log. Be prepared to discuss your responses with your small group and the class.

Investigate

Part A: Identifying Household White Powders

In this part of the activity, you will test each of six white powders with a set of reagents (water, phenolphthalein, silver nitrate solution, and acetic acid), looking for signs of a physical or chemical change. For safety reasons, you will use common white powders found around the house.

1. How would you design an experiment to carry out these tests? You can share your design with your teacher and you may be given permission to proceed. Alternatively, your teacher may suggest you use the procedure outlined here because the materials have all been prepared and safety considerations taken into account.

Safety goggles and a lab apron must be worn *at all times* in a chemistry lab.

White powder	Solubility in water	Phenolphthalein (PHTH)	Silver nitrate solution ($AgNO_{3(aq)}$)	Acetic acid ($HC_2H_3O_2$)
calcium carbonate $CaCO_3$				
calcium sulfate $CaSO_4$				
sodium bicarbonate $NaHCO_3$				
sodium carbonate Na_2CO_3				
sodium chloride NaCl				
sodium hydroxide NaOH				

2. Obtain a set of six labeled white powders. Check to make sure the set contains calcium carbonate, calcium sulfate, sodium hydrogen carbonate, sodium carbonate, sodium chloride, and sodium hydroxide.

   a) In your *Active Chemistry* log, prepare a data table similar to the one shown.

3. Obtain four clean test tubes. Label the first test tube "solubility," the second test tube "PHTH," the third test tube "$AgNO_3$," and the fourth tube "$HC_2H_3O_2$." These labels correspond to the four tests you will use on each of the six white powders.

4. Place the four tubes in a test-tube rack and add 10 mL of distilled water to each test tube.

5. Add a small scoop of calcium carbonate ($CaCO_3$) to each of the test tubes. Stir each test tube using a clean stirring rod. Be very gentle when stirring. It is quite easy to break the bottom of the test tube with the glass rod. Observe the first test tube.

   a) Record your observations on your data table.

Do not mix powders or other chemicals unless instructed to do so by your teacher. Report spills to your teacher immediately.

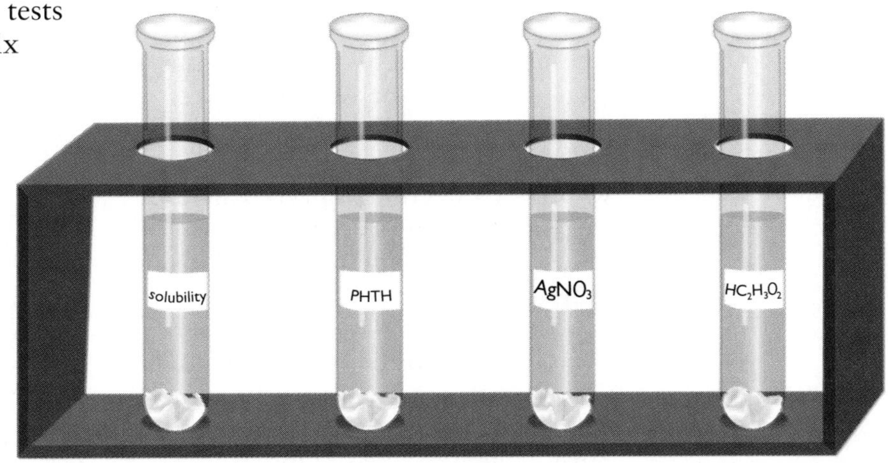
solubility
PHTH
$AgNO_3$
$HC_2H_3O_2$

6. Add 1-2 drops of phenolphthalein solution (PHTH) to the second test tube. Gently swirl the contents of the test tube.

   a) Record your observations in your data table.

7. Add a couple of drops of silver nitrate solution, $AgNO_{3(aq)}$, to the third test tube. Gently swirl the contents and observe.

   a) Record your observations in your data table. Note the symbol (aq) following the chemical symbol. Recall that this stands for aqueous and means the compound is in a solution with water. Other symbols can be used to represent the states of matter for compounds including (s) for solids, (l) for liquids, and (g) for gases.

8. To the fourth test tube, add a small pipette full of acetic acid solution, $HC_2H_3O_2$. Gently swirl the contents.

   a) Record your observations in your data table.

Wash your hands and arms thoroughly after the activity.

9. Dispose of the contents of the test tubes as indicated by your teacher. Clean the test tubes using a test-tube brush. Rinse them twice with a small amount of distilled water.

10. Now that you are familiar with lab techniques for each material, repeat *Steps 4* to *9* for the remaining five powders, substituting the next white powder in your data table where the directions call for calcium carbonate, $CaCO_3$. Your teacher may have your sodium hydroxide samples already measured for you. In the event that your teacher wants you to do the preparation, you must be extremely careful with solid sodium hydroxide, as it will burn. (Chemically speaking, it will saponify your skin, i.e., make soap). Use gloves in measuring out your solid sodium hydroxide for the different test tubes.

11. You are given a white powder.

    a) What test results would you expect if the white powder were NaCl?

    b) What test results would you expect if the white powder were $NaHCO_3$?

    c) Does each material have a unique set of properties?

Part B: Reading and Creating Flowcharts

Now that you can identify each compound based on its solubility in water and reaction with the other three reagents, you need a way to represent this simply. In this part of the activity, you will learn how to use a type of map called a flowchart. Flowcharts can be used to illustrate a deductive reasoning process, so they are useful to a forensic scientist.

1. What does the first flowchart on the next page represent?

   a) Write down your thoughts in your *Active Chemistry* log and be prepared to share them with the class.

2. The next flowchart can be used to identify the six modes of transportation shown. Choose a mode of transportation and see if the flowchart identifies it correctly. Choose a second one and try it again.

   a) Copy the flowchart into your *Active Chemistry* log and fill in all the blanks. Is each blank unique? If so, the flowchart works.

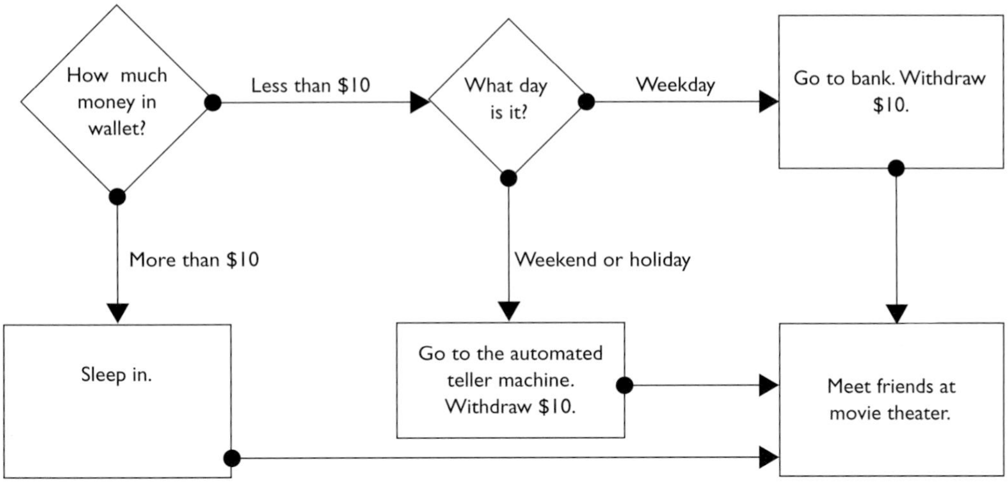
How much money in wallet?
Less than $10
What day is it?
Weekday
Go to bank. Withdraw $10.
More than $10
Weekend or holiday
Sleep in.
Go to the automated teller machine. Withdraw $10.
Meet friends at movie theater.

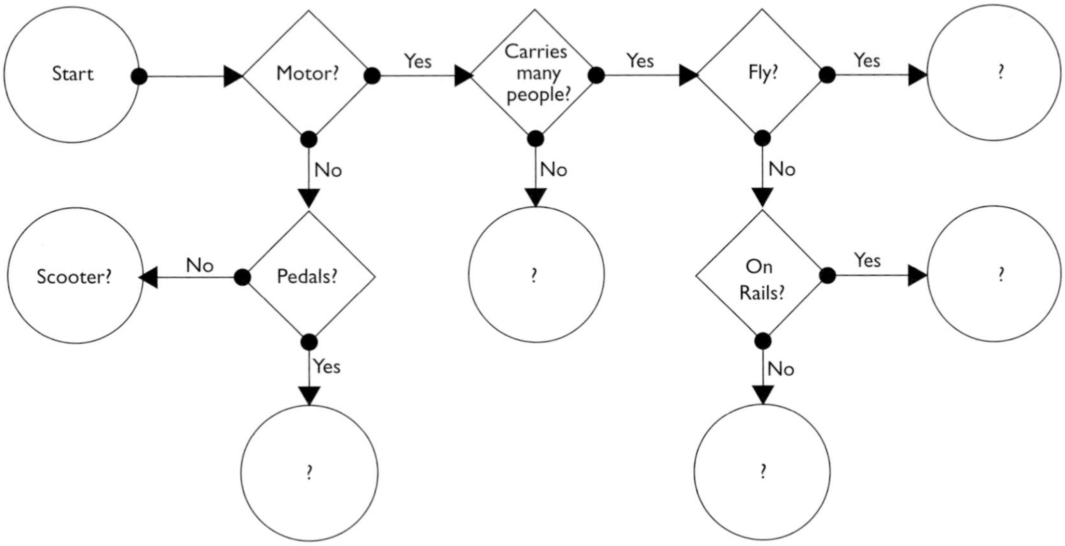
Start
Motor?
Yes
Carries many people?
Yes
Fly?
Yes
?
No
No
No
Scooter?
No
Pedals?
?
On Rails?
Yes
?
Yes
No
?
?

Notice that a flowchart does not need to be based on yes-or-no questions to work. For example, one of the questions could have been, "How many wheels does it have?" Answers to this could have been, "two," "four," and "more than four."

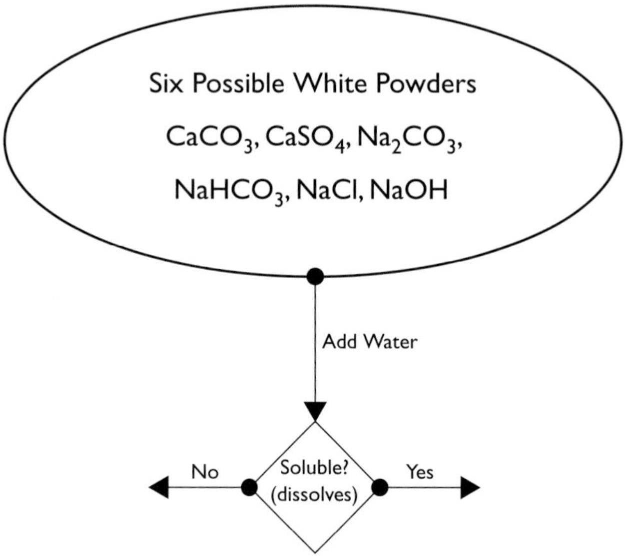
Six Possible White Powders
$CaCO_3$, $CaSO_4$, Na_2CO_3,
$NaHCO_3$, NaCl, NaOH
Add Water
No
Soluble? (dissolves)
Yes

3. Now that you've had some practice creating flowcharts, use your test results from *Part A* to create a flowchart for identifying the household white powders. Hint: you might want to start with whether the solid dissolves in water as your first decision. (See the example flowchart shown.)

4. Once you have created your chart, try it out using at least two of the white powders to test its validity. (See if it works!). If your flowchart does not correctly identify all six of the powders, revise it and test it again.

   a) Once you have a flowchart that works, copy it into your *Active Chemistry* log.

Chem Words

qualitative analysis: the determination of which substances are present in the sample with little or no regard to the exact amount of each.

Chem Talk

IDENTIFYING UNKNOWNS IN CHEMISTRY

Qualitative Analysis

Forensic chemists are often faced with the challenging task of identifying unknown compounds. There are millions of possible compounds and mixtures of compounds to choose from. Forensic chemists must develop tests that identify each one! The use of tests to determine the identity of an unknown compound is called **qualitative analysis**. In this type of analysis, it is the identity of the unknown—the *qualities* that make it unique—that is important and not the quantity, or amount, of the substance. In this experiment, you used the results from a series of tests performed on six different compounds to develop a flowchart. This flowchart will allow you to identify one or more unknown white powders found at the *Chapter Challenge* crime scene, if the powder or powders are the ones you have tested in this activity.

The key to identifying a white powder is testing properties that allow one powder to be differentiated from another. For example, both sugar and salt dissolve easily in water. Therefore, testing a powder that may be either sugar or salt by dissolving the powder in water would not help tell them apart. But sugar melts at a relatively low temperature, while salt melts at a much higher temperature, so if the white powder melts in a pan on the stove, you know that it cannot be salt. The tests used in a qualitative analysis depend on the properties of the possible unknown substances. If the number of possible substances is large or some of the possible substances have many physical and chemical properties in common, a scientist might have to conduct several different tests before accurately identifying the unknown substance.

Ionic Compounds

The white powders you used in this activity are all **ionic compounds**. Ionic compounds are made of a combination of positive and negative **ions**. Sodium chloride is an ionic compound, so its chemical formula, NaCl, means there is one positive sodium ion (Na^+) for every one negative chloride ion (Cl^-).

Ionic compounds form on the basis that opposite charges attract. The positive sodium ion is attracted to the negative chloride ion. This attraction between the positive ion (also called a **cation**) and the negative ion (also called an **anion**) is called an **ionic bond**, and the substance formed by the bond is the ionic compound. The sodium ion and chloride ion join to form the ionic compound sodium chloride, NaCl, as shown.

$$Na^+ + Cl^- \rightarrow NaCl$$

In calcium chloride, $CaCl_2$, there is one positive calcium ion (Ca^{2+}) for every two negative chloride ions (again, Cl^-).

$$Ca^{2+} + 2Cl^- \rightarrow CaCl_2$$

Notice since there are two chloride ions for every one calcium ion there is a 2 in front of the chloride ion. You must always have the same number of ions or atoms of each element on both sides of a chemical equation. This is due to the **Law of Conservation of Matter**. It states that matter cannot be created or destroyed. Chloride ions must be equal in the reactants and products, so there must be two on each side.

In an ionic compound the cations take the name of the element. The anions take the name of the element but the ending is changed to *–ide*. Notice that metals form positive ions and nonmetals form negative ions.

Chem Words

ionic compound: a compound that is composed of positive ions (cations) and negative ions (anions).

ion: an electrically charged atom or group of atoms that has acquired a net charge, either negative or positive.

cation: an ion that has a positive charge.

anion: an ion that has a negative charge.

ionic bond: the attraction between oppositely charged ions.

Law of Conservation of Matter: the amount of matter present before and after a chemical change remains the same.

Chem Words

polyatomic ion: an ion that consists of two or more atoms that are covalently bonded and have either a positive or negative charge.

solubility: the amount of a substance that can dissolve in a given quantity of solvent at a given temperature.

soluble: a substance that dissolves in a liquid.

solution: a homogeneous mixture of two or more substances.

insoluble: a substance that will not dissolve in a liquid.

Some Common Ions

Formula	Name	Formula	Name
Na^{+}	sodium ion	Cl^{-}	chloride ion
K^{+}	potassium ion	F^{-}	fluoride ion
Ag^{+}	silver ion	O^{2-}	oxide ion
Ca^{2+}	calcium ion	S^{2-}	sulfide ion

Groups of atoms may act as a single ion in an ionic compound, like in calcium carbonate, $CaCO_3$. There is one calcium cation (Ca^{2+}) for every one carbonate anion (CO_3^{2-}). Ions like carbonate, (CO_3^{2-}), are called **polyatomic ions**. Sulfate (SO_4^{2-}), hydroxide (OH^{-}), nitrate (NO_3^{-}), acetate ($C_2H_3O_2^{-}$) and bicarbonate (HCO_3^{-}) are other polyatomic anions found in the white powders and reagents used in this activity.

Solubility

In *Part A*, you placed a sample of each white powder in water to see if it would dissolve. This property of matter is called **solubility**. The powders that dissolved in water are **soluble**. When a solid dissolves in water the mixture of the dissolved solid and the water is called a **solution**. The powders that did not dissolve are **insoluble**. Whether or not a particular powder dissolves in water is a complex matter that depends on many factors. Fortunately, the solubility of many substances in water has been investigated. The results of some of the investigations are summarized in the table.

You can use the thousands of hours of work of chemists that resulted in this table to help you make identifications. Chemists don't memorize these tables, though some remember parts of the table. For example, some chemists through their repeated experiences with chlorides may remember which ones are not soluble.

This table can be used to predict if a given solid will dissolve in water. To determine if a solid is soluble, look at the chemical formula for the solid,

Solubility Rules

Nitrates (NO_3^{-})	All are *soluble*.
Chlorides (Cl^{-})	All are *soluble* **except** those containing ions of silver, mercury (I), and lead (II).
Sulfates (SO_4^{2-})	All are *soluble* **except** those containing ions of barium, calcium, strontium, silver, lead (II), and mercury (I).
Carbonates (CO_3^{2-})	All are *insoluble* **except** those containing ions of the Group I metals or the ammonium ion.
Hydroxides (OH^{-})	All are *insoluble* **except** those containing ions of the Group I metals or the ammonium ion.

and identify which of the five negatively charged ions listed in the table the solid contains. Then read the rule for solids containing that ion and the exceptions to the rule. For example, sodium carbonate, Na_2CO_3, contains the ion carbonate, CO_3^{2-}. According to the table, all carbonates are insoluble except for the ones containing Group I metals. Sodium is a Group I metal, so sodium carbonate is an exception to the general rule that carbonates are insoluble. Therefore, sodium carbonate is soluble and dissolves in water. Other examples are given below.

- KCl is soluble because all chlorides are soluble except those containing ions of silver, mercury (I), and lead (II). KCl does not contain any of the exceptions.
- $Mg(OH)_2$ is insoluble because hydroxides are insoluble except for those containing Group I metals, and magnesium is not a Group I metal.

Determining whether a given solid is soluble is another example of deductive reasoning using both the table of solubility rules and the periodic table.

Phenolphthalein: An Acid-Base Indicator

In the second test, you added phenolphthalein (PHTH) to your sample. PHTH is one of a class of compounds known as acid-base indicators. **Acids** are compounds that form H^+ ions in solution and strong acids are 100% dissociated in water. Acids taste sour (citric and maleic acids are used in sour candies), react with metals (corrosive), neutralize bases, and react with indicators to produce a color change. **Acid-base indicators** are substances that change color when exposed to an acid or a base. Some common acids and their uses are listed in the table. Unlike HCl, weak bases are only slightly dissociated in water.

Common Acids and their Uses

Name	Formula	Use	Strength
acetic acid	$HC_2H_3O_2$	vinegar	weak
carbonic acid	H_2CO_3	carbonated sodas	weak
hydrochloric acid	HCl	stomach acid	strong

Bases are compounds that form hydroxide ions (OH^-) in solution. Bases taste bitter, are corrosive, feel slippery, saponify fats (turns fats into soaps), neutralize acids, and cause indicators to change color.

Chem Words

acid: a solution that has a pH value less than 7.

acid-base indicator: a substance that changes color when exposed to either an acid or a base.

base: a solution that has a pH value greater than 7.

Chem Words

double-replacement reaction: a reaction in which two elements or groups of elements in two different compounds exchange places to form new compounds.

precipitate: an insoluble salt that is formed when two solutions are mixed together.

Bases cause phenolphthalein to turn bright pink. Some common bases and their uses are listed in the table.

Common Bases and their Uses

Name	Formula	Use	Strength
sodium hydroxide (lye)	$NaOH$	drain cleaners	strong
ammonia	NH_3	window cleaners	weak
magnesium hydroxide	$Mg(OH)_2$	antacids	strong
sodium carbonate	Na_2CO_3	glass manufacture	strong

Reactions of Ionic Compounds: Double-Replacement Reactions

Ionic compounds can form insoluble solids in chemical reactions. For example, when silver nitrate solution is added to sodium chloride solution, a milky white solid is formed. The chemical equation for this reaction is shown below.

silver nitrate + sodium chloride → sodium nitrate + silver chloride

$$AgNO_{3(aq)} + NaCl_{(aq)} \rightarrow NaNO_{3(aq)} + AgCl_{(s)}$$

By examining the reaction, you can see that the metals, sodium (Na) and silver (Ag), exchange places to form two new compounds. This reaction is called a **double-replacement reaction.** You can determine the identity of the milky white solid, called a **precipitate**, by looking at the two products and using the solubility rules. The first product, sodium nitrate, dissolves in water because all nitrates are soluble. The second product, silver chloride, is insoluble because all chlorides are soluble with the exception of mercury (II), lead (II), and silver. Because of silver chloride's insolubility, instead of dissolving and being invisible like the sodium nitrate, the silver chloride that is formed is visible as a milky white precipitate.

Here are more examples of double-replacement reactions.

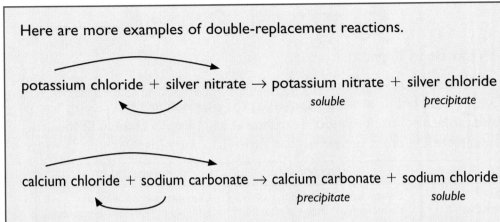

potassium chloride + silver nitrate → potassium nitrate + silver chloride
soluble *precipitate*

calcium chloride + sodium carbonate → calcium carbonate + sodium chloride
precipitate *soluble*

Another example of a double-replacement reaction from this activity is the reaction of acetic acid solution with sodium carbonate solution.

$$2HC_2H_3O_{2(aq)} + Na_2CO_{3(aq)} \rightarrow 2NaC_2H_3O_{2(aq)} + H_2CO_{3(aq)}$$

The hydrogen ion in acetic acid trades places with the sodium ion in the sodium carbonate. The carbonic acid product, H_2CO_3, immediately decomposes to produce carbon dioxide gas (the bubbles in *Part A*) and water.

$$H_2CO_{3(aq)} \rightarrow H_2O_{(l)} + CO_{2(g)}$$

Whenever carbonic acid is a product in a chemical equation, it is replaced with water and carbon dioxide.

$$2HC_2H_3O_{2(aq)} + Na_2CO_{3(aq)} \rightarrow 2NaC_2H_3O_{2(aq)} + H_2O_{(l)} + CO_{2(g)}$$

Generally, acetic acid and other acids react with carbonates and hydrogen carbonates to form carbon dioxide gas. The gas is in the bubbles that form in the solution. A carbonate is a compound that contains the CO_3^{2-} ion. Some common carbonates include sodium carbonate (Na_2CO_3) and calcium carbonate ($CaCO_3$). Hydrogen carbonates are compounds that contain the bicarbonate ion HCO_3^-. The most common bicarbonate is sodium bicarbonate, $NaHCO_3$, commonly known as baking soda. Bicarbonates react with acids in a manner similar to carbonates.

Checking Up

1. In your own words, explain the difference between a quantitative and a qualitative analysis.
2. What is a polyatomic ion?
3. Is sodium chloride (NaCl) soluble? Explain how you arrived at your answer.

What Do You Think Now?

At the beginning of this activity you were asked:

- **What information would you need to tell different white powders apart?**
- **Can you think of any methods you could use to identify what they are?**

Review your ideas about these questions. Now that you have completed this activity, you should have more informed answers to the two questions. Re-answer the two questions in your *Active Chemistry* log using terms and specific concepts from this activity.

Chem Essential Questions

What does it mean?

Chemistry explains a macroscopic phenomenon (what you observe) with a description of what happens at the nanoscopic level (atoms and molecules) using symbolic structures as a way to communicate. Complete the chart below in your *Active Chemistry* log.

MACRO	NANO	SYMBOLIC
What are some of the macroscopic properties that you observed with the white powders in this activity?	*Explain what is happening at the nano level during a double-replacement reaction. You can use potassium chloride and silver nitrate as examples.*	*Chemists use formulas as symbols to represent elements and compounds. Explain the meaning of the formula NaOH. How do chemists name this ionic compound?*

How do you know?

What was the evidence in the laboratory of physical and chemical changes? Explain.

Why do you believe?

Explain a situation where you have seen a chemical and physical change in your experiences outside of the classroom.

Why should you care?

List at least two concepts from this activity that you think would be useful in analyzing a crime scene. Explain why you chose each concept.

Reflecting on the Activity and the Challenge

You have learned how to identify white powders based on their chemical and physical properties. If your crime scene includes a white powder, you will need to analyze it to determine its identity. You will also need to assign different powders to different suspects so that the identity of the powder will help to identify the suspect.

Chem to Go

1. Use the list of ions below to answer the questions.

   Cl^-, Na^+, Al^{3+}, SO_4^{2-}, MnO_4^-, NH_4^+, O^{2-}, Fe^{2+}

   a) Which ions are cations?

   b) Which ions are anions?

   c) Which ions are polyatomic ions?

2. Which of the following compounds are insoluble in water?

   K_2CO_3, Na_2SO_4, $MgCO_3$, $Ba(OH)_2$, $FeCl_3$, $Cu(NO_3)_2$, $PbCl_2$

3. Which of the following are double-replacement reactions?

   a) $AgNO_3 + NaBr \rightarrow NaNO_3 + AgBr$ b) $CaCO_3 \rightarrow CaO + CO_2$

   c) $FeCl_3 + 3KOH \rightarrow 3KCl + Fe(OH)_3$ d) $Zn + CuSO_4 \rightarrow ZnSO_4 + Cu$

4. Complete the word equations for the following double-replacement reactions.

   a) potassium chloride + lead (II) nitrate →

   b) iron (III) chloride + potassium hydroxide →

   c) sodium hydroxide + calcium nitrate →

5. Identify the precipitates formed in each of the reactions in *Question 4*.

6. Name one other physical property and one other chemical property you could use to identify any powdered chemical found at a crime scene.

7. How could a defense attorney prove that a white powder was NOT the chemical that the prosecutors claimed it to be?

8. In the reaction described in the *Chem Talk* section,

   $2HC_2H_3O_2 + Na_2CO_3 \rightarrow 2NaC_2H_3O_2 + H_2O + CO_2$

   a) Show that the number of H, C, O and Na atoms are identical on both sides of the equation.

   b) Why must the number of these elements be identical on both sides of the equation?

9. List a few properties of one of the white powders so another team can use their flowchart to identify the powder.

10. What is the minimum number of tests you must conduct to determine if the white powder is NaCl, if the only possibilities are the powders you used in the activity?

11. ***Preparing for the Chapter Challenge***

    Each of the chemicals in this lab was called a "household" chemical. Create a table with three columns: white powder, possible uses of the white powder, and crime scenes where you might find this chemical. Use the Internet and references suggested to you by your instructor to determine each chemical's possible use or uses.

Inquiring Further

Instrumental techniques

On many of the crime dramas, you will notice researchers using machines to identify samples from the crime scene, or more commonly, they send it off to the lab and get back a printed report. Research instrumental methods forensic chemists use to identify white powders found at a crime scene. Identify the name of one of these instruments and explain how it functions on the physical or chemical properties of the white powder.

Chapter mini Challenge

Your challenge for this chapter is to create a crime scene and prepare evidence so that some other team can solve the crime. Having completed four activities, this is a good time to give your forensics challenge a *first try*. It's time to create a crime scene using one or two bits of evidence reflecting chemistry principles. Of course, being limited to the chemistry content of four activities will limit the types of evidence you can expect. However, this *first try* will give you a good sense of what the challenge entails and how you and other teams are going to approach your forensics task.

Your *mini-challenge* is to create a crime scene, evidence, and a police report. You will only be providing the class with three minutes to try to solve your crime. After this time, you will share the solution to the crime. The class will then provide feedback. You will not be given much preparation time for your *mini-challenge*.

Chemistry Content

Your team should first review the chemistry content that may be included in this forensics challenge. Each content area can be creatively used as a piece of evidence. Toward the end of each activity is a section called *Reflecting on the Activity and the Challenge,* which can provide hints as to the application of chemistry content to the forensics challenge. You may decide to review this section.

Activity 1: You learned about deductive reasoning. You also learned about elements and their properties.

Activity 2: You investigated glass fragments and found that they could be distinguished by their densities. Density is a characteristic property of matter.

Activity 3: You observed the luminol reaction and discovered that blood will be detected by luminol. You also learned that other substances will also produce light from a luminol reaction. The luminol reaction can be used as evidence of blood or can be used to confuse the crime detectives. You also learned about energy levels and the emission of light in addition to the need for catalysts.

Activity 4: You practiced a set of lab techniques that can be used to distinguish one white powder from another. The identification of unknown chemicals involves sets of reactions. You also learned how to set up a flowchart to help clarify the logic of identifying the chemical.

Criteria

Your team should also review the criteria that you discussed on the first day of this chapter. Your crime scene, police report, and evidence should be creative and engaging, as well as have accurate chemistry explanations.

Preparing for Your mini Challenge

Your team should begin the process of creating the crime scene and evidence by brainstorming ideas about possible storylines you may use, while keeping in mind that the chemical evidence must be from one of the four activities. You can try to be suspenseful, mysterious, or humorous. Some crime shows are quite serious but some movies mix crime solving with fun, such as *Austin Powers* or *The Pink Panther*. Of course, you are limited in the evidence that you can include since you have only completed four of the activities in this chapter. Your final crime scene, after you complete all eight activities, will have more possibilities.

Engineering/Technology Design

The engineering-design process involves a number of distinct steps. In creating a crime scene, you are involved in a design process. Note how your efforts follow the design model described.

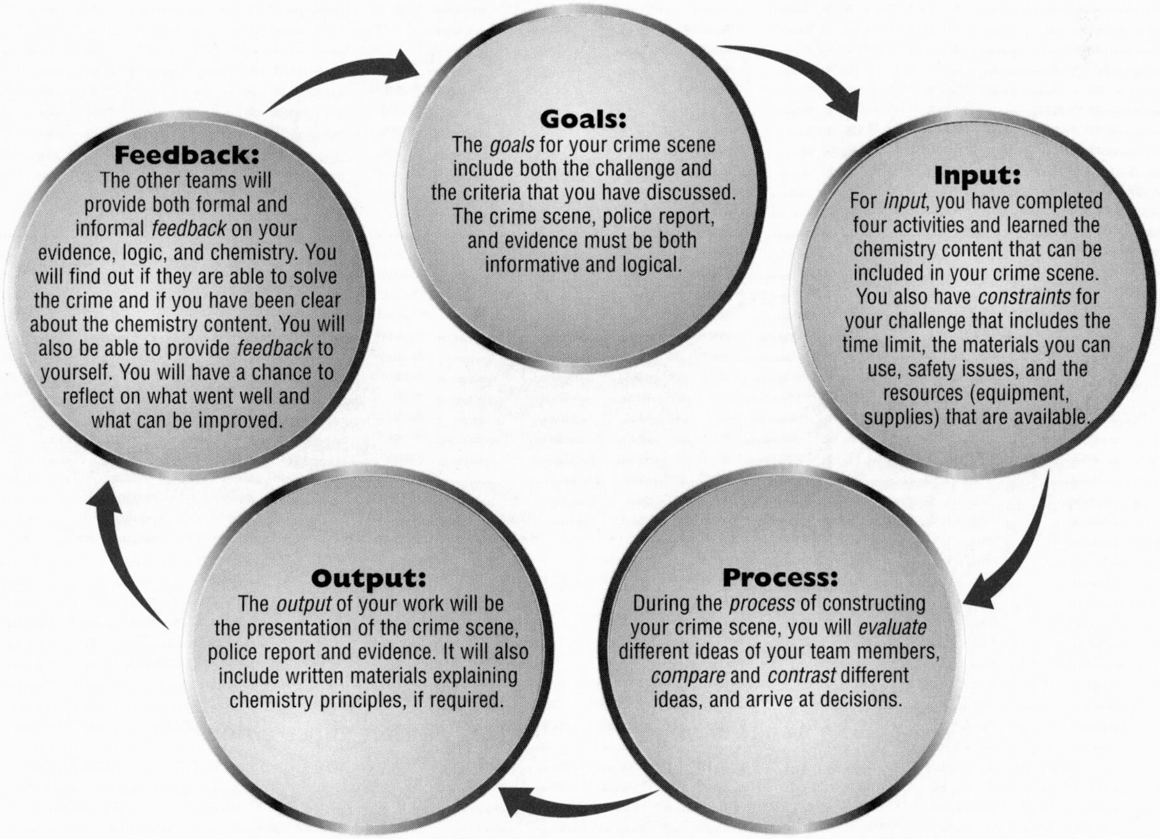

Goals:
The goals for your crime scene include both the challenge and the criteria that you have discussed. The crime scene, police report, and evidence must be both informative and logical.
Input:
For input, you have completed four activities and learned the chemistry content that can be included in your crime scene. You also have constraints for your challenge that includes the time limit, the materials you can use, safety issues, and the resources (equipment, supplies) that are available.
Process:
During the process of constructing your crime scene, you will evaluate different ideas of your team members, compare and contrast different ideas, and arrive at decisions.
Output:
The output of your work will be the presentation of the crime scene, police report and evidence. It will also include written materials explaining chemistry principles, if required.
Feedback:
The other teams will provide both formal and informal feedback on your evidence, logic, and chemistry. You will find out if they are able to solve the crime and if you have been clear about the chemistry content. You will also be able to provide feedback to yourself. You will have a chance to reflect on what went well and what can be improved.

Remember: This is a *first try*. The feedback that you get from this brief presentation of a crime scene will be extremely valuable when you prepare for the full crime show at the end of the chapter. At that point, you will begin the entire design cycle again. That's why it is called a cycle. You go through it over and over to improve your design or, in this case, the forensics challenge.

Activity 5 Developing Latent Prints

What Do You See?

Who has seen my MISSING COOKIE
The MISSING COOKIE MYSTERY

GOALS

In this activity you will:

- Learn how to identify fingerprints.
- Develop **latent** (invisible) fingerprints using the silver nitrate method.
- Explain, using specific terms and concepts, the chemistry behind the silver-nitrate method from the macroscopic, nanoscopic, and symbolic perspectives.

What Do You Think?

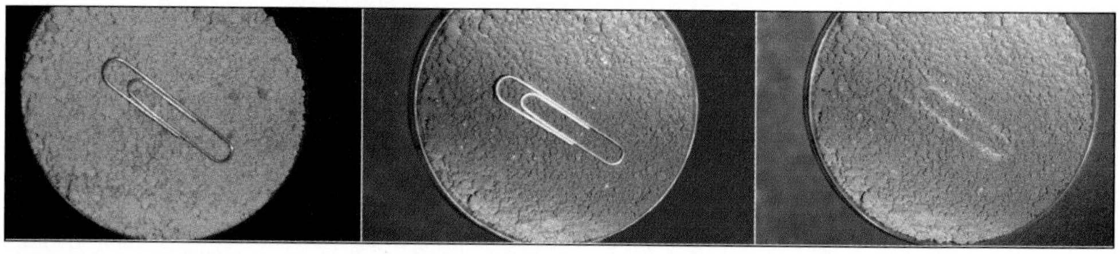

The picture above shows a dish of silver chloride with a paper clip on top of it. The picture in the middle shows the same dish after exposure to ultraviolet light. The picture on the right shows the dish after the paper clip is removed.

- **What changes do you observe after silver chloride has been exposed to UV light?**
- **Why have these changes occurred?**

Record your ideas about these questions in your *Active Chemistry* log. Be prepared to discuss your responses with your small group and the class.

Investigate

In this *Investigate* section you will explore how one chemical, silver chloride, and its properties aid forensic chemists in their discovery and identification of fingerprints at a crime scene. First, you will learn more about silver chloride and its synthesis. Then, you will investigate the properties of fingerprints and determine how forensic scientists make their identifications. Finally, you will create your own procedure to analyze fingerprints using silver chloride. Be sure to ask plenty of questions in the first two parts of this investigation, so you create the most effective procedure to identify latent prints!

Part A: Properties of Silver Chloride

1. Using a clean, graduated cylinder measure 50 mL of 0.1 *M* silver nitrate solution and place it in a 250-mL beaker. Recall that the symbol *M* stands for *molarity* and represents the concentration of the ionic compound that is dissolved in the water.
2. Using a second clean graduated cylinder add 50 mL of 0.1 *M* sodium chloride solution to the beaker containing the silver nitrate solution.
   a) What happens? Record your results in your *Active Chemistry* log.
3. Filter the white precipitate.
   a) Write the word equation for the double-replacement reaction between silver nitrate and sodium chloride. Use the solubility rules in *Activity 4* to identify which product is a precipitate.
4. When you finish separating the precipitate from the solution, remove the filter paper from the funnel, unfold it and place it on a paper towel.
   a) What does the precipitate look like? Record your observations in your *Active Chemistry* log.
5. Using a spatula or a stirring rod spread the precipitate evenly over the surface of the filter paper.
6. Place a penny in the center of the paper and expose the paper to UV light for about three to five minutes.
   a) Record your observations in your *Active Chemistry* log.
7. Remove the penny from the center of the paper.
   a) How does the precipitate that was under the penny compare to the precipitate that was exposed to UV light?

Part B: Types of Fingerprints

1. Ink your right index finger on an inkpad. Place the left side of the inked finger onto a sheet of white paper. Slowly roll the finger to the right using even pressure. If your print is blurry, try again. Wash your finger with soap and water.
2. Examine your fingerprint with a magnifying glass. Using the figure below, classify your print as an arch, loop, or whorl.

Safety goggles and a lab apron must be worn *at all times* in a chemistry lab.

Silver nitrate will irritate skin and eyes. Be careful when handling it. Keep silver nitrate away from flames.

arch loop whorl

a) When a print is made, does the print represent the ridges of the fingerprint or the valleys? Record your observations and answers in your *Active Chemistry* log.

3. Compare your print to your classmates' prints.

a) Are there any similarities between prints?

b) How many of the index prints are arches, loops, or whorls?

c) Are any two prints exactly the same?

d) Can a person be identified based only on the type of print (arch, loop, or whorl)? Explain.

e) When identifying a person based on fingerprints, scientists often look for tiny features within the print itself. These features are called ***minutiae.*** Compare whorls from two people. How do they differ?

Part C: Developing Latent Prints

In *Part A* of this investigation you observed that silver chloride, AgCl, is a light-sensitive compound. It turns from white to dark gray when it is exposed to UV light. Can this property of silver chloride be used to visualize hidden prints?

Wash your hands and arms thoroughly after the activity.

1. One way to observe latent prints is the silver-nitrate method. Silver nitrate solution contains silver nitrate dissolved in water. When silver nitrate is placed on a print, a double-replacement reaction occurs between the silver nitrate in the solution and the sodium chloride (salt) in the print. You saw this type of reaction before in *Activity 4*. A double-replacement reaction is a reaction in which the positive ions in the compounds switch places.

As you observed in *Part A*, silver nitrate will react with sodium chloride to form the precipitate silver chloride, AgCl.

2. Devise a procedure to develop invisible fingerprints on a piece of paper. Hint: Before making a fingerprint on paper, wipe your index finger against your nose or behind your ear to ensure your print contains an ample amount of oils and salt.

3. When you have created a procedure, have it approved by your teacher before you begin.

a) Record your procedure and your observations in your *Active Chemistry* log. Place the developed print in your *Active Chemistry* log.

b) How does your developed print compare to the print you made in *Part B*?

c) Can you tell if the developed print is an arch, loop, or whorl?

d) Can you see the fine details (minutiae) in the print?

e) How did your image compare to those made by the other groups in class? How did your procedure compare to the other groups' procedures?

4. Dispose of the materials as directed by your teacher. Clean up your workstation.

Chem Talk

FINGERPRINTING

Fingerprint Basics

Englishman Francis Galton calculated that there are over 64 billion different possible fingerprint patterns. Although this number has since been disputed, it is agreed that the probability of any two people having the same print is very, very low. The skin on all fingertips has numerous ridges and valleys. The ridges contain sweat pores. The sweat pores excrete fatty oils, salts, and water onto the ridge surfaces. When a finger touches an object, the mixture of oils, salts such as sodium chloride (NaCl), and water is transferred to the surface of the object. This creates an "invisible" fingerprint of oil, salt, and water on the object. These prints, which cannot be seen with the naked eye, are called **latent prints**. There are three factors that make fingerprints valuable evidence. Besides their uniqueness, fingerprints also don't change as a person gets older, and they can be classified.

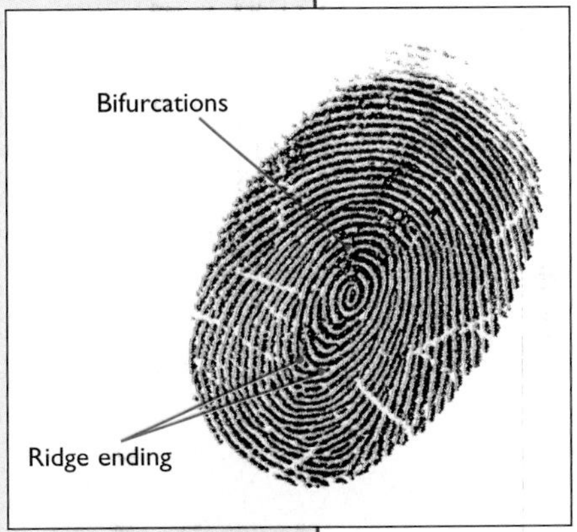
Bifurcations
Ridge ending

The Classification of Fingerprints

A fingerprint may be characterized by its ridge characteristics and its ridge patterns. A single fingerprint may contain up to 150 individual ridge characteristics called **minutiae**. It is the type and location of minutiae that make a print unique. The diagram below illustrates some of the many different types of minutiae. Generally, 10-16 identical minutiae are required to consider two prints to be a match.

Fingerprints also contain general ridge characteristics that allow them to be classified. As mentioned in the *Investigate* section, there are three different types of ridge patterns: the arch, the loop, and the whorl.

The loop is the most common pattern of ridges. Approximately 65% of the population's fingerprints are loops. In a loop, the ridges enter and exit the print from the same side of the finger. The whorl is the second most

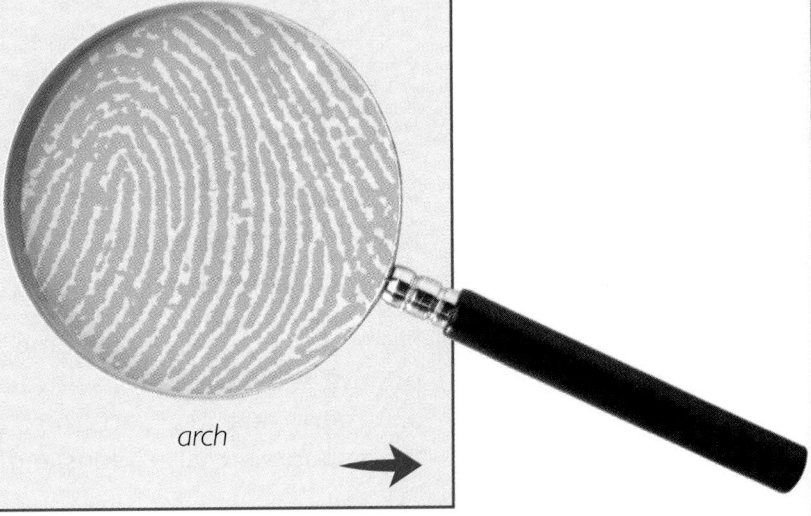

arch

Chem Words

latent prints: in forensics, fingerprints that cannot be seen by the naked eye.

minutiae: in forensics, the ridge characteristics in a fingerprint.

common pattern at 30%. A whorl must have two deltas (triangular patterns of ridge lines) on either side of the center of the print. Finally, the arch is the least common type of fingerprint at 5%. Arches look like little tents or hills in the middle of the print. It is important to remember fingerprints cannot be considered a match based on the ridge patterns alone. A match is determined by the position and type of minutiae.

Developing Latent Prints

As you have probably seen on television and in the movies, there are numerous ways to develop latent prints. They include dusting, iodine fuming, superglue fuming, and silver nitrate developing. All the methods work by interacting with one of the three components in the print: the fatty oils, the salts, or the water. In this activity you studied the silver-nitrate method.

If all else fails when looking for latent prints, one of the last methods to be used is the silver-nitrate method. Silver nitrate solution contains silver nitrate dissolved in water. When silver nitrate is placed on a print, a double-replacement reaction occurs between the silver nitrate in the solution and the sodium chloride (salt) in the print. Recall that a double-replacement reaction is a reaction in which the positive ions in the compounds switch places.

As you observed in *Part A*, silver nitrate will react with sodium chloride to form the precipitate silver chloride, AgCl. This same reaction happens on the surface of a latent print when it is painted with silver nitrate solution:

$$AgNO_{3(aq)} + NaCl_{(s)} \rightarrow AgCl_{(s)} + NaNO_{3(aq)}$$

$AgNO_{3(aq)}$	$NaCl_{(s)}$	$AgCl_{(s)}$	$NaNO_{3(aq)}$
painted on the print	*salt in the print*	*precipitate formed on the print*	

Silver chloride is formed on the surface of the print. However, at this point the print is still invisible.

Why Silver Chloride Turns Gray

Silver chloride is an ionic compound. Ionic compounds are composed of positive and negative ions attracted to each other. They are arranged in an orderly repeating pattern to maximize the attractive forces between the oppositely charged ions and to minimize the repulsive forces

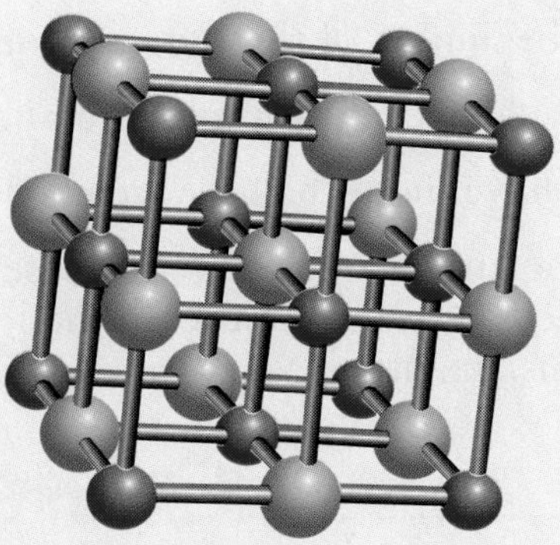

between the like charged ions. This regular repeating pattern is called the **crystalline structure** of the compound. The crystalline structure for silver chloride is shown in the diagram.

Notice the alternating pattern of positive silver ions and negative chloride ions. When a crystal of silver chloride is exposed to light, the light has enough energy to promote electrons in the crystal to a higher energy level. When electrons are in the higher level (called an "excited state," remember *Activity 3* and the luminol reaction) they can undergo reactions that do not usually occur. Ultimately, a chloride ion in the crystal loses one of its electrons to a silver ion. The silver ion gains the electron and becomes silver metal. The chlorine atom combines with another chlorine atom that has lost an electron to form chlorine gas. Silver metal is gray; its presence explains why the precipitate turns gray. This process is repeated throughout the crystal and the net reaction is:

oxidation (from $2Cl^-$ to Cl_2^0)

$$2Ag^+{}_{(aq)} + 2Cl^-{}_{(aq)} \rightarrow 2Ag^0{}_{(s)} + Cl_2{}^0{}_{(g)}$$

reduction (from $2Ag^+$ to $2Ag^0$)

When an atom or ion loses an electron we say that it has been **oxidized**. In this reaction the chloride ion loses an electron and is oxidized. The silver ion takes the electron and becomes silver metal. When an atom or ion gains an electron we say that it has been **reduced**. This type of reaction is an **oxidation-reduction reaction**. Keep these basic terms in mind, because you will learn more about oxidation-reduction reactions in the next activity.

Upon exposure to UV light, the silver ion in the silver chloride is converted into silver metal and the print turns gray. This creates a visible image of the print in much the same manner as photography. Also, silver nitrate reacts with the proteins in your skin. If you were to spill silver nitrate on your skin, then go outside, a similar developing reaction would occur. The UV light from the Sun would end up leaving a black or brown stain on your skin. As a last note, if the silver-nitrate method is used by forensic chemists when analyzing evidence, it is one of the last methods used to visualize the prints. This is because silver nitrate destroys other forms of evidence, such as DNA.

Chem Words

crystalline structure: the regular arrangement of the oppositely charged ions of the compound, geometric bonding pattern, and the packing of the metal atoms in the structure in solid salts, compounds, and metals.

oxidized: an atom, molecule, or ion that has lost one or more electrons to gain a certain positive charge.

reduced: an atom, molecule, or ion that has gained one or more electrons to gain a certain negative charge.

oxidation-reduction reaction: a chemical reaction in which an atom, molecule, or ion transfer electron(s) to another atom, molecule, or ion.

Checking Up

1. Why are fingerprints valuable pieces of evidence in forensics?
2. What are three components of a fingerprint that are used in developing latent prints?
3. Why does silver chloride turn gray when exposed to UV light?

What Do You Think Now?

At the beginning of this activity you were asked:

- **What changes do you observe after silver chloride has been exposed to UV light?**
- **Why have these changes occurred?**

Read the answers you gave to these questions. In a detailed paragraph, write what happened from the picture on the left to the picture on the right. Use the vocabulary from this activity as you write your response.

Chem Essential Questions

What does it mean?

Chemistry explains a macroscopic phenomenon (what you observe) with a description of what happens at the nanoscopic level (atoms and molecules) using symbolic structures as a way to communicate. Complete the chart below in your *Active Chemistry* log.

MACRO	NANO	SYMBOLIC
What was required to observe latent prints?	*Describe the reaction of silver nitrate and the salt in your sweat in developing latent prints.*	*Draw a picture of an NaCl crystal.*

How do you know?

How could you demonstrate that it is the salt from your skin that reacts with the silver nitrate when "lifting" latent fingerprints?

Why do you believe?

What else might involve oxidation or reduction that you've experienced outside this class? Provide a positive and negative consequence of having everybody's fingerprints on file.

Why should you care?

Fingerprinting has always been considered an excellent way in which to determine the identity of a person. How can you use fingerprints in a creative way as part of the crime scene that you develop?

Reflecting on the Activity and the Challenge

Part of the problem you are facing in creating a crime scene is to understand how to observe something that is not initially visible. In this activity you focused on how to develop hidden prints. Think about how you can use hidden prints to enhance your crime scene. Also, think about the types of surfaces that will work best with the silver-nitrate method. Finally, keep in mind the limitations of the silver-nitrate test and how you can use those limitations in your crime scene.

Chem to Go

1. In your own words, describe how the silver-nitrate technique works in developing latent prints.
2. When placing the silver nitrate solution on the paper, why is a soft bristle brush used?
3. What would happen to the image if the print was not left under the UV light long enough? What would happen to the image if you left the print under the UV light too long? Explain.
4. Would the silver-nitrate technique work best on construction paper, the trigger guard for a gun, or a window? Explain.
5. Would the silver-nitrate technique work on a piece of evidence that had been soaked in water? Explain. (Hint: think back to the solubility rules in *Activity 4*.)
6. Which of the following reactions are double-replacement reactions?

   a) $CuSO_4 + BaCl_2 \rightarrow CuCl_2 + BaSO_4$

   b) $Mg + Cl_2 \rightarrow MgCl_2$

   c) $Na_2CO_3 + 2HCl \rightarrow 2NaCl + H_2O + CO_2$

   d) $CdCl_2 + Na_2S \rightarrow CdS + 2NaCl$
7. Complete the following double-replacement word equations. Circle the precipitates.

   a) copper (II) sulfate + sodium carbonate →

   b) cadmium (II) chloride + sodium hydroxide →

   c) lead (II) nitrate + sodium sulfate →

   d) nickel (II) chloride + sodium carbonate →
8. Can a suspect be identified as a criminal based on his ridge patterns? Explain.
9. ***Preparing for the Chapter Challenge***

   Fingerprints need fingers to create them. It is time to begin to create some of your characters for your crime scene. Look through your original table from the first *Preparing for the Chapter Challenge* from *Activity 1* at the types of evidence throughout this entire chapter. Reflect back on the details of the evidence from the first five activities. After thinking back on your work this far and the possibilities from the upcoming activities, create at least four characters for your crime scene. For each character create a brief biography, a picture, and of course, a unique fingerprint!

Inquiring Further

Methods of identifying fingerprints

Conduct the experiment you design only under adult supervision.

As you can tell from your previous laboratory activities in this chapter, a good forensic scientist relies on the physical and chemical properties of her evidence to identify more specifics on that piece of evidence. In the glass analysis you used the physical property of density; when studying blood you relied on a chemical property of the iron (II) ion; and in your study of white powders you used both chemical and physical properties of the white powder to make a positive identification.

A forensic scientist's treatment of the most commonly identified form of evidence —fingerprints—is no different. In the lab you relied on physical and chemical properties of fingerprint residues to make a positive identification through the silver-nitrate method. Other methods can be used that also rely on the properties of the fingerprint: dusting for prints, iodine fuming (through sublimation of iodine), and cynoacrylate (superglue) fuming. Under the guidance of your teacher, research and perform one or more of these techniques. Present your findings to the class, highlighting *how* your technique relies on chemical and/or physical properties.

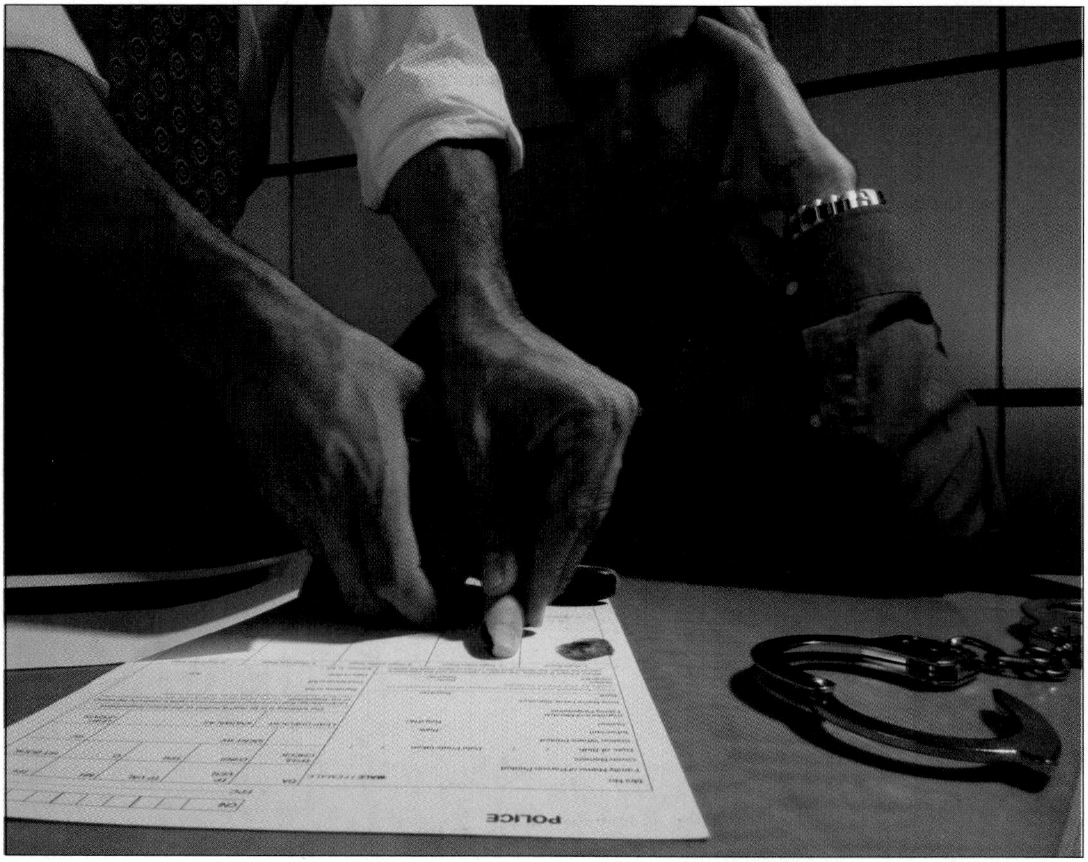
POLICE

Activity 6 Metal Activity Series

What Do You See?

METAL
BATHS
SPA

GOALS

In this activity you will:

- Use chemical properties and deductive reasoning to identify a pattern in metal reactions.
- Compare and contrast single-replacement and double-replacement reactions.
- Define and explain the concepts of oxidation and reduction.
- Gain an understanding of the activity series of metals.

Safety goggles and a lab apron must be worn *at all times* in a chemistry lab.

What Do You Think?

Aluminum was once so valuable that kings used to impress their guests with aluminum forks and spoons. Aluminum now sells for 20¢ per pound. Gold sells for $550 per ounce.

- **What is the difference between aluminum and gold?**
- **Why has the value of aluminum decreased over the years?**

Record your ideas about these questions in your *Active Chemistry* log. Be prepared to discuss your responses with your group and the class.

Investigate

A piece of metal is left at the crime scene. Could this be a clue? In this activity, you'll look at a way of identifying a pure metallic element.

1. Obtain small strips of aluminum (Al), copper (Cu), iron (Fe), magnesium (Mg), tin (Sn), and zinc (Zn). Other forms of metal can be used (shavings or filings, like steel or copper "wool," shot), but strips work best. Use sandpaper or steel wool to clean off the surface of the strips as thoroughly as possible.

   a) Why is it necessary to clean the strips? Record your thoughts in your *Active Chemistry* log.

Color							
	$Al(NO_3)_3$	$Cu(NO_3)_2$	$Fe(NO_3)_3$	$Mg(NO_3)_2$	$SnCl_4$	$Zn(NO_3)_2$	HCl
Al							
Cu							
Fe							
Mg							
Sn							
Zn							

Mix chemicals only as instructed by your teacher.

Wash your hands and arms thoroughly after the activity.

2. Set up a 6 × 7 grid on a 48-well reaction plate or a combination of well plates. Place a piece of blank white paper underneath the reaction plate. This will make it easier to observe the reactions that will occur.

3. Make sure the wells are as clean as possible. Cut seven 3 mm squares from the aluminum strip and place one in each well of the first row. Repeat with the other five metals in the next six rows of wells. A sample grid is provided above. Each box represents one well on your well plate.

   a) Draw the grid in your *Active Chemistry* log.

4. Make a note of the color of each original solution above its column. These colors are characteristic of the metal ions in these solutions. For example copper (II) nitrate, $Cu(NO_3)_2$, is blue. The blue is due to the Cu^{2+} ion in solution.

5. Add ten drops of the specific 0.2 *M* ionic solution to each well in the column, starting with aluminum nitrate, $Al(NO_3)_3$ in the first column. Many of these solutions are called solutions of nitrates, because they have the anion nitrate, NO_3^-. Instead of tin (IV) nitrate, tin (IV) chloride is used. In the last column of wells, add 10 drops of 1.0 *M* HCl.

   a) Record what you see in each well on the corresponding square of your grid. Look for color changes in the solutions or the metals. You may also see precipitates, bubbles, or other evidence of the occurrence of a reaction. You may want to use a magnifying glass to help you see very small changes. (Hint: some of these changes take longer than others, so be patient.)

   b) If after a second look you still see no changes, then write "N.R." in that box to represent no chemical reaction has happened.

6. Once you stop seeing new evidence of chemical reactions, look for a pattern in the results you have recorded. If you can't find one, try rewriting your table of results.

   a) First, next to the metal's atomic symbol, write the number of solutions each metal reacted with.

   b) Next, beside the solution's chemical formula, write the number of metals each solution reacted with.

7. Dispose of the materials as directed by your teacher. Clean up your workstation.

8. Make a second results grid, but this time you will change the order of the metals and solutions. Order the metals from the greatest number of reactions at the top row

to the least number of reactions as the bottom row. Order the solutions from the greatest number of reactions in the first column to the least number of reactions in the final column. Then fill in your results in the new grid. Write a brief summary of the pattern you see now.

a) Record your arrangement and your answer in your *Active Chemistry* log.

9. The analysis of diagrams is just as important as being able to draw them. Take a look at the diagrams shown here. Analyze the diagrams carefully and discuss them with your partners before tackling the questions below.

a) What metal elements are represented in these diagrams?

b) How is the structure of a metallic element similar to that of an ionic compound? How is it different?

c) What is the difference between Cu and Cu^{2+} at the macroscale (i.e., in the test tubes)?

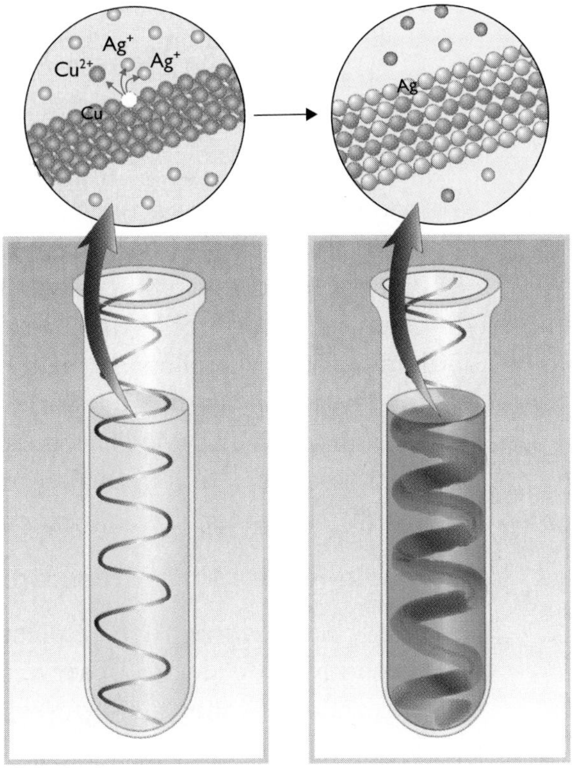

Cu²⁺
Ag⁺
Ag⁺
Cu
Ag

Chem Talk

METAL ACTIVITY SERIES

Metals and Transition Metals

Metals vary in their reactivity. Some metals lose their outer electrons so easily that they rarely are seen in their pure form. They react with too many common substances, like water. Metals that are in Group I of the periodic table, such as sodium and potassium, fall into this category. Group II metals tend to be slightly less reactive. However, not all Group I metals are more reactive than Group II metals. Other metals are so unreactive that they are found in nature in their pure state. Gold and silver fall into this category. This property accounts in part for the high value placed upon them.

Chem Words

single-replacement reaction: a chemical reaction in which a free element replaces an ion in a compound.

Gold and silver, along with many of the metals you tested in this activity, are transition metals. Transition metals are located in the center section of the periodic table, making the "transition" from the metals on the left side of the periodic table to the nonmetals on the right side.

Iron is an example of a transition metal. Like many transition metals, iron can form cations with different charges and properties. As you saw in the luminol reaction from *Activity 3*, iron (II) and iron (III) ions had different chemical properties. When naming most transition metals, a roman number is used, following the metal name. The numeral represents the charge on the metal ion in the compound. For example, you used $SnCl_{4(aq)}$ in this activity. This is called tin (IV) chloride, since tin is a transition metal and in this compound the tin ions have a charge of +4. Tin (II) is another possible cation of tin. It has a charge of +2.

Single-Replacement Reactions

In this activity, you placed a piece of metal into a solution of an ionic compound in order to observe a possible chemical reaction. This type of reaction is called a **single-replacement reaction**. An example of a single-replacement reaction you didn't observe is the reaction between copper metal and silver nitrate solution.

copper + silver nitrate → copper (II) nitrate + silver

$$Cu_{(s)} + 2AgNO_{3(aq)} \rightarrow Cu(NO_3)_{2(aq)} + 2Ag_{(s)}$$

It is called a single-replacement reaction because a free element replaces an ion in the compound. The ion in the compound becomes a free, neutral element. In the example, the metal copper replaces the silver metal ion in the compound silver nitrate, forming copper (II) nitrate. The silver ions that are replaced become neutral silver atoms. This type of reaction is similar to the double-replacement reaction you studied in the last activity. In a double-replacement reaction, ions from two different compounds exchange places. In a single-replacement reaction a free element replaces an ion in a compound. An example of each type of reaction is shown below.

Single replacement $Zn_{(s)} + Cu(NO_3)_{2(aq)} \rightarrow Zn(NO_3)_{2(aq)} + Cu_{(s)}$

Double replacement $NaCl(aq) + AgNO_3(aq) \rightarrow AgCl(s) + NaNO_3(aq)$

Other examples of single-replacement reactions include:

zinc + copper (II) sulfate → zinc sulfate + copper

$$Zn(s) + CuSO_4(aq) \rightarrow ZnSO_4(aq) + Cu(s)$$

aluminum + sulfuric acid → aluminum sulfate + hydrogen gas

$$2Al(s) + 3H_2SO_4(aq) \rightarrow Al_2(SO_4)_3(aq) + 3H_2(g)$$

Single-replacement reactions differ from double-replacement reactions in that electrons are transferred in single-replacement reactions but not in double-replacement reactions. In double-replacement reaction ions are switching places. In a single-replacement reaction the free metal is losing electrons (thus becoming a positively charged ion) and the metal ion is gaining electrons (thus becoming a neutral atom). Because of this electron transfer, single-replacement reactions are classified as oxidation-reduction reactions.

Oxidation and Reduction

Atoms that have an equal number of protons and electrons are neutral and have no charge. Any metal in its natural state, when it is not combined with any other element, such as copper metal, aluminum metal, and iron metal, is neutral. So, iron metal $Fe(s)$, copper metal $Cu(s)$, and aluminum metal $Al(s)$ are all neutral. If the metal loses electrons, it becomes a cation, an ion with a positive charge.

In *Activity 4*, you learned that when a metal forms a compound, it loses electrons. So, in a single-replacement reaction, the free metal loses electrons to the cation in the compound. Look at the reaction you did in this activity between aluminum metal and iron (III) nitrate:

$$Al(s) + Fe(NO_3)_3(aq) \rightarrow Fe(s) + Al(NO_3)_3(aq)$$

In this reaction aluminum metal loses three electrons to iron ions, forming aluminum ion.

$$Al(s) \rightarrow Al^{3+}(aq) + 3e^-$$

When a substance loses electrons it has been oxidized. Oxidation is the loss of electrons. In this case aluminum metal has been oxidized to form aluminum ion. Also, in oxidation, the charge, or **oxidation number** as it is called, is becoming more positive, 0 to +3.

Chem Words

oxidation number: a positive or negative number assigned to each atom in a compound to help keep track of the electrons in a chemical reaction.

Chem Words

oxidation-reduction (redox) reaction: a chemical reaction (change) in which electrons are transferred from one substance to another.

valence electrons: the number of electrons in the outermost shell.

activity series of metals: a list of the metals based on their ability to be oxidized. The easier it is to oxidize the more active the metal is in comparison to other metals.

However, electrons cannot just be lost. Another element has to accept them. In this case, iron (III) ions from the iron nitrate accept the electrons from aluminum to form iron metal.

$$Fe^{3+}(aq) + 3e^- \rightarrow Fe(s)$$

When a substance gains electrons, it has been reduced. In this case, iron (III) ion has been reduced to form iron metal. Notice that in reduction, the oxidation number, or charge, gets smaller, +3 to 0. The net reaction is (nitrate, NO_3^-, is omitted because it is not changed in the reaction):

oxidation (Al → Al³⁺)

$$Al(s) + Fe^{3+}(aq) \rightarrow Al^{3+}(aq) + Fe(s)$$

reduction (Fe³⁺ → Fe)

Another example is the reaction between zinc and a copper (II) solution:

oxidation (Zn → Zn²⁺)

$$Zn(s) + Cu^{2+}(aq) \rightarrow Zn^{2+}(aq) + Cu(s)$$

reduction (Cu²⁺ → Cu)

Metal Activity Series

Name	Symbol
lithium	Li
potassium	K
calcium	Ca
sodium	Na
magnesium	Mg
aluminum	Al
zinc	Zn
iron	Fe
tin	Sn
lead	Pb
hydrogen*	H
copper	Cu
mercury	Hg
silver	Ag
platinum	Pt
gold	Au

* Hydrogen is not a metal but it behaves like a metal in some chemical reactions so it is included in the activity series.

An easy way to remember oxidation and reduction is the saying "***LEO** the lion says **GER***"– **L**oss of **E**lectrons is **O**xidation, **G**ain of **E**lectrons is **R**eduction. Since oxidation does not occur without reduction, these types of reactions are called **oxidation-reduction** reactions.

The Activity Series of Metals

As you observed in this activity, not all metals will react to replace all of the metal ions. Some elements do not lose their outer, or **valence**, electrons in single-replacement reactions as easily as other elements.

Some elements are not oxidized as easily as others. The **activity series of metals**, ranks the metals in order of ease of oxidation. The elements at the top of the activity series lose their electrons in single-replacement reactions more easily than do elements at the bottom of the list. The activity series can be used to predict if a single-replacement reaction will take place. For a single-replacement reaction to occur, the free, neutral metal must be higher on the list than the metal ion it is trying to replace. For example, the following reaction will not occur:

$$Au_{(s)} + FeCl_{3(aq)} \rightarrow \text{no reaction}$$

No reaction will occur in this case and therefore Au, the free atom, is lower than Fe, the metal ion, on the activity series. Another example is below. This reaction will take place:

$$3Mg_{(s)} + 2FeCl_{3(aq)} \rightarrow 3MgCl_{2(aq)} + 2Fe^{3+}{}_{(aq)}$$

This reaction will occur and therefore Mg, the free atom, is higher on the activity series than Fe, the metal ion. Magnesium is oxidized more easily than iron, and magnesium will transfer its outer electrons to iron.

Checking Up

1. Are all Group I metals more reactive than Group II metals?
2. Where are the transitional metals found on the periodic table? Why are they called transitional metals?
3. Explain the difference between single-replacement reactions and double replacement reactions.
4. Is an oxidation-reduction reaction an example of a single-replacement or double-replacement reaction?
5. How would you use the activity series of metals as a student chemist?

What Do You Think Now?

At the beginning of this activity you were asked:

- **What is the difference between aluminum and gold?**
- **Why has the value of aluminum decreased over the years?**

What have you learned about these metals and their reactivity from this activity? Finding pure gold may be difficult because of its scarcity but not because it reacts with other substances. How might this explain why the value of aluminum has changed so drastically over time?

Chem Essential Questions

What does it mean?

Chemistry explains a macroscopic phenomenon (what you observe) with a description of what happens at the nanoscopic level (atoms and molecules) using symbolic structures as a way to communicate. Complete the chart below in your *Active Chemistry* log.

MACRO	NANO	SYMBOLIC
What reactions did you observe between metals and the nitrate solutions?	*Explain what is happening at the nanoscopic level to the atoms of metals in the single-replacement reactions.*	*To assist in predicting what will happen when a metal is placed in a nitrate solution, you can use the activity series of metals. How can you use this chart?*

How do you know?

What evidence do you have that copper will replace iron or that iron will replace copper when the metal is placed in a nitrate solution?

Why do you believe?

When the outside of a car is damaged and the paint is scraped away, the exposed steel (mostly iron) soon becomes reddish-brown with rust. Explain what is happening. What is oxidized? What is reduced?

Why should you care?

What are the advantages and disadvantages to using chemical properties to identify metals from a crime scene? How could you use these advantages or disadvantages in your crime scene?

Reflecting on the Activity and the Challenge

In this activity you learned that some metals are more reactive than others, and that more reactive metals will replace less reactive metals as part of ionic compounds in aqueous (water) solutions. You can use this information to identify what metal fragment you find at a crime scene. In the next activity, you will examine one way of using this knowledge to gather information about a crime.

Chem to Go

1. List the metals you examined in order of decreasing activity in single-replacement reactions.
2. Based on your results with HCl, where do you think hydrogen would belong in this activity series? Explain using your specific results.
3. Use the Metal Activity Series to determine which of these combinations you would expect to produce a reaction. For each, explain why.

   a) aluminum with iron (III) sulfate
   b) zinc with copper (II) sulfate
   c) calcium with zinc sulfate
   d) magnesium with zinc nitrate
4. Complete the word equations for the single-replacement reactions in *Question 3.*
5. The chemical formula for rust is Fe_2O_3. Iron metal is simply Fe. When iron is converted to iron (III) oxide, what chemical process occurs?
6. Sometimes a piece of zinc metal is attached to a steel pipe. Why?
7. Which reactions are redox reactions? For the redox reactions identify the reactant that is oxidized and the reactant that is reduced.

   a) $Sn(s) + Cu^{2+}(aq) \rightarrow Sn^{2+}(aq) + Cu(s)$

   b) $2Zn(s) + Sn^{4+}(aq) \rightarrow 2Zn^{2+}(aq) + Sn(s)$

   c) $Cu^{2+}(aq) + 2OH^{-}(aq) \rightarrow Cu(OH)_2(s)$
8. ***Preparing for the Chapter Challenge***

   Now that you have practiced writing a crime scene story and received feedback on it, it is time to begin drafting your group's story with the cast of characters you created in the previous activities. With your group, spend some time talking about a possible story, not forgetting the pieces of evidence we have yet to investigate (serial number recovery and ink identification). A good place to start may be to share your *C.S.I.* scripts. In your group, have a recorder write down your ideas and hold them for the group, and a leader to keep the conversation on task and moving. After the discussion, write your reflection of the conversation in your *Active Chemistry* log. Be sure to include any final decisions made on the direction or plot of the story.

Inquiring Further

Removing oxidation

One of the first steps you used in this activity was to sand or steel wool each metal strip. You were asked to respond to why this was important. With the guidance of your teacher, design an experiment to determine if the sanding really was an important step. Report your results. Explain your observations, reflecting on the nanoscopic and symbolic meanings presented in this and other activities.

Activity 7 Serial-Number Etching

What Do You See?

564738
IRON SOLUTION
564738
THE RETURN OF THE SERIAL NUMBER!
564738

GOALS

In this activity you will:

- Apply the chemical and physical properties of metals to serial-number stamping and recovery.
- Explain what happens at the nanoscopic level when serial numbers are stamped and recovered.
- Use and create models to represent the nanoscopic physical and chemical changes of metals.

What Do You Think?

All matter is made of atoms. Metals are matter, so logically they are also made of atoms. Keep this in mind as you respond to the next two statements.

- **What do you think happens to the atoms in a piece of metal when a serial number is stamped into the metal?**
- **Without referencing any sources, draw a picture to illustrate your idea.**

Record your ideas about these questions and draw the picture in your *Active Chemistry* log. Be prepared to discuss your responses with your small group and the class.

Investigate

In this activity you will use the chemical and physical properties of metals to investigate the science behind serial-number recovery.

Part A: Stamping a Serial Number

1. Obtain a rectangular piece of aluminum metal approximately 3 inches long, 1/2 inch wide, and 1/8 inch thick.

JH4NA1153PT000391

2. Before proceeding consider what will happen if you hit the die too hard. If you hit the die too hard it will take a long time to obliterate the number. If you hit the die too softly, it will not penetrate far enough under the metal's surface to allow the number to be restored later. Your instructor may have you practice stamping a scrap piece of aluminum a few times.

3. Using a hammer and dies, carefully stamp eight different numbers into the aluminum bar to create a serial number like the one in the diagram. Do not use the same number more than twice. Also, make sure to hit the die evenly. Important: Record the serial number you have stamped and its position on the aluminum bar in your *Active Chemistry* log because you may not remember these things exactly later on.

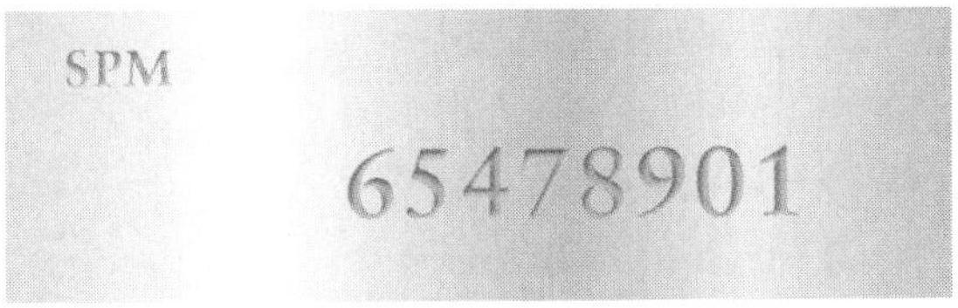
SPM
65478901

4. In the upper left corner, stamp your initials or your group's identification number by hitting it extremely hard with the hammer. Look at the back side of the metal where you put your initials. What do you see? Try to explain why this has happened.

   a) Record your observations and your answers in your *Active Chemistry* log.

5. Record the number or combination of letters written on the back of your piece of aluminum using a black marker. This number is there for your instructor to match and for you to know which side formerly had the serial number!

6. Turn your sample in to your teacher so that the serial numbers can be ground off.

Part B: Etching to Recover Serial Numbers

1. Examine the front of the aluminum piece under a hand lens or stereoscope.

   a) Sketch your observations in your *Active Chemistry* log.

2. You must first prepare the surface for the etching process by sanding the surface until it is perfectly smooth. Any rough surface will cause the powerful etching solutions to pool, giving you poor results. Sand the surface first using 100-grit sandpaper, followed by 150-grit, and finally 220-grit, wiping the surface with a damp towel between each of the grits. Sand the bar in an up and down motion as shown in the diagram.

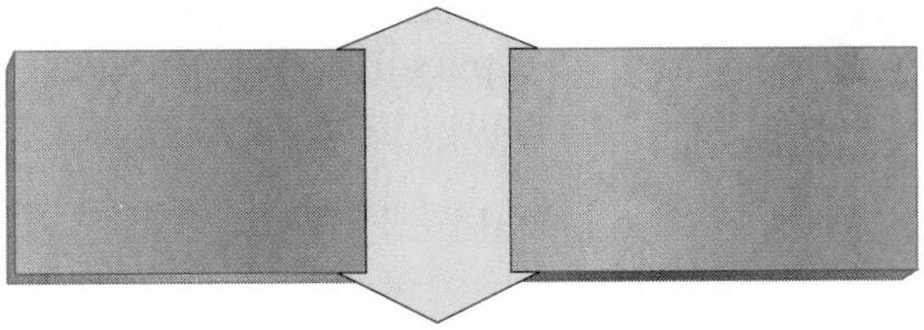

3. Again examine the front of the aluminum piece under a hand lens or stereoscope. Even at this early stage, you may start to see the beginnings of a serial number.

   a) Sketch your observations in your *Active Chemistry* log.

Safety goggles and a lab apron must be worn *at all times* in a chemistry lab.

Report any spills of the etching solution to your teacher immediately.

4. Using gloves, wipe the metal thoroughly with a cotton ball soaked in ethanol. This removes all of the oils from the surface. Oil and the aqueous solutions you'll use do not mix. A layer of oil will keep the etching solution from reacting with the surface of the metal evenly, so it is very important to keep the surface oil free.

5. Still using gloves (keep them on throughout the first portion of this activity), use a cotton ball to evenly apply the etching solution of hydrochloric acid and iron (III) chloride.

6. Repeat *Step 5* every two minutes.

The etching solution contains a concentrated strong acid, so you must be careful not to get any on your skin or clothing.

7. This process is not quick, so be patient. While working on the applications (which may take up to 40 minutes), begin the next portion of the laboratory activity. Occasionally you may want to look at the metal with a hand lens or under the stereoscope to see what is happening. Be sure that the gloved person uses only the etching solution and touches the bar. The gloved person should not touch the material in the next portion of the lab.

8. When you are finished, rinse the bar in a solution of sodium bicarbonate.

   a) Sketch your observations in your *Active Chemistry* log.

   b) What happened? Were you able to discern the serial numbers? How long did it take? Record your answers in your *Active Chemistry* log.

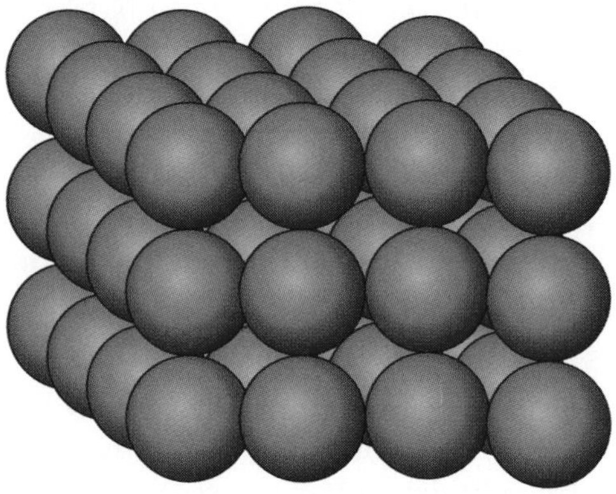

   c) A metal is made of atoms packed in a regular repeating pattern, called a lattice. Based on the figure and your observations, what do you think happened to the atoms when you hit the die to create a serial number? What do you think the solution did to restore the serial number?

Part C: Making a Model

1. Obtain two different colored blocks of modeling clay. Working on a piece of wax paper, cut 20 thin layers, approximately 1 mm thick (about the thickness of a penny), from the rectangular end of each block of clay. Each of these layers will represent a layer of metal atoms in the sample.

2. Using ten layers of each color, create two stacks of alternating colors.

3. Take the wooden dowel and carefully roll out each stack so that it is about 3⁄4 of its original thickness. Carefully trim the edges so that you can see each layer and so it is rectangular again.

4. Cut each rectangle into two squares. You have now created four copies of a simple model of a metal sample. You will use three of the squares. The fourth square is an extra, in case you make a mistake.

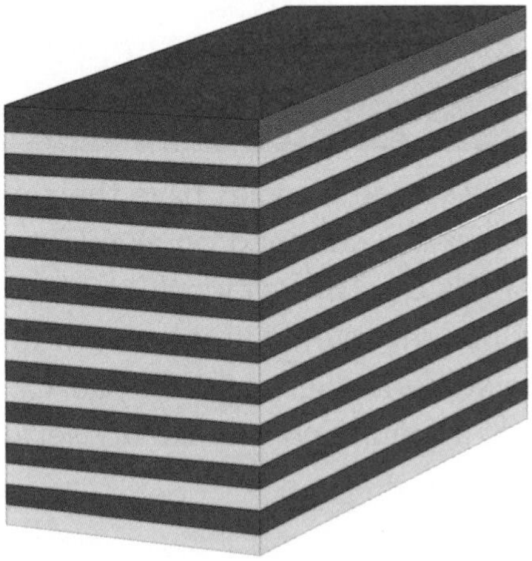

   a) Take one of the square models and make a drawing of what it looks like in your *Active Chemistry* log. Label this model the "unstamped" model.

   b) What do you think will happen to the layers of metal atoms when the square is stamped? Record your prediction in your *Active Chemistry* log. Explain the reasoning behind your prediction.

5. Carefully press the end of an unsharpened pencil 2–3 mm into one square of the clay model. This will simulate stamping the metal with a blunt stamp. Set the model aside.

6. Take a second square model. Using a sharpened pencil, press the sharpened end 2–3 mm into the surface of the metal.

   a) Create two new drawings in your *Active Chemistry* log. The first drawing should illustrate what you think the layers will look like under the blunt stamp. The second drawing should illustrate what you think the layers will look like underneath the sharp stamp. Leave space underneath each drawing.

7. Once you have finished your drawings, cut each square in half using a thin blade. Make sure you cut through the middle of the stamped areas.

   a) Underneath the drawings you made previously, draw what the layers actually look like now that you can see the middle of the stamped areas. How did your prediction compare to the actual results? What happens to the metal atoms underneath the stamped areas? Record your answers in your *Active Chemistry* log.

   b) Compare the results of the blunt stamp and sharp stamp. Which process affects the metal layers the most? Explain your reasoning. Record your answers in your *Active Chemistry* log.

8. Dispose of the materials as directed by your teacher. Clean up your workstation.

Wash your hands and arms thoroughly after the activity.

Chem Talk

Chem Words

lustrous: a characteristic property of how much a metal shines.

ductile: a characteristic property of how easy it is to pull metal into the form of a wire.

malleable: a characteristic property of how easy it is to flatten a piece of metal.

grain: a small piece of metal that shows how the atoms are arranged.

Identification Numbers

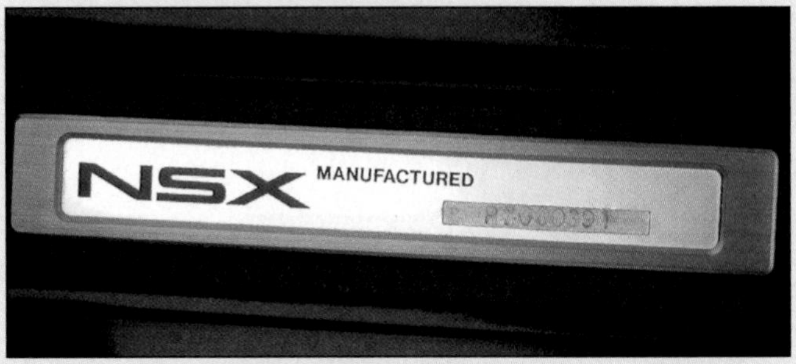
NSX
MANUFACTURED

Many expensive personal items are stamped with an identification or serial number. Automobiles also have a series of letters and numbers, a Vehicle Identification Number (VIN), to identify each car. All registered vehicles have their own unique number. Many of these VIN numbers are stamped on aluminum plates and mounted in different parts of the car. Thieves work to hide this identification number by scratching out the aluminum plates on the engine and front of car. Clever forensics student scientists, like you, can apply your knowledge of the structure of a metal and the activity series to recover the scratched-out serial number.

The Nanoscopic View of Metals

Everyone is familiar with metals. They are an integral part of society. Metals are used in cars, airplanes, skyscrapers, and many common household items such as kitchen stoves, utensils, and pots and pans. What classifies a material as being metallic? Metals are a class of elements that have many common properties. Most metals are **lustrous** (shiny), they feel cool to the touch because of their ability to conduct heat, they conduct electricity, they are **ductile** (they can be drawn into wires), and they are **malleable** (they can be hammered into thins sheets). And as you learned earlier, metals are located on the left side of the stair-step line in the Periodic Table of the Elements.

But why does serial-number etching work? To understand this you need to take a much closer look at the metal, zooming in on its nanoscopic structure. In a metal, the atoms are arranged in tiny regions called **grains**. These grains range in size from 0.01 mm to 0.1 mm.

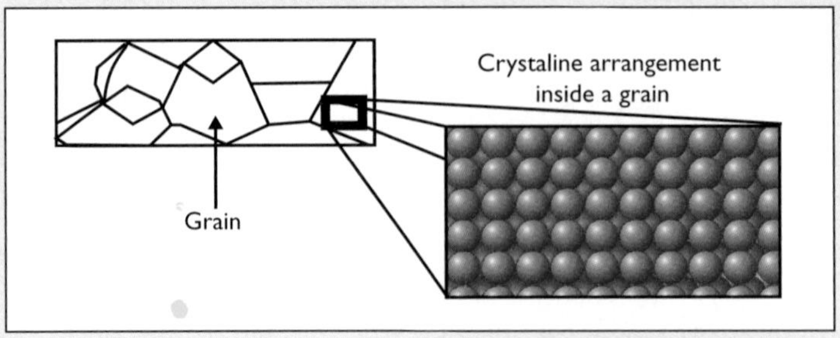
Crystaline arrangement inside a grain
Grain

Within each grain, the metal's atoms are arranged in an orderly or crystalline arrangement. Within the crystalline structure of the grain, however, there are tiny irregularities called **dislocations**.

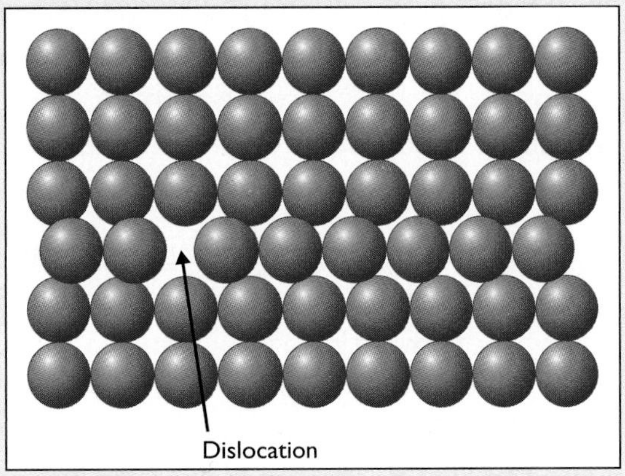
Dislocation

When a metal is bent repeatedly, the dislocation moves inside the crystal creating other dislocations. This increases the stress inside the metal until the metal becomes brittle and breaks. You can try this yourself by bending a paper clip or a coat hanger back and forth numerous times. Eventually, the paper clip or the coat hanger will break. If you were to heat the metal and allow it to cool slowly, the metal will anneal, that is, the metal atoms will rearrange themselves to relieve the stress and the metal will be malleable (bendable) again. High temperatures and slow cooling are needed for annealing to give the metal atoms sufficient energy to move and rearrange.

The Chemistry behind Serial Numbers in Metals

Serial numbers are usually stamped into metal with hard, blunt metal dies. When this is done at a fairly low temperature, such as room temperature, the metal is said to be "cold-worked" or "work-hardened." The die strikes the surface of the metal with a strong force, causing the die to penetrate the metal. The atoms just below the surface of the metal undergo a **plastic** (permanent) **deformation**. This creates a huge number of dislocations in the metal beneath the surface of the stamp. As you saw in your model, the layers of the clay were compressed directly underneath the stamped area, with the blunt "stamp" compressing more area than the sharp "stamp." The compression in your clay model is an example of plastic deformation. The further away from the stamp, the less compressed the layers were.

The same kind of physical deformation happens in the metal when it is stamped. In metals there are grains instead of layers like in the clay. The dislocations force the electrons of the atoms in the stamped grains to get closer together. This creates a lot of stress in the crystalline structure of the grain and hardens the material in that region.

Chem Words

dislocations: atoms misplaced in a crystalline structure.

plastic deformation: a permanent dislocation of atoms in an area of a metal that has been struck with a strong force.

Chem Words

etching: reproducing an engraving on the surface of a metal plate with acid.

In these stressed areas some of the energy used to make the deformation is stored in the stressed (stamped) grains. This stored energy gives the stressed (stamped) grain a higher energy than the unstamped grains. As a result, when an etching solution is applied to the surface, the stamped areas react faster than the unaltered metal. The products of this reaction have a different appearance than does the unreacted metal, so the serial number reappears as impressions, made of the reaction products, in the metal.

The **etching** method works by using single-replacement chemical reactions. As you learned in *Activity* 6, a single-replacement reaction is a type of oxidation-reduction reaction. The etching solution used for aluminum was made of hydrochloric acid and iron (III) chloride. Aluminum (Al), being higher on the activity series than iron and hydrogen, will donate some electrons to the iron (III) ions and the hydrogen ions in the etching solution. Since the iron (III) ions and the hydrogen ions are gaining electrons from the aluminum, they are being reduced and the aluminum is being oxidized (see equations below). This results in the formation of iron metal atoms, hydrogen gas, and aluminum ions. Remember, the stamped aluminum atoms have a higher energy than the unstamped atoms, so the stamped atoms will react faster with the two compounds than the unstamped aluminum atoms.

Reaction 1 from the etching solution:

$$Al_{(s)} + Fe^{3+}{}_{(aq)} \rightarrow Al^{3+}{}_{(aq)} + Fe_{(s)}$$

Reaction 2 from the etching solution:

$$2Al_{(s)} + 6H^{+}{}_{(aq)} \rightarrow 2Al^{3+}{}_{(aq)} + 3H_{2(g)}$$

If you wanted to etch a metal other than aluminum, such as iron, you would need to consult the activity series for an appropriate replacement for the iron (III) chloride solution.

Checking Up

1. What is a crystalline structure?
2. What are dislocations in a crystalline structure?
3. What type of reaction is the etching reaction?

What Do You Think Now?

At the beginning of this activity you were asked:

- **What do you think happens to the atoms in a piece of metal when a serial number is stamped into the metal?**
- **Without referencing any sources, draw a picture to illustrate your idea.**

Look back at your answers. Write a paragraph critiquing your original response. Comment on what was correct, what was incorrect, and how you would change your answers and diagram now that you've completed the lab.

Chem Essential Questions

What does it mean?

Chemistry explains a macroscopic phenomenon (what you observe) with a description of what happens at the nanoscopic level (atoms and molecules) using symbolic structures as a way to communicate. Complete the chart below in your *Active Chemistry* log.

MACRO	NANO	SYMBOLIC
Explain what events took place at the macroscopic level when you sanded, etched, and reconstructed the serial numbers.	*What oxidation-reduction reaction was able to reconstruct the serial numbers?*	*Draw a structure for the metal and the serial-number etching to explain why you were able to retrieve the numbers once they were "gone."*

How do you know?

What evidence do you have from this activity that the serial numbers can still be retrieved after they have been sanded off the metal?

Why do you believe?

In tracking stolen cars, the police often use the serial numbers to identify the vehicles. What other items can be tracked using serial numbers etched in metal?

Why should you care?

How can you increase the interest in your crime-scene drama by adding a serial-number component?

Reflecting on the Activity and the Challenge

Part of the problem you are facing in creating a crime scene is to understand how to observe something that is not initially visible. To restore an obliterated serial number, you used knowledge developed from a model and from reading about the microscopic structure of metals, combined with knowledge about the Metal Activity Series from the last activity. There are many different metals and you should begin thinking of ways to etch different metal samples. You can now also use the concepts that you have learned to describe the chemistry behind the technique.

Chem to Go

1. Describe two ways that the original serial number could be obscured so that the etching method would not be useful to reveal the serial number. Use your model to explain why it would keep the etching process from working.
2. Based on what you learned in the previous activity on the activity series, why is iron (III) chloride used to etch aluminum instead of magnesium chloride?
3. Based on the activity series, what other metals could be etched by a hydrochloric acid and iron (III) chloride mixture?

4. Why did the etching solution bubble? Explain.
   Hint: you can start to explain by writing a reaction that occurs.
5. A more complete activity series is:
   Mg > Al > Zn > Fe > Pb > H > Cu > Hg > Ag.
   Answer the following questions using this information.
   a) Which is the most active of these metals?
   b) Which is the least active of the metals?
   c) If a magnesium ion has a +2 charge and a zinc ion has a +2 charge, write the reaction that occurs spontaneously between them when one is a metal and the other is an ion. Be sure to write the aqueous or solid information in parentheses.
   d) Name two other metal ion solutions, besides Fe^{3+} (which you used), that could be used to restore a serial number in aluminum.
6. Complete the word equations for the following reactions. If a reaction does not occur, write "N.R."
   a) zinc + sodium nitrate →
   b) zinc + silver nitrate →
   c) tin + zinc nitrate →
7. ***Preparing for the Chapter Challenge***

   Using the chemistry and techniques in this chapter, you must create a crime scene, analyze the evidence, and link the evidence so that it implicates one of the four suspects. Write a paragraph describing how you can use what you learned in this activity to analyze a metal piece of evidence. In addition, write a paragraph that describes how you can link that piece of evidence to one of your characters.

Inquiring Further

1. Etching other metals

Pick a common metal other than aluminum, such as iron or copper. Using the activity series, predict what might be a good reagent to use with that metal. Research serial-number etching further to determine a method for etching the metal you select. Under the supervision of an adult, test the method.

2. Restoring serial numbers on nonmetallic materials

Research serial-number restoration methods that are used on nonmetallic materials. Begin by reading the article titled, *A Compilation of Techniques and Chemical Formulae used in the Restoration of Obliterated Markings*, by Ernest E. Massiah, in the *AFTE Journal*, volume 8, number 2, 1976. Under the supervision of an adult, experiment with one of the methods you read about.

Activity 8 Chromatographic Capers

What Do You See?

The WHO-WROTE-The-RANSOM-LETTER MYSTERY
Ransom Letter
INK

GOALS

In this activity you will:

- Identify an unknown ink based on a set of standards.
- Explain, from the macroscopic, nanoscopic, and symbolic perspectives, how the components of a mixture are separated in chromatography.
- Calculate, compare, explain, and predict R_f values for substances.

What Do You Think?

A detective searches a crime scene, looking for pieces of evidence and comes across a stack of threatening letters written in black ink. Each is unsigned and has no fingerprints except the victims', but the detective still knows they can be used as evidence.

- **How can a detective use black ink as evidence?**
- **What properties of black ink make it possible evidence at a crime scene?**

Record your ideas about these questions in your *Active Chemistry* log. Be prepared to discuss your responses with your group and the class.

Investigate

In this activity you will explore one way forensic scientists identify inks—paper chromatography.

Part A: Analyzing Ink

1. Your teacher will give you a piece of chromatography paper with a small spot of black ink at one end.
2. Tape a large paper clip to the top of the paper and attach a binder clip to the bottom of the paper to weigh down the paper once it's resting in the water as pictured in the diagram on the next page.

Safety goggles and a lab apron must be worn *at all times* in a chemistry lab.

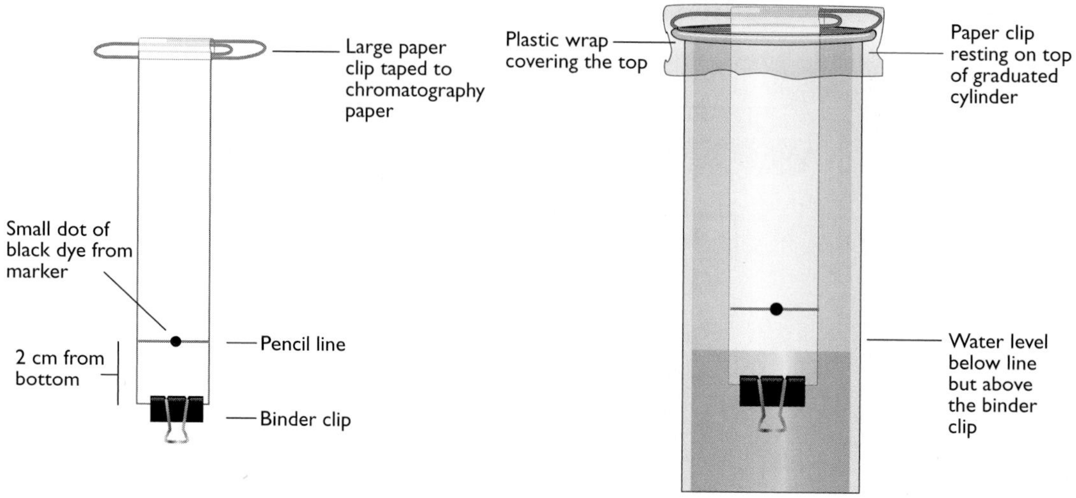
Large paper clip taped to chromatography paper
Small dot of black dye from marker
2 cm from bottom
Pencil line
Binder clip
Plastic wrap covering the top
Paper clip resting on top of graduated cylinder
Water level below line but above the binder clip

Wash your hands and arms thoroughly after the activity.

3. Add distilled water to a graduated cylinder to barely cover the binder clip when the paper is placed into the cylinder.
4. Place the piece of paper into the cylinder. Cover the top of the cylinder with plastic wrap. Do not let the sides of the paper touch the sides of the graduated cylinder. Observe.
5. When the level of the water is within 1.0 cm of the top of the paper, remove the chromatogram (the paper with the finished separation on it), mark the distance that the water traveled using a pencil, and hang the chromatogram to dry.
6. When the paper is dry, label it "Unknown." You will use this paper as a comparison when working through the *Chem to Go* section.
7. Attach the chromatogram to your *Active Chemistry* log. Record your observations in your *Active Chemistry* log. Where did the colors come from? Why are they in different locations instead of staying together? Record your answers in your *Active Chemistry* log.

Part B: A Model of How the Separation Works

1. In your model you will use a set of two different colored poker chips to represent black ink. An "X" on the chip represents the side that faces up. Examine the two different poker chips with a hand lens.

   a) How are they alike? How are they different?

2. A felt board will be used to represent the chromatography paper. Examine the felt board with your hands and with the hand lens.

   a) Is the surface textured or smooth? Record your observations in your *Active Chemistry* log.

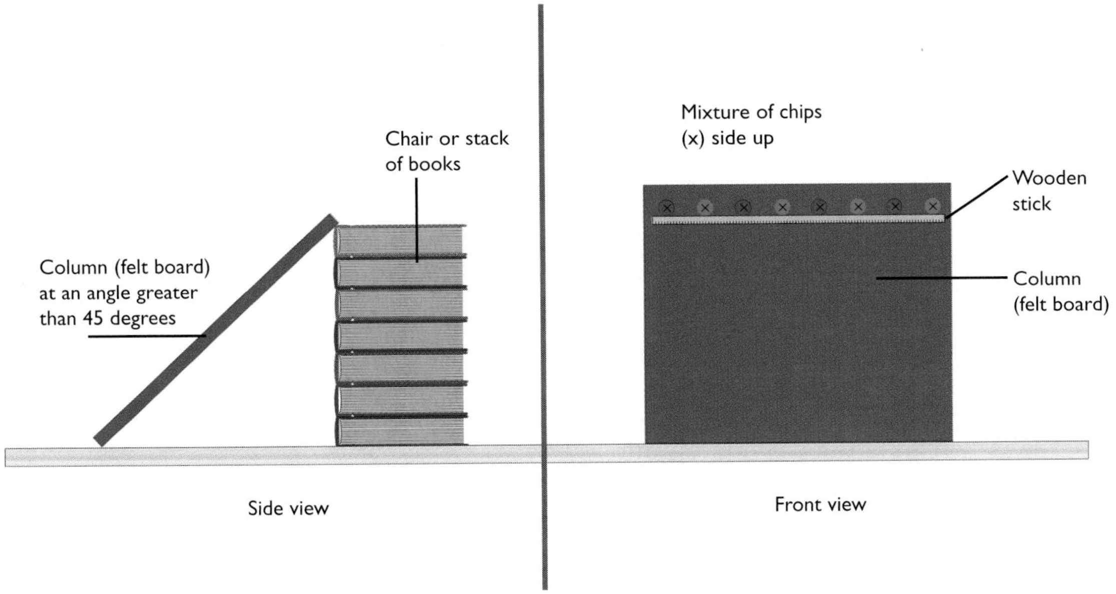
Chair or stack
of books
Column (felt board)
at an angle greater
than 45 degrees
Side view
Mixture of chips
(x) side up
Wooden
stick
Column
(felt board)
Front view

3. Compare the texture of the bottoms of the two different colored chips to the texture of the felt.

   a) Which color of chip has a bottom surface closest to that of the felt?

4. Angle the long side of the felt board up against a stack of books or a chair so that it is angled between 45° and 70°, as shown in the diagram.

5. Place the meter stick across the felt board. The surface of the felt board should hold it in place. Place the components of the mixture (the chips), X-side up, onto the felt board above the meter stick.

   a) Based on your observations of the chips and the felt board, predict which component of the mixture (which colored chip) will travel down the felt board the faster. Explain. Record your prediction in your *Active Chemistry* log.

6. Remove the meter stick and observe what happens.

   a) Record the results in your *Active Chemistry* log.

7. Repeat *Steps 5* and 6 two more times.

   a) In your *Active Chemistry* log, make a series of drawings that show what happens as you remove the meter stick.

   b) Based on your observations, explain why the mixture of chips separated as it traveled down the felt board. Record your explanation in your *Active Chemistry* log.

   c) Which component of the mixture (which chip color) is similar to the yellow dye in your chromatogram from the black ink? Which component of the mixture is like the blue dye? Record your answer and explain your logic in your *Active Chemistry* log.

Part C: Applications to Forensics

1. To match inks, you will be spotting all of the markers, including the "Unknown," on the same sheet of wide chromatography paper, so you will have to run the separation in a

large 600-mL beaker. Also, you will attach the paper to a pencil instead of a paper clip because the pencil will stretch across the mouth of the beaker.

a) Why do you think it is important to run all of the samples on the same sheet?

b) Using what you have learned about paper chromatography separations, write down the procedure you will use for creating the chromatogram in your *Active Chemistry* log.

Wash your hands and arms thoroughly after the activity.

2. Show your procedure to your teacher for approval before proceeding.

    a) After you have completed your chromatogram, identify the "Unknown." Record and justify your answer in your *Active Chemistry* log.

3. Dispose of the materials as directed by your teacher. Clean up your workstation.

Chem Talk

Chem Words

mixture: a combination of two or more substances.

SEPARATING MIXTURES USING CHROMOTOGRAPHY

Mixtures

In this activity you explored a method for separating mixtures. Mixtures are all around you and make up many common household items such as soda, baking powder, cleaning solutions, and of course, black ink. A **mixture** is defined as a physical combination of two or more substances. Mixtures can be separated based on differences in their physical properties. Salt water is a mixture of salt and water. The salt can be separated from the water by evaporating the water. The salt will remain in the container and the water vapor (steam) can be collected above the container. Chromatography is another means that chemists can separate mixtures.

Chromatography

Chromatography is a method of separation that was originally invented for separating different colored plant pigments. Its name derives from the Greek words *chroma*, meaning color, and *graphein*, meaning write. In this experiment you used chromatography to separate the components in black ink. However, this technique is not limited to colored materials. It may be used to separate colorless mixtures of gases, drugs, or liquids. It is important to note that chromatography does not separate materials because of their different colors, but because of their different properties. In this activity you used components of different colors because this makes them easy to see as they separate. However, it has nothing to do with the way chromatography works.

In chromatography you have two different phases: the **stationary phase** and the **mobile phase**. In your experiments, the chromatography paper was the stationary phase because it does not move. The mobile phase was the water that moved up the paper. In chromatography, the components of the mixture interact with both the mobile and stationary phases. The higher the polarity of a component, the more it will interact with the mobile phase (the water) and the faster it will travel. The more a component interacts with the stationary phase (the paper) the slower it travels. Since every component has a different polarity, each will interact with the mobile and stationary phases to different degrees. Therefore, each different chemical in the mixture will pass through at different rates, thus separating the substances in the mixture.

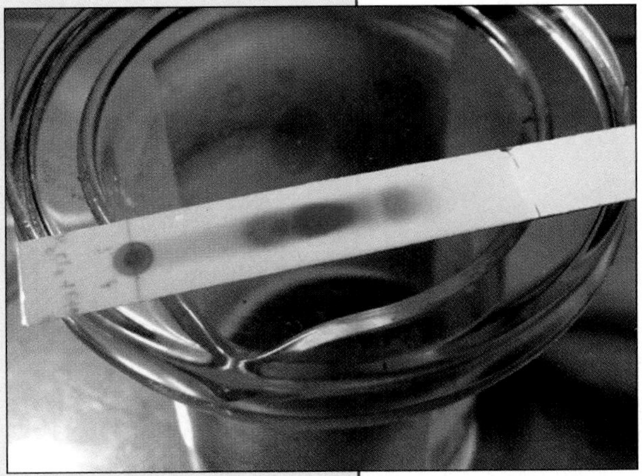

In *Part B* of this activity you modeled the chromatography process. The stationary phase was represented by the felt board and the mixture was made of two different substances—represented by the different surfaces on the chips. The poker chips with a rough surface interact with the felt board more than the smooth poker chips. The chips with the rough bottoms attach and detach on the fuzzy surface of the board. This slows them down as they travel down the board. The smooth chips do not catch on the surface as much as the rough chips, so they travel down the board at a much faster rate. The difference in the attraction to the stationary phase causes the separation of the different poker chips in the mixture.

Chem Words

chromatography: an experimental technique that separates a mixture by the speed at which they migrate over a stationary phase.

stationary phase: the absorbent in chromatography. In paper chromatography, the paper is the stationary phase.

mobile phase: the fluid that contains the mixture that is analyzed in chromatography. Water can be the mobile phase in paper chromatography.

Chem Words

R_f factor: the retention factor and the ratio of the distance a component traveled compared to the distance the mobile phase moved.

Application of Chromatography to Forensic Chemistry

In forensics, chromatography has a wide variety of applications, such as ink analysis, toxicology, and arson investigations. As you saw in *Part C* of the *Investigate* section, chromatography can be used to identify different brands of black ink by separating them into their individual components. In toxicology it can be used to separate mixtures of different drugs and other chemical substances, such as a mixture of heroin and baking soda. In arson investigations, samples taken from the site of the fire can be analyzed for the presence of gasoline or other flammable substances.

Unknown components in mixtures can be identified by comparing the chromatogram of the unknown sample to a set of standard chromatograms. Standard chromatograms are made using the same stationary phase and mobile phase that were used for the "Unknown." In addition to comparing the chromatogram of the Unknown to the standard, a quantitative measure known as the R_f can be used to identify components. The **R_f factor** is defined as the distance traveled by the component divided by the distance traveled by the solvent. An example is shown in the diagram.

$$R_f = \frac{\text{distance traveled by component}}{\text{distance traveled by solvent (mobile phase)}}$$

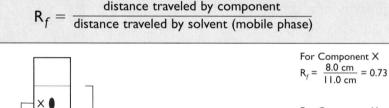

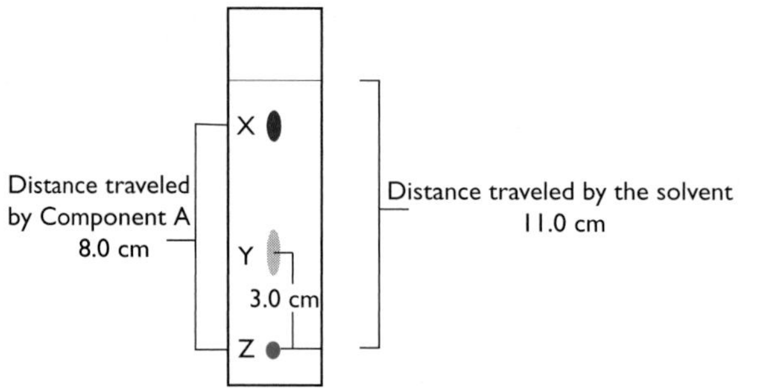
Distance traveled
by Component A
8.0 cm
X
Y
3.0 cm
Z
Distance traveled by the solvent
11.0 cm

For Component X
$$R_f = \frac{8.0 \text{ cm}}{11.0 \text{ cm}} = 0.73$$

For Component Y
$$R_f = \frac{3.0 \text{ cm}}{11.0 \text{ cm}} = 0.27$$

For Component Z
$$R_f = \frac{0.0 \text{ cm}}{11.0 \text{ cm}} = 0$$

For a given stationary-mobile phase combination, the R_f factor of a compound is constant. So if a yellow dye in the unknown has R_f factor different from the R_f factor of the yellow dye in the standard chromatogram, then it can be assumed the two dyes are not the same.

Finally, the relative quantities of each component can be qualitatively determined by comparing their intensities. The more intense the color the higher the concentration of the component with that color is in the mixture. If the intensities of all of the spots are the same, the components are present in nearly equal quantities in the mixture.

Checking Up

1. Give two examples of mixtures you use every day.
2. What was the stationary phase and what was the mobile phase in the chromatography experiments you did?
3. In a chromatography test, Component A traveled 5.0 cm. The solvent (mobile phase) traveled 10.0 cm. Calculate the R_f factor of Component A.

What Do You Think Now?

At the beginning of this activity you were asked:

- **How can a detective use black ink as evidence?**
- **What properties of black ink make it possible evidence at a crime scene?**

Answer the two questions again, this time using the theory and chemistry words you learned in this investigation.

Chem Essential Questions

What does it mean?

Chemistry explains a macroscopic phenomenon (what you observe) with a description of what happens at the nanoscopic level (atoms and molecules) using symbolic structures as a way to communicate. Complete the chart below in your *Active Chemistry* log.

MACRO	NANO	SYMBOLIC
What did you observe with your sense of sight during the chromatography activity?	*Explain why some molecules are able to travel larger distances on the paper.*	*You used poker chips as a model to explain how chromatography works. How is this model of poker chip motion not like the movement of the molecules?*

How do you know?

What evidence do you have that all black inks are not identical?

Why do you believe?

Ink makers often change the component ingredients of their inks. How would this add a complication to a crime investigation?

Why should you care?

Notes at the crime scene can now be a chemical tool for investigation. Create a part of a crime scene that fits in with your general story that uses ink marks in a creative fashion.

Reflecting on the Activity and the Challenge

In this activity you separated various colored mixtures using chromatography. Consider the types of evidence that paper chromatography would be good for analyzing. Black ink used in a ransom note may be the same as the ink in the pen of one of the suspects. Think of how you can use standards and R_f values to determine the type of ink used.

Chem to Go

1. Classify the following as mixtures or pure substances:

   a) sugar water
   b) copper wire
   c) ammonia cleaning solution
   d) table salt (sodium chloride, NaCl)

2. Based on your knowledge of chromatography, which dye in *Part A* interacted more with the mobile phase than the stationary phase? Explain your reasoning.

3. How would varying the size of the piece of paper change your results? What would remain the same? Explain your answers to both questions.

4. Why is it important to use a pencil when making any markings on the chromatogram?

5. What is the maximum possible value for R_f? Where would the component be on the column when R_f is the maximum value?

6. Calculate the R_f factors for the Unknown from *Part A* of the *Investigate* section. How do these values compare to the R_f factors of the dyes in each of the standards and the same Unknown in *Part C*? Explain your findings.

7. In this activity, you constructed a model to illustrate how chromatography works. While you were able to explore some of the factors that affect the separation of components in chromatography using this model, the model is not effective for explaining everything about chromatography. Where are some areas the model breaks down? Consider what in the model represents each of the components and the two phases (mobile and stationary).

8. ***Preparing for the Chapter Challenge***

   Consider how you could use chromatography as a part of your *Chapter Challenge*. In a few sentences, describe the types of evidence that you could analyze in class using chromatography. In a paragraph, describe how chromatography works and how it can be used to analyze a piece of evidence retrieved from a crime scene.

Inquiring Further

1. Investigating factors influencing chromatography

There are many different factors that can influence your chromatogram. Some of these include the length of the stationary phase, the size of the original sample, and the types of mobile phases that you can use with paper chromatography. Choose one of these variables to change. If applicable, research the variable to develop a hypothesis. Under the supervision of an adult, investigate how changing specific variables affects the separation of black ink.

2. Investigating permanent inks

In this activity you used water-based black inks. Can permanent black ink be separated using paper chromatography? Research the properties of permanent inks. Under the supervision of an adult, investigate what types of mobile phases are needed to separate permanent ink.

5
5

Chem at Work

Jacqueline Leith

Forensic Chemist, Miami Dade Crime Lab, Miami, FL

One of the most popular shows on television today is *CSI: Miami*. The show features a team of criminologists who solve crimes by gathering evidence and analyzing it with state-of-the-art forensic technology. Jacqueline Leith's job is like a real-life version of the show. She is a forensic chemist in Miami's crime lab.

Jacqueline is an expert at identifying unknown substances. "We mostly deal in analyzing controlled substances like drugs. Later, we present the evidence at trial to a jury." She feels that this is the most satisfying part of her job.

Jacqueline does three tests when a controlled substance comes into the lab. First, she conducts a "spot test" or "color test," in which a chemical reagent is added to a sample of the unknown substance. If there is a color change, Jacqueline can usually identify it as heroin or cocaine. Next, she performs a "micro-crystalline test" which involves another chemical reagent. Jacqueline then views the sample under a light microscope. If she sees "feathered crystals" form, the unknown substance is cocaine. The last test utilizes a complex machine with a robotic arm. This machine, called a gas chromatograph mass spectrometer, breaks the sample apart chemically. "Just like on TV," Jacqueline adds with a smile.

Jacqueline finds her job fulfilling in many ways. She loves the work she does because she has always been fascinated by science and always wanted a career that involved science.

Doug Lerner

Arson Investigator, Sheriff's Dept., Rockland County, NY

Doug Lerner and his "K-9" partner, "Scooter," are arson investigators with the Rockland County Sheriff's Department in New York. Their job is to determine the causes of fires. Lerner knows melted aluminum means the fire exceeded 1200°F. Scooter, a yellow Labrador, can sniff out fire accelerants like gasoline and kerosene.

Dr. Ed Espinoza

Chief Forensic Scientist at U.S. Fish and Wildlife Service, Ashland, OR

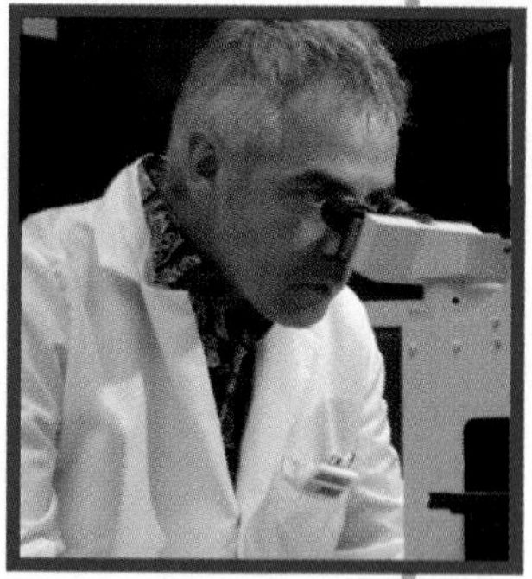

Ed Espinoza plays an important part in the fight to protect and preserve wildlife by solving crimes against endangered species and protected animals. His lab uses techniques rooted in chemistry to identify, for example, animal species from blood samples. The evidence he gathers helps to track down smugglers, poachers and illegal hunters.

CSI Chemistry Assessment

Your *Chapter Challenge* is to create a crime scene, write a police report, and prepare evidence so that another team can solve the crime. The crime scene must include evidence that can be analyzed using chemistry techniques that were learned in this chapter. Your crime story should include a police report, description of the crime, a diagram of the crime scene, a list of all the evidence found at the scene, and anything else that will make the story come to life. Each piece of evidence should point to more than one suspect while the totality of evidence should be able to link the crime to only one suspect.

You will also create dossiers (descriptions) for at least four different suspects. Each dossier will include personal information about the subject such as a mug shot, fingerprint of right index finger, the suspect's name, occupation, and any other information that will be needed to link the suspect to the crime or eliminate him or her as a suspect. You may be creative with your characters, but using names or lives of students is not allowed. It is important that you develop the story and the characters of the suspects so that the evidence you were given logically points to a single guilty suspect. However, you may also want to include a piece of evidence that implicates more than one suspect so that the audience of the crime show cannot immediately guess the guilty party.

Your classmates will have a chance to solve your crime. You will write down the solution to the crime (which suspect is guilty), including a flowchart illustrating the expected outcomes of the analysis of evidence. All of the solution material should be sealed in an envelope. Once the students testing your package have analyzed the evidence and presented their case, they will open the envelope and compare what they decided to what you intended.

Chemistry Content

Activity 1: You learned about deductive reasoning. You also learned about elements and their properties.

Activity 2: You investigated glass fragments and found that they could be distinguished by their densities. Density is a characteristic property of matter.

Activity 3: You observed the luminol reaction and discovered that blood will be detected by luminol. You also learned that other substances will also produce light from a luminol reaction. The luminol reaction can be used as evidence of blood or can be used to confuse the crime detectives. You also learned about energy levels and the emission of light in addition to the need for catalysts.

Activity 4: You practiced a set of lab techniques that can be used to distinguish one white powder from another. The identification of unknown chemicals involves sets of reactions. You also learned how to set up a flowchart to help clarify the logic of identifying the chemical.

Activity 5: You learned how to develop latent prints and investigated the double-replacement reaction of sodium chloride and silver nitrate.

Activity 6: You investigated single-replacement reactions and redox reactions in order to develop the Metal Activity Series.

Activity 7: As investigators you learned how to lift the serial numbers from sanded pieces of metal. The explanation for why this is possible required you to look at metals at the molecular or nanoscopic level.

Activity 8: You practiced chromatography techniques in order to analyze different inks that may be present at a crime scene.

You may want to make a chart that shows the activity number, some chemistry concepts in the activity and some ideas as to how you can use these concepts as part of your *CSI Chemistry* mystery. You should pay particular attention to the sections *Reflecting on the Activity and the Challenge, Chem Essential Questions*, and *Preparing for the Chapter Challenge*. You should also compare your list with the *Chem You Learned* summary.

Activity #	Chemistry concepts	How to use concepts

You may decide to do the first activity as a group in order to ensure that everybody understands how to proceed. After completing the first activity, each team member can be assigned two or three activities. You can then review all of the activities as a group with the activity expert reviewing each summary.

Criteria

You and your team should review the criteria by which you will be graded. Before beginning the chapter, your teacher discussed what criteria should be used to judge the quality of work for the *CSI Chemistry* challenge. This included:

For the Crime Scene You Create

- How many techniques must be used to evaluate the evidence?
- How creative is the short story that sets the scene?
- How authentic is the police report?
- How well are your dossiers of suspects integrated with your story?
- The quality of your crime scene including interest and the ability to solve it.
- The chemistry in your story and chemical principles required to solve the crime.
- How do the chemistry concepts apply at the macroscopic, nanoscopic, and symbolic levels for each of the principles you've chosen?

For the Crime Scene You Create (continued)

- How carefully must you work to analyze the evidence? Were there twists and turns?
- How convincing is the logic in identifying the guilty suspect "beyond a reasonable doubt"?
- How should you provide feedback on the groups' analysis of the chemistry within their story?

Preparing for the Chapter Challenge

- **Decide How to Build Your Story**

Your team's next step is to decide whether to begin with the story and then put together the evidence, or whether you compile the evidence and then build your story around that evidence. Somewhere in the process you will also have to create suspects for the crime as well. Always keep in mind that the chemistry content is crucial to the success of your challenge.

- **Chemistry content is necessary but not sufficient.**

All your knowledge of chemistry will be necessary for use in developing the *CSI* challenge but it won't be sufficient for the success of the story. You must also create characters and an intriguing and challenging crime scene that your classmates can solve after gathering sufficient evidence that you provide. Your entire team should have input and everyone on the team should be comfortable with the plan.

- **Manage Your Time**

You have a sense of how you want to proceed and what you want the final product to be. You now have to allocate the work. How much time do you have to complete the project? When is the project due? How will you get everything done in this time frame? Who will be working on the written materials including the instructions? Who will ensure that the chemistry principles include explanations at both the macroscopic and nanoscopic levels. Who will prepare the chemistry descriptions? Will each team member contribute one chemistry concept? How will you ensure that everybody's work meets the standard of excellence to ensure that everybody on the team gets an A? Will you need materials for your crime scene? Where will these come from? Planning a project well does not ensure success, but poor planning almost always leads to disappointment.

- **Practice Solving Your Crime Story**

You will need to make sure that you have enough time to put all the components together. You have to have both the crime-scene story and evidence and the written materials ready on the due date. You also want to have saved some time for a practice run. You may be able to make some last minute adjustments to your story based on the results of the practice session.

As students try to solve your crime, you will get to solve theirs. Use your chemistry knowledge and logic models to decide on which suspect is responsible for the crime. Don't jump to conclusions. Remember that the team creating the story has probably added some extra information to confuse you.

Engineering/Technology Design

Reflect on the engineering/technology design process. Recall the successes and disappointments from the *mini-challenge*. How can you build upon what went right and what could have been improved? What warm and cool feedback did you receive from the other members of the class?

Enjoy your CSI Chemistry mystery!

Chem You Learned

- **Deductive reasoning** involves the use of observable data and the use of that data to solve a problem.
- Because of the increasing size of atoms with increasing atomic number, five ***d*-orbitals** are filling with electrons in the **transition metals**.
- **Physical properties** and **chemical properties** help to characterize the various **elements** and **compounds** in our physical world.
- Every pure **substance** has a **density**, a physical property which is characteristic of that substance under standard conditions.
- In **forensics**, blood testing at a crime scene is always "**presumptive**." A **luminol** reagent is used to show the possibility of the presence of blood residue.
- With the **catalyst** of hydrogen peroxide, the **luminol** reagent will show a **chemiluminescent** yellow-green color in the presence of blood.
- **Electrons** can exist at several **energy levels**, depending upon the situation. Normally, they occupy the lowest energy level, the **ground state**. When an electron absorbs energy, it can rise to higher energy levels, called **excited states**.
- An excited electron will return to the **ground state**, with the emission of energy, typically light energy of a very specific **wavelength**.
- **Qualitative analysis** is used to determine *whether* a substance is present in a sample whereas **quantitative analysis** is required to determine *how much* of that substance is present.
- **Ionic compounds** always contain a **cation** and an **anion**, and are formed by the complete transfer of one or more electrons.
- **The Law of Conservation of Matter** is a key concept in chemistry and it makes possible the balancing of chemical equations.
- Some ions are composed of two or more atoms which are **covalently** bonded together. These are called **polyatomic ions**. Two examples are NH_4^+ and CO_3^{2-}.
- A **solution** is a homogeneous mixture of two or more substances. The substance in greater concentration is called the **solvent** and those in lesser concentrations are called **solutes**.
- Predictions about **solubility** can be made by using a table of **solubility rules**.
- **Double-replacement reactions** always involve the formation of a **precipitate** or a gas.
- **Oxidation** and **reduction** occur simultaneously as one substance loses electrons (is oxidized) and another substance gains those electrons (is reduced).
- **Single-replacement reactions** always involve the reduction-oxidation process (**redox**).
- Copper can be oxidized to the (I) state or the (II) state with the corresponding **oxidation numbers** of +1 and +2.
- Most metals have the physical properties of being **lustrous**, **ductile**, **malleable**, and have the ability to **conduct** heat and electricity well.
- The technique of **chromatography** is used for the separation of mixtures based on differing physical properties.
- In a chromatographic separation, a **mobile phase** carries the mixture through a **solid phase**.

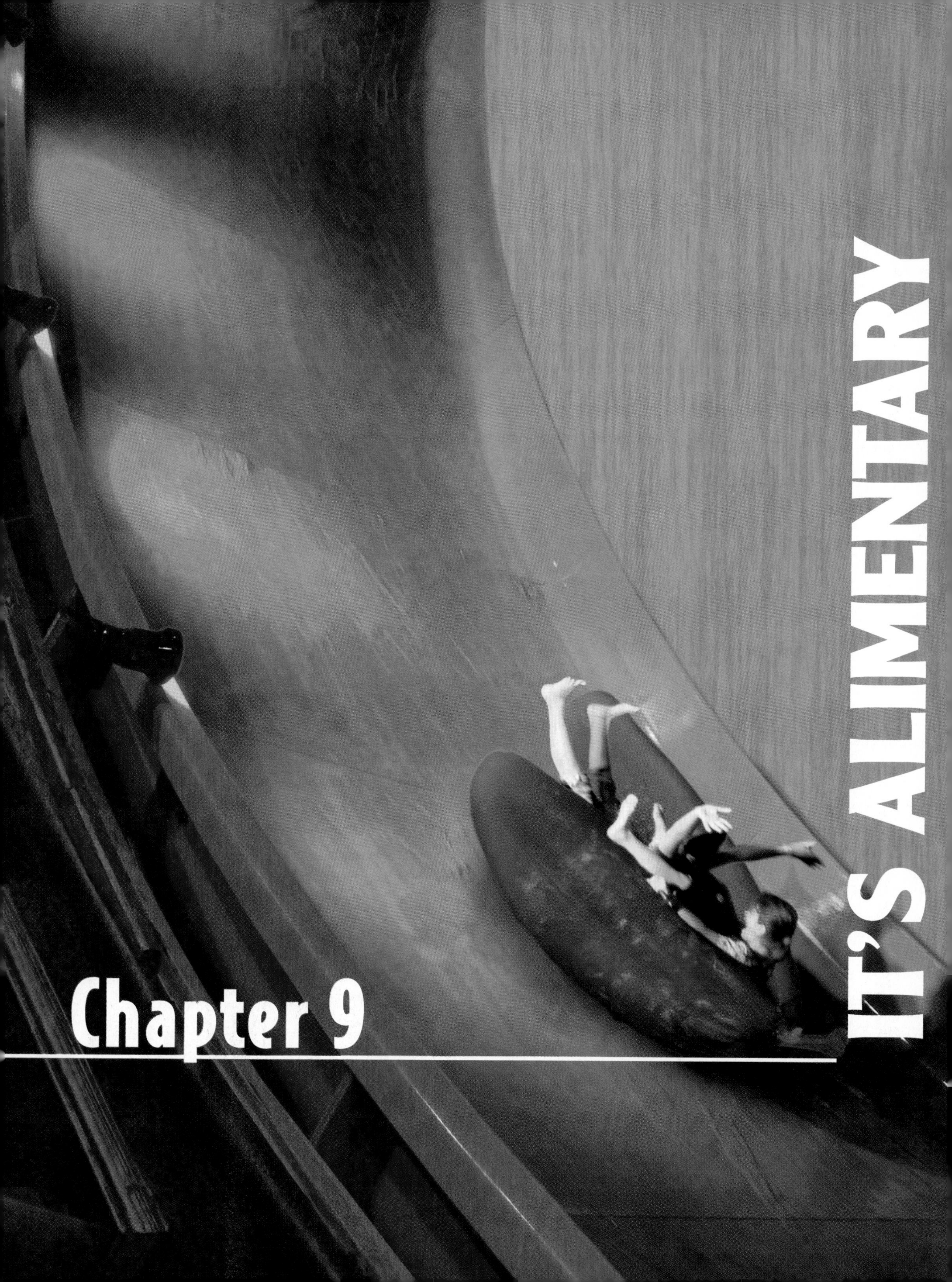

Chapter 9

IT'S ALIMENTARY

Chapter Challenge

9 It's Alimentary

Scenario

In the last thirty years many amusement parks have been built around a theme. They are so common now that we refer to them as theme parks instead of amusement parks. Imagine that an amusement park is being designed around the systems of the human body. The name of the park is going to be Anatomy World. It will consist of rides through giant body systems, interactive encounters, and three-dimensional working simulations of all the body systems. Its intent is to serve as an exciting entertainment experience, but also to teach participants how the body functions.

TICKETS

Your Challenge

Your *Active Chemistry* team has been asked to design and plan a ride for Anatomy World based around a trip down the alimentary canal. The overall idea of the ride is that on entering the alimentary canal, the riders assume the size of a common nutrient molecule. If they are two meters tall before their trip, they would become two nanometers tall as they enter the alimentary canal. Their vehicle is a microscopic particle of food. You are to identify the physical and chemical perils that would be encountered by your food vehicle upon entering one of the sections of the alimentary canal. Next, you are to demonstrate, on a macroscopic level with real food, what would happen chemically to your food vehicle under these conditions. Finally, you are to conduct a skit, staged at the molecular level, depicting both the physical and chemical challenges that would need to be duplicated for a full-scale ride to be built at Anatomy World.

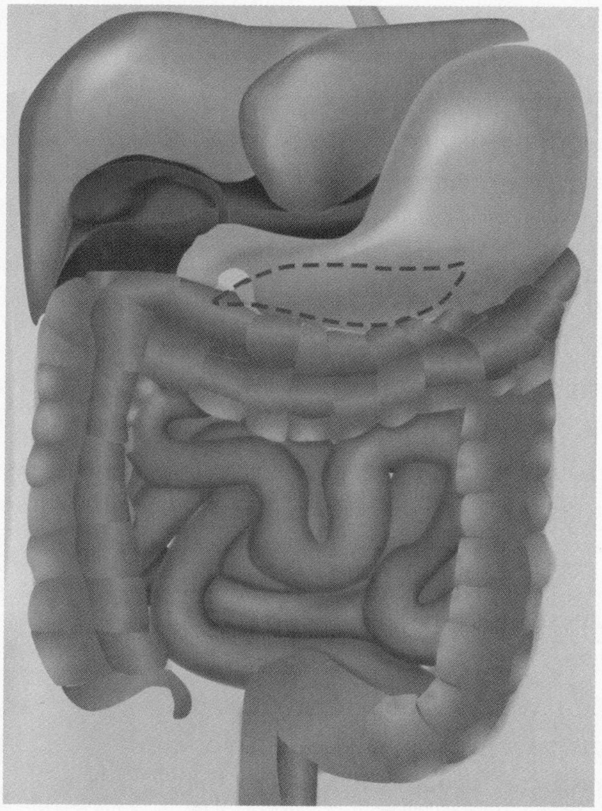

You will need to complete the following tasks:

- Choose a portion of the alimentary canal that you will concentrate on for this ride at Anatomy World.
- Identify the chemical and physical changes that take place along that portion of the alimentary canal.
- Choose the components of a meal that will start down the ride.
- Using real food, document the changes that at least one part of your meal undergoes as it passes through the part of the alimentary canal that you have selected.

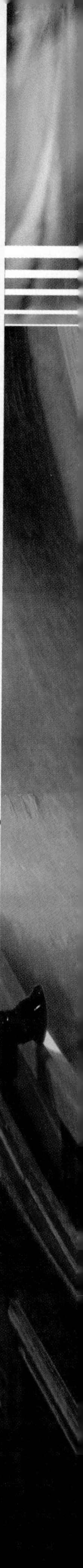

ChemCorner

Chemistry in *It's Alimentary*

- Carbohydrates
- Starches
- Sugars
- Benedict's solution
- Hydrolysis
- Polymers
- Antacids
- Limewater
- Charles's Law
- Kelvin scale
- Pepsin
- Lactase
- Proteins
- Amino acids
- Peptide bonds
- Gay-Lussac's Law
- Kinetic Molecular Theory
- Ideal gas

H_2O + ACID
PEPSI
Beef Jerky
ACID + PE
ACTIVE CHEMISTRY

- Write the script for a skit that demonstrates, at the molecular level, the chemistry that your food vehicle would experience on its trip down the alimentary canal. The script must be based on real chemical principles. Provide additional background to the script that describes the chemistry principles in detail. This could include the results of activities you performed to learn about each concept.
- Perform the skit before the class. Members of the class can be recruited to play the parts of "extras" but your team must play the starring roles.

Criteria

How will your part of the ride be graded? What will make your classmates and your teacher say that your presentation was great? How much of your grade should come from the visible evidence of how your meal actually changed? How much should come from the accuracy of your script? And how much should come from the performance of your skit? Discuss these issues in small groups and with your class.

You may decide that some or all of the following components should be graded:

- Presentation of the details of the digestion of food.
- Accuracy of the chemistry in the script and additional background.
- Number of chemistry concepts in the script.
- Quality of the additional chemistry background relating to activities.
- Thoroughness of the script.
- Audience appeal of the skit.
- Cleverness and quality of props used in the skit.

Once you have determined the areas that contribute to a great presentation, you and your classmates should decide how many points should be given for each area. Because you will be working in groups and dividing up the work, you need to agree how each member's contribution to the team effort should be rewarded. If you address these concerns before a grade is given, there is a much better chance of success.

Activity 1 The Upper End of the Alimentary Canal

What Do You See?

BENEDICT SOLUTION
EYE DROPS
EYE DROPS
Benedict Solution

GOALS

In this activity you will:

- Experience both the mechanical and chemical digestions of a cracker.
- Test for the presence of starch and its hydrolysis products.

What Do You Think?

About 65 million Americans (25%) have digestive problems and must take medications.

- **Where in your body does the digestion of your food first take place?**
- **What chemical and physical changes occur there?**

The *What Do You Think?* questions are provided to get you engaged in the activity. They are meant to grab your attention. They are also used to find out what you already know or think you know. Don't worry about being right or wrong. Discussing what you think you know is an important step in learning.

Record your ideas about these questions in your *Active Chemistry* log. Be prepared to discuss your responses with your small group and the class.

Investigate

Part A: Past the Teeth and into the Mouth

1. Imagine that you've just been given either a piece of pizza, a potato chip, or a chocolate-chip cookie.

   a) Describe what happens when you put the food in your mouth. Be as detailed as possible. How many bites do you take? How long do you chew before swallowing? Which teeth do you use to chew? What is happening in your mouth?

Be sure the food is not contaminated by anything in the lab before you eat it.

Safety goggles and a lab apron must be worn *at all times* in a chemistry lab.

Be sure to carefully dispose of the cracker that has been tested with iodine. Clean up any iodine spills immediately.

b) Which of the changes are physical changes of the food?

c) Which of the changes are chemical changes of the food?

2. In the classroom area (not the lab), place a piece of unseasoned cracker on your tongue. No chewing is allowed.

a) Record any taste changes in two minutes.

3. Take another piece of cracker and chew it for 30 seconds. Do not swallow. Time how long it takes from when you start to chew until the cracker starts to change taste.

a) Record the time and describe the taste change.

b) Write an explanation on why you think the two times were different.

4. In the lab, break off a small piece of a cracker. Put a drop of the Lugol's (iodine/iodide) solution on it.

a) What do you observe happening?

b) Lugol's solution is a positive test for starch. Describe your observation in terms of starch presence.

Part B: What Does Saliva Do?

1. You saw a positive test for starch in *Part A* when you applied a drop of Lugol's solution to the cracker. You will now see if you can gather evidence of what type of chemical digestion started in your mouth as you chewed the cracker.

2. Your teacher will show you a demonstration by setting a warm water bath at 37°C, which is body temperature (equal to 98.6°F).

3. Your teacher will deposit about 1.0 mL of saliva in one test tube. Then your teacher will add 1.0 mL water to a second test tube.

4. Your teacher will add two drops of starch solution to each test tube. Both are then placed in the 37°C water bath.

a) What is the importance of the test tube containing water?

b) Record your observations in your *Active Chemistry* log.

5. Wait at least three minutes after the starch has been added.

a) During this time, predict what will be observed when Lugol's solution is added to each test tube.

b) You teacher will now add one drop of Lugol's solution. What do you observe? Record your observations and possible explanations for the results of this investigation in your *Active Chemistry* log.

Part C: What Chemical Digestion Takes Place in the Mouth?

1. The substance in saliva that is responsible for digestion is an enzyme called salivary amylase. You will look at the beginning of digestion in the mouth in more detail. Use five test tubes, each to represent a set of conditions in the mouth. Label them A, B, C, D, E.

2. Begin heating water in a large beaker on a hot plate. You will need this for a boiling water bath later.

3. Put a second beaker of water on another hot plate. Hang a thermometer from a ringstand so that the tip of the thermometer remains submerged in the water. Adjust the hot plate to maintain a temperature of 55°C.

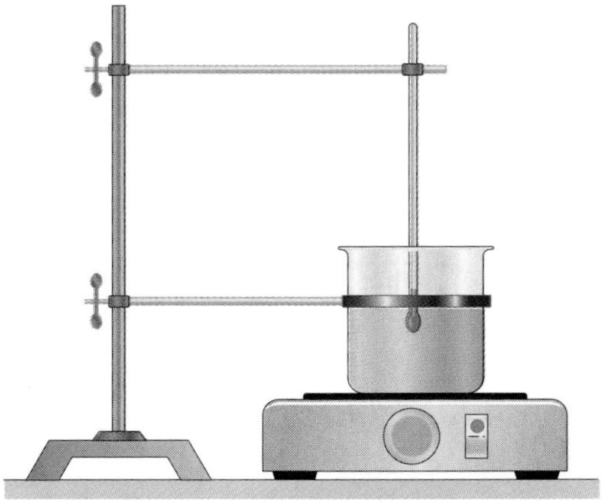

4. Add 5 mL of distilled water only to tube A.
5. Place 5 mL of 1% fungal amylase solution into test tubes B, C, D, E.
6. Place all five tubes in the 55°C water bath.
7. Get four pieces of cracker that are about the same size.
8. Crumble a piece of cracker in tube B. After five minutes, crumble another piece in tube C. After another five minutes, crumble a piece of cracker in tube D. After four more minutes, crumble the last piece in tube E. Make sure that the entire cracker is covered by the solution in each test tube. You may need to push it down with a glass stirring rod.
9. When the piece of cracker has been in tube E for one minute, remove all five test tubes from the 55°C water.
10. Place 10 drops of Benedict's solution into test tubes A to E. Benedict's solution is used to check for the presence of sugar in a substance. The darker the red, the more sugar there is. Since there is no sugar in the distilled water, you would expect that the Benedict's solution does not indicate the presence of sugar in tube A.
11. Using a test-tube clamp, place the five test tubes (A to E) in the boiling water bath for 10 minutes.
12. After 10 minutes, remove the test tubes with a test-tube clamp. Place them in a test-tube rack.
    a) Prepare a table similar to the one below, in your *Active Chemistry* log. Enter your observations. (Reminder: Benedict's solution is used to check for the presence of sugar in a substance. The darker the red, the more sugar there is.)
    b) In addition to the observations, you can also make inferences explaining what has happened. How can you explain these results? Where did the sugar come from? Why aren't all the tubes the same color?
13. Dispose of the materials as directed by your teacher. Clean up your workstation.

Wash your hands and arms thoroughly after the activity.

	Tube A no cracker	Tube B 15 min	Tube C 10 min	Tube D 5 min	Tube E 1 min
color before boiling					
color after boiling					
place in order according to sugar content					

Chem Talk

Chem Words

digestion: the physical and chemical breakdown of food into smaller nutrient particles.

starch: a complex molecule (polymer) made up of thousands of glucose units linked together.

hydrolysis: the breaking down of a larger molecule into smaller ones through a reaction with water.

THE BEGINNING OF DIGESTION

Parts of the Digestive System

The alimentary canal (digestive tract) is essentially a long hollow tube that extends from the mouth to the anus. You can think of it as a chemical factory located inside a 7.6 m long tube. Its purpose is to store and break down the organic molecules of the food you eat into smaller particles. The tissues of the body can then absorb these smaller particles. A smooth-running operation can process its food in anywhere between 24 and 72 hours (depending upon what you eat). This process is called **digestion**. It starts in the mouth, as you found in this activity.

You eat and digest food every day. You probably rarely think about the process of digestion unless something goes wrong. For example, you can get a stomach ache, vomit, or develop diarrhea.

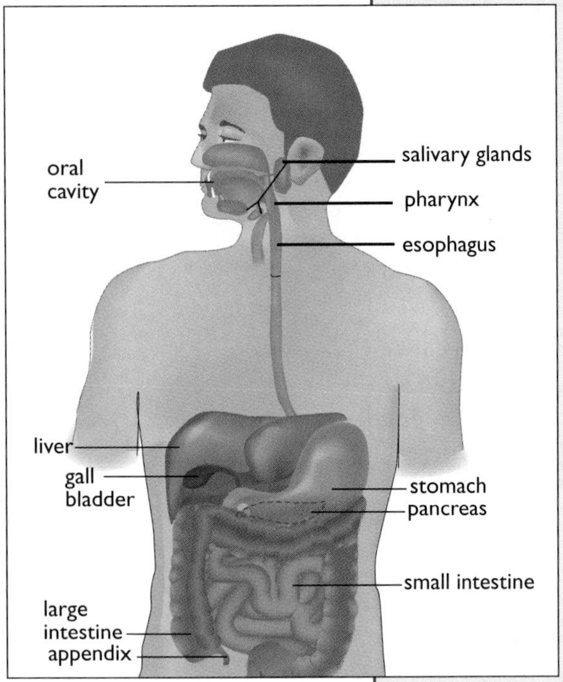
oral cavity
salivary glands
pharynx
esophagus
liver
gall bladder
stomach
pancreas
small intestine
large intestine
appendix

Hydrolysis of Starch

When you first let the cracker dissolve in your mouth, you probably noticed that the starchy taste became a sweet taste. **Starch** molecules, after interaction with the saliva or the amylase solution, become sugar molecules.

The process of digestion begins in the mouth. Because food is in the mouth for such a short time, only partial digestion takes place there. Essentially, the digestion that occurs in the mouth is a chemical process called **hydrolysis**.

You can understand this better by looking at both starch and sugar at the molecular level. Starch is made of a string of glucose (sugar) molecules. By adding water, hydrolysis takes place. This means that the bonds connecting subunits of complex foods are broken down through the reaction with water (hydro means water). The long string of glucose molecules are broken into pairs of glucose molecules which are a sugar called maltose. In the activity, the Lugol's (iodine/iodide) solution showed the presence of starch in the cracker. It reacted and formed a dark blue/black product, indicating that starch is present. The Benedict's solution then showed the presence of the maltose. Many, but not all, sugars react with Benedict's solution to form a brick-red precipitate of copper (I) oxide, Cu_2O.

Hydrolysis of Starch

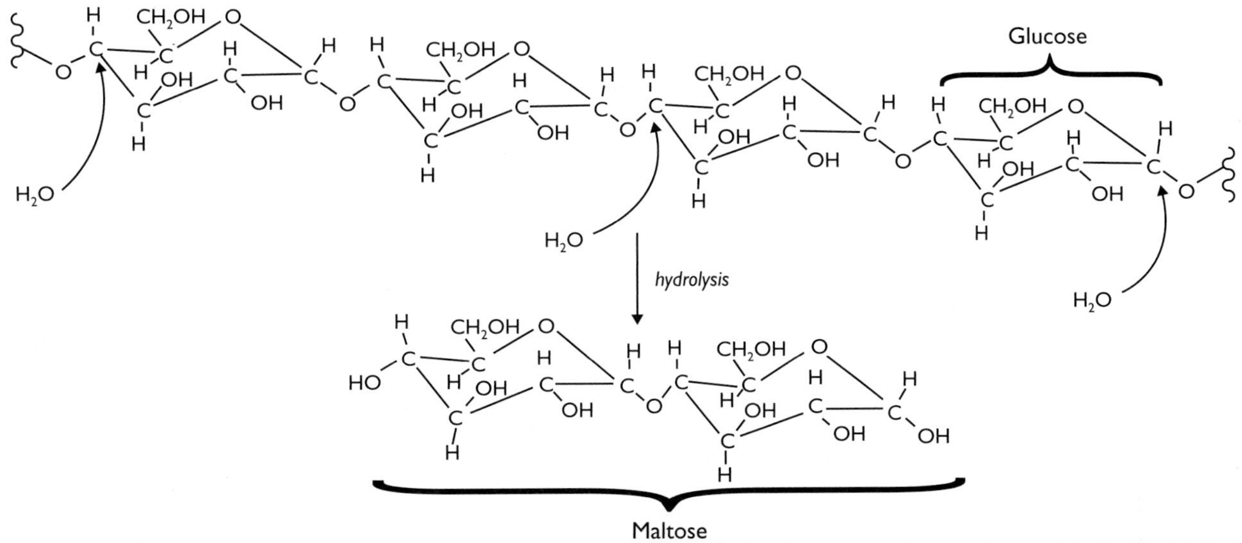
Glucose
H_2O
H_2O
hydrolysis
H_2O
Maltose

The diagram above shows starch and maltose molecules. At first, the diagram appears to be quite overwhelming, but it simply shows that starch combines with water to produce sugar through a process called hydrolysis. You can decipher this complex picture by noticing the following:

- The starch molecule is composed of a string of glucose molecules. In the starch molecule shown, you can see four of the many, many glucose molecules. Some starches have as many as 6000 glucose molecules.
- Water is added to the starch as shown with the H_2O arrows pointing toward the bonds holding the glucose molecules together.
- The arrow pointing down indicates that hydrolysis is taking place.
- The bottom part of the diagram shows that maltose is created. Maltose is two glucose molecules bound together and is a simple sugar. If there were four glucose molecules in the starch, there would be two maltose sugars created. The diagram just shows one of the maltose molecules.

The Role of Amylase Enzymes

Hydrolysis is one of the most important reactions occurring in the digestive process. But it cannot take place with water alone, as you observed in the activity. Water alone cannot change the starch to sugar. Saliva in the mouth contains a substance called salivary amylase. It makes the hydrolysis of starch in the mouth possible. As you learned, starch is a natural polymer made up of many smaller subunits that are bonded together. These smaller units are molecules of a simple sugar called glucose. Sugars are molecules made up of C, H, and O, and starch is a set of glucose molecules hooked together in a special way. The amylase enzyme in your saliva enables the hydrolysis of some of the bonds hooking the glucose subunits together to occur.

Other Changes That Occur in the Mouth

Physical digestion also takes place in the mouth. The teeth are an important part of digestion. They bite, tear, and grind the food into a bolus (a ball). Saliva contains amylase. However, saliva is a watery fluid that also dissolves food particles. You can only detect flavor if the food is in solution, and you know how important tasting your food is!

Just the sight and smell of food can activate the salivary glands, which produce saliva.

Checking Up

1. What does hydrolysis have to do with digestion?
2. What are the chemical subunits that make up starch?
3. What are you testing for when you use the Benedict's test?
4. What are you testing for when you use the iodine test?
5. What physical changes take place in the mouth?

What Do You Think Now?

At the beginning of this activity you were asked:

- **Where in your body does the digestion of your food first take place?**
- **What chemical and physical changes occur there?**

How does digestion begin before food gets to the stomach?
What kind of chemical do you have in your mouth that starts the digestion process?

Chem Essential Questions

What does it mean?

Chemistry explains a macroscopic phenomenon (what you observe) with a description of what happens at the nanoscopic level (atoms and molecules) using symbolic structures as a way to communicate. Complete the chart below in your *Active Chemistry* log.

MACRO	NANO	SYMBOLIC
In Part A, why did the cracker become sweet as it sat in your mouth? In Part B, which test tube tested positive for starch? In Part C, what does the time have to do with the variation in color for the different test tubes?	*What is meant by hydrolysis? What enzyme is needed and how does time play a role in this process?*	*Make a simple sketch to describe what happens to the starch when it comes in contact with saliva and water, and becomes the sugar maltose. In this simple sketch, glucose can be drawn as a small shape.*

How do you know?

What evidence do you have to support the idea that amylase will hydrolyze starch into sugars?

Why do you believe?

Recently our nation has experienced a nutritional trend that stresses a "low-carb" diet. "High-carb" foods like pasta, breads, potatoes, etc., are full of starch. How can you use the information you gained in this activity to explain the benefits of a low-carbohydrate diet?

Why should you care?

Your theme park ride might include the concept that digestion actually begins in the mouth. How will your vehicle simulate the effects of amylase on your particle of food?

Reflecting on the Activity and the Challenge

In creating your portion of the ride down the alimentary canal, you must remember that you and your vehicle have become microscopic. You have become the size of a molecule and not the size of food you normally see. In this activity, you observed the result of physical and chemical changes that food undergoes in the mouth. The saliva in the mouth contains the enzyme amylase, which broke down starch into the sugar maltose. There are two tests that can help you to identify two important substances in food: the iodine test for starch, and Benedict's test for sugar. You should begin thinking of ways in which your skit might show how food is changed inside the mouth. You can now use the concepts of chemistry to describe what is occurring at the beginning of the alimentary canal.

Chem to Go

1. Digestion consists of physical and chemical changes in food.
   a) What physical changes go on in the mouth as food starts its trip down the alimentary canal?
   b) What chemical changes go on in the mouth as food starts its trip down the alimentary canal?
2. What are the products of the hydrolysis of starch?
3. What is the color change that takes place when iodine is added to a starch?
4. What is the color change that takes place when iodine is added to maltose or glucose?
5. Why did you not get the same color in each of the test tubes containing the cracker when Benedict's solution was added?
6. Suppose you added the Lugol's solution to the test tubes containing the crackers instead of Benedict's solution. What would you predict that you would see? How would you explain these observations?
7. Why did you set your water bath temperature to 37°C in *Part B*?
8. ***Preparing for the Chapter Challenge***

   You can begin designing your ride. You can begin your ride by depicting chewing as a physical change. Then, show the chemical changes that occur as the starch molecules become sugar molecules.

Inquiring Further

Other uses for starch

What are some uses of starch other than being in foods? Research this question and present your findings to the class.

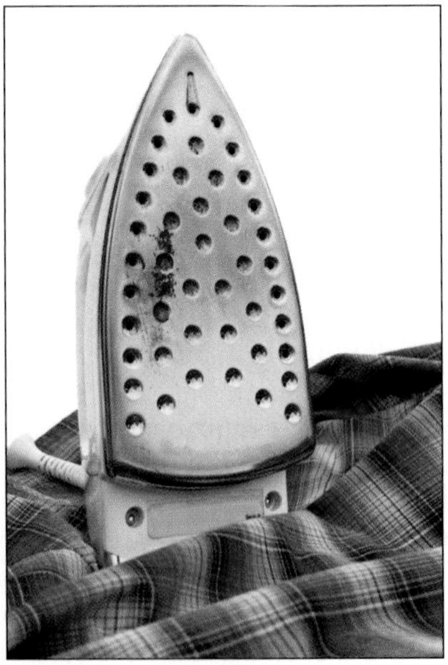

Activity 2 Antacids in the Stomach

What Do You See?

ANTACID
ANT ACID
Al_2O_3
MG(OH)
$NaHCO_3$
$CaCO_3$
ANT ACID

GOALS

In this activity you will:

- Explore the chemical environment in the stomach, especially how it responds in the presence of bromophenol blue indicator.
- Observe how commercial antacids work in the stomach.
- Experimentally determine whether equal masses of different antacids have equal ability to lower the acidity of a sample, and thereby determine which one is the most effective.

Safety goggles and a lab apron must be worn *at all times* in a chemistry lab.

What Do You Think?

People may eat too much of various foods that will work together to cause an upset stomach, acid indigestion, or heartburn.

- **How does taking an antacid relieve the discomfort that accompanies these digestive problems? Do they work?**

Record your ideas about these questions in your *Active Chemistry* log. Be prepared to discuss your responses with your small group and the class.

Investigate

1. Add 2 mL 0.5 *M* hydrochloric acid to each of four test tubes. (Hydrochloric acid will be used to simulate stomach acid.)
2. Place one drop of bromophenol blue indicator in each test tube.
   a) What is the color of the indicator when it is in the presence of the acid?
3. The question you will investigate is: How will the acid, similar to what is in your stomach, react when different bases are added to it? Bases are the active ingredients of antacids.

4. To the first test tube, add some of the base called sodium bicarbonate, $NaHCO_3$.

   a) Observe and record what happens. Is there a color change after the base has been added? What is the color of the indicator when an excess of antacid has been added? Did any other change occur?

5. Add some ground-up calcium carbonate antacid tablets to the second test tube.

   a) Observe and record what happens.

6. Add some liquid antacid to the third test tube.

   a) Observe and record what happens.

   b) In your *Active Chemistry* log, describe what seems to be consistent about the color of the indicator when it is in the presence of an acid and when it is in the presence of a base.

7. Save the fourth test tube with its acid and indicator as a comparison to use in the following part of the activity.

8. Grind up the three commercially available antacids. Measure out 0.25 g samples of each.

   a) Record the cost of the bottle and the number of doses per bottle. Use this information to calculate the price per dose. Be aware that for some products, a dose may require more than one tablet.

9. Place the 0.25 g of each antacid into a small plastic cup that has a volume of about 150 mL.

10. Add 20 mL of water to each container. Then add 10 drops of bromophenol blue indicator to each container.

    a) Observe and record the color of the solution in each container.

11. Using an eyedropper, slowly add 0.50 *M* hydrochloric acid to the mixture of water and antacid. Carefully count the drops of hydrochloric acid that are required to change the color of the indicator to the color it had in acid solution. (Remember, you saved the fourth tube for this purpose.)

    You will need to swirl the container and solution after each addition of the acid. Some of the antacids will change color but will turn back to the original color in a few seconds. You must continue to add acid and swirl until the new color remains for at least 60 seconds.

    a) Record the final number of drops.

    b) Use the data you collected to decide which antacid provides the most neutralizing power. Discuss what evidence you used to make this decision.

    c) Which is the most economical antacid to use?

Be careful with the acid used in this activity. It can cause chemical burns.

Do not eat anything used in the lab.

Dispose of the chemicals carefully as your teacher instructs.

Wash your hands and arms thoroughly after the activity.

Chem Talk

ANTACIDS

Is It Heartburn or Acid Indigestion?

Why are there so many commercials for **antacids** on TV? One reason is that almost 50% of the population in the U.S. has heartburn at least once a month, and 7% experience it every day. Statistics on acid indigestion are difficult to find because the definition is vague, but it's probably almost as common as heartburn.

Heartburn is the burning feeling in the middle of your chest caused by **acid** leaking upwards from the stomach into the esophagus. Your esophagus doesn't have a protective lining like the stomach. The acid leaking up into the esophagus can cause pain and sometimes even damage. Even though it is called heartburn, it has nothing to do with your heart. The pain is experienced in the general area of the heart.

Like heartburn, acid indigestion causes a similar burning discomfort, but it is in the pit of your stomach. The entire surface of the stomach is covered with a mucus lining that protects the stomach from the corrosive effects of the acid. However, this protective layer sometimes breaks down and results in the feeling of acid indigestion. Severe damage to the stomach lining can result in an ulcer. An ulcer is a lesion in the surface of the lining of the stomach.

Until recent times, doctors believed lifestyle factors like stress and diet caused ulcers. Although it is true that smoking, drinking alcohol, and using caffeine are still suspected of causing problems, scientists now believe that the primary cause of most ulcers is infection caused by the bacterium *Helicobacter pylori* (H. pylori).

pH in the Stomach

An empty stomach has a pH of about 1 to 2 and is therefore very acidic. (Recall that solutions with pH values less than 7 are acids and those greater than 7 are **bases**.) When foods are consumed, the pH will change and cause the contents in the stomach to be less acidic. For instance, the pH might rise to 4. The bromophenol blue indicator that you used has different colors depending on the acidity of the solution. If the pH is 3 or less, the indicator solution will be yellow.

Chem Words

antacid: a substance that will increase the pH in the stomach.

acid: a solution that has a pH less than 7.

base: a solution that has a pH greater than 7.

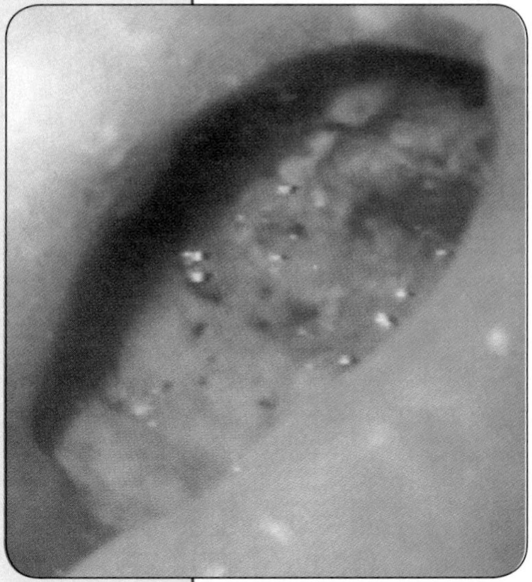

Ulcers are open sores that develop on the lining of the esophagus, stomach, or upper small intestine.

If the pH of the solution is 4.6 or greater, it will become a purple color. Notice that between 3 and 4.6, it will be changing colors.

Relieving Heartburn and Acid Indigestion

Those who suffer from more than occasional heartburn sometimes find the need to take steps to prevent stomach acid from leaking back up into the esophagus. Avoiding alcohol, peppermint/spearmint, chocolate, all caffeinated drinks, and fatty foods helps maintain the proper connection between the esophagus and the stomach. Waiting two or three hours after eating before lying down is also recommended. To prevent acid indigestion and to protect the stomach lining, aspirin and tobacco products should not be used. To reduce the production of extra acid, smoking, caffeinated products, citrus juices, and milk (yes, milk) should be avoided.

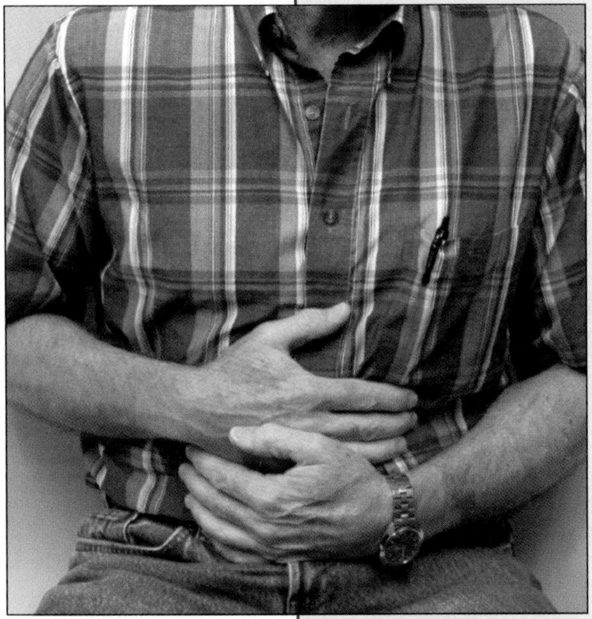

There are two types of over-the-counter medicines proven to work against heartburn and acid indigestion. They are antacids and hydrogen blockers. They both reduce the acidity of stomach fluids. Antacids work quickly and are relatively cheap. They do not stop the production of the acid. They simply use up the excess stomach acid to provide a short period of relief.

One active ingredient in some antacids is calcium carbonate $CaCO_3$. This ingredient is often found in chewable antacid tablets. Calcium carbonate is a solid (s) that reacts with some of the hydrochloric acid (HCl), a liquid (aq). The products of this reaction are calcium chloride, water, and carbon dioxide (CO_2), a gas (g). The reaction is:

$$CaCO_{3(s)} + 2HCl_{(aq)} \rightarrow CaCl_{2(aq)} + H_2O_{(l)} + CO_{2(g)}$$

Another active ingredient, magnesium hydroxide, is also able to react with the hydrochloric acid in the stomach. This active ingredient is frequently found in many of the liquid antacids. The reaction is:

$$Mg(OH)_{2(s)} + 2HCl_{(aq)} \rightarrow MgCl_{2(aq)} + 2H_2O_{(l)}$$

A third active ingredient commonly found in antacids is aluminum hydroxide, which also reacts with the hydrochloric acid. The reaction is:

$$Al(OH)_{3(s)} + 3HCl_{(aq)} \rightarrow AlCl_{3(aq)} + 3H_2O_{(l)}$$

In this activity, the color of the **acid-base indicator** tells you the pH of the stomach acid. When the antacid was added it neutralized some of that acid and the pH of the mixture changed. The pH went up and changed the color of the indicator. You saw that all of the antacids changed the color of the indicator. In the first equation on the preceding page, the calcium carbonate, $CaCO_3$, used up the hydrochloric acid (HCl) and made carbon dioxide (CO_2), calcium chloride ($CaCl_2$), and water. But in the other two equations, the active ingredient in the antacid actually neutralized the acid. This means that the number of molecules (or moles) of acid consumed equals the number of molecules (or moles) of water produced. Even though the different types of antacids reacted in different ways, they all lowered the amount of acid and made the pH go up. This was shown by the change in color of the indicator. An indicator is one simple way to show that the amount of acid is changing. Remember that as the acidity goes up, the pH goes down, and as the acidity goes down, the pH goes up.

After taking an antacid, a smaller amount of acidic gastric fluid will reflux into the esophagus, causing less heartburn. As you have seen in this activity, different products have different abilities to reduce the acid concentration. Part of this depends on which active ingredients the product contains. The other factor deals with how much of each of the ingredients a particular product contains. Reading the label can help explain which reactions are going on in the stomach.

Hydrogen blockers, rather than neutralizing some of the acid like antacids do, actually reduce the amount of acid being produced in the stomach. However, the only way for the blocker to do this is to be absorbed through the intestine and into the blood stream. This takes longer than an antacid to work, but the hydrogen blocker will provide relief longer than an antacid (6–12 hours).

The obvious question is, "Why not put both an antacid and a hydrogen blocker in the same product?" That way a person could get temporary relief from excess acid as well as future reduction in the production of acid. It would appear that you are thinking in the same way as the big drug companies. At least one product now available, has done just that. It contains calcium carbonate and magnesium hydroxide along with a hydrogen blocker, which is used to restrict the production of hydrochloric acid.

Chem Words

acid-base indicator: a substance that changes color when exposed to either an acid or a base.

hydrogen blocker: a compound that is used to inhibit the production of hydrogen ions in the stomach and intestines.

Checking Up

1. What are the differences between heartburn and acid indigestion?
2. What is an ulcer?
3. a) How do antacids work against heartburn and acid indigestion differently?
   b) How do hydrogen blockers work against heartburn and acid indigestion differently?
4. Lowering the concentration of acid has what effect on the pH of a solution?
5. Which type of product produces relief from heartburn and acid indigestion faster, antacids or hydrogen blockers? Explain.

What Do You Think Now?

At the beginning of this activity you were asked:

- **How does taking an antacid relieve the discomfort that accompanies these digestive problems? Do they work?**

Now that you have completed this activity, how would you explain the purpose of antacids and how they work? Are all antacids the same in chemical composition and in their ability to neutralize acids?

Chem Essential Questions

What does it mean?

Chemistry explains a macroscopic phenomenon (what you observe) with a description of what happens at the nanoscopic level (atoms and molecules) using symbolic structures as a way to communicate. Complete the chart below in your *Active Chemistry* log.

MACRO	NANO	SYMBOLIC
What observations did you use to determine the general acidity of the different solutions tested?	*At the molecular level, what is the reaction between the hydrochloric acid HCl and the sodium bicarbonate base $NaHCO_3$?*	*In chemisty, you can use equations to represent reactions. Use equations to show how the hydrochloric acid of the stomach can be neutralized.*

How do you know?

Antacids are advertised to reduce the acid in your stomach. What evidence do you have from the activity that this is true?

Why do you believe?

You or someone you know may have experienced the discomforts of acid indigestion. What do people you know do to relieve acid indigestion? (Note: Relief from acid indigestion may not involve the use of a drug at all. It may involve preventative steps you can take to avoid these problems.)

Why should you care?

Finding ways to avoid acid indigestion or heartburn are important. If these conditions occur often you can expect to have more serious problems at a later time of life. How can you incorporate this into your presentation?

Reflecting on the Activity and the Challenge

In this activity, you expanded your knowledge about acids, antacids, bases, and indicators. The stomach contains gastric fluids, which are mostly hydrochloric acid, and antacids may be used to neutralize this acidity. In this activity, you examined various antacids and their abilities to neutralize hydrochloric acid. This information could come in handy as you plan your skit as part of the ride down the alimentary canal.

Imagine what might happen if all of a sudden some antacid dropped into the stomach where you were trapped. Would something different happen if it were a calcium carbonate tablet as compared to a dose of aluminum hydroxide or magnesium hydroxide? Remember, in your skit you must represent what is chemically occurring by acting out the roles that the individual molecules would play.

Chem to Go

1. Write a balanced chemical equation for the neutralization reaction between sodium hydrogen carbonate (sodium bicarbonate) and hydrochloric acid. (Hint: One of the products is the gas discussed in *Activity 3*.)
2. What simple method can be used to identify an acid or base?
3. Classify the following household products as acidic or basic based on their pH.
   a) Vinegar, pH 3.0
   b) Drain cleaner (contains sodium hydroxide), pH 12.0
   c) Tomato sauce, pH 4.4
   d) Household ammonia, pH 10.0
   e) Citric juices, pH 3.0
   f) Baking soda, pH 9.0
4. It takes twice as much of antacid X as antacid Y to neutralize a certain mass (or volume) of an acid. Which antacid contains more base?
5. Solution A is tested with blue litmus paper. It stays blue. Solution A is then tested with red litmus paper. The red litmus paper stays red. What can you conclude about the solution?
6. Create a chart like the one below in your *Active Chemistry* log and record the information gathered by reading the labels of different antacid products at a grocery or drug store:

Ingredients	Antacid #1	Antacid #2	Antacid #3
recommended dose			
cost per container			
cost per recommended dose			

7. *Preparing for the Chapter Challenge*

   Create a few lines of exciting dialog that can be used to describe what happens in the stomach as the antacid is ingested. Is there a way you can include a chemical equation into your ride or dialog?

Inquiring Further

1. Choosing relief for an upset stomach

If you were traveling through the alimentary canal and the stomach was upset, would you want your host body to calm the stomach down with a dose of magnesium hydroxide, sodium bicarbonate, or calcium carbonate?

2. Structure and function of the stomach

Research the structure and function of the stomach. What controls the movement of food into and out of the stomach? What is the pH of gastric fluids? In addition to acid, what other fluid is secreted in the stomach? What protects the stomach lining from the acid?

3. GERD (gastroesophageal reflux disease)

Research and report to your team about acid-reflux disease (GERD).

4. Definitions of acids and bases

What are the definitions of acids and bases according to Arrhenius, Brønsted and Lowry, and Lewis? Review your previous work with acids and bases and summarize these definitions.

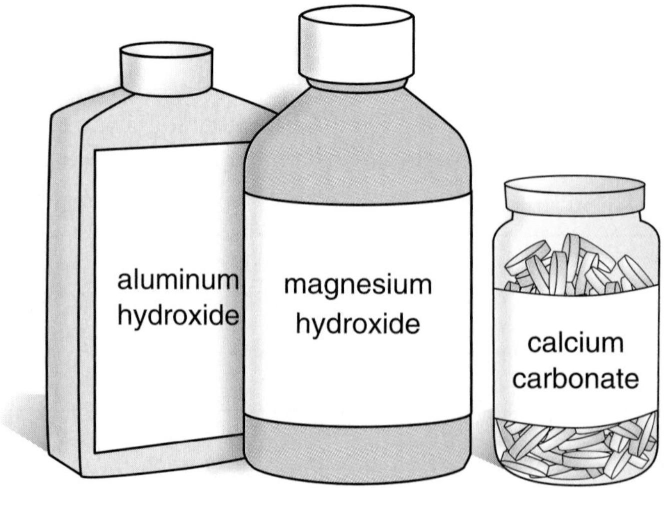
aluminum hydroxide
magnesium hydroxide
calcium carbonate

Activity 3 Studying Carbon Dioxide

What Do You See?

SO
DA
CO_2

GOALS

In this activity you will:

- Generate CO_2 by various methods, then collect and characterize it.
- Explore how the volume of a gas varies with temperature.
- Compare the Celsius and Kelvin temperature scales.

What Do You Think?

An effervescent antacid tablet and a carbonated beverage produce a fizz that tickles your nose when you take the first mouthful.

- **What causes you to burp after drinking a carbonated beverage?**

Record your ideas about this question in your *Active Chemistry* log. Be prepared to discuss your responses with your small group and the class.

Investigate

All carbonated beverages give off gases. Under pressure, the gas can stay in the beverage. When you open the top and release the pressure, some of the gases are released but some remain in the beverage and give it the fizz. In this investigation, you will try to determine how the temperature of the drink affects the amount of gas that the liquid can hold.

Part A: Collecting and Testing Carbon Dioxide Gas

1. You will first have to learn a technique for collecting a gas. The technique that you will use involves the displacement of water. First place 3 mL of water in a test tube (#1). Then place a one-hole rubber stopper fitted with a short piece of glass tubing into the mouth of the test tube. Attach rubber tubing to the glass tubing.

Safety goggles and a lab apron must be worn *at all times* in a chemistry lab.

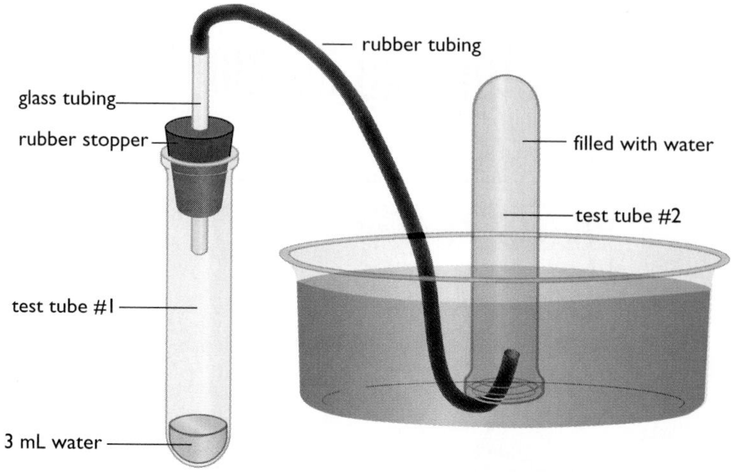
rubber tubing
glass tubing
rubber stopper
filled with water
test tube #2
test tube #1
3 mL water

2. Completely fill another test tube (#2) with water and submerge it, upside down, in a container of water. Place the end of the rubber tubing from test tube #1 into test tube #2.

3. Drop one-half tablet of an effervescent antacid tablet into test tube #1. Quickly place the rubber stopper back into the mouth of the tube.

4. The water will be displaced from tube #2 by the gas coming from the effervescent antacid tablet. Keep the mouth of test tube #2 below the surface of the water. When all of the water has been displaced, place a small square of plastic wrap over the mouth of the tube. Now the test tube can be removed from the water. Put a rubber band around the mouth of the test tube to keep the plastic wrap in place. This should keep the gas from escaping.

5. Remove the plastic wrap from test tube #2 and insert a glowing splint into the tube.

   a) What did you observe happening? Record these observations in your *Active Chemistry* log.

Be careful with the glowing splint and other burning materials. Dispose of it carefully.

Avoid breathing the gas given off by the tablet.

6. Continue to generate gas by adding more effervescent antacid tablets to test tube #1. This time, place the rubber hose into a new test tube containing 5 mL of limewater. (This time the test tube is not submerged in the water.) Observe what happens at first when the gas bubbles through the limewater. As the bubbling continues, you may have to add more effervescent antacid tablets to maintain generation of the gas. What further change do you see?

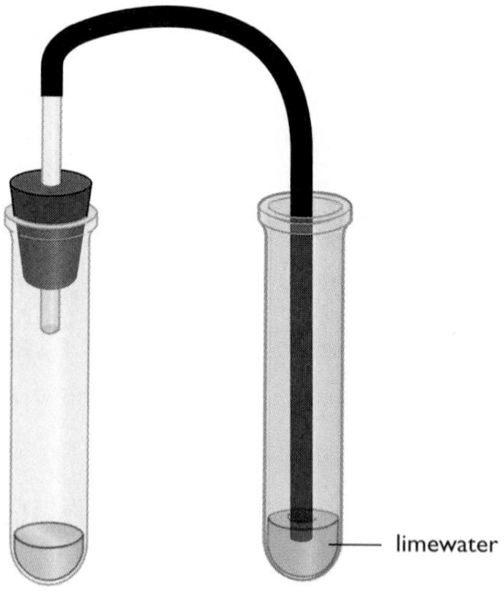
limewater

   a) Record these observations in your *Active Chemistry* log.

7. The gas carbon dioxide CO_2 is able to extinguish a glowing splint. It reacts with limewater to form a white solid, or ***precipitate***. The gas oxygen O_2 will ignite a splint and has no reaction with limewater. The gas hydrogen H_2 will cause a small explosion when exposed to a fire and does not react with limewater.

   a) On the basis of this information and your results, identify the gas produced by the effervescent antacid tablet.

8. Dispose of the materials as directed by your teacher.

Part B: Temperature and Solubility of a Gas

1. Design an experiment that would help you investigate the question: How does temperature affect the solubility of the gas in carbonated beverage? (The solubility of a gas in a liquid is a measure of how much gas can remain in the liquid.)

   With the approval of your teacher, you may be able to move ahead with your design. Alternatively, your teacher may ask you to use the following steps, for which the equipment is available and safe.

2. Put water in a large beaker, set it on a hot plate and heat it to 37°C. Suspend a thermometer from a ringstand in the water so that the temperature can be monitored. Adjust the hot plate setting so that a temperature of 37°C can be maintained.

3. Obtain two balloons and stretch them back and forth about a dozen times. Blow into them and inflate them two or three times. This will make it easier for them to expand. Open two small cold glass bottles of a carbonated beverage and immediately place the balloons over the mouths of the bottles.

4. Submerge one bottle of the beverage in a beaker of 37°C water. Maintain the temperature of the water at 37°C. With the balloon still on the mouth of the bottle, agitate or swirl the bottle. When no more bubbles of gas are given off, use a twist-tie to tie off the balloon. Twist it tightly so none of the gas leaks out.

5. At the same time as you did in *Step 4*, submerge the other bottle in a beaker of ice and water. With the balloon still on the mouth of the bottle, agitate or swirl the bottle vigorously. When no more bubbles of gas are given off by the beverage, make a knot in the neck of the balloon to tie it off so that no gas can leak out. *Do not use a twist-tie on this second balloon.*

Do not heat glass bottles directly on the hot plate. Also, do not heat the glass bottles higher than 37°C. They can break.

6. Without taking measurements, roughly compare the volume of gas released from the bottle in the 37°C water with the volume of gas released from the bottle in the ice water.

   a) Record in your *Active Chemistry* log any conclusions you can make about these volumes. What does this tell you about the relationship between temperature and the solubility of a gas in a liquid?

Part C: Temperature and Volume of a Gas

Safety goggles and a lab apron must be worn *at all times* in the lab.

1. To compare the volume of a gas at different temperatures, you need to be sure that you are comparing the volume of the same number of particles of gas. You cannot be sure that this is the case in the two balloons of gas collected above. To overcome this problem:

   Take the balloon of gas that you tied off. Place it in a 1000-mL beaker that contains 200 mL of ice water. There should be no pieces of ice floating in the beaker.

   Place a 600-mL beaker inside the first beaker so that it rests on the top of the balloon. With your hand push the 600-mL beaker down until the balloon is just submerged. In other words, the bottom of the 600-mL beaker should just be at the surface of the water but not submerged in the water. Record the volume to which the water rises in the beaker. Using the graduations on the beaker, you will have to estimate to the nearest 10 mL the total volume of the (balloon + water).

2. Remove the balloon and place it in the 600-mL beaker so that it won't get mixed up with other balloons in the room.

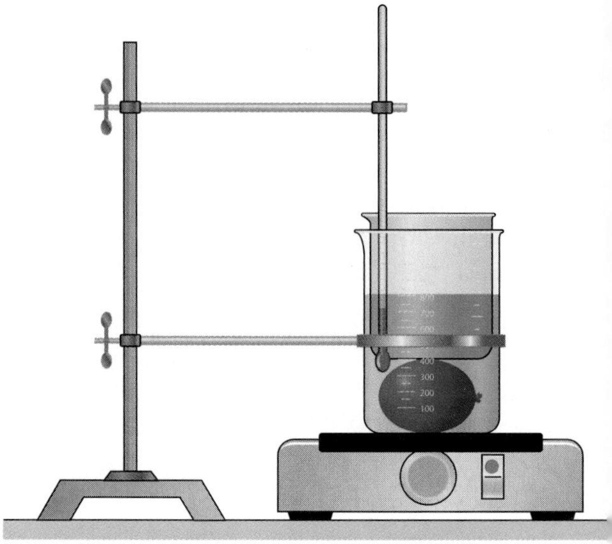

3. Place a thermometer in the beaker containing the 200 mL of water.

   a) Record this starting cold temperature.

4. Heat the 200 mL of water in the 1000-mL beaker to about 80°C. Using beaker tongs or hot pads, remove the beaker from the heat source and place it on the workbench. Return the balloon to this beaker containing the 200 mL of hot water.

5. Once again, push down (with a rubber glove to limit heat on your hand) on the 600-mL beaker to entirely submerge the balloon below the surface of the water. Allow the balloon to remain submerged for a few minutes so that the gas in the balloon may come to the same temperature as the water.

6. With your hand, move the 600-mL beaker upward until the balloon is just submerged. In other words, the bottom of the 600-mL beaker should just be at the surface of the water.
   a) Record the new volume to which the water has risen in the beaker. Once again, you will only be able to estimate to the nearest 10 mL the total volume of the balloon plus water.
   b) Remove the balloon and use the thermometer to obtain the temperature of the warm water. Record this temperature in your *Active Chemistry* log.
7. Dispose of the materials as directed by your teacher. Clean up your workstation.
8. Use the data that you have recorded in your *Active Chemistry* log to compute the volume of the balloon at the cold temperature. Also, compute the volume of the balloon at the hot temperature.
   a) Record the volumes of the balloon at the cold and hot temperatures.
   b) Write a statement that describes the change in volume of the gas as the temperature increased.
   c) By what factor did the volume of the balloon increase?
   d) By what factor did the temperature increase?
   e) Did the volume increase by the same factor that the temperature increased?

Wash your hands and arms thoroughly after the activity.

Chem Talk

THE RELATIONSHIP BETWEEN TEMPERATURE AND THE VOLUME OF A GAS

Testing for Carbon Dioxide

In this activity, you collected carbon dioxide CO_2 gas from the effervescent antacid tablets dissolved in water. As you saw in *Activity* 2, gas was formed when some antacids underwent a reaction. The common chemical test for CO_2 is to bubble it through **limewater** (a basic, aqueous solution of calcium hydroxide). The formation of a white solid, or **precipitate**, confirms the presence of CO_2. The equation for this is:

$$CO_{2(g)} + Ca(OH)_{2(aq)} \rightarrow CaCO_{3(s)} + H_2O_{(l)}$$

Upon further addition of CO_2, the white precipitate dissolves according to:

$$CaCO_{3(s)} + CO_{2(g)} + H_2O_{(l)} \rightarrow Ca(HCO_3)_{2(aq)}$$

Another identifying feature of CO_2 is that it does not burn and it will not support combustion. Therefore, sticking a glowing splint into a bottle of CO_2 will cause it to go out immediately. This is the basis of using a CO_2 fire extinguisher.

Chem Words

limewater: a saturated aqueous solution of calcium hydroxide.

precipitate: a solid that separates from a solution usually as the result of a chemical reaction of two other solutions.

Solubility and Volume of Gas and Temperature

As the name indicates, carbonated beverages (drinks) contain CO_2 that has been dissolved in the liquid under pressure. Opening the can or the bottle allows the gas to be released and the pressure to be reduced. You found in the activity that as the temperature increased, more gas was released from the liquid. The solubility of the gas in the liquid decreased as the temperature increased. If the beverage is cold when it enters the stomach, it gets warmed up because the temperature of the stomach is around 37°C, about 30° warmer than the cold, carbonated drink. More CO_2 will be released in the stomach than if the carbonated beverage remained at room temperature. This is because CO_2 is less soluble in warm liquids than in colder liquids. All that gas in your stomach causes you to burp.

You also found that increasing the temperature of the gas increased the volume of the gas.

Chem Words

Charles's Law: a gas law that says if the mass of a gas and the pressure of the gas are held constant, the volume of the gas will vary in a direct proportion to the temperature of the gas.

direct proportion: a mathematical relationship that says, as one quantity increases the other one will increase so that their ratio remains constant, or if one quantity decreases the other one will decrease so that their ratio remains constant.

Charles's Law

This relationship between temperature and volume is called **Charles's Law**. Jacques Charles was an avid hot-air balloonist back in the 1800s. Because he was concerned about the volume his balloon must maintain, he very carefully measured the relationship between the temperature and volume of the gas in his balloon. With the help of another Frenchman, Joseph Louis Gay-Lussac, the law known today as Charles's Law was formulated. It says that there is a **direct proportion** between temperature and volume if a constant mass of gas remains at constant pressure. This means that if the temperature goes up, the volume will go up proportionally. And, if the temperature goes down, the volume will also go down proportionally. Note that this relationship is only valid if the pressure and the mass of the gas remain constant while the volume and temperature change.

Examine the following data that scientists from the 1800s might have collected:

A 1.00 L volume of gas with an initial temperature of 15°C was warmed to 30°C. The volume increases to 1.05 L. Just as you found, increasing the temperature also increases the volume.

By using Kelvin as the temperature scale, the result is more profound. The **Kelvin** scale has the same increments as the Celsius scale, but 0 K is equal to –273°C and this temperature is known as **absolute zero** and is thought to be the coldest temperature possible. (The Kelvin scale does not use the degree symbol.) You can see the relationship between Celsius and Kelvin on the thermometer pictured.

The Kelvin temperature is found by adding 273 to the Celsius temperature.

As a conversion equation, you can write that

$$K = 273 + {}^{\circ}C.$$

Returning to the sample data, you now see that the temperature increase in kelvins was from an initial temperature of 15°C, or 288 K to a final temperature of 30°C or 303 K. The Kelvin temperature ratio is 303/288 = 1.05 times as big. This is identical to the volume change.

This is an enormous breakthrough in thinking about gases. This means that the absolute temperature and volume really are directly proportional. As the absolute temperature went up by a factor of 1.05, the volume also went up by a factor of 1.05.

In the equation for Charles's Law, the amount and pressure are constant:

$$\frac{V_1}{T_1} = \frac{V_2}{T_2}$$

and V is the volume and T is absolute temperature (°C + 273.15 = K)

If you want to double the volume of a gas, you must also double the temperature of the gas (using the Kelvin scale). In your initial example of 1.0 L of gas at 15°C, or 288 K, you would have to double the temperature to 2 × 288 K = 576 K to double the volume to 2.0 L. (576 K is equal to 303°C.) Doubling the Kelvin temperature in this case increases the Celsius temperature by a factor of 20.

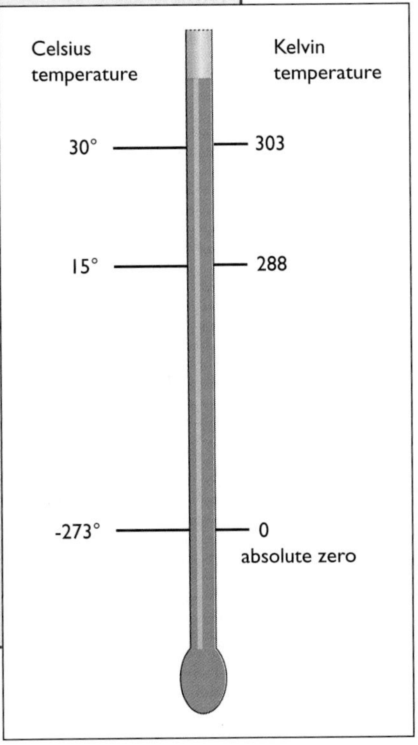
Celsius temperature
Kelvin temperature
30°
303
15°
288
-273°
0
absolute zero

Chem Words

kelvins: the base unit of temperature. One kelvin represents the same temperature difference as one degree Celsius.

absolute temperature scale: a temperature scale where absolute zero is taken as 0 K and on which there are 100 divisions between the freezing point of water (273.15 K) and the boiling point of water (373.15 K).

Checking Up

1. What is a chemical test for the presence of CO_2?
2. What does Charles's Law say?
3. Define the term "directly proportional."
4. Which temperature scale must be used when solving problems using Charles's Law?
5. What are two properties of CO_2 that make it useful in a fire extinguisher?

There are other gas laws that you will be learning about and they will all be simpler to understand when you use absolute Kelvin temperatures instead of Celsius temperatures.

Increasing Temperature at the Molecular Level

You have investigated some of the macroscopic properties of gases. As student chemists, you are also interested in what is happening at the molecular level. The molecules of CO_2 gas are in constant motion. The temperature is a measure of the average kinetic energy of these molecules. The higher the temperature, the faster the molecules move and the greater the kinetic energy associated with this motion. When the temperature increases, you expect that the faster-moving higher energy molecules will be able to push on the balloon more than slower-moving molecules. This is why the volume of the balloon begins to increase. As the volume gets larger, fewer particles hit the wall every second. The enlarged balloon stops expanding when the increase of the energy of the molecules is exactly balanced by the decrease in the number of particles hitting the balloon per second.

What Do You Think Now?

At the beginning of this activity you were asked:

- **What causes you to burp after drinking a carbonated beverage?**

Now that you have completed this activity, how would you answer the question?

Chem Essential Questions

What does it mean?

Chemistry explains a macroscopic phenomenon (what you observe) with a description of what happens at the nanoscopic level (atoms and molecules) using symbolic structures as a way to communicate. Complete the chart below in your *Active Chemistry* log.

MACRO	NANO	SYMBOLIC
What happens to the size of a balloon filled with gas as you heat it?	*On the molecular level, explain how increasing the temperature of the gas will increase the volume.*	*Draw a sketch that depicts the different behavior of gas molecules at 288 K and then at 576 K.*

How do you know?

Use your data to explain Charles's Law:

$$\frac{V_1}{T_1} = \frac{V_2}{T_2}$$

Why do you believe?

To celebrate a friend's birthday, you purchase a mylar balloon (a shiny balloon material). It's very cold outside and when you leave the store, you see that your balloon is no longer inflated. You go back into the store to complain about the leak in the balloon. But as you explain the problem, the balloon inflates again. Explain what is occurring.

Why should you care?

If your ride were to have the riders navigate the potential problem of being burped out of the body, how would you describe this?

Reflecting on the Activity and the Challenge

Recall that in this activity you investigated the properties of carbon dioxide and various ways that carbon dioxide can be produced. Certain medicines, foods, and beverages may produce carbon dioxide in a chemical reaction. Carbonated beverages contain carbon dioxide gas that can escape from the liquid. If you drink a cold soft drink, the volume of carbon dioxide gas will expand as it warms in your stomach. This knowledge of chemistry can be applied to the skit needed for your part of the ride through the alimentary canal. Imagine what you would experience when you are in the stomach, clinging to a particle of food, and the carbonated beverage that has just entered the stomach starts warming up. Molecules of CO_2 as big as you are being released and are moving toward you at a high speed. More and more of them keep coming! The ride might get a little rocky for a while.

Chem to Go

1. Charles's Law in chemistry states that the temperature and the volume of a gas are directly proportional if the pressure and amount remain constant.
   a) Write this as an equation.
   b) Draw a graph that represents a direct proportion between the variables of volume (y-axis) and temperature (x-axis).
2. To test for the presence of CO_2 you bubbled the gas through limewater.
   a) What is limewater?

b) Write the balanced chemical equation for the chemical reaction that occurs when carbon dioxide is bubbled into limewater.

c) What is the chemical name of the white solid product (precipitate) formed in the test for carbon dioxide?

3. Which is the higher temperature, 27°C or 270 K? By what factor is one bigger than the other?

4. Explain why Kelvin temperatures are always positive.

5. The average human body temperature is 98.6°F, which is 37.0°C.

   a) What is this temperature on the Kelvin scale?

   b) What is done mathematically to change a Celsius temperature to a Kelvin temperature?

6. Convert 150 K to its Celsius equivalent.

7. If the volume of a gas in a flexible container is 444 L at a temperature of 200 K, what will the volume be if the temperature falls to 100 K, assuming that the pressure remains constant?

8. The temperature outside the city bank reads 278 K (the bank president is a former chemistry teacher).

   a) What would be the appropriate clothes for the day, a bathing suit, or a heavy jacket?

   b) Because some of the people in the bank do not understand the Kelvin scale, the other side of the flashing temperature sign gives the temperature in °C. If the one side flashes 310 K, what does the other side flash in °C?

9. ***Preparing for the Chapter Challenge***

   You can certainly use the concept of the effect of temperature of a gas on its solubility and on its volume. Determine a way in which your ride will use these relationships. Write an explanation of the chemistry principles and how you know about them as part of your challenge.

Inquiring Further

1. Who were Fahrenheit, Celsius, and Kelvin?

Compare the scientific work of Gabriel Fahrenheit, Anders Celsius, and Lord Kelvin. What did they have in common?

2. Dry Ice

What is dry ice? At what temperature is dry ice stored? What are some uses of dry ice?

Activity 4 Observing Real Food in Artificial Stomachs

What Do You See?

WATER
WATER + ACID
WATER + PEPSIN
ACID + PEPSIN
Beef Jerky

GOALS

In this activity you will:

- Construct four artificial "stomachs" containing combinations of water, pepsin, and hydrochloric acid.
- Investigate, in a systematic way, the effects of water, hydrochloric acid, and pepsin on various foods placed in the artificial stomachs.
- Use a chemical equation to represent what is happening inside the artificial stomachs.

Safety goggles and a lab apron must be worn *at all times* in a chemistry lab. Be careful not to get the hydrochloric acid on you or your clothing. It can cause chemical burns.

What Do You Think?

The pH of the hydrochloric acid in the stomach is about 2. That's strong enough to burn your skin. Thankfully, your stomach has a layer that protects it from this strong acid.

- **What do you think happens to food like a hamburger or potatoes when they are in the stomach?**

Record your ideas about this question in your *Active Chemistry* log. Be prepared to discuss your responses with your small group and the class.

Investigate

1. Prepare four artificial "stomachs." Place a plastic sandwich bag inside a 250-mL beaker. Fold down the top of the bag over the lip of the beaker. Use either a piece of string or a rubber band to secure the bag to the beaker.

"Stomach"	Water	0.05 *M* HCl	2% pepsin	Raw potato	Egg white	Beef jerky	Raw cabbage
A	100 mL			X	X	X	X
B	50 mL	50 mL		X	X	X	X
C	50 mL		50 mL	X	X	X	X
D		50 mL	50 mL	X	X	X	X

Stomach A: Add 100 mL of distilled water to the bag.
Stomach B: Add 50 mL of distilled water and 50 mL of 0.05 *M* HCl to the bag. Mix the contents by gently swirling.
Stomach C: Add 50 mL of distilled water and 50 mL of a 2% pepsin solution to the bag. Mix the contents by gently swirling.
Stomach D: Add 50 mL of a 2% pepsin solution and 50 mL of 0.05 *M* HCl to the bag. Mix the contents by gently swirling.

2. Prepare "food" for the "stomachs."

   Get four equal pieces of potato, four equal pieces of hard-boiled egg white, four equal pieces of beef jerky, and four equal pieces of raw cabbage.

   To each of four of the sticks, tie a piece of potato and a piece of egg white. To each of the other four sticks tie a piece of beef jerky and a piece of raw cabbage.

3. Lay one stick across the mouth of the beaker so that the two food samples dangle below into the liquid. Now lay another stick, with the other two foods, crisscross to the first stick. All four food samples should now be submerged in the "stomach" fluid.

4. Prepare the other three "stomachs" in the same manner.

5. Cover each of the artificial stomachs with a strip of plastic wrap.

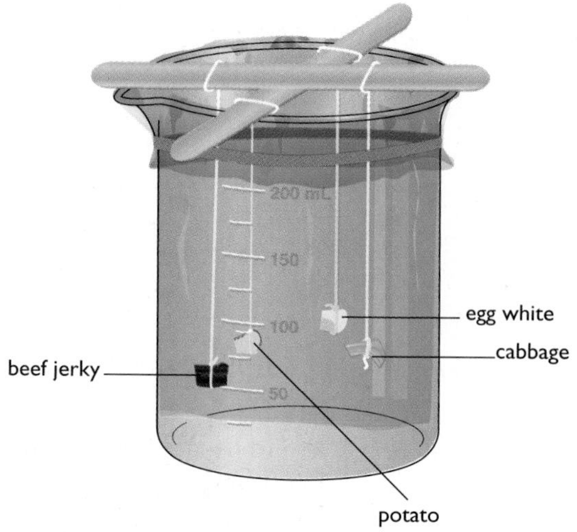
200 mL
150
100
50
egg white
cabbage
beef jerky
potato

6. Observe each of the foods in each of the stomachs after 15 minutes, 24 hours, 48 hours, and 72 hours. Your teacher may have prepared some of these in advance.

   a) Record all of your observations.

   b) What have you decided goes on in each "stomach?" What kind of digestion appears to be taking place? Record in your *Active Chemistry* log your predictions and interpretations.

Chem Talk

DIGESTION IN THE STOMACH

Observing Human Digestion in the Stomach

Dr. William Beaumont

In 1822, a young army doctor, Dr William Beaumont, was the first person actually to see digestion in a live stomach. On June 6, 1822, a French-Canadian man named Alexis St. Martin was shot in the stomach. Dr. Beaumont arrived 30 minutes after the accident. He treated the wound, but he could not fully close the hole in the man's stomach. The hole remained "large enough that Beaumont could insert his entire forefinger into the stomach cavity." A year from the time of the accident, the hole was still about 2.5 inches in circumference and had to be continually closed with a compress and bandage.

In 1825 Dr. Beaumont began his experiments with St. Martin, ". . . becoming the first person to observe human digestion as it occurs in the stomach." He tied pieces of food to a silk string and dangled the food through the hole into St. Martin's stomach. Some of the kinds of food he tested were beef, pork, and raw cabbage. In 1831 he experimented with a much wider range of foods. He took samples from St. Martin's stomach that had spent various times in the stomach and examined the progressive stages of digestion.

Alexis St. Martin lived 58 years after the accident and died at the age of 86. Because you will not be able to find volunteers like St. Martin, you carried out your investigation in artificial plastic bag stomachs.

Pepsin Helps in the Digestion of Protein

There are numerous differences between a real stomach and the artificial ones you used in this activity. The environment of the stomach is not calm and contented as your artificial stomachs might lead you to believe. When food is present, the stomach is in constant motion. The stomach continually squeezes the food as it undergoes **peristalsis**. This is the involuntary muscle contraction that moves food around in the stomach and intestines. If you were clinging to a morsel of food

Chem Words

peristalsis: this is the involuntary muscle contraction that moves food around in the stomach and intestines.

Chem Words

amino acid: an organic compound linked together to form protein.

catalyst: a reagent that speeds the rate of a chemical reaction without getting used up in the process.

enzyme: a substance that is a protein but is a specific catalyst found in the body.

pepsin: an enzyme that acts as a catalyst for the hydrolysis of proteins.

protein: a molecule that contains a long chain of amino acids.

inside the stomach, the ride would be pretty violent. In addition, the environment would be very acidic. From cells embedded in the entire surface of the stomach, hydrochloric acid is secreted into the mix.

From this activity you learned that hydrochloric acid alone will not digest the vehicle in which you are riding through the alimentary canal. You have seen that digestion requires both hydrochloric acid *and* pepsin. Only foods containing proteins (i.e., beef jerky and egg white) seemed to be affected.

Recall from *Activity 1*, that the enzyme amylase was needed to hydrolyze the starch. Similarly, **pepsin** is an enzyme that helps hydrolyze proteins within the stomach. Amylase is specific to starch and pepsin is specific to proteins.

What exactly is a protein? **Proteins** are very large chain-like molecules made out of carbon, hydrogen, oxygen, nitrogen, and sometimes sulfur. Just as a bicycle chain is made up of many links, a protein is made up of many smaller molecules called **amino acids**. Foods such as meat, peanuts, cheese, and eggs contain proteins that must be broken down. Digestion of proteins is the chemical attack of these long-chain molecules.

Enzymes as Catalysts

Pepsin is an enzyme that acts as a catalyst for the hydrolysis of proteins. A **catalyst** is a reagent that speeds the rate of a chemical reaction without getting used up in the process. **Enzymes** themselves are proteins, and are highly specific catalysts. Often, their only job is to catalyze one particular reaction and nothing else. They work best at a particular pH and temperature. Specific conditions vary for different enzymes, but most of them work best at around 40°C. That's very close to normal body temperature of 37°C.

The graph shows you enzyme activity (how well it works) vs. temperature. At temperatures above 45°C enzymes become denatured, or their shape changes and they are no longer effective.

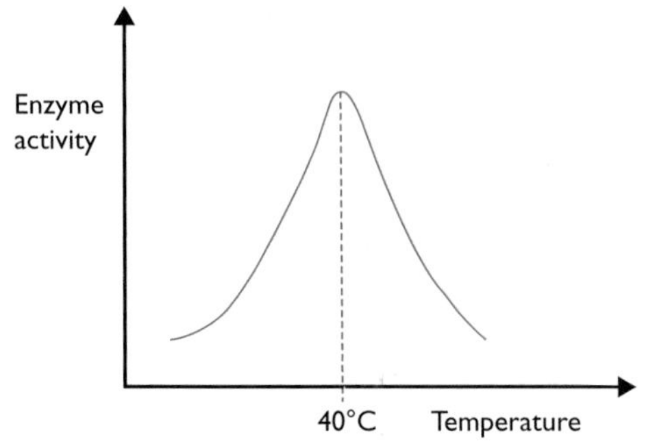
Enzyme activity
40°C
Temperature

You could draw a similar looking graph for pH vs. enzyme activity, as pH can also denature enzymes (proteins) and make them ineffective.

The enzymes that get secreted in the stomach are called gastric enzymes. Pepsin is the main gastric enzyme. It is active only in the acid environment of the stomach (pH 1.5–2.5 or less); it is ineffective in the intestine (~pH 7, neutral). Pepsin in the stomach works best at pH = 2. Amylase in the mouth works best at pH = 7.

Other Functions of the Stomach

Contrary to what many people believe, very little digestion goes on in the stomach. As you have seen in your artificial stomachs and as Dr. Beaumont learned from observing his patient, food is only digested to a small degree in the stomach. The stomach does perform other important functions, however. When food first enters the stomach, it is thoroughly mixed through peristalsis, the mechanical contraction of stomach muscles.

The gastric juice present in the stomach turns the food into a mushy substance called "chyme," preparing it to move down the digestive tract. If a person eats food that has lots of bacteria, or if the stomach gets irritated by a virus or other germ, the stomach may say, "Hey, this food's not going any further!" At this point, the muscles of the stomach squeeze themselves together to push the food out the way it came–back out through the esophagus and mouth. Vomiting is an important line of defense. It can remove dangerous food and prevent more serious problems that could show up further down the line.

Unusual Uses for Pepsin

Pepsin is used commercially in some cheese-making, in the leather industry to remove hair and residual tissue from hides, and in the recovery of silver from discarded photographic films by digesting the gelatin layer that holds the silver.

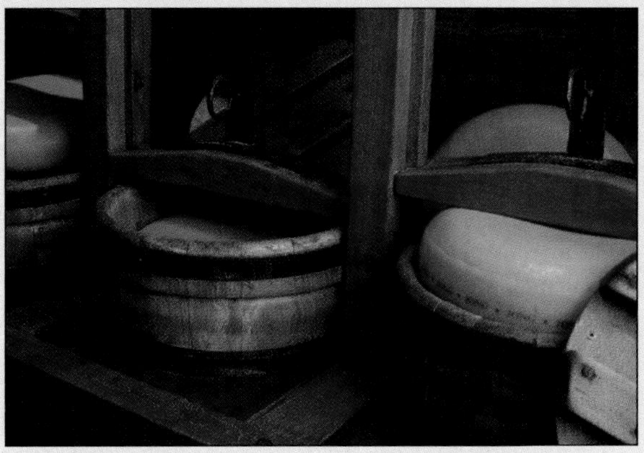

Checking Up

1. What important function does peristalsis perform?
2. What smaller units combine to make up proteins?
3. What are two of the requirements that must be present to start the digestion of protein in the stomach?
4. Which type of food seems to be the only kind that can undergo digestion in the stomach?
5. What causes food to be vomited?

What Do You Think Now?

At the beginning of this activity you were asked:

- **What do you think happens to food like a hamburger or potatoes when they are in the stomach?**

How have your predictions about the fate of a hamburger and potato changed as a result of your investigation?

Chem Essential Questions

What does it mean?

Chemistry explains a macroscopic phenomenon (what you observe) with a description of what happens at the nanoscopic level (atoms and molecules) using symbolic structures as a way to communicate. Complete the chart below in your *Active Chemistry* log.

MACRO	NANO	SYMBOLIC
Describe the disintegration of the foods in the different "stomachs" over time.	*What does an enzyme do at the molecular level to aid in digestion?*	*Data is often shown in graphical form. Explain the meaning of the graph showing enzyme activity vs. temperature.*

How do you know?

What evidence do you have that the only "stomach" that promoted digestion was the one containing the enzyme pepsin and hydrochloric acid, and that the only type of food that went through the digestion process was food containing protein.

Why do you believe?

Contrary to what many would predict, hydrochloric acid cannot digest food without the enzyme. Apparently pepsin does not promote the digestion of carbohydrates, at least not with the low pH found in the stomach. With the evidence from *Activity 1*, it appears that enzymes are highly important in digesting food. Can the enzymes in the mouth digest the proteins in meat?

Why should you care?

Enzymes pose a major danger for riders traveling down the alimentary canal. Even though an enzyme is very specific with which substances it will react, there are many different enzymes in the alimentary canal. This might need to be addressed in your *Chapter Challenge* in some manner.

Reflecting on the Activity and the Challenge

In this activity, you saw evidence that the enzyme pepsin, along with hydrochloric acid in the stomach, begins the digestion of proteins. You may have also gotten some hints concerning which types of foods would be relatively safe to choose as your vehicle through this portion of the alimentary canal. Remember that the skit for your portion of the ride down the alimentary canal has to be from the point of view of what might be happening at the molecular level. What might you incorporate into your skit from what you have learned about the stomach in this activity? Seat belts might be in order!

Chem to Go

1. Which foods seem to undergo digestion in the artificial stomachs?
2. Which set of conditions allowed the digestion to begin?
3. After 72 hours, had the foods been digested? Does it take more than 72 hours to digest these same foods inside you? Explain the difference in time required for digestion in this artificial setting compared to what goes on inside your stomach.
4. The chemical breakdown of a protein is called ___________. In this process, the _______of the protein is broken.
5. Make a sketch of a graph that represents enzyme activity vs. pH. Be sure to label your axes and make the pH axis to scale.
6. ***Preparing for the Chapter Challenge***

   The stomach is not a calm, motionless, plastic bag filled with liquid. When food is observed or smelled, as it enters the mouth and stomach, signals from the brain are sent to get the stomach ready for its part in digestion. Develop a working model that you can use to demonstrate with real food what kind of action (both chemical and physical) would be going on in the stomach.

Inquiring Further

1. Stomach stapling

Even though the stomach is important, could a person survive if a part or all of the stomach were removed? What would the effect be if a physician surgically stapled a patient's stomach to decrease the stomach's size? Research stomach stapling and report to your class what you learn.

2. Carbohydrates and proteins

How does the structure of a protein differ from a carbohydrate?

3. pH dependency of pepsin and amylase

Design and carry out an experiment investigating the pH dependency of pepsin or amylase. That is, at what pH do these enzymes show the most activity? Be sure to identify your independent and dependent variables, and include the use of a control. This exercise could help you with your *Chapter Challenge* as you need to identify the chemical perils that your food particle may encounter.

Chapter mini Challenge

THE BRIDGE
HONK

Your challenge for this chapter is to design a ride for the theme park Anatomy World. Having completed four activities, this is a good time to give your ride a *first try*. This *first try* will give you a good sense of what the challenge entails and how you and other teams are going to approach your design task.

Your *mini-challenge* is to design a part of a ride for Anatomy World that includes some chemistry concepts. The passenger in the ride will be a tiny, tiny piece of food that will experience both the physical and chemical changes as the food moves through the digestive system. You will only be providing the class with a two-minute explanation of your ride. Within your two minutes, you should perform part of the skit illustrating the ride, explain some of the design for the ride, and explain some of the chemical or physical changes that a player will experience during the ride.

Chemistry Content

Your team should first review the chemistry content that may be included in this design for a ride in Anatomy World. Each content area can be creatively used as a part of the ride. Following each activity was a section called *Reflecting on the Activity and the Challenge*, which can provide hints as to the application of chemistry content to your ride design.

Activity 1: You learned about both physical and chemical changes that occur in the mouth. You learned about how starch becomes sugar during hydrolysis. You also investigated the use of iodine to detect starch and Benedict's solution to detect sugar.

Activity 2: You investigated the use and function of antacids in the stomach. You also learned about pH as an indicator of acids and bases. You tested the effectiveness of different antacids in decreasing acidity.

Activity 3: You generated carbon dioxide (CO_2) gas and then investigated properties of this gas. You investigated the effect of temperature changes on the volume of the gas. You also studied the effects of pressure changes on the volume of the gas. In exploring the behavior of gases, you found the value of using Kelvin rather than Celsius as a measure of temperature.

Activity 4: You conducted experiments to determine the role of the stomach in digestion. By building an "artificial stomach" you investigated the role of hydrochloric acid and pepsin in the hydrolysis of proteins. You also learned how pepsin acts as a catalyst in the reaction.

Criteria

Your team should also review the criteria that you discussed on the first day of this chapter. Your ride for Anatomy World should be fun and original. It should demonstrate an understanding of chemistry concepts and help the riders experience these concepts.

Preparing for Your mini Challenge

Your team should begin the process of designing a ride by brainstorming ideas about rides that you enjoy that may be adapted for this purpose. You should then discuss how you can include chemistry concepts from at least two of the activities in the ride. You can then decide on the design of the ride. How will you make the ride fun? How will you demonstrate the ride in your skit? In the *mini-challenge*, you will have only two minutes to describe the design for your ride, perform a brief skit of someone on the ride and to explain the physical and chemical changes in the ride.

Engineering/Technology Design

The engineering-design process involves several distinct steps. In designing a ride for an amusement park, you will use a design process. Note how your efforts follow the design model below.

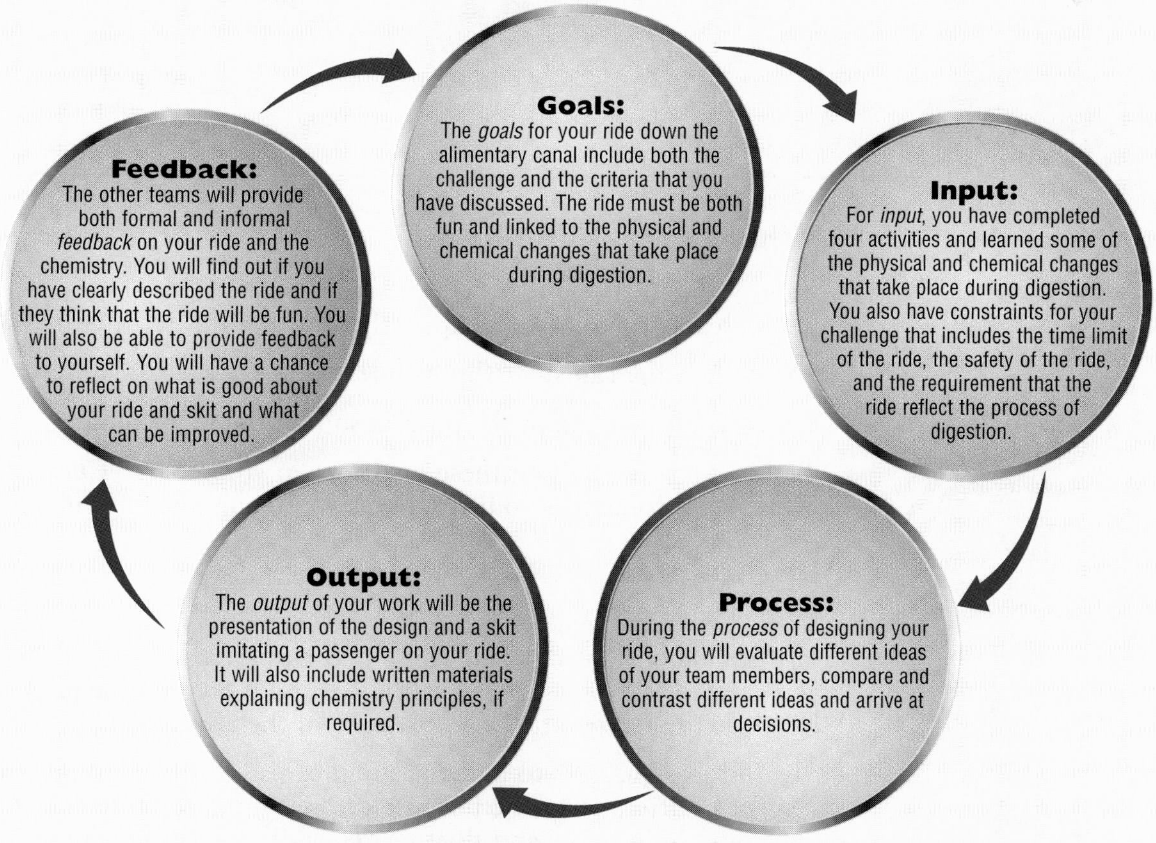
Goals:
The goals for your ride down the alimentary canal include both the challenge and the criteria that you have discussed. The ride must be both fun and linked to the physical and chemical changes that take place during digestion.
Input:
For input, you have completed four activities and learned some of the physical and chemical changes that take place during digestion. You also have constraints for your challenge that includes the time limit of the ride, the safety of the ride, and the requirement that the ride reflect the process of digestion.
Process:
During the process of designing your ride, you will evaluate different ideas of your team members, compare and contrast different ideas and arrive at decisions.
Output:
The output of your work will be the presentation of the design and a skit imitating a passenger on your ride. It will also include written materials explaining chemistry principles, if required.
Feedback:
The other teams will provide both formal and informal feedback on your ride and the chemistry. You will find out if you have clearly described the ride and if they think that the ride will be fun. You will also be able to provide feedback to yourself. You will have a chance to reflect on what is good about your ride and skit and what can be improved.

Remember: This is a *first try*. The feedback that you get from this brief presentation of your ride will be extremely valuable when you prepare for the final ride down the alimentary canal that you will develop at the end of the chapter. At that point, you will begin the entire design cycle again. That's why it is called a cycle. You keep going through it over and over to improve your design or, in this case, the ride for Anatomy World.

Activity 5 Gas Pressure

What Do You See?

GOALS

In this activity you will:

- Generate CO_2 by reacting an effervescent antacid tablet with water.
- Examine the relationship between temperature and pressure produced by an enclosed gas.
- Relate Charles's Law and Gay-Lussac's Law with the Kinetic Molecular Theory.

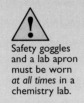

Safety goggles and a lab apron must be worn *at all times* in a chemistry lab.

What Do You Think?

After putting water and an effervescent antacid tablet into a film canister, gas is created and you can expect the film canister to "flip its lid."

- **Why does the canister "flip its lid?"**
- **How could you adapt the process so that the top would not blow off?**

Record your ideas about these questions in your *Active Chemistry* log. Be prepared to discuss your responses with your small group and the class.

Investigate

As you have learned in *Activity 3*, gases are made of tiny molecules that are in constant motion. These particles are constantly colliding and creating gas pressure inside the container holding the gas. How are the temperature and pressure of the gas related?

1. Add five quarters to an empty film canister. Add 6 mL of water. The quarters serve the purpose of preventing the film canister from tipping over and floating. They do not participate in the chemical reaction.

2. Grind up some effervescent antacid tablets in a mortar with a pestle. Weigh out some of the powder and then add it to the film canister.
   a) Record the mass in your *Active Chemistry* log.
3. Quickly snap on the lid, place it on the table, and step back.
   a) Record how long it takes before the lid pops off.
4. Continue to alter the amount of powder until the lid remains on the canister for a period of between 25 and 35 s (seconds) before popping. That means that it can't pop before 25 s, but it will pop before 35 s. Examine the contents left in the film canister. There should not be any white solid remaining. If there is, reduce the amount of effervescent antacid tablets and try again. (You must empty out the contents of the canister and wipe it dry before repeating the experiment.) You might choose to use a table similar to the one shown below to keep track of your data.
5. Using the same canister, number of quarters, and volume of water as in *Step 4*, place the canister in a flat-bottom dish. Pour cold water in the dish to surround the canister to within 1 cm of its rim. You might want to add some ice to cool the water down to a temperature at least 15°C lower than the room temperature.
6. Allow the water and quarters to cool down to the temperature of the water in the dish.
   a) Measure and record the temperature of the water in the dish.
7. Add the same amount of powdered effervescent antacid tablets to the canister as determined in *Step 4*. Quickly snap on the lid, place it back in the cold water, and step back.
   a) Measure and record the time until the lid pops off.
   b) If the lid does not pop off, what must this tell you about the pressure of the gas inside the film canister at this lower temperature? Check to make sure no white solid remains.
   c) In your *Active Chemistry* log, analyze what you have seen and formulate the relationship between the pressure of a constant volume of gas and its temperature. State your evidence. How could you test this relationship?
8. Dispose of the materials as directed by your teacher. Clean up your workstation.

Wash your hands and arms thoroughly after the activity.

Trial	Mass of Antacid Tablets (mg)	Time it Takes Top to Pop (s)
1		
2		
3		

Chem Talk

Chem Words

Gay-Lussac's Law: a gas law that states if the mass of a gas and the volume of a gas are held constant, the pressure of the gas will vary in a direct proportion to the absolute temperature of the gas.

GAS LAWS

Gay-Lussac's Law

Carbon dioxide is a very important and common chemical that is found in the stomach. Many antacids neutralize excess stomach acid and at the same time produce CO_2. All carbonated beverages have large amounts of CO_2 dissolved under pressure in the water. Some of this gas escapes when the bottle or can is opened, but a lot of gas still remains dissolved, which can be released upon warming. This is what makes a cold carbonated drink fizzy or effervescent on a hot day. Everyone has probably tasted a soft drink that has been left open and has been warmed. Most of the CO_2 has escaped and so the soft drink tastes flat.

Gay-Lussac

When a large amount of gas is ingested or generated in the stomach quickly, there is a certain amount of discomfort. When there is too much gas in the stomach, it comes up through the esophagus and out the mouth as a burp. There is a specialized muscle at the junction of the esophagus and the stomach that remains closed except to allow food to pass from the esophagus to the stomach. Just as in the activity with the film canister, where the pressure rose until the cap popped, the gas pressure in your stomach rises until it overcomes the pressure of the muscle that is acting like a valve. The gas that rushes up the esophagus and out your mouth results in a burp. The warming of a carbonated drink in the stomach makes the CO_2 less soluble, releasing considerable gas. This almost always makes you burp after quickly drinking a cold soda. It is often mentioned that in some countries and cultures (probably not the USA) a burp after eating is a sign that the meal was very well prepared, and is a compliment to the cook!

Another important relationship that is useful when working with gases has been demonstrated in this activity. Just as in *Activity 3* where the relationship between volume and temperature was referred to as Charles's Law, the relationship between pressure and temperature is often referred to as **Gay-Lussac's Law.** Yes, it is the same Joseph Louis Gay-Lussac associated with Charles's Law. From the behavior of the CO_2 in the film canister, it is easy to see the relationship expressed in Gay-Lussac's Law. The temperature and the pressure are directly proportional, if the mass and volume of the gas remain constant.

Remember, a direct proportion means that as one quantity goes down the other one goes down proportionately; and if one goes up, the other goes up proportionately. Don't forget, all temperatures must be absolute temperatures. In other words, all temperatures must be changed from Celsius temperatures into absolute Kelvin temperatures. To change from Celsius to absolute Kelvin temperatures add 273 to the Celsius temperature. When the temperature of the gas trapped in the film canister went down, so did the pressure. In fact, the pressure went down enough so that the cap was not blown off.

Gay-Lussac's Law is the basis for the warning on aerosol cans that says "do not incinerate." Even though the can appears empty, it retains a reasonable amount of gas. Exposing an aerosol can to extreme heat would be very dangerous because it will raise the temperature of the gas. Because the gas is trapped in a constant volume, it will explode as the pressure rises beyond the strength of the can. In doing so, it could splatter dangerously hot and/or flammable material all around.

Kinetic Molecular Theory of Gases

In *Activity 3* and in this activity you have seen examples of Charles's Law and Gay-Lussac's Law. There are many other situations where these relationships among volume, temperature, and pressure hold. These laws led to the development of a theory that attempted to explain why these relationships were observed. It is known as the **Kinetic Molecular Theory of Gases**. The assumptions of this theory apply to all gases, but the equations derived from the theory are only accurate for what is known as an **ideal gas**. To understand what this theory says you must think small, at the molecular (nanoscopic) level. The fundamental assumptions that the scientists agreed upon in formulating this theory are:

1. All gases are made up of tiny particles. These particles are called atoms or molecules.
2. The particles in gases are very far apart in comparison to their own diameter. In other words, a gas is made up of mostly empty space.
3. These particles are in constant motion and move in straight paths until they collide with something.
4. When the particles collide they bounce off each other. Energy may be transferred to whatever they run into, but no energy is lost.
5. At any particular instant, all of the particles do not possess the exact same amount of energy.

→

Chem Words

ideal gas: a hypothetical gas that has zero intermolecular forces of attraction between molecules over all ranges of temperature and pressure.

Kinetic Molecular Theory of Gases: a model that explains gas behavior in terms of particles in constant random motion that move in straight lines until collisions occur between them.

Chem Words

pressure: force applied per unit of surface area.

temperature: the measure of the average kinetic energy of molecular motion.

However, the average kinetic energy of all the particles is directly proportional to their absolute (or Kelvin) temperature.

The equations that relate the pressure, volume, and absolute temperature of gases under different conditions are accurate only for an ideal gas (one whose molecules exert no attraction whatever for each other). However, as long as the temperature and pressure of a gas is close to room temperature and ordinary atmospheric pressure, these ideal gas equations can be used to describe real gases as well.

Pressure

Now, try to think what is happening at the molecular level. The gas **pressure** is due to the collisions that the particles have with the walls of the container. Two major factors should be considered in terms of the pressure that the gas exerts. The first is how often the particles collide with the walls, and the second is with what force they collide with the walls. The gas pressure inside a balloon will be greater if either the number of collisions in one second increases or if the molecules hit the inside walls with more forceful collisions. If you could be shrunk down and put inside a balloon, the beating that you would take from the gas molecules inside would depend on how often they were hitting you as well as how hard they hit you.

Temperature

Temperature is measured with a thermometer. Although your sense of touch gives you some indication of temperature, it does not have the precision of a thermometer. For example, the tile floor and the carpet in a bathroom will probably have the same temperature, but the tile floor may feel much colder because of how well it conducts heat energy. When working with gases, you find that temperature is a measure of the average kinetic energy of the particles in the gas. Some particles are traveling very fast and have large kinetic energies. They may collide with other slower-moving particles in the same gas and lose some of that kinetic energy. The average kinetic energy of all the particles is the temperature of the gas.

Applying Charles's Law

Charles's Law states that volume and temperature are directly proportional when the pressure of a constant mass of gas is held constant (refer back to *Activity 3*).

Imagine particles of gas inside a box with a moveable weighted cover, as shown in the diagram. The pressure of the gas is equal to the weight of the cover. What would happen if someone put the box in an oven?

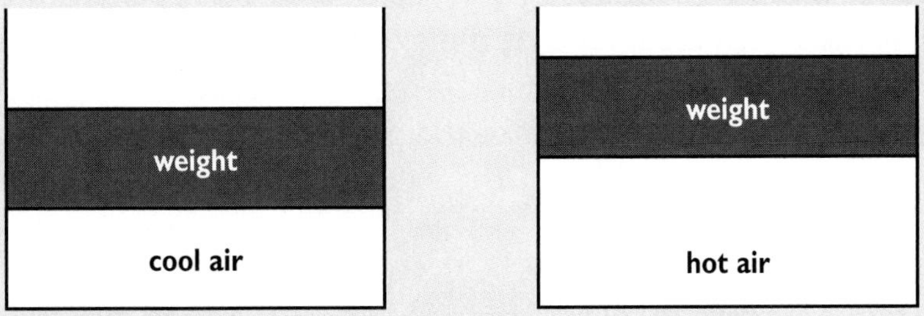
weight
cool air
weight
hot air

- The temperature of the container and the gas inside would increase.
- The velocity of the particles of the gas and the kinetic energy would increase.
- The particles would be hitting the walls and cover with more force and more often. The pressure of the gas would increase.

If the pressure of the gas were to increase, the weight would move up until the pressure of the gas once again equaled the weight of the cover.

You can now compare the situation with the cold air and the hot air. The pressure is the same and is equal to the weight of the cover. The cool air requires a small volume and the hot air requires a large volume.

Charles's Law can be used to determine how much the volume changes as a result of a change in temperature. If the old volume is divided by the old temperature, it will equal the new volume divided by the new temperature. This is one mathematical way of expressing a direct proportion.

$$\frac{V_{old}}{T_{old}} = \frac{V_{new}}{T_{new}}$$

For example, a balloon has a volume of 240.0 mL at the beach where the atmospheric pressure is 760 torr and the absolute temperature is 298 K. The pressures on the inside and outside of the balloon are equal, so the gas pressure is also 760 torr. When the Sun came out in the afternoon, the volume of the balloon increased to 245 mL.

What was the temperature in the afternoon? The atmospheric pressure was still 760.0 torr.

$$\frac{240.0\text{ mL}}{298\text{ K}} = \frac{245\text{ mL}}{T_{new}}$$

Solving for T_{new} gives a temperature of 304 K.

Now check to make sure the answer seems reasonable. The pressure remained constant, so if the temperature goes up, the volume must also; and so it does. Always check to see if your answer seems reasonable! 304 K is 31°C (88°F) which is a reasonable value. This analysis of the balloon at the beach assumes that the extra stretch of the balloon does not add an additional pressure. Taking into account the pressure of the balloon material would make the problem more difficult but more accurate.

Applying Gay-Lussac's Law

Gay-Lussac's Law says that pressure and temperature are directly proportional if volume is held constant. Imagine yourself shrunk down again to molecule size but trapped in a 55-gallon oil drum. All the oil has been removed and your only companions are the many, many particles that make up the air filling the drum. This time the volume cannot change. What would happen if somebody put a blowtorch to the outside of the drum?

- The particles would start moving faster. This means that they would be hitting the walls with force.
- Those fast-moving particles will also be hitting you and the wall more often.
- Because the volume can't change, Gay-Lussac's Law seems to make sense when it predicts pressure will also increase as the temperature increases.

If the drum rolled into the river, the temperature of the gas would decrease. This means the speed of the particles would decrease. And the number of collisions on you would also decrease.

Gay-Lussac's Law can be used to find how much the pressure changes as a result of the change in the temperature. If the old pressure is divided by the old temperature, it will equal the new pressure divided by the new temperature.

$$\frac{P_{old}}{T_{old}} = \frac{P_{new}}{T_{new}}$$

For example, an aerosol can having a volume of 450 mL and a temperature of 292 K and a pressure of 950.0 torr was left out in the bright Sun and the temperature of the gas inside rose to 310 K. What was the resulting pressure inside the can?

$$\frac{950.0 \text{ torr}}{292 \text{ K}} = \frac{P_{new}}{310 \text{ K}}$$

Solving for P_{new} gives a pressure of 1010 torr (or 1.3 atm).

Checking Up

1. What causes a burp after rapidly drinking a soft drink?
2. With a fixed mass of a gas, the Kinetic Molecular Theory describes the relationship among which three variables?
3. What are two factors that account for a gas's pressure?
4. How are the temperature and average rate of motion in a gas related?

What Do You Think Now?

At the beginning of this activity you were asked:

- Why does a canister "flip its lid?"
- **How could you adapt the process so that the top would not blow off?**

How would you describe what the pressure of a gas is?

How would you describe what the temperature of a gas is?

Using a constant volume of gas, how are the behaviors of the temperature of the gas and the pressure of the gas related? Is it possible to change one without changing the other?

Chem Essential Questions

What does it mean?

Chemistry explains a macroscopic phenomenon (what you observe) with a description of what happens at the nanoscopic level (atoms and molecules) using symbolic structures as a way to communicate. Complete the chart below in your *Active Chemistry* log.

MACRO	NANO	SYMBOLIC
Describe how the pressure inside a film canister changed when temperature increased.	*How do the moving gas particles in a canister exert pressure? Explain using the Kinetic Molecular Theory of Gases.*	*Using the gas law equations, show how they can be used to predict direct and indirect proportions.*

How do you know?

What evidence do you have that the pressure of a gas increases with an increase in the temperature?

Why do you believe?

What happens to the pressure inside an automobile tire when the winter arrives and the temperature drops?

Why should you care?

Propose a miraculous escape from a section of the alimentary canal through using an apparatus that operates on a gas-law principle.

Reflecting on the Activity and the Challenge

In this activity, you learned about CO_2, one of the most important gases associated with your body. It also allowed you to learn about some of the relationships involving the pressure, temperature, and volume of gases as observed in the macroscopic world.

Now, try to put yourself into the nano-world of individual molecules. This would be a world where you would be shrunk down to one-billionth of your current size. Try to understand these relationships from this new perspective. This should enable you to better envision what the environment in the alimentary canal might be like. In this nano-world, the release of CO_2 from a soda would be a catastrophic event, greater even than a hurricane here in the macroscopic world.

Chem to Go

1. What happens to the pressure inside a sealed rigid container when the temperature of the container and gas increase?
2. What is the cause of a burp after drinking a cold soft drink?
3. What happens to the solubility of carbon dioxide gas as the temperature increases?
4. In your experiment involving the effervescent antacid tablet and water in the film canister, the cap blew off quickly in the first experiment and there was white solid powder left. The next time you used less antacid until finally you reduced the amount of material so that there was no white solid left when the reaction was over. What would happen if you did one more experiment and used even less antacid?
5. At room temperature, which is 300 K, an empty aerosol can contained 200 mL of gas under a pressure of 1.5 atm. The highest pressure that the can's wall will withstand before exploding is 2.5 atm. If the can is exposed to extreme heat, at what temperature will it explode?
6. Air is pumped into a tractor tire at a pressure of 1500 torr. At dawn the temperature of the air in the tire is 295 K. At 3:00 PM in the afternoon the temperature is 308 K. What is the pressure in the tire now? (Assume that the volume of the tire did not change.)

7. ***Preparing for the Chapter Challenge***

   You know that the stomach is a very violent rocking and rolling environment when food is undergoing digestion. If your host body just guzzled a whole bottle of soda and it had made its way down the esophagus and was just entering the stomach and you were in the area, you might be in danger of being burped up and out through the mouth. It is very hard to match the conditions you would find in the stomach at this point, but it brings up an interesting problem. Do you think that you could "burp" off the lid of the film canister by pouring an ice-cold soda into a canister with a temperature of 37°C? You know it works in the stomach, but will it work in the film canister? See if you can devise a way to "burp" off the lid.

Inquiring Further

1. Aerosol cans

Read the label on two aerosol cans concerning safety and cautions with heat. What temperature is mentioned on the cans? What happens if you exceed that temperature?

Do not attempt any experiments using aerosol cans. They are unsafe.

2. Oxygen in water

Dissolved oxygen in a lake or pond is important for fish to survive. What happens to the solubility of oxygen when the temperature gets much hotter in the summer? Why have fountains been installed in some newly made lakes and ponds at apartment complexes, subdivisions, and golf courses?

Activity 6 Size of Molecules

What Do You See?

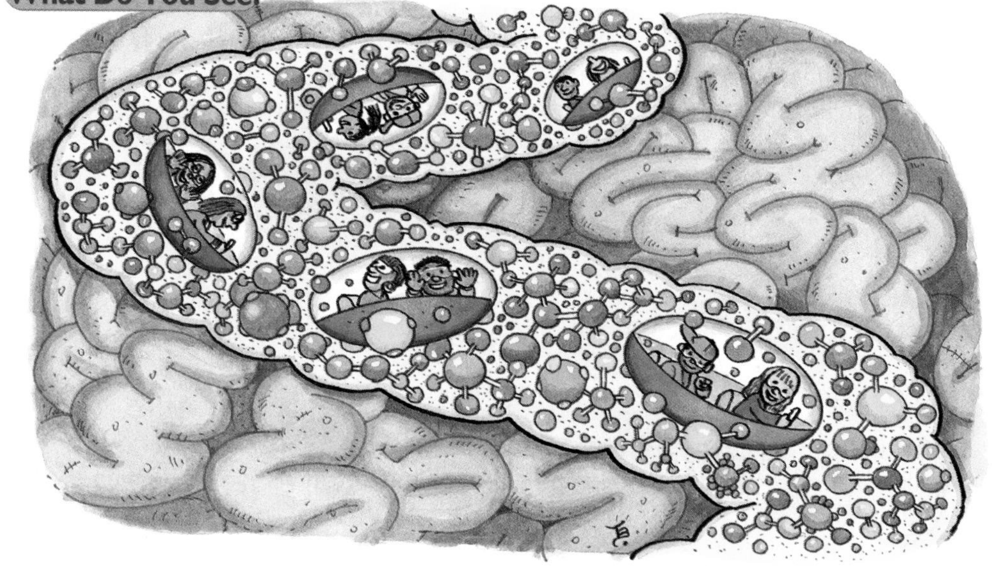

GOALS

In this activity you will:

- Use the physical property of particle size to separate a mixture.
- Compare, on both a nanoscale and macroscale, important molecules found in the alimentary canal.
- Deduce which molecules can be easily absorbed through the intestinal wall.

What Do You Think?

Your eyes can see things that are smaller than 1/10th of a millimeter. A microscope can see things that are 1000 times smaller than this.

- **Compare the size of a human hair and a water molecule. What would each look like through a microscope?**

Record your ideas about this question in your *Active Chemistry* log. Be prepared to discuss your responses with your small group and the class.

Investigate

Part A: Separating a Mixture

1. Prepare a mixture of sand, BBs, gravel, and marbles. Observe the mixture. Without touching the materials with your hands or tweezers, invent a method to separate the three types of materials into different containers.

   a) What physical property could you take advantage of to separate this mixture?

   b) Describe your process to your teacher before moving forward.

   c) If you were given three different-sized molecules, could you use a similar method to separate them?

Part B: Relative Sizes in the Macro- and Nano- Worlds

1. Some of the important molecules that you have studied about in this chapter are water, starch, enzymes like pepsin and amylase, and glucose.

   a) What are the relative sizes of these molecules? Use the table to answer this question.

   b) How would they relate to you in size if you were shrunk down into their "nano-world?" The prefix "*nano*" means one-billionth. In other words, 1 nm = 1×10^{-9} m. For the purpose of your *Chapter Challenge*, when you enter the alimentary canal you become one-billionth of your normal size. Assuming that you are about 2 m tall now, you would be 2 nm in height for your ride through the alimentary canal. By folding yourself up into a ball, you could have an even smaller size of about 0.5 mm. Copy the table in your *Active Chemistry* log.

   c) Because it is difficult to think in such small terms, magnify everything in the table by a factor of one billion. A list of examples that are in the same relative size as the entries in the table is given. If you can arrange the "macro-world" examples according to their relative sizes in the proper boxes in column three of the table, you will get a sense of the relative sizes of the molecules and materials in the examples. Complete the table above with the following entries. (A couple of entries have been done for you.)

"Nano-world" example	Diameter (nm)	"Macro-world" example	Diameter (m)
water molecule	0.1	baseball	0.1
glucose	0.5		
you	2 (or 0.5)	you	2 (or 0.5)
protein	5		
enzyme	50		
starch	5000		
blood cell	50,000		
human hair	150,000		
period in a textbook	500,000		

- baseball
- distance from Chicago to Detroit
- distance from Chicago to the suburbs
- downtown Chicago
- hotel lobby
- hotel room
- width of Lake Michigan

2. Now, imagine the cell membrane of the small intestine. It is here that many molecules are absorbed through the lining of the intestine so that they can enter the blood stream and be carried off to other parts of the body. Molecular size is very important in determining which substances can pass through the membrane. Assume that the thickness of the cell membrane is 10 nm. Also, assume that the opening through the membrane is 1 nm.
   a) Which molecules that you have been studying could pass through and which could not?

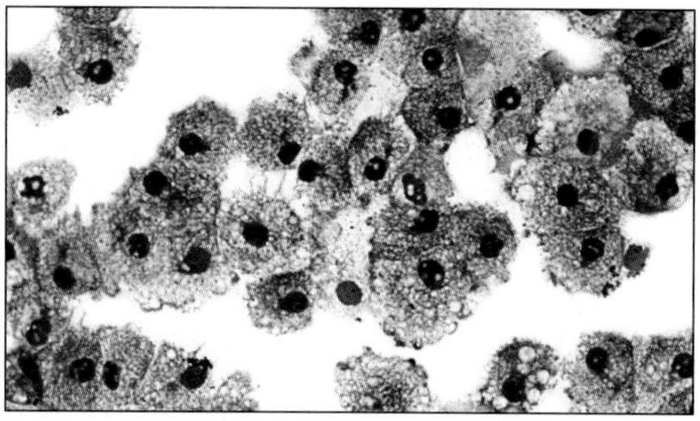

3. To make it easier to understand, return to the "macro-world." Here, everything is one billion times larger than the objects in the "nano-world." The 1 nm opening through the cell membrane multiplied by one billion gives you 1 m. This is approximately the width of the door to your classroom. Depending on how large your classroom is, the thickness of the cell membrane, if blown up to the "macro-world," would be about the distance from your door to the opposite wall.
   a) With this perspective, how many of the molecules you have studied would be able to pass through your classroom door? Use the "macro-world" examples that you arranged in the table to help you make a decision.

Chem Talk

COMPARING THE MACRO- AND NANO- WORLDS

This activity helped you to picture the relative sizes of the molecules and enzymes that have been presented so far. At your reduced nano-size, a bite of food would seem as big as the whole state of Illinois! Recall the prefix "nano" means one billionth. One **nanometer** is one-billionth of a meter (1 nm = 1×10^{-9} m). Just think, a food particle that would seem as large as the state of Illinois would ultimately have to be chopped up into pieces about the size of your classroom door in order to be absorbed into the body. Without ever thinking about it, food enters your mouth every day, and over a 24–36 hour period, passes down the alimentary canal, getting smaller and smaller until it is broken down into molecules that your body can finally use. The next time you eat a meal, think about all the high-powered chemistry that is required to keep you healthy and active.

Chem Words

nanometer: one-billionth of a meter (1 nm = 1×10^{-9} m).

Checking Up

1. Approximately how long does it take to digest a meal?
2. Approximately how many times bigger is a piece of food that enters your mouth than the small molecules that are formed at the end of the digestion process?

What Do You Think Now?

At the beginning of this activity you were asked:

- **Compare the size of a human hair and a water molecule. What would each look like through a microscope?**

If you were located in the small intestine and encountered a molecule of amylase, how many times bigger would it be than you? How many times bigger than you might a starch molecule be? How small must the units of starch become before they can pass through the intestinal wall?

Chem Essential Questions

What does it mean?

Chemistry explains a macroscopic phenomenon (what you observe) with a description of what happens at the nanoscopic level (atoms and molecules) using symbolic structures as a way to communicate. Complete the chart below in your *Active Chemistry* log.

MACRO	NANO	SYMBOLIC
Compare the "macro-world" examples to the "nano-world" of cells and hair.	*How many times smaller must you be to fit inside the alimentary canal, and fit through the intestinal cell membrane?*	*For what purpose did you model the size of molecules in terms of objects in the city of Chicago?*

How do you know?

In this activity you compared important molecules to objects found in Chicago, all the way from a baseball used by the Chicago Cubs to the size equal to the width of Lake Michigan. What can you now conclude about the importance of the hydrolysis of starch or proteins? (Reminder: Hydrolysis is the breakdown of the starches and proteins into smaller and smaller sizes by breaking the chemical bonds of these macromolecules.)

Why do you believe?

You used the idea of a scale model to help you better understand the sizes of molecules. How are a world map, a globe, and an architectural model of a new building helpful as models?

Why should you care?

This activity may be the most important in providing a perspective of the relative size of molecules you would encounter in an alimentary canal ride. How can you explain the ride of different molecules through the intestine with the information gathered in this activity?

Reflecting on the Activity and the Challenge

The first purpose of this activity was to try and give you a sense of the relative size of the molecules that you have been learning about. The second purpose was to provide you some appreciation of how really, really, really small the molecules have to be before they can be absorbed. With this new perspective, you should be able to better formulate events that will take place in your skit. Being only 2 nm tall, can you imagine what would happen to you if a huge enzyme or protein molecule collided with the piece of food on which you were riding? Splat! A drop of acid dripping off the roof of the stomach takes on a different meaning if you are in its path below. Truly, the digestive tract is a dangerous place when you are only 2 nm tall.

Chem to Go

1. The "macro-world" examples used in the table all dealt with Chicago. Develop a new set of examples that have the same scale as the "nano-world" and "macro-world" examples in the table in *Step 1*. (Don't just use a city other than Chicago.)
2. If shrunk down to nano-size, how many of your objects would pass through the intestinal wall?
3. A drop of hydrochloric acid would have a volume of about 0.05 cm^3. If it dropped from the roof of the stomach towards you, how much larger would it be than you? The formula of a sphere is $V = \frac{4}{3}\pi r^3$.
4. ***Preparing for the Chapter Challenge***

   Make a scale model of three things that you have seen in your ride down the alimentary canal. The three things are you (in your nano-size body), a molecule of starch, and a molecule of amylase. You must use multiples of the same object to represent the heights of the three substances. For example, if you used sugar cubes, you would represent the height of one of the objects with a certain number of sugar cubes. The other objects must be represented by enough sugar cubes to indicate their relative height to your first object. It is up to you as to what you choose the unit object to be.

Inquiring Further

Bacteria and viruses

Research the sizes of a bacterium, a virus, an atom, and a blood cell. How do they compare to the molecules in the table in this activity?

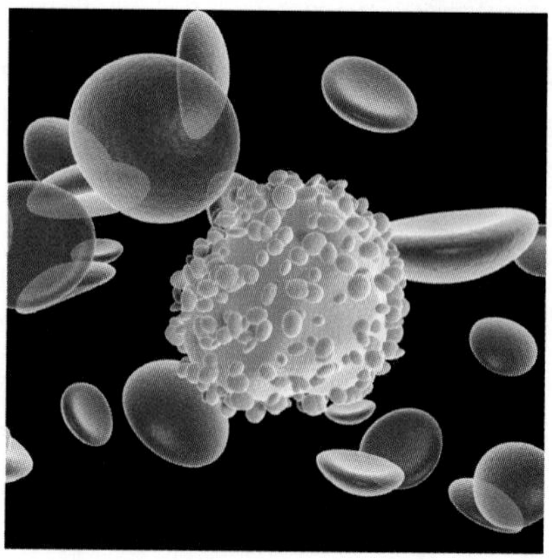

Activity 7 Hydrolysis of Lactose

What Do You See?

MILK
0%
MILK
2%
MILK
1%
GLU-
COSE
LACTOSE
GALA-
CTOSE
LACTEEZE
TEST STRIPS
Whole
MILK

GOALS

In this activity you will:

- Develop a procedure for analyzing milk and sugar samples for the presence of glucose.
- Develop a procedure to investigate the effect that lactase has on hydrolyzing lactose into glucose and galactose.

What Do You Think?

Some cultures use lots of cheese and milk products in their foods. Italian food includes meats mixed with cheeses in dishes like chicken parmigiana, ricotta-stuffed pasta, and pizza. Other cultures have little or no cheese and milk products in their foods. Chinese and Japanese foods do not use either cheese or milk.

- **Why do you think a culture that has cows for meat does not use these cows to produce milk and cheese for their food products?**

Record your ideas about this question in your *Active Chemistry* log. Be prepared to discuss your responses with your small group and the class.

Investigate

1. Glucose is a simple sugar that your body can readily use. Lactose is a complex sugar. If lactose passes through the small intestine without having been hydrolyzed, and if it passes into the large intestine, a very uncomfortable condition normally occurs. Complex sugars like lactose need to be broken down into smaller sugars like glucose before they leave the small intestine. Lactase is an enzyme that can successfully hydrolyze the lactose into simple sugars like glucose which can easily be digested.

Safety goggles and a lab apron must be worn *at all times* in a chemistry lab.

Do not consume any of the food used in this activity.

Wash your hands and arms thoroughly after the activity.

You can test for the presence of glucose with a glucose test strip. It will show that glucose is present by changing color.

2. Design a procedure to find out which of the six substances, listed below, lactase can hydrolyze into glucose units. These glucose units can then readily be absorbed through the wall of the intestine. You will use lactase enzyme drops. If it successfully hydrolyzes lactose found in food, a positive test for glucose should be seen.

   Review procedures you have used in other activities in this chapter as you plan your experiment. Also, consult the directions on the package of the lactase enzyme drops and on the package of the glucose test strips in planning your procedure.

   a) Record your procedure in your *Active Chemistry* log.

3. Obtain samples of the following six substances:

   - **whole milk**
   - **2% milk**
   - **skim milk**
   - **5% solution of lactose**
   - **5% solution of glucose**
   - **5% solution of galactose**

   When your teacher has approved your procedure carry out your experiment.

   a) Record your observations and your conclusions.

4. Dispose of the materials as directed by your teacher. Clean up your workstation.

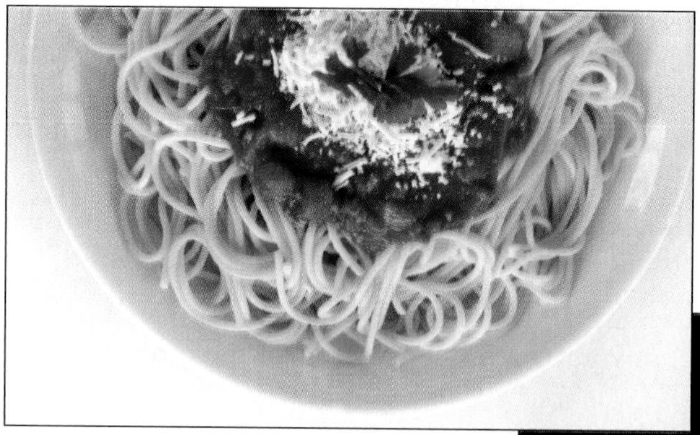

Chem Talk

DIGESTING LACTOSE

As you read, glucose is a simple sugar that your body can readily use. There are more complex sugars and starches that are actually composed of strings of glucose chemically bonded together. In digestion, enzymes break these complex sugars and starches into the simple glucose units. The breakdown of these complex molecules into simpler molecules is called hydrolysis. You have studied some examples of this in previous activities.

Millions of Americans experience gas, bloating, cramps, and diarrhea after drinking something as innocent as milk. The culprit in milk is **lactose**. This sometimes is referred to as milk sugar. There are many different sugars that you come in contact with every day. The simplest sugars are called **monosaccharides**. The most important of these is glucose. Another common monosaccharide is fructose. This is the sugar in many soft drinks. Lactose is an example of a complex sugar made up of two simple sugars bonded together. This type of sugar is called a **disaccharide**. The monosaccharides making up lactose are glucose and galactose. Another common disaccharide is sucrose, the chemical name for table sugar. It is made up of glucose and fructose.

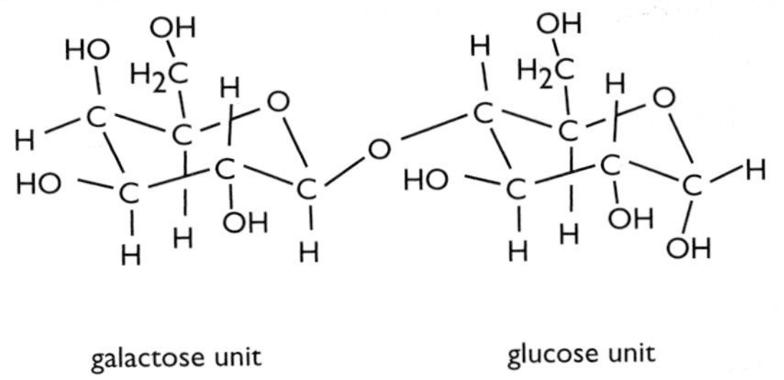
galactose unit
glucose unit
lactose

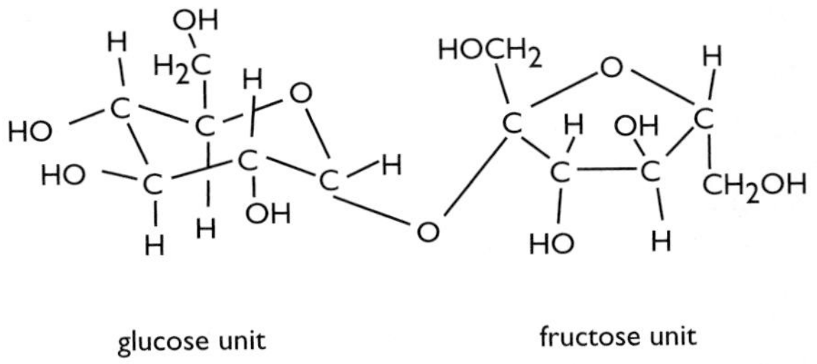
glucose unit
fructose unit
sucrose

Chem Words

lactose: a disaccharide made up of the simple sugars glucose and galactose.

monosaccharide: a simple sugar (consisting of three to nine carbons) that cannot be hydrolyzed further.

disaccharide: two simple sugars linked together forming a carbohydrate that can be hydrolyzed.

Chem Words

lactase: an enzyme that catalyzes the hydrolysis of lactose into glucose and galactose.

Why does lactose in milk cause these problems in some people and not others? Most people have in their digestive tract an enzyme, **lactase**, that can digest the lactose found in milk and many other milk-containing foods. Consequently, the lactose becomes glucose and galactose. These simple sugars are routinely absorbed in the small intestine. For people with insufficient production of lactase, the lactose passes through the small intestine undigested on into the large intestine. Living in the large intestine are millions of bacteria that are hungry. Some of these bacteria thrive on lactose. The products that they form, mostly gases, cause bloating, cramping, and other uncomfortable symptoms.

As people age, sometimes the production of lactase declines, and people who never had these problems before, experience them later in life. There are some ethnic groups who do not traditionally integrate milk products into their diet and thereby have mostly lost their ability to produce lactase at all. Lactose intolerance is most often found among older adults as well as those of African, Asian, Jewish, and Mediterranean descent.

Removing milk and milk products from one's diet is very serious. A serious calcium deficiency may occur when milk is eliminated. Not to worry! Lactase can be harvested from various dairy yeasts and fungi that produce it as a byproduct of their digestive systems. Because lactase is readily available, it has been marketed in various convenient forms: tablets, chewable tablets, caplets, and liquid drops. Lactase can be found in any drugstore and in many supermarkets. There are many national brands available. Some chain stores have their own generic products containing lactase.

If you have been diagnosed as "lactose intolerant," all that you have to do is take a few tablets when you eat dairy food. The lactase breaks down the lactose during the digestive process, and lactose intolerant people have no more of the uncomfortable symptoms. If your prefer, you can treat your own milk with drops of lactase enzyme, another supplier of lactase.

There are many dairy products that can be found in some stores that have already been treated with lactase. For example, you can buy treated milk where the lactase has already broken down the lactose in the milk before you buy it. Other products such as ice cream, yogurt, and frozen yogurt are available too.

The tricky part for lactose intolerant consumers is being aware of products where lactose might not be an obvious ingredient. The common dairy products are easy. Milk chocolate seems obvious, although semi-sweet or bittersweet chocolate may be fine. Aged cheeses are normally okay because much of the lactose was converted to lactic acid as the cheese ripened. Mozzarella cheese, cream cheese, and ricotta cheese all contain lactose and should be avoided unless eaten along with lactase. The best defense is to read food labels. The following ingredients are suspect: whey, caseinate, dry milk solids, non-fat dry milk, curds, and margarine.

Because ingredients making up the greatest percentage of the product must be listed first on a label, the higher up on the list, the more potential there is for lactose being present in sufficient quantity to cause problems. Other sources of lactose are prepared cakes and sweet rolls, sandwich cookie fillings, caramels, fudge, instant potatoes, creamed vegetables, dried soup mixes, powdered soft drink mixes, chewing gum, and pudding mixes. One of the most unexpected places is in prescription and over-the-counter drugs, such as coated aspirin. Lactose is used as a bulking agent, a tablet-binding agent, and a coating for many pills.

Checking Up

1. In what food is lactose found?
2. What is lactase and where is it found in the body?
3. What problem do people who suffer from lactose intolerance have? How can this be treated chemically?
4. How could people who eat no milk products still be subjected to ingesting lactose?

What Do You Think Now?

At the beginning of this activity you were asked:

- **Why do you think a culture that has cows for meat does not use these cows to produce milk and cheese for their food products?**

What is lactose intolerance? How can people be helped to overcome the symptoms of this problem? What causes this problem?

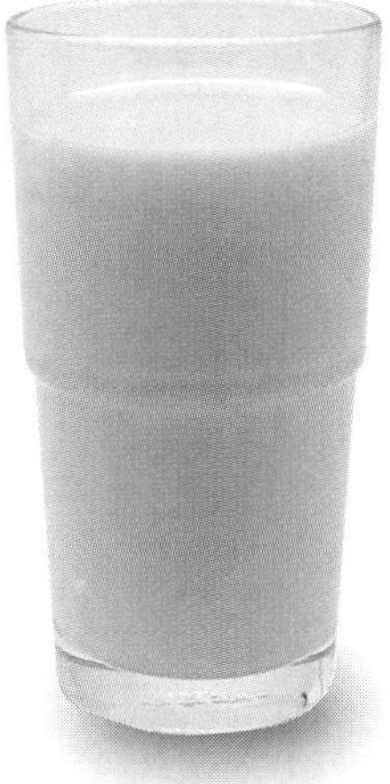

Chem Essential Questions

What does it mean?

Chemistry explains a macroscopic phenomenon (what you observe) with a description of what happens at the nanoscopic level (atoms and molecules) using symbolic structures as a way to communicate. Complete the chart below in your *Active Chemistry* log.

MACRO	NANO	SYMBOLIC
What evidence can you point to that proves lactase helped to hydrolyze lactose?	*Show how the enzyme lactase breaks the disaccharide lactose into the two monosaccharides glucose and galactose. What is the ultimate fate of these sugars?*	*Use structural formulas to represent the hydrolysis of lactose into simple sugars.*

How do you know?

How can a glucose strip tell you whether lactose is present?

Why do you believe?

How have the diets for cultures that have high rates of lactose intolerance evolved?

Why should you care?

With some imagination, you should be able to incorporate the perils of entering the large intestine into your skit. Maybe you can use it to show what could happen if lactase doesn't come to your rescue.

Reflecting on the Activity and the Challenge

The lining of the small intestine produces a variety of enzymes. Other important enzymes are received from the pancreas and liver. Some of these enzymes break down proteins, some break down starches to sugars, and others break down complex sugars into simple sugars. After sugars have been digested, absorption can take place in the small intestine. A deficiency in the production of the enzyme lactase results in the inability to properly break down lactose (milk sugar). Recall the procedure that you developed to test for the presence of the products formed when lactose breaks down. Do you think that your experiment gave you enough information to decide whether your lactase supplement works? How would this activity be useful in planning for perils that a nanoscopic rider through the alimentary canal might experience? What if the intestine you are riding through cannot produce lactase? How would this affect the rest of your ride?

Chem to Go

1. What enzyme will hydrolyze the disaccharide sugar lactose (found in milk) into the simpler sugars glucose and galactose?
2. a) When someone is lactose intolerant and says he cannot drink milk, eat cheese, or eat any milk products, what uncomfortable physical symptoms can occur if he eats these products?

   b) What problem in the small intestine causes these people to be lactose intolerant?

   c) Who are the most likely people to suffer from lactose intolerance?
3. You used liquid drops of lactase in your experiment. Solid tablets containing the lactase enzyme are also commercially available. But the fine print on the package of these tablets might indicate that glucose was used in formulating the tablet. Why might this information influence you to use another product instead? How would your results have turned out if you had used a product made with glucose?
4. *Preparing for the Chapter Challenge*

   Assume that you know that the host body of the alimentary canal in which you are riding cannot produce lactase. Propose how your trip might be different if your host body could produce lactase. What strategy might you use to aid you in safely escaping from the alimentary canal into the blood stream?

Inquiring Further

Enzyme-based food supplements

There are other enzyme-based food supplement products found in drugstores that are used to relieve gas and bloating in the large intestine. Investigate such a product and find out whether it could be used in the place of a lactase product.

Chem at Work

Dr. Siaka Yusuf

Gastroenterologist, East Lansing, MI

Dr. Yusuf can recall the exact moment he decided to become a gastroenterologist. When he was a young man in Nigeria, his grandfather was stricken with a preventable intestinal ailment. Yusuf accompanied him to the hospital where they were forced to wait a very long time for treatment. When the doctor arrived, he administered an antibiotic injection that cured his grandfather right away. That was the moment Yusuf made his decision. "It was amazing how quickly the medicine worked," he says. "I thought about how many people I could help if I were a doctor."

A gastroenterologist is a doctor who specializes in the treatment of disorders of the gastrointestinal tract. Gastrointestinal diseases are the leading causes of human death worldwide. The primary causes of such diseases are poor hygiene and sanitation. These health hazards are not allowed to get a strong foothold here in America, but they are common problems in impoverished countries, where there is little money to construct effective waste-removal systems and to support programs that could educate the population on the importance of good hygiene.

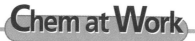

Dr. Yusuf has had wide experience in treating various kinds of gastroenterological diseases. He did his internship in Nigeria, and also practiced medicine near the Zimbabwe/Mozambique border, where he assisted people suffering from dysentery and viral cholera. He counsels all his patients on the importance of hygiene and other preventative measures.

Dr. Yusuf now has a busy practice in East Lansing, Michigan where he sees up to 2,400 patients a year. Yusuf finds the work he does very satisfying because he believes he is making a difference by educating the patients he treats. To stay healthy, he advises patients to see their doctor regularly.

Theresa Giannone

Pharmacist, Katonah Pharmacy, New York

Theresa enjoys being a pharmacist because she likes helping people, and because of her interest in science. "Pharmacy is all about chemistry," she says. Because of growing demand in the business, she anticipates robots will eventually be used to fill prescriptions, "but you'll always need a human pharmacist to relate to people."

Jacques Saisselin

Consultant, Vitamin Shop, Chappaqua, NY

Jacques is a vitamin consultant and manages a store that sells nutritional supplements, minerals and vitamins. He feels that his products can make a significant difference in health maintenance, and believes that science backs him up. "Chemistry is all life," he says. "Your body is a chemical factory."

It's Alimentary Assessment

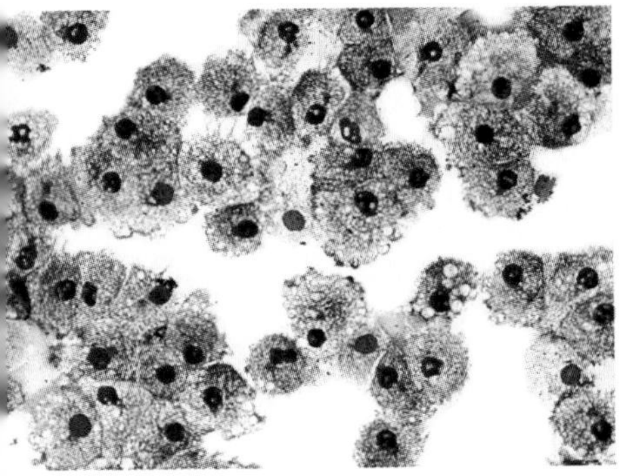

Your *Chapter Challenge* is to design and plan a ride for Anatomy World based around a trip down the alimentary canal. The overall premise of the ride is that upon entering the alimentary canal, the riders assume the size of a common nutrient molecule. If they are 2 meters tall before their trip, they would become 2 nanometers tall as they enter the alimentary canal. Their vehicle for this ride is a microscopic particle of food from a recent meal. You are to identify the physical and chemical perils that would be encountered by your food vehicle upon entering one of the sections of the alimentary canal. Next, you are to demonstrate, on a macroscopic level with real food, what would happen chemically to your food vehicle under these conditions. Finally, you are to conduct a skit, staged at the molecular level, depicting both the physical and chemical challenges that would need to be duplicated for a full-scale ride to be built at Anatomy World.

You will need to complete the following tasks:

- Choose a portion of the alimentary canal that you will concentrate on for this ride at Anatomy World.
- Identify the chemical and physical changes that happen along that portion of the alimentary canal.
- Choose the components of a meal that will start down the ride.
- Using real food, document the changes that at least one part of your meal undergoes as it passes through the part of the alimentary canal that you have selected.
- Write the script for a skit that demonstrates, at the molecular level, the chemistry that your food vehicle would experience on its trip down the alimentary canal. The script must be based on authentic chemical principles.
- Provide additional background to the script that describes the chemistry principles in detail. This could include the results of activities you performed that helped illuminate each concept.
- Perform the skit before the class. Members of the class can be recruited to play the parts of "extras" but your team must play the starring roles.

Chemistry Content

Activity 1: You learned about both physical and chemical changes that occur in the mouth. You learned about how starch becomes sugar during hydrolysis. You also investigated the use of iodine to detect starch and Benedict's solution to detect sugar.

Activity 2: You investigated the use and function of antacids in the stomach. You also learned about pH as an indicator of acids and bases. You tested the effectiveness of different antacids in decreasing acidity.

Activity 3: You generated carbon dioxide (CO_2) gas and then investigated properties of this gas. You investigated the effect of temperature changes on the volume of the gas. You also studied the effects of pressure changes on the volume of the gas. In exploring the behavior of gases, you found the value of using Kelvin rather than Celsius as a measure of temperature.

Activity 4: You conducted experiments to determine the role of the stomach in digestion. By building an "artificial stomach" you investigated the role of hydrochloric acid and pepsin in the hydrolysis of proteins. You also learned how pepsin acts as a catalyst in the reaction.

Activity 5: You learned about the production of carbon dioxide and how gas pressure is affected by temperature and can cause a belch. The kinetic theory of gases provides a model for the observations.

Activity 6: You investigated the size of molecules. Since your ride requires you to shrink to the size of molecules, the relative sizes of different molecules may play a big role in the interest and accuracy of the ride.

Activity 7: You compared the digestion of simple sugars like glucose with more complex sugars like lactose. You learned about people who are lactose intolerant and what they may do to relieve discomfort.

You may want to make a chart that shows the activity number, some chemistry concepts in the activity and some ideas as to how you can use these concepts as part of your Anatomy World ride. You should pay particular attention to the sections *Reflecting on the Activity and the Challenge*, *Chem Essential Questions* and *Preparing for the Chapter Challenge.* You should also compare your list with that given in the *Chem You Learned* summary.

Activity #	Chemistry concepts	How to use concepts

You may decide to do the first activity as a group in order to ensure that everybody understands how to proceed. After completing the first activity, each team member can be assigned two or three activities. You can then review all of the activities as a group with the activity expert reviewing each summary.

Criteria

You and your team should review the criteria by which you will be graded. Before beginning the chapter, your teacher led a class discussion to get a sense of what criteria should be used to judge the quality of work for your ride and skit. Your class should now make a final decision on the grading of each of the following requirements (it may be decided that some or all of the following components should be graded):

- Presentation of the documentation of the food digesting
- Accuracy of the chemistry in the script and additional background

- Number of chemistry concepts in the script
- Quality of the additional chemistry background relating to activities
- Thoroughness of the script
- Audience appeal for the skit
- Cleverness of props used in the skit

Preparing for the Chapter Challenge

• Choose Your Section of the Alimentary Canal

Your team's next step would then be to decide whether your ride will include all portions of the digestive system or a limited portion. You know the chemistry of food digestion, but you will have to decide how to turn that into an entertaining ride. Finally, you have to prepare the skit. How will you add elements to the skit to best communicate the excitement of the ride and the chemical processes?

• **Chemistry content is necessary but not sufficient.**

All your knowledge of chemistry will be necessary for use in creating your ride for Anatomy World, but it won't be sufficient for the success of the *Chapter Challenge*. You must also create excitement, humor or fear in your ride so that people will want to ride it again and again. Your skit will publicize the ride. Creating your ride is a creative process. Your entire team should have input and everyone on the team should be comfortable with the plan and the skit.

• Plan Your Project and Manage Your Time

You have a sense of how you want to proceed and what you want the final product to be. You now have to allocate the work. How much time do you have to complete the project? When is it due? How will you get everything done in this time frame? Who will be working on the written materials? Who will ensure that the chemistry principles include explanations at both the macroscopic and nanoscopic levels. Who will prepare the chemistry descriptions? Will each team member contribute one chemistry concept? How will you ensure that everybody's work meets the standard of excellence to ensure that everybody on the team gets an A? Will you need materials for the skit, and if so, where will you get them? Create a time chart showing how much time you have. Allocate responsibilities to everybody including work that must be done in class and work that can be done individually for homework. Leave time to review each other's work.

• Practice Your Presentation

You will need to make sure that you have enough time to put all the components together. You must have the ride description, the chemistry details and the skit ready on the due date. You also want to have saved some time for a practice run of the skit. You may be able to make some last minute adjustments to your ride or skit based on the results of the practice session.

Engineering/Technology Design

Recall the successes and disappointments from the *mini-challenge*. How can you build upon what went right and what could have been improved? What warm and cool feedback did you receive from the other members of the class?

Enjoy your ride down the alimentary canal!

Chem You Learned

- **Hydrolysis** is a chemical reaction catalyzed by enzymes or acid where a large molecule, e.g., starch, is decomposed into smaller units by the addition of water.
- **Enzymes** are bio-catalysts which can speed up specific reactions by lowering the activation energy of the reaction.
- One **chemical test for starch** is its reaction with the iodine/iodide reagent to produce a dark, blue-black color.
- An **antacid** is a basic substance that is used to control excess stomach acid by neutralizing a part of the acid.
- One important function of an **acid-base indicator** is to determine the pH of a solution.
- **Hydrogen blockers** are drugs designed to inhibit the production of hydrogen ions within the stomach and intestines.
- Qualitative and quantitative analysis often use the formation of an insoluble **precipitate** as a procedural technique.
- **Charles's Law** states that the volume of a gas is directly proportional to the absolute temperature when the moles of a gas and its pressure are held constant.

$$\frac{V_1}{T_1} = \frac{V_2}{T_2}$$

- The **Kelvin (K)** scale is the SI unit of temperature and must be used in calculations using the gas laws. To convert Celsius to kelvin, add 273.15 to the Celsius temperature.

$$°C + 273.15 = K$$

- **Absolute zero** (0K) is equal to −273.15 °C and is assumed to be the coldest temperature that can be achieved and where molecular motion is at a minimum.
- A **catalyst** is a substance that speeds the rate of a chemical reaction without being permanently changed itself.
- **Proteins** are long chains of bio-polymers which are composed of various amino acids.
- **Gay-Lussac's Law** states that the pressure is directly proportional to the absolute temperature when the moles of gas and its volume are held constant.

$$\frac{P_1}{T_1} = \frac{P_2}{T_2}$$

- The **Kinetic Molecular Theory** is a model that assumes that the gas molecules are in constant, random motion, have zero volume, have no attractive or repulsive forces, and whose collisions are completely elastic.
- A **nanometer (nm)** is a unit of measurement equal to one-billionth of a meter.

$$1 \text{ nm} = 1 \times 10^{-9} \text{ m}$$

- A **monosaccharide** is a simple sugar containing three to nine carbon atoms. Examples are glucose, galactose, and fructose.
- A **disaccharide** is a sugar that consists of two simple sugars. An example is sucrose (table sugar) which is composed of a glucose and a fructose unit.

Chapter 10

SOAP SENSE

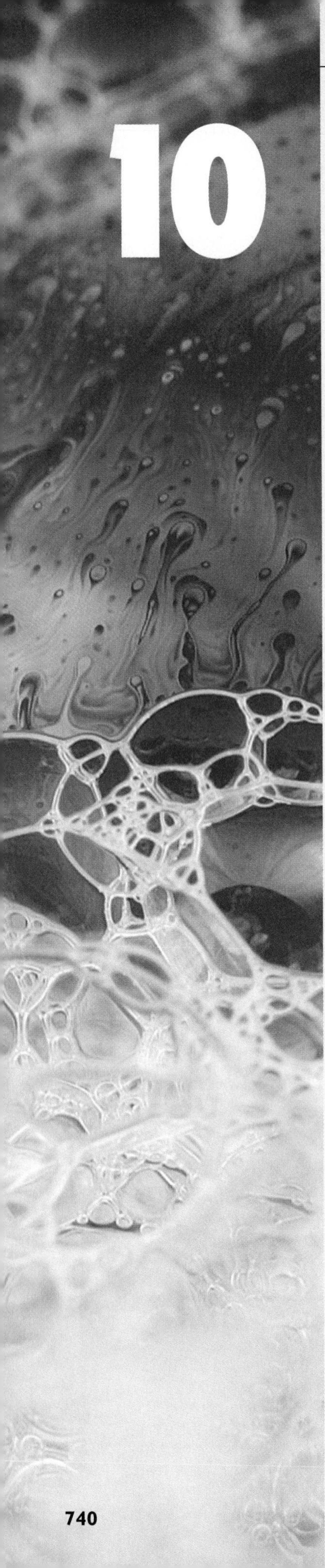

10

Soap Sense

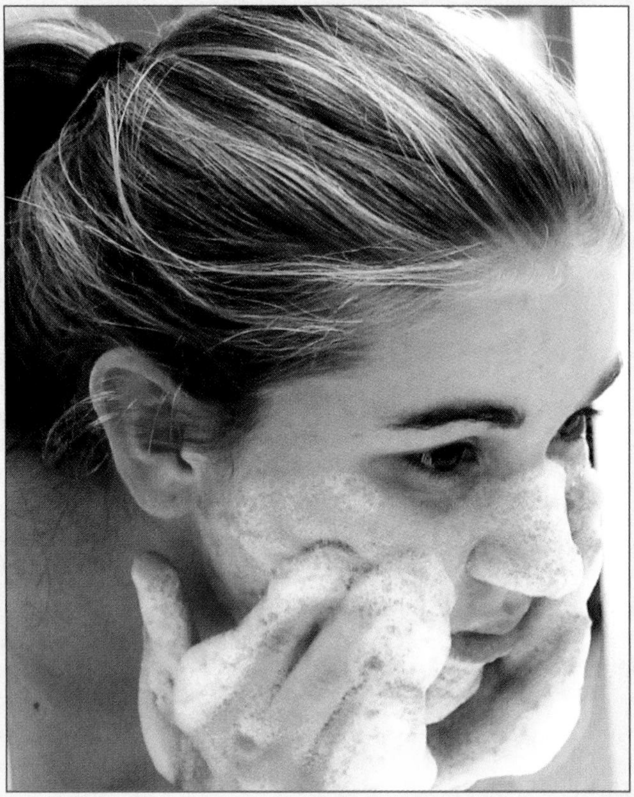

Scenario

You have probably used soap in many forms in your home. However, have you ever considered how soap is made? Long before there was a soap industry, people made their own soap. It is relatively easy to make soap, but it is difficult to make it well. In this chapter, you will have the opportunity to explore soap-making and determine how to improve upon a soap.

Your group will represent a chemical consulting firm. You have been asked to design a soap using natural products. Your soap will need to be an improvement over a soap that is currently on the market. It can be a bar soap, a liquid soap, or a powdered soap. You will provide enough information that the company that hired your firm can take to potential investors to raise funding to make the soap you propose. Go to a store and locate a soap that does what you want it to do. You will use this as a standard to compare to the soap you make. You may want to buy the soap or provide the purchase information to your teacher. Try to design a soap that is better than the soap you bought. The soap you make will not be perfect the first time, or the second. In developing a soap for market, soap manufacturers go through various stages of improving it. There are a lot of variables to consider and you will have to keep good notes of your observations before you create a recipe for a final product.

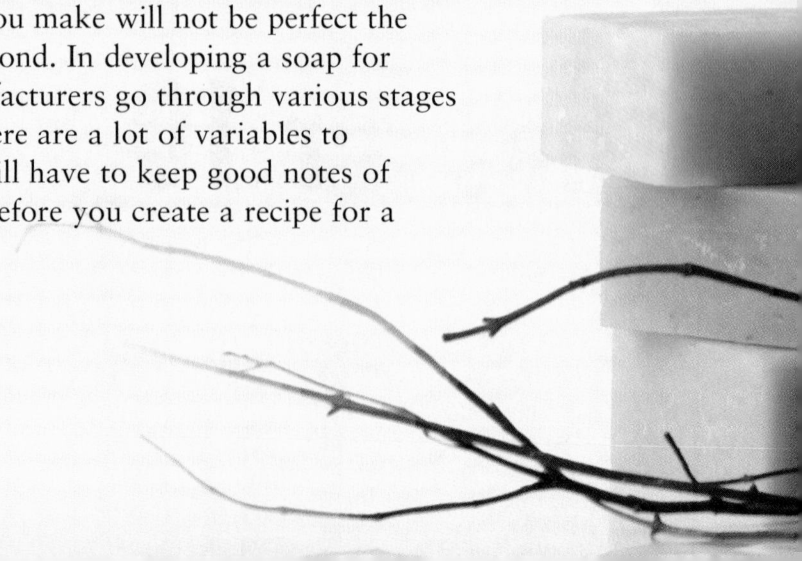

Your Challenge

Your challenge is to create a procedure to make a soap from natural products that can be sold at local stores. In working through the activities, you will test several variations of the two main ingredients in soap. You will learn why these variations have the effects they do on a soap's properties, so that you can design a recipe that will produce a soap with the properties you desire. However, none of the ingredients for making soaps are pure, so you will have to spend some time analyzing your results to determine how to proceed. You will have to play with the process in an organized way to figure out how to create a soap that is better than the commercial soap you are trying to beat.

le savon
de perfumed
Aromatherapy Herbal Soap
Wisteria Mountain
goats milk soap

ChemCorner

Chemistry in *Soap Sense*

- Household cleaning agents
- Experimental design
- Lewis dot structures
- Effect of structure on properties
- Saturated and unsaturated fats
- Carbon chain length
- Intermolecular forces
- Arrhenius acids and bases
- Hydrophilic and hydrophobic interactions
- Tetrahedral structure of carbon
- Hard water
- Detergents
- Quantitative experiment
- Qualitative experiment
- Saponification
- *Cis-* and *trans-* double bonds
- Functional group
- Micelles
- Polar and non-polar bonds

MAKING A SOAP
LAURYL SULFATE
CITRIC ACID
LARD
NaOH
DYE
SCENT
LANOLIN
CITRIC ACID
WAX
SALT
MOLD
SOAP

You will prepare two presentations for your company—one for the corporation executives, and a second for the marketing department.

In the presentation for the corporation executives, explain your objectives in designing your soap, and the steps you went through to achieve those objectives. You should create a display board to accompany this presentation. (You can use a science fair board for your display.) On your display, you should include a representation of the soap-making process you used, photos or drawings to illustrate it, and descriptions of all of the ingredients, including the additives, with explanations of the chemistry behind how these ingredients give your soap the properties it has.

The presentation for the marketing department should be a more detailed written report. It should give them information they can offer potential investors, explaining why your soap will have the properties you expect, and analyzing which methods you rejected and why you rejected them. In this presentation, it is important to illustrate the strengths your soap will have in the marketplace and the type of marketing campaign that you think would be effective in selling the soap. You may design packaging, magazine or newspaper ads, radio spots, TV commercials, billboards, or any other support materials you believe will be useful.

le sayone
de perfumed
call 1-800-555-9032
ORDER NOW!

Criteria

How will the soap procedure you propose and accompanying materials be evaluated? What qualities should a quality product have? How good do your explanations of the chemistry need to be? Discuss these issues in small groups and with your class. You may decide that some or all of the following qualities should be graded.

- How many ingredients, including additives, did you use?
- How engaging is the display?
- How understandable is your display to a corporation executive who does not have a background in science?
- How clear are your explanations of the chemistry?
- What is the pH of your soap?
- How compatible is your soap to the skin?
- Is your soap compatible with all types of materials or fabrics?
- How thorough is your written report for investors?
- How appealing is the packaging or other advertising you suggest?
- How convincing are your arguments for why the soap you propose would have the properties you desire it to have?

Activity 1 What Makes a Good Soap?

What Do You See?
SOAP
WATER A
LIQUID DISHWASH
WATER B

GOALS

In this activity you will:

- Recognize that soaps are chemicals that vary in their characteristics.
- Consider the importance of market research in product design.
- Examine sampling issues in administering a survey.
- Compare the information provided by a qualitative experiment.

What Do You Think?

Soap is a multi-billion dollar industry; some of the biggest corporations in the U.S. are soap companies.

- **How many different cleaning products does your family have at home?**
- **Why are there so many?**
- **Are they all needed?**

The *What Do You Think?* questions are provided to get you engaged in the activity. They are meant to grab your attention. They are also used to find out what you already know or think you know. Don't worry about being right or wrong. Discussing what you think you know is an important step in learning.

Record your ideas about these questions in your *Active Chemistry* log. Be prepared to discuss your responses with your small group and the class.

Investigate

About a month ago, your teacher instructed you to make several soaps using a recipe. The reason you needed to make the soaps ahead of time is that the chemical reaction of soap-making, called saponification, is very slow. It takes anywhere from 3–8 weeks for the process to complete.

In this activity, you will create and use a survey to learn more about what your consumers want, so that you can design a soap to meet their needs. You will also invent a laboratory test to determine which soaps are most effective, and you'll practice the test on several commercial soaps.

Part A: Market Research

1. Think about your kitchen, bathroom and storage areas. List at least five different types of household cleaners in one minute. Then combine your list with the other students in your group and describe each type of cleaner.

   a) Write down your group's entire list in your *Active Chemistry* log.

2. How do the cleaners differ from each other?

   a) Organize your list by focusing on the differences between cleaners. Write down lists under different categories in your *Active Chemistry* log. Some categories to consider might include shampoos, liquid soaps, special purpose soaps (hand soap, dish soap, laundry soap), etc. How did you decide which cleaner belongs in which category?

   b) Define your categories, and write down these definitions in your *Active Chemistry* log.

3. Focus on bar soaps only.

   a) With your group, list the qualities you look for in a bar soap. Decide which of these qualities are most important.

4. Using your list of important qualities, write a survey to discover what features other people think are most important in a bar soap. Your survey should have between 5 and 10 questions.

   a) Write down your survey questions in your *Active Chemistry* log.

5. You will need to get five people to answer your survey.

   a) In your group, decide together on this question: Does it matter which five people you choose to answer your survey? Explain your answer.

6. Combine your survey results with the results of the other members of your group. Organize the responses and decide on the qualities of a bar soap that are most important to consumers, including yourselves. Discuss the qualities and make some preliminary decisions on what you will design into your own bar-soap recipe.

   a) Keep notes from your conversation in your *Active Chemistry* log. You will refer back to these later in the chapter.

Part B: Testing the Effectiveness of a Bar Soap

1. Look over your list of most important qualities from *Step 6* of *Part A*. Choose one quality that you think you can measure in different bar soaps to help determine a bar soap's effectiveness. You should be able to measure a result for each bar soap rather than just describe it. One example may be how much time it requires for a piece of each bar soap to dissolve in water, if you think that affects the cleaning ability of the soap. Your teacher will list materials that are available for you to use in the test that you design. You will need to ask about any other materials you may need.

   a) Brainstorm some ideas with your group and write down in your *Active Chemistry* log some possibilities for tests you could do.

2. Your teacher will lead a class discussion about the different ways of measuring soap effectiveness that different groups have thought about. Once some ideas have been discussed, confer with your lab partners and choose a test the group wants to use. You will use this test now to compare several commercially available soaps, and you will use the same test later in this chapter to evaluate the soaps that you make.

3. Invent a procedure that you will use to test the effectiveness of soaps, and write down general notes on the steps of your procedure. You should do some brainstorming to invent your own test. Your teacher may be able to help you with some suggestions. Once you have invented a test, describe your procedure to your teacher, who must approve the procedure before the next step.

   a) After you receive your teacher's approval, write down your procedure in your *Active Chemistry* log before you do the test.

4. Perform the test and note any modifications of the procedure. You will use your test again in this chapter, so it is important that you develop a procedure that is repeatable and gives reliable results.

5. Use your test to compare two commercially available bar soaps provided by your teacher.

   a) Note the results in your *Active Chemistry* log.

   b) After conducting the test, ask yourself: Was this test a good way to measure what I wanted to test? What changes would improve my test? Write down your thoughts on these questions in your *Active Chemistry* log.

6. Dispose of the materials as directed by your teacher. Clean up your workstation.

Safety goggles and a lab apron must be worn *at all times* in a chemistry lab.

Be sure to have your teacher check your plan before beginning any part of it.

Wash your hands and arms thoroughly after the activity.

Chem Talk

CLEANING AGENTS

Removing Unwanted Substances

Soaps and other cleaning agents allow you to remove unwanted substances from your body, your clothes, or other objects. Some substances, like a splash of muddy water, can be removed very easily. Others, like grease from an auto-repair shop, are very hard to remove. You use soaps to help you remove the more difficult ones. In this chapter, you will begin to learn why some materials are more difficult to remove than others and what soap does to make it easier to remove them. You will also learn how soaps differ from each other and →

Chem Words

soap scum: an insoluble precipitate that forms when soap reacts with the mineral salts in hard water.

hard water: water that contains a large amount of mineral salts (mostly calcium and magnesium) that prevent it from forming lather with soap.

from the other classes of cleaning agents that you listed. You will also begin to see how understanding the structure of a chemical helps you to predict how it will behave.

How Cleaning Agents Differ

Cleaning agents differ in many ways. They differ in the materials they are intended to clean. For example, some are meant to be used on the body, while others are not. They also differ in how harsh they are. Very harsh cleaners usually clean so thoroughly that they strip away all protective coatings. Cleaners also differ in the kinds of dirt they will dissolve and wash away. And of course, different cleaners have different ingredients.

Soaps and shampoos are usually made from naturally occurring animal or vegetable fats and oils. Solid bar soaps most often contain sodium ions. As you know from making your soap, bar soaps begin as liquids and become harder as the soap-making (saponification) reaction occurs over several weeks.

The process for making liquid soaps is slightly different. Liquid soaps usually contain potassium ions, so these soaps are made using potassium hydroxide instead of sodium hydroxide. Potassium soaps are generally softer and more soluble in water than sodium soaps. The addition of extra water to a soap made with potassium ions keeps it from hardening.

Tile-o
Tile Cleaner

Soap Scum

The biggest drawback to soaps is the formation of **soap scum**. Soap scum, such as a bathtub ring, is an insoluble white or yellowish residue that can collect over anything you wash with soap. Soap scum is most noticeable in places with **hard water**. Hard water is water that is rich in salts of calcium and magnesium. These salts are dissolved in water as it flows through the ground. They are present in varying amounts depending on where you live. When the calcium or magnesium ions in the hard water replace the sodium or potassium ions in the soap molecules, the soap molecules with calcium or magnesium ions attached to them precipitate as soap scum. In places with hard water, you need much more soap to get something clean than in places with soft water. Soap scum can be removed with commercial products containing sodium hydroxide or ammonia.

Other Cleaners

Shine
Soft
powder
cleanser

Detergents are a different class of cleaners that resolves the problem of soap scum. Detergents are chemicals that have sodium and potassium ions combined with slightly different chemical structures than those of soaps. This change of chemical structure creates compounds that are water soluble even when combined with calcium and magnesium ions. There is no such thing as detergent scum. Another difference between soaps and detergents is that soaps are made of materials found in nature while detergents are synthetic, although some of the ingredients in detergents may be natural.

Abrasive cleaners have grit mixed into soap in very high percentages and work just like sandpaper to remove dirt. Some hand cleaners also employ this principle.

Waterless hand cleaners are usually soaps mixed into ethanol (grain alcohol) or turpentine (paint cleaner). There are a few advantages to dissolving the soaps with these solvents instead of water. One advantage is that ethanol and turpentine are better at dissolving some dirt, so they help the soap clean.

Bleach
PLUS

Some household cleaners, such as window cleaners, tile cleaners, all-purpose surface cleaners, and toilet bowl cleaners, do not contain much, if any, soap. These cleaners work not by just dissolving the dirt, but by reacting with what needs to be removed (cleaned away). The reaction forms substances that either dissolve or can be washed away readily. These cleaners must be used and disposed of carefully so that they do as little damage as possible to the environment.

Chem Words

detergents: a class of cleaners that have sodium and potassium ions combined with slightly different chemical structures than those of soaps. Detergents remain soluble even when combined with calcium and magnesium ions.

Chem Words

quantitative measurement: a measurement that has a numerical value.

qualitative measurement: a measurement that does not have a numerical value.

Soap Business

Have you ever received a phone call from a "market researcher" asking your opinions on a topic? If you were going into the soap business, you would probably want to do some market research before you began. The survey you designed represents a very simple form of market research. The answers to your survey will help you decide what you want your soap to do and how it should be better than other soaps.

Market researchers have to think about whose opinions to collect. You probably found that some people take their choice of soaps very seriously. Others have very little interest. You may have decided to give different weights to different opinions, depending on how strongly they are held. If you make a soap that appeals strongly to men, but women make 80% of the buying decisions, your soap may not be very successful.

Designing a Test for Soap Effectiveness

In designing a test for soaps, the requirement of a measurable result may seem difficult. Scientists often prefer experiments with results that can be measured numerically (called **quantitative**) to tests that do not give some kind of numerical answer (called **qualitative**). Reaching for measurements often gives much more information about the topic being explored than qualitative experiments do. Also, it is much easier to compare the results from two different materials when those results are numerical. If your test only asks, "Is the material cleaner after washing with your soap than before?" you won't be able to say which cleans better. It is worth the extra time to devise a quantitative experiment, because it will give you much more information.

Checking Up

1. How does the behavior of soaps and detergents differ in hard water?
2. Label the following statements as either quantitative or qualitative:
   a) This soap is harsh on the skin.
   b) A popular soap has a flowery smell and is red in color.
   c) One soap removed 25% more dirt than another.
3. Which is more harmful to the environment, soaps or detergents?

What Do You Think Now?

At the beginning of this activity you were asked:

- **How many different cleaning products does your family have at home?**
- **Why are there so many?**
- **Are they all needed?**

Revisit your answers. How has this activity changed the way you view cleaning products in your home?

Reflecting on the Activity and the Challenge

In this activity, you have begun the process of choosing a specific objective, which is a very important step for any project you begin. You have to decide exactly where you are trying to go in order to have a chance of getting there. It is also crucial to have some way of telling whether you are getting closer to or further from your goal. A well thought-out test should do that for you. A valid test will also help you to persuade buyers. After you have finished creating your new and improved soap, you will need to convince others of its merits in order to sell it. If your test is believable to others, you might use it as the basis of an advertising campaign.

Chem to Go

1. a) Walk around your home and make a list of the different cleaning agents in your home.
   b) Categorize the cleaning agents in your home according to the categories of cleaning agents described in the *Chem Talk* section.
   c) Are there any cleaning agents that don't fit into a category? How would you describe this category?
   d) Are there any cleaning agents that might fit into more than one category? Explain.
2. Describe two real-world situations where a survey like yours would be used.
3. Describe two qualitative measurements you have done at some point in a science class. Then describe two quantitative measurements you have done. For each of these quantitative measurements, explain the advantage the numerical measurement gave you over a qualitative measurement.
4. Look back over your notes from the soap effectiveness test you did in *Part B*. Write a procedure for this test so that someone in another chemistry class could repeat your test on the same soaps you tested and obtain the same results.
5. Soaps can contain either sodium ions or potassium ions. Look at the periodic table—what do the elements sodium and potassium have in common?
6. Soft freshwater:
   a) contains few magnesium and calcium ions
   b) contains many magnesium and calcium ions
   c) contains few sodium and potassium ions
   d) contains many sodium and potassium ions
7. Which soap is more likely to sell well?
   a) One designed to clean paper towels
   b) One designed to clean the underside of a cement truck
   c) One designed to clean lawn mowers
   d) One designed to clean pans

8. *Preparing for the Chapter Challenge*

   Take the time now to clearly state the goal of your research for the *Chapter Challenge*. What soap do you want to compete against? In what way will you plan to have your soap be better than the soap you chose to compete against? You may modify this goal as you learn more about soaps, but it is important that you begin with a clear goal. Write down your clearly stated goal in your *Active Chemistry* log and discuss this with your teacher.

Inquiring Further

Market-research methods

Research different methods of deciding whom to include in a market-research survey. Redesign your survey more professionally, based on what you learned. Conduct your survey (you'll need to interview at least 40 people to have good statistics) and analyze the results numerically, calculating averages and standard deviations for each question.

VERY IMPORTANT
IMPORTANT
NOT IMPORTANT

Activity 2 Modeling Molecules

What Do You See?

Na+
SOAP

GOALS

In this activity you will:

- Connect the two-dimensional drawing of a simple organic molecule to the three-dimensional structure it assumes.
- Examine the differences in molecular shape that result from small differences in molecular structure and the differences in properties of substances that can result from these differences in shape.
- Model the chemical reaction that takes place during the soap-making process.
- Predict the structures formed by atoms by examining their bonding (valence) electrons.

What Do You Think?

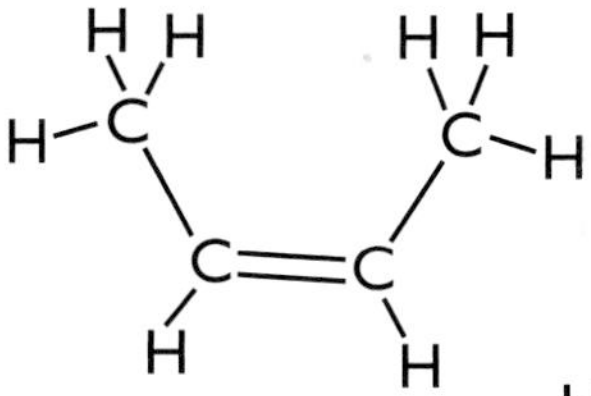

Here are the structures of two different four-carbon molecules that have the same numbers of carbons and hydrogens.

- **Describe the differences in these two molecules' shapes.**

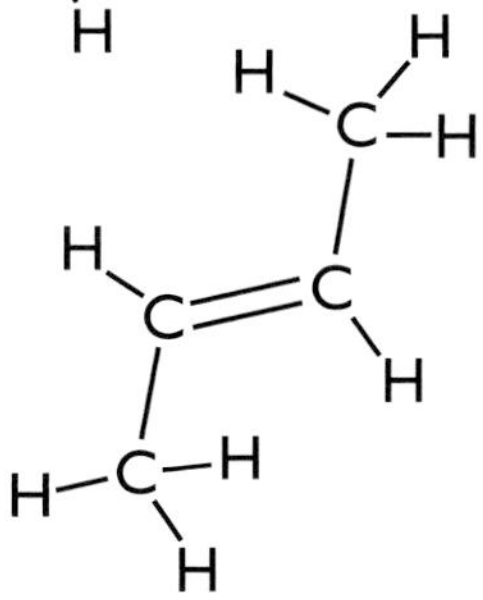

Record your ideas about this question in your *Active Chemistry* log. Be prepared to discuss your responses with your small group and the class.

Investigate

In this activity, you will use molecular model sets to build some hydrocarbons and other molecules so that you can see what shapes soap molecules take. Understanding the shapes of molecules is crucial to understanding how the molecules interact with each other.

It is these interactions that determine the behaviors of substances. To design a soap that has certain properties, you have to decide what kinds of molecules should be included in the ingredients used to make the soap. Therefore, you have to be able to predict the shapes of molecules.

1. Work individually or in pairs. Open a molecular-model set and organize the balls and sticks in it. What categories of balls and sticks are there?

   a) Write down what information describes each color of a ball. For example, a black ball has four holes that appear to be equally spaced apart. (It can make four bonds.)

2. A hydrogen atom will make 1 bond, an oxygen atom will make 2 bonds, a nitrogen atom will make 3 bonds and a carbon atom will make 4 bonds. (This can be remembered as HONC – 1, 2, 3, 4.)

   a) Which colors in your set could represent each of these elements? Of course, the actual atoms aren't red or blue or any color at all. The different colors make it easier to keep track of which atoms are where.

3. Use sticks and balls to make a structure consisting of no more than six different balls. Also, make sure that all the holes in the balls have sticks in them that are connected to other balls. If you are able to make a structure, then you have constructed a model of a molecule that could exist.

   a) Sketch a copy of your model in your *Active Chemistry* log.

4. The covalent bonds formed by these atoms are each composed of an electron pair. Because all electron pairs have a negative electrical charge, they repel other electron parts. You will use strings to model the positions in space of these bonds or electron pairs. Working in a group of four, have one person hold one end of four 20-cm strings in one hand. Each person (including the one already holding all four strings) should take the other end of one string and hold it out away from the center. Try to make each string (or at least its far end) as far away from *all* the other strings as possible.

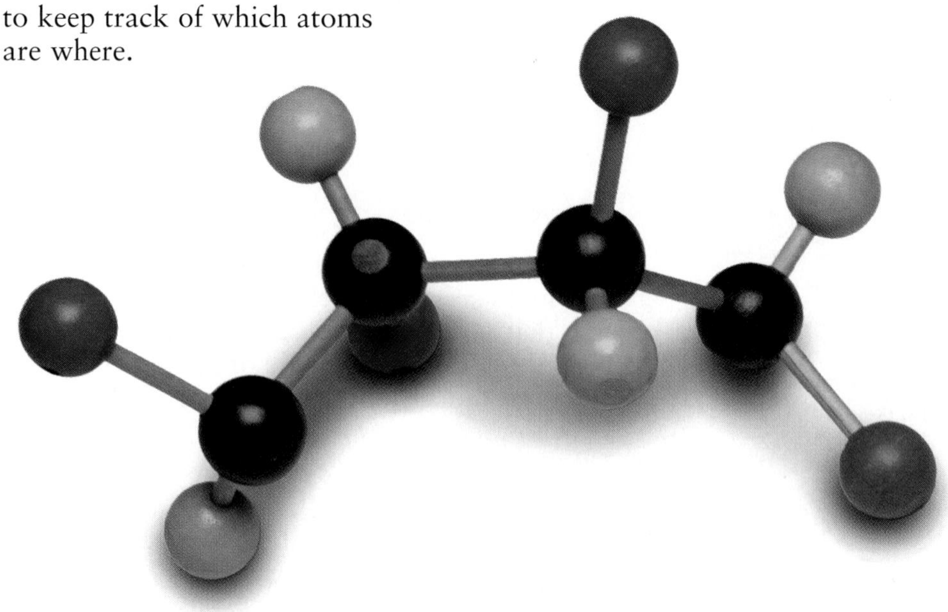

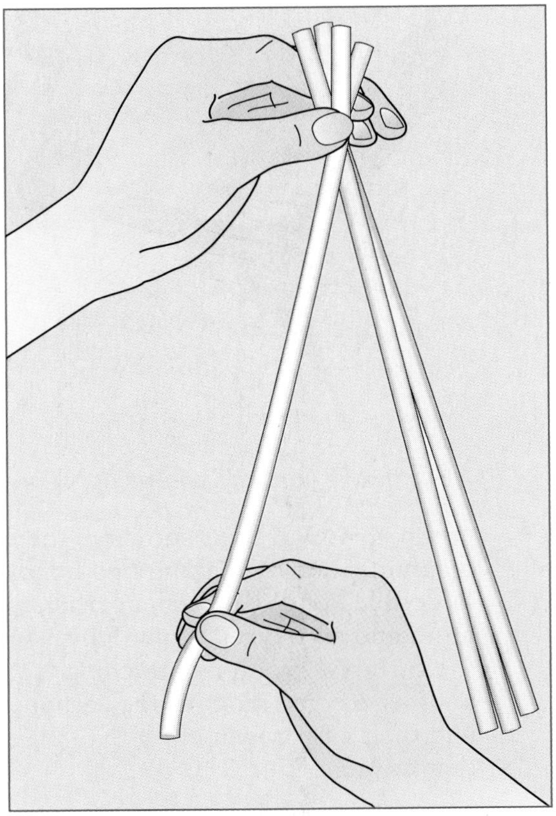

a) Describe the shape you have made.

b) If a carbon atom had four bonds to hydrogen atoms, each of which repelled the other three, this is the shape the molecule would take.

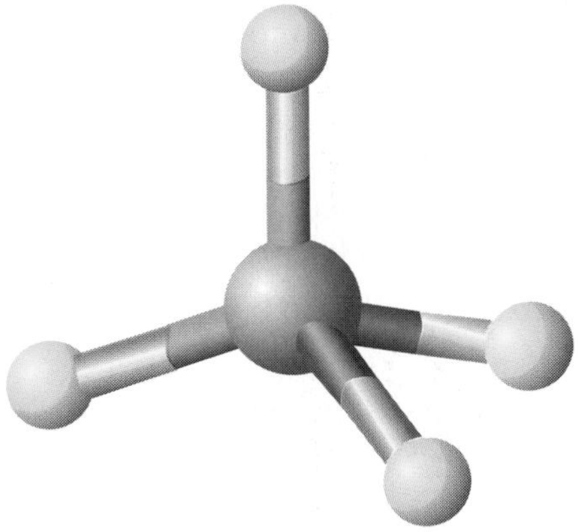

Ball-and-stick model of methane (CH_4)

5. Now, use the molecular-model set to build a molecule of methane (CH_4) or natural gas, using one carbon atom and four hydrogen atoms from the molecular-model kit. The name of this molecular shape is a *tetrahedron*. In geometry, a tetrahedron is a four-sided figure in which each side is a triangle.

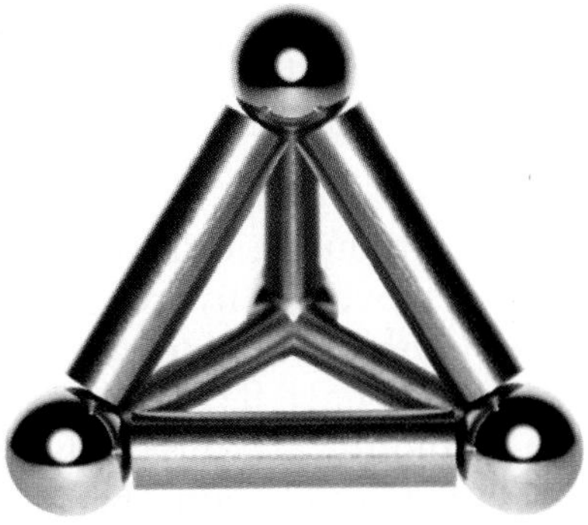

A tetrahedron

6. Next, make a two-carbon molecule by joining two carbon atoms together and filling the rest of the holes in the carbon atoms with hydrogen atoms.

   a) Write down the formula of the molecule you have made.

   Now replace one of the hydrogen atoms with another carbon atom, and surround the new carbon atom with hydrogen atoms.

   b) Write down the formula of the molecule you have made. This molecule is propane, the gas used in gas grills.

   Replace a hydrogen atom with another carbon so that you have four carbon atoms in the chain. Add hydrogen atoms as needed.

c) What does the molecule look like? Draw it in your *Active Chemistry* log. Write down its formula. This compound is called butane, the liquid fuel in most lighters.

7. Make the four-carbon molecule have different shapes by twisting around the center C—C bond.

   a) Draw the two shapes that are the most different in your *Active Chemistry* log.

8. Now, remove the bond that you twisted around (in the center), and also remove one hydrogen from each of the two middle carbons. Most kits have flexible bonds that can bend for making double bonds. Create a double bond between the two middle carbons with two of those flexible bonds.

   a) Is it possible any more to twist around the center bond?

   b) Draw the shape of the molecule you just made.

   c) Which of the two molecules in *What Do You Think?* is it like? Which one must be bent and which one can be more like a straight line?

   d) How can you make the other molecule in the *What Do You Think?* section? Answer this question in your *Active Chemistry* log.

   In the first molecule shown in *What Do You Think?*, the arrangement of carbons around the double bond is called a *cis* arrangement. In the second molecule, the arrangement of carbons is called a *trans* arrangement.

9. Take apart your molecules and begin anew. Build one methane (CH_4) molecule. Start another molecule by beginning a carboxyl group (—COOH), as shown in the diagram. Start by making *two* bonds (a double bond) between a carbon atom and an oxygen atom. Finish the carboxyl group by attaching another oxygen atom to the carbon, and then a hydrogen atom to that oxygen.

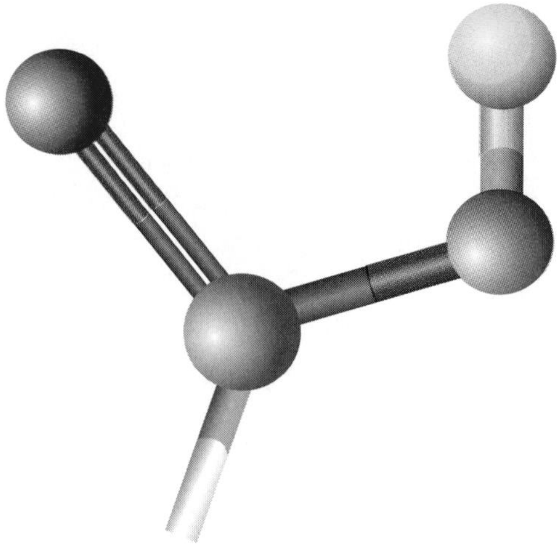

Carboxylic acid functional group

Such a cluster of atoms (—COOH) is called a ***functional group***. The name of this functional group is carboxyl. Molecules that have this functional group attached are called carboxylic acids.

The carbon atom has room for one more bond. Remove a hydrogen atom from the methane molecule you made earlier and attach the carboxyl group at that point. This molecule is acetic acid (the acid in vinegar), CH_3COOH. The carboxyl group makes it an acid.

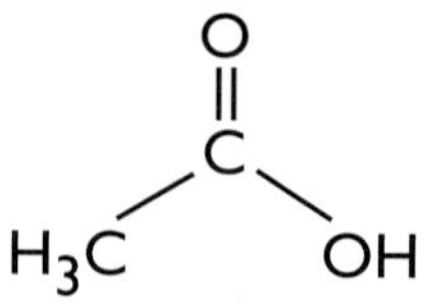
O
C
H3C
OH

Acetic acid

10. Make a glycerol molecule (used in cosmetics) by connecting three carbon atoms together with single bonds, and then connecting an —OH group to each carbon. Fill in the other empty holes on the carbon atoms with hydrogen atoms.

    a) Write the formula for this molecule. Do not take apart this glycerol molecule because you will need it again later.

11. Next, construct a fatty acid by replacing one of the hydrogen atoms in the CH_3 part of your acetic acid (CH_3COOH) model with a carbon atom, then adding another one to that one, and so on, to create a long chain of carbon atoms.

    When your molecule contains 18 carbon atoms, you have the backbone for a molecule of stearic acid. You will probably need to combine with another group in order to have enough atoms to use or you may have to stop at a smaller molecule with fewer carbon atoms. A complete stearic acid molecule is shown in the two diagrams below. (Make sure your larger group keeps one glycerol molecule to use later.) Finally, fill in all the empty holes in the carbon atoms with bonds to hydrogen atoms.

    You can see that the molecule you have made can be stretched out in more or less a straight line.

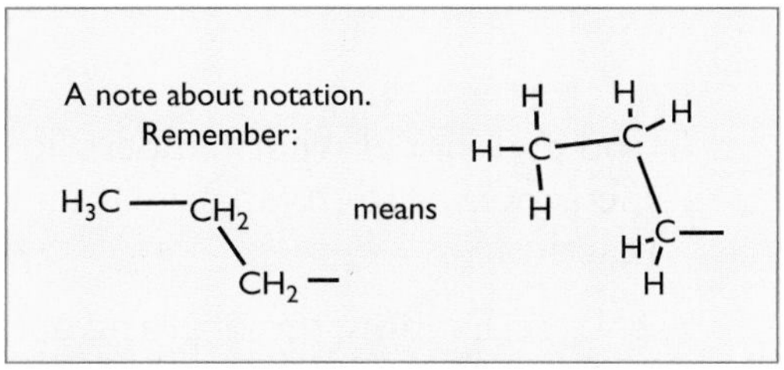
A note about notation.
Remember:
H₃C — CH₂
CH₂ —
means

The carbon backbone zigzags back and forth, but the overall shape of the molecule can be more or less linear, as in the drawing below. In this kind of notation, the chain of carbons forms the skeleton or "backbone" of the molecule and the hydrogen atoms form the other bonds on each carbon atom.

Take your molecule and put it on a table next to other stearic acid molecules. Gently push them together. You can see that they can be packed together quite tightly.

12. Take one of the stearic acid molecules and change its structure. Create a *cis*-double bond between the ninth and tenth carbons in the carbon chain (begin counting at the carboxyl group) by removing a hydrogen atom from each one and connecting them with a second bond. This is *cis*-oleic acid, a mono-unsaturated fatty acid. Have your teacher put the oleic acid molecule back in the middle of the pile of stearic acid molecules.

    a) How does this affect the way the pile can be packed together?

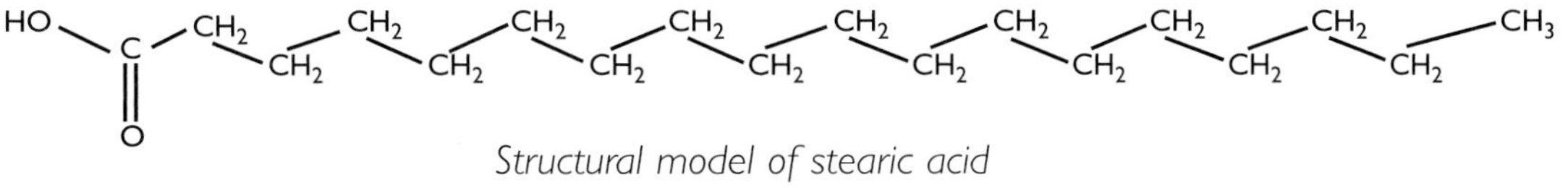

Structural model of stearic acid

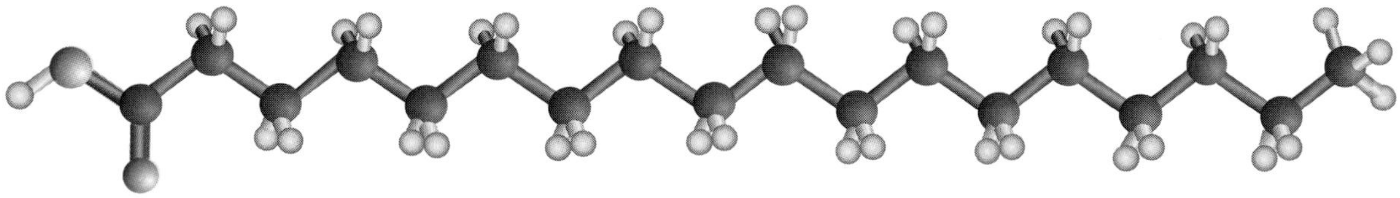

Ball-and-stick model of stearic acid

13. You can model what happens in the saponification (soap-making) reaction.

    a) Describe how three stearic acid molecules can be attached to a single glycerol molecule to create a fat (as shown in the diagram).

    b) In your log, draw this diagram and identify the parts from the original three stearic acid molecules and the single glycerol molecule.

14. When this fat molecule reacts with three NaOH units, three units of soap (shown in the diagram) and one glycerol molecule are created.

    a) In your log, describe how this occurs.

15. Describe a skit for the class that could illustrate the saponification reaction. Have different people represent different parts of the soap molecule. (Actually, soap isn't a molecule. Each unit of soap is two charged ions: a positively charged sodium ion and a long hydrocarbon chain whose oxygen atom at the end carries a negative charge.)

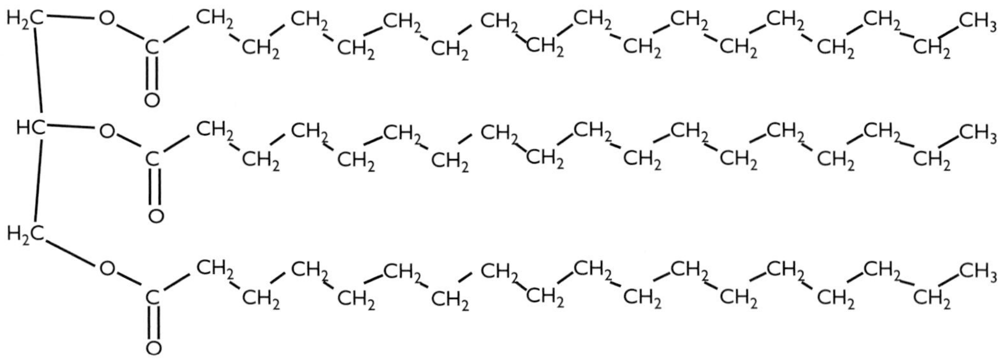

Fat made from three stearic acid residues linked to a glycerol molecule

Na^+ OH^-
Na^+ OH^-
Na^+ OH^-

Three units of sodium hydroxide. (The reaction requires three units of NaOH.)

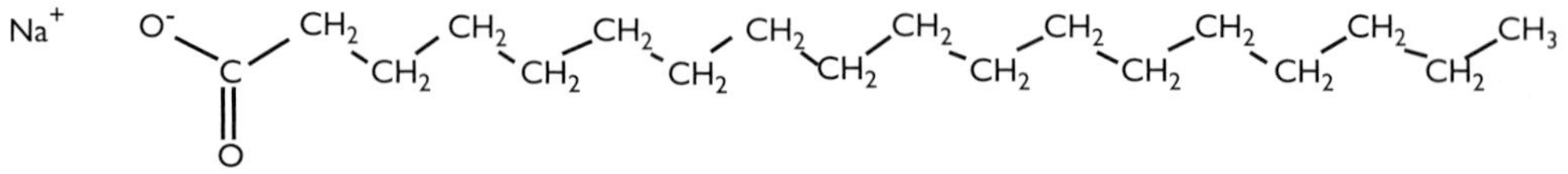

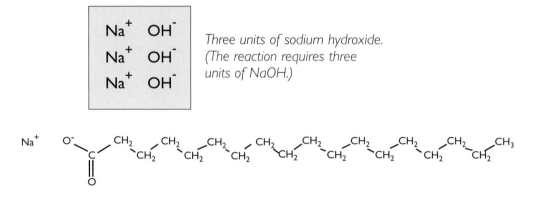

One unit of soap. (The saponification reaction produces three of these.)

Chem Talk

CHEMICAL STRUCTURES

Chemical Structures and Isomers

One of the things chemists want to know about a compound is its chemical structure. The beauty of organic chemistry is the ability of the carbon atom to bond with itself to form very large and very complex structures. A simple hydrocarbon formula such as butane, C_4H_{10}, can represent two different compounds. Such compounds are called **isomers**. You saw this with the models you built in the *Investigate* section. Each isomer of butane has the four carbons attached in a different arrangement and each will have its own characteristic physical and chemical properties.

$CH_3CH_2CH_2CH_3$	CH_3 (attached to the central C of) CH_3CHCH_3
n-butane (for normal butane)	2-methylpropane (or isobutane)

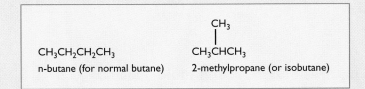

Another way to draw isomers is to use "line-bond" drawings. These show only how the carbons are connected to one another. The line-bond drawings do not show the hydrogen atoms and their bonds. Instead, they only show the bonding of the carbon atoms. It is an easy way to quickly draw structures for comparison purposes. (Note: this is *only* done with carbon atoms.)

 = $CH_3CH_2CH_2CH_3$

n-butane (for normal butane)

 = 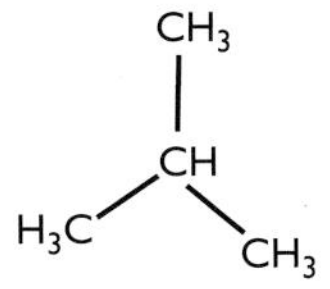
CH3
CH
H3C
CH3

2-methylpropane (or isobutane)

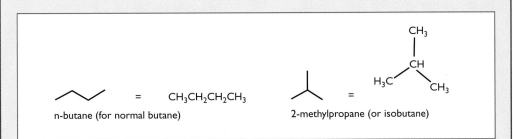

A hydrocarbon where all carbons have single bonds is called a **saturated hydrocarbon**. An **unsaturated hydrocarbon** contains one or more carbon-carbon double or triple bonds. (Remember, all carbons must have four bonds!) To convert butane into a simple unsaturated hydrocarbon, C_4H_8, two hydrogen atoms must be replaced with one double bond. The formula C_4H_8 represents four different

Chem Words

isomers: compounds that have the same chemical formulas but different structural formulas.

saturated hydrocarbon: a hydrocarbon with no double or triple bonds. It is "saturated" because the maximum number of hydrogen atoms are bound to the carbon atoms.

unsaturated hydrocarbon: a hydrocarbon (organic compound) with one or more carbon-carbon double or triple bonds.

compounds, again each with its own physical and chemical properties. You can see how quickly the number of organic molecules increases when you add more carbon atoms, double bonds, and atoms such as oxygen and nitrogen.

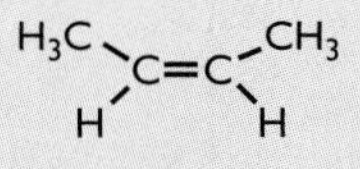

cis-2-butene

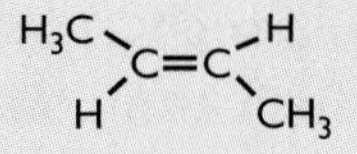

trans-2-butene

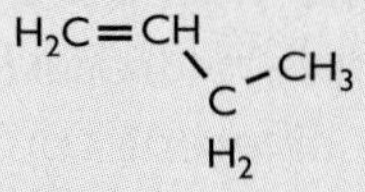

1-butene

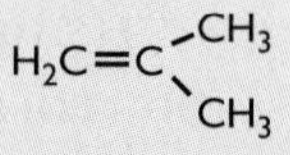

2-methylpropene

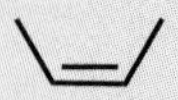

cis-2-butene

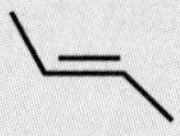

trans-2-butene

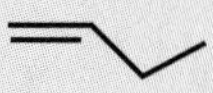

1-butene

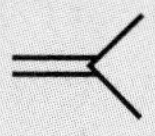

2-methylpropene

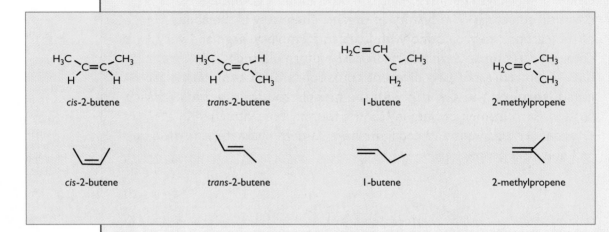

Lewis Structures of Atoms and Molecules

Recalling the octet rule and the special stability attained in filling an electron shell, you can see that a carbon atom (in Group IVA) needs four more electrons. However, carbon almost never gives up electrons or takes on electrons. Because of this, nearly all carbon compounds are covalent and contain four bonds to other atoms. **Lewis structures** are diagrams that show only the outer-shell valence electrons. These are the electrons used in bonding. A look at the Lewis structures in the diagram of some common atoms (H, C, N, O, F) allows you to figure out how many electrons each needs to fully bond and how many bonds it will usually form. Hydrogen requires only two electrons to fill its shell for stability.

Chem Words

Lewis structure: a system of showing chemical structure in which the valence electrons of an atom are placed around the atom. Bonds are shown as a pair of dots or as a line. Non-bonding valence electrons are shown as dots that are not placed between the symbols or elements in the compound.

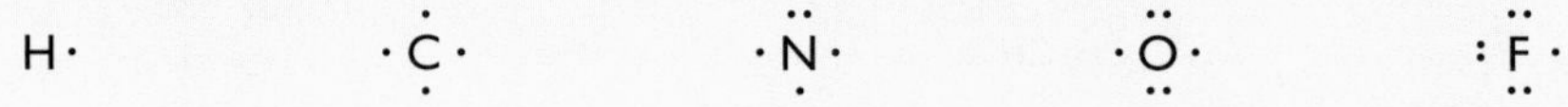

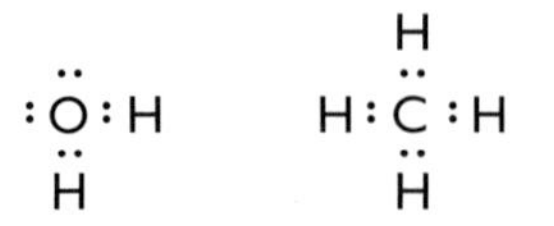

water methane

Look at a few simple molecules with full electron shells after bonding. The Lewis structures of water and methane would look as shown in the diagram. The hydrogen always has two electrons and the oxygen or carbon has eight electrons.

Shared pairs of electrons *between* two atoms represent covalent bonds, while unshared pairs of electrons on one atom belong only to that atom. These are called "lone pairs" or "non-bonding pairs."

One shorthand method for drawing structures uses a single line to represent a single bond. In this fashion, the two molecules can be drawn as shown.

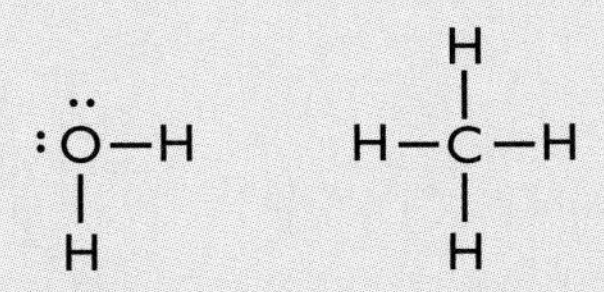

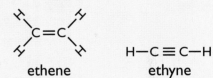

water methane

You can draw very complicated structures such as the structure of a fat molecule, in this way. As suggested previously, each atom will form a standard number of bonds, depending on how many valence electrons it has. Carbon always forms four bonds, while nitrogen forms three, oxygen forms two, and the halogens (F, Cl, Br, I), like hydrogen, form one bond. A **structural formula** of this type tells you the number of each kind of atom and how they are connected to one another. In molecules having **polar covalent bonds**, you can also deduce the polarity of the molecule by considering its geometry.

Double and Triple Bonds

Sometimes two or three bonds can form between two atoms. When double or triple bonds are formed, atoms share more than one pair of electrons. These fall into the unsaturated class of compounds and have their own unique physical and chemical properties. The two simplest of these organic compounds are ethene and ethyne, as shown in the diagram.

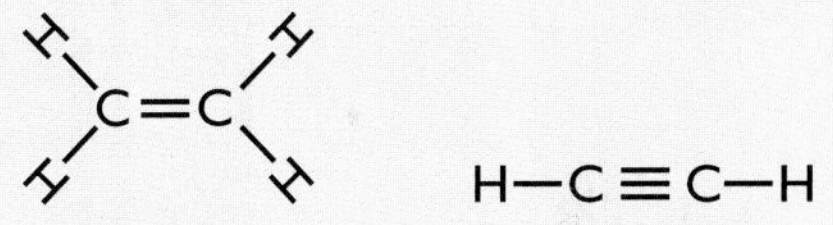

ethene ethyne

Note that the "*-ane*" ending as in methane (ethane, propane, butane) indicates a saturated hydrocarbon. The "*-ene*" ending indicates an unsaturated molecule with at least one double bond. The "*-yne*" ending indicates an unsaturated molecule with at least one triple bond. The terms "saturated" and "unsaturated" are in reference to the total number of hydrogen atoms. An unsaturated hydrocarbon has fewer hydrogen atoms than it could have and can react to take on more hydrogens.

You observed during the activity that single bonds allow free 360° rotation about the bond. The result of this is that the molecule can adopt many different shapes. When you made a C=C double bond, you found that it was rigid and could not be rotated without breaking the bond. In the same way, the two carbons of a triple bond cannot be rotated without breaking the bond between them. Compounds with

Chem Words

structural formula: a formula of a molecule that shows not only all of the atoms but also how they are connected to each other.

polar covalent bond: a bond between two atoms of different electronegativity. The center of electron density is found nearer to the more electronegative atom.

Chem Words

***cis-* double bond:** a geometric arrangement of a carbon to carbon double bond where the hydrogen atoms are located on the same side of the double bond.

***trans-* double bond:** a geometric arrangement of a carbon to carbon double bond where the hydrogen atoms are located on opposite sides of the double bond.

double and triple bonds in their structure have more rigid structures than saturated compounds. This generally results in higher melting and boiling points.

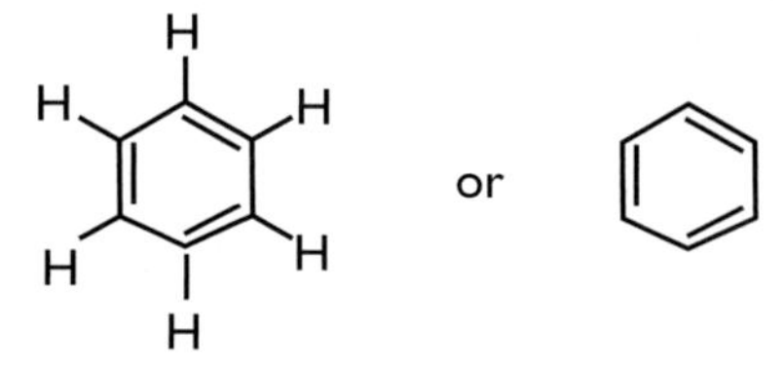

One of the most interesting natural unsaturated cyclical compounds to be discovered early on was benzene, C_6H_6. Benzene can be isolated from coal tar and is a known carcinogen. Although the formula was known by 1825, its structure puzzled chemists for decades and many odd structural formulas were proposed. Credit was given to the chemist Friedrich August Kekulé von Stradonitz for being the first to deduce a reasonable structure for this unusually stable unsaturated compound. Although later found to be incorrect, the alternating single and double bonds found in benzene became known as "Kekulé" structures in his honor.

cis and *trans* Structures

In the *What Do You Think?* section at the beginning of this activity, you were shown two molecules. They had the same formula and name (C_4H_8 and 2-butene), and yet, they were clearly different molecules. The compound on the left is a ***cis*** isomer and the other isomer is called ***trans***. Typically, a *trans* compound will be more stable than the *cis* isomer. It will pack into a crystalline structure better and have a higher melting point. The *trans* isomer is more stable than the *cis* isomer. Therefore, it is less reactive than the cis isomer.

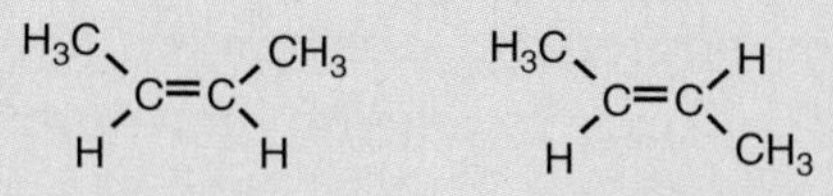

cis-2-butene *trans*-2-butene

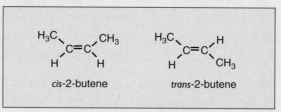

You often hear on television that *trans*-fatty acids are bad for you and that *cis*-fatty acids are healthier in your diet. The *cis* compounds are the natural form of most fats. Enzymes can more easily digest them by breaking them into smaller molecules that your body can use.

The Tetrahedral Carbon

Each carbon bond is made of two shared electrons. As your group discovered by using the four strings representing the four bonds, the molecule takes on the shape of a **tetrahedron** when the four bonds are positioned to minimize the electrical forces of repulsion of the hydrogen atoms. It is this tetrahedral shape that gives two-dimensional drawings of carbon chains their "zig-zag" appearance. More importantly, the tetrahedral carbon atom provides a multitude of interesting, complex, and useful structures. The specificity of many bio-molecules, such as enzymes, are dependent upon this unique feature of carbon bonding.

What is Soap?

The soaps you made before you began this chapter were produced by a chemical reaction between two ingredients: a naturally occurring animal or vegetable fat, and NaOH, a strong base. The name for this type of reaction is **saponification** and it occurs between any fat and a strong base. Fats, also called triglycerides, are organic (carbon-containing) molecules produced by living organisms. They are composed of three long hydrocarbon chains, each one attached to one of the three —OH groups on a glycerin molecule by a carboxyl group.

Two ways of drawing the chemical structure of stearic acid

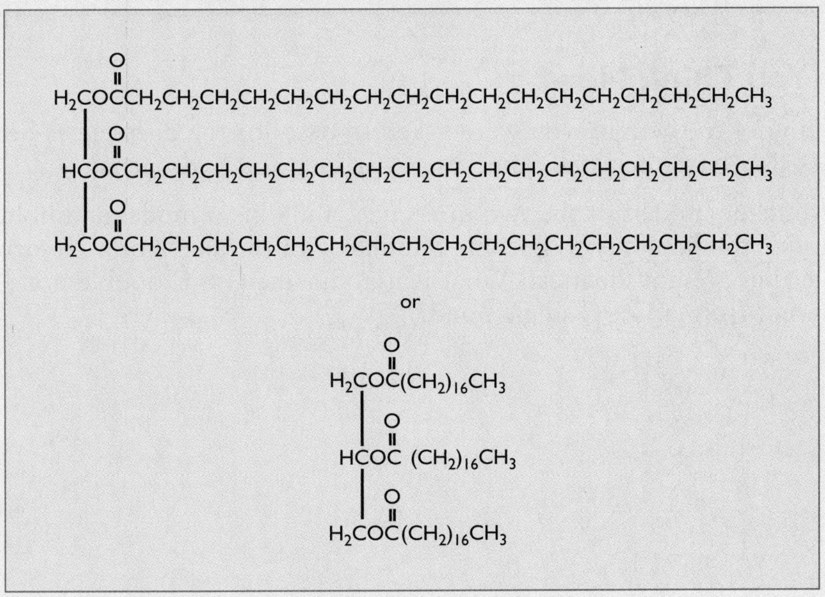

Chem Words

tetrahedron: in geometry, a pyramid with four sides that are equilateral triangles. In chemistry, the term used for molecular structures in which there are four bonds at equal angles between each other (109.5°) around an atom.

saponification: the hydrolysis of triglyceride in the presence of a base.

Chem Words

carboxyl functional group: the characteristic functional group of organic acids (—COOH).

functional group: the characteristic group of an organic molecule.

In the soap-making process, when you mix the fat and the base together, the molecule comes apart, creating glycerin and three unattached fatty acids as products. The fatty acid molecules have a long non-polar hydrocarbon chain and a **carboxylic functional group** on one end. A **functional group** is the characteristic group of an organic molecule.

Under basic conditions, the carboxyl group loses an H^+ ion. The negative ion formed is attracted to the positive sodium ions (Na^+) in the solution. This new ionic compound formed is the soap. One example of a soap compound is shown using the "zig-zag" convention.

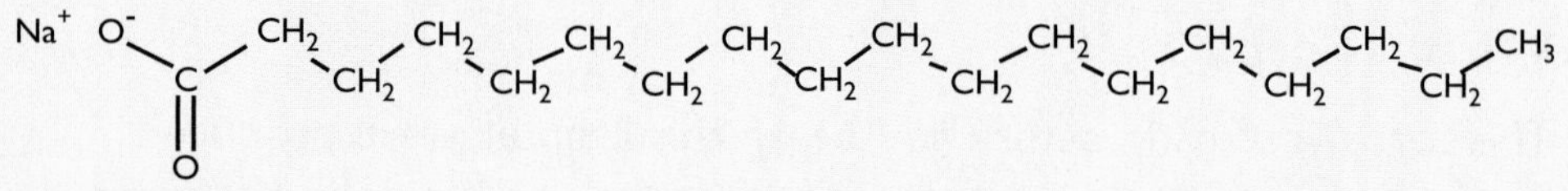

Na^+ O^-
C
O
CH_2
CH_3

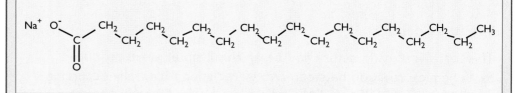

Soap has been made this way for thousands of years. Traditionally, the fats used in making soap have been some kind of animal fat like tallow (from beef) or lard (from pork), although vegetable oils like olive or coconut have also been used. You used sodium hydroxide as the base. In the past, wood ashes have been used as the base (also called lye). Other ingredients can be added to change the properties of the soap somewhat, but the basic recipe has not changed much over time.

Checking Up

1. From the periodic table determine how many valence electrons each of these atoms have:

   a) Mg c) Ne

   b) S d) Al

2. What bases may be used in the soap-making process?
3. What is the name for the soap-making process?
4. Draw a structure of any fatty acid.
5. Draw a structure of a *cis*-double bond and a *trans*-double bond.

What Do You Think Now?

At the beginning of the activity you were asked to describe the differences between two molecules that have the same numbers of carbons and hydrogens.

You now have made models of the two molecules. Building a model and holding it in your hand is the best way to become familiar with the shape of a molecule. The two molecules are not identical. What is it about the C═C double bond that makes it different from a C—C single bond?

Chem Essential Questions

What does it mean?

Chemistry explains a macroscopic phenomenon (what you observe) with a description of what happens at the nanoscopic level (atoms and molecules) using symbolic structures as a way to communicate. Complete the chart below in your *Active Chemistry* log.

MACRO	NANO	SYMBOLIC
Describe at least two properties of animal fat that you have observed when cooking or eating beef or chicken.	*Describe a fat molecule in terms of its molecular structure.*	*Draw a structural model for a fat molecule.*

How do you know?

What are the types of models explored in this activity? Which model would be the best for predicting the number of bonds an atom will form?

Why do you believe?

Diamond is one of the hardest substances known, so it is very difficult to break. Graphite is so soft and slippery that it is often used as a lubricant. (This property makes it a good writing material, because it helps the point of your pencil slide easily across the paper, leaving a trail of graphite bits behind.) Yet both of these materials are made of only one kind of atom, carbon. What do you think accounts for their differences?

Why should you care?

For the design and presentation of your soap, it will be helpful to have a solid understanding of the process of saponification. Explaining to your company how the soap is formed will assure your boss that you are competent and knowledgeable. Using models in your presentation will help others to understand your vision for the world's best soap. How will you do this in your presentation?

Reflecting on the Activity and the Challenge

The world is filled with many different compounds. In order to fully understand their differences and produce materials with the properties you want, you have to look at both the macroscopic properties of those compounds and the properties that arise at the atomic level. The ways the atoms are connected and the three-dimensional shape of the molecules contribute to the properties of the material. You can draw diagrams and build models of those atomic structures to better visualize and understand the structures of substances, and in turn, their properties. Understanding the structure of a soap molecule can help you predict how the properties of soaps change as you change the ingredients used to make the soap.

Chem to Go

1. Are the shapes of these two molecules different? If so, why?

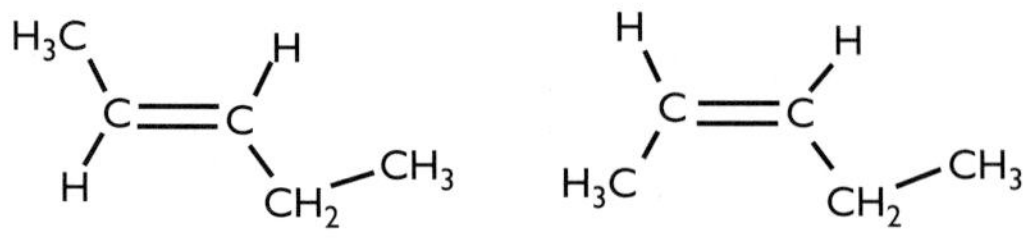

2. Which of the two molecules in *Question 1* has a *cis* arrangement about the double bond, and which has a *trans* arrangement? Explain.

3. Are these two molecules different or the same? Explain.

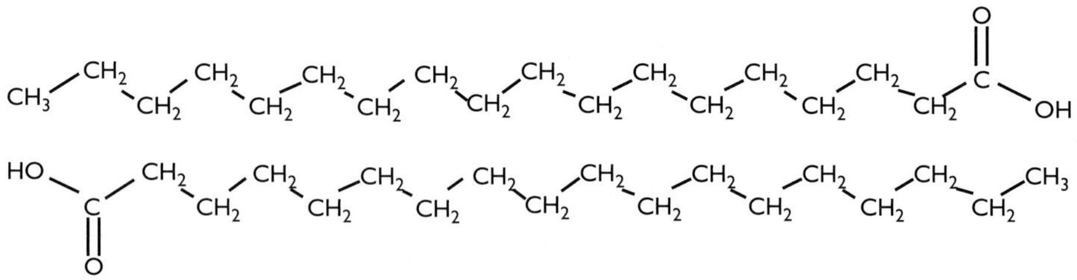

4. Draw the Lewis structure of each of the following atoms. Use the Roman numeral group number in the periodic table for the number of valence electrons.

   a) N   b) S   c) F   d) Ar

5. Which of the atoms you drew in *Question 4* can make bonds and which ones cannot? How many bonds can each one make?

6. a) Draw the Lewis structure of ammonia, NH_3.

   b) Draw the chemical structure of ammonia, showing the bonds as lines.

   c) Would you expect ammonia to be a polar molecule? Explain.

7. The following problems are about ethanol (grain alcohol), CH_3CH_2OH.

   a) Using a line to represent each bond, draw the chemical structure for ethanol.

   b) How many bonds does each carbon atom make? Does carbon always make the same number of bonds? Why?

8. The structure below represents a fat that could be used to make a soap. Draw the chemical structure of one unit of soap in the *cis* form that would be created by reacting this fat with three units of NaOH.

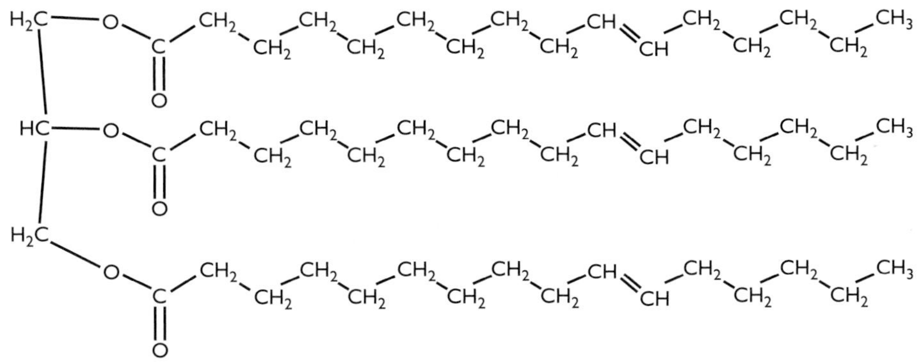

9. ***Preparing for the Chapter Challenge***

In the *Chapter Challenge*, you will need to explain the chemical reaction in which soap is made from the ingredients you choose to use. You will need to represent the molecules involved in this chemical reaction. There are different ways to represent a molecule: Lewis diagrams and two kinds of structural diagrams (one with all the C-H bonds shown, and the other without). In your *Active Chemistry* log, use the glycerol molecule as an example, and represent it in all three ways. It may help to build glycerol first using the molecular-model sets.

Activity 3 How Do You Clean Dirty Laundry?

What Do You See?

AMMO NIA
LIQUID DETERGENT
JAX
KEROSENE
AMMONIA
BLEACH
BLEACH
SOAP

GOALS

In this activity you will:

- Discover that different types of dirt vary in what is required to remove them from cloth, and that most dirt falls into one of two categories.
- Determine the type of cleaning solution best able to remove all types of dirt.
- Create a demonstration of electrostatic attraction/repulsion.
- Demonstrate that water is subject to electrostatic forces, but kerosene is not.

Safety goggles and a lab apron must be worn *at all times* in a chemistry lab.

What Do You Think?

Sometimes, just rinsing something in water is enough to get it clean. Other times, you need soap or something stronger to clean something dirty.

- **What determines how hard it is to clean something?**
- **What does soap do that helps get something clean?**

Record your ideas about these questions in your *Active Chemistry* log. Be prepared to discuss your responses with your small group and the class.

Investigate

There are different types of dirt. To design a recipe for a soap that will clean several different kinds of dirt well, you have to know how soaps clean. To understand this, you have to figure out what soap molecules actually do when they clean, and what special features soap molecules have that enables them to do this.

Part A: Types of Dirt

1. Your teacher will provide the class with the following types of dirt:
   - dirt (potting soil)
   - grease
   - coffee or tea
   - grass or other ground-up plants

- grape juice
- ketchup or mustard
- markers (non-permanent)
- charcoal

Divide the dirt samples among the different groups in your class. Later, you will pool your class data.

2. Put about a teaspoon (5 mL) of one of the dirt types in the center of a square of white cloth. Fold the cloth in half, and then again in half. Rub the substance into the cloth. Make sure that there is dirt over the entire cloth. You will be cutting the cloth into several pieces and you need to have dirt on each piece. Open the cloth. Use a spatula to scrape off any excess substance not absorbed by the cloth.

3. Repeat this step using a new cloth for each of the additional dirt that your group is assigned.

4. Using scissors, cut each cloth into six equal pieces.

5. Take one piece of blank $8\frac{1}{2}$ by 11-inch paper for each dirt sample you are studying. On each paper, label the rectangles.

   - The first box should have your group's name and which dirt you are studying.
   - The second box should be labeled Control.
   - The next five boxes should be labeled with each of the five cleaning agents (see *Step 6*).
   - The last box will be a summary.

Group: Dirt:	Control	Water	Kerosene
Kerosene/ water	Detergent	Bar soap	Summary

6. For each type of dirt, set aside one of the six pieces of cloth as the control.

   a) Why do you need a control?

   With the other five pieces, try to rinse the dirt out of each cloth using the following cleaning agents (or combination) and then allow them to dry:

   - water
   - kerosene
   - first kerosene, then water
   - powdered laundry detergent
   - bar soap

   b) Record your results in your *Active Chemistry* log.

7. Place the dried cloth pieces on the $8\frac{1}{2}$ by 11-inch paper you labeled.

   a) In the summary rectangle, list the cloths in order of cleanest to dirtiest.

8. When you have finished with your cloth pieces, gather all the pieces that were rinsed in kerosene and wash them out using detergent. Rags or other materials with kerosene on them can very easily catch on fire, even when it seems that there should be no danger. The detergent will enable water to wash the kerosene out of the fabric.

9. Dispose of the materials as directed by your teacher. Clean up your workstation.

You will be working with kerosene, which can damage your skin. Kerosene is also highly flammable, so be extremely careful not to work near any sparks or flames.

Make sure you know where the fire blanket and fire extinguisher are located in your laboratory and how to use them, before you begin this next step.

Use the kerosene in a well-ventilated area, such as a fumehood. Do not breath the vapors.

Wear gloves and use tongs to rinse the cloth with kerosene so it does not get on your hands.

Clean up any spills immediately. Rinse towels coated with kerosene in detergent and water before throwing them away.

Soap can make things slippery. Clean up spills and be careful when holding equipment that may have soap on it.

Wash your hands and arms thoroughly after the activity.

10. Pool your class data. Then as a class, discuss which cleaning agents worked best and worst for various dirt samples.

    a) Are there different categories of dirt that are cleaned better by different agents? Write down the class consensus in your *Active Chemistry* log.

Part B: Behavior of Water and Kerosene toward a Charged Balloon

1. Your teacher will demonstrate how two charged balloons (balloons rubbed against a wool sweater) react when suspended by strings and placed near each other.

    a) Record your observations in your log.

2. Your teacher will set up two burettes in a ringstand, as shown. One contains water and the other kerosene. After the valve on the burette is opened and adjusted so that the water exits in a very thin stream, observe what happens when the charged balloon is brought close to the water.

    a) Record your observations in your *Active Chemistry* log.

3. Your teacher will repeat this with the kerosene burette.

    a) Record your observations in your *Active Chemistry* log.

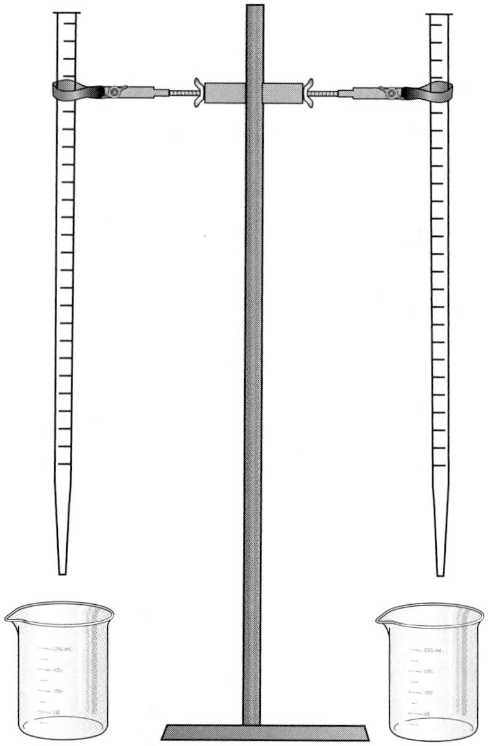

4. When you rub the balloon against a wool sweater, a negative static-electric charge builds up on the surface of the balloon.

    a) What does the behavior of the water stream when the balloon is held closely to it tell you about the water molecules? What could account for its behavior?

    b) What does the behavior of the kerosene stream when the balloon is held closely to it tell you about the kerosene molecules? What could account for its behavior?

Chem Talk

POLAR AND NON-POLAR MOLECULES

Two Classes of Materials and How Soap is Related to Them

In *Part B* of this activity, you observed a basic difference in the way that water and kerosene respond to a charged balloon. You know that unlike charges attract and like charges repel. Compounds like water are attracted to the electric charge on the balloon. The balloon is negatively charged, so the positively charged parts of water molecules are attracted to the negatively charged balloon. On the other hand, no part of the kerosene molecule has a distribution of electric charge to allow it to be attracted to the balloon. This difference results from the chemical structure of each molecule.

If you used an object with a positive charge (like a glass rod that has been rubbed with a silk cloth, for example), you would find that once again the water stream would be attracted to it. In this case, the negatively charged part of the water molecules are attracted to the positive rod. In liquid water, the molecules are constantly rotating rapidly. They will rotate to face whichever direction that maximizes the attractive forces.

Part of the water molecule has a small, or *partial*, negative charge on the oxygen atom, and part of the molecule has a partial positive charge on the hydrogen atoms. The symbols $\delta+$ and $\delta-$ stand for a partial positive and partial negative charge, respectively. The positively charged parts of the water molecule are attracted to the negatively charged balloon, and so a stream of water bends toward it. The negatively charged parts of water molecules are attracted to a positive charge. Similarly, a stream of water will also bend toward a positively charged object.

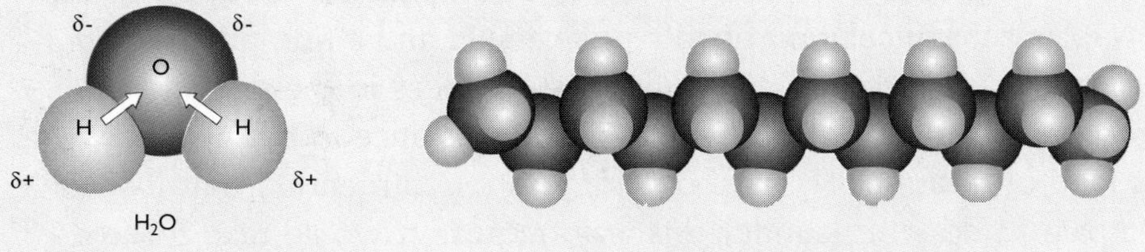
δ-
δ-
O
H
H
δ+
δ+
H₂O

water (has partial charges) *kerosene (no partial charges)*

Kerosene molecules, a mixture of hydrocarbons with carbon chains of about 10 to 12 carbons, have no net charged portions at all. Carbon and hydrogen atoms, of which kerosene is composed, have about the same attraction for the electrons, so there is no net charge imbalance.

Chem Words

polar molecule: a molecule that has a negative region (pole) and positive region (pole) due to the arrangement of the polar bonds.

A stream of kerosene will not be attracted to either positively or negatively charged objects. This is an important difference between water and kerosene. Neither one is made up of charged particles. In a water molecule, the small positive charges are exactly balanced by the small negative charge, so that the molecule is neutral overall. The difference between water and kerosene is that, within the water molecule, there is a positively charged region and a negatively charged region, while within the kerosene molecule, the regions are all essentially neutral.

Based on this evidence, chemists conclude that water is a **polar molecule** and kerosene is a non-polar molecule. Polar molecules have partial positive and partial negative regions within the molecule.

In the activity, you also observed that water and kerosene do not mix. Based on this evidence, you can make the following hypothesis: polar and non-polar molecules do not mix. This is the key to cleaning.

Dirt composed of polar substances will mix with water because it is polar. These substances dissolve in the water, and the water washes them away. The water thereby cleans the cloth. Dirt composed of non-polar substances will not mix with water because water is polar. These substances do not dissolve in water, and water is unable to wash them away. The cloth, therefore, remains dirty.

This is where kerosene, a non-polar molecule, comes to the rescue. The dirt composed of non-polar substances will mix with kerosene because both are non-polar. These substances dissolve in kerosene, which then washes them away. The kerosene cleans the cloth.

In the activity, you observed that sometimes it takes both water (or a water-like agent) and kerosene (or a kerosene-like agent) to clean all of the dirt off a piece of cloth. To clean dirt composed of both polar and non-polar substances, you need a polar liquid and a non-polar liquid. The water rids the cloth of the polar substances in the dirt and the kerosene rids the cloth of the non-polar substance in the dirt. However, this kind of treatment is hard on clothes, not to mention that it would be a pain to do your laundry this way because it would take twice as long to launder dirty clothes.

Soap is a chemical that has one part that is polar and one part that is non-polar. The polar part of the soap cleans the dirt made up of polar substances, while the non-polar part of the soap cleans the dirt made up of non-polar substances. That is what makes soap such a great cleaner.

Soap can do the job of both water and kerosene. (When we refer to water and kerosene, we also mean water-like and kerosene-like liquids.)

The two classes of materials (water-like and kerosene-like) are termed **hydrophilic** (water-loving) and **hydrophobic** (water-avoiding). The names of the classes refer to water because water is so important that it is natural to compare things to it. A soap is a chemical that has both a hydrophobic and a hydrophilic part, so it is able to dissolve in both kinds of chemicals and clean both classes of dirt. The technical name for such a chemical is a **surfactant**. Sodium stearate, shown in the diagram, is a typical surfactant.

Chem Words

hydrophilic: a substance that is attracted to water and is soluble in water.

hydrophobic: a substance that is not attracted to water and is insoluble in water.

surfactant: a substance that lowers the surface tension of a liquid and allows wetting, such as soap added to water.

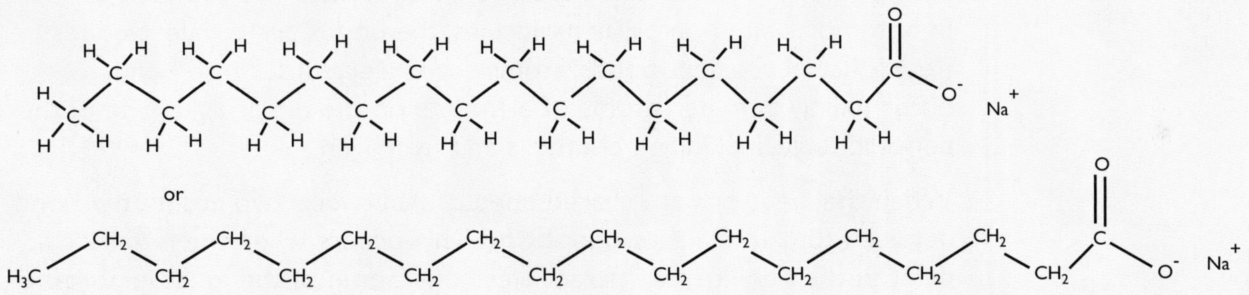

Sodium stearate

These are two ways of representing the same molecule. In the first representation, all the C–H bonds are shown. In the second representation, only the C–C bonds are shown, and the C–H bonds are collapsed into $-CH_2-$ inside the chain, or a $-CH_3$ (or H_3C-) at an end. It is often simpler to represent large molecules the second way, without drawing all the C–H bonds. However, it is important to remember that the C–H bonds are also there. The hydrophilic end of this chemical is the one with the ions (Na^+ and $-COO^-$). The hydrophobic part is the long carbon chain.

What Makes a Molecule Hydrophobic or Hydrophilic?

There is a saying in chemistry: *like dissolves like*. Better expressions would be polar dissolves polar and non-polar dissolves non-polar. Water-like molecules are hydrophilic because they are polar, as is water. Polar molecules attract each other, so you can dissolve one substance that is polar in another that is polar. In other words, some substances (hydrophilic ones) "love" being with water. Kerosene-like molecules are hydrophobic, or they "fear" water because they are not polar. Non-polar molecules and polar molecules do not attract each other, so a non-polar substance will not dissolve in a polar substance. Kerosene, being non-polar, cannot dissolve in water, which is polar.

Chem Words

polar bond: a bond in which the two atoms have a difference in attractive force, causing one atom to be slightly negative and the other slightly positive.

non-polar bond: a bond in which the two atoms share the electrons more or less equally.

electronegativity: a scale that determines how much an atom will attract electrons toward it in a covalent chemical bond.

It is helpful to think of this attraction as a kind of "competition." Imagine one water molecule surrounded by many other water molecules. These other water molecules are all attracted to the first one and to each other. A non-polar molecule will not be attracted in this way to the water molecule. It cannot break the attraction that water molecules have for each other as this attraction is fairly strong. Any non-polar molecules will be "shut out." The polar molecules will all stick together, while the non-polar molecules (which are only weakly attracted to each other) will band amongst themselves.

What makes molecules polar or non-polar in the first place? Molecules are made of atoms that are bonded together in various structures. Bonds result when electrons are shared or transferred between atoms. In both polar and non-polar molecules, the bonds are covalent bonds. Recall that in covalent bonds, atoms share electrons. These bonds occur mainly between atoms of elements on the upper right side of the periodic table, including nonmetals and hydrogen.

When the electrons are shared unequally between two atoms, the bond between the atoms is a **polar bond**. This occurs when the two atoms differ in their abilities to attract electrons. Some of the most important (and common) polar bonds are bonds between H and any one of N, O, F, or Cl atoms. For other atoms that are bonded, a good rule of thumb for telling if the atoms are not similar enough to form a polar bond is to look at where the elements are on the periodic table. If they are far apart, they tend to form polar bonds.

When the electrons shared between two atoms are shared more or less equally, the bond is a **non-polar bond**. This occurs when the two atoms are similar to each other. Obviously, a bond between two atoms of the element, such as the bond between two oxygen atoms in an O_2 molecule, is perfectly non-polar, because the atoms are the same. Other bonds that are considered non-polar exist between elements that are near each other on the periodic table, such as C and N.

However, a bond between C and H is nearly non-polar, even though these atoms are not close together on the periodic table. A more precise way of determining if a bond is polar or non-polar becomes necessary.

Determining Whether Molecules Are Polar or Non-polar

There is a convenient concept called **electronegativity (EN)** that can be used to describe the attraction that an atom has for electrons it shares in a covalent bond. A scale of electronegativity values for the elements was developed by the late American chemist, Linus Pauling. On the partial periodic table shown here, some elements are shown with their assigned electronegativity values. For example, fluorine is assigned the value of 4.0, oxygen is assigned 3.5, etc. You can see that electronegativity values generally increase as you move up any column on the periodic table or across any row from left to right. Electronegativity values can be used to predict whether electrons will be shared equally or unequally between atoms in a bond, making the bond either polar or non-polar.

Linus Pauling

To predict the polarity of a bond, you just look at the electronegativity values of the atoms that are bonded together. If the electronegativity values are similar, then the electrons are shared more equally between the atoms, and the bond is non-polar.

Electronegativity values generally increase as you go up a column or across a period from left to right.

Electronegativities of Some Elements
(on the arbitrary Pauling scale)

H 2.1						
Li 1.0	Be 1.5	B 2.0	C 2.5	N 3.0	O 3.5	F 4.0
Na 0.9	Mg 1.2	Al 1.5	Si 1.8	P 2.1	S 2.5	Cl 3.0
K 0.8	Ca 1.0	Ga 1.6	Ge 1.8	As 2.0	Se 2.4	Br 2.8
Rb 0.8	Sr 1.0					I 2.5
Cs 0.7	Ba 0.9					

For example, if you are looking at a bond between carbon and chlorine, then you look at the difference between carbon's electronegativity value (2.5) and chlorine's value (3.0). You can get two pieces of information from these numbers. First, chlorine is a stronger attractor of electrons because it has a higher EN value. Second, the bond must be polar because there is a relatively large difference between the electronegativities ($3.0 - 2.5 = 0.5$). This means that the chlorine atom will have a partial negative charge, and the carbon atom will have a partial positive charge. The charges are partial because the chlorine atom didn't gain an entire extra electron (as it does when an electron is transferred to form a chlorine ion, Cl^-), but it receives more than half of the charge of the pair of electrons it shares with carbon. Chemists usually use a scale of electronegativity differences to determine polarity of bonds. If the difference lies between 0 and 0.4, the bond is considered non-polar.

If the difference lies between 0.5 and 1.7, the bond is considered polar. The larger the difference, the more polar the bond is.

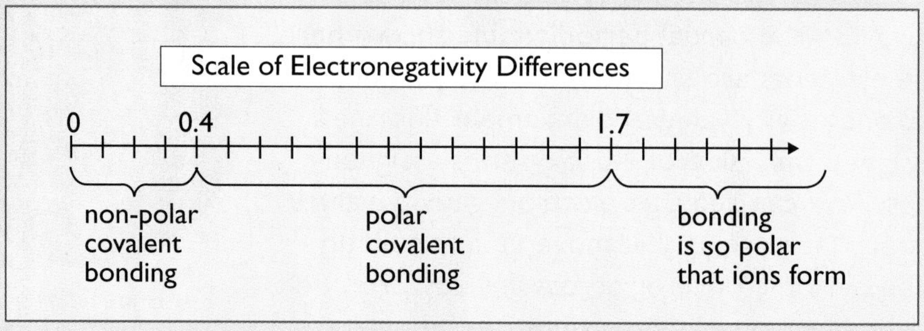
Scale of Electronegativity Differences
0
0.4
1.7
non-polar covalent bonding
polar covalent bonding
bonding is so polar that ions form

Electronegativity can also be used to predict whether a bond between two atoms will be covalent or ionic. A covalent bond is formed when the electrons in the bond are shared between the two atoms, whether equally (non-polar) or unequally (polar). When the difference between the atoms' abilities to attract electrons becomes great enough, one atom fully takes up the electrons from the bond, and the other atom loses them. This transfer of electrons results in an ionic bond because two ions form. (One ion is negative, with the additional electron, and the other ion is positive, because it now lacks an electron.) Bonds with electronegativity differences greater than 1.7 will usually be ionic.

So you can predict whether a molecule will be polar or non-polar by examining its structure. If the atoms in the molecule are connected in a way that produces one or more polar bonds, then the molecule is probably polar. (The shape of a molecule also determines whether it is polar or not, but we will ignore that for now.) If a molecule contains no polar bonds, it is non-polar.

Why "Like Dissolves Like" and Surfactants Dissolve in Both Polar and Non-polar Substances

Polar molecules are attracted to each other because the positive part of one molecule is attracted to the negative part of the next. So, in a glass of water, each water molecule is attracted to the others around it, making a very stable situation. Attraction between molecules of a substance raises its melting and boiling point. Adding a non-polar molecule like oil would disrupt this attraction, breaking the attraction/stabilization feature between water molecules. A solution in which the oil and water molecules are mixed together is therefore less stable than one in which they are separated, so oil and water don't mix. In general, polar and non-polar molecules don't mix. On the other hand, if you mix another polar compound like sugar (sugar has lots of –OH bonds, which are polar) into water, it dissolves easily. When a polar sugar molecule comes between two polar water molecules, the positive parts of these molecules attract the negative parts of the water molecules, so a stable solution is formed. This is why water and sugar mix easily.

Many ionic compounds will also mix easily with water, because they separate into ions (charged particles), which are attracted to the polar water molecules. You saw an electrostatic (plus-minus) attraction when the negatively charged balloon was attracted to the positive charges on the water molecules. Polar molecules are hydrophilic because water is polar and other polar compounds will mix easily with it. Non-polar molecules are hydrophobic because they don't mix easily with water.

Surfactants are chemicals with both polar and non-polar ends, so they can dissolve in both polar and non-polar substances. Sodium stearate, the surfactant presented early in this activity, has one end (with the oxygen ion) that is charged or polar, while the other end is a non-polar hydrocarbon chain. The polar end of a surfactant dissolves in water or other polar compounds, and the non-polar end of a surfactant dissolves in kerosene, oil, grease, or other hydrophobic compounds.

Checking Up

1. Why did the balloon attract the stream of water, but not kerosene?
2. Do kerosene and water mix? Why or why not?
3. Explain the terms hydrophilic and hydrophobic.
4. What is a surfactant?
5. What is the EN difference between F and H? What type of bond is formed?
6. Explain the difference between a polar and an ionic bond.
7. Draw an H_2S molecule and use arrows to show any polar bonds. Is this molecule polar?

What Do You Think Now?

At the beginning of this activity you were asked:

- **What determines how hard it is to clean something?**
- **What does soap do that helps get something clean?**

Refer to the ideas you wrote down at the beginning of the activity. How has your thinking changed? How would you answer the questions now?

Chem Essential Questions

What does it mean?

Chemistry explains a macroscopic phenomenon (what you observe) with a description of what happens at the nanoscopic level (atoms and molecules) using symbolic structures as a way to communicate. Complete the chart below in your *Active Chemistry* log.

MACRO	NANO	SYMBOLIC
Draw a sketch showing charged balloons next to a stream of water and a stream of kerosene.	*Show the water molecules in the stream of water as they are attracted to the charged balloon.*	*How is electronegativity used to determine if a molecule is polar?*

How do you know?

What evidence do you have that water and kerosene are both needed to clean certain dirt? What evidence do you have that soap alone can do the same cleaning?

Why do you believe?

You are familiar with using water to clean clothes. Now you have begun to learn how it works at the molecular level. Another method for getting clothes clean is called dry cleaning. Discuss with your small group what this means and how it might work. Record your thoughts in your *Active Chemistry* log and be prepared to go over this with your teacher and the class.

Why should you care?

Soaps are used to remove substances from fabrics or other materials. Write a description of electrostatic attractions for your soap presentation.

Reflecting on the Activity and the Challenge

Your challenge is to create a useful soap. You will need to include both polar and non-polar regions in your surfactant. You will not be able to create a soap that does everything. If you think about it, no cleaning agent on the market can do that. Cleaning agents are specialized. You wouldn't want to wash your hands with laundry detergent, for example. You will need to think about what kinds of dirt you want your soap to clean. Some options include cleaning dirt and grease from your hands, cleaning dirt from laundry, or cleaning food off dirty dishes. There is a wide variety of options to choose from.

Chem to Go

1. You may have noticed that salad dressing separates into oil and water. That is because oil and water don't mix. If you had tried using a stream of oil from the burette in *Part B* of the activity, what result would you expect? Explain why.
2. Return to the list of "dirts" your class tried to clean.
   a) Organize this list into these categories: hydrophilic, hydrophobic, and contains both.
   b) If you had gasoline on hand instead of water or kerosene, which dirt would gasoline clean the best? (Hint: Gasoline has the polarity of kerosene.)
   c) What if you had vinegar? Which dirt would vinegar clean? (Hint: Vinegar is 95% water.)
3. List six common liquid materials in your household that have not been discussed in this chapter. Which of them contain polar molecules, and which contain non-polar molecules? How could you determine this?
4. Determine which of the following molecules are polar and which are non-polar by comparing the electronegativity values of the atoms. In each case, explain how you made the determination.

a) CH_4 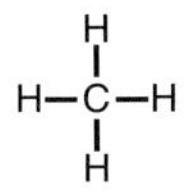

d) CH_3OH 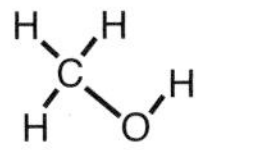

b) NH_3 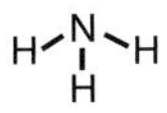

e) CH_3COOH 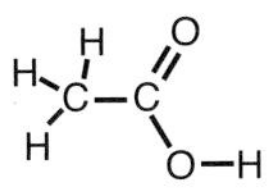

c) HCl H—Cl

5. For each of the substances in *Question 4*, indicate whether the substance would dissolve in water or would separate from water. Explain your reasoning.
6. ***Preparing for the Chapter Challenge***

   Part of the *Chapter Challenge* requires you to explain the chemistry of how your soap will work to clean what you intend it to clean. Write a paragraph in your *Active Chemistry* log that will serve as a rough draft for this part of the report in your *Chapter Challenge* presentation.

Inquiring Further

1. Temperature and cleaning agents

Do not use kerosene for this activity if you are going to try heating the cleaning agent using a flame or hot plate. Heating a flammable liquid can be dangerous. Have your teacher check your plan before beginning any part of it.

Does temperature affect the ability of a cleaning agent to remove dirt? Design an experiment to investigate this. With the approval of your teacher, carry out the experiment. Report your findings to the class.

2. Surfactants

In the *Chem Talk* section, you learned that soaps are part of a class of materials called surfactants. What does the word surfactant mean? What do surfactants do to the properties of water? Why?

3. Home remedies for cleaning stains

Investigate home remedies for cleaning stains. Ask your grandmother for advice, look in old cookbooks, search on the Internet, or use one of the home remedies that your teacher provides. Can you make sense of these home remedies in light of what you have learned about cleaning agents? Try to explain why each step of a home remedy works to clean the stain. Use the following words in your explanation: hydrophobic, hydrophilic, surfactant, temperature. Write down any questions that this exercise prompts, and try to learn the answers to these questions as you proceed through this chapter.

Activity 4 How Does Soap Work?

What Do You See?

H_2O
H_2O
1
2
SOAP
SOAPY WATER
ALCO HOL
AC

GOALS

In this activity you will:

- Identify polar and non-polar materials.
- Explain the behavior of a mixture of two immiscible liquids.
- Explain the effect of a surfactant on such a mixture.

What Do You Think?

Soap molecules have both polar and non-polar parts that allow them to dissolve both hydrophilic and hydrophobic substances.

- **How can molecules of soap dissolve both hydrophilic and hydrophobic substances?**

Record your ideas about this question in your *Active Chemistry* log. Be prepared to discuss your responses with your small group and the class.

Investigate

If you know what soap molecules do when they clean and what parts of the soap molecules can be varied, you can design a soap with molecules that can clean some things better than others.

Part A: Properties of Water

1. If you take a cup of water and pour it on your desk, it spreads out over the surface of the desk and spills onto the floor. Gravity pulls down on the pile of water molecules you temporarily create. It pulls them down off the pile to the surface of the desk, and then down to the floor. Liquids do not hold their shape like a solid.

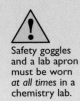

Safety goggles and a lab apron must be worn *at all times* in a chemistry lab.

Do this activity on a tray or absorbent surface so the liquid does not run onto the floor. Clean up any spills immediately.

Avoid breathing the alcohol fumes. Keep the alcohol away from sources of flames and sparks.

They usually spread out flat unless they are held in a container.

a) Predict and record in your *Active Chemistry* log the number of drops of water you will be able to place on a penny.

Put a penny on your desk. Slowly add drops of water onto it, one at a time. Add as many drops as you can.

b) Record in your log the maximum number of drops of water that fit on the penny.

c) How high does the water extend above the surface of the penny?

d) Why doesn't gravity make the water sticking up above the surface flow down the side and onto the desk?

2. Predict the number of drops of alcohol you will be able to place on a penny.

a) Record your prediction in your log.

Repeat the procedure in *Step 1* with drops of alcohol on a penny.

b) Record the number of drops of alcohol you are able to place on a penny.

c) Compare and contrast the results of water drops and alcohol drops.

d) Can you create a hypothesis for any differences you observed?

3. Fill a cup with water nearly to the top. Place a sewing needle onto the surface of water so that it floats. (Hint: To place the needle, use tweezers.)

a) What keeps this steel needle from sinking?

4. Make some soapy lather in your hands, as you would when washing them. Touch the surface of the water on the penny with a soapy finger (gently so as not to disturb it).

a) Record what happens.

Touch the surface of the water in the cup containing the needle with a soapy finger (again, gently so as not to disturb it).

b) Record your observations.

5. Take a bubble wand and try to blow bubbles using a water solution, an alcohol solution, and a soap solution.

a) Record your observations.

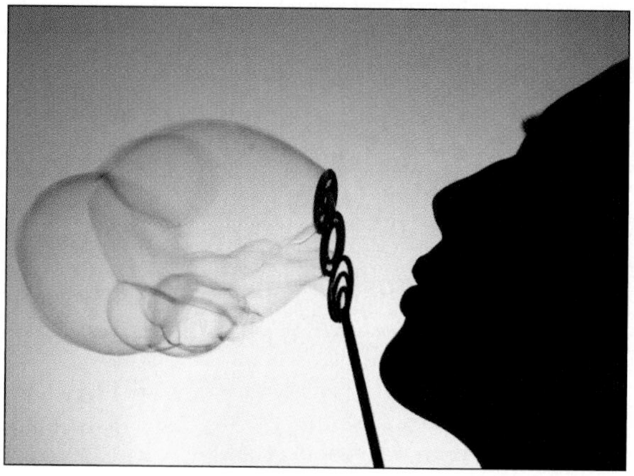

6. Think about the investigations you just completed.

a) In your *Active Chemistry* log, summarize the similarities and differences between the behavior you have observed in the three liquids you have tested on surfaces and tried blowing bubbles with: plain water, isopropyl alcohol, and soapy water.

Part B: Mixing Materials

1. Your teacher will provide you with the following materials:

   - vegetable oil
   - mineral oil
   - ethanol
   - kerosene
   - honey
   - liquid soap
   - water

   Explore what happens when you mix any two of these materials. (If two substances are able to be mixed to form a solution, they are said to be miscible. If they cannot be mixed, they are immiscible.) Do not attempt to test every possible combination of two. Instead, choose a representative sample. Do a minimum of 12 tests.

   a) Write down your procedure in your log and have it approved by your teacher before you begin.

   b) Organize your observations in a table (or tables) in your *Active Chemistry* log.

2. Recall from the previous activity that there are two categories of pure materials, polar and non-polar. The saying, "like dissolves like" refers to these two categories. That is, polar materials will dissolve in other polar materials, non-polar materials will dissolve in other non-polar materials, and polar and non-polar materials separate from each other. Water is polar.

   a) Use your data from the previous step to categorize all the other materials as either polar or non-polar. You may have to pool your data with data from the rest of the class.

   b) Does any material fit in both categories? In your *Active Chemistry* log, write down some of your conclusions from your observations.

3. Now conduct a set of tests to determine which of the liquids will dissolve the following solid materials:

   - salt
   - sugar
   - butter
   - powdered soap
   - aspirin
   - aspartame or saccharine

   Test each one to see if it will dissolve in water, and then in vegetable or mineral oil. Crushing or grinding any solid that is not in powdered form can speed up dissolving.

   a) Organize your data in a table, and classify each material as polar or non-polar.

   b) Does any material fit in both categories?

Part C: Modeling the Action of Soap

1. You are going to model the behavior of polar and non-polar materials. Prepare the following models from toothpicks and small foam spheres:

   Soap-molecule models
   Take 20 toothpicks and 20 small foam spheres. Attach the spheres to the toothpicks as shown on the next page. The foam sphere represents the polar end of the soap molecule, and the rest of the toothpicks represent the non-polar end of the soap molecule.

Safety goggles and a lab apron must be worn *at all times* in a chemistry lab.

Be careful with all of the fluids. Clean up any spills immediately. Oils can make things slippery to hold.

Kerosene and ethanol are both very flammable and are toxic. Review with your teacher how to handle them safely before beginning the activity.

Do not consume any substances in a chemistry lab.

Wash your hands and arms thoroughly after the activity.

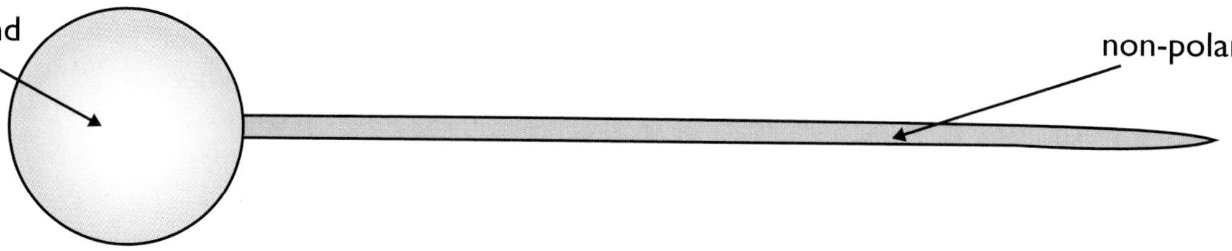
polar end
non-polar end

Polar molecules (water) Take about 20 more foam spheres. These represent polar water molecules.

Non-polar molecules (kerosene or oil) Take about 10 toothpicks and break each one into several pieces. These small toothpick pieces represent non-polar molecules.

2. Now you will use the models to figure out how soap can dissolve in polar and non-polar substances.

   Place a large white piece of paper on your desk or lab bench. To represent a sample of water, take all the polar water molecules and place them randomly all over the white paper.

   Show what happens when you add kerosene or oil to the water. Add 5 or 6 non-polar molecules. Remember that polar molecules attract each other much more strongly than they attract non-polar molecules or than non-polar molecules attract each other.

   a) What arrangement will minimize this contact? Draw this in your *Active Chemistry* log and label your drawing, "How oil and water molecules are arranged in a mixture of oil and water."

   Remove the non-polar molecules from the paper on your desk to prepare for the next step.

3. Think about what happens when you dissolve soap in water. Remember that polar and non-polar materials do not wish to come into contact with each other. How can you arrange the 20 soap molecules you made so that they are *inside* the water sample? Is there a structure that mixes the soap molecules in smaller groups throughout (and inside) the water? The structure you have to create to do this is called a ***micelle***.

   a) Draw a picture of the arrangement in your *Active Chemistry* log, and label your drawing, "How soap molecules are arranged when they are dissolved in water." Draw an arrow pointing to the micelle and label it "micelle."

4. Add a few non-polar oil molecules to your water/soap solution. How can you arrange the molecules so that the oil as well as the soap is dissolved in the water?

   a) Draw a picture of this arrangement in your *Active Chemistry* log, and label your drawing, "How soap molecules and oil molecules are arranged when soap and oil are dissolved in water."

   b) Make a drawing in your *Active Chemistry* log of how soap can be dissolved in a non-polar substance. You may use the models to figure this out, if you wish. Label the drawing, "How soap molecules are arranged when they are dissolved in a non-polar substance."

5. You have been exploring a model to show how soap dissolves in polar and non-polar materials. However, the model has limitations. Not the least of these is that real materials are three-dimensional, not two-dimensional. To determine what a three-dimensional micelle looks like, imagine that a 1 m by 1 m by 1 m box on your desk is filled with water molecules.

   a) How would a soap micelle have to be structured to be able to dissolve in the water? Describe it in your *Active Chemistry* log. It is difficult to represent such a structure in a drawing on paper. Remember that the two-dimensional drawings of micelles that you will see here are really cross-sections of three-dimensional micelles.

6. How does soap act to clean? If a shirt with oil spilled on it were laundered in a soapy water solution, where would the oil particles prefer to be?

   a) Write a one-paragraph explanation in your *Active Chemistry* log of how you think soapy water works to clean oil off a shirt. Use drawings where necessary to illustrate your explanation.

7. You will now determine what happens to soapy water when you add oil to it. Add the same amount of water to each of four test tubes (about half full). To tubes #2 and #3, add equal amounts of liquid dish soap. To tubes #3 and #4, add equal small amounts of oil.

   Capping each test tube with a stopper or with your thumb, shake each test tube the same number of times. Set the test tubes side by side in a test-tube rack and compare their contents.

   a) Write down your observations in your *Active Chemistry* log.

Wash your hands and arms thoroughly after the activity.

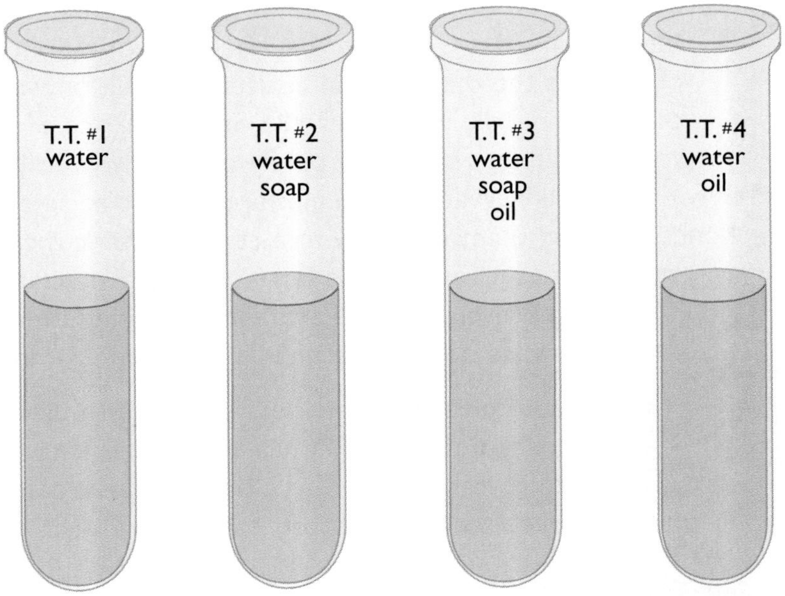
T.T. #1
water
T.T. #2
water
soap
T.T. #3
water
soap
oil
T.T. #4
water
oil

Chem Talk

ACTION OF SOAP AND WATER

Micelles

In this activity, you modeled the micellular structures that soap molecules take when dissolved in polar and non-polar liquids. You may have also concluded that soap's cleaning action takes place by surrounding non-polar particles with **micelles** of soap dissolved in water. When the soapy water is washed away, the non-polar particles remain encased in the micelles, so they are washed away with the water as well.

When you shake soapy water, bubbles form. Fewer bubbles form when soap molecules are working to dissolve oil in water, so the amount of bubbling can tell you how much soap is being used to dissolve oil in water. Bubbles are a result of the unique polar/non-polar structure of soap molecules interacting with a special property of water called **surface tension**. To understand why bubbles form, you have to know a little about surface tension of water.

Surface Tension of Water

Water is a very unusual and important molecule. It is the basis of life on Earth because it has lots of properties that allow it to do things that other molecules cannot. One of these properties is its strong surface tension. Surface tension of water is the reason small insects can walk on water, you can rest a needle or a paper clip on the surface of water, and you can pile up water on a penny or slightly overfill a cup of water without spilling. Water molecules are very polar, so they form strong bonds between themselves. Up to a certain extent, these strong bonds create a force larger than the gravitational force and prevent light objects from breaking through (as in the case of a sewing needle or lightweight insect).

Soap molecules come between water molecules but don't stick to them as strongly as water molecules stick to each other. Therefore, soap decreases the surface tension of water. If you overfill a cup of water

Chem Words

micelle: an aggregation of molecules that have a polar or ionic end and a non-polar end such that in aqueous solution, the polar ends will be outside the aggregate, attracted to water and the non-polar ends will be inside the aggregate, away from the water.

surface tension: the result of intermolecular attraction force that causes the liquid to minimize its surface area.

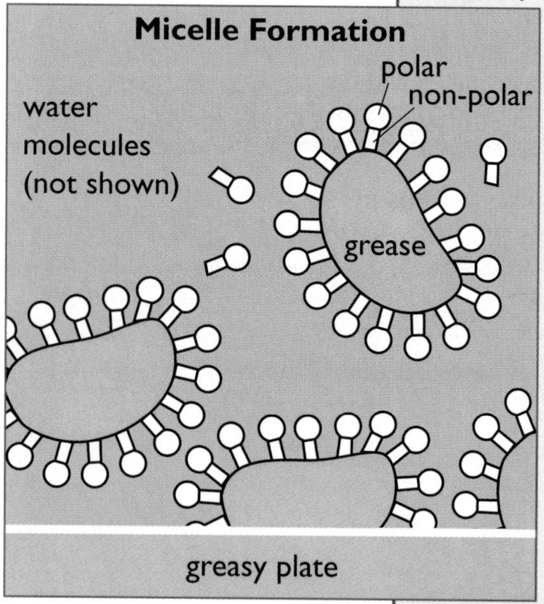
Micelle Formation
polar
non-polar
water molecules (not shown)
grease
greasy plate

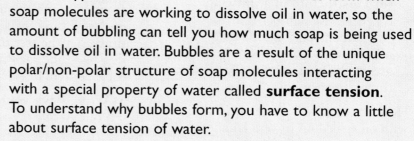

and then touch a soapy finger to the top of the water, the soap molecules come in between the water molecules and break the surface tension. The water flows over the rim of the cup. Likewise, if you have a sewing needle floating on top of some water and you touch a soapy finger to the water, the sewing needle will break through the water.

From your attempts to blow a bubble with plain water, you know that it is difficult to get the bubble to even start to form. There are two reasons for this. One is that the surface tension of water is too high. The water molecules attract each other too strongly. The other reason is that water evaporates too easily. Soapy water can form bubbles for the same reason that micelles form. The hydrophilic part of the soap molecules are attracted strongly toward water molecules and water molecules are strongly attracted to each other, leaving the hydrophilic parts away from the water, pointing toward the outside of the soap bubble. If the soap and water mixture is drawn or splashed into a thin layer, the soap molecules will form a very thin layer (one molecule thick) on either side of that layer, with water molecules trapped in between. That way, the hydrophobic end of each soap molecule can be away from water (on the outside of this thin layer), and the hydrophilic end can be next to the water (on the inside). The water molecules don't pull together into a tight drop as they would without the soap because they are just as stable next to soap molecules as next to water molecules. So, they can be stretched into a thin layer. Also, this thin layer of soap molecules on the outside of the water molecules insulates the water from the air and keeps it from evaporating. This film then forms a bubble.

Formation of a Bubble

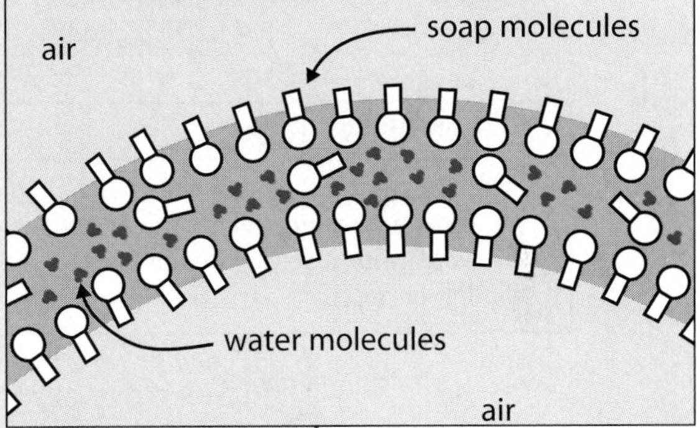
air
soap molecules
water molecules
air

Soap Decreases Surface Tension

Soap decreases the surface tension of water by about one-third, enabling bubbles to form. This property is crucial to the effectiveness of soap. The reduction of the water's surface tension allows soapy water to "wet" a surface that is being washed much more thoroughly and quickly than plain water could. The water molecules have to reach the dirt before there is any possibility of washing it away. Water molecules attract each other strongly, so the water separates itself from hydrophobic dirt. The soap/water mixture is able to get right next to the dirt, allowing the soap to perform its next task. The soap then mixes with the dirt so that small dirt particles surrounded by soap molecules form a micelle that can then be easily washed away.

Checking Up

1. What is a micelle and what role does it play in dissolving soap?
2. What property of water molecules is responsible for its high surface tension?
3. Explain how a bubble is formed.

What Do You Think Now?

At the beginning of this activity you were asked:

- **How can molecules of soap dissolve both hydrophilic and hydrophobic substances?**

Review your answer. How are soap molecules arranged inside a hydrophilic substance, such as water, so that the non-polar parts of the soap molecules don't contact the substance? How are soap molecules arranged inside a hydrophobic substance, such as kerosene, so that the polar parts of the soap molecules don't make contact with the substance?

Chem Essential Questions

What does it mean?

Chemistry explains a macroscopic phenomenon (what you observe) with a description of what happens at the nanoscopic level (atoms and molecules) using symbolic structures as a way to communicate. Complete the chart below in your *Active Chemistry* log.

MACRO	NANO	SYMBOLIC
Describe what happened when you touched a soapy finger to the water with a sewing needle floating on top.	*On a molecular level, describe what happened when the soap was added to the water.*	*Draw a diagram of soap molecules dissolved in water.*

How do you know?

What evidence do you have that a strong attraction exists between water molecules?

Why do you believe?

Cleaning clothes requires the use of soap and water. Why can water alone not do the job of cleaning clothes?

Why should you care?

An understanding of the interactions among water molecules or water molecules and other polar molecules will be required in order to produce a soap that has desirable properties. Creating a soap requires you to be aware of its molecular structure. What molecular structure will you require for your new soap?

Reflecting on the Activity and the Challenge

In this activity you have learned how soap works to clean dirty things. An effective cleaning agent is "at home" in both polar and non-polar materials so that it can clean both. Very big molecules can be polar on one end and non-polar on the other end. You can vary a soap's properties by changing how polar the polar end of the soap molecule is or how non-polar the non-polar end happens to be. You will explore both of these variations in the next few activities. When you design your soap recipe, think about what kinds of things you want to be able to clean with the soap.

Chem to Go

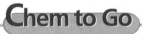

1. Which is easier to clean with room temperature soapy water: a dish with liquid oil on it or a dish with solid butter on it? Why? Describe what happens at the molecular level.
2. How does using hot soapy water improve cleaning dirty dishes? Use the example of oil versus butter of the previous question and explain why hot soapy water cleans both equally easily.
3. Try the overfilled cup of water experiment described in the *Chem Talk* section (you could also try floating a sewing needle or a paper clip). When you touch a soapy finger to the top of the water, does it matter what kind of cleaning agent you have on your finger? Try different cleaning agents you have at home (do not use any cleaning agents that are dangerous to contact with your skin). Report your observations. Based on your observations, what can you conclude about the different cleaning agents you tried?
4. Design an experiment to determine the minimum amount of soap necessary to wash a dirty dish. Clearly describe how you would do this experiment so that another person repeating your experiment somewhere else would arrive at the same result.
5. Is determining the minimum amount of soap necessary to wash a dirty dish a quantitative or qualitative measurement? Why?
6. You are probably aware of a property of matter called density. If two liquids do not mix, the liquid having lower density will float on the top of the liquid with higher density. Based on your data from this activity, which has a higher density—water or oil?
7. Liquid X is polar and liquid Y is non-polar. On the basis of this information, which of the following would you expect to happen?

   a) NaCl would dissolve in both liquids.

   b) Water would be miscible (mix well) with liquid Y.

   c) Water would be miscible with liquid X.

   d) Both liquids would be miscible in another non-polar liquid Z.

8. ***Preparing for the Chapter Challenge***

   Part of the *Chapter Challenge* requires you to present a convincing argument for the marketing department to use with potential investors to explain why your soap will be effective in cleaning the kinds of dirt you designed it to clean. In your *Active Chemistry* log, write a sales pitch for the soap you will design. Make a convincing argument for how your soap will corner a particular market because it will be uniquely effective in cleaning __________ (what you design it to clean).

Chapter mini Challenge

HONK
THE BRIDGE

Your challenge for this chapter is to design a soap using natural products that will be an improvement over a soap that is currently on the market. It can be a bar soap, a liquid soap, or a powdered soap. You will provide enough information that the company that hired you can take to potential investors to raise funding to make the soap you propose. Having completed four activities, this is a good time to share your soap idea for the first time. Your *mini-challenge* is to prepare a one-minute presentation for either the corporate executives or the marketing department. A corporate presentation should include a description of the properties of the soap and the chemistry associated with these properties. A marketing presentation should include what special features your soap will have and the chemistry associated with how the soap is able to clean. The class will then provide feedback. They will comment on your soap design and your description of chemistry principles. You will not be given much preparation time for your *mini-challenge*. It is a way to get a sense of what you will be involved with at the end of the chapter.

Chemistry Content

Your team should first review the chemistry content that may be included in the soap design. Each content area can be creatively placed into your presentation or outline. Following each activity was a section called *Reflecting on the Activity and the Challenge* which can provide hints as to the application of chemistry content to the soap-design challenge. You may decide to review this section.

Activity 1: You investigated the effectiveness of soaps including solubility and properties that may be required for different situations. You also learned about hard versus soft water, the problems associated with soap scum, and the difference between soap and detergent.

Activity 2: You learned about molecular structure, and Lewis dot diagrams. Understanding the shapes of molecules is crucial to understanding how the molecules interact with each other and how the interactions create the behavior of substances like soap.

Activity 3: You observed the difference between polar and non-polar substances and found which could be removed by water (a polar molecule) and which could be removed by kerosene (a non-polar molecule). You also learned that soap is a chemical that has one part that is polar and one part that is non-polar.

Activity 4: You modeled the micellular structures that soap molecules take when dissolved in polar and non-polar liquids. You also learned that soap's cleaning action is to surround non-polar particles with micelles of soap dissolved in water. When the soapy water is washed away, the non-polar particles that remain encased in the micelles are washed away with the water.

Criteria

Your team should also review the criteria that you discussed on the first day of this chapter. Your soap design should demonstrate an understanding of chemistry concepts and help both the corporate executives and the marketing department understand the product.

Preparing for Your mini Challenge

Your team should begin the process of designing a soap by brainstorming ideas about soaps that you prefer and soaps that your target consumer would find appealing. Will your new soap be for teenagers or for young children? You should then discuss how you can include chemistry concepts from at least two of the activities. You will have one minute for the presentation. You will also have to prepare an outline for the report that will accompany your final work. At the end of the chapter, you will know much more chemistry and much more about soap. At that time, your presentation and report will be more comprehensive.

Engineering/Technology Design

The engineering-design process involves a number of distinct steps. In designing and manufacturing a soap, you are involved in a design process. Note how your efforts follow the design model described.

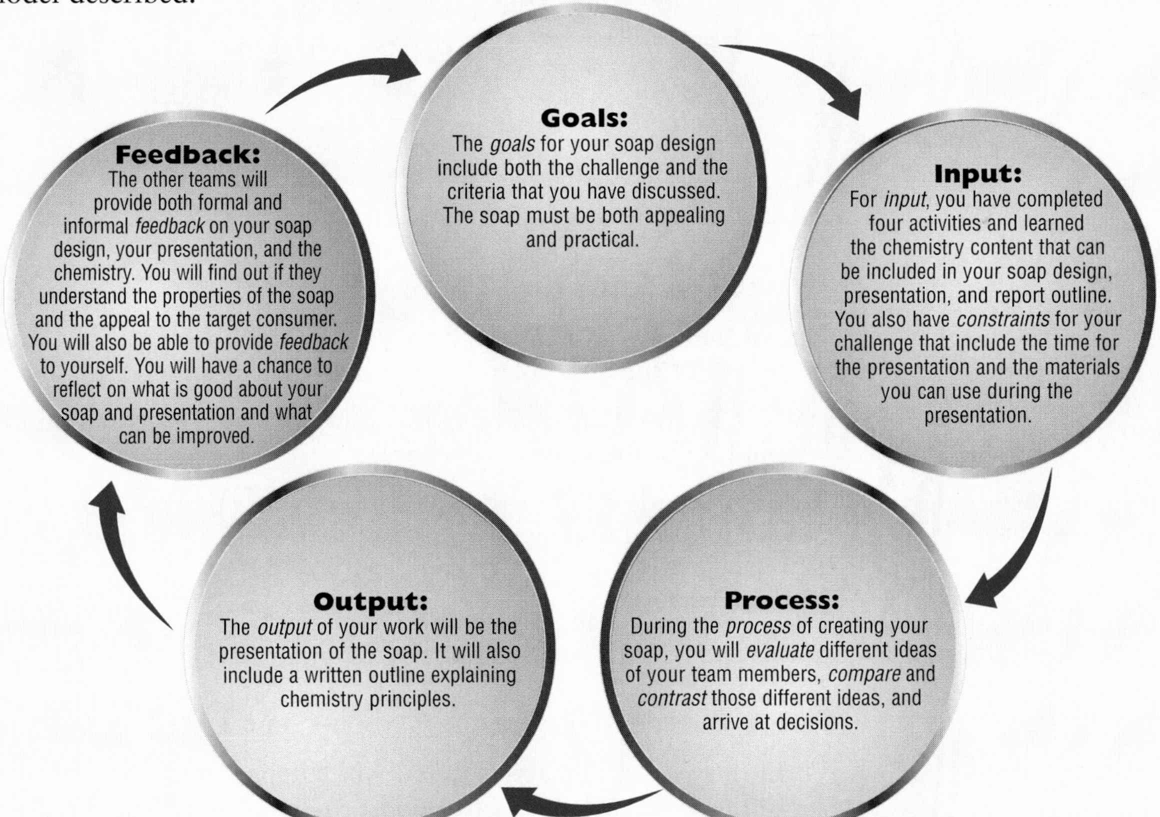
Goals:
The *goals* for your soap design include both the challenge and the criteria that you have discussed. The soap must be both appealing and practical.
Input:
For *input*, you have completed four activities and learned the chemistry content that can be included in your soap design, presentation, and report outline. You also have *constraints* for your challenge that include the time for the presentation and the materials you can use during the presentation.
Process:
During the *process* of creating your soap, you will *evaluate* different ideas of your team members, *compare* and *contrast* those different ideas, and arrive at decisions.
Output:
The *output* of your work will be the presentation of the soap. It will also include a written outline explaining chemistry principles.
Feedback:
The other teams will provide both formal and informal *feedback* on your soap design, your presentation, and the chemistry. You will find out if they understand the properties of the soap and the appeal to the target consumer. You will also be able to provide *feedback* to yourself. You will have a chance to reflect on what is good about your soap and presentation and what can be improved.

Remember: This is a *first try*. The feedback that you get from this brief presentation of your soap will be extremely valuable when you prepare for the full soap manufacturing design and presentation that you will develop at the end of the chapter. At that point, you will begin the entire design cycle again. That's why it is called a cycle. You keep going through it over and over to improve your design or, in this case, the design of a new soap.

Activity 5

Changing the Fat: How Does Chain Length Affect Properties?

What Do You See?

FATTY ACID 2
ICE CUBES
FATTY ACID 2

GOALS

In this activity you will:

- Measure the melting and freezing points of three different fatty acids.
- Relate differences in freezing points of these acids to differences in their molecular structures.
- Evaluate properties (including cleaning effectiveness) of three soaps made from these fatty acids and look for correlations with increasing chain length.

What Do You Think?

One of the ways you can vary the properties of a soap is to change the length of the non-polar part of the soap molecule.

- **What do you think changing the non-polar part of a soap molecule would do to the soap's properties?**

Record your ideas about this question in your *Active Chemistry* log. Be prepared to discuss your responses with your small group and the class.

Investigate

In this activity, the focus is on the non-polar part of the soap molecule.

Part A: Effects of Varying the Carbon-Chain Length of a Molecule

1. In this part of the activity, you will compare a measurable property of the following three fatty acids:

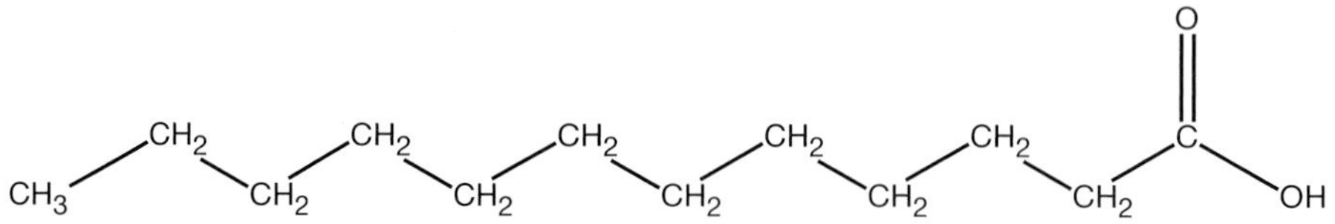
CH3
CH2
CH2
CH2
CH2
CH2
CH2
CH2
CH2
CH2
CH2
C
O
OH

lauric acid

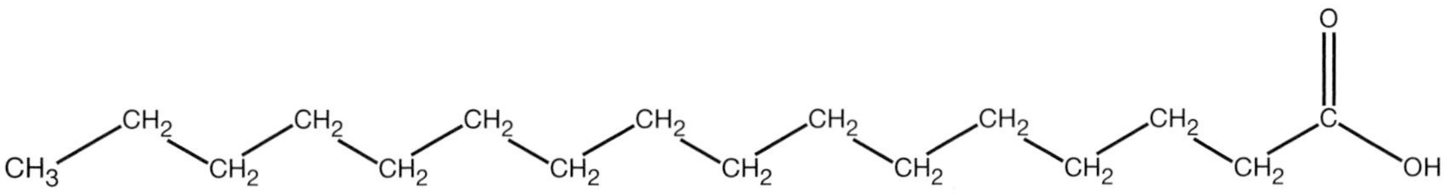

palmitic acid

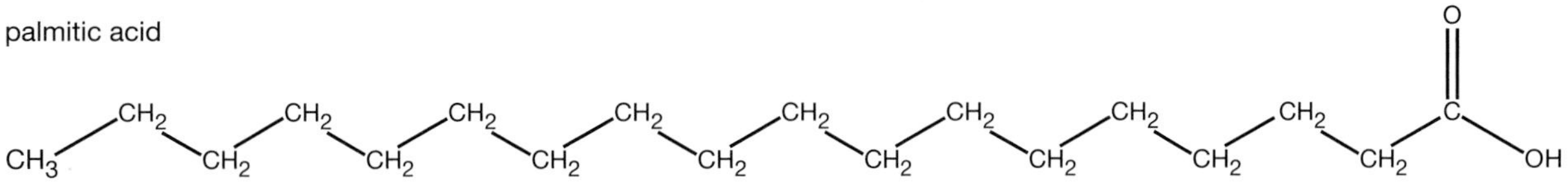

stearic acid

Fatty acid	Number of carbons in chain	Molecular formula	Melting point	Other properties
lauric acid				
palmitic acid				
stearic acid				

How are these molecules similar? How are they different? How many carbons are in each molecule's chain?

a) In your *Active Chemistry* log, make a table like the one shown.

b) Write down the number of carbons in each chain and the molecular formula of each acid.

c) Record any other physical properties that you observe.

2. All of these fatty acids are solids at room temperature (about 22°C). You are going to compare the melting temperatures of the three fatty acids. You will heat all of these solids until they become liquids. As each cools down, you will be able to record the temperature at which it becomes a solid. Note that the melting point is identical to the freezing point. Water freezes at 0°C and ice melts at 0°C.

There will be a number of steps going on at the same time. Read through the entire set of directions carefully so that you can organize a working plan.

3. Set up a beaker with water on top of a hot plate and bring the water to near boiling. Use heatproof gloves. Carefully take the beaker off the hot plate. Place it on a heatproof surface on your table. Secure a thermometer in the beaker.

Safety goggles and a lab apron must be worn *at all times* in a chemistry lab.

Assign a monitor to stay with the beaker of hot water so others do not touch it and get burned.

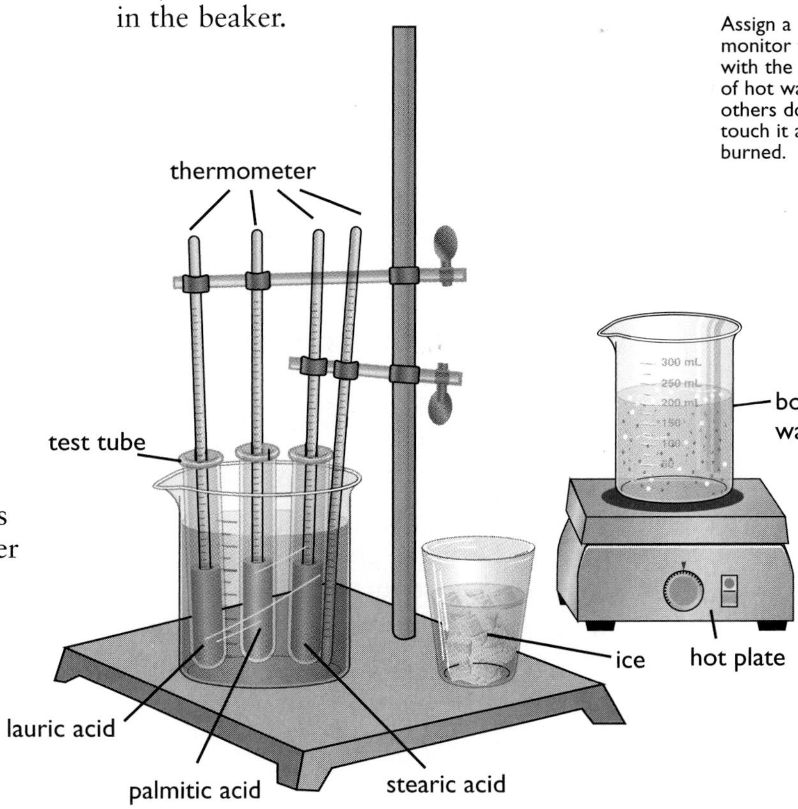
thermometer
test tube
boiling water
ice
hot plate
lauric acid
palmitic acid
stearic acid

The soaps you made are probably still somewhat dangerous to your skin because they have not continued to react for long enough (soap makers usually let soaps sit for several months). Do not let the soaps contact any bare skin.

Wash your hands and arms thoroughly after the activity.

4. Obtain some crushed ice. (Another person in the group can do this.)
5. Obtain three test tubes and label them with the names of the three fatty acids. (A third person in the group can do this.) Place a small amount of each fatty acid in its labeled test tube. Put a thermometer in each test tube.
6. Set all three test tubes in the beaker of hot water. You may have to hold them with test-tube holders.
7. Wait until all three fatty acids have melted in their test tubes. Then, begin adding tiny amounts of ice to the hot water in the beaker.
   a) Record the temperatures of each fatty acid every 30 s and watch the contents of the test tubes as the temperature decreases.
   b) When the first fatty acid begins to solidify or crystallize, note the temperature on the table in your *Active Chemistry* log.
8. Continue adding ice slowly to the hot water to cool it.
   a) What happens to the temperature of the fatty acid while it is freezing, compared to the temperature of the water around it that's getting colder?
   b) When the second fatty acid begins to crystallize, record its temperature in your *Active Chemistry* log. Continue adding ice slowly to the water to cool it.
   c) When the third fatty acid begins to crystallize, record its temperature.
9. Clean up your workstation following your teacher's directions.
10. You have now measured the melting points of the three fatty acids.
    a) What conclusion can you draw about the relationship between chain length and melting temperature?

Part B: Comparing Soaps Made with the Three Fatty Acids

You can now compare the properties of the three soaps you made a month ago from coconut oil, palm oil, and beef tallow. Relate the properties of the three soaps to the chain lengths of the non-polar parts of the soap molecules.

1. Make a data table in your *Active Chemistry* log with three columns, labeled:
   - coconut oil soap (lauric acid soap, 12 carbons)
   - palm oil soap (palmitic acid soap, 16 carbons)
   - beef tallow soap (stearic acid soap, 18 carbons)

   Obtain small amounts of each of these three soaps, made a month or so ago by your class. Observe the properties of the three soaps.
   a) Write down your observations in your data table.
2. Return to your *Active Chemistry* log notes from *Activity 1*. Use the procedure you developed in that activity to compare quantitatively the effectiveness of the three soaps.
   a) Record your results in your data table.
   b) What relationships exist between trends in the properties of the three soaps and the three different chain lengths (C12, C16, C18)? Record your conclusions in your *Active Chemistry* log.

Chem Talk

CARBON-CHAIN LENGTHS AND PROPERTIES OF FAT

The Saponification Reaction

Fats differ in the hydrocarbon chains from which they are made. The chemical structure of a typical fat is shown in the top diagram.

Chemical Structure of a Typical Fat Molecule

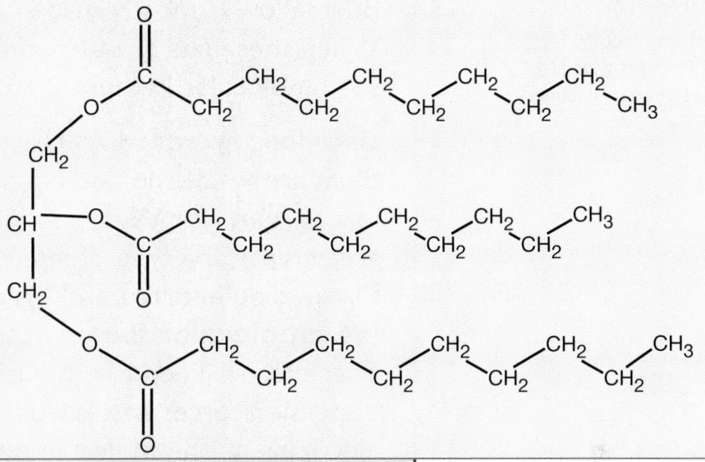

When fats react in a saponification reaction, the bonds between the three-carbon glycerol backbone and the long chains break, and three soap molecules (plus a glycerol molecule) result from each fat molecule. For example, the three soap molecules shown in the diagram below would result from the fat molecule shown above.

Three Soap Molecules Resulting from Saponification

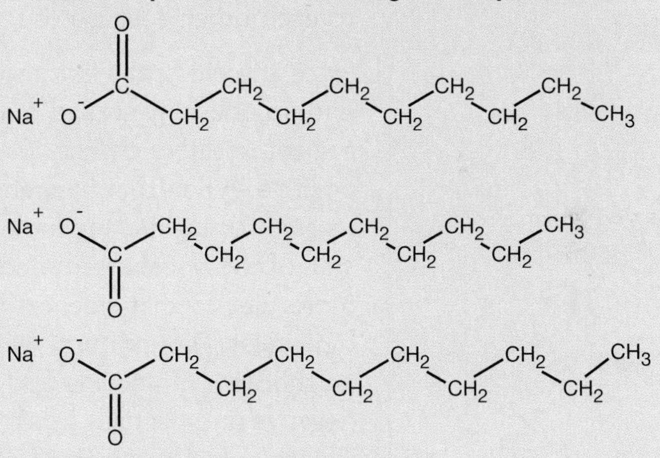

Pure 18-carbon soap (made from pure stearic acid) is white in color, as are all pure soaps. Naturally occurring fats are all mixtures of several different fat molecules, each with different lengths of carbon chains. Most fat molecules contain more than one type of fatty acid residue. For example, coconut oil contains about 50 % lauric acid fat (12-carbon chains). But coconut oil also contains smaller amounts of other fats: 17 % myristic acid fat (14-carbon chains) and 9 % palmitic acid fat (16-carbon chains). The soaps resulting from stearic acid (18-carbon), palmitic acid (16-carbon), and oleic acid (also 18 carbons, but with a different structure than stearic acid) are the most common ingredients in bar soaps that are commercially sold. Due to impurities, the soap resulting from palmitic acid can be reddish-brown in color. Similarly, impurities in the soap resulting from oleic acid often make it look yellow. The colors of many natural soaps (without additives to change the color) vary from yellowish-brown to reddish-brown, and many of them are off-white.

Chem Words

van der Waals forces: weak intermolecular attraction forces between molecules.

intermolecular forces: the forces that are between molecules.

How Chain Length Affects the Properties of a Substance

Coconut oil is mostly made of fats with chains the length of lauric acid. Palm oil is mostly made of fats with chains the length of palmitic acid. Beef tallow is mostly made of fats with chains the length of stearic acid. When these fats are turned into soaps, each fat molecule makes three soap molecules because it has three carbon chains on it.

Since long hydrocarbon chains are non-polar, the interactions between them are weak and fleeting, and depend on attractions called dispersion forces (**van der Waals forces**). (Forces called van der Waals forces are actually any type of intermolecular forces including dispersion forces, dipole forces, and hydrogen-bonding forces.) These are called **intermolecular forces** because they occur between molecules. These forces keep the molecules bound together in the solid state. The dispersion forces result from momentary shifts in the negatively charged electrons of one molecule due to attraction to the positively charged nuclei of neighboring molecules. The two molecules are attracted to each other much as two objects that have been rubbed together adhere to each other because of static electricity.

Since the electrons in a molecule are always in motion, they sometimes end up unevenly spread out. The side with more electrons will have a slight negative charge. The side with fewer electrons will be slightly positive. When that happens, a similar imbalance will be *induced* or *created* in neighboring molecules. This happens because the positive side of the unbalanced molecule will attract electrons of neighboring molecules to that side, creating an unbalanced situation in those molecules. They, in turn, will induce an unbalanced situation in other neighboring molecules, and so on. This unbalanced state of partially negative and partially positive charges gives rise to a polarized molecule. This is only fleeting and temporary, however.

The result is that the initial unbalanced molecule will end up surrounded by other molecules and the initial molecule will attract *all of them*. These imbalances can cause large numbers of molecules to be attracted to each other.

When taken one at a time, these forces are too small to make any difference. However, since there are many molecules, the forces add up. Most importantly, the forces become stronger when the molecules are bigger, because more electrons are involved. Also, the momentary polarity is spread out over a larger area. Therefore, materials made of larger molecules have stronger dispersion (van der Waals) forces. It takes a higher temperature to break the forces and melt these materials.

Looking back at your data from *Part A* of the activity, you found that the longer the carbon chain, the higher the melting point was. There are stronger attractions in the longer molecules, so more energy is required to break the attractions and send the molecules into the liquid state.

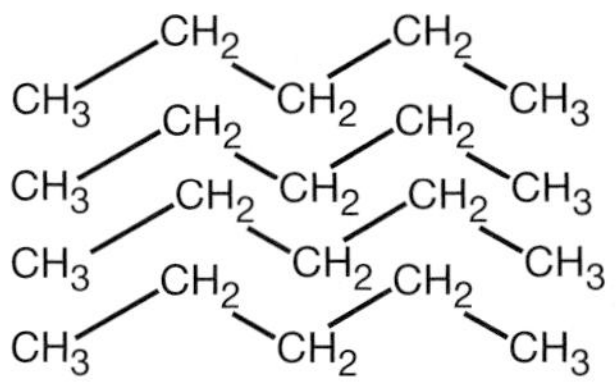

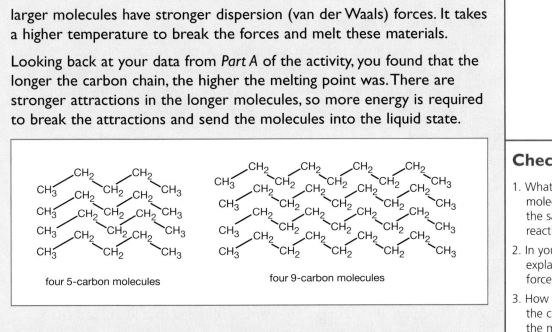

four 5-carbon molecules

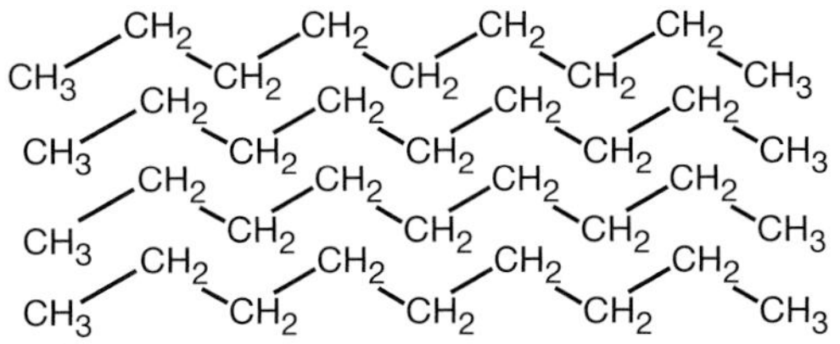

four 9-carbon molecules

The 9-carbon molecules will melt at a higher temperature than the 5-carbon molecules, because there are stronger dispersion (van der Waals) forces holding them in the solid state.

Checking Up

1. What occurs to fat molecules during the saponification reaction?
2. In your own words, explain dispersion forces.
3. How does the length of the carbon chain affect the melting point?
4. Explain why the length of the carbon chain affects the melting point.

What Do You Think Now?

At the beginning of this activity you were asked:

- **What do you think changing the non-polar part of a soap molecule would do to the soap's properties?**

Look at your answer to this question. How would you answer the question now?

Chem Essential Questions

What does it mean?

Chemistry explains a macroscopic phenomenon (what you observe) with a description of what happens at the nanoscopic level (atoms and molecules) using symbolic structures as a way to communicate. Complete the chart below in your *Active Chemistry* log.

MACRO	NANO	SYMBOLIC
Describe how you can measure the melting point of a fatty acid.	*Describe the origin of the attractive forces among non-polar molecules.*	*What type of symbolic representation would best describe the forces of attraction between molecules? Use such a model to show the intermolecular attractions between palmitic acid molecules.*

How do you know?

What evidence do you have to support the idea that increased chain length (or larger molecules in general) increases melting points?

Why do you believe?

Hair shampoos are products that have been extensively studied. The ingredients in successful commercial shampoos have been studied under many different conditions. People want to have a shampoo that rinses out completely, leaving hair clean and fresh. Would a study such as the one in this activity be helpful in developing a shampoo? Explain.

Why should you care?

Making changes one at a time and keeping other factors constant allows you to draw conclusions about the relationship of the structure of a molecule and its properties. Write a paragraph to explain the forces that hold molecules together and how they affect the action of soap. You can use this to enhance your sales pitch to the company.

Reflecting on the Activity and the Challenge

There are an essentially unlimited number of different compounds that you could try using as soaps. Few of them would work well. Fortunately, chemistry allows you to not only uncover the properties that allow a compound to work as a soap, but also to discover principles that govern the ways that properties vary as the structure of the molecules vary. As the chain length of a fatty acid increases, the attraction between its molecules increases, and so its melting and boiling points increase. For similar reasons, soaps made from these fatty acids become harder as chain length increases, and they produce less lather or suds. Consider how you will incorporate structure/activity relationship studies in your presentation for the corporate executives.

Chem to Go

1. In *Part A*, you compared the melting points of three different fatty acids that differed in their chain lengths. What kind of test was the melting point measurement: quantitative or qualitative? Explain.
2. Draw one of the soap molecules that would result from using the following fat molecule to make soap.

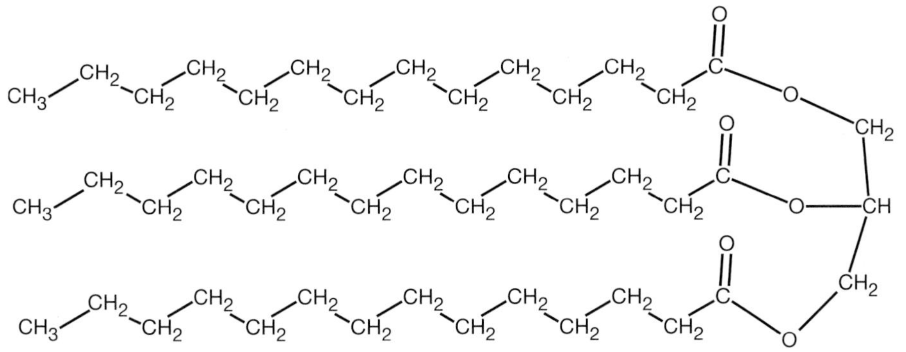

3. At approximately what temperature would you expect myristic acid, a 14-carbon chain fatty acid, to melt?
4. Answer the following questions based on the four molecular structures shown below.

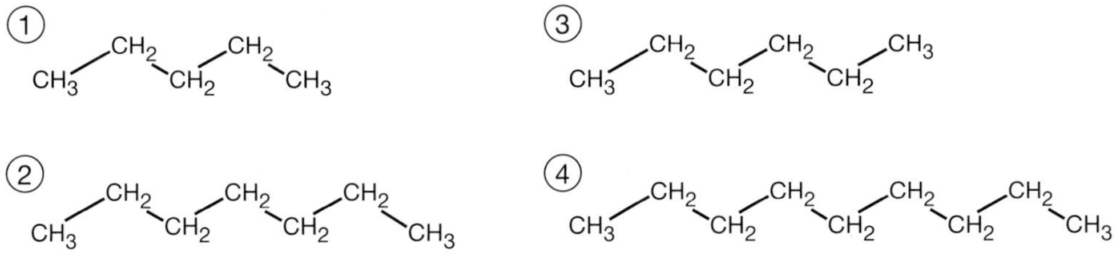

   a) Arrange the molecules (1-4 above) in order from lowest melting temperature to highest melting temperature.

   b) Which of these hydrocarbons would melt first if you placed a little of each one in its own test tube and placed all the test tubes in a hot-water bath? Explain.
5. If there was a naturally occurring fat that had mostly 14-carbon chains in it, how would you expect the properties of a soap made from it to compare to the three soaps you tested in *Part B*?
6. One of the properties you observed when testing the three soaps was how much the soaps lathered. Given what you learned in a previous activity about how soap molecules form lather, propose an explanation for why the lathering ability of the soaps depends on the carbon-chain length of the soap molecules.

7. It is possible to make soaps from fatty acids instead of from naturally occurring fats. The reaction that occurs is simpler and does not produce glycerol because there is no three-carbon backbone that the carbon chains are attached to. Assume you have access to the following fatty acids:

Fatty acid	Chemical formula	Carbon-chain length
butyric acid	$C_4H_8O_2$	four carbons
caproic acid	$C_6H_{12}O_2$	six carbons
capric acid	$C_{10}H_{20}O_2$	ten carbons
lauric acid	$C_{12}H_{24}O_2$	twelve carbons
myristic acid	$C_{14}H_{28}O_2$	fourteen carbons

a) Draw the chemical structures of any three of the fatty acids in the table.

b) If you make soaps from pure fatty acids, then the soap molecules produced are all the same (as opposed to making soaps from naturally occurring fats, which are all mixtures of different fats). Design an experiment to investigate the lathering ability of pure soaps made from carbon chains of varying length.

c) Besides lathering ability, in what other properties might you expect to see differences between the five pure soaps made from these five fatty acids?

8. What would be the formula of a fatty acid with eight carbons?

a) $C_8H_{10}O_2$ b) $C_8H_{16}O$ c) $C_8H_{16}O_2$ d) $C_8H_{18}O_2$

9. ***Preparing for the Chapter Challenge***

How does chain length relate to melting point for the soaps prepared? What is the right chain length to use in the soap that you are designing for your *Chapter Challenge*? You might try a combination of different fats to take advantage of the properties of both short and long chain length soaps. Write down some notes on these ideas in your *Active Chemistry* log.

Inquiring Further

1. Investigating the chain lengths of other molecules

Choose another molecule series (alkanes, alkenes, alcohols, aldehydes, amides, etc.) and research the effect of increasing the chain length by linking up several of these molecules in a series.

2. Water temperature and clean laundry

Research the effect of temperature on the cleaning effectiveness of soaps and detergents. Does it matter whether you do your laundry in hot water, warm water, or cold water?

Activity 6

Changing the Fat: Does Unsaturation Make a Difference?

What Do You See?
SATURATED FATTY ACID
UNSATURATED FATTY ACID
PAPER CLIPS

GOALS

In this activity you will:

- Make useful models of the shapes of 18-carbon fatty acids with increasing numbers of double bonds.
- Predict and then measure the melting points of these fatty acids.
- Evaluate soaps made with these fatty acids as before and look for trends related to the number of double bonds.
- Extrapolate these results to untested fatty acids and oils.

What Do You Think?

Health and nutrition reports often talk about eating "good" fats and avoiding "bad" fats.

- **What is a "good" fat and what is a "bad" fat?**

Record your ideas about this question in your *Active Chemistry* log. Be prepared to discuss your responses with your small group and the class.

Investigate

There is another feature of carbon chains that can be varied: degree or amount of *unsaturation*. Unsaturation is a measure of the number of multiple (double or triple) bonds in a molecule. In *Part A* of this activity, you will use a model to predict the melting point of three fatty acids with the same number of carbons but with different degrees of unsaturation. Then you'll determine the melting temperatures of the three fatty acids and see how well your predictions worked. In *Part B*, you will examine the behaviors of four soaps made from fats with four different degrees of unsaturation.You can combine what you conclude in this activity with what you learned from the previous one to design a soap that has a variety of properties.

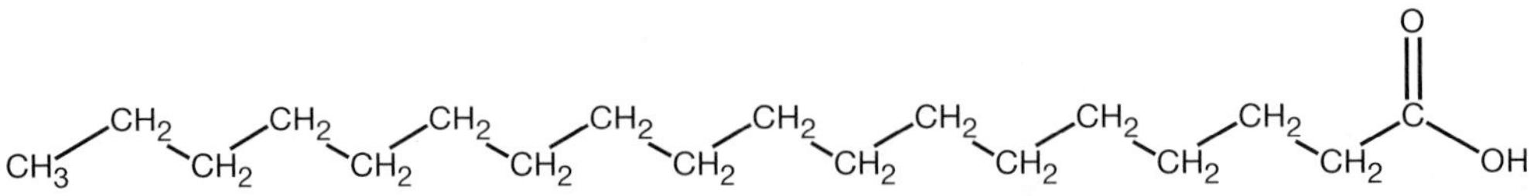

stearic acid

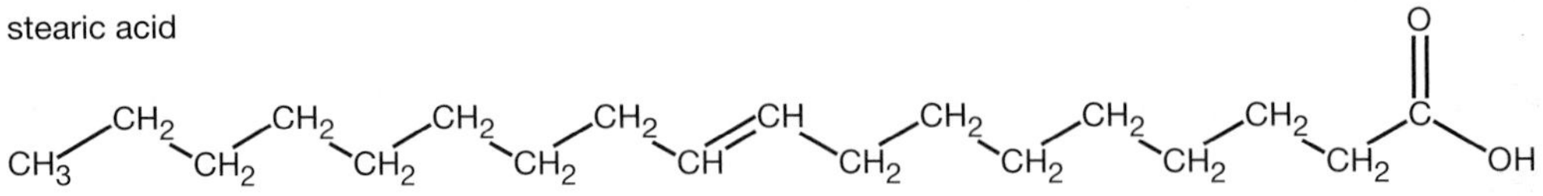

oleic acid

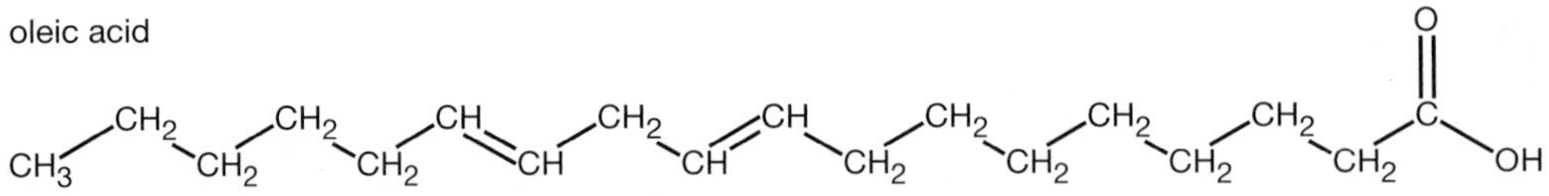

linoleic acid

Part A: Effects of Varying the Degree of Unsaturation in a Hydrocarbon

1. You will compare the melting points of three fatty acids shown above. These fatty acids are the primary carbon-chain components of the major ingredients in the three soaps you already made. Once you know more about how these three fatty acids differ, you can explain why the properties of the three soaps differ.

   Look at the structural formulas of each molecule. How are these molecules similar? How are they different?

   a) Make a three-column table in your *Active Chemistry* log, similar to the one in the previous activity. Label each row with the name of one fatty acid. Write down the information about each of the fatty acids that is revealed from the molecular structures shown above.

2. Atoms can twist around single bonds. However, when there is a double bond in a molecule, atoms that are around it are locked in place because they can't twist or rotate around a double bond. Double bonds also give rise to specific atom-to-atom bond angles. In a carbon chain with a double bond between two carbons in the middle of the chain (as in oleic acid), there are two ways the double bond can be arranged as shown below.

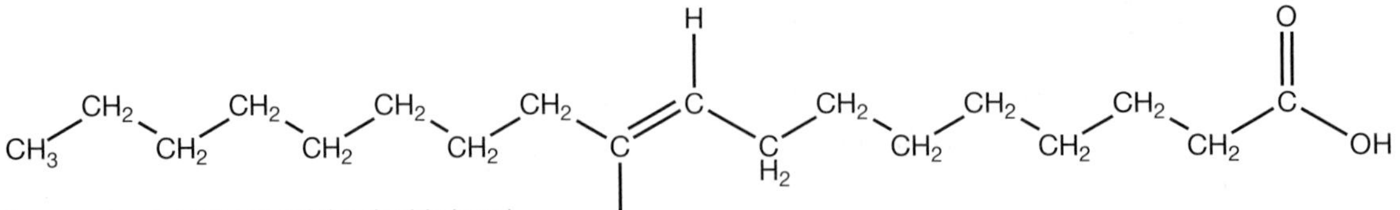

trans arrangement around the double bond

and

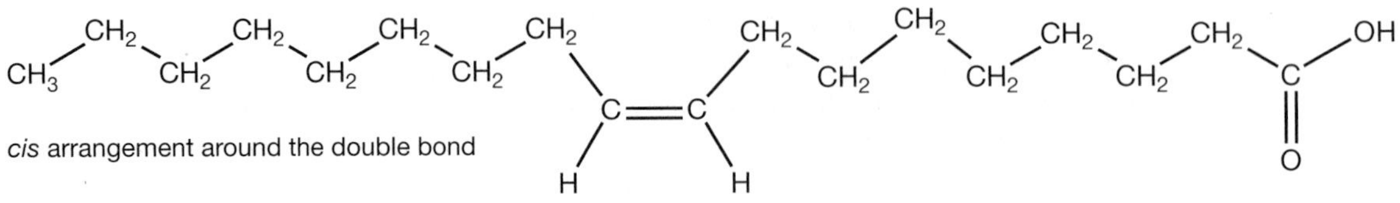

cis arrangement around the double bond

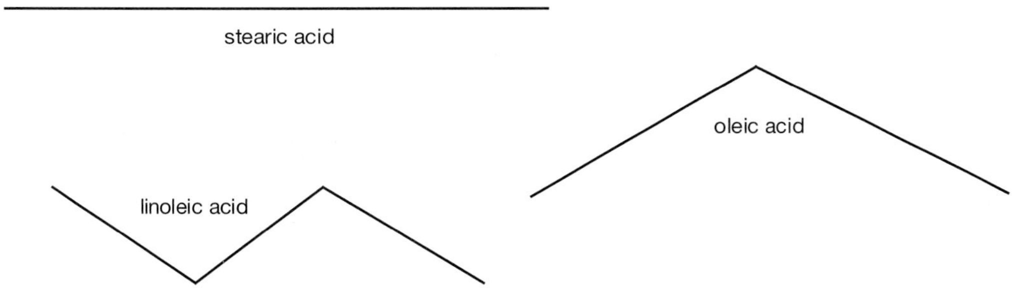
stearic acid
oleic acid
linoleic acid

The *trans* double bond arrangement allows for the zig-zag shape shown. A *cis* double bond has a different three-dimensional arrangement of atoms, also shown. The double bonds in naturally occurring fatty acids are *nearly always* in *cis* arrangements.

When molecules are in the solid state, even though they can twist a bit around their C—C single bonds, they mostly stretch out into long straight zig-zag shapes wherever possible. This means that for solid stearic acid, the molecules can be modeled as long sticks. For oleic acid (with one double bond), the molecules can be modeled as bent sticks, like the shape of a boomerang. And for linoleic acid (with two double bonds), the molecules can be modeled as zig-zag shapes with two bends, like a picture of a lightning bolt.

3. To model how molecules are arranged in the solid state in these three fatty acids, you will create models out of paper clips. Take about 60 paper clips in total. Stretch each paper clip by unfolding it and making it as straight as possible. Set aside 20 of the straight paper clips to serve as stearic acid molecule models. Take another 20 and make a single bend in the middle of each one, at about a 120° angle, to represent oleic acid molecules. With the remaining 20, make two bends, at about 120° angles, to represent linoleic acid molecules.

   a) Draw the shapes of the three molecules in the table you created in *Step 1*.

4. To get a picture of the arrangement of molecules when stearic acid molecules are in the solid state, take the stearic acid paper clip molecules and set them all in a paper clip box. Close the cover of the box, and then shake the box gently a few times. Open the box. How are the molecules arranged?

   a) Make a drawing of the arrangement of the molecules in your *Active Chemistry* log, and label the drawing "stearic acid (solid)."

   b) Repeat the procedure for oleic-acid paper clip molecules. Label the drawing in your *Active Chemistry* log, "oleic acid (solid)."

   c) Do the same for the linoleic acid model. How is this arrangement different than the other two? Label this drawing, "linoleic acid (solid)" in your *Active Chemistry* log.

5. All three of these fatty acids have the same numbers of carbons. They do differ in their melting points (which you will measure shortly), but it is not due to having different chain lengths, as in the previous activity. Use what you learned about dispersion forces (van der Waals attractions) in the previous activity, and the drawings you just made, to make a prediction about which fatty acid will have the lowest melting point and which will have the highest.

   a) Write down your prediction in your *Active Chemistry* log, and explain how you arrived at it.

6. In the previous activity, you already measured the melting temperature of stearic acid. Now you will repeat that measurement technique and measure the melting points of oleic acid and linoleic acid.

   a) Record that melting temperature of stearic acid in a table.

   b) Both oleic acid and linoleic acid exist as liquids at room temperature. What does this already tell you about their melting points?

Safety goggles and a lab apron must be worn *at all times* in a chemistry lab.

Wash your hands and arms thoroughly after the activity.

7. In preparation for measuring the melting points, you will need to have temperatures that go below 0°C. In a large plastic cup, make an ice-saltwater slurry. First, place crushed ice in the cup. Then, add salt to the crushed ice. Add a tiny amount of water, only enough to make it possible to stir the slurry. Use a spoon to stir the slurry until the salt is well mixed in. Place a thermometer in the slurry. What is the temperature? If the temperature is not below –10°C, add more salt and stir, until the temperature reaches –10°C.

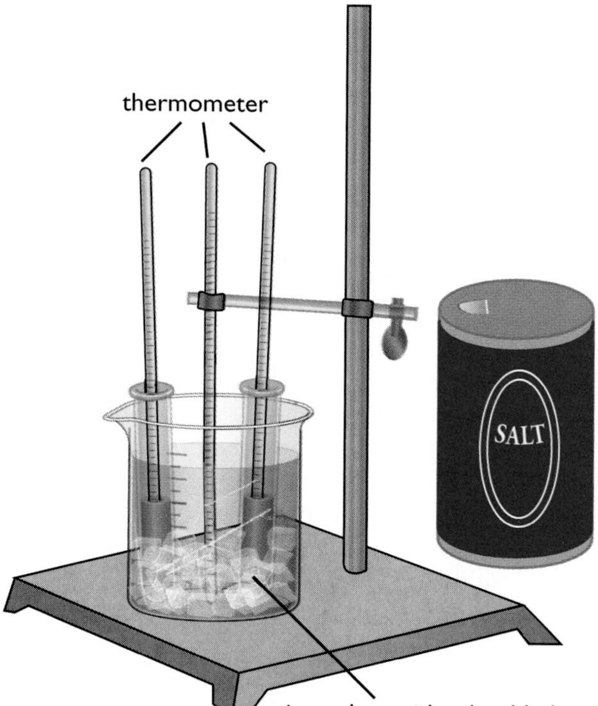
thermometer
SALT
ice cubes with salt added

8. Take the thermometer out of the slurry and gently wash it. Label the two test tubes: "oleic acid" and "linoleic acid." Add some oleic acid to the oleic acid test tube, and add some linoleic acid to its test tube. Do not fill the test tubes more than a quarter of the way. Carefully place a thermometer in each test tube, *making sure not to puncture the bottoms of the test tubes*. Set the test tubes in the cold slurry. Observe the test tubes for the first crystals.

   a) Record the freezing/melting points for the two acids.

   b) Compare your data with the rest of the class. Compare your data with your predictions. Did you predict the order of the melting points correctly? Write down some conclusions in your *Active Chemistry* log.

9. Dispose of the materials as directed by your teacher. Clean up your workstation.

Part B: Comparing Soaps Made with Four Fatty Acids of Differing Numbers of Double Bonds

You will now compare the properties of the four soaps made from four naturally occurring fats. You will try to relate trends in the properties of the four soaps to the number of double bonds in their soap-molecule carbon chains.

1. Obtain small amounts of the four soaps you made a month or so ago. Observe the physical properties of the four soaps.

   a) Make a data table in your *Active Chemistry* log with four columns:

   - Beef tallow soap (stearic acid soap, no double bonds)
   - Olive oil soap (oleic acid soap, one double bond)
   - Safflower/sunflower oil soap (linoleic acid soap, two double bonds)
   - Linseed oil soap (linolenic acid soap, three double bonds)

   b) Record your observations.

2. Return to your *Active Chemistry* log notes from *Activity 1*. Use the procedure you developed in that activity to compare quantitatively the effectiveness of the four soaps.

   a) Record your results.

   b) What relation or relations exist between the properties of the four soaps and the number of double bonds (zero, one, two, or three)? Write down your conclusions.

Safety goggles and a lab apron must be worn *at all times* in a chemistry lab.

Wash your hands and arms thoroughly after the activity.

Part C: Putting Together Chain-Length and Double-Bonding Data

You have now investigated two different ways of modifying the non-polar part of a soap molecule. Since there are two different modifications you can do, you can also work with combinations of these differences.

1. Copy the following table into your *Active Chemistry* log. Organize your observations of the behaviors of soaps made of different chain lengths and numbers of double bonds into the table.

Length of carbon chain	Number of double bonds				Increased lathering	Property 2	Property 3	Property 4
	Zero	One	Two	Three				
18	beef tallow	olive oil	safflower oil sunflower oil	linseed oil				
16	palm oil							
14								
12	coconut oil							
Increased soap hardness								
Property 5								
Property 6								

For example, you investigated the effect of soaps with different chain lengths (C12, C16, and C18) on how much the soaps lathered. Indicate in the table the direction that the lathering increased. Draw an arrow pointing up if the longest carbon chain produced the most lathering. Draw an arrow pointing down if the longest carbon chain produced the least lathering.

An opportunity is also provided to investigate the effect of the number of double bonds on the soap's hardness. Use an arrow pointing left or right to show the results of your investigation. Organize all your other observations from the previous activity and from this one in the same table.

Chem Talk

SATURATED AND UNSATURATED FATS

Animal and Vegetable Fats and What They Contain

All fats have sizable numbers of carbon chains that often contain double bonds (unsaturated fats). These fats vary a great deal. Beef tallow and lard have many more fats with chains that look like stearic acid (all C–C single bonds). A month or so ago, you also used three other fats to make soaps. Olive oil is made mostly of fats with chains that look like oleic acid (one C=C double bond). Safflower and sunflower oils are made mostly of fats with chains that look like linoleic acid (two C=C double bonds). And linseed oil is made mostly of fats with chains that look like linolenic acid (three C=C double bonds.) You probably have an idea now of where some of the fatty acids get their names. No animal or vegetable fat is purely one kind of fat. And no soap made from animal or vegetable fats can be purely one kind of soap molecule. While the fats used to make

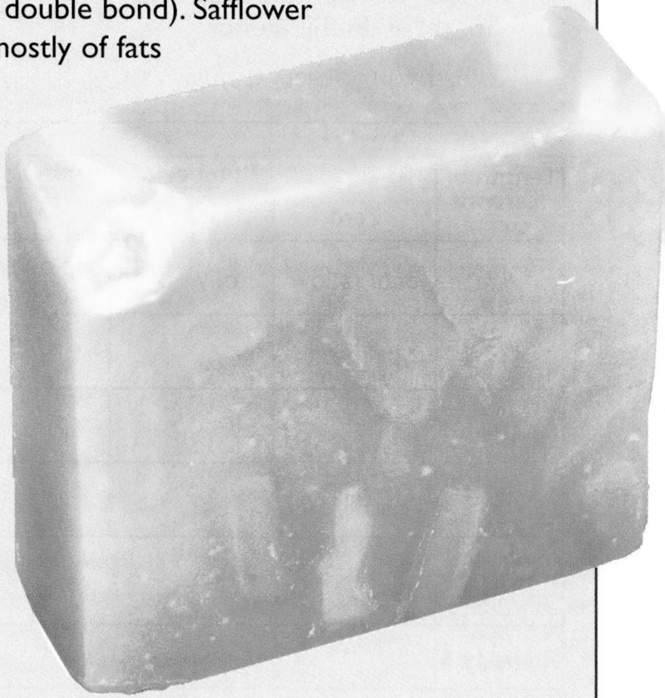

the soaps you experimented with were mostly made of one kind of fatty acid each, there were other fatty acids present in them as well. Since it is not possible to obtain a naturally occurring fat that is made entirely of one kind of fatty acid, you experimented with pure fatty acids first, in order to understand the effects on the properties of soaps due to the features of the different fatty acids.

Two Classes of Fatty Acids

Fatty acids are grouped into two classes, **saturated** and **unsaturated**. Saturated means that none of the carbon atoms form double or triple bonds with other carbon atoms. Unsaturated molecules contain carbon-carbon double bonds and/or triple bonds. Hydrogen atoms can be added to the carbon-carbon double bonds and triple bonds of unsaturated molecules to make less unsaturated or fully saturated molecules. Here are examples of saturated and unsaturated versions of a five-carbon molecule.

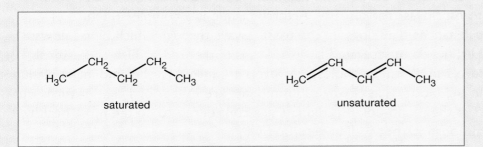

H_3C CH_2 CH_2 CH_2 CH_3
saturated
H_2C CH CH CH CH_3
unsaturated

Saturated fatty acids come primarily from animal products like meat and dairy products. Unsaturated fatty acids come primarily from plants and are usually vegetable oils: peanut oil, safflower oil, corn oil, soybean oil, sesame oil, and sunflower oil.

Hydrogen atoms can be easily added to a double bond to change an unsaturated compound into a saturated compound. This process is called **hydrogenation** and requires a platinum catalyst. At any double bond, the weaker of the two bonds can be broken, allowing a hydrogen atom to be attached to each of the two carbons.

$$CH_3CH{=}CHCH_2CH_3 + H_{2(g)} \xrightarrow{Pt} CH_3CH_2CH_2CH_2CH_3$$

Hydrogenation is used commercially to manufacture saturated fats for cooking that are more stable to heat and oxidation. However, they are more difficult to digest. The reverse process of making an unsaturated compound from a saturated one is far more difficult.

Chem Words

saturated: a class of fatty acids in which the molecules contain no carbon-carbon double or triple bonds.

unsaturated: a class of fatty acids in which the molecules contain at least one carbon-carbon double bond or triple bond.

hydrogenation: a chemical reaction in which hydrogen is added to a compound. In this case, the addition of hydrogen to unsaturated bonds between carbon atoms.

Chem Words

mono-unsaturated: molecules with carbon chains that have only one double bond (like olive and canola oils, as well as some fish oils).

poly-unsaturated: molecules with carbon chains that have more than one double bond (like corn or soybean oils).

Some fats are **mono-unsaturated**, meaning that carbon chains have only one double bond (like olive and canola oils, as well as some fish oils), and others are **poly-unsaturated**, meaning carbon chains have more than one double bond (like corn or soybean oils).

Keep in mind the distinction between unsaturated *fatty acids* and unsaturated *fats*. Unsaturated fatty acids clearly possess one or more double bonds. Unsaturated fats (which contain three fatty acid chains) can possess chains that are both unsaturated and saturated, and can still be called unsaturated. That is, you might encounter a fat that has one unsaturated chain and two saturated chains and it will still fall into the category of unsaturated fats.

Unsaturated and Saturated Fats and Diet

You have probably heard the terms unsaturated and saturated fats in discussions of food and nutrition. Saturated fats have been linked to cardiovascular diseases. Arterial plaque is a complex mixture of substances that clogs up the passageways through which blood flows. High levels of saturated fat in a diet is correlated to high cholesterol levels. In turn, high cholesterol levels are linked to the amount of plaque in the blood. That is why saturated fats are called "bad" fats. It turns out that the mono-unsaturated fats are considered to be the most healthy, although it's not well understood why.

In their pure form, one of the ways in which saturated fats differ from unsaturated fats is in the temperature at which they change from liquid to solid. Saturated fats are usually solids at room temperature (although sometimes barely, as in the case of butter). Unsaturated fats are usually liquids at room temperature. This is because the double bonds in unsaturated fats cause "kinks" in the carbon chains that interfere with their packing closely together as their temperature drops. Remember that if molecules are packed more closely together, the attractive dispersion forces (van der Waals interactions) are stronger, so it takes more energy to separate the molecules in the solid state. Another way of thinking of this is that to be a solid, the molecules have to pack

Saturated fatty acids pack together well.

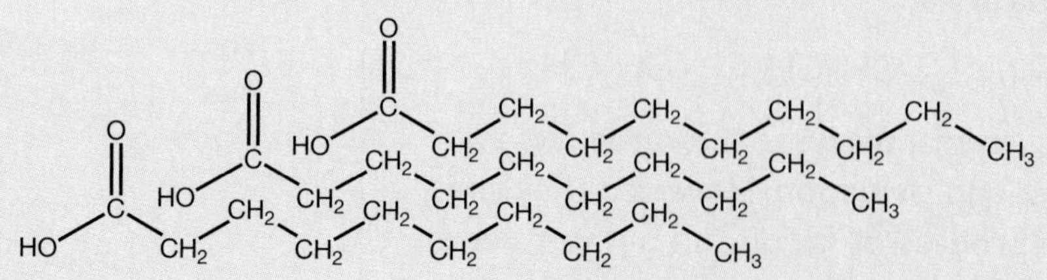

themselves closely enough so that attractive dispersion forces (van der Waals interactions) can hold them together. Saturated fats, lacking these "kinks," pack together easily as they are cooled, and remain solids at higher temperatures. Unsaturated fats must be cooled to lower temperatures before they pack together tightly enough to become solid. This changes the feel of these fats. Saturated fats feel greasy, while unsaturated fats feel oily.

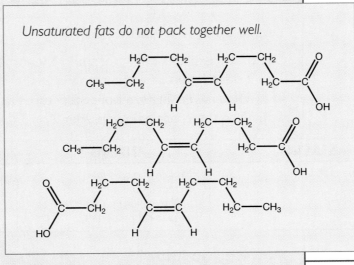

Unsaturated fats do not pack together well.

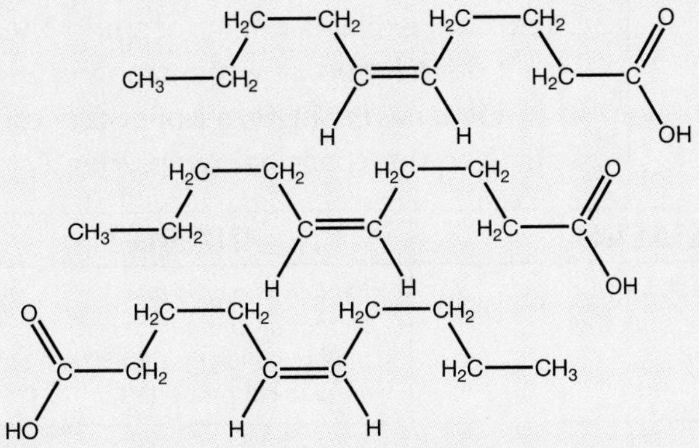

Within these two large categories, saturated and unsaturated, fatty acids also differ from each other in the lengths of their carbon chains. Some are long, some are short, and some are intermediate. The lengths of the carbon chains also affect the properties of the soap. To design a soap, you have to take both of these factors (chain length and amount of unsaturation) into account.

Checking Up

1. What is the difference between a saturated and an unsaturated fatty acid?
2. What would you call an unsaturated fat that has three carbon-carbon double bonds?
3. A vegetable oil would contain mostly what kind of fats?

What Do You Think Now?

At the beginning of the activity you were asked:

- **What is a "good" fat and what is a "bad" fat?**

Now that you have investigated saturated and unsaturated fats, in what category would you place saturated fats? Why?

Chem Essential Questions

What does it mean?

Chemistry explains a macroscopic phenomenon (what you observe) with a description of what happens at the nanoscopic level (atoms and molecules) using symbolic structures as a way to communicate. Complete the chart below in your *Active Chemistry* log.

MACRO	NANO	SYMBOLIC
List some macroscopic properties of soap that you observed.	*Explain in words how increasing the number of double bonds in a fat alters its physical properties.*	*Use drawings to show how increased numbers of double bonds affects the properties of fats.*

How do you know?

What evidence do you have that unsaturated and saturated fats have different melting points?

Why do you believe?

In advertising and in the news, you often hear terms related to fats such as: saturated, unsaturated, poly-unsaturated, partially hydrogenated, etc. What effect will hydrogenating a poly-unsaturated fat have in terms of its physical state?

Why should you care?

Showing how changes bring about desirable properties will be a major bonus when it comes to selling your idea of a new improved soap to company executives. Explain whether or not your soap will be unsaturated and the basis of your choice in terms of desirable properties.

Reflecting on the Activity and the Challenge

The amount of unsaturation that a fatty acid molecule contains is another feature that determines the properties of the soap it will make. *Cis*-double bonds in fatty acids keep them from packing together as tightly and therefore decrease their melting points. In soap, *cis*-double bonds make the soap softer; the hardest soaps have more saturated fatty acid salts. Now you have a sense of how to line up the properties of a soap, based on the fats you chose to use in the recipe. In the table at the end of this activity are listed most of the fats that you can obtain in stores. Consider what fat or fats you would like to use in your recipe to give your soap particular important properties.

Chem to Go

1. Identify the following hydrocarbons as saturated or unsaturated.

a) 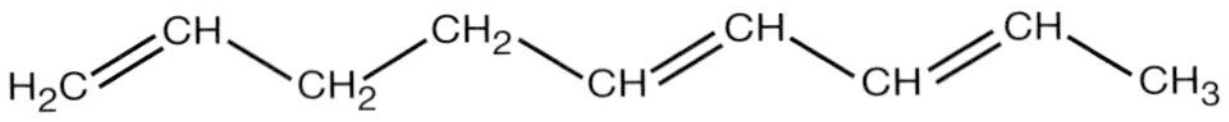

b) 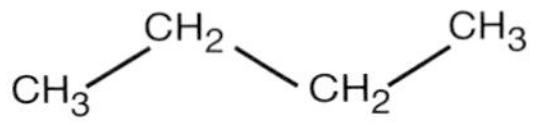

c) 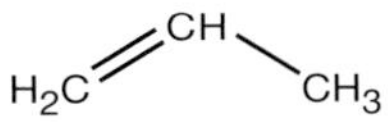

d) H_3C-CH_3

e) $HC\equiv CH$

f) 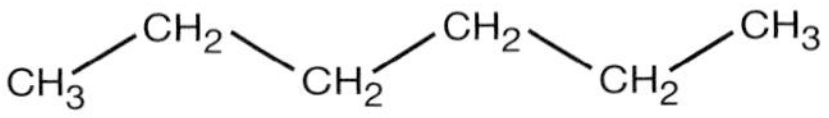

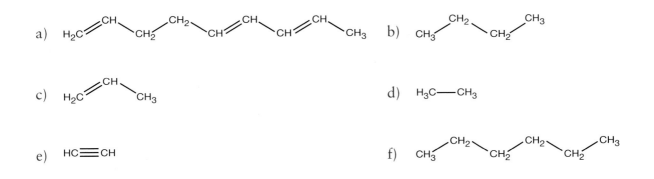

2. Answer the following questions based on the three molecular structures shown below.

(1)

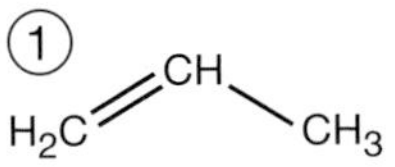

(2)

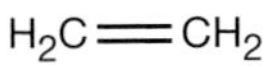

(3)

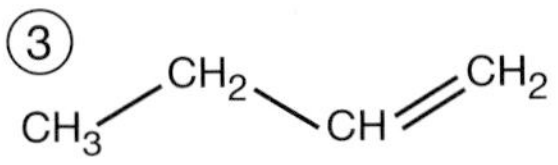

a) Arrange the molecules (1–3) above in order from lowest melting temperature to highest melting temperature.

b) Which of these hydrocarbons would solidify first if you placed a little of each one in its own container and placed all the containers in a very cold place? Explain.

3. When testing the properties, you observed differences in the four soaps. One difference was how hard the soaps were. Given what you learned about the properties of the fatty acids you tested in *Part A* of this activity, explain why the hardness of a soap depends on the degree of unsaturation (the number of double bonds) of the soap molecules.

4. The following hydrocarbons all have ten carbons in them. The chains are all liquids at room temperature and have melting points below room temperature. (Decane is a component of gasoline.) Naphthalene (moth balls) is a solid at room temperature. Based on what you know about the interactions between molecules in the solid state, explain why the melting points are in the order shown.

Chemical structure	Chemical name	Melting point
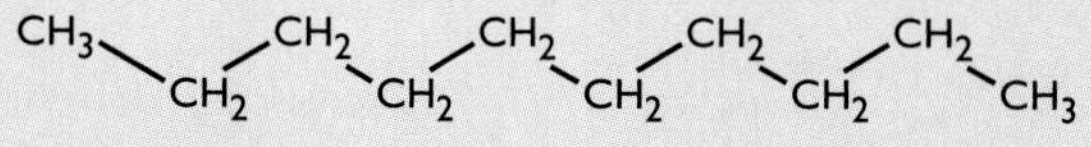	decane	–30°C
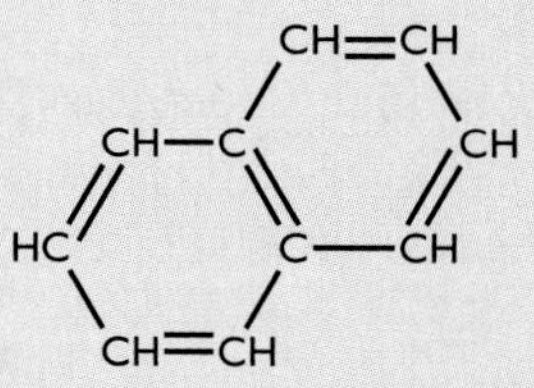	naphthalene (molecule has a flat shape due to double bonds)	81°C
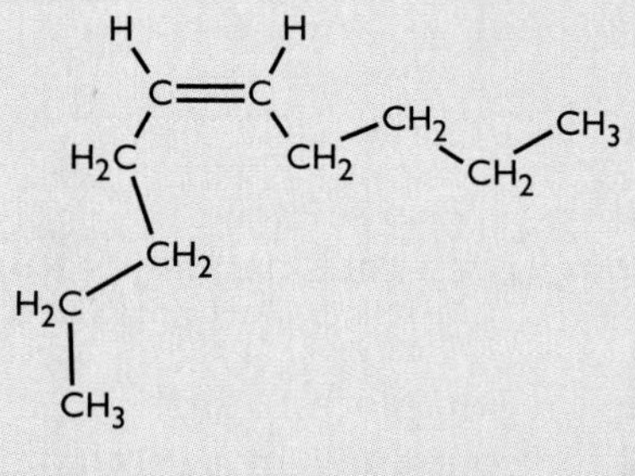	*cis*-5-decene	–112°C
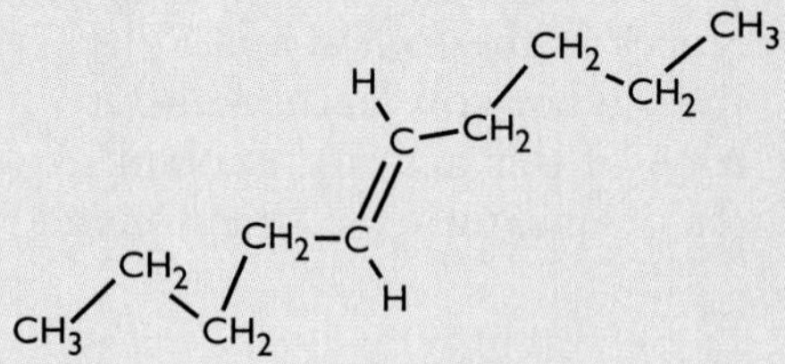	*trans*-5-decene	–73°C

5. Palm kernel oil has the same amount of lauric acid as coconut oil, but it also has a significant amount of oleic acid. What would you expect a soap made from palm kernel oil to do that a soap made from coconut oil would not do?

6. Cocoa butter is nearly equal portions of palmitic, oleic, and stearic acids. Based on what you know from the last activity and this one, what properties might you expect a soap made from cocoa butter to have?

7. Corn oil is almost entirely oleic and linoleic acids. Based on what you know from the last activity and this one, what properties might you expect a soap made from corn oil to have?

8. Which one of the following fatty acids is most likely to be found in greater amounts in an animal fat?

   a) *cis*-oleic acid b) linoleic acid c) palmitic acid d) *trans*-oleic acid

9. ***Preparing for the Chapter Challenge***

   As part of the *Chapter Challenge*, you'll need to explain why you chose the ingredients you did to give your soap the properties you desire. Now that you've completed two studies of how the two features of fats (chain length and degree of unsaturation) affect the properties of a soap, and you have a table organizing fats according to the number of C=C double bonds and chain length, you can make some predictions about which fats (or combination of fats) might give your soap the properties you desire. In your *Active Chemistry* log, make a prioritized list of properties you desire your soap to have. Decide which properties can be controlled by the features of fats that you have control over. Then, for each property of the soap you wish to design, predict which fat (or combination of fats) would give the soap the desired property. Write down some possible recipes based on these predictions.

Percentages of Different Fatty Acids in Common Animal and Vegetable Fats

Fatty acid / Fat	Capric C10 no d.b.	Lauric C12 no d.b.	Myristic C14 no d.b.	Palmitic C16 no d.b.	Linolenic C18 3 d.b.	Linoleic C18 2 d.b.	Oleic C18 1 d.b.	Stearic C18 no d.b.
beef tallow		1	4	27	1	3	39	20
canola oil*				1	1	15	32	
castor oil†		0.6	0.6	0.6		3	7	0.6
cocoa butter				24		2	38	35
coconut oil	7	48	17	9		2	6	2
corn oil			1	10		34	50	3
lard			1	28		6	48	12
linseed oil				6	47	24	19	3
olive oil				7		5	84	2
palm kernel oil	7	47	14	9		1	19	1
palm oil			1	40		10	43	6
peanut oil				8		26	56	3
safflower oil		1	1	1	3	70	19	1
sesame oil				9		40	45	4
soybean oil				10	7	51	29	2
sunflower oil				6		66	25	2

"d.b." stands for double bonds.

**Canola oil also contains 50% erucic acid, which is C22 with one double bond.*

†Castor oil also contains 87% ricinoleic acid, which is identical to oleic acid except there is an –OH group at carbon #12.

Composition of many fats varies widely. These figures are general averages.

Activity 7 Soap, Other Bases, and pH

What Do You See?

pH 1-4 5 6 7 8 9 10
COLOR
← ACIDIC
BASE →
LIQUID DETERG
H_2O
pH Test Strips
SOAP

GOALS

In this activity you will:

- Measure the pH of a number of common soaps.
- See the effect on pH when an acid is used to neutralize a base.
- Change the pH of an acid by dilution, and discover the amount of water necessary to do so.
- Relate changes in pH to changes in hydrogen ion concentration.

Safety goggles and a lab apron must be worn *at all times* in a chemistry lab.

What Do You Think?

Baking soda and drain cleaner are both bases. You can brush your teeth with baking soda. You would never brush your teeth with drain cleaner. Vinegar and battery acid are both acids. You can use vinegar as salad dressing but you cannot use battery acid in the same way.

- **Why is baking soda safe for brushing teeth and drain cleaner is not?**
- **Why is vinegar safe as a food, but battery acid is not?**

Record your ideas about these questions in your *Active Chemistry* log. Be prepared to discuss your responses with your small group and the class.

Investigate

A strong base (NaOH) was one of the two ingredients you used to make soap (fat was the other). If you change the base used to make soap, you also change the properties of the soap. In this activity, you'll learn why that is, so that you can decide which base to use in your soap recipe for the *Chapter Challenge*.

Part A: Comparing Commercial Soaps

1. Your teacher will provide you with, or ask you to provide samples of different commercially available soaps. You will test those soaps for their pH values. Label each soap with the following information:

- the name of the soap
- where the soap was purchased or obtained

Open the soap containers and place all the soaps and labels in a line. Place a plastic utensil (knife, fork, or spoon) with the soap to take a small amount.

2. Make a drawing of a 24-well plate in your *Active Chemistry* log.

Obtain from your teacher a 24-well plate, some distilled water in a beaker, a disposable dropper, some pH test paper, and as many toothpicks as there are different soaps to test. Send two people from your group to the line of soaps — one who will obtain a tiny amount of each soap and place it in one well of a 24-well plate, and the second who will record on a drawing of the well plate the location and identity of each soap in the plate. Use a drawing like this.

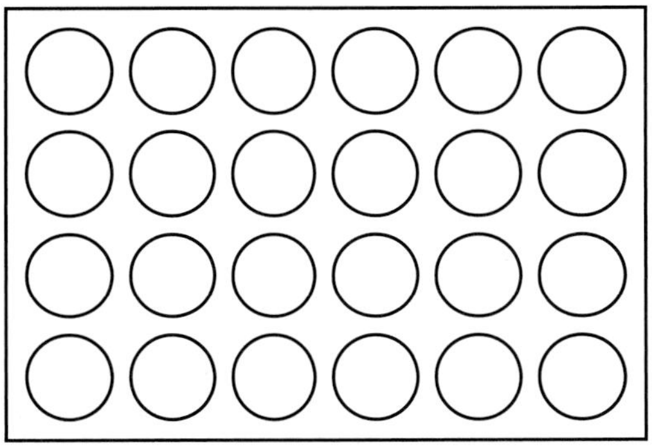

3. Use a sheet piece of paper (8.5" × 11") to draw a table. The table should have enough boxes in it so that there is one for each soap to be tested. At the top of each box, write the identifying information for the soap to be tested. Then, place the paper flat on the table, and place a small (torn off) piece of pH test paper in each box.

4. Obtain a very small amount of each soap. Place it in a well of a 24-well plate. Identify the location of each soap on your drawing of the plate.

5. Make a soap solution of each soap gathered. To each well that has soap in it, add a small amount (a few drops) of distilled water. Stir it with a toothpick to get some of the soap dissolved in the water. Then take the toothpick and touch it to the pH paper in the corresponding box. Afterward, throw away the toothpick so that you won't accidentally use it again with a different soap.

   a) Why is it important to use a different toothpick for each soap solution?

   b) Once all of the soaps have been tested for pH, read the pH of each soap using the color chart. Write the pH in the data table. Then copy the data table into your *Active Chemistry* log.

   c) Organize the soaps in order of increasing pH. Write down your organized lists in your *Active Chemistry* log.

   d) Do you see any similarities between the soaps within a pH group?

6. The pH scale runs from 0 to 14. Solutions can be classified according to their pH as follows:

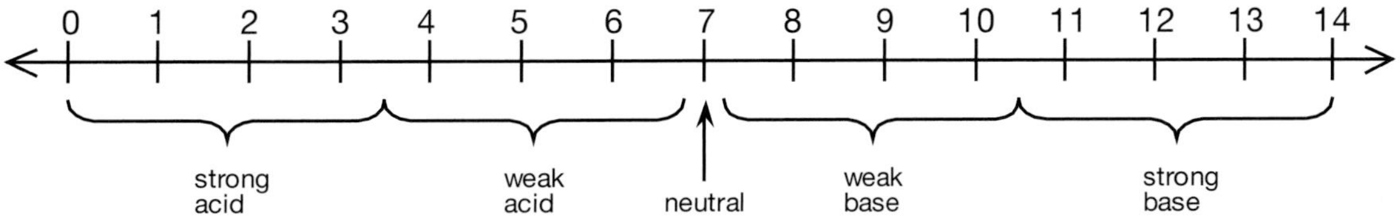
0
1
2
3
4
5
6
7
8
9
10
11
12
13
14
strong acid
weak acid
neutral
weak base
strong base

Some of the soaps you will be working with are strong enough bases to be dangerous to your skin, eyes, and clothing, so safety precautions are important.

Avoid touching your face, especially around your eyes, during this activity. Tell your teacher if you feel any skin or eye irritation.

Wipe up any spills immediately.

a) Return to your lists of soaps by pH in your *Active Chemistry* log. Assign each group of soaps one of the following labels: strong acid, weak acid, neutral, weak base, strong base.

7. Does the amount of soap solution you test affect its pH? Design an experiment to find out.

   a) Record your experimental design in your *Active Chemistry* log.

   With the approval of your teacher, complete your experiment.

   b) Based on your experimental evidence, does the amount of soap solution affect its pH?

Safety goggles and a lab apron must be worn *at all times* in a chemistry lab.

HCl is a strong acid. Be careful with it. Keep it off your skin and clean up any spills immediately.

Wear gloves!

8. Does the amount of water you add to a soap solution affect its pH? Design an experiment to find out.

   a) Record your experimental design in your *Active Chemistry* log. (Hint: Use the soap with the highest pH.)

   With the approval of your teacher, complete your experiment.

   b) Based on your experimental evidence, does the amount of water you add to the soap solution affect its pH?

9. What happens when you mix an acid and a base? Most of your solutions are probably bases. Obtain a dropper bottle containing a strong acid solution (hydrochloric acid, HCl dissolved in water), and some new toothpicks. Add *one drop* of HCl solution to each well that has a soap in it. Tear off new pieces of pH paper for testing and place them in the boxes in the data table. Use new toothpicks and mix in the HCl solution, and then retest each soap.

   a) What happens? Write down your observations in your *Active Chemistry* log.

10. Dispose of the materials as directed by your teacher. Clean up your workstation.

Part B: What is pH?

1. You know that pH is a measure of the strength of an acid or base. You probably found that diluting a soap solution with water lowered its pH. Now you are going to be more quantitative about this. Your teacher will measure the pH of a beaker of hydrochloric acid (HCl) solution. Obtain a 5-mL sample of the acid.

   a) When you measure the pH of the HCl solution you receive, do you expect it will be the same or different? The question is, "Does the pH change if the amount of a solution changes?" Write an answer to this question, using a complete sentence, in your *Active Chemistry* log.

2. You can think of acids and bases as the two parts of water when it breaks up into ions. A water molecule H_2O or HOH can break apart into an H^+ ion and an OH^- ion. The H^+ part is acidic and the OH^- part is basic. When you have pure water, you have equal amounts of H^+ and OH^-.

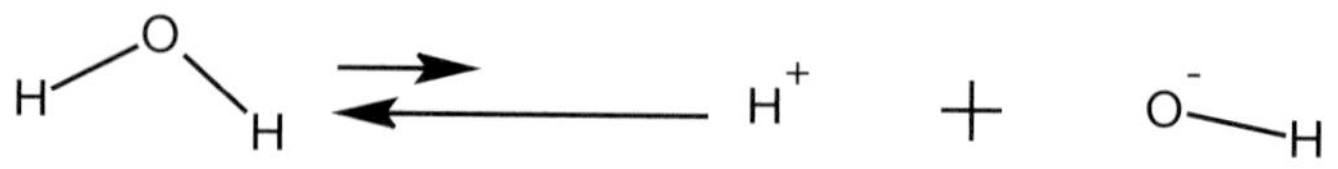

What makes a solution acidic is an excess of H^+ ions. So, if you add something to water that adds H^+ ions, but not OH^- ions, then you have created an acidic solution.

a) Do you think the large volume of acid (that your teacher tested) has more H^+ ions or the same amount as the 5-mL volume that you received? Why?

b) Draw a picture of what's inside the large volume of acid with its H^+ ions.

c) Now draw a picture of half of it, with the H^+ ions that remain. What happens to the number of H^+ ions?

d) Should the pH change?

e) *What exactly does pH measure, if not the total number of H^+ ions in a solution?* Write an answer to this question, using a complete sentence, in your *Active Chemistry* log.

3. Measure the pH of the acid your teacher gave you. Use a glass stirring rod to touch a drop of the acid to a small piece of pH paper.

a) Record the pH of your HCl solution in your *Active Chemistry* log.

b) Is the pH the same or different than the pH your teacher found for the large amount of HCl solution?

4. Measure the pH of distilled water.

a) Record the pH of the distilled water.

5. Predict about how much distilled water you would need to dilute your HCl solution in order to change its pH value by 1.

a) Record your prediction.

b) In which direction will the pH change when you dilute the acid with water? Why?

6. Measure the amount of distilled water you have decided to use. Place the water into a test tube or beaker. Add the acid slowly and carefully to the test tube or beaker. When you add acid to water, at first you have only a small amount of acid mixing with a larger amount of water. The acid is immediately diluted. The acid being added to the water only gradually comes up to its final derived concentration.

a) Record the amount of water you used.

b) Measure and record the pH of the resulting solution.

c) Did it change as much as you expected?

7. Based on these results, make another estimate of how much water you would need to use to dilute the original acid enough to change the pH value by one unit. Calculate how much additional water you need to reach this amount. Add the acid to this amount of water. Never add water to acid. Measure the pH again. Repeat the process until you have changed the pH by one. Try not to overshoot your target (that is, try not to change the pH by more than one unit).

a) Show your work in your *Active Chemistry* log.

8. How much water do you think you would need to dilute 5 mL of this final (diluted) acid to change its pH by one more unit (so that it is two pH units away from the value originally given to you by your teacher)? Carry out your procedure.

When working with strong acids or bases, always add the acid or base slowly to the water or other solution, rather than adding water to the acid or base. Acids and bases can sometimes react violently with water.

Adding water to acid puts a small amount of water in contact with a large amount of acid at its maximum concentration (with the greatest potential for a violent reaction).

Wash your hands and arms thoroughly after the activity.

a) Record your experiment and results in your *Active Chemistry* log.

b) How does this dilution compare to the dilution you used in previous steps?

9. With your group, predict how large a dilution you would need to change the pH of your new (*Step 8*) solution by one more pH unit. What would you need to do to change the pH of your (*Step 8*) solution by two pH units?

a) Write down your predictions in your *Active Chemistry* log.

10. pH is a measure of the concentration of H^+ ions in a solution. A special notation $[H^+]$ is used to write the concentration of H^+ ions. This notation represents the number of H^+ ions in a standard volume, which is always one liter.

Assume that the starting concentration of H^+ ions was some arbitrary number like one mole of H^+ ions per liter.

a) If the starting concentration of H^+ ions in the HCl solution your teacher gave you was 1.0 *M* of H^+ ions per liter of solution, what was the concentration by the time the pH had changed by one unit (*Step 7*)? By two units (*Step 8*)? What would you predict the concentration to be by the time the pH had changed by three units? By four units?

b) Show the position of these concentrations on a number line drawn in your *Active Chemistry* log.

11. You might have had difficulty putting the concentration numbers on a number line, because they are so different in size. It turns out that an exponential scale is a much more convenient and useful way of representing a range of numbers where each division varies from the next by being one fraction of the previous one (such as one-tenth).

a) Copy these three scales (A, B, and C) into your *Active Chemistry* log, and indicate on them where your initial concentration of HCl solution was (*Step 3*), where one-tenth of this concentration was (*Step 7*), and where one-hundredth of the initial concentration was (*Step 8*).

b) In what direction did the pH change as you diluted the solutions? Why? Write down your answers in your *Active Chemistry* log.

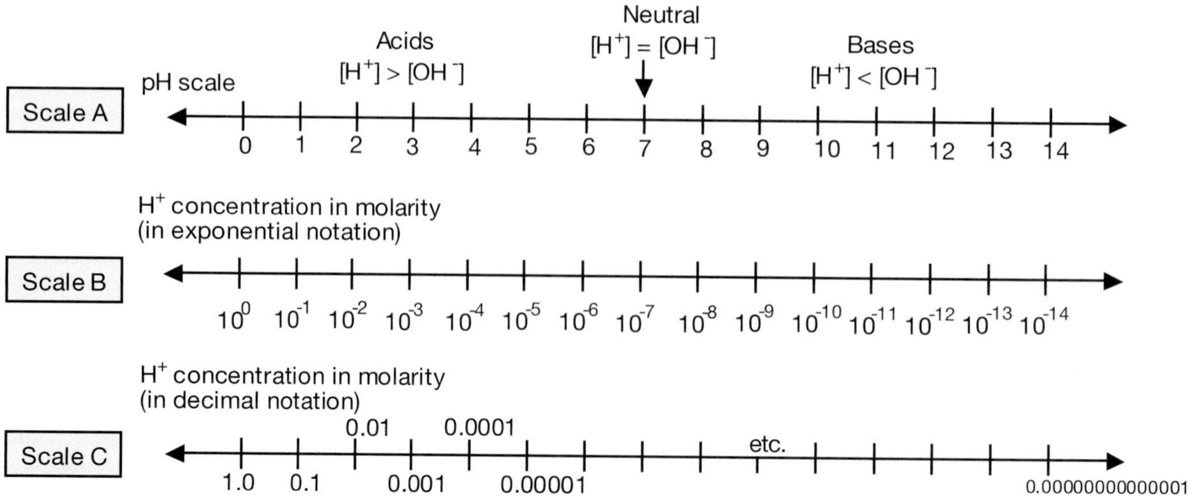
Scale A
pH scale
Acids
[H+] > [OH-]
Neutral
[H+] = [OH-]
Bases
[H+] < [OH-]
0 1 2 3 4 5 6 7 8 9 10 11 12 13 14
Scale B
H+ concentration in molarity
(in exponential notation)
10^0 10^-1 10^-2 10^-3 10^-4 10^-5 10^-6 10^-7 10^-8 10^-9 10^-10 10^-11 10^-12 10^-13 10^-14
Scale C
H+ concentration in molarity
(in decimal notation)
1.0 0.1 0.01 0.001 0.0001 0.00001 etc. 0.00000000000001

Chem Talk

ACIDS AND BASES

Defining Acids and Bases

Chemists often consider bases and acids together, because the two concepts are related. Especially important is the concept of acids and bases in water solution. Your body is largely water, so the biochemical reactions in your body take place in an aqueous environment. There are several historical levels for the definition of acids and bases. Let's review those definitions.

The earliest definition was the **Arrhenius** definition in which an acid was defined as a chemical that releases hydrogen ions, H^+ (in water, hydronium ions, H_3O^+). A base releases hydroxide ions, OH^-. This is an easily understood definition, but somewhat limited and little used today. A better definition of an acid is the **Brønsted-Lowry** concept. They proposed that an acid is an H^+ donor and a base is a H^+ acceptor. This is a broader definition and includes the Arrhenius definition while expanding it to other substances. However, the most general and most useful definition is the **Lewis** acid-base concept. Here, an acid is an electron-pair acceptor (such as HCl) and a base is an electron-pair donor (such as NH_3).

Pure water is mostly made of complete H_2O molecules. However, even in pure water, two in every billion water molecules is ionized, that is, broken into a H^+ ion (actually, H_3O^+) and an OH^- ion. That is not very many. This is symbolized in the equation by the longer arrow going from right to left.

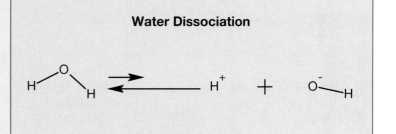

Water Dissociation

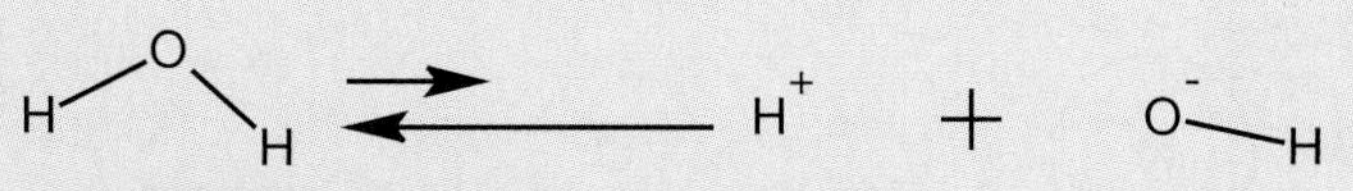

H
O
H
H+
+
O-
H

This equation shows an equilibrium where water molecules form ions (forward reaction with the arrow to the right). And it also shows the reverse reaction of the ions reacting to form water (reverse reaction with the arrow to the left).

Pure water has equal quantities of H^+ and OH^- ions. This condition is called neutral. The concentration of these ions has been measured and calculated. Symbolically, concentrations are shown as $[H^+]$ and $[OH^-]$. In solution chemistry, $[H^+]$ means moles per liter of hydrogen ions (in water, hydronium ions, $[H_3O^+]$).

Chem Words

Arrhenius acid: a substance that releases hydrogen ions.

Brønsted-Lowry acid: a substance that can donate hydrogen ions.

Brønsted-Lowry base: a substance that accepts hydrogen ions.

Lewis acid: a substance that is an electron-pair acceptor.

Lewis base: a substance that is an electron-pair donor.

What a lot of bases have in common chemically is the release or creation of hydroxide (OH^-) ions. Most strong bases are ionic compounds with hydroxide anions bound to metal cations. When dissolved in water, these hydroxide ions are released into the solution. Sodium hydroxide, NaOH, is an example of a strong base. When solid NaOH is added to water, it dissolves, dissociating (breaking apart) into Na^+ cations and OH^- anions. This happens easily because NaOH is a polar *ionic* compound and water is a polar solvent. The ions are stabilized in solution by the surrounding polar water molecules.

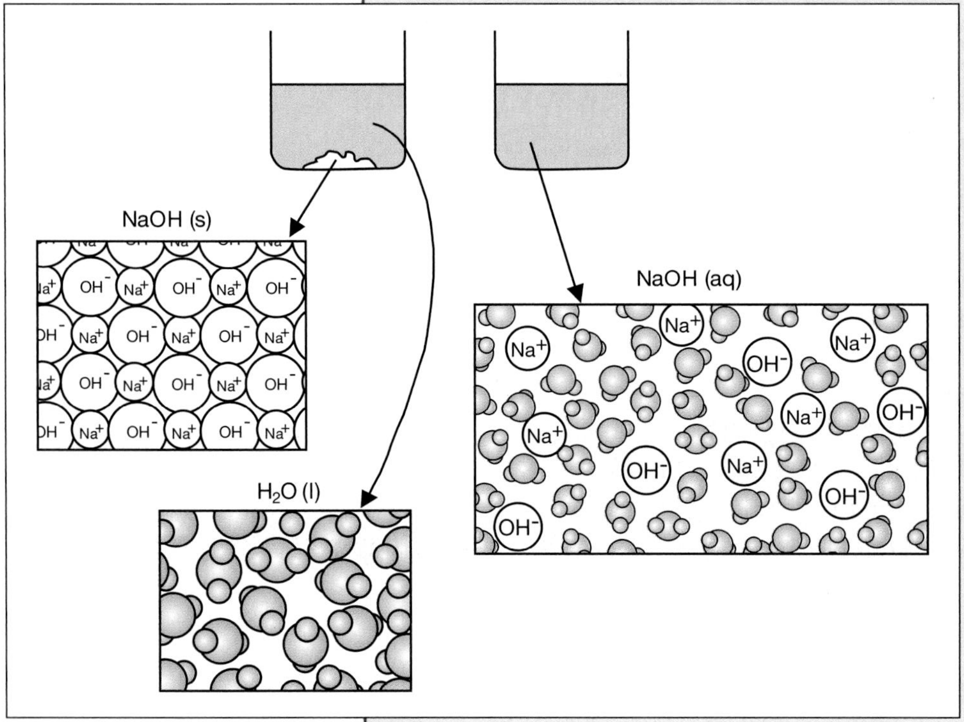
NaOH (s)
H_2O (l)
NaOH (aq)

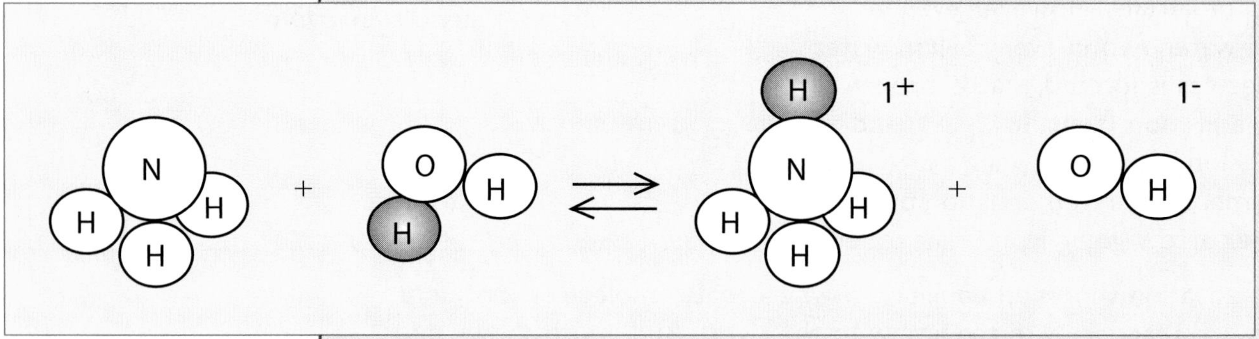
1+
1-

Some bases work by binding hydrogen ions (Brønsted and Lewis definitions), thereby decreasing the hydrogen ion concentration. Ammonia (NH_3), for example, can remove an H^+ from a water molecule, resulting in NH_4^+ and OH^-. This is also an equilibrium reaction which produces an $[OH^-]$ of about 10^{-5} mol/L. And so, NH_3 is a base, but a weak base.

Neutralization

Large amounts of H^+ and OH^- ions cannot exist together in aqueous solution. When an H^+ ion collides with an OH^- ion, the chances of forming a water molecule are very high. The chances of a water molecule breaking up into H^+ and OH^- ions is very low. The water molecule is much more stable than the pair of ions. Imagine starting with a basic solution that has far more OH^- ions than H^+ (H_3O^+) ions. If you add H^+ (H_3O^+) ions to this basic solution, the collisions of the negative ions (OH^-) and the positive ions (H^+ or H_3O^+) will occur quite quickly due to attractions and their rapid velocities. This is called **neutralization**. Excess base is neutralized by the addition of acid. Excess acid is neutralized by the addition of base.

You can use a base to neutralize an acid in just the same way as you used an acid in this activity to neutralize a base. As you add OH^- ions to a solution containing a high concentration of H^+ ions (H_3O^+ ions in water), you do not get a mixture of the two, but instead a reduction in the number of H^+ ions and an increase in the number of water molecules. There is another product as well. When the H^+ ion breaks apart from an acid, it usually leaves a negatively charged ion (called an anion) behind. Hydrochloric acid (HCl), for example, breaks apart into H^+ and Cl^- ions. Bases like NaOH similarly form a cation (Na^+) along with the OH^- ion. Unlike the reaction of H^+ and OH^- ions, the Na^+ and Cl^- ions do not form a covalent compound when dissolved in water. Instead, these ions are attracted to and surrounded by water molecules. When the water is evaporated, they form a stable, solid, ionic compound called a salt. When you add aqueous solutions of HCl to NaOH to each other, you form water molecules and dissolved ions. If you evaporate the water, you have gaseous water (vapor) and a salt. This is an example of a double-replacement reaction.

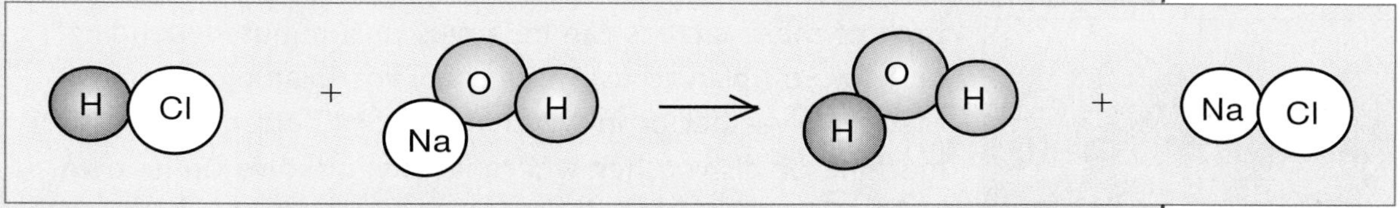
H
Cl
+
O
Na
H
O
H
H
+
Na
Cl

If you add potassium hydroxide (KOH, a strong base) to nitric acid (HNO_3, a strong acid), water and potassium nitrate (KNO_3, another salt) is formed. In each case, you are neutralizing an acid or a base with the opposite type of solution to form water and a salt.

Chem Words

neutralization: the reaction between an acid and a base to form water and a salt (usually the reaction between hydrogen ions and hydroxide ions to form water molecules).

Choosing the Base for Soap-Making

While you should consider changing the type of base used to make a soap, doing so is difficult. The first major problem is that most strong bases are metal hydroxides. Most Group II and Group III metal hydroxides will not dissolve in water. If a base doesn't dissolve, it becomes difficult to get the base and the fat in close enough contact to allow the saponification reaction to proceed in a reasonable amount of time. Of the Group I hydroxides, only NaOH and KOH are cost effective. Lithium, cesium, and rubidium are rare elements and are very expensive.

The second problem is that weak bases do not work very well in the soap-making process. The "soaps" they produce usually have properties that are undesirable for personal use. In fact, it is the cations present in "hard water," calcium and magnesium, that make an unattractive insoluble "sludge." So most personal care soaps are made with either NaOH or KOH.

There is a meaningful choice to be made between NaOH and KOH, however. KOH produces softer soaps, and is used for producing liquid soaps. This is due to differences between the sodium and potassium ions. Chemically, both sodium and potassium atoms lose a single electron to form 1^{+} charged ions. However, potassium is a larger atom because it has one more shell of electrons than sodium does. The larger potassium ion does not match the size of the negative ion of the soap ion (a group of atoms O-C-O with an angle of about 120° between them and with a negative charge spread over the two oxygen atoms) as well as the smaller sodium ion. Because of the size mismatch, the solid formed from the potassium ion and the soap ion is not as stable and dissolves more readily.

Each of these factors can be a plus or a minus, depending on how you plan to use your soap. For example, a soap that dissolves better in water may work better in a washing machine or dishwasher, where it must dissolve on its own before it can begin to do its job. However, it may be a drawback for a bar soap that will be used in the shower, because it wouldn't last as long. Increased lather is often valued by consumers, but can cause problems in machines that wash items in an enclosed space, such as a dishwasher.

Understanding pH

To understand pH, you must consider two variables. First, you want to know what the concentration of the acidic or basic chemical in the solution is. Obviously, the higher the concentration of the acid, the higher the concentration of H^+ ions and the stronger the acidic solution. Second, you want to know what fraction of the acidic molecules separate into an H^+ ion and its corresponding anion. Molecules like hydrochloric acid and nitric acid separate entirely into ions. That is, every molecule of the substance separates, or "dissociates," into a cation and an anion. These are **strong acids**. But **weak acids**, like acetic acid (found in vinegar) only partially dissociate. Most of the acetic acid molecules remain whole, so fewer H^+ ions are present in a weak acid, even when the concentration of the acidic chemical is high.

Now consider the case where there is a large concentration of H^+ ions. Because there is a large concentration of H^+, there must be a scarcity of OH^- because any OH^- ions have been incorporated into H_2O molecules. So, in an acidic solution, the balance is tipped. There are more H^+ ions than in pure water, and there are fewer OH^- ions than in pure water. This inverse proportionality leads you to be able to predict the concentration of OH^- ($[OH^-]$) if you know the concentration of H^+ ($[H^+]$), and vice versa. In fact, the product of the two concentrations is equal to a constant (K_w), 1×10^{-14}.

$$K_w = [H^+][OH^-] = 1 \times 10^{-14}$$

So if the $[H^+]$ of a solution is known to be $1 \times 10^{-3}\ M$, the $[OH^-]$ must be:

$$[H^+]\ [OH^-] = 1 \times 10^{-14}$$

$$[1 \times 10^{-3}\ M]\ [OH^-] = 1 \times 10^{-14}$$

$$[OH^-] = \frac{1 \times 10^{-14}}{1 \times 10^{-3}\ M}$$

$$= 1 \times 10^{-11}\ M$$

pH and Neutralization

Here is where **pH** finally makes an appearance. pH is a measure of the H^+ ion concentration. The lower the pH is, the higher the H^+ ion concentration is. Because H^+ ion concentration and OH^- ion concentration are tied together (inversely proportional), pH also

Chem Words

strong acid: an acid that completely ionizes in water to produce H_3O^+. Strong acids include HCl, H_2SO_4, and HNO_3.

weak acid: an acid that slightly dissociates to release a small amount of hydrogen ions into the solution. Vinegar or acetic acid is an example of a weak acid.

pH: a measure of the acidity or alkalinity of a solution. Solutions with pH less than 7 are acidic, solutions with pH greater than 7 are basic. Mathematically, $pH = -\log[H^+]$.

serves as a measure of OH^- ion concentration (pH + pOH = 14). When the pH of a solution is low (in other words, when H^+ ion concentration is high), the OH^- ion concentration must be low because usually OH^- ions encounter H^+ ions and re-form water molecules. Conversely, the higher the pH, the higher the OH^- ion concentration is (and the lower the H^+ ion concentration). You have already learned that the pH scale customarily runs from 0 (representing a very strong acid with a high H^+ ion concentration) to 14 (representing a very strong base with a high OH^- ion concentration). Pure water is neutral, with a pH balanced right in the middle at 7. Now you know enough to understand where this pH scale comes from.

If you begin with a strong acid with a pH of 2, and slowly add base to it, most of the added OH^- ions will not survive in the solution. They will instead form water molecules as soon as they encounter the H^+ ions. Adding a base to an acid acts to reduce the H^+ ion concentration because every OH^- ion that is converted to a water molecule takes an H^+ ion with it. The strong acid becomes weaker as the H^+ ion concentration declines. Eventually, you will have added as many OH^- ions as there were H^+ ions to begin with. The solution is now neutral with a pH of 7. If you keep on adding the base, excess OH^- ions begin to accumulate, and the solution becomes basic (with a pH now increasingly greater than 7). The H^+ ion concentration continues to fall as the OH^- ion concentration continues to rise.

Concentration of Solutions

The way to quantify the amount of solute in a solution is by measuring its **concentration**. Concentration is a measure of how much **solute** is contained in a certain amount of **solution**. This way of describing solutions has the advantage of being independent of the amount of solution involved. There are a number of different ways or units for measuring concentration.

If you like sugar in tea or coffee there is probably a certain concentration of sugar that you like. You want the sweetness to be the same every time, but you don't necessarily want the amount of sugar to be the same every time. If you usually put two teaspoons of sugar in a cup of coffee, then, if you only have half a cup, you will only want one teaspoon. The amount of sugar goes down proportionally with the amount of coffee. However, the ratio or concentration stayed the same in each case.

Chem Words

concentration: the measured amount of solute dissolved in a solution. Molarity (*M*, moles per liter) is an example of concentration.

solute: a substance in lesser concentration that interacts with a solvent to form a solution.

solution: a homogeneous mixture that consists of a solvent and at least one solute.

In chemistry, concentration is measured in units of **molarity**, which is abbreviated as *M*. Molarity stands for the number of moles of a solute that are dissolved in one liter of a solution.

$$M = \frac{\text{number of moles of solute}}{\text{liter of solution}}$$

Moles are just quantities, and the quantity of any items in a mole is: 602,200,000,000,000,000,000,000 or 6.022×10^{23} of those things.

pH and Dilution

In this activity, you reduced the strength of the strong acid not by adding base, but just by adding water, or by diluting it. You reduced the concentration of H^+ ions not by taking them away, but by increasing the amount of solution they reside in. Look at the relationship of ion concentration and volume:

$$\text{ion concentration} = \frac{\text{number of ions}}{\text{volume of solution}}$$

If you increase the volume, you reduce the concentration. If you began with a solution of 0.10 mol of pure HCl in 1.0 L of aqueous solution (which would make a 0.10 *M* solution of HCl), and then added 1.0 L of additional water, you would have 0.10 mol of HCl, now dissolved in 2.0 L of solution. The concentration has been reduced by $\frac{1}{2}$, or is now 0.10 mole / 2.0 L = 0.050 mole/ L or 0.050 *M* HCl.

In this activity, instead of increasing the volume of the solution by a factor of 2 each time, you increased the volume by a factor of 10 each time. So if you began with 0.10 *M* HCl, the first dilution should have produced 0.010 *M* HCl. The second dilution should have produced 0.0010 *M* HCl, and the third dilution should have produced 0.00010 *M* HCl, and so on. You can see that after many dilutions, the amount of excess H^+ ions would be extremely small.

To find the pH of any solution, you first write the H^+ ion concentration as a power of 10; so 0.10 *M* HCl = 1.0×10^{-1}, and 0.000010 *M* HCl = 1.0×10^{-5}. The pH of each solution is just the exponent, without the negative sign, so these two solutions are of pH 1 and 5, respectively. That's why each ten-fold dilution produces a change of 1 pH unit (until you approach a pH of 7). Mathematically stated,

$$pH = -\log[H^+]$$

Chem Words

molarity: the number of moles of solute dissolved in a liter of solution.

Checking Up

1. Explain the Arrhenius, Brønsted-Lowry, and Lewis concepts of acids and bases.
2. What is neutralization?
3. How does a strong acid differ from a weak acid?
4. How is the molarity of a solution determined?
5. How is the pH defined mathematically?
6. Calculate the following:
   a) If the $[OH^-]$ of a solution is 0.2 *M*, what is the $[H^+]$?
   b) If the $[H^+]$ of a solution is 1×10^{-2} *M*, what is the pH?
   c) If the $[H^+]$ of a solution is 0.0004 *M*, what is the pH?
   d) If the $[OH^-]$ of a solution is 0.02 *M*, what is the pH?

What Do You Think Now?

At the beginning of this activity you were asked:

- **Why is baking soda safe for brushing teeth and drain cleaner is not?**
- **Why is vinegar safe as a food, but battery acid is not?**

How would you now explain to someone that, while it is safe to brush your teeth with baking soda, using drain cleaner (NaOH) would not be a good idea, even though they are both bases. In your explanation, use the terms hydrogen ion concentration, hydroxide ion concentration, pH, and strong base/weak base.

Chem Essential Questions

What does it mean?

Chemistry explains a macroscopic phenomenon (what you observe) with a description of what happens at the nanoscopic level (atoms and molecules) using symbolic structures as a way to communicate. Complete the chart below in your *Active Chemistry* log.

MACRO	NANO	SYMBOLIC
How can you measure the pH of a solution?	*What are you actually measuring when you take the pH of a solution?*	*How can you symbolically represent the acidity of a solution?*

How do you know?

Use your data from this activity to show that as the hydrogen ion concentration decreases, the pH of a solution increases.

Why do you believe?

You often hear advertising for shampoo products that claim they are "pH balanced." What does that mean?

Why should you care?

You will want to assure your customers that the soap you are providing has a gentle effect on the skin, even though harsh chemicals were used in making the soap. How will you describe the gentleness of your soap product?

Reflecting on the Activity and the Challenge

In this activity, you learned about acids and bases and the use of the pH scale to measure the strength of these solutions. Soap-making requires the use of a strong base, and the pH of the final product must be brought down to a safe level, so an understanding of these topics is essential. Understanding acid/base and neutralization reactions allows a much better working knowledge of the soap-making process. Different bases produce soaps with different properties, so choosing the proper base is important to producing the type of soap you want.

Chem to Go

1. An advertisement for a shampoo claims that it is the very best because it has the lowest pH of all shampoos. Would you buy this shampoo? Why or why not?
2. Answer the following questions about dilutions.
   a) What would the pH be if you diluted a solution with a pH of 10 by one-tenth?
   b) What would the pH be if you mixed together one part solution with a pH of 4 and nine parts water?
   c) What would the pH be if you mixed 10 mL of a solution with a pH of 3 with 90 mL of water to make a total of 100 mL of solution?
   d) What would the pH be if you mixed 1.0 mL of a solution with a pH of 3 with 99 mL of water to make a total of 100 mL of solution?
3. Which acid is stronger and more dangerous, a solution with a pH of 2 or a solution with a pH of 6? Why?
4. If you take 5 mL of a solution with a pH of 3 and add it to 5 mL of a solution with a pH of 11, what would be the pH of the resulting solution? Why? (Think about what's in the solution with a pH of 3 and what's in the solution with a pH of 11.) What is the name of the special reaction that occurs when you mix these two solutions?
5. If you have a bar soap that is too basic to be used on the skin, describe how you could make it less basic. How would the pH change?
6. What is the pH of a solution whose H^+ concentration, $[H^+]$, is 0.00001 *M*?
7. In many areas of the world, the soil is relatively acidic. Most plants grow best at a neutral pH, and some plants will not grow at all in acidic soil.
   a) Farmers often add a chemical called "lime" to the acidic soil to cause the soil to be more neutral. What kind of chemical is lime?
   b) Soil with a pH of 3 is how many times more acidic than soil with a pH of 6?
   c) Some plants (like rhododendrons and blueberries) grow better in acidic soil. What advice would you give to someone planting these plants?
8. Explain how you can use the same scale to measure how acidic a solution is and also how basic it is. Why don't you need two different scales?
9. Identify whether each chemical is an acid, a base, or neither, according to the Arrhenius definition.

a) KOH	c) NH_4^+	e) HNO_2	g) $HClO$
b) HBr	d) $Mg(OH)_2$	f) H_2SO_4	h) CN^-

10. ***Preparing for the Chapter Challenge***

    Clarify further the type of soap you would like to produce, and select the base you would like to try using to make this soap. Explain in your *Active Chemistry* log your reasoning for choosing the base you chose.

Activity 8 Making Soap Functional and Appealing

What Do You See?

COLOR DYE
FOAMING AGENT
EDTA
SODIUM LAURYL SULFATE
LANOLIN
WAX
CITRIC ACID
MOLD
SOAP FACTORY
DYE
TEST TUB
SHAM POO
DIRT

GOALS

In this activity you will:

- Compare a store-bought soap to soaps made by classmates using a variety of measures, including a quantitative test of cleaning effectiveness.
- Evaluate the pros and cons of different fats as foundations for a soap product.
- Make a decision about other additives to your soap, after considering four broad classes of additives.
- Produce the soap you have designed.

What Do You Think?

When you change the fat in the starting materials for soap, you have control over the lathering ability and hardness of a soap. When you change the base, you have control over whether the soap is a solid or liquid. Many soaps on the market claim to be moisturizing soaps.

- **How can you develop a soap that has a moisturizer?**

Record your ideas about this question in your *Active Chemistry* log. Be prepared to discuss your responses with your small group and the class.

Investigate

In this activity, you will need to decide what other chemicals you might add to your soap to give it additional appealing properties that the fat and base do not create. Then, you will invent your recipe for your soap, and you'll make it.

1. Obtain a sample of the store-bought soap that you are trying to compete against. Perform the soap effectiveness tests that you used on all the other soaps on the store-bought soap. Compare the results from the store-bought soap to your results from testing the six soaps you made before beginning this chapter.

   a) What special qualities does the store-bought soap have that you are going to improve?

b) What features do the six soaps have that are improvements on the commercially available soaps? What features are worse?

c) Write notes in your *Active Chemistry* log to help you decide on how to build your recipe for the *Chapter Challenge*.

2. Discuss with your group the data you collected over the chapter. Decide on the fat(s) and base you will use to make your soap.

a) Write down in your *Active Chemistry* log your rationale for using the fats and base you decide on.

3. Once you know what your ingredients will be, submit them in writing to your teacher.

4. Decide on any additives to use. You can learn about what different additives do in the *Chem Talk* section for this activity. Your teacher can give you an idea of how much to use of different additives and at what point in the procedure to add them.

5. Make the soap you propose. Use the basic recipe that you used when making the soaps before you began the chapter.

Safety goggles and a lab apron must be worn *at all times* in a chemistry lab.

Review procedures for safely handling the substances you will use before you begin.

Wash your hands and arms thoroughly after the activity.

NaOH is a strong base. Keep it off your skin and clean up any spills immediately.

Chem Talk

SOAP APPEAL

Additives

There are many factors that can increase the appeal of a soap. We will focus on four **additives**:

- moisturizers like lanolin or cetyl alcohol
- thickeners (usually waxes)
- ingredients to adjust pH, such as citric acid or extra fatty acids
- foaming agents that enhance lathering (like sodium lauryl sulfate or sodium laureth sulfate).

Other additives you might consider could include:

- dyes (must be FDA-approved) to alter the color
- fragrances such as **essential oils** or **esters**
- preservatives and antioxidants, such as EDTA or vitamin E.

You could probably extend this list. You can find out more information about what the other additives do in books about soap-making in the library and by searching on the Internet. →

Chem Words

additives: substances that are added to alter the characteristics of the material. An example in soaps would be the addition of a foaming agent to increase the lather of the soap.

essential oils: in soaps, oils or esters that are added to give it desirable fragrance.

ester: the reaction product when an organic acid and an alcohol combine and eliminate a water molecule.

Chem Words

humectant: an additive that attracts water. In soaps, glycerol is added to help in attracting water to the skin surface.

emollient: an additive that helps to retain water or prevent water from escaping from the skin.

sebum: an emollient that the skin produces naturally.

FUNCTIONAL AND APPEAL OF SOAPS

Moisturizers

There are two ways to moisturize skin: add molecules to the skin that draw water vapor in from the air, or coat the surface of the skin with molecules that prevent the skin's own water from escaping into the air. The first kind of moisturizers are called **humectants**, and the second kind are called **emollients**.

A humectant must be a molecule that attracts water. The most common humectants are glycerin (already a product of the saponification reaction), propylene glycol, sorbitol, and cetyl alcohol. All of these molecules have alcohol (—OH) groups. The O—H bond is very polar, so it helps the molecule to be polar. Water molecules are also very polar. The attraction of polar molecules for each other is a crucial chemistry concept. The process you are using to make soap leaves the glycerin produced by saponification in the soap, although many commercial soap-making processes do not. You could consider adding more glycerin or other humectants to your soap to increase its ability to attract water.

An emollient must be a molecule that sticks to the skin but repels water. Emollients act by trapping water within the skin, preventing its evaporation. They form a thin layer of molecules that the water molecules cannot cross. Skin produces its own emollient, called **sebum**. Unfortunately, the more frequently and thoroughly you wash your skin, the more of it you wash away. So, emollients are added to soaps to replace what is being removed. Lanolin is a typical emollient. It is a naturally occurring animal oil that is a mixture of molecules made of cholesterol and various fatty acids. Lanolin is often removed from sheep's wool in the process of cleaning it. Its function in the sheep's wool is to protect and waterproof the wool. Other animal oils can be used as emollients (such as mink oil). Plant and vegetable oils are also used — avocado, sesame, and aloe vera oils are common ingredients in moisturizers.

aloe vera plant

Fats can also act as emollients. In order for this to happen, of course, the fats must not be saponified. This is arranged by using less than the amount of base needed to completely saponify all of the fat used in the soap recipe. With more chemistry knowledge, it is possible to calculate exactly the amount of a particular base needed to completely saponify the amounts of the specific fats used in a soap recipe. Then, in order to leave some of the fat intact, the calculated amount of base is reduced by some small percentage, which will be the percentage of fat left in the soap. The six soaps you made had a base reduction of about 6%. Some soap makers reduce the base by as much as 15%, but this can sometimes result in a soap that feels somewhat greasy.

Thickeners

Waxes are sometimes added to soaps to thicken or harden them. A thicker, harder soap preparation will dissolve more slowly in water, and last longer as a bar of soap. Most waxes such as beeswax, a commonly used natural soap ingredient, are complex mixtures of many chemicals. The major component is a mixture of chemicals in which a saturated fatty acid is linked to a saturated fatty alcohol. A fatty alcohol has an —OH group at the end of a long hydrocarbon chain. The linkage is like that in a fat molecule, but there is only a single —OH group in the fatty alcohol instead of the three —OH groups found in glycerol. This results in a molecule with properties somewhat similar to those of a fat, but which can take a more or less straight shape (much less complicated than the shape of a fat, with those three fatty acid chains all attached to the same molecule). This straight shape allows the molecules to pack together more closely, so it is harder and melts at a higher temperature.

Many waxes are solids at room temperature, but melt at relatively low temperatures, so they are easy to work with and easy to add to soap. When soaps are made from fats that are liquids at room temperature, the soaps tend to be softer. It is helpful to add wax to thicken and harden them (so the bar lasts longer). As you learned in *Activities 5* and *6,* attractive dispersion forces (van der Waals interactions) are stronger when hydrocarbon chains are longer and more saturated, and when molecules stack more neatly, the substance becomes solid and hard. Stronger attractive dispersion forces require more energy to break and send the molecules from the solid phase into the liquid phase. Therefore, longer saturated-chain molecules melt at higher temperatures. Paraffin, for example, consists of hydrocarbon chains containing at least 26 carbon atoms. (Paraffin is a wax sometimes used in home canning or candle-making as well as soap-making.)

Adjusting pH

When you dissolve soap in water, some of it reacts with water and produces a somewhat basic solution (pH > 7). The negatively charged carboxylate group, R–COO⁻, is a weak base and will increase the concentration of OH^- ions according to the equilibrium equation below. Typically, only 1 in 100,000 soap molecules react at any given time.

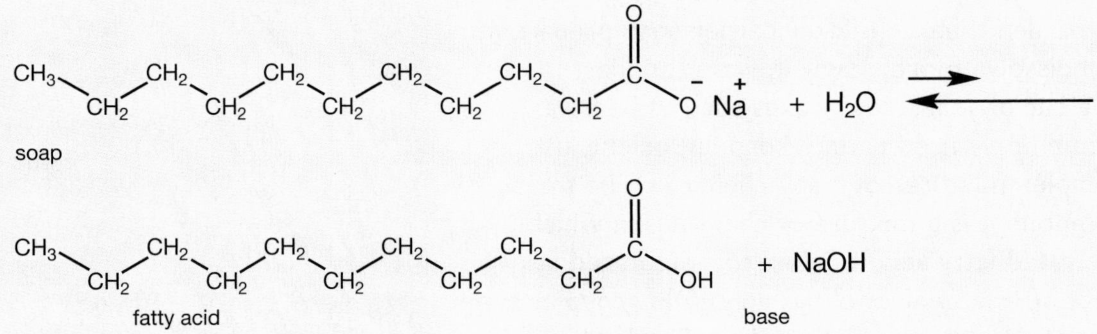
soap
+ H_2O
+ NaOH
fatty acid
base

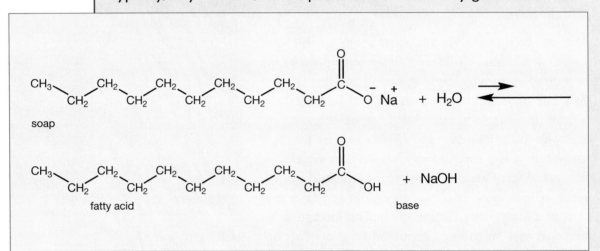

This basic solution can be harsh on your skin. One way to counteract this is to add an acid (to neutralize the base). Typically, citric acid is added because it occurs naturally (so people will be less likely to react to it) and it has a pH of 4 to 4.5, so it can lower the pH but not to a dangerous level. If you combine an acid at pH 4 with a base at pH 9, the pH of the resulting solution will have to be somewhere in between 4 and 9.

Foaming Agents

Foaming agents increase the lathering in soaps. They do this by lowering the surface tension of water. (Look back at *Activity 4* to see more details about the surface tension of water.) Lather is not necessarily related to cleaning ability, but most consumers think it is because of heavy advertising that pushes this idea. Laundry detergents for washing machines, for example, are carefully designed to clean with a minimum of suds, because suds interfere with the operation of the machine. But many people like lots of lather in their personal care products, so products like hand soaps and shampoos are often designed to produce extra bubbles. Fats that are used to increase lather are primarily coconut oil and palm kernel oil. These two oils contain nearly 50% lauric acid, a very short (12 carbon atoms) saturated fatty acid, as well as large amounts of myristic acid, a slightly larger (14 carbon atoms) saturated fatty acid. Soaps are rarely made from these oils alone, but they are often added to the mixture of fats to increase lather.

Bubbles (lather) can form more easily if the surface tension is reduced further. Soap is not the only molecule that can break the surface tension of water. Foaming agents also do this. Typical foaming agents are sodium lauryl sulfate and sodium laureth sulfate. Both are derived from coconuts.

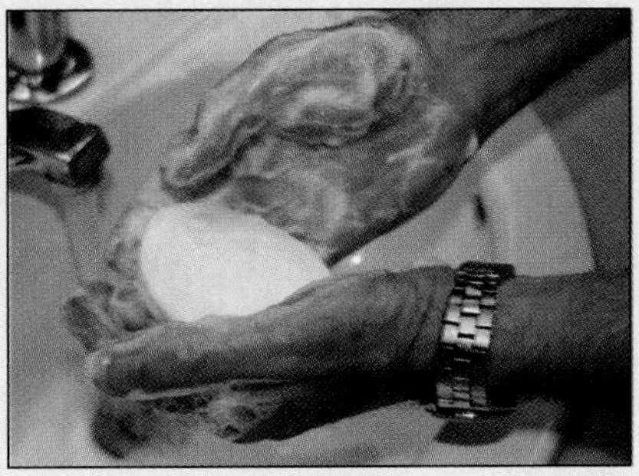

Checking Up

1. List four additives that you could include in making a soap.
2. Explain the difference between a humectant and an emollient.
3. Give three examples of emollients you could use in your soap.
4. What additive can be used to thicken a soap?
5. In your own words, explain how a thickening agent works.

What Do You Think Now?

At the beginning of this activity you were asked:

- **How can you develop a soap that has a moisturizer?**

What additives have you now decided to add to your soap recipe? Be sure to consider your marketing target group when choosing your additives. Will some of your chosen ingredients appeal to all soap users?

Chem Essential Questions

What does it mean?

Chemistry explains a macroscopic phenomenon (what you observe) with a description of what happens at the nanoscopic level (atoms and molecules) using symbolic structures as a way to communicate. Complete the chart below in your *Active Chemistry* log.

MACRO	NANO	SYMBOLIC
The look, feel, and odor of your soap must appeal to your target group. Make a list of the properties your soap will have.	*At the molecular level, what is responsible for the desired macroscopic properties of your soap? For example, the smell of your product might be due to an added chemical fragrance, often essential oils or ester compounds.*	*Be sure you know the structures of the chemical ingredients you are adding to your soap. Look them up and record them in your Active Chemistry log.*

How do you know?

Which chemical ingredients in the commercial soap are responsible for the desired properties that you will want in your soap?

Why do you believe?

There are many soap products designed specifically for hair, face, dry skin, oily skin, dandruff, laundry, dishes, etc. Would it be smart to use facial soap to remove tough automobile grease from your hands? Make sure that your soap's ingredients are chosen not only for marketing, but also the chemicals you add will get the job done.

Why should you care?

You want your soap to be commercially successful, so choosing your ingredients to satisfy your corporate executives, marketing department, and the target group must be done carefully. Explain why the ingredients you have chosen will do the job that the soap was intended to do.

Reflecting on the Activity and the Challenge

You now have compared the soap you are improving upon for your challenge, and the six soaps you made from different animal and vegetable fats. You also know what some different additives will do to your soap. You designed your final soap recipe and made the soap. A month from now, after the reaction is nearly complete, you can find out how well it worked. Now it's time to turn your attention to the fun part of completing the *Chapter Challenge* and marketing your soap.

Chem to Go

1. Look at the ingredients in a bottle of shampoo that you have at home. List all the ingredients and identify the functions of as many of the ingredients as you can. (See the *Chem Talk* section.)
2. What advantages would a soap made from two different fats have if one fat was a liquid at room temperature and the other was a solid at room temperature? Which additive(s) could help fix the problems arising from a bar soap made from a fat containing a single kind of fatty acid (one that was a liquid)?
3. What is the difference between a humectant and an emollient? List two examples of each.

4. ***Preparing for the Chapter Challenge***

   Devise several recipes for soap that you could try. Figure out which one will be the best one to try. Write down the reasons why you chose the one you did, and also the reasons why you rejected the others. Write down in your *Active Chemistry* log a detailed recipe for the soap you will make for your *Chapter Challenge*.

Inquiring Further

Esters

Research techniques for the synthesis of specific esters to add fragrance to your soap. (Your teacher may have procedures for producing esters in chemistry lab manuals that come with college chemistry books or other high school chemistry textbooks.) Identify an ester with a fragrance appropriate for a soap and develop a plan to synthesize it. After approval by and under the supervision of your teacher, make the ester.

Be sure your teacher reviews your plan before you begin and that you understand the safe handling of substances you will use. Carry out your plan only under adult supervision.

Chem at Work

Susan Soros

Owner, Soap Goddess® Handmade Soap Company, Avalon, TX

Susan Soros is part of a booming cottage industry, making and selling soaps from her home in rural Texas. As the founder and primary operator of the Soap Goddess® Handmade Soap Company, Susan makes her products from scratch in her own workshop and sells them over the Internet to customers worldwide—some as far away as Japan!

Susan's interest in soap-making began when she saw homemade soap products at a farmer's market. She went to the library and found information about the chemical processes involved in making soap. "The chemistry is amazing," she says. "Sodium hydroxide (NaOH) is a dangerous chemical that can cause severe burns if it is not handled safely. But when you add oil . . . there's a transformation into a product that can moisturize and keep skin healthy."

Susan went to work creating her own soap recipes, experimenting with different oils, scents and natural additives. Once she realized that it wasn't very complicated, the idea of launching her own company was born.

Susan's experiments taught her a lot about the chemistry of soap, which involves a reaction called *saponification*. "The process itself involves adding an acid (fatty acids, oils) to a base (lye or sodium hydroxide) to create a salt, which is technically what a soap is," she says. "I experiment by using different oils in different quantities."

She has learned that different oils can yield different results. Palm oil, she says, makes soap harden. Coconut oil creates lather, but too much can dry out the skin. On the other hand, she says, olive oil is a great moisturizer.

Dr. Donald Orth

Research Scientist, Neutrogena Corp., Los Angeles, CA

Dr. Orth is the director of research for a major manufacturer of soaps and other skin products. He oversees the tests on products in the company's labs. In a stability test, a product is exposed to different temperatures for long periods of time to determine the effects on its chemical composition.

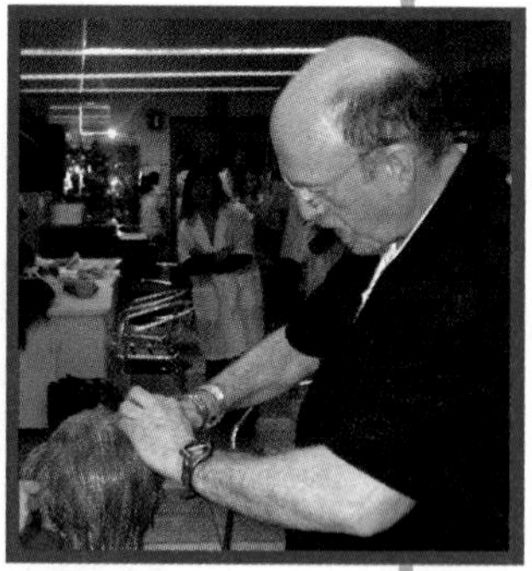

Steven Milit

Beauty School Instructor, New York, NY

Steven Milit teaches cosmetology at a Manhattan beauty school. He knows a lot about the chemistry that is used in hair styling. He explains that hair dyes are a solution of two reactive ingredients, hydrogen peroxide (H_2O_2) and ammonia (NH_3), that have dramatic effects on the follicle.

Soap Sense Assessment

Your *Chapter Challenge* is to create a procedure to make a soap from natural products that can be sold at local stores. You will prepare two presentations for your company—one for the corporation executives, and a second for the marketing department.

In the presentation for the corporation executives, explain your objectives in designing your soap, and the steps you went through to achieve those objectives. You should create a display board to accompany this presentation. On your display, you should include a representation of the soap-making process you used, photos or drawings to illustrate it, and descriptions of all of the ingredients, including the additives, with explanations of the chemistry behind how these ingredients give your soap the properties it has.

The presentation for the marketing department should be a more detailed written report to give them information they can offer potential investors explaining why your soap will have the properties you expect. It should also analyze which methods you rejected and why you rejected them. In this presentation, it is important to illustrate the strengths your soap will have in the marketplace and the type of marketing campaign that you think would be effective in selling the soap. You may design packaging, magazine or newspaper ads, radio spots, TV commercials, billboards, or any other support materials you believe will be useful.

Chemistry Content

To begin, you should review all of the activities that you have completed. You can skim through the text and your *Active Chemistry* log to help remind you of the chemistry concepts in each activity.

Activity 1: You investigated the effectiveness of soaps, including solubility and which properties you may require for different situations. You also learned about hard versus soft water, the problems associated with soap scum and the difference between soap and detergent.

Activity 2: You learned about molecular structure and the Lewis dot diagrams. Understanding the shapes of molecules is crucial to understanding how the molecules interact with each other and how the interactions create the behavior of substances like soap.

Activity 3: You observed the difference between polar and non-polar substances and found which could be removed by water (a polar molecule) and which could be removed by kerosene (a non-polar molecule). You also learned that soap is a chemical that has one part that is polar and one part that is non-polar.

Activity 4: You modeled the micellular structures that soap molecules take when dissolved in polar and non-polar liquids. You may have also surmised that soap's cleaning action is to surround non-polar particles with micelles of soap dissolved in water. When the soapy water is washed away, the non-polar particles remain encased in the micelles, so they can be washed away with the water as well.

Activity 5: You compared soaps made from fats that have carbon chains of different lengths. You learned how varying the length of the carbon chain changes the properties of a soap, such as the melting temperature.

Activity 6: You used a model to predict the melting point behaviors of three fatty acids with the same number of carbons but different degrees of unsaturation. You then tested your prediction by determining the melting temperatures. You also examined the behaviors of four soaps made from fats with four different degrees of unsaturation.

Activity 7: You measured the pH of a number of common soaps. You learned ways in which to make the soap less dangerous.

Activity 8: You compared a purchased soap to soaps made by classmates using a variety of measures, including a quantitative test of cleaning effectiveness. You also evaluated the pros and cons of different fats as a foundation for a soap product. You read about factors that could appeal to people purchasing soap, such as moisturizers, thickeners, ingredients to adjust pH, and foaming agents that enhance lathering.

You may want to make a chart that shows the activity number, some chemistry concepts in the activity, and some ideas as to how you can use these concepts as part of your Soap Manufacturing Presentation. Your chart may include whether the activity provides content for the corporate presentation or the marketing presentation. You should pay particular attention to the *Reflecting on the Activity and the Challenge*, *Chem Essential Questions*, and *Preparing for the Chapter Challenge* sections. You should also compare your list with that given in the *Chem You Learned* summary.

You may decide to do the first activity as a group to ensure that everybody understands how to proceed. After completing the first activity, each team member can be assigned two or three activities.

Activity #	Chemistry concepts	How to use concepts

Criteria

Before beginning the chapter, your teacher led a class discussion to get a sense of what criteria should be used to judge the quality of work for this Soap Manufacturing Presentation. Now that you have considerable understanding of the chemistry concepts, think about and discuss what would make an informative corporate presentation and a great, entertaining marketing presentation. What characteristics should a quality product have? How good do your explanations of the chemistry need to be? How much weight should be given to the presentation and how much to the accompanying written materials? The rubric your class develops can be a useful tool for your team to check the quality of your work and to ensure that you have included all necessary parts of the project.

Preparing for the Chapter Challenge

- Choose Your Soap

Your team's next step would then be to decide on the soap that you want to present and the properties of that soap.

- Write Your Explanations

Your presentation to the corporate board will have to include the chemistry involved in your soap-making process. Your presentation and related literature to the marketing group will have to include the design process, including rejected ideas, modifications on earlier ideas and how your soap's properties make it a desirable consumer product.

- **Chemistry content is necessary, but not enough.**

You must also find an interesting and informative way of presenting your information. Remember also, that when you are presenting your ideas you are in the role of a teacher. Teachers use models that help promote learning. One model is the 7E instructional model. In the 7E model, you begin by *engaging* the audience as well as *eliciting* their prior knowledge. This means that you use a way to find out what they already know so that you can be more aware of this during the teaching and learning process. This is then followed by an *explore phase* where the participants are involved in finding out about something and experiencing some phenomenon. After the explore phase, you can help them *explain* what they experienced. You can then *elaborate* on the concepts and describe where else they may observe similar events. You then end with an *extend* where you give the audience something to think about that is beyond what you have introduced. The last stage of the 7E model is *evaluate*. The evaluation of whether the corporate executives or marketing team understood your presentation takes place throughout the cycle—through the *engage, elicit, explore, explain, elaborate* and *extend*.

- Manage Your Time

You have a sense of how you want to proceed and what you want the final product to be. You now have to allocate the work. How much time do you have to complete the project? When is the presentation? How will you get everything done in this time frame? Who will be working on the written materials and the posters, including the description of chemistry concepts? How will you ensure that each member's work meets the standard of excellence so that everybody on the team gets an A? Create a time chart for the challenge. Divide the responsibilities. How much time will each take? Some work can be done individually as homework. Leave time to review each other's work.

Engineering/Technology Design

Reflect on the engineering/technology design process. Recall the successes and disappointments from the *mini-challenge*. How can you use the feedback that you received to improve your show? At this point, you are starting the design cycle again.

Good Luck with Your Soap Sales Pitch!

Chem You Learned

- **Saponification** is the hydrolysis of a triglyceride fat with a strong base to make **soap**.
- **Quantitative analysis** involves valid observations using measurements and calculations.
- **Qualitative analysis** involves valid observations made without measurements.
- **Valence electrons** are those electrons located in the outermost energy level of an atom.
- The **Lewis dot structure** of an atom represents the valence electrons of the atom.
- The sharing of an electron pair between two bonded atoms is a **covalent bond**.
- The ability of an atom to attract electrons to its nucleus is called its **electronegativity**.
- When there is a significant difference in the electronegativity of two covalently bonded atoms, it is called a **polar covalent bond**.
- When there is little or no difference in the electronegativity between the two atoms involved in a covalent bond, it is a **non-polar covalent bond.**
- Charged particles with like charges exhibit **electrostatic repulsion**.
- **Electrostatic attraction** occurs between charged particles that have opposite charges.
- When a small clump of soap molecules encircles a "dirt" particle, it is called a **micelle**.
- **Saturated fats**, such as stearic acid, contain only single bonds between two carbon atoms.
- Other fats, such as oleic and linolenic acid, can have double bonds between carbon atoms and these are classified as **unsaturated fats**.
- **Hydrogenation** is a process where hydrogen molecules are added to the double bonds of an unsaturated fat.
- The double bonds of unsaturated fats can exist in either the ***cis-*** or ***trans-*** form. Most animal fats are found to exist in the ***cis-*** form.
- Common **functional groups**, such as **esters**, **alcohols**, and **carboxyl groups** are found in the hydrolysis reaction of fats.

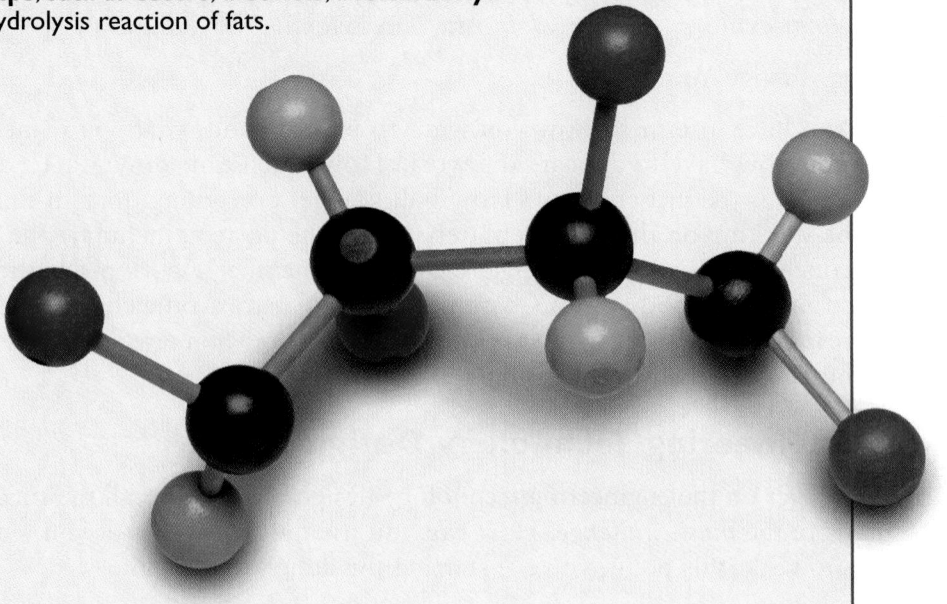

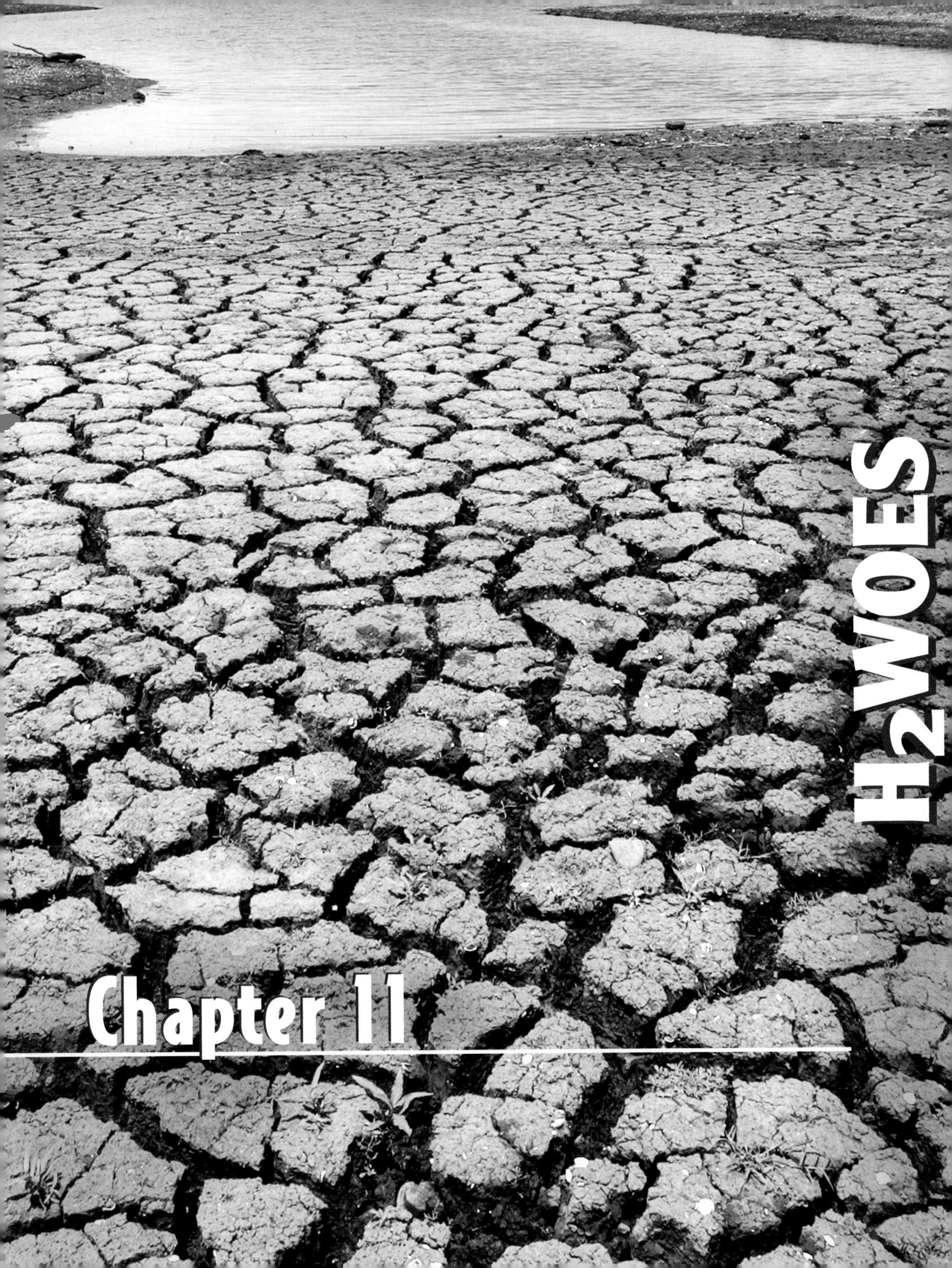

Chapter 11

H_2WOES

Chapter Challenge

11

H_2Woes

Scenario

Thirsty? If you'd like to quench that thirst, you could head to the sink, turn on the tap, and fill a tall glass with cool, clean water. While this is a common experience for most of us, nearly one-quarter of the people in the world do not have access to quality drinking water. As the world population increases and industrialization spreads to the less developed regions, the supply of safe water is becoming endangered and even scarcer

throughout the world. Currently, one-third of deaths throughout the world are due to the lack of clean water. Approximately 80% of all diseases are related to water quality and sanitation. In addition, the United Nations Educational, Scientific and Cultural Organization, UNESCO, reports that during your adult life, 70% of the world could be facing water shortages. All of this should make your next trip for a glass of water a bit more thought provoking!

Your Challenge

You have been assigned by an international health organization, like UNESCO, to improve the water supplies of a number of communities in Latin America. Because of water-borne chemicals and microbes, the communities have been forced to rely on bottled water for drinking. Many streams in the areas are suspected of being contaminated with toxic minerals and organic chemicals, possibly introduced by drainage from mines, agricultural fields or industrial sites.

The communities are of three types:

- mining and logging areas that have drawn water from mountain streams
- farming areas that rely on wells, rivers, swamps, or lakes as sources of water
- industrialized areas that depend on water reservoirs fed by rivers and wells.

Naturally occurring contaminants of water sources in the areas vary widely because the minerals range from those of volcanic origin in the mountainous areas to principally sedimentary rocks in the farming or urbanized areas. You must predict the most likely contaminants in each area and specify a series of preferred steps for purifying the water. You must be prepared to explain to the organization the chemical processes that are behind these steps and why they are the best choices for assuring the purity of the water supplies.

ChemCorner

Chemistry in H_2*Woes*

- Solubility factors
- Periodic trends
- Carcinogens
- Precipitation reactions
- Chemical bonding
- Spectral absorption
- Ion-specific electrodes
- Electrostatic forces
- Ionic equilibria
- Tyndall Effect
- Laws of thermodynamics
- Toxicity limits
- Chlorination of water
- Chemical reaction rates
- Order and disorder
- Suspensions
- K_{sp}

DISINFECTION
FILTER
CHLORINE
ULTRAVIOLET PURIFICATION
DRINKING WATER
POND WATER

The same decisions were made in your own community, probably many years ago, and the choice of the water purification system can serve as a guide for how an efficient, economical system may be designed.

You will need to complete the following tasks:

- Decide what major water contaminants may be expected in each area, and how they got there.
- Estimate the amounts of contaminants that purification plants should be designed to remove.
- Develop a process diagram or flowchart for the water purification procedures that you will propose.
- Explain the chemistry behind the steps in purifying the water.
- Present to the class the merits of your approaches toward water purification.

Criteria

How will you determine whether your purification measures will work for the various types of communities? How could you make it clear to your classmates that the purification steps you choose are essential? How will you explain the science that makes the purification processes possible? You must decide as a class what evidence should be used to decide if your team has successfully completed the classroom challenge. Come to a consensus on what you will address in your rubric for this project and determine how you will value each piece. As you discuss, you may decide that some or all of the following qualities should be graded:

- Demonstration of an understanding of the culture's water issues.
- Assessment of the solutes in your specific area.
- Success of your procedures for your specific area.
- Variety of purification techniques you explain and justify.
- Difficulty and length of the procedures you carry out.
- Accuracy of the chemistry principles involved at the macroscopic, nanoscopic, and symbolic levels.
- Clarity, thoroughness, and organization of the documentation of your purification activities.

Activity 1 What's in Natural Water?

What Do You See?

TAP
RIVER
OCEAN
POND

GOALS

In this activity you will:

- Explain the pathways that water takes in cycling between ocean, air, and land.
- Review ionic and covalent bonds and their corresponding properties.
- Learn the identities and properties of some solutes that enter our water supply.
- Practice presenting and reporting on water and its basic chemistry.

What Do You Think?

Look at the picture of pond water. This may resemble one natural source that you will face in your purification task. Compare this to a glass of tap water.

- **What type of substances, both living (biotic) and nonliving (abiotic), are found in a sample of pond water?**
- **How do you think these substances end up in each water sample?**

The *What Do You Think?* questions are provided to get you engaged in the activity. They are meant to grab your attention. They are also used to find out what you already know or think you know. Don't worry about being right or wrong. Discussing what you think you know is an important step in learning.

Record your ideas about these questions in your *Active Chemistry* log. Be prepared to discuss your responses with your small group and the class.

Investigate

In this activity, you will look at the composition of natural waters. In *Part A*, you will look at the natural cycle of water and the sources of the drinking water. Then in *Part B*, your group will explore four possible substances that enter the water supply as they go through the natural water cycle: minerals, gases, fertilizers, and organic molecules.

Safety goggles and a lab apron must be worn *at all times* in a chemistry lab.

Keep the powders away from your skin, eyes, and mouth. Some can be irritating and/or abrasive.

Part A: Analysis of the Flow of Water

1. In a simplified model of the water cycle, water is found both on the surface of the Earth and in the ground. This water can move into the atmosphere through evaporation and transpiration (the release of water vapor by plants). The water in the atmosphere can return to Earth by condensation and precipitation.

   a) Draw a diagram that shows the water cycle.

2. Most of the Earth's water is saltwater and is found in the oceans. A small fraction (2.6%) of the water on Earth is fresh water and 76% of this is found in ice caps and glaciers.

   a) What other information about water is shown in the diagram below?

Distribution of Earth's Water

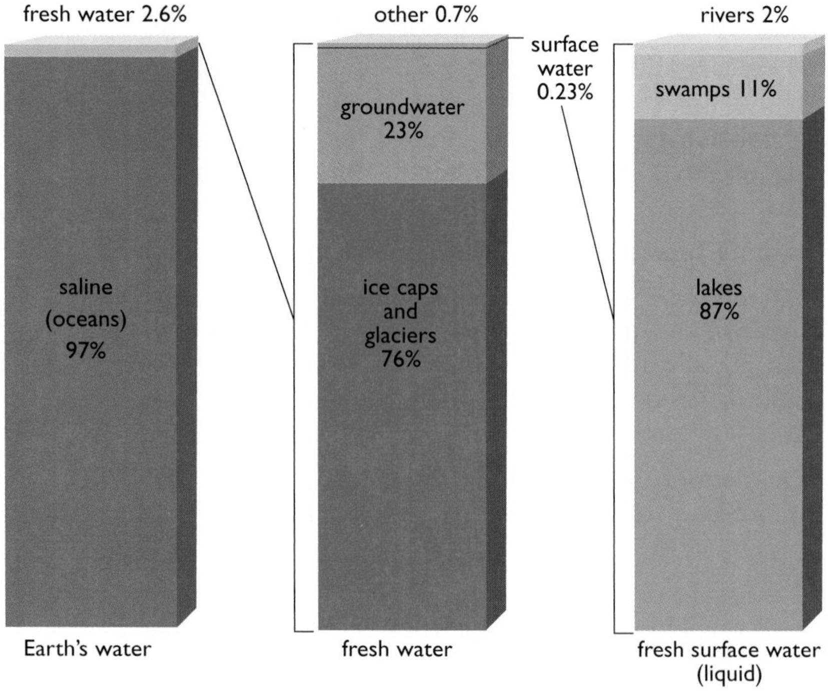

fresh water 2.6%
saline (oceans) 97%
Earth's water
other 0.7%
groundwater 23%
ice caps and glaciers 76%
fresh water
surface water 0.23%
rivers 2%
swamps 11%
lakes 87%
fresh surface water (liquid)

   b) In your *Active Chemistry* log, write a brief story about what happens to a typical drop of water over 100 years. Consider where it would spend most of this time. Be sure to use the terms shown in the diagram. Be creative, but do your best to accurately represent the "life" of the water drop. When finished, share your story with your group.

   c) What water sources provide the world with its drinking water?

   d) What specific water source provides your community with its drinking water?

Part B: Becoming an Expert on the Solutes of Natural Waters

In this part of the activity, you will divide your group into four *expert* groups: (I) minerals, (II) gases, (III) organic compounds, and (IV) fertilizers. Experts from different groups will work together. After they complete their analyses, the experts will return to their groups and report findings. Each expert group will investigate one group of solutes present in the natural water supply. Follow the directions for your expert group.

Expert Group I: Solubility of Minerals

Surface water and groundwater may encounter many minerals as they move toward a water-treatment facility. Some of these minerals may dissolve in the water. The minerals can be healthful and good tasting or they may reduce water quality and even be hazardous. You will have an opportunity to test some common minerals to see if they are soluble in water. Your teacher will provide samples of minerals such as halite, calcite, gypsum, dolomite, magnesite, and pyrite.

Mineral	Formula	Cation	Anion	Observation of solubility (yes or no)
halite	$NaCl$	Na^+	Cl^-	
calcite	$CaCO_3$	Ca^{2+}	CO_3^{2-}	
gypsum	$CaSO_4{\cdot}2H_2O$*	Ca^{2+}	SO_4^{2-}	
dolomite	$CaMg(CO_3)_2$	Ca^{2+}, Mg^{2+}	CO_3^{2-}	
magnesite	$MgCO_3$	Mg^{2+}	CO_3^{2-}	
pyrite	FeS_2	Fe^{2+}	S^{2-}	

** The "$2H_2O$" in this formula indicates that two water molecules per $CaSO_4$ are part of the crystalline solid.*

1. Obtain a sample of each mineral from your teacher.
2. The table above shows the ions that make up each of the minerals. Copy the table into your *Active Chemistry* log. If your instructor has given you extra or different minerals, add or substitute their names, chemical formulas, and positive ions (*cations*) and negative ions (*anions*) in the table.
3. Use a mortar and pestle to grind a small sample of each mineral into a powder.
4. Test the solubility of each mineral in water by observing if a *very small* amount of a ground sample of the mineral seems to disappear into the water as the test tube is shaken.

   a) Record the results in your *Active Chemistry* log.

   b) Compare your results to the Table of Solubility Rules in the appendix. Do these minerals follow the solubility rules?

Expert Group II: Forms of Gases in Solution

You may not think of gases such as nitrogen (N_2), oxygen (O_2), carbon dioxide (CO_2), sulfur dioxide (SO_2), and ammonia (NH_3) as solutes in water. However, they are part of natural waters. You will use universal indicator (UI) to observe the pH when these gases are dissolved in water.

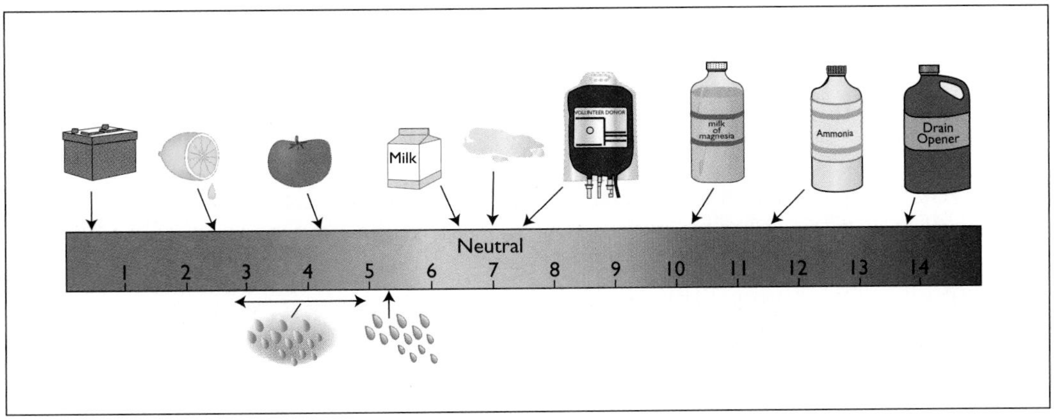
Milk
milk of magnesia
Ammonia
Drain Opener
Neutral
1 2 3 4 5 6 7 8 9 10 11 12 13 14

Gas	Formula	Final UI color	pH in solution
carbon dioxide			
sulfur dioxide			
ammonia		(predicted)	(predicted)

Sulfur dioxide is a toxic gas. Please be careful when generating this. You should work with your bag under the hood. When finished, leave this bag under the hood sealed. Only use it to extract the small sample of SO_2.

Sulfuric acid is caustic; be careful when handling this chemical.

Even small amounts of the acids used can cause injuries to skin and eyes, as well as damaging clothing.

Be sure to wash well after handling the acids, and clean up even small spills immediately.

Have a large beaker or pan ready to place the zipper bag in when you are finished so the contents do not spill.

1. Copy the table above into your *Active Chemistry* log.
2. Fill a well of a spot plate with UI.
3. You will next need to generate CO_2, carbon dioxide. To do this, take approximately 2.00 g of the calcium carbonate ($CaCO_3$) and place it in a plastic zipper-seal bag. Squeeze all of the air out of the bag and seal it almost all the way.
4. In the small opening, add two droppers full (whole droppers full —not drops) of hydrochloric acid (HCl). Completely seal the bag and shake *gently*.
5. You will collect some of the carbon dioxide with a plastic pipette. To do this, first squeeze all of the air out of the pipette. Slide it, still squeezed, into the bag. Use the tip of the pipette to open the bag slightly. Then release the pipette and let it collect the carbon dioxide gas.
6. Bubble the carbon dioxide gas in the spot plate of UI.
   a) Record the final UI color after the bubbling.
   b) Record the pH.
7. Fill another one of the spot plates with UI.
8. If your instructor has not prepared a sulfur-dioxide solution, you will need to generate SO_2, sulfur dioxide. Place about 2.00 g of sodium sulfite (Na_2SO_3) in the bottom corner of a plastic zipper-seal bag. Squeeze out all of the air out of the bag and seal it almost all the way.
9. In the small opening, add two droppers full (whole droppers full—not drops) of sulfuric acid (6 M H_2SO_4). *Seal the bag immediately.*
10. You will collect some of the sulfur dioxide with a plastic pipette. To do this, first squeeze all of the air out of the pipette. Slide it, still squeezed, into the bag. Use the tip of the pipette to open the bag slightly. Then release the pipette and let it collect the sulfur dioxide gas.
11. Bubble the sulfur dioxide gas in the spot plate of UI.
    a) Record the final UI color after the bubbling.
    b) Record the pH.
12. When many gases dissolve in water, they react with the water to form ***polyatomic ions***. For example, when CO_2 dissolves in water, you can represent it by $CO_2(aq)$. Once in solution, it can react with the water to form the bicarbonate ion, HCO_3^-, and the hydrogen ion, H^+, according to the equation:

$$CO_2(aq) + H_2O(l) \leftrightharpoons HCO_3^-(aq) + H^+(aq)$$

    a) In your *Active Chemistry* log, write a complete reaction for aqueous sulfur dioxide and water. You may want to use the polyatomic ion chart on the next page to help you predict this reaction.
13. Other gases, such as ammonia, have different effects on the pH of a solution.
    a) Complete the following equation for aqueous ammonia $NH_3(aq)$.
    $NH_3(aq) + H_2O(l) \rightarrow$??

Common Polyatomic Ions

acetate (CH_3COO^-)	cyanide (CN^-)	nitrate (NO_3^-)
ammonium (NH_4^+)	dichromate ($Cr_2O_7^{2-}$)	nitrite (NO_2^-)
arsenate (AsO_4^{3+})	hydrogen carbonate, bicarbonate (HCO_3^-)	oxalate ($C_2O_4^{2-}$)
arsenite (AsO_3^{3+})	(di)hydrogen phosphate ($H_2PO_4^-$)	perchlorate (ClO_4^-)
benzoate ($C_6H_5COO^-$)	(mono)hydrogen phosphate (HPO_4^{2-})	periodate (IO_4^-)
borate (BO_3^{3-})	hydrogen sulfate, bisulfate (HSO_4^-)	permanganate (MnO_4^-)
carbonate (CO_3^{2-})	hydrogen sulfide, bisulfide (HS^-)	phosphate (PO_4^{3-})
chlorate (ClO_3^-)	hydrogen sulfite, bisulfite (HSO_3^-)	phosphite (PO_3^{3-})
chlorite (ClO_2^-)	hydroxide (OH^-)	silicate (SiO_3^{2-})
chromate (CrO_4^{2-})	hypochlorite (ClO^-)	sulfate (SO_4^{2-})
cyanate (CNO^-)	iodate (IO_3^-)	sulfite (SO_3^{2-})

b) In your table, fill in your predictions for what would happen if ammonia was bubbled into a solution of universal indicator. Use the equation you wrote on the previous page and your knowledge of pH to help you in your prediction.

Expert Group III: Solubility of Organic Compounds

Natural waters interact with a number of organic compounds. Some of these compounds come from natural sources. Others are the result of human interaction with the environment.

1. Obtain vials of sample organic compounds from your teacher. Each vial contains approximately 0.10 g (2–3 drops) of the compound.
2. Copy the table below into your *Active Chemistry* log. The table shows the structural formula of each compound. If your teacher has given you extra or different organic compounds, add or substitute their names and chemical formulas.
3. Add 3.0 mL of water to each vial. Stopper the vial and shake vigorously. Allow to settle and separate (15-30 s).

The organic compounds must all be considered toxic (some are very toxic). Do not breathe the fumes, or allow exposure to skin or eyes.

Some of the organic compounds are flammable. Do not get them near flames or sparks.

Clean up even small spills of the organic compounds immediately and rinse any towels used thoroughly with water before disposing of them.

Organic compound	Chemical formula	Observation of solubility
ethanol	CH_3CH_2OH	
1-hexanol	$CH_3CH_2CH_2CH_2CH_2CH_2OH$	
n-hexane	$CH_3CH_2CH_2CH_2CH_2CH_3$	
n-octane	$CH_3CH_2CH_2CH_2CH_2CH_2CH_2CH_3$	
urea	$(NH_2)_2CO$	
glucose	$CH_2(OH)CH(OH)CH(OH)CH(OH)CH(OH)CHO$	
oleic acid	$CH_3(CH_2)_7CH{=}CH(CH_2)_7COOH$	
ethylene glycol	$CH_2(OH)CH_2OH$	

Dispose of the materials as directed by your teacher.

Clean up your workstation.

Wash your hands and arms thoroughly after the activity.

a) Record the appearance of the mixture in your *Active Chemistry* log. Note if the substance is soluble, slightly soluble, or insoluble.

b) Review each result and the corresponding chemical formula. In your *Active Chemistry* log, suggest why some of the organic compounds are much more soluble than others.

Expert Group IV: Fertilizers in Water

Plants require three primary mineral nutrients: nitrogen, phosphorus, and potassium. These are the nutrients found in commercial fertilizers. Some commercial fertilizers containing these elements are: ammonium nitrate, NH_4NO_3; calcium superphosphate, $Ca(H_2PO_4)_2$; and potassium carbonate, K_2CO_3.

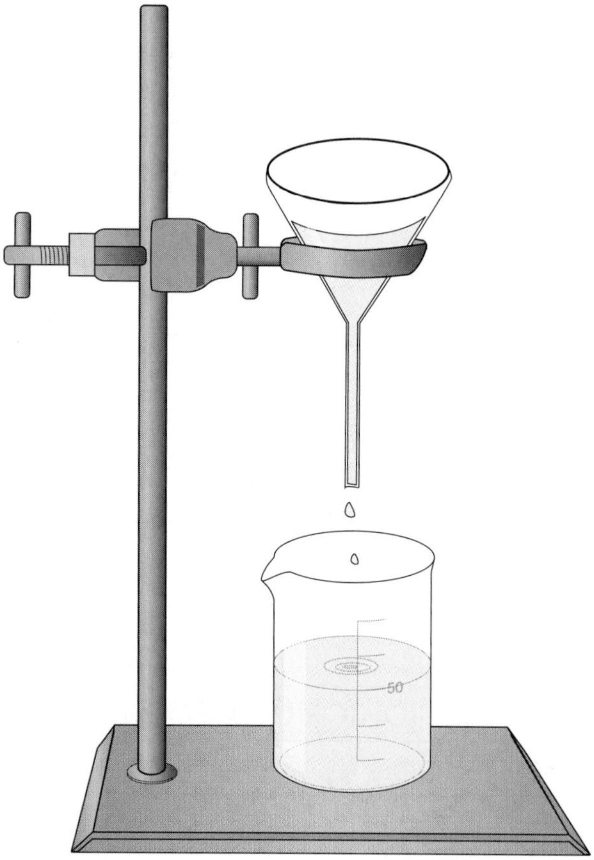
50

1. Add 10.0 mL of de-ionized water to a clean beaker. Measure the water temperature.

   a) Record the temperature in your *Active Chemistry* log.

2. With stirring, add solid compound to the water until no more solid will dissolve. Measure the temperature of the solution. If the temperature changed as the solid dissolved, wait for it to settle close to its initial value.

3. Find the mass of a clean 50-mL beaker and a clean watch glass. You will use the watch glass as a lid for the beaker.

   a) Record this mass in your *Active Chemistry* log.

4. Filter the solution into the clean 50-mL beaker.

5. Evaporate the water from the solution using a hot plate set on low heat. Be careful to evaporate the filtrate slowly to avoid splattering. Use the watch glass to catch any splatter. When it is nearly dry, you might prefer to leave it overnight in a warm place to dry out completely.

   a) Determine the mass of solid that dissolved in the 10.0 mL of water by subtracting the mass of the beaker, watch glass, and solid from the earlier recorded masses of the beaker and the watch glass. Record this solubility value, in grams per 100 mL of water, in your *Active Chemistry* log.

   b) Convert your g/100 mL of water value to ppm (mg/L of water). The term ppm stands for parts per million. The concentration expressed in mg/L has the same numerical value when expressed in ppm for water solutions. Show your mathematical steps and your value in your *Active Chemistry* log.

Chem Talk

THE COMPOSITION OF NATURAL WATERS

The Hydrological (Water) Cycle

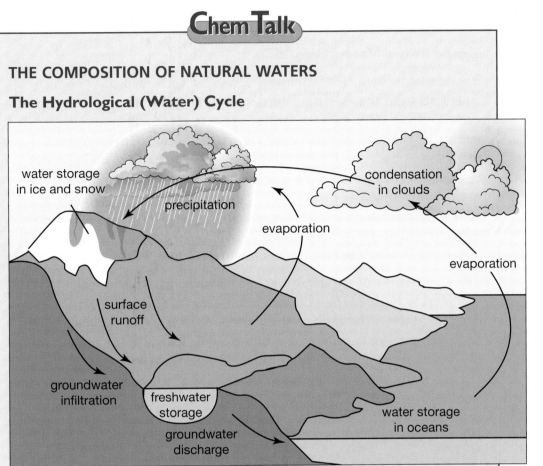

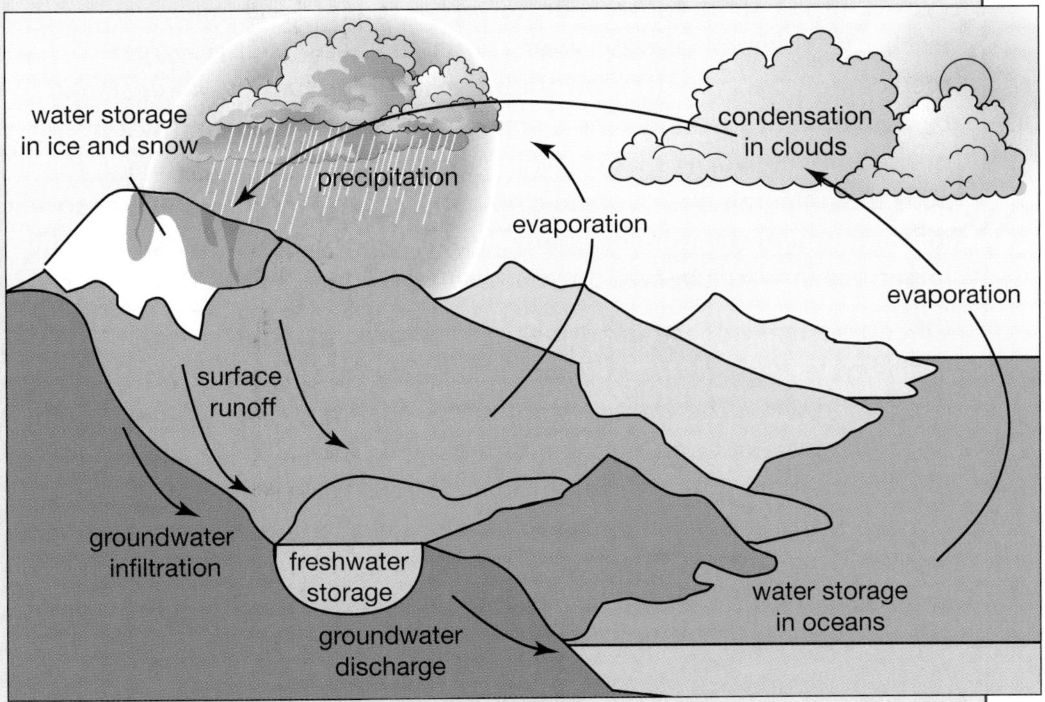
water storage
in ice and snow
precipitation
condensation
in clouds
evaporation
evaporation
surface
runoff
groundwater
infiltration
freshwater
storage
groundwater
discharge
water storage
in oceans

In order to know what impurities might be present in a water supply it is useful to trace the pathways water takes in cycling around the globe. The collection of pathways is called the **hydrologic cycle**. It includes:

- flowing surface water in oceans, lakes, reservoirs, rivers and streams
- frozen water in snow and glaciers
- atmospheric water as vapor and as droplets in clouds and rain
- groundwater in underground **aquifers** running through porous rocks.

In addition to flowing between regions as a liquid, water can be transported as vapor.

Water available for purification comes from both the surface fresh waters and groundwaters. The water available for purification from groundwater or lakes and rivers is being depleted rapidly in some regions, largely by irrigation of crops. Once depleted, the aquifers are replenished very slowly because of the slow movement of water underground.

Chem Words

hydrologic cycle: the constant circulation of water from the sea, through the atmosphere, to the land, and eventual return to the atmosphere by way of transpiration and evaporation from the land and evaporation from the sea.

aquifer: a structure of porous rock, sand, or gravel that holds water underground.

Chem Words

polar covalent bond: a covalent bond in which one end of the bond is more negatively charged than the other because of unequal sharing of electrons.

hydrogen bond: a very strong type of dipole-dipole attraction in which a hydrogen atom is bridged between two highly electronegative atoms, usually F, O, or N. The H is covalently linked to one of the electronegative atoms, and a hydrogen bond results from the strong electrostatic attraction to the other.

Water in the Natural World

Because water is such a wonderful solvent, it ends up picking up many chemicals from the environment during its trip through the hydrological cycle. Despite strict controls on sewage treatment and industrial discharge, pollution of waterways continues. Water is also a great medium for the growth of organisms that can be harmful if consumed by humans. In short, the simple answer to "What's in natural water?" is *practically everything* that the water contacts. As you have seen in the activities, minerals, gases, organic compounds, and fertilizers will dissolve in water. You might wonder how you could ever hope to remove all the impurities in water. In fact, do you have to remove them all?

Of course, many of the impurities are removed naturally at some point in the cycle. Most of the salts and other impurities in ocean water are left behind when the water evaporates. Wetlands are sometimes referred to as "nature's kidneys" because of their ability to improve the quality of water. Organisms that live in wetlands, rivers, lakes, and oceans can remove many harmful chemicals through their natural processes. As water slowly moves through the ground on its way to aquifers, many impurities are filtered out. Material suspended in the water can settle out in reservoirs.

However, as cities grow and wetlands are drained, many of these processes are being overwhelmed. Also, drainage of fertilizers, pesticides, and herbicides from farms, lawns, and golf courses has sent these dangerous chemicals into water supplies. Preventing some of these sources of contamination might be one part of the answer. However, for the purposes of your *Chapter Challenge*, you will focus on the treatment of contaminated water in order to purify it. First, consider why water is such a good solvent for a variety of compounds.

The Chemistry behind Water as a Solvent

Water is a unique molecule because of its small size and the two **polar covalent bonds** between the hydrogen and oxygen atoms. This polarity is a result of the difference in electronegativity (EN) beween the two atoms, with oxygen being more electronegative. The two partially positive H atoms of water are attracted to the partially negative O atom of nearby water molecules, forming what are called **hydrogen bonds**. These transient intermolecular attractions between adjacent water molecules are not true bonds but they are responsible for water's unusual physical properties.

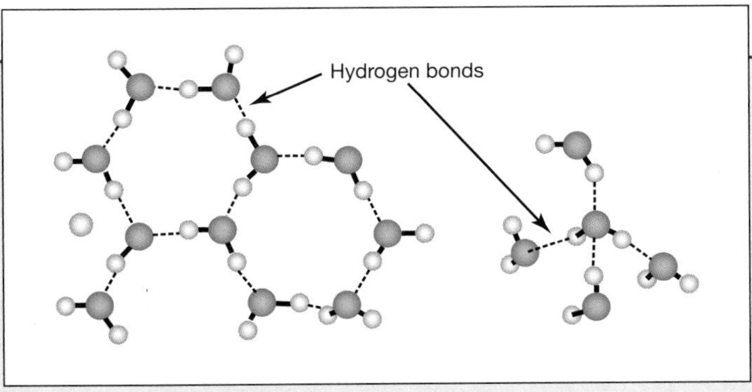
Hydrogen bonds

The hydrogen bonds result in water having four properties that allow for life to exist on this planet:

- the cohesive nature of water molecules (low volatility, high boiling point)
- the ability to moderate temperature (heat capacity)
- the lower density of ice (ice floats in water)
- water's remarkable ability to act as a solvent (as revealed in this activity).

In general, the more polarized a compound is, the more readily it dissolves in water. This is because of the strong electrostatic interaction of the water dipole with cations, anions, and other dipolar substances. You can make predictions about whether a bond is ionic or covalent by referring to the **electronegativity** of each individual atom. Electronegativity (EN) is an arbitrary scale, ranging from 0 to 4.0. It measures the difference in attraction for electrons between two atoms in a chemical bond. The atom that has the greater attraction for the electrons is assigned the higher electronegativity. Thus, the atom with the higher EN is the more negative of the atoms in the bond. F is the most electronegative and the alkali metals the least. Each element's electronegativity can be found in chemistry tables (see appendix). A large difference of EN between two atoms gives a more **ionic bond**. A small difference of EN will produce a non-polar **covalent bond**. However, ionic compounds with multiple charges on the ions (such as $Ca_3(PO_4)_2$) or small ions (such as LiF) may have limited solubility because of the large energy required to separate the ions in the solid.

Bond Types Based on Electronegativity (EN) Differences

EN difference	Bond type	Example
greater than 2.0	ionic bond	NaCl, where Na = 0.9, Cl = 3.0
1.6 – 2.0	polar covalent (if both nonmetals)/ ionic (if one is a metal)	H_2O, where H = 2.1, O = 3.5 LiBr, where Li = 1.0, Br = 2.8
0.5 – 1.6	polar covalent bond	CO_2, where C = 2.5, O = 3.5
less than 0.5	non-polar covalent bond	CH_4, where C = 2.5, H = 2.1

Chem Words

electronegativity: a measure of the ability of an element to pull electrons towards itself. In a chemical bond, a difference in electronegativities of two bonded atoms makes the bond polar, or ionic, if the difference is sufficiently large.

ionic bond: a bond resulting from attractions between oppositely charged ions. The ions may be formed by electron transfer from metallic elements to nonmetallic elements or they may be composed of several atoms (polyatomic ions).

covalent bond: a bond between atoms in which electrons are shared.

Chem Words

mineral: a naturally occurring, inorganic solid material that consists of atoms and/or molecules that are arranged in a regular pattern and has a characteristic chemical composition and physical properties.

polyatomic ion: a group of atoms strongly bound to each other and carrying a definite positive or negative charge. Most polyatomic ions have a negative charge.

organic compound: a compound that usually contains hydrogen and carbon joined by covalent bonds, and may also contain atoms such as O, N and S.

Four Classes of Compounds: Minerals, Gases, Organic, and Fertilizers

Minerals in general are ionic compounds, consisting of positive or negative ions or collections of atoms carrying a positive or negative charge, called **polyatomic ions**. When an ionic compound dissolves in water, each of the ions is surrounded by polar water molecules, effectively separating the ion from other ions. As observed in this activity, water is able to dissolve most minerals, at least in limited amounts.

Gases are generally not very soluble in water unless they contain polar covalent bonds such as those in SO_2, CO_2, and NH_3. A gas such as methane (CH_4, "swamp gas") has only non-polar covalent bonds and is virtually insoluble in water. The C-H bond, which is a characteristic of organic molecules, has very little polarization because the EN of C (2.5) and H (2.1) are similar. Compounds containing mostly C-H bonds are insoluble or only slightly soluble in water because the water molecules are more strongly attracted to each other than to the compound.

Organic compounds are based on carbon and the ability of carbon to form multiple covalent bonds. They can interact strongly with water if they have polar functional groups like −OH and −NH. Organic substances that contain O and N can form hydrogen bonds with water molecules, making them more soluble. Pesticides and herbicides are among the organic compounds that are a hazard in drinking water. While they are not always very soluble in water, they are often toxic in trace amounts.

The three primary plant nutrients are nitrogen, phosphorus, and potassium and these are usually found in fertilizers that are applied to crops. Nitrogen is supplied as a salt containing ammonium ions or nitrate ions. Phosphorus is supplied as a soluble phosphate, such as ammonium phosphate. Fertilizers may contain a salt of potassium, such as KNO_3. Note that all salts containing ammonium ions, nitrate ions, or potassium ions are completely soluble in water and easily find their way into the water supplies. It is excess nutrient run-off from farms and golf courses that contribute to the occasional "algae bloom" that occurs in ponds and other bodies of water.

The above principles can be used to explain solubility rules that emerge from sampling a large number of ionic and covalent compounds. These solubility rules are provided in the appendix.

In this activity, you have looked at some of the types of contaminants that must be removed from water. The type and amount of these contaminants

Maximum Contaminant Levels (MCL) *From US EPA Drinking Water Standards and Health Advisories.*	
Organic Chemicals	**MCL (mg/L)**
bromoform, $CHBr_3$	0.08
chloroform, $CHCl_3$	0.08
2,4-dichlorophenoxyacetic acid, $C_8H_6Cl_2O_3$	0.07
endrin, $C_{12}H_8OCl_6$	0.002
malathion, $C_7H_{13}O_5PS$	(.01)*
polychorinated biphenyls	0.0005
simazine, $C_7H_{12}ClN_5$	0.004
styrene, $C_6H_5CH{=}CH_2$	0.1
2,4,5-trichlorophenoxyacetic acid (agent orange), $C_8H_5Cl_3O_3$	(0.07)*
2,3,7,8-TCDD (dioxin), $C_{12}H_4O_2Cl_4$	0.00000003
toluene, $C_6H_5CH_3$	1
1,1,1-trichloroethane, CCl_3CH_3	0.2
1,1,2-trichloroethane, $CHCl_2CH_2Cl$	0.005
vinyl chloride, $CH_2{=}CHCl$	0.002

**Lifetime health advisory is given since no MCL is enforced.*

are different in different areas. For example, river water or groundwater are likely to have much higher amounts of dissolved metal and carbonate ions because the water has been in contact with minerals. The amount of minerals that can dissolve in water increases in areas with acidic water. SO_2 and NO_2 are produced when coal is burned and returns to Earth as "acid rain." Discharges from mining or other industries may also acidify water supplies. The Environmental Protection Agency (EPA) has set **maximum contaminant levels** (MCL) for all contaminants that it requires water-treatment plants to monitor. A complete table of drinking water standards is available at the U.S. Environmental Protection Agency website. The tables shown represent only a small portion of the entire list. In the same document, the agency has also established **Secondary Drinking Water Regulations** (SDWR). These are non-enforceable federal drinking water guidelines. They regulate cosmetic effects (such as tooth or skin discoloration) or aesthetic effects (such as taste, odor, or color).

Chem Words

maximum contaminant level (MCL): the maximum concentration of a water contaminant that is allowed by the EPA to be present in water provided by water-treatment plants.

Secondary Drinking Water Regulations (SDWR): non-enforceable federal drinking water guidelines regarding cosmetic effects, taste, odor, or color.

Checking Up

1. Name three areas where fresh water is stored in nature.
2. Explain why water is a good solvent.
3. What are three types of contaminants that can be found in water naturally?
4. How can electronegativity be used to determine the type of bond that will occur between two atoms?
5. What government agency is responsible for setting water standards?

Maximum Contaminant Levels (MCL) *From US EPA Drinking Water Standards and Health Advisories.*	
Inorganic element or anion	**MCL (mg/L)**
antimony, Sb	0.006
arsenic, As	0.01
barium, Ba	2
beryllium, Be	0.004
bromate, BrO_3^-	0.01
cadmium, Cd	0.005
chloramine, NH_2Cl	4
chlorine, Cl_2	4
chlorine dioxide, ClO_2	0.8
chlorite, ClO_2^-	1
chromium, Cr	0.1
copper, Cu	1.3
cyanide, CN^-	0.2
fluoride, F^-	4
lead, Pb	0.15
mercury, Hg	0.002
nickel, Ni	(0.1)*
nitrate, NO_3^-	10
nitrite, NO_2^-	1
selenium, Se	0.05
silver, Ag	(0.1)*
thallium, Tl	0.002
zinc, Zn	(2)*

Secondary Drinking Water Regulations (SDWR) *From US EPA Drinking Water Standards and Health Advisories.*	
Chemicals	**SDWR (mg/L)**
aluminum, Al	0.05 to 0.2
chloride, Cl^-	250
copper, Cu	1.0
fluoride, F^-	2.0
foaming agents	0.5
iron, Fe	0.3
manganese, Mn	0.05
pH	6.5-8.5
silver, Ag	0.1
sulfate, SO_4^{2-}	250
Total Dissolved Solids (TDS)	500
zinc, Zn	5

Choosing a Source of Water

Whenever a source of water is chosen for a community, it must be capable of yielding an adequate amount for the future needs of the community. Also, the source cannot be so contaminated that it is too expensive to purify adequate amounts. In choosing your source, you will need to consider what is available and what is practical to use. You will want to include this consideration in your research of the area.

**Lifetime health advisory is given since no MCL is enforced.*

What Do You Think Now?

At the beginning of the activity, you were asked:

- **What type of substances, both living (biotic) and nonliving (abiotic), are found in a sample of pond water?**
- **How do you think these substances end up in each water sample?**

Based on what you learned in this activity, what questions would you ask to better determine some of the solutes in the pond-water sample? Which solutes are most likely to be found in the tap water?

Chem Essential Questions

What does it mean?

Chemistry explains a macroscopic phenomenon (what you observe) with a description of what happens at the nanoscopic level (atoms and molecules) using symbolic structures as a way to communicate. Complete the chart below in your *Active Chemistry* log.

MACRO	NANO	SYMBOLIC
What can you observe about a water sample and its properties as a natural solvent?	*Create a picture of how water molecules would interact with particles from a piece of the mineral halite (NaCl).*	*How do you symbolically represent ionic solid and molecular gases in solution? How do you represent the measure of solute in solution?*

How do you know?

Making specific reference to your data and using terms from the *Chem Talk* section, explain what solutes may appear in natural waters.

Why do you believe?

Cite one specific portion of this activity and explain how it relates to your past experience with water outside the classroom.

Why should you care?

How do the contaminants in natural water relate to the *Chapter Challenge*? What questions must you ask about the type of area you are studying?

Reflecting on the Activity and the Challenge

Now that you're aware of the types of contaminants that may be in your own water supply before and after it is treated, you are in a better position to propose what contaminants may reasonably be expected in the three areas described in the *Chapter Challenge*.

You may also be ready to decide why one natural water source may be more appropriate to use than others for each of the areas. The choice will be influenced by the geology of the region, the types of contaminants arising from human activities, and whether the amount of water will be adequate. Part of the challenge will be to create realistic descriptions of the three areas in enough detail to allow you to predict the best approaches for developing clean and abundant supplies of water.

Chem to Go

1. Why is it important to consider what happens on farmland, when considering a water supply? How is this connected to the hydrological cycle?
2. Name three potential contaminants of a water supply that would make it unusable. Which of these characteristics arise from human activities?
3. Characterize the following compounds as soluble or insoluble in water: $Ca_3(PO_4)_2$, $SrSO_4$, $ZnCl_2$, CaS, CuS, and Na_2CO_3.
4. Give a reason why some parts of the United States have higher concentrations of substances dissolved in their groundwater.
5. Methane, which has the formula CH_4, is insoluble in water. Explain why this natural gas is not soluble in water.
6. Industrial factories and urban areas have a history of producing an excess of sulfur dioxide gas, among other pollutants. Explain how this gas would change the original water supply downwind.
7. The MCLs for fluoride (F^-) and nitrate (NO_3^-) ions are given below. Express these values in ppm.

   a) F^- MCL = 4 mg/L

   b) NO_3^- MCL = 10 mg/L
8. ***Preparing for the Chapter Challenge***

   You must consider the geology of your chosen area in order to assess best what solutes will be present in your natural water supply. To get a better idea of what the area may be like, explore the Hydrology for the Environment, Life and Policy (HELP) website sponsored by UNESCO. In particular, read through a profile of one of the HELP basins. Your teacher may direct you to a particular basin that would represent an area most like your chosen area. Your teacher may distribute materials from the website if you do not have easy access to the Internet. In your group, submit a proposed assessment of the area, indicating what solutes from this activity may be present in your area.

Inquiring Further

Exploring other biogeochemical cycles

The hydrological cycle is just one of many biogeochemical cycles (cycles of chemicals throughout the living Earth). Research another biogeochemical cycle. Create an illustration of that cycle and write a narrative that would explain the cycle.

Activity 2 Factors Affecting Solubility of Solids

What Do You See?

SUGAR
FOOD COLORS

GOALS

In this activity you will:

- Discover how temperature changes the solubility of specific solids.
- Understand the energetics of dissolution.
- Consider other factors that may affect solubility.

What Do You Think?

Table sugar, the only ingredient in pure rock candy, is a water-soluble molecule called sucrose. Here are the directions for making rock candy.

1. *Put 500 mL of water in a saucepan and heat to boiling.*
2. *Add 200 g of sugar to the boiling water while stirring. Keep stirring until the sugar dissolves.*
3. *Remove the pan from the heat. Pour the mixture into a jar and place a string with dried sugar in it.*
4. *Let the sugar water sit and cool. The crystals will begin to form along the string in a few hours.*

- **Since sugar can dissolve in cold water, why do you think the water is heated to dissolve the 200 g of sugar?**

Record your ideas about this question in your *Active Chemistry* log. Be prepared to discuss your responses with your small group and the class.

Investigate

In this investigation, you will explore the effects of temperature on the solubility of various solutes.

Part A: Endothermic and Exothermic Formation of Solutions

1. Place a pea-sized sample of ammonium chloride (NH_4Cl) into a 10-mL test tube.
2. Add 5.0 mL of distilled water to the test tube. Mix to create an aqueous solution of ammonium chloride, $NH_4Cl(aq)$.
   a) Record your observations for the formation of this solution in your *Active Chemistry* log. Does the test tube feel cold or warm?
3. Repeat *Steps 1* and *2* for calcium chloride ($CaCl_2$).
   a) Record your observations for the formation of the aqueous solution of calcium chloride, $CaCl_2(aq)$, in your *Active Chemistry* log. Does the test tube feel cold or warm?
4. a) Which ***dissolution*** (dissolving process) is ***exothermic***, giving out heat energy to the surroundings and resulting in a negative change in enthalpy?
   b) Which dissolution is ***endothermic***, taking in heat energy from the surroundings and resulting in a positive change in enthalpy?

Safety goggles and a lab apron must be worn *at all times* in a chemistry lab.

Dispose of the materials as directed by your teacher.

Clean up your workstation.

Wash your hands and arms thoroughly after the activity.

Part B: Adding Heat to a Solution

1. Fill a large test tube with 10 mL of distilled water.
2. Prepare a ***saturated aqueous solution*** of $CaCl_2$ by adding slightly more solid than will dissolve. Mix vigorously to assure that no more solid will dissolve and there is a small amount of solid left in the test tube. Allow the solution to come to room temperature.
3. Gently heat the solution over a Bunsen-burner flame. Be sure to point the open test tube away from you and your classmates. While heating, carefully observe the solution.
   a) Write down your observations in your *Active Chemistry* log.
   b) Compare your observations as to the direction of heat flow with your earlier observation of $CaCl_2$ dissolving. Discuss this with your group and write your answer in your *Active Chemistry* log.

Chem Talk

FACTORS AFFECTING DISSOLUTION

Exothermic and Endothermic Processes

A process is called **exothermic** if it releases heat to the surroundings. A process is **endothermic** if heat must come from the surroundings for the process to occur. When this change in heat energy occurs at a constant pressure, the heat energy changes are called **enthalpy**. In chemistry, the symbol ΔH is used for a change in enthalpy. Enthalpy

Chem Words

exothermic process: a process that releases heat energy and has a negative value of ΔH.

endothermic process: a process that requires heat energy to be added in order for it to occur and has a positive value of ΔH.

enthalpy: change in heat energy for a process that occurs at constant pressure; symbolized by ΔH.

changes can be negative or positive, as you observed in the exothermic and endothermic reactions in the activity.

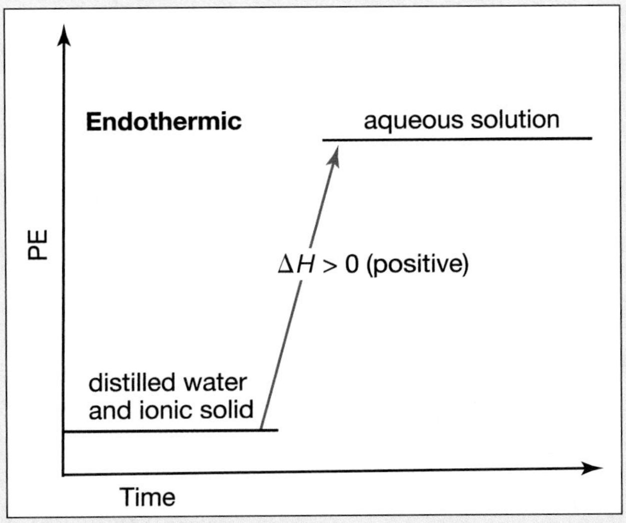
PE
Endothermic
aqueous solution
$\Delta H > 0$ (positive)
distilled water
and ionic solid
Time

Enthalpy

If the **dissolution** is exothermic, then the ions in solution must have a lower enthalpy than the starting solid plus pure water. That is true because the heat released to the surroundings had to come from somewhere. In this case, the source of heat is the increased stability of the ions as they move to their new environment. You can think of it like the heat exchange when a bowling ball is dropped. The potential energy of the ball becomes kinetic energy as it falls but is transferred almost completely to heat upon impact. If, on the other hand, the dissolution is endothermic, the ions in solution must have a higher enthalpy than the starting solid plus pure water. The energy removed from the surroundings as they cooled had to go *somewhere*. That *somewhere* can only be the ions in solution as they move to a less stable form in their new environment.

Entropy: An Additional Driving Force behind Formation of a Solution

There is a tendency for a system to move toward the lowest, most stable energy state. If this were the only important factor, all reactions would be exothermic. Since you have observed a dissolution process that is endothermic, it is apparent that there must be some other driving force for forming a solution than just this tendency. This other driving force is **entropy**. Entropy is a measure of the disorder in a system represented by the symbol "*S*." The change in entropy (ΔS) is associated with the extent of disorder in the substance. When a solid such as sugar dissolves in a liquid such as water, entropy has increased. The lower entropy state has all the sugar in a cube in a single location. The higher entropy (more disordered) state has the sugar spread throughout the water in all possible locations. If a process occurs in isolation from

Chem Words

dissolution: the process of dissolving through the interaction of one substance with another. It is also referred to as solvation.

entropy: a thermodynamic property of a substance associated with the extent of disorder in the substance. If a process occurs in isolation from the surroundings, then the entropy change for the process must be positive, that is, the disorder spontaneously increases. A substance is more ordered as a solid than it is as a liquid, and it is more ordered as a liquid than it is as a gas.

Chem Words

Gibbs free energy: a thermodynamic property that can be used to predict whether a process, such as the dissolution of a substance, will occur spontaneously at constant temperature and pressure.

thermodynamics: the study of the role of energy in physical and chemical changes.

the surroundings, then the entropy change for the process must be positive ($+\Delta S$) as the disorder spontaneously increases. When considering different states of matter or changes in states of matter, a substance is more ordered as a solid than it is as a liquid, and it is more ordered as a liquid than it is as a gas. Increasing the disorder, or entropy, therefore accompanies the formation of a solution. This increase in entropy is the additional driving force in forming a solution.

Thermodynamics

A process is spontaneous if it can occur on its own without intervention of any sort. You can use properties of substances to predict whether solution formation will take place spontaneously. In this activity, you have considered the forces that can drive the formation of a solution: a decrease in energy and an increase in disorder. The **Gibbs free energy** change for a process carried out at constant temperature and pressure is based on both the enthalpy change associated with the process, ΔH, and the entropy change, ΔS, through the Gibbs free energy equation:

$$\Delta G = \Delta H - T\Delta S$$

ΔH = enthalpy (heat content)	$\Delta H = -$ (reactions exothermic)
	$\Delta H = +$ (reactions endothermic)
ΔS = entropy (randomness)	ΔS = the more positive, the more disorder (when solids melt or dissolve, ΔS is positive)
ΔG = free energy	$\Delta G = -$ (reactions spontaneous)
	$\Delta G = +$ (reactions non-spontaneous)
T = temperature	T = Kelvin (K) Note: K = °C + 273.15

Thermodynamics, the study of the role of energy in chemical and physical changes, indicates that ΔG should have a *negative* sign if the dissolution process occurs *spontaneously*. When a solution is formed, ΔS is usually positive. By spreading freely to any part of the solution, the solute becomes less ordered. Therefore, the ΔS term in the equation makes a negative contribution to ΔG ($-T\Delta S$ is negative since ΔS is positive and T is always positive in Kelvin.) If the reaction is exothermic, then ΔH is also negative. Thus, ΔG must be negative and the reaction is spontaneous. When a solid material dissolves in a liquid material and is exothermic, you expect the reaction to be spontaneous as indicated by the Gibbs free energy.

If the solid material dissolving in a liquid material is endothermic, the calculation of the Gibbs free energy will indicate whether the reaction is spontaneous or not. In this case, the ΔH is positive. For the reaction to occur spontaneously, the Gibbs free energy must be negative. This can only happen if the $-T\Delta S$ term is larger than the ΔH term.

$$\Delta G = \Delta H - T\Delta S$$

At low temperatures, $-T\Delta S$ will be small and ΔG will probably be positive. At some point, the temperature becomes large enough that the $T\Delta S$ term will be larger than the ΔH term and the Gibbs free energy will be negative. At this temperature, the reaction becomes spontaneous.

The final situation is where the reaction is exothermic but entropy decreases. This may be the case where two solutions react to form a solid precipitate. At low temperatures, this could be spontaneous because the Gibbs free energy ΔG could be negative.

These situations are summarized in the table.

Gibbs Free Energy with Respect to Entropy and Enthalpy		
ΔG, free energy	**ΔH, enthalpy or heat content**	**ΔS, entropy or disorder**
Always spontaneous (ΔG is always $-$)	$-$, (exothermic reaction)	$+$, (increased disorder)
Always non-spontaneous (ΔG is always $+$)	$+$, (endothermic reaction)	$-$, (decreased disorder)
Spontaneous at high temperatures (ΔG is $-$ at high temperatures; ΔG is $+$ at low temperatures)	$+$, (endothermic reaction)	$+$, (increased disorder)
Spontaneous at low temperatures (ΔG is $-$ at low temperatures; ΔG is $+$ at high temperatures)	$-$, (exothermic reaction)	$-$, (decreased disorder)

So, if you know the entropy, enthalpy, and temperature values, then a thermodynamic quantity can be calculated that will indicate whether a substance will dissolve. The same equation can be used to decide whether a chemical reaction is spontaneous.

Chem Words

lattice energy: the energy needed to separate a crystalline ionic compound into gas-phase ions.

hydration energy: the energy change when gas-phase ions are solvated by liquid water.

Ionic Dissolution and Thermodynamics

Breaking an actual process down into separate imagined steps that end up with the same overall change is a commonly used technique in thermodynamics. Clearly, when you prepare solutions of solids in the laboratory, you do not separate the ionic solid (NaCl) compound into gas-phase ions (Na^+ and Cl^-) before dissolving the ions. However, it is easier to understand the forces and energies for the two separate steps than it is to deal with the whole process.

The dissolution of an ionic compound can be analyzed as two steps: (1) separation of the ions in the solid into gas-phase ions and (2) solvation of the gas-phase ions by surrounding them with liquid water molecules. In practice, these separate steps are very difficult to achieve directly in actual experiments, but the separation allows you to better understand the energy changes that are involved. The energy needed in the first step is called the **lattice energy**. The energy change of the second step is called the **energy of hydration**. Both of these steps involve large changes in energy. The first is endothermic and positive, while the second is exothermic and negative. However, the net process, dissolution, may have a relatively small change in energy.

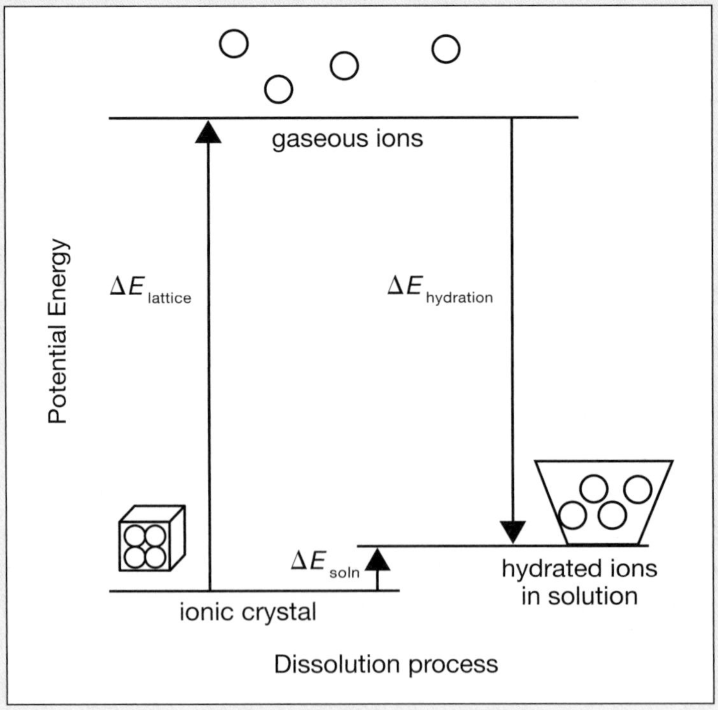

gaseous ions
Potential Energy
$\Delta E_{lattice}$
$\Delta E_{hydration}$
ΔE_{soln}
hydrated ions in solution
ionic crystal
Dissolution process

Checking Up

1. If the dissolution is endothermic, do the ions in solution have a lower or higher enthalpy than the starting solid plus pure water?
2. What is entropy?
3. Is the entropy of sugar in solution higher or lower than solid sugar?
4. Write the Gibbs free energy equation.
5. In addition to entropy and enthalpy, what other two factors affect solubility?

Temperature and Solubility

As you saw in *Part B* of this activity, when a solution is **saturated**, the concentration of the solution does not change unless you change the temperature or pressure. This fixed value is called the solubility. Temperature has an effect on solubility that cannot necessarily be predicted by the enthalpy change alone. The graph shown was created by experimentation with solubilities and temperature. It can be used to predict solubilities at various aqueous temperatures. As you can see from the data, as the temperature increases, the solubility of most, but not all, ionic solids increases. This graph can come in handy when working on your *Chapter Challenge*!

A substance that dissolves under one set of conditions may become insoluble as conditions change. In this activity, you discovered how solubilities can be influenced by changes in temperature. Likewise, changes in the pH also affect the solubilities of water contaminants.

Chem Words

saturated solution: a solution in dynamic equilibrium having both a dissolved and undissolved compound present. The compound enters solution and leaves solution at the same rate at equilibrium, maintaining a constant solution concentration at a fixed temperature.

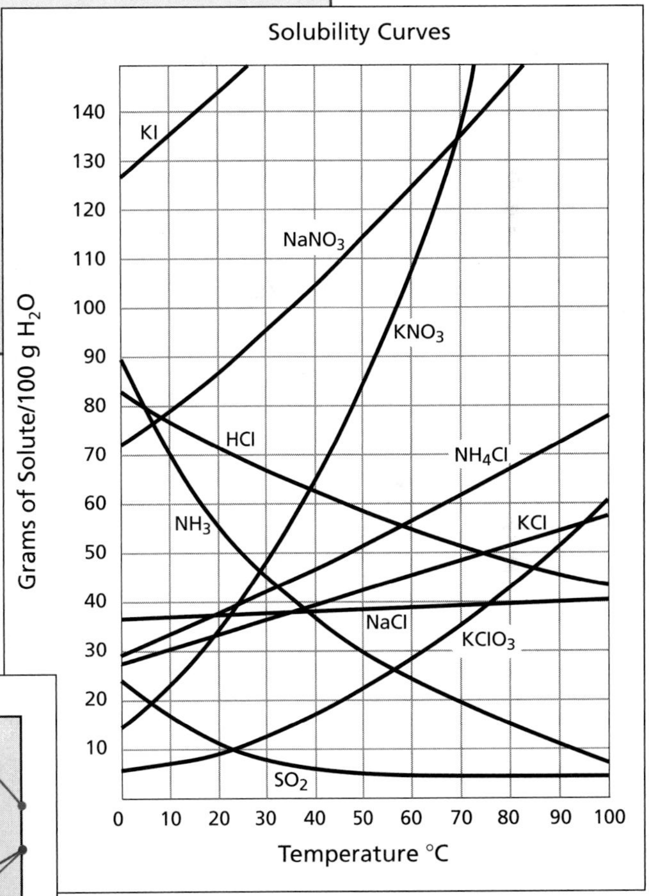
Solubility Curves
Grams of Solute/100 g H2O
Temperature °C
KI
NaNO3
KNO3
HCl
NH4Cl
NH3
KCl
NaCl
KClO3
SO2
0 10 20 30 40 50 60 70 80 90 100
10 20 30 40 50 60 70 80 90 100 110 120 130 140

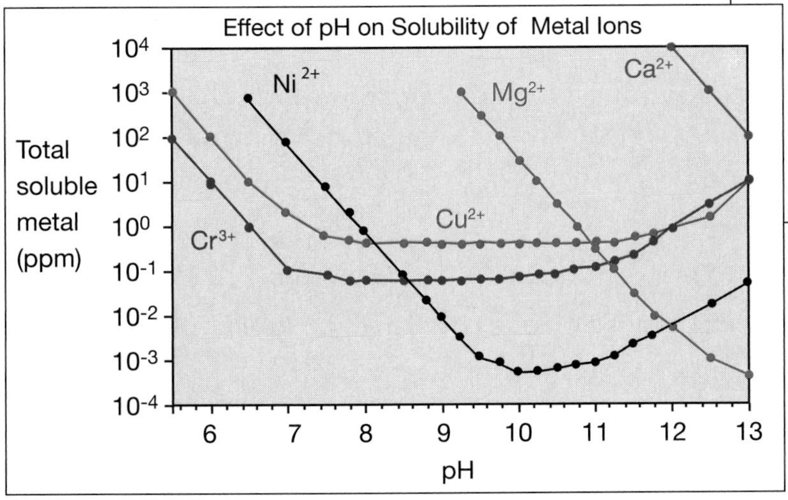
Effect of pH on Solubility of Metal Ions
Total soluble metal (ppm)
pH
Ni 2+
Mg2+
Ca2+
Cu2+
Cr3+
10^4 10^3 10^2 10^1 10^0 10^-1 10^-2 10^-3 10^-4
6 7 8 9 10 11 12 13

What Do You Think Now?

At the beginning of this activity you were asked:

- **Since sugar can dissolve in cold water, why do you think the water is heated to dissolve the 200 g of sugar?**

Clearly, the chemistry behind making rock candy isn't just kids' play. Look back at the direction for making rock candy in the *What Do You Think?* section. Using the terms presented in this activity, explain what you think is happening at the nanoscale level in the process of creating rock candy.

Chem Essential Questions

What does it mean?

Chemistry explains a macroscopic phenomenon (what you observe) with a description of what happens at the nanoscopic level (atoms and molecules) using symbolic structures as a way to communicate. Complete the chart below in your *Active Chemistry* log.

MACRO	NANO	SYMBOLIC
How can you detect changes in enthalpy when dissolving a solid in a liquid?	*Create a conceptual diagram illustrating the formation of a solution from distilled water and an ionic salt.*	*Using the solubility chart, identify two ionic solids whose solubility always increases with temperature and one ionic solid whose solubility decreases with temperature increases.*

How do you know?

Making specific reference to your data and using terms from the *Chem Talk* section, explain how you know temperature has an effect on solubility.

Why do you believe?

How might you be able to relate the content in this activity to another experience in the kitchen besides making rock candy? Explain.

Why should you care?

How is the gathered data and information relevant to the *Chapter Challenge*?

Reflecting on the Activity and the Challenge

In this activity, you investigated what makes one substance more soluble than another and how you can predict and change the solubility of a substance. You might think that such basic questions are not very important for purposes of water purification because it usually deals with contaminants whose solubilities have been extensively measured. In the real world, though, the problem of dealing with solubilities ends up being much more complicated than simply looking up their values.

In planning to meet the challenge, you will want to consider what influence these variables may have on the solubility of major contaminants that are picked up by natural waters. What could happen to solubilities of substances dissolved in cold waters as they enter warmer rivers, or vice versa? Some examples of ionic compounds that are very common in water supplies are $Ca(HCO_3)_2$ and $FeCl_3$, and you should be sure to consider how their solubilities might be influenced by the temperature and pH. Also, you will have to be prepared to predict whether some minor but toxic contaminants, like chromium, copper, or lead, have a good chance of remaining in solution all the way to the point where water treatment takes place.

Chem to Go

1. Dissolving NaOH in water in a test tube makes the test tube warmer.
   a) Is the dissolution of NaOH exothermic or endothermic? Explain briefly.
   b) Predict how you could change the solubility of NaOH by changing the temperature.
2. If you wanted to minimize the amount of potassium nitrate in your solution, what temperature would you want your solution to be, 20°C or 60°C?
3. Explain why substances in forming a solution reach a state of less order.
4. Recall whether heat was released or absorbed when you dissolved NH_4Cl and $CaCl_2$. What are the signs of ΔH and ΔS for the dissolution of NH_4Cl and $CaCl_2$?
5. Is the Gibbs free energy of solution positive or negative for the dissolution of $CaCl_2$? Explain the basis for your answer.
6. When dissolving ammonium nitrate solid into distilled water, the following enthalpy, entropy, and temperature were calculated or measured.

$$\Delta H = 28.05 \text{ kJ}$$

$$\Delta S = 0.1087 \text{ kJ/K}$$

$$T = 25°\text{C } (298 \text{ K})$$

   a) What is the value of ΔG for this solution? Show your work.
   b) Is the dissolution spontaneous? Explain.

7. ***Preparing for the Chapter Challenge***

The solubility of common solutes in your waters will be changed by temperature and pH. Considering your region and the probable solutes, create a table that shows the probable solutes, effects of changes in temperature, and effects of changes in pH. Use the graphs presented in this activity as well as other tables.

Inquiring Further

Changing the solubility of gases with temperature

Research how the solubility of gases in aqueous solution changes with temperature. Report your findings to your class, including why considering this change is important in natural waters.

Activity 3 How Much Solute Is in the Water?

What Do You See?

ST. LOUIS
NEW YORK

GOALS

In this activity you will:

- Experience three methods for quantifying solutes in natural waters.
- Use and convert between different concentration units.
- Experimentally determine the concentration of total dissolved solids (TDS), iron (III) ions, nitrate ions, and total water hardness (calcium and magnesium ions) in your water sample.

What Do You Think?

Four water samples were tested: distilled water, agricultural water, industrial water, and mining water. A conductivity probe determined the total dissolved solids (TDS) measure for each sample. The results were as follows:

1. distilled water, 0–10 ppm
2. agricultural water, 400 ppm
3. industrial water, 150 ppm
4. mining water, 5000 ppm

- **Generally, what type of dissolved solids do you think a conductivity probe measures? Explain.**
- **Specifically, what dissolved solids do you think are present in each sample?**

Record your ideas about these questions in your *Active Chemistry* log. Be prepared to discuss your responses with your small group and the class.

Investigate

In this activity you will explore how to quantify solutes in your specific "natural" water sample (from either your agricultural, industrial, or mining region of Latin America) through different techniques: titration, semi-qualitative colorimetry, and possibly ion-specific probeware.

Trial	Concentration of EDTA (*M*)	Initial volume of EDTA (mL)	Final volume of EDTA (mL)	Volume of EDTA titrated (L)	Moles of EDTA titrated (mol)	Moles of M^{2+} in the water sample (mol)	Volume of water sample (L)	Concentration of M^{2+} in the water sample (mol)
trial 1	0.010						0.050	
trial 2	0.010						0.050	

Safety goggles and a lab apron must be worn *at all times* in a chemistry lab.

Part A: Titration for Water Hardness

1. Copy the table above into your *Active Chemistry* log.

2. The hardness of water may be found by ***titrating*** the water sample with a 0.010 *M* solution of EDTA (ethylenediaminetetraacetic acid). EDTA forms a soluble complex with the Mg^{2+} and Ca^{2+} ions. (These ions make water hard and are referred to as Mg^{2+}.) Both the soluble ions and EDTA are clear in solution so you will use a small amount of indicator dye called EBT (Eriochrome Black T).

   Set up your equipment as shown in the diagram.

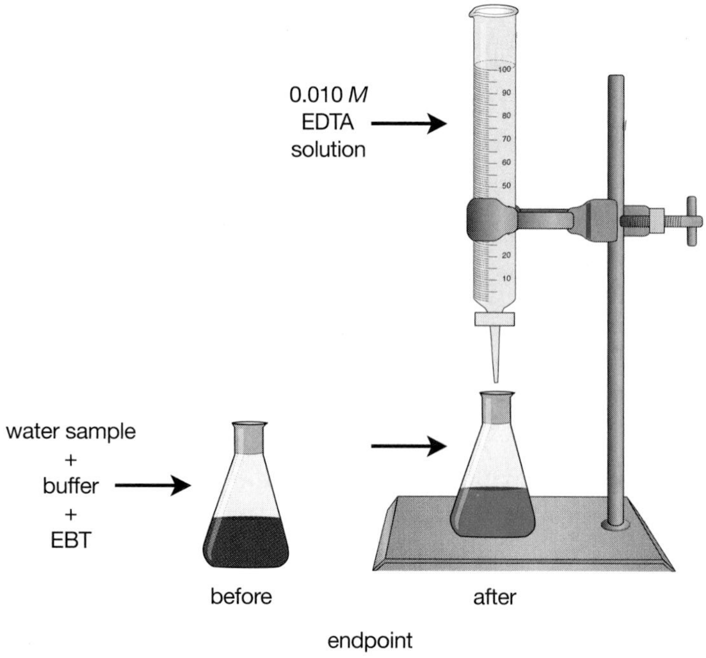
0.010 M EDTA solution
water sample + buffer + EBT
before
after
endpoint

3. Fill the burette with 0.010 *M* EDTA solution.

   a) Record the initial volume reading on the burette in the table in your *Active Chemistry* log.

4. In a 250-mL Erlenmeyer flask add 50.0 mL of a water sample, 3.0 mL of pH 10 buffer, and 6 drops of EBT indicator. The solution in the Erlenmeyer flask should be a purplish color.

5. Slowly add the 0.010 *M* solution of EDTA in the burette to the EBT-M^{2+} solution in the Erlenmeyer flask. Swirl the solution as you add the EDTA solution. When the color flashes blue in the Erlenmeyer flask, add the EDTA drop by drop until the solution in the Erlenmeyer flask stays blue. The color blue indicates the endpoint of the titration has been reached. EDTA has formed a complex with all of the Mg^{2+} and Ca^{2+} ions in solution.

   a) Record the final volume of EDTA in the table in your *Active Chemistry* log.

   b) Calculate and record the volume of the EDTA solution titrated into the water sample. Convert this number from milliliters to liters. Recall that 1.0000 L = 1000.0 mL. Record this value in your *Active Chemistry* log.

6. Complete the first row of the table by performing the necessary stoichiometric calculations and conversions. A sample problem can be found in the *Chem Talk* section for additional guidance.

   a) The moles of EDTA are found by multiplying the solution concentration (0.010 *M*) times the volume (L) that had to be added to reach the endpoint.

   b) Use the equation:

   $M^{2+}(aq) + EDTA(aq) \rightarrow M^{2+} \cdot EDTA(aq)$

   From the equation, you see that one EDTA molecule combines with one Mg^{2+} or Ca^{2+} ion. Therefore, the moles of EDTA added equals the total moles of Mg^{2+} and Ca^{2+} in the water sample when the titration is complete.

   c) The unknown concentration of the Mg^{2+} and Ca^{2+} ions $[M^{2+}]$ is equal to the total moles of M^{2+} ions divided by the volume of the water sample (0.050 L).

7. Repeat *Steps 3* to *6* for a second 50.0-mL sample of water. Be sure you have cleaned and rinsed the Erlenmeyer flask well.

Part B: Semi-qualitative Colorimetry for Iron Concentration

1. Obtain the prepared reference standards (water samples) with known concentrations of iron (III) (Fe^{3+}) of 1.0 ppm, 5.0 ppm, 10.0 ppm, and 100.0 ppm.

2. Measure 10.0 mL of each of the reference standards into four individual test tubes or four flat-bottom vials. Lightly label the top of each test tube or vial with the corresponding concentration.

3. Add 1.0 mL of 0.50 *M* NH_4SCN to each of the reference standards. Place the standards over a light box, either by standing them on the source (if they have flat bottoms) or by placing them in a wire test-tube rack on top of the light source.

4. Prepare your sample vial. Measure 10.0 mL of your water sample into a test tube or vial. Add 1.0 mL of 0.50 *M* NH_4SCN to your untreated water sample.

5. Compare the intensities of the colors of the reference standards with your water sample. Answer the following questions in your *Active Chemistry* log.

   a) What two reference standards does your sample fall between?

   b) What is the estimated Fe^{3+} concentration?

Part C: Ion-Specific Electrode for Nitrates (Optional)

1. Prepare the nitrate probe according to the probe's specific directions. This often involves soaking the probe in a concentrated solution for an hour before class.

2. Calibrate the probe according to the probe's specific directions. Your instructor will let you know if this step has been done for you prior to class.

3. Take the reading for your water sample. Pour 100 mL of your water sample into a clean beaker. Rinse the probe with distilled water and carefully blot it dry. Insert your probe into the water sample and gently swirl for a few seconds.

   a) When the reading stabilizes, record the value from the ion-specific probe in your *Active Chemistry* log.

Glass probes are very fragile. Use caution when handling.

Dispose of the materials as directed by your teacher.

Clean up your workstation.

Wash your hands and arms thoroughly after the activity.

Chem Talk

Chem Words

titration: an analytical process that determines the unknown concentration of a substance by reacting a solution containing it with a solution of another substance of known concentration.

titrant: a solution of known concentration that is used to determine an unknown concentration in a titration.

endpoint (of a titration): the stage in a titration when just enough titrant has been added to the solution being analyzed to cause the complete reaction of the substance whose concentration is being found.

indicator: a substance added to a solution to help visually follow the course of a titration, which is normally complete when the indicator changes color.

water hardness: the concentration of Mg^{2+} and Ca^{2+} in water, which form insoluble soap scum. It is expressed as milligrams of $CaCO_3$ per liter of water.

QUANTIFYING SOLUTES IN NATURAL WATERS

Getting Analytical

Analytical chemistry has two broad goals: identifying what chemicals are present and measuring the amounts of those chemicals. In *Activities 1* and 2, you learned ways in which you can identify and predict what chemical solutes are present in the water. In this activity, you learned three techniques to analyze the amounts of chemical solutes in natural water supplies: titration, colorimetry, and ion-specific probes.

Amounts of substances in solution are often compared using molar concentrations. A solution with a concentration of 1.0 *M* has 1.0 mol of the substance dissolved in each liter of the solution. For example, 1.0 L of a 1.0 *M* aqueous solution of NaCl has 1.0 mol of Na^+ ions and 1.0 mol of Cl^- ions dissolved in it. As you may have noticed, water chemistry tends to use the units ppm or mg/L. You can convert between molar concentration units and parts per million using the following steps.

$$1.0\ M \text{ of } Cl^- = \frac{1.0 \text{ mol of } Cl^-}{\text{L of solution}}$$

$$\left(\frac{1.0 \text{ mol of } Cl^-}{\text{L of solution}}\right)\left(\frac{35.45 \text{ g of } Cl^-}{1.0 \text{ mol of } Cl^-}\right)\left(\frac{1000 \text{ mg}}{1 \text{ g}}\right) = \frac{35{,}450 \text{ mg of } Cl^-}{\text{L of solution}} = 3.5 \times 10^4 \text{ mg/L } Cl^- = 3.5 \times 10^4 \text{ ppm } Cl^-$$

Titrations and Total Water Hardness

Titration is a process that finds the concentration of a substance by reacting a solution containing it with a **titrant**. A titrant is a solution of another substance of known concentration. The process occurs until the precise point where all of the original substance has reacted. That point is referred to as the titration **endpoint**. It is often represented visually by the addition of a reaction-specific **indicator**. The indicator is a substance that is added to a solution to follow the course of a titration, which is normally complete when the indicator changes color. In this activity, you measured the **hardness** of water through titration.

In some regions of America, people speak of "soap scum." It forms in a ring around a bathtub or in the shower. That soap scum is a result of hard water forming insoluble precipitates with soap molecules. Water is described as *hard* when it contains a high concentration of Mg^{2+} and Ca^{2+} ions. In the *Investigate* section, you found the concentration of these ions in your water sample by adding another solution, EDTA (ethylenediaminetetraacetic acid). This solution can remove the Mg^{2+}

and Ca^{2+} ions completely from the water sample. The titration is complete when all of the Mg^{2+} and Ca^{2+} ions have been bound to EDTA molecules.

The total water hardness simply reflects the total concentration of Mg^{2+} and Ca^{2+} ions. Normally, though, it is assumed that $CaCO_3$ is solely responsible for the water hardness. There is one mole of $CaCO_3$ for each mole of Ca^{2+}. The mass of $CaCO_3$ is just the moles of Ca^{2+} times the formula mass of one mole of $CaCO_3$. Finally, the total water hardness is normally expressed in milligrams of $CaCO_3$ per liter of water. Therefore, you must convert the molar concentration to ppm. The following sample problem represents the calculations you must perform in order to go from water sample and EDTA titrant to the total water hardness.

Sample Problem

A 0.020 *M* solution of EDTA with EBT indicator was used to titrate 25.0 mL of tap water. As the EDTA solution was added to the water, the indicator changed to a purple color. More EDTA was slowly added until the entire solution turned to blue and the purple color was not visible in the solution. At the endpoint of this titration, it was found that 5.92 mL of 0.020 *M* EDTA had been added to the water. Calculate the mg/L of $CaCO_3^-$ contained in the water, assuming that the water hardness was entirely due to this compound.

It is given that 1 mol of EDTA titrates 1.0 mol of Ca^{2+}, which is equivalent to 1.0 mol of $CaCO_3$.

$$Ca^{2+} + \text{EDTA} \rightarrow Ca^{2+}\cdot(\text{EDTA})$$

Then $\dfrac{0.020 \text{ mol EDTA}}{\text{volume (L)}} \times 5.92 \times 10^{-3} \text{ L solution} \times \dfrac{1 \text{ mol } CaCO_3}{1\text{mol EDTA}} = 1.2 \times 10^{-4} \text{ mol } Ca^{2+}$

The $CaCO_3$ in water $= \dfrac{1.2 \times 10^{-4} \text{ mol } CaCO_3}{2.5 \times 10^{-2} \text{ L}} = 4.8 \times 10^{-3}$ *M* and in mg/L it would be:

$$\frac{4.8 \times 10^{-3} \text{ mol } CaCO_3}{\text{L}} \times \frac{100.1 \text{ g } CaCO_3}{1 \text{ mol } CaCO_3} \times \frac{1000 \text{ mg}}{\text{g}} = 480 \text{ mg/L or } 480 \text{ ppm}$$

In future activities you will deal with ways in which the total water hardness can be reduced to prevent precipitation of soap scum. Water having a total hardness of less than 75 mg of $CaCO_3$ per liter of water is classified as *soft*. Water with a total hardness greater than 150 mg of $CaCO_3$ per liter of water is classified as *hard*. Hard water is

Analyses of Ion Concentrations in Typical Water Supplies			
Constituent	Oakland, CA, reservoir	Niagara Falls, NY, river	Dayton, OH, well
Ca^{2+}(aq)	13	36	92
Mg^{2+}(aq)	2.7	8.1	34
Na^{+}(aq)	4.5	6.5	8.2
K^{+}(aq)	1.4	1.2	1.4
$Fe^{2+/3+}$(aq)	0.015	0.02	0.09
HCO_3^{-}(aq)	27	119	339
SO_4^{2-}(aq)	16.2	22	84
Cl^{-}(aq)	10.3	13	9.6
NO_3^{-}(aq)	0.7	0.1	13
SiO_2(aq)	2.4	12	10
TDS	68	165	434
total hardness	44	123	369

not a concern in some areas like the Northeast U.S. and the West Coast where rather insoluble granitic minerals are common. In the Midwest, though, sediments are mostly limestone, which is $CaCO_3$. Therefore, natural water supplies throughout the Midwestern U.S. are generally hard and basic. Bedrock, such as clay and some soils, also can produce water hardness associated with other anions, particularly sulfate and chloride. The table shows sample readings from three different places around the United States.

Modern Methods of Analyzing Water

Modern analytical methods generally use complex instruments for quantitative measurements, but the principles behind the operation of the instruments resemble those used in the simple comparisons carried out as part of this activity. You used an *ion-specific electrode* to measure quantitatively the concentration of nitrate ions, which must be monitored in a water-treatment plant.

Nitrate ions (NO_3^{-}) are found in waters through a variety of natural sources, including nitrogen-fixing plants and decomposing animals and plants. Human activity, though, contributes an excess of nitrate ions into the natural water supply. Areas with agriculture and livestock can have excess nitrate in the surface and groundwaters because of pollution from man-made fertilizers. As you learned in *Activity 1*, these fertilizers contain high amounts of soluble nitrate. Urban areas are also at risk of high nitrate levels. In these areas the excess nitrates are a result of industrial water treatment and emissions from automobile engines and factories.

Ion-specific electrodes work by using membranes, little plastic disks with special pores, which are specific to the ion of interest. These electrodes can be found for a number of ions commonly present in natural waters, including hydrogen ion (pH), chloride, ammonium, calcium, phosphate, and nitrate.

Colorimetry also is a more "high tech" option for measuring the concentration of Fe^{3+} ions. The method you used in this activity was just color comparison using your eye as the instrument, making it semi-quantitative. An optical instrument called a spectrophotometer can be used to measure amounts of substances based on the color of light that they absorb. Your activity uses the color of a complex formed when iron (III) (Fe^{3+}) binds to thiocyanate indicator ions to estimate the Fe^{3+} concentration by comparing with standard solutions of known concentration. The spectrophotometer measures absorption of light of a specific wavelength by a sample. The reading obtained using the spectrophotometer is compared with a **Beer's Law** plot, a graph of known concentration and their absorbancies at the same specific wavelength. The accuracy is much better but the same molecular property is the basis for both methods.

Iron is commonly found in water supplies as it is one of the most abundant substances, making up nearly 5% of the Earth's crust. Some igneous rocks contain iron in a variety of forms like ferromagnesian minerals, mica, iron (II) sulfide (FeS), iron pyrite (FeS_2), hematite (Fe_2O_3), and magnetite (Fe_3O_4). Sandstone rocks also contain iron as oxides, carbonates, sulfides, and clay minerals. Iron also frequently enters water supplies through pipes and waterways. Although iron can occur in water in two oxidation states, iron (II) (Fe^{2+}) and iron (III) (Fe^{3+}), the Fe^{2+} quickly converts to Fe^{3+} when the water is exposed to air. Small amounts of iron (III) are safe in water supplies; therefore, iron (III) is considered a secondary contaminate by the EPA.

Total dissolved solids (TDS) used to be measured through a *gravimetric method*, based on weighing the solids after evaporation of all the water. A more convenient method for determining TDS is now used. It measures the conductivity of the water, which is caused by dissolved ions. With some assumptions about which ions are responsible for most of the conductivity, i.e., Ca^{2+}, Mg^{2+}, Na^+, K^+, HCO_3^-, SO_4^{2-}, Cl^-, and NO_3^-, the TDS can be calculated and used as a secondary standard to watch.

Chem Words

colorimetry: measurement of the intensity of light transmission in the visible region of the electromagnetic spectrum. It is used extensively for the determination of concentrations of substances in solution.

Beer's Law: states that the absorbance varies linearly with both the cell path length and the analyte concentration according to the equation $A = \alpha lc$.

Checking Up

1. What are the two goals of analytical chemistry?
2. What three techniques did you use in this activity to analyze the solutes present in your water sample?
3. Explain the process of titration in your own words.
4. How is modern, high-tech colorimetry different in technique than the one you used in the activity?

What Do You Think Now?

At the beginning of this activity you were asked:

- **Generally, what type of dissolved solids do you think a conductivity probe measures? Explain.**
- **Specifically, what dissolved solids do you think are present in each sample?**

Return to the *What Do You Think?* questions and reconsider your original answers. Do you think any of the three solutes measured in class constitute a large percentage of the total dissolved solids for your specific water sample? If yes, which solute seemed to be the largest portion of the total dissolved solids? If no, what other ions do you predict are a large part of the TDS for your water sample? Explain your answer.

Chem Essential Questions

What does it mean?

Chemistry explains a macroscopic phenomenon (what you observe) with a description of what happens at the nanoscopic level (atoms and molecules) using symbolic structures as a way to communicate. Complete the chart below in your *Active Chemistry* log.

MACRO	NANO	SYMBOLIC
Each technique had its own macroscopic phenomenon to observe. Choose ***two*** *and explain what you observe on the macroscopic level.*	*Describe at the nano level what is occurring during a titration.*	*Mathematics is used to calculate concentrations during titration. Provide an example of such a calculation.*

How do you know?

Which of the two methods for determining iron concentration gave the highest values? Make specific reference to your data and observations from each technique presented in this activity.

Why do you believe?

Does natural water conduct electricity? Does distilled water conduct electricity? Explain your answer to both of these questions, referring back to the activity when appropriate.

Why should you care?

Why is it important that you understand how to measure hardness of water and what effect it has on your daily use?

Reflecting on the Activity and the Challenge

In this activity you dealt with ions in water that are not necessarily toxic. However, they can affect water quality. In deciding whether it's worth lowering the amounts of these undesirable ions in water, you will have to know their initial levels in untreated water, the cost of removal, and whether the removal process will cause other, possibly worse problems. Also, note that different water supplies have widely varying amounts of these ions depending on the geology and land use in your region.

Chem to Go

1. What chemical compounds are the sources of hardness in natural waters?
2. Water supplies having too much hardness can create soap scum and scale inside water heaters and water pipes. Offer reasons why dealing with these effects can be costly.
3. Total water hardness is calculated by making the assumption that most of the water hardness is due to calcium ions from calcium carbonate ($CaCO_3$). For every one mole of calcium ion, there would be one mole of calcium carbonate. Assume a 25.0 mL water sample had 1.2×10^{-4} mol Ca^{2+}. Calculate the total water hardness in ppm (mg/L) for this sample, assuming the water hardness is entirely due to $CaCO_3$. Show all your work.
4. Compare the total dissolved solids reading from *What Do You Think?* and the water hardness of your water sample. Which should be larger? Why?
5. The concentration of chloride ions (Cl^-) in a water sample may be determined by titrating a water sample with a known concentration of silver nitrate ($AgNO_3$) solution using sodium chromate (Na_2CrO_4) as an indicator. It is found that 7.0 mL of 0.010 *M* silver nitrate ($AgNO_3$) is titrated into 10.0 mL of a tap water sample to get the faint orange tint of silver chromate (Ag_2CrO_4) from the sodium chromate indicator. It is assumed that when this happens all of the chloride ions (Cl^-) in the tap water have now reacted and precipitated with the titrated silver ions (Ag^+) as silver chloride ($AgCl$).
   a) What is the equation for precipitating chloride ions with silver ions?
   b) How many moles of silver ions were titrated into the sample of tap water? Show your work.
   c) How many moles of chloride ions were present in this tap water solution?
   d) What is the molar concentration (*M*) of the chloride ions in the tap sample?
   e) How many ppm (mg/L) of chloride ions are in the tap water sample?
6. The maximum contaminant level (MCL) for nitrate ion in a water supply is 10.0 mg/L.
   a) Express this concentration in molar units (*M*). Show the work behind your calculations.
   b) Did your water sample meet this regulation?

7. The National Secondary Drinking Water Regulations (SDWR) from the U.S. Environmental Protection Agency recommend a level of Fe^{3+} of 0.05ppm.

   a) Express this concentration in molar units (*M*). Show the work behind your calculations.

   b) Did your water sample meet this regulation?

8. ***Preparing for the Chapter Challenge***

   You have now four measures for solutes in your water sample: TDS, nitrate ion, total water hardness (mainly calcium ion), and iron (III) ion. Add these to your table of solutes, if they are not already there. As you did in *Activity 2*, fill in any effects that temperature or pH may have on the solubility. Now, for all of the solutes that you felt may be present as well as those presented in this activity, use the tables provided in *Activity 1* to research the MCL or SDWR. Record these in a table to keep and use with your *Chapter Challenge*.

Inquiring Further

Colorimetry with a spectrophotometer

Your calculations of iron (III) ion concentrations were semi-qualitative. An optical instrument, called a spectrophotometer, can be used to measure concentrations of substances based on the color of light an indicator (or the substance, if the solute is normally colored) may absorb. The spectrophotometer measures absorption of light of a specific wavelength by a sample and compares it with a Beer's Law plot, a graph of known concentrations and their corresponding absorbencies at the same specific wavelength. With your teacher's guidance, determine your water sample's concentration of iron (III) ion or some other ion in solution using a spectrophotometric device. Report your methods and results to your class.

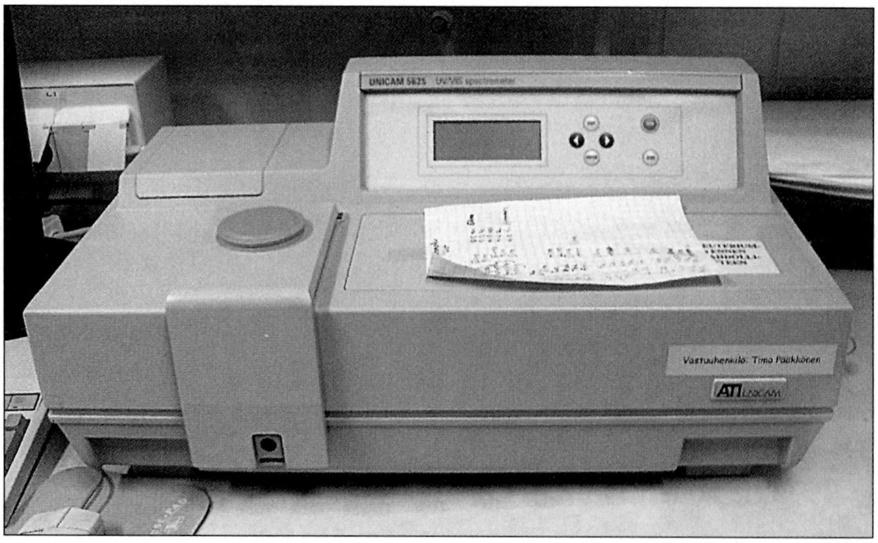

Activity 4 Aqueous Balance: Equilibrium

What Do You See?

WHERE IS H +OH ?

GOALS

In this activity you will:

- Determine pH and understand its meaning.
- Learn the basic principles behind equilibrium and the law of mass action.
- Calculate a solubility product constant (K_{sp}) and an equilibrium constant (K_{eq}) from experimental data.
- Learn how to shift the equilibrium concentrations by applying LeChatelier's stressors to an aqueous chemical equilibrium.

What Do You Think?

Water, water, everywhere,
And all the boards did shrink;
Water, water, everywhere,
Nor any drop to drink.

The Rime of the Ancient Mariner
by Samuel Taylor Coleridge (1772–1834)

- **If there was water everywhere, why was there no water to drink?**
- **What is de-ionized water?**

Record your ideas about these questions in your *Active Chemistry* log. Be prepared to discuss your responses with your small group and the class.

Investigate

In this investigation you will learn about chemical equilibrium. Your main objective is to understand enough so that you can better calculate the concentration of a solute and predict the effect of changing the equilibrium on other solutes and the purity of water.

Sample solution	pH	$[H^+]$ (*M*)	$[OH^-]$ (*M*)
de-ionized water	7.0	1.0×10^{-7}	1.0×10^{-7}
0.10 *M* $HCl_{(aq)}$			
0.10 *M* $NaOH_{(aq)}$			
your water sample			

Safety goggles and a lab apron must be worn *at all times* in a chemistry lab.

Part A: pH and the Equilibrium of Water

1. Copy the table above in your *Active Chemistry* log.
2. Pour a small amount of each sample into a small beaker. If you are using a pH probe, be sure to pour enough of each sample to cover the tip of the probe.
3. Using the method recommended by your teacher, determine the pH of the 0.10 *M* HCl, 0.10 *M* NaOH, and your water sample. If you are using a pH probe, be sure to completely rinse the probe with distilled water as demonstrated by your teacher.
   a) Record your pH values in your *Active Chemistry* log table.
4. Calculate the concentration of hydrogen ions, $[H^+]$, in each solution. Note that $[H^+] = 10^{-pH}$.
   a) Record these molar concentration values in the table in your *Active Chemistry* log.
5. Water is very stable and very little dissociation takes place. One in 10 million (10^{-7}) water molecules dissociate into H^+ and OH^- ions. The dissociation equation or equilibrium equation is:

   $HOH \leftrightarrows H^+(aq) + OH^-(aq)$.

   Determining the value of the equilibrium constant, K_w:

   $$K_w = [H^+][OH^-]$$
   $$= (1 \times 10^{-7} M)(1 \times 10^{-7} M)$$
   $$= 1 \times 10^{-14}$$

   Another way that you can look at this is:

   $$pK_w = pH + pOH$$
   $$= 14$$

   If you know the pH or the $[H^+]$ then you can determine pOH or $[OH^-]$.

   As an example, if the $[H^+] = 1 \times 10^{-3}\ M$ you can substitute this value into the equation ($K_w = [H^+][OH]$) and show that

   $$[OH] = \frac{1 \times 10^{-14}}{1 \times 10^{-3}}$$
   $$= 1 \times 10^{-11}\ M$$

   From this you can then say that the pOH = 11.

   a) Using K_w, calculate the concentration of hydroxide ions, $[OH^-]$, in each solution in your table. Record these molar concentration values in your *Active Chemistry* log.

A 0.10 *M*	B 0.010 *M*	C 0.0010 *M*	D 0.00010 *M*	E 0.000010 *M*
$Na_2C_2O_4$ (the original solution)	9 drops distilled water + 1 drop of solution A	9 drops distilled water + 1 drop of solution B	9 drops distilled water + 1 drop of solution C	9 drops distilled water + 1 drop of solution D

Part B: Determining the Value of the Solubility Product of Calcium Oxalate

1. Obtain 0.10 *M* solutions of both $Na_2C_2O_4$ (sodium oxalate) and $Ca(NO_3)_2$ (calcium nitrate).

2. Dilute these concentrations serially by a factor of 10 each time using a multi-well microplate. To dilute by a factor of 10, you add 9 parts distilled water to 1 part of the solution to be diluted. A serial dilution means diluting each subsequent solution by a factor of 10, leaving you with a microplate with the following concentrations of each solute, labeled $Na_2C_2O_4$ A–E and $Ca(NO_3)_2$ A–E.

3. Mix the two solutions (A with A, B with B, and so on) in separate wells and check for formation of a CaC_2O_4 precipitate.

   a) For which mixtures was *no precipitate* observed? This means then the solution is now too dilute for any solid CaC_2O_4 (calcium oxalate) to exist in equilibrium with the solution.

4. To approach the experiment from the opposite direction, mix the two solutions that are more diluted (E with E, D with D, and so on) until you observe the barest amount of precipitate.

   a) Once you discover the concentrations to mix to get a small amount of CaC_2O_4, record these concentrations in your *Active Chemistry* log.

   b) Calculate the concentrations of $C_2O_4{}^{2-}(aq)$ and $Ca^{2+}(aq)$ using the mixture of the two solutions that gave the first noticeable precipitate. Note that when you mix one drop of sodium oxalate with one drop of calcium nitrate, the concentrations of the calcium and oxalate ions will be cut in half. For example, if one drop of 0.10 *M* oxalate ion is mixed with one drop of 0.10 *M* calcium ion, the concentration of each of the ions will now be 0.05 *M*.

   c) The reaction can be written

   $$Na_2C_2O_4(aq) + Ca(NO_3)_2(aq) \rightarrow 2NaNO_3(aq) + CaC_2O_4(s)$$

   The total ionic equation for the reaction that shows all of the ions is:

   $$2Na^+(aq) + C_2O_4{}^{2-}(aq) + Ca^{2+}(aq) + 2NO_3{}^-(aq) \rightarrow 2Na^+(aq) + 2NO_3{}^-(aq) + CaC_2O_4(s).$$

   Notice that the Na^+ and $NO_3{}^-$ ions appear in the same form before and after the reaction takes place. Any such ions that are not changed by a reaction are called spectator ions. They may be omitted in writing what is called the net ionic equation. Cancel the Na^+ and $NO_3{}^-$ spectator ions that appear on both sides of the total ionic equation to obtain the net ionic equation:

   $$Ca^{2+}(aq) + C_2O_4{}^{2-}(aq) \rightarrow CaC_2O_4(s).$$

   Write this net ionic equation in your *Active Chemistry* log.

5. Every chemical equilibrium has an equilibrium constant expression, also called a mass-action expression. The ***law of mass action*** is a result of many experimental observations and states for a general reaction: ***a*** moles of reactant A with ***b*** moles of reactant B forms ***c*** moles of product C, ***d*** moles of product D and ***e*** moles of product E ($aA + bB \rightarrow cC + dD + eE$) is expressed as

$$K_{eq} = \frac{[C]^c[D]^d[E]^e}{[A]^a[B]^b},$$

where [C] stands for the molar concentration (*M*) of C and so on for D, E, A, and B. If a reactant or product is a solid or water, then you do not include it in the mass-action expression because its concentration is constant.

Also note the powers of concentration used in the equilibrium constant correspond to the coefficients in front of each substance in the equation.

a) In your *Active Chemistry* log, write the mass-action (equilibrium constant) expression for both the total ionic equation and the net ionic equation.

Note the states of matter of each species in each equation!

b) Are the expressions equal? Explain.

c) Calculate your K_{eq} using your concentration values calculated in *Step 5*, expressing your answer in scientific notation. Have these checked by your teacher before moving onto *Step 6*.

6. Since the reaction is reversible, it can also be written as:

$2NaNO_3(aq) + CaC_2O_4(s) \rightarrow Na_2C_2O_4(aq) + Ca(NO_3)(aq)$

When the reaction is written in the direction of the solid dissolving the equilibrium constant K_{eq} is also called the solubility product (K_{sp}).

a) Calculate your K_{sp} using your concentration values calculated in *Step 5*, expressing your answer in scientific notation.

7. The agreed-on experimental value of the calcium oxalate K_{sp} at 25°C is 2.3×10^{-9}.

a) How does your value compare to your experimentally determined value?

b) If there are differences, offer a few reasons why this may be.

$AgNO_3$ solution will stain your skin. Always use latex gloves when working with a solution of $AgNO_3$.

Part C: Shifting Equilibrium—LeChatelier's Principle

To observe LeChatelier's Principle, you will work with the following chemical reaction, which will be in a state of equilibrium when you prepare it:

$Ag_2SO_3(s) + 4NH_3(aq) \rightarrow 2Ag(NH_3)_2^{+}(aq) + SO_3^{2-}(aq)$

1. Add 5.0 mL of 0.050 *M* $AgNO_3$ containing 0.20 *M* NH_4OH into a 75-mL test tube or a 100-mL beaker.

> ***Note:*** This solution does not yet contain the reaction in equilibrium because it is missing $Ag_2SO_3(s)$ and $SO_3^{2-}(aq)$. A reaction in equilibrium must contain all of the reactants and products in contact with each other so that the rate in one direction is equal to the rate in the other direction. The solution does contain 0.050 *M* of $Ag(NH_3)_2^{+}(aq)$ because all of the $Ag^{+}(aq)$ in the prepared solution converts to a *complex ion* $Ag(NH_3)_2^{+}(aq)$. Exactly two molecules of NH_3 are bound to each Ag^{+} ion. By bonding to Ag^{+}, the NH_3 concentration has been reduced by twice the starting concentration of Ag^{+}. In other words, the concentration of NH_3 is now:
>
> $0.20\ M - (2 \times 0.05\ M) = 0.10\ M.$

2. Add 3.0 mL of 0.10 *M* Na_2SO_3 to the solution and mix thoroughly.

   a) Record any changes in the appearance of the solution in your *Active Chemistry* log.

3. Repeat this addition of 3.0 mL of 0.10 *M* Na_2SO_3 three more times for a total of 12.0 mL.

   a) Record any changes in the appearance of the solution after each addition.

   b) Using the volume of added Na_2So_3 when you *first noticed* the appearance of solid (precipitate) $Ag_2SO_3(s)$, calculate the concentrations of $Ag(NH_3)_2^+$, NH_3, and SO_3^{2-}, assuming that they change only because of the dilution of the original amounts. In other words, find the moles of each substance you added to the reaction mixture and divide by the new total volume of the reaction mixture. A sample calculation is shown. Record your calculations and the final concentrations in your *Active Chemistry* log.

For a chemical reaction such as $Ag_2SO_3(s) + 4NH_3(aq) \rightarrow 2Ag(NH_3)_2^+(aq) + SO_3^{2-}(aq)$, the constant ($K_{eq}$) that relates concentrations at equilibrium is found by multiplying the product concentrations, $[Ag(NH_3)_2^+]^2[SO_3^{2-}]$, and dividing by the reactant concentrations, which is simply $[NH_3]^4$ in this case. The concentrations of pure solids like Ag_2SO_3 are effectively constant and are not included in the expression for the equilibrium constant.

Sample Calculation

In a titration, 22.7 mL of 0.043 *M* Na_2SO_3 is added from a burette to 10.0 mL of 0.050 *M* $AgNO_3$ containing 0.20 *M* NH_3 in order to reach the point where Ag_2SO_3 begins to precipitate. Calculate the equilibrium constant, K_{eq}, using the following equation:

$$Ag_2(SO_3)(s) + 4NH_3(aq) \leftrightarrows 2Ag(NH_3)_2^+(aq) + SO_3^{2-}(aq)$$

Note that the starting concentration of NH_3 is 0.10 *M* because one-half is used to react with silver ion.

Solution: The amount of NH_3 in the reaction mixture is given by its initial volume times its molarity, or

$$10.0\text{ mL} \times \frac{1\text{L}}{1000\text{ mL}} \times \frac{0.10\text{ mol}}{\text{L}} = 1.0 \times 10^{-3}\text{ mol.}$$

The volume at equilibrium is $(1.0 \times 10^{-2}\text{ L}) + (2.27 \times 10^{-2}\text{ L}) = 3.27 \times 10^{-2}\text{ L}$.

So $[NH_3] = \dfrac{1.0 \times 10^{-3}\text{ mol}}{3.27 \times 10^{-2}\text{ L}} = 0.031\ M$ at equilibrium.

Similarly, the amount of $Ag(NH_3)_2^+$ ions is $1.0 \times 10^{-2}\text{ L} \times 0.050\text{ mol/L} = 5.0 \times 10^{-4}\text{ mol}$.

The $[Ag(NH_3)_2^+] = \dfrac{5.0 \times 10^{-4}\text{ mol}}{3.27 \times 10^{-2}\text{ L}} = 0.015\ M$ at equilibrium.

Finally, the amount of SO_3^{2-} is $2.27 \times 10^{-2}\text{ L} \times 0.043\text{ mol/L} = 9.8 \times 10^{-4}\text{ mol}$.

The equilibrium concentration of the sulfite ion is

$$\frac{9.8 \times 10^{-4}\text{ mol}}{3.27 \times 10^{-2}\text{ L}} = 0.030\ M.$$

Note that you are assuming that the small amount of Ag_2SO_3 that was observed to precipitate did not affect the concentration of $NH_3(aq)$, $Ag(NH_3)_2^+(aq)$, or $SO_3^{2-}(aq)$.

You then calculate an equilibrium constant based on these results by multiplying the product concentrations and dividing this number by the product of all the reactant concentrations, all at equilibrium. Given this, the following expression is used for the equilibrium constant:

$$K_{eq} = \frac{(Ag(NH_3)_2{}^+)^2(SO_3{}^{2-})}{(NH_3)_4} = \frac{(0.015)^2(0.030)}{(0.031)^4} = 7.2$$

Solid Ag_2SO_3 was left out in defining an equilibrium constant because its concentration is considered to be constant.

4. What is the mass-action (equilibrium constant) expression for this reaction?

   a) Record this in your *Active Chemistry* log.

5. Using your concentrations calculated in *Step 3* and the expression you wrote in *Step 4*, determine the experimental K_{eq} at your room temperature.

6. Now that you have a chemical system at equilibrium, you will apply one of LeChatelier's stresses, a change in concentration, to see how it shifts the equilibrium.

   Add 5.0 mL of 0.5 *M* NH_4OH(aq) to the test tube or beaker to see the equilibrium shifting from left to right.

   a) Record your observations in your *Active Chemistry* log.

   b) What do you predict would happen if you added a source of $SO_3{}^{2-}$? Write your prediction in your *Active Chemistry* log.

   c) Explain your observations and hypothesis using ***LeChatelier's Principle***, that states when a change (a change in concentration, temperature, pressure, or volume) is imposed on a system at equilibrium, the system responds by attaining a new equilibrium condition that minimizes the imposed change.

Dispose of the materials as directed by your teacher.

Clean up your workstation.

Wash your hands and arms thoroughly after the activity.

Chem Talk

EQUILIBRIUM

Overview

Some chemical reactions are reversible. If you mix hydrogen gas and iodine gas, hydrogen iodide gas will form. That hydrogen iodide gas will then decompose into hydrogen gas and iodine gas. If confined to a closed container, a state of **equilibrium** would be reached where the amount of hydrogen gas and iodine gas producing hydrogen iodide would be equal to the amount of hydrogen iodide decomposing into the hydrogen and iodine.

An experiment can be performed that begins with equal concentrations of hydrogen and iodine and no hydrogen iodide. After a given time, the

Chem Words

equilibrium: the condition when the forward rate of the reaction is equal to the reverse rate of the reaction and the concentrations of reactants and products are unchanging.

$aA + bB \rightleftarrows cC + dD + eE$

system will reach equilibrium and the concentrations of hydrogen, iodine, and hydrogen iodide can be measured. A second experiment can be performed which begins with only hydrogen iodide. After a given time, the system will reach equilibrium and the concentrations of hydrogen, iodine and hydrogen iodide can be measured. A third experiment can be performed which begins with different concentrations of hydrogen and iodine. After a given time, the system will reach equilibrium and the concentrations of hydrogen, iodine, and hydrogen iodide can be measured.

In each of the experiments, the initial concentrations are different. The final concentrations for the hydrogen, iodine, and hydrogen iodide gases in each of these experiments will also be different. However, there is a quantity that is identical in all experiments. This is the **mass-action expression**, also called the **equilibrium constant**. This quantity will be the same for the different experiments as long as the temperature is constant.

The **law of mass action** is a result of many experimental observations and states. For a general reaction of *a* moles of reactant A with *b* moles of reactant B to form *c* moles of product C, *d* moles of product D, and e moles of product E ($aA + bB \rightarrow cC + dD + eE$):

$$K_{eq} = \frac{[C]^c[D]^d[E]^e}{[A]^a[B]^b},$$

where [C] stands for the molar concentration (*M*) of C, and so on for D, E, A, and B. If a reactant or product is in the solid or liquid phase, then you do not include it in the mass-action expression because its concentration is more or less constant. Also, K_{eq} is temperature dependent; therefore, the values of K_{eq} will change for systems at different temperatures.

Sample Problem I

Nitrosyl chloride, $NO_2Cl(g)$, is in equilibrium with $NO_2(g)$ and $Cl_2(g)$:

$$2NO_2Cl(g) \rightarrow 2NO_2(g) + Cl_2(g)$$

The concentrations of the three substances at equilibrium are $[NO_2Cl] = 0.00106\ M$, $[NO_2] = 0.0108\ M$, and $[Cl_2] = 0.0054\ M$.

Find the equilibrium constant using:

$$K_{eq} = \frac{[NO_2]^2[Cl_2]}{[NO_2Cl]^2} = \frac{(0.0108)^2(0.0054)}{(0.00106)^2} = 0.56.$$

Chem Words

law of mass action: a reaction equilibrium expression where the product of the product concentrations divided by the product of the reactant concentrations is equal to a constant.

mass-action expression (equilibrium constant):

$$K_{eq} = \frac{[C]^c[D]^d[E]^e}{[A]^a[B]^b}$$

Chem Words

solubility product: the equilibrium constant for the dissolution of an ionic substance in water.

$K_{sp} = [A^+]^a[B^-]^b$

The Equilibrium of Water

To understand the pH of water, you must remember that the water will be in equilibrium with a small amount of H^+ and OH^-. So, for the reaction $H_2O(l) \rightarrow H^+(aq) + OH^-(aq)$, the equilibrium constant is defined as $K_{eq} = [H^+] \times [OH^-]$. Note that since the concentration of $[H_2O(l)]$ is too large (55.5 *M*/L) it is considered a constant, and is omitted from this expression.

This equilibrium constant is also called the ionization constant of water and is given the special symbol K_w:

$$K_w = [H^+][OH^-] = 1.0 \times 10^{-14}$$

You can use this expression to solve mathematically for the pH of de-ionized water using the following steps.

- First, in de-ionized water the concentration of hydrogen ions is equal to the concentration of hydroxide ions or $[H^+] = [OH^-] = 1 \times 10^{-7}$ $K_w = [H^+][OH^-] = 1.0 \times 10^{-14}$
- Then, remembering $pH = -\log_{10}[H^+]$, you substitute 1.0×10^{-7} for the hydrogen ion concentration and find the pH is 7 and the $pOH = -\log_{10}[OH^-] = 7$ as well.

In this activity, you explored the pH of your natural water sample, as well as solutions of hydrochloric acid ($HCl(aq)$) and sodium hydroxide ($NaOH(aq)$), and determined the concentrations of hydrogen ions and hydroxide ions in your water sample.

Calculating the Solubility Product (K_{sp})

In a saturated solution of an insoluble ionic compound, a constant called the **solubility product** can be used to determine the equilibrium concentrations of ions in solution. In this part of the activity, you determined the value of the solubility product for a solution of calcium oxalate (CaC_2O_4). You wanted to form only the smallest amount of CaC_2O_4 because forming additional precipitate would change the ion concentrations from their initial values and require you to measure the amount of precipitate in order to know how much of the ions remain in solution at equilibrium.

For dissolution of an ionic solid, the equilibrium constant is called the solubility product, and it is simply the product of the concentrations of all the ions that become solvated. For this type of equilibrium constant, knowledge of its value is enough information to tell you the equilibrium concentrations. This makes calculation of the equilibrium ion concentrations very straightforward if you prepare a saturated solution of a single salt.

$$AB(s) \rightarrow A^{+}(aq) + B^{-}(aq), \text{ so } K_{sp} = [A^{+}] \times [B^{-}].$$

The concentrations are found using $[Ca^{2+}][C_2O_4^{2-}] = [Ca^{2+}]^2 = K_{sp}$. You can solve for the $Ca^{2+}(aq)$ concentration by taking the square root of both sides of this last equation. So $[Ca^{2+}] = \sqrt{K_{sp}}$. Note that the solution must be saturated in order to assure that the equilibrium between dissolved and undissolved CaC_2O_4 is established. However, that was not how you prepared the solution containing $Ca^{2+}(aq)$ and $C_2O_4^{2}(aq)$. In your preparation, it was not essential that $[Ca^{2+}]$ and $[C_2O_4^{2-}]$ be equal since they came from separate solutions.

The following sample problem shows you how to use the solubility product constant, like the one you calculated, to determine the solubility of an ionic compound. This calculation can lead you to the solubility of any ionic compound if you know the K_{sp} for a specific temperature in an aqueous system. Tables of K_{sp} values can be found in numerous references. Values at 25°C can be found in the appendix of this text.

Sample Problem 2

What is the solubility of $CaSO_4$?

The solubility is determined by measuring the amount of compound dissolved per liter of solution when equilibrium exists between dissolved and solid compound.

K_{sp} for $CaSO_4$ is given in the appendix solubility chart as 2.4×10^{-5}.

Now $K_{sp} = [Ca^{2+}][SO_4^{2-}] = [Ca^{2+}]^2$ since $[Ca^{2+}] = [SO_4^{2-}]$.

Hence $[Ca^{2+}]^2 = 2.4 \times 10^{-5}$. Find the square root of both sides to find $[Ca^{2+}] = 4.9 \times 10^{-3}\ M$.

Since one mol of Ca^{2+} goes into solution for each mole of $CaSO_4$ dissolved, the solubility of $CaSO_4$ is 4.9×10^{-3} mol/L of solution.

The solubility in grams per liter is readily found by multiplying the moles of $CaSO_4$ times its formula mass of 136.1 g/mol.

So the solubility is $\dfrac{4.9 \times 10^{-3} \text{ mol } CaSO_4}{L} \times \dfrac{136.1 \text{ g } CaSO_4}{1 \text{ mol } CaSO_4} = \dfrac{0.67 \text{ g } CaSO_4}{L}$.

Calculating Equilibrium Constant (K_{eq})

For a chemical reaction such as $Ag_2SO_{3(s)} + 4NH_{3(aq)} \rightarrow 2Ag(NH_3)_2{}^{+}{}_{(aq)} + SO_3{}^{2-}{}_{(aq)}$, the constant ($K_{eq}$) that relates concentrations at equilibrium is found by multiplying the product concentrations, $[Ag(NH_3)_2{}^{+}]^2[SO_3{}^{2-}]$, and dividing by the reactant concentrations, which is simply $[NH_3]^4$ in this case. The concentrations of pure solids like Ag_2SO_3 are effectively constant and are not included in the expression for the equilibrium constant. The equilibrium constant does not fix the values of the concentrations at equilibrium. Equilibrium values of concentrations depend on how the equilibrium was prepared. They will differ if different initial values of concentrations or temperatures are used.

Sample Problem 3

Suppose that 22.7 mL of 0.037 *M* Na_2SO_3 was added from the burette to 10.0 mL of 0.050 *M* $AgNO_3$ containing 0.20 *M* NH_4OH in order to reach the point where Ag_2SO_3 begins to precipitate.

The starting NH_3 concentration is 0.1 *M*.

The amount of NH_3 in the reaction mixture is given by its initial volume times its molarity, or

$$10.0 \times 10^{-3}\ \text{L} \times \frac{0.10\ \text{mol NH}_3}{\text{L}} = 1.0 \times 10^{-3}\ \text{mol}.$$

The volume at equilibrium is $(10.0 \times 10^{-3}\ \text{L}) + (22.7 \times 10^{-3}\ \text{L}) = 3.27 \times 10^{-2}\ \text{L}$.

So $[NH_3] = \dfrac{1.0 \times 10^{-3}\ \text{mol}}{3.27 \times 10^{-2}\ \text{L}} = 0.031\ M$ at equilibrium.

Similarly, the amount of $Ag(NH_3)_2{}^{+}$ ions is $10.0 \times 10^{-3}\ \text{L} \times 0.050\ \text{mol/L} = 5.0 \times 10^{-4}$ mol.

The equilibrium concentration is equal to $\dfrac{5.0 \times 10^{-4}\ \text{mol}}{3.27 \times 10^{-2}\ \text{L}} = 0.016\ M$.

Finally, the amount of $SO_3{}^{2-}$ ions is $22.7 \times 10^{-3}\ \text{L} \times 0.37\ \text{mol/L} = 8.4 \times 10^{-4}$ mol.

The equilibrium concentration is equal to $\dfrac{8.4 \times 10^{-4}\ \text{mol}}{3.27 \times 10^{-2}\ \text{L}} = 0.026\ M$

Note that you are assuming that the small amount of Ag_2SO_3 that was observed to precipitate did not affect the concentration of $NH_{3(aq)}$, $Ag(NH_3)_2{}^{+}{}_{(aq)}$ or $SO_3{}^{2-}{}_{(aq)}$. You then calculate an equilibrium constant based on these results by multiplying all equilibrium product concentrations and dividing by the product of all the equilibrium reactant concentrations. $2Ag(NH_3)_2{}^{+}{}_{(aq)}$ and $SO_3{}^{2-}{}_{(aq)}$ appear on the right side of the equation and are considered to be the products. The reactants then are $Ag_2SO_{3(s)}$ and $4NH_{3(aq)}$. Hence, the following expression is used for the equilibrium constant:

$$K_{eq} = \frac{[Ag(NH_3)^{+}]^2[SO_3{}^{2-}]}{[NH_3]^4} = \frac{(0.022)^2(0.056)}{(0.044)^4} = 7.2.$$

Note that the solid Ag_2SO_3 was left out in defining an equilibrium constant because its concentration is considered to be constant.

Also note that the powers of concentration used in the equilibrium constant correspond to the coefficients in front of each substance in the equation.

To more accurately determine the actual numerical value of the equilibrium constant, you could follow the same procedure as in *Part C* except the Na_2SO_3 solution would be added very slowly with a burette so that the addition is stopped at exactly the point where the Ag_2SO_3 just begins to precipitate. At that point, the reaction would be in equilibrium but only a tiny amount of the ions would have left the solution in forming the solid. If only a very slight amount of Ag_2SO_3 is formed, then the change in the moles of $Ag(NH_3)_2^+$ in the solution is negligible. Thus, the concentrations of all species in solution would be known at equilibrium, and K_{eq} could be found as in the previous two sample problems.

For a reaction to be at equilibrium, all of the products and reactants must be present and in contact with each other so that both forward and reverse reactions continue at equal rates. You can cause a reaction at equilibrium to shift to create more products or more reactants by changing the rate of the forward reaction or the reverse reaction. **LeChatelier's Principle** states when a change in concentration, temperature, pressure, or volume is imposed on a system at equilibrium, the system responds by attaining a new equilibrium condition that minimizes the impact of the imposed change.

To observe LeChatelier's Principle, you worked with the following chemical reaction in a state of equilibrium:

$$Ag_2SO_{3(s)} + 4NH_{3(aq)} \rightarrow 2Ag(NH_3)_2^{+}{}_{(aq)} + SO_3^{2-}{}_{(aq)}.$$

Chem Words

LeChatelier's Principle: when a reaction at equilibrium is "stressed" by a change in concentration of a reactant or product, the reaction will shift in the direction to relieve the "stress" and establish a new equilibrium.

Checking Up

1. In your own words, describe a dynamic equilibrium.
2. What is the law of mass action?
3. Define pOH. What is its value when the pH is 5?
4. What is a saturated solution?
5. Why are solids and solvents not included in the K_{sp} expression for a solid which is in equilibrium with its ions?
6. In your own words, explain LeChatelier's Principle.

What Do You Think Now?

At the beginning of this activity you were asked:

- **If there was water everywhere, why was there no water to drink?**
- **What is de-ionized water?**

Go back and reread your answers to the *What Do You Think?* section. It probably seems much easier to answer the questions now that you better understand chemical equilibrium.

Chem Essential Questions

What does it mean?

Chemistry explains a macroscopic phenomenon (what you observe) with a description of what happens at the nanoscopic level (atoms and molecules) using symbolic structures as a way to communicate. Complete the chart below in your *Active Chemistry* log.

MACRO	NANO	SYMBOLIC
What evidence did you see that helped you determine the pH of different solutions?	*Explain what will happen when calcium ions are added to a saturated calcium oxalate solution.*	*How can you make the two equilibrium equations favor the creation of more product(s)?* *a)* $Ag_2SO_3(s) + 4NH_3(aq) \rightarrow 2Ag(NH_3)_2^{+}(aq) + SO_3^{2-}(aq)$ *b)* $Ca^{2+}(aq) + C_2O_4^{2-}(aq) \rightarrow CaC_2O_4(s)$

How do you know?

Making specific reference to your data and using terms from the *Chem Talk* section, explain your observations in *Part C* of this activity.

Why do you believe?

How does this concept of equilibrium make sense conceptually? How does it relate to you in your life?

Why should you care?

How can you use your understanding of equilibria to develop a method for water purification in your *Chapter Challenge*?

Reflecting on the Activity and the Challenge

In this activity, you have learned how the concentrations of various substances in equilibrium can often be calculated rather than measured. You related the concentration of one solute to other solutes using equilibrium constants. The equilibrium constants can change, however, if the temperature changes. The techniques used in applying equilibrium constants are the same whether you are dealing with a chemical reaction, a dissolution process, or the dissociation of water. They are extensively used in making predictions about the composition of water in various stages of treatment. You have introduced these three types of equilibrium as though they were isolated processes with no complications from other species in solution. In reality, water chemistry involves multiple equilibria that have to be treated simultaneously.

Chem to Go

1. Is the pH of your sample of tap water within the Secondary Drinking Water Standard pH range of 6.5–8.5?
2. How is the solubility product, K_{sp}, defined for the ionic substance Ag_2SO_3?
3. Use the solubility product, K_{sp}, of $MgCO_3$ (3.5×10^{-8}) to calculate the concentrations of $Mg^{2+}(aq)$ and $CO_3{}^{2-}(aq)$ in a saturated solution of $MgCO_3$.
4. MgF_2 has limited solubility in water, whereas $MgCl_2$ and NaF are highly soluble. Suppose that a student adds $MgCl_2(s)$ to a 0.001 *M* solution of NaF. Use the solubility product of MgF_2 (6.6×10^{-9}) to find the concentration of $Mg^{2+}(aq)$ if just enough $MgCl_2$ is added to precipitate a tiny amount of MgF_2.
5. Write an expression for the equilibrium constant, K_{eq}, for the reaction $N_2O_4(g) \rightleftarrows 2NO_2(g)$.
6. A mixture of $N_2O_4(g)$ and $NO_2(g)$ at equilibrium has concentrations of 0.0457 *M* for NO_2 and 0.448 *M* for N_2O_4. What is the equilibrium constant for the reaction shown in the previous question?
7. How do you think you would calculate the equilibrium constant for the reaction $CO_2(aq) + H_2O(l) \rightleftarrows HCO_3{}^-(aq) + H^+(aq)$? What concepts might tie into a problem like this?
8. In *Activity 3*, you observed the effect of temperature on solutions in equilibrium with undissolved solids. How is it possible for solubility to increase or decrease if the solubility product is a constant?

Chapter mini Challenge

HONK
THE BRIDGE

Your challenge for this chapter is to improve the water supplies in a few Latin American communities. Because of water-borne chemicals and microbes, the communities have had to rely on bottled drinking water. Many streams in these areas may be contaminated with toxic minerals and organic chemicals, possibly introduced by drainage from mines, farm land or industrial sites. Naturally occurring contaminants of water sources vary widely because the minerals range from those of volcanic origin in the mountainous areas to principally sedimentary rocks in the farming or urbanized areas. You must predict the most likely contaminants in each area.

Your *mini-challenge* is to prepare a one-minute presentation and an outline to the international organization about the problems of contaminants in water supplies. You will decide what major water contaminants may be expected in each area, and how they got there. You will estimate the amounts of contaminants that purification plants are designed to remove.

The class then will provide feedback. This will give you a good sense of what you will need to complete your *Chapter Challenge*, when you will have more chemistry content and can also explain purification methods.

Chemistry Content

Activity 1: Your group explored four possible substances that enter the water supply as they go through the natural water cycle. This exploration included the solubility of minerals, the effect of soluble gases on pH, the solubility of organic compounds, and the solubility of fertilizers.

Activity 2: You investigated how temperature changes the solubility of specific solids. You also learned about how the Gibbs free energy can help you determine if a reaction is spontaneous.

Activity 3: You learned how to quantify solutes in your specific "natural" water sample (from either your agricultural, industrial, or mining region of Latin America) through different techniques including titration and semi-qualitative colorimetry.

Activity 4: You determined the pH and learned the principles of equilibrium and the law of mass action. You also calculated a solubility product constant (K_{sp}) and an equilibrium constant (K_{eq}) from experimental data.

Criteria

Your report and presentation should be informative and articulate. It should show an understanding of chemistry concepts and help convince an international health organization of your expertise.

Preparing for Your mini Challenge

Your team should begin the process of creating the report by deciding what information should be provided for your target group, the international health organization. What information do you think the international health organization will be most interested in learning? Keep in mind that your group's presentation should not only be informative, but also interesting. Brainstorm ideas that will make your presentation and report effective. Will you include charts and descriptions of experiments and data? Will you introduce a human element by inventing a story about someone living in an area without clean water? You can then discuss how you can include chemistry concepts in the presentation. You will only have one minute for the presentation. You will also have to prepare an outline for the report that will accompany your final report completed at the end of the chapter. At the end of the chapter, you will know much more about purification techniques, and can include them to make your presentation more comprehensive.

Engineering/Technology Design

The engineering-design process involves a number of distinct steps. In designing the steps for purifying the water, you are involved in a design process. Note how your efforts follow the design model described.

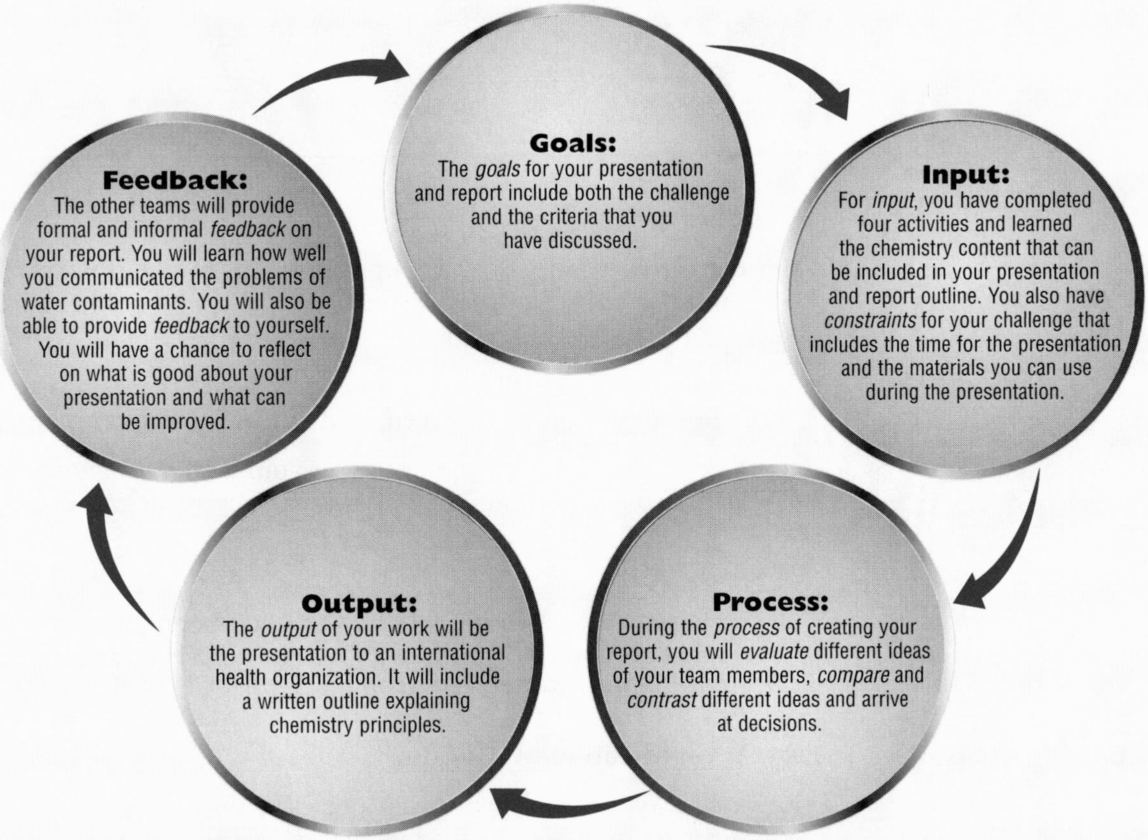
Goals:
The *goals* for your presentation and report include both the challenge and the criteria that you have discussed.
Input:
For *input*, you have completed four activities and learned the chemistry content that can be included in your presentation and report outline. You also have *constraints* for your challenge that includes the time for the presentation and the materials you can use during the presentation.
Process:
During the *process* of creating your report, you will *evaluate* different ideas of your team members, *compare* and *contrast* different ideas and arrive at decisions.
Output:
The *output* of your work will be the presentation to an international health organization. It will include a written outline explaining chemistry principles.
Feedback:
The other teams will provide formal and informal *feedback* on your report. You will learn how well you communicated the problems of water contaminants. You will also be able to provide *feedback* to yourself. You will have a chance to reflect on what is good about your presentation and what can be improved.

Remember: This is a *first try.* The feedback that you get from this brief presentation of the water issues will be extremely valuable when you prepare for the full presentation that you will develop at the end of the chapter. At that point, you will begin the entire design cycle again. That's why it is called a cycle. You keep going through it over and over to improve your design or, in this case, the recommended means of purifying water in a community.

Activity 5 Removing Suspended Particulates and Iron

What Do You See?

NO DUMPING

GOALS

In this activity you will:

- Create floc to remove colloidal particles in a solution.
- Compare the flow and batch methods for filtering water.
- Begin to create a schematic diagram for purifying your particular water sample.

What Do You Think?

Consider three samples of water in clear containers: tap water, distilled water, and natural water that is similar to the samples you've been assessing in the previous activities.

- **What do you think will happen to a laser beam that is projected through samples of tap, distilled, and natural water? Explain.**

Record your ideas about this question in your *Active Chemistry* log. Be prepared to discuss your responses with your small group and the class.

Investigate

You have spent the past four activities predicting and assessing what solutes may be found in your natural water supply. You will now turn your attention to the other half of the *Chapter Challenge*, purification.

Part A: Clarification of a Water Sample

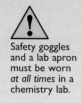

Safety goggles and a lab apron must be worn *at all times* in a chemistry lab.

1. Watch as your teacher projects a laser beam through three samples of water: tap water, distilled water, and natural water.

   a) Record your observations.

   b) What do you think is happening on the nanoscopic level that explains these observations?

Water sample	Volume of 0.10 *M* $Al_2(SO_4)_3$ (mL)	Mass of CaO needed to complete reaction (g)	Predicted mass of $Al(OH)_3$ formed (g)	Mass of dry filter paper (g)	Mass of dry floc and filter paper (g)	Mass of dry floc (g)
untreated (natural)	10.0					
distilled	10.0					

2. ***Alum***, $Al_2(SO_4)_3$, can be used to form an insoluble gel of aluminum hydroxide, $Al(OH)_3$, by the following reaction with quicklime, CaO:

   $3CaO(s) + 3H_2O(l) + Al_2(SO_4)_3(aq) \rightarrow$
   $2Al(OH)_3(s) + 3CaSO_4(aq)$

   The aluminum hydroxide gel serves to ***coagulate*** (clump together) and collect finely suspended particles like those that caused the laser beam to scatter in *Step 1*.

   a) Copy the table above into your *Active Chemistry* log.

3. Using the balanced equation for the reaction between alum and quicklime, calculate the mass (g) of quicklime needed to react with 10.0 mL of a 0.10 *M* alum solution.

   Hints for your calculation:

   - You will first need to calculate the moles of alum in 10.0 mL of a 0.10 *M* alum solution.
   - You will then need to use the balanced equation to calculate the number of moles of quicklime needed to react with the number of moles of alum.
   - Using the molar mass of quicklime, you can convert moles of quicklime into grams of quicklime needed to fully react with 10.0 mL of a 0.10 *M* alum solution.

   a) Using steps similar to those given, calculate the mass (g) of the insoluble gel of aluminum hydroxide, $Al(OH)_3(s)$, that will form in the reaction between 10.0 mL of a 0.10 *M* alum solution and your calculated mass (g) of quicklime. Record this value in the table in your *Active Chemistry* log.

4. Pour 100 mL samples of the untreated (natural) water and distilled water into 150-mL beakers.

   a) Record observations of each sample in your *Active Chemistry* log.

5. Add 10.0 mL of the 0.10 *M* alum solution and your calculated amount of quicklime to each of the water samples. Using a glass stir rod, stir each mixture for a minute.

6. While allowing the precipitate to settle, use a pencil to label the edge of two pieces of filter paper, one for each water sample. Weigh two dry, labeled pieces of filter paper.

   a) Record these values (g) in the table in your *Active Chemistry* log.

   b) After allowing the precipitate to settle, record your observations of each beaker.

   c) If available, shine a laser beam through each sample. Record your observations in your *Active Chemistry* log.

Mix chemicals only as directed by your teacher.

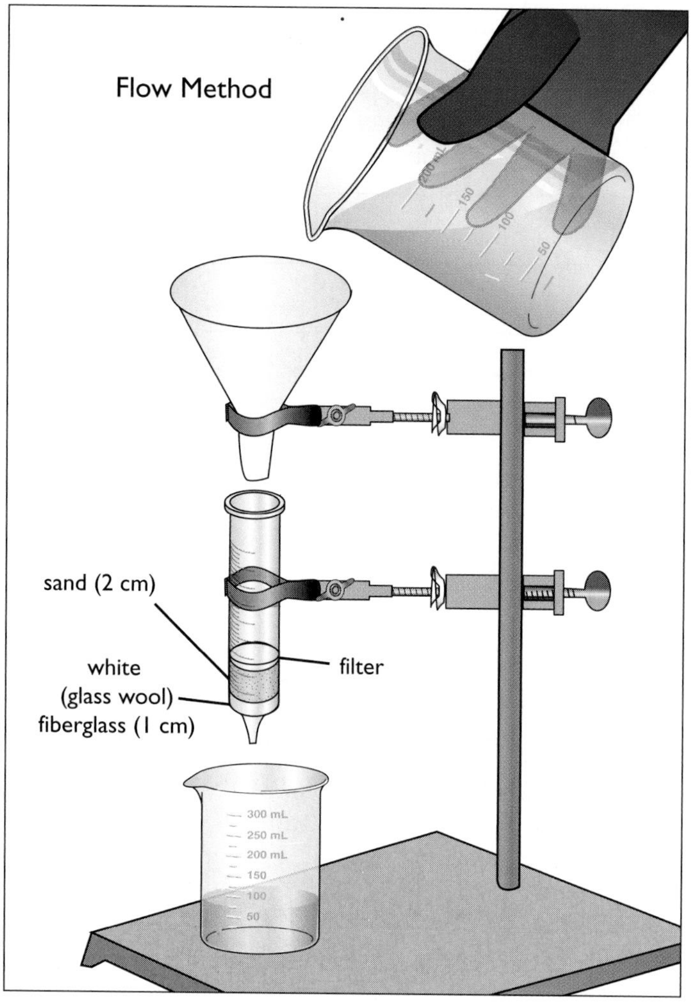
Flow Method
sand (2 cm)
white
(glass wool)
fiberglass (1 cm)
filter
300 mL
250 mL
200 mL
150
100
50

7. Filter each sample using the method demonstrated by your teacher. Allow the precipitate on the filter paper to dry. Discard the filtrate.

8. Once dry, measure the mass of the filter paper and precipitate. Determine the mass (g) of the precipitate, called ***floc.***

   a) Record these values in your *Active Chemistry* log.

   b) Compare the masses of floc from each sample to the predicted amount of the aluminum hydroxide gel. Explain similarities or differences in your *Active Chemistry* log.

Part B: Removing Iron—The Flow and Batch Methods

Iron, as $Fe^{3+}(aq)$, is a secondary contaminate which you may choose to remove because of taste, odor, etc. This can be achieved by precipitating the iron in solution with sodium hydroxide (NaOH) through the following reaction.

$$Fe^{3+}(aq) + 3NaOH(aq) \rightarrow$$
$$Fe(OH)_3(s) + 3Na^{+}(aq)$$

In removing the iron from a water sample, you will experiment with two methods used in water-treatment schemes to remove dissolved solids: (I) the ***flow method*** and (II) the ***batch method.*** Your teacher will assign half the class to perform the flow method and the other half to perform the batch method. Once you have your results, you will report your results back to the other group.

I. Removing Iron: Flow Method

1. Using the diagram as a guide, construct a filtration column. Use care with the glass wool.

2. Copy the table below into your *Active Chemistry* log.

	Volume of 100 ppm $Fe^{3+}(aq)$ (mL)	Volume of 0.01 *M* $NaOH(aq)$ needed (mL)	Flow rate (mL/min)	$[Fe^{3+}]$ of treated sample (ppm)
trial 1	10.0			
trial 2	10.0			

3. Calculate the volume of 0.010 *M* sodium hydroxide solution needed to precipitate all of the iron in 10 mL of a 100 ppm iron solution.

   a) Record this value in your *Active Chemistry* log.

4. Measure the calculated volume in a 10-mL graduated cylinder and prepare to pour it into your column. You will want to pour this *immediately* before you pour your water sample into the column in *Step 5*.

5. Pour the NaOH solution into the column and then immediately pour 10 mL of the 100 ppm solution of iron ions into the column. After pouring, start a timer to record the time it takes for the 10.0 mL sample to run through the filtration column. It may be necessary to push the sample through using the syringe.

   a) Once the sample has run through the column, note the final time.

   b) Calculate the flow rate. Record this flow rate for trial 1 in the table in your *Active Chemistry* log.

6. Save the sample and label it trial 1. Set this aside for analysis in *Step 9*. Clean your filtration column, discarding materials as directed by your teacher.

7. You will repeat *Steps 1, 4,* and *5* for trial 2. You will want to vary the flow rate for this second trial. To *increase* the flow rate, you may apply more pressure with the syringe. To *decrease* the flow rate, you may add two or three additional pieces of filter paper when constructing your column.

8. Save the sample and label it trial 2. Set this aside for analysis in the next step. Clean your filtration column, discarding materials as directed by your teacher.

9. Analyze your trial 1 and trial 2 samples using the semi-quantitative technique from *Activity 3, Part B.* Your teacher has a wider variety of sample iron concentrations for you to use for color comparison than in *Activity 3.* They range in value from 0 ppm to 100 ppm.

   a) Record your estimated concentration for each treated sample in the table in your *Active Chemistry* log.

II. Removing Iron: Batch Method

1. Use the diagram shown for the flow method as a guide. Construct a filtration column. Use care with the glass wool.

2. Copy the table below into your *Active Chemistry* log.

	Volume of 100 ppm $Fe^{3+}(aq)$ (mL)	Volume of 0.01 *M* NaOH(aq) needed (mL)	Stir time (s)	Standing time (min)	$[Fe^{3+}]$ of treated sample (ppm)
trial 1	10.0				
trial 2	10.0				

3. Calculate the volume of 0.010 *M* sodium hydroxide solution needed to precipitate all of the iron in 10 mL of a 100 ppm iron solution.
   a) Record this value in your *Active Chemistry* log.
4. Determine the stir and standing times for your two trials. You will want to have a variety of times to compare in the class, ranging from 5–100 s for stir times and 1–20 min for standing times.
5. Prepare your batch by measuring 10.0 mL of 100 ppm iron solution and pouring the solution into a small beaker.
6. Pour your calculated amount of 0.010 *M* sodium hydroxide solution into the beaker containing your iron solution to create the batch. *Immediately* start a timer. Stir for your determined stir time for trial 1.
   a) Record the stir time in your *Active Chemistry* log.
   b) Let the sample stand for trial 1. Record this stand time in your *Active Chemistry* log.
7. Carefully decant the solution into your filtration column. Take care not to transfer the precipitated particles. You may need to use the syringe to push the sample through the column.
8. Save your filtrated sample and label it trial 1. Clean the filtration column, discarding the substances as directed by your instructor.
9. Repeat *Steps 1, 5, 6, 7,* and *8* for trial 2. You may want to start trial 2 during the standing time for trial 1.
10. Analyze your trial 1 and trial 2 samples using the semi-quantitative technique from *Activity 3, Part B.* Your teacher has a wider variety of sample iron concentrations for you to use for color comparison than in *Activity 3.* They range in value from 0 ppm to 100 ppm.
    a) Record your estimated concentration for each treated sample in the table in your *Active Chemistry* log.

Wash your hands and arms thoroughly after the activity.

Dispose of the materials as directed by your teacher.

Clean up your workstation.

Chem Words

suspension: a mixture containing suspended particles that may be large enough to precipitate slowly.

colloid: a mixture containing suspended particles much larger than molecular dimensions but small enough that precipitation does not occur.

Chem Talk

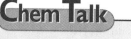

PURIFYING WATER

Removing Larger Particulates

Large objects can be readily removed from a water supply by passing the water through a screen. However, solid material such as dirt can be so finely divided in water that it remains suspended indefinitely. The thermal motion of the water molecules keeps the tiny particles uniformly distributed. This type of **suspension** is called a **colloid**, and it appears at first sight like a homogeneous solution. However, as you observed in the activity, the light from the laser beam was scattered off the tiny particles suspended in the solution. The beam helped you distinguish the particles

that were invisible to your unaided eye. This scattering is known as the **Tyndall Effect.**

In principal, a filter with small enough pores could remove the particles, but the flow rate through the filter would be very slow and it would require frequent replacement. Hence, chemicals are added to the water, forming precipitates that are capable of adsorbing the fine particles in the process of settling out. In this activity, by mixing **alum** ($Al_2(SO_4)_3$) and quicklime (CaO) you created one such chemical. It was an insoluble gel of aluminum hydroxide, $Al(OH)_3$. The reaction was as follows:

$$3CaO_{(s)} + 3H_2O_{(l)} + Al_2(SO_4)_{3(aq)} \rightarrow 2Al(OH)_{3(s)} + 3CaSO_{4(aq)}$$

The aluminum hydroxide gel served to **coagulate** (clump together) finely suspended particles. The solid material that settled out is known as **floc.** The floc should have had a mass greater than the predicted amount of $Al(OH)_3$, since it contained the suspended particles causing the Tyndall Effect as well as the insoluble gel. If the water sample was free of particulates, like the distilled sample, then the floc should consist of just the $Al(OH)_3$. Remaining in solution were the soluble Ca^{2+} and SO_4^{2-} ions you added in the chemical reactants. Subsequent water softening steps, to be introduced in *Activity 6,* can be used to reduce the amount of Ca^{2+}.

Filtration

If a precipitation reaction is used to remove a dissolved ion, such as Fe^{3+}, from the solution, then the treated sample must be filtered. You have investigated whether it is better to allow settling of the sediment before attempting to filter as in the **batch method**, or whether the precipitate can be removed as the treated water stream moves continuously through a filter as in the **flow method**. In either method, adequate time must be allowed for all precipitation reactions to occur to remove enough of the contaminant to meet the water standards. As you have observed in this activity, though, filtration tends to slow down as the filter gets filled with particulates. Therefore, you must experimentally find the appropriate timing and techniques for each particular water sample.

Chem Words

Tyndall Effect: the scattering of a collimated beam of light by suspended particles in a colloid.

alum: $Al_2(SO_4)_3$, which is one of the reagents needed to produce a gel of $Al(OH)_3$.

coagulate: to clump together particles suspended in a colloid so that they will settle out.

floc: a clump of solids formed in sewage by biological or chemical action.

batch method: a process in which an operation is carried out on a fixed amount of material to allow time for chemical or physical transformations to go to completion. The batch method for purifying water allows time for sedimentation followed by filtration.

flow method: a process in which an operation is carried out on a continuously moving stream of material. In the flow method for purifying water, the water flows continuously through stages of filtration.

Water-treatment plants typically use a batch method for removal of sediments because of the large amount that must be removed. Separate settling basins are used for removal of suspended particulates, removing iron, or the water-softening process to be studied in *Activity 6*. The sediment from each basin is regularly pumped out of a settling basin and buried in soil. The residual solids that fail to settle out can then be handled by filtration without clogging the filter very often. Just as in your syringe filtration column, water-treatment plants use a range of filtration materials progressing from coarse to fine. Typically, gravel is followed by sand and finally coal or charcoal. That also helps prevent clogging because most of the particulates are retained before they can reach the fine-pore filter. The rate of flow out of the settling basin can be adjusted to assure that all of the reactions have had time to come to equilibrium.

As you should have discovered through the comparison of your flow and batch results, the flow method for water purification is generally not used on large scale because it would not allow enough time for reactions to reach equilibrium. Small water-purification columns based on the flow method may be effective at low flow rates, provided the reactants in the filtration column have very small grain size and do not escape. Such units are commonly installed in homes under sinks or attached to faucets.

Checking Up

1. How is a colloid different from other suspensions?
2. What is the Tyndall Effect?
3. Describe the difference between the batch method and the flow method.
4. Why is the batch method used for large-scale water purification?

What Do You Think Now?

At the beginning of this activity you were asked:

- **What do you think will happen to a laser beam that is projected through samples of tap, distilled, and natural water? Explain.**

You began this activity by making an observation of a laser beam being passed through each water sample. Explain your observations using terms you learned in this activity.

Chem Essential Questions

What does it mean?

Chemistry explains a macroscopic phenomenon (what you observe) with a description of what happens at the nanoscopic level (atoms and molecules) using symbolic structures as a way to communicate. Complete the chart below in your *Active Chemistry* log.

MACRO	NANO	SYMBOLIC
Describe the Tyndall Effect that is observed when laser light is projected through a natural water sample.	*Sketch a diagram showing how a laser beam behaves when it strikes a colloidal particle.*	*What affect would a solution of sodium oxalate have on a filtration system that contained a mixture of alum and quicklime? Discuss this using the equation in the* Chem Talk *section.*

How do you know?

Making specific reference to your data and using terms from the *Chem Talk* section, explain how you know the batch method was more effective than the flow method for water purification.

Why do you believe?

Why do you know that the batch method must be used in your water purification? Explain.

Why should you care?

What is the importance of the batch method for your *Chapter Challenge*?

Reflecting on the Activity and the Challenge

In this activity, you have learned about physical processes that must take place in order for the chemistry of water purification to be effective. Physical processes are changes in the phase or condition of materials rather than chemical composition. They have great practical importance because they often control how fast the overall water treatment can be performed. They also influence the cost of materials and equipment required to get the job done.

It is apparent that as you develop water-purification plans, you must learn some engineering strategies for applying chemistry in a real-world setting. Often, a plan is best developed empirically (using experiments and experience). Instead of trying to calculate the rates of incompletely understood processes, several alternatives are tried to see which works best.

Chem to Go

1. What limits how quickly water can be purified when a flow method is used for removing particulates?
2. What limits how quickly water can be purified when a batch method is used for removing particulates?
3. When alum and quicklime are added to water, what ions remain in solution?
4. A sample of water has an Fe^{3+} concentration of 0.0010 *M*.
   a) How many moles of Fe^{3+} are in 10.0 mL of the water?
   b) How many moles of NaOH are needed to precipitate the Fe^{3+} as $Fe(OH)_3$?
   c) Assuming that the precipitation reaction goes to completion, what mass of $Fe(OH)_3$ will be formed?
5. When NaOH is added to a sample of water containing Fe^{3+} in order to precipitate $Fe(OH)_3$, a small amount of Fe^{3+} will remain in equilibrium with the $Fe(OH)_{3(s)}$. You can calculate $[Fe^{3+}]$ at equilibrium using K_{sp} for $Fe(OH)_3$ (6.3×10^{-38}).
   a) What is $[Fe^{3+}]$ at equilibrium when the OH^- concentration is 0.0010 *M*?
   b) Is the value you found for $[Fe^{3+}]$ below the secondary drinking water regulation for Fe?
6. Ingesting too much $Na^+(aq)$ may cause high blood pressure in humans, and excess sodium in a water supply can make it unusable. The following bases may be preferred over NaOH for precipitating Fe^{3+} ions: KOH, $Mg(OH)_2$, or $Ca(OH)_2$. Do these have any disadvantages?
7. Explain why water treatment calls for a sequence of filtering materials such as gravel, sand, glass wool, and filter paper. What would happen if the order were reversed?

8. ***Preparing for the Chapter Challenge***

   Begin a flow diagram or schematic for the various stages that must be part of the water-treatment plants required for the challenge. At each stage that you add to the diagram in this and other activities, you should specify the chemical reactions, the separation methods, and the contaminants removed.

Inquiring Further

1. pH effects on coagulation

As you learned in prior activities, an engineer designing a chemical treatment plant must consider pH throughout the entire purification process. This is especially true when using the alum and quicklime to remove the suspended particles in solution, as you will want to create the most aluminum hydroxide gel to coagulate the colloidal suspensions. Under the guidance of your teacher, design and conduct an experiment to determine the pH that creates the most aluminum hydroxide, i.e., the pH where aluminum hydroxide is the least soluble. Report your findings to your class.

Do this activity only under adult supervision.

2. Other coagulants

Alum is just one reactant used in the reaction to create floc. Its use has recently been scaled back because aluminum is on the maximum contaminant list and has been tentatively linked to cases of dementia (specifically Alzheimer's). Another popular chemical to use in place of alum is iron (III) sulfate. This chemical creates a floc very similar to your precipitate in *Part B* of the *Investigate* section. Research other coagulants used to clarify water by creating floc. Write a report for the class that names the other coagulants, provides the chemical reactions involved, and expresses the advantages and disadvantages of each coagulant including safety, possible health hazards, complications to the treatment process, and cost.

Activity 6 Water Softening

What Do You See?

HARD WATER
SOFT WATER

GOALS

In this activity you will:

- Investigate the equilibria behind water softening.
- Determine which reduces water hardness more, precipitation reactions or ion-exchange resins.
- Learn about any drawbacks connected with softening water.

What Do You Think?

Hard water can cause more problems than leaving a soap-scum ring around the bathtub. It can leave scaling inside water pipes. Hard water must be softened in order to avoid long-term system damage.

- **What reaction can be used to remove the Ca^{2+} and Mg^{2+} ions from water? Show the chemistry and explain your reasoning.**
- **Can all of the Ca^{2+} and Mg^{2+} ions be removed? Explain your reasoning.**

Record your ideas about these questions in your *Active Chemistry* log. Be prepared to discuss your responses with your small group and the class.

Investigate

Part A: Precipitation of Calcium

Using the same water sample you analyzed in *Activity 3*, add sodium carbonate to remove calcium ions by precipitation of calcium carbonate. Since calcium carbonate is slightly soluble in water, you will have to account for this in your calculations and the assessment of the amount of calcium left in the solution. This activity is a good review of all of the chemistry you have applied thus far in the chapter, so it would be wise for you to look back in your *Active Chemistry* log if you are unsure about how to make a calculation!

Calculation/Observation	Result
total water hardness of your water sample (ppm)	
amount of $Ca^{2+}{}_{(aq)}$ in 100.0 mL of your water sample (mol)	
amount of $Na_2CO_{3(s)}$ needed to precipitate the $Ca^{2+}{}_{(aq)}$ in your sample (g)	
theoretical amount of $CaCO_{3(s)}$ formed (mol)	
amount of $Ca^{2+}{}_{(aq)}$ remaining in solution due to slight solubility of $CaCO_{3(s)}$ (mol)	
percent of $Ca^{2+}{}_{(aq)}$ remaining in solution	
theoretical amount of $CaCO_{3(s)}$ formed, accounting for the slight solubility of $CaCO_{3(s)}$ (g)	
actual amount of $CaCO_{3(s)}$ formed (g)	
results of soap test	

1. You will use sodium carbonate to remove calcium ions by precipitating calcium carbonate.

   a) Write the reaction for the formation of calcium carbonate using sodium carbonate. Be sure to include the states of matter and properly balance the equation.

2. Copy the table above into your *Active Chemistry* log.

3. Assuming that Ca^{2+} was responsible for all the water hardness measured in *Activity 3*, perform the following theoretical calculations and record your answers in the table in your *Active Chemistry* log.

   a) How many moles of $Ca^{2+}{}_{(aq)}$ are in 100.0 mL of your particular sample of water?

   b) Theoretically, how many grams of Na_2CO_3 should be added so as to cause all of the calcium ions to precipitate into solid calcium carbonate if the above reaction goes to completion?

   c) How many moles of $CaCO_3$ would be formed?

4. The reaction to precipitate Ca^{2+} does not go to completion since $CaCO_3$ is slightly soluble. Use the solubility value for $CaCO_3$ ($K_{sp} = 8.7 \times 10^{-9}$ at 25°C) to perform the following calculations. Record your answers in the table in your *Active Chemistry* log.

   a) Write the solubility expression for $CaCO_3$.

   b) Calculate the moles of Ca^{2+} when $CaCO_{3(s)}$ is in equilibrium with equimolar amounts of $Ca^{2+}{}_{(aq)}$ and $CO_3{}^{2-}{}_{(aq)}$.

   c) Calculate the percent of Ca^{2+} remaining in the solution after precipitation. (Hint: Use your amount from *Step 3(a)* as the original total.)

   d) Calculate the theoretical mass (g) of $CaCO_{3(s)}$ formed, taking into account the slight solubility of $CaCO_{3(s)}$.

5. Using the batch method, treat the 100.0 mL sample of water with the quantity of $Na_2CO_{3(s)}$ that you calculated is necessary to precipitate $CaCO_3$ according to the initial reaction stoichiometry.

Safety goggles and a lab apron must be worn *at all times* in a chemistry lab.

Mix chemicals only as directed by your teacher.

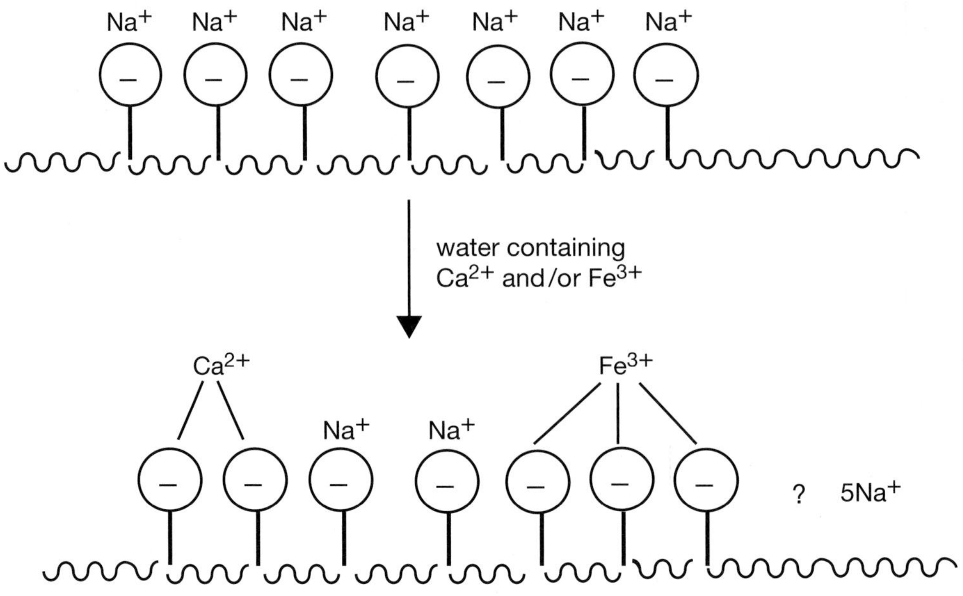
Na+ Na+ Na+ Na+ Na+ Na+ Na+
water containing
Ca2+ and/or Fe3+
Ca2+
Fe3+
Na+ Na+
? 5Na+

6. Find the mass of the batch precipitate.

   a) Measure the mass of a dry piece of filter paper and record this value in your *Active Chemistry* log.

   Filter according to your teacher's directions. Dry the precipitate on the filter paper as directed by your teacher.

   b) Calculate the mass of your $CaCO_{3(s)}$ precipitate. Record this value in the table in your *Active Chemistry* log.

7. Test the filtrate qualitatively for water hardness by adding some soap to it and observing whether the solution is cloudy.

   a) Record your results in the table in your *Active Chemistry* log.

Part B: Ion-Exchange Resins

1. Choose either the batch or flow technique that you used in *Activity 5*.

2. Create a table in your *Active Chemistry* log to collect all of the necessary data. In addition to the data collected for the particular method in *Activity 5*, you will want to include the amount of resin used and have a column for the analysis of the filtered water.

3. Load the mixing flask or filtration column with the recorded amount of acidic anion ***ion-exchange resin.*** An acidic ion-exchange resin is a polymeric material that has negative sites on its surface. These negative sites attract and absorb positive ions such as Ca^{2+} and Mg^{2+}, removing them from water. As the water sample comes into contact with the resin beads, the Ca^{2+} and Mg^{2+} ions are attracted to the negative sites, replacing the Na^+ ions originally on each bead.

4. Process a sample of untreated water with the ion-exchange resin.

5. Analyze your filtered solution for total water hardness. For a quantitative analysis, follow the experimental design in *Activity 3* for the analysis of total water hardness (*Investigate, Part A*). For a qualitative analysis, add some soap to a portion of your water sample before and after the treatment with ion-exchange resin. Shake the solution to see if it becomes cloudy.

   a) Record the results in the table in your *Active Chemistry* log.

Dispose of the materials as directed by your teacher.

Clean up your workstation.

Wash your hands and arms thoroughly after the activity.

Chem Talk

TREATING HARD WATER

Water Hardness

As you learned in *Activity 1*, natural waters can differ a great deal in the amounts and types of minerals they contain. The most common positive ions are Ca^{2+} and Mg^{2+}, and they are responsible for making water hard. They are not dangerous to consume in the usual quantities contained by natural waters. However, they lower the quality of the water and may create expensive complications when present in elevated amounts. They cause the formation of "scale." This gradually builds up and closes the inside of iron water pipes. Scale is caused by calcium and magnesium ions when they precipitate as $CaCO_3$ and $Mg(OH)_2$.

Klean
fabric detergent

The soap scum that appears in bathtubs and sinks can be traced to hard water as well. Soaps are salts of long-chain molecules called fatty acids. The non-polar end of the soap molecule allows greasy molecules to dissolve. Ca^{2+} and Mg^{2+} bond strongly to the carboxylate ions ($-COO^-$) of soaps to form insoluble residues.

Considerably more soap is needed to wash laundry with hard water than soft. Much of the residue remains in fabrics after rinsing and prevents thorough cleaning. Many detergents, on the other hand, can work better in hard water than soaps because they contain phosphate ions that can attach to Ca^{2+} and Mg^{2+} ions without forming an insoluble residue. Sodium salts of alkylbenzenesulfonic acids are also widely used as detergents, because like the phosphate ions, they are able to form soluble salts with the Ca^{2+} and Mg^{2+} ions.

Treating Water Hardness: Precipitation

Water-treatment plants typically use a mixture of soda ash, Na_2CO_3, and slaked lime, $Ca(OH)_2$, to remove the Ca^{2+} and Mg^{2+} ions. As you observed in your investigation, Na_2CO_3 causes the precipitation of calcium carbonate, $Ca(CO_3)$. Slaked lime, $Ca(OH)_2$ causes the precipitation of magnesium hydroxide, $Mg(OH)_2$. This is commonly

Chem Words

soda-lime process: a process adopted on a large scale in water-treatment plants for removing Ca^{2+} and Mg^{2+} by the addition of Na_2CO_3 (soda) and $Ca(OH)_2$ (lime).

ion-exchange resin: a polymeric material that has negative sites on its surface where various positive ions are adsorbed. Positive ions of higher charge are more strongly adsorbed, but still may be replaced by ions of lower charge having a sufficiently high concentration.

referred to as the **soda-lime treatment**, a chemical treatment based on a location-specific balance of the following chemical reactions.

$$Na_2CO_{3(s)} + Ca^{2+}{}_{(aq)} \leftrightarrows 2Na^{+}{}_{(aq)} + CaCO_{3(s)}$$

$$Mg^{2+}{}_{(aq)} + 2OH^{-}{}_{(aq)} \leftrightarrows Mg(OH)_{2(s)}$$

While the chemistry behind the soda-lime treatment is complicated, it is a preferred method. It is convenient to use with a settling basin followed by filtration, and the chemicals are cheap. Soda ash is currently about $1.20 per kilogram and slaked lime is about $0.50 per kilogram.

In this activity, you encountered some of the drawbacks of the soda-lime treatment. The Ca^{2+} cannot be completely removed because precipitation is not complete. At equilibrium, some calcium ions remain dissolved. This is true for the Mg^{2+} ions as well. The equilibrium concentrations of these ions are determined by the solubility products of the precipitates and the concentrations of added $CO_3{}^{2-}$ and OH^-. It is unwise to add too much slaked lime, because it adds to the Ca^{2+} removal problem. The addition of Na_2CO_3 is limited by the health hazard of a high concentration of Na^+, which can lead to high blood pressure in some individuals. Hence, water softening is not complete in water-treatment plants and may not be performed at all in some areas. In those places, homeowners may choose to soften water that is to be used for cleaning by installing commercial water softeners.

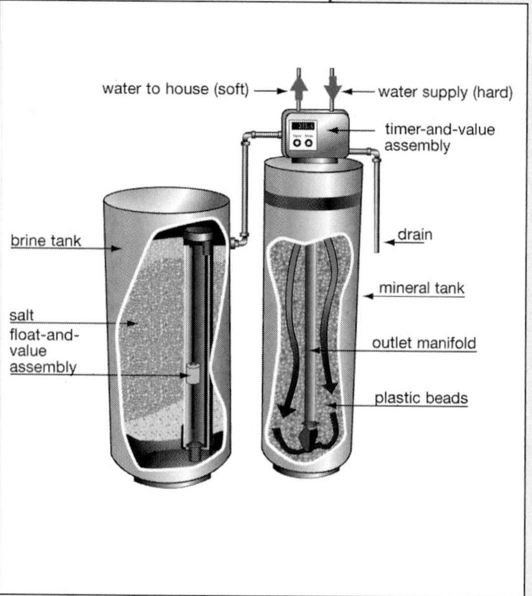
water to house (soft)
water supply (hard)
timer-and-value assembly
brine tank
drain
mineral tank
salt
float-and-value assembly
outlet manifold
plastic beads

Treating Water Hardness: Ion-Exchange Resin

Water softening by **ion-exchange resins** is based on a very different principle. Instead of being removed in precipitates, the positive ions are attached to a polymerby being attracted to negatively charged sites on the surface of the polymer. The polymer cannot be prepared with a net negative charge, but rather starts with Na^+ ions adhering to the negative sites. Since the Ca^{2+} and Mg^{2+} are more strongly attracted to the negative sites than the Na^+, they readily replace the Na^+. The net effect is the same as in the soda-lime treatment. The stream of water ends up with Na^+ ions instead of Ca^{2+} and Mg^{2+}. However, instead of separating a precipitatefrom the stream of water, it is necessary to reload the ion-exchange resin with Na^+ ions by temporarily exposing it to a high concentration of sodium chloride solution.

During the reloading process, dissolved $CaCl_2$ and $MgCl_2$ are carried away and the Na^+ adheres to the polymer. As you may have noticed in your investigation, water softened by this technique can have considerably lower Ca^{2+} and Mg^{2+} concentrations than is possible with the soda-lime process.

The drawbacks to ion-exchange resins were not as easily observed. In a water softener's "flush" cycle, Na^+ is washed from the resin down a drain. Some may remain and be carried into the home's water lines. Therefore, some homeowners choose to have lines used for consuming water bypass the softener. In addition, at about $3.00 per kilogram, ion-exchange resins are more expensive than soda and lime. However, they are not consumed in the full treatment and reloading cycle and can be reused for years.

Checking Up

1. What causes "hard" water?
2. What are the disadvantages of hard water?
3. Why is the soda-lime treatment of hard water a preferred method?
4. How do ion-exchange resins work to remove Ca^{2+} and Mg^{2+} ions from hard water?
5. What are the drawbacks of ion-exchange resins?

What Do You Think Now?

At the beginning of this activity you were asked:

- **What reaction can be used to remove the Ca^{2+} and Mg^{2+} ions from water? Show the chemistry and explain your reasoning.**
- **Can all of the Ca^{2+} and Mg^{2+} ions be removed? Explain your reasoning.**

Were any of the reactions you predicted in the *What Do You Think?* section part of this activity? You were asked if you could completely remove the ions causing water hardness. How would your answer to this question change after performing the two techniques?

Chem Essential Questions

What does it mean?

Chemistry explains a macroscopic phenomenon (what you observe) with a description of what happens at the nanoscopic level (atoms and molecules) using symbolic structures as a way to communicate. Complete the chart below in your *Active Chemistry* log.

MACRO	NANO	SYMBOLIC
When sodium carbonate solution was added to hard water, what evidence did you see that confirmed that the hard water contained calcium ions?	*The surface of the resin-exchange column is saturated with sodium ions. Explain what is taking place when the hard water that contains calcium ions comes in contact with the sodium-charged resin-exchange column.*	$Na_2CO_3(s) + Ca^{2+}(aq) \rightarrow 2Na^+(aq) + CaCO_3(s)$ *and* $CaCO_3(s) \rightarrow Ca^{2+}(aq) + CO_3^{2-}(aq)$ *From the equations that are shown, explain why you cannot totally remove all of the calcium ions.*

How do you know?

How did you see that the water had been softened? Explain.

Why do you believe?

Why are water softeners so popular in the homes of people living in the Midwestern states like Ohio?

Why should you care?

Is it important to remove the water hardness from your water sample? Explain.

Reflecting on the Activity and the Challenge

In this activity, you have tried procedures that can be used to soften water. Softening water does not make water any safer to consume. It does make water a better cleaning solvent. It may end up saving a lot of money by reducing soap purchases and avoiding the need to replace appliances and supply lines.

In designing water treatment procedures for different communities, you should decide whether a water-softening step is essential. Consider whether attempts to remove other contaminants will be as successful if they have not been preceded by water softening.

Chem to Go

1. In *Part A* of this investigation did the treatment with Na_2CO_3 noticeably reduce the water hardness? What was your evidence?
2. Suppose that you use $CaCl_2$ to precipitate F^- in a water sample.
   a) Write the reaction as if it would go to completion.
   b) How many moles of $CaCl_2$ should you add to 10.0 mL of water containing 12 mg/L of $F^-_{(aq)}$ if the reaction goes to completion? Show all of your work.
   c) When the resulting precipitate comes to equilibrium, not all of the F^- will be removed from solution. Write this equation.
   d) Find the equilibrium concentration of F^- using the K_{sp} for CaF_2 (3.9×10^{-11}). Show all of your work.
3. If twice the stoichiometric amount of Na_2CO_3 calculated in *Part A* is added to a 100.0 mL sample of water, will more $CaCO_3$ be formed than before? If so, how much more will form? Show the work behind your answers.

4. Why is $Ca(OH)_2$ added to water as part of the overall softening process even though it contains the hard-water Ca^{2+} ions?

5. Why are Ca^{2+} and Mg^{2+} ions more strongly attracted than Na^+ ions to negative sites in ion-exchange resins?

6. What is the purpose of periodically adding highly concentrated sodium chloride solutions to ion-exchange resins?

7. Nitrate is commonly removed from water through the use of ion-exchange resins.

   a) Propose how you think these resins would work on the nanoscale.

   b) How would you be able to test to see if the ion-exchange resin you proposed would be effective in removing nitrate from your water supply?

8. ***Preparing for the Chapter Challenge***

   Continue your diagram for the water purification from the previous activity. Decide if water softening is necessary for your particular region. If so, decide whether you will use ion-exchange resins or precipitation. Be prepared to justify your decision.

Inquiring Further

1. Magnesium removal

Removing magnesium from a water sample involves the consideration of additional chemical equilibria, including the bicarbonate equilibrium. First, research ways in which this precipitation occurs in water purification systems. Under the guidance of your teacher, apply your methods to your water sample and record your results. Write a report for your class on the complex chemistry behind these steps and your results in purifying your water sample.

Do this activity only under adult supervision.

2. Nitrate removal

Nitrate is removed from water sources through two common methods: ion-exchange resins and biological treatments. Research each of these methods as they relate to removing nitrate from the water supply. Present your findings to your class, including the advantages and drawbacks of each method.

Activity 7 Removing Toxic-Metal Ions

What Do You See?

Heavy Metal PHISH
STARRING: ARSENIC, MERCURY, ZINC And LEAD

GOALS

In this activity you will:

- Discover what steps can be taken to keep toxic-metal ions out of the drinking water supply.
- Apply the chemical concepts you have learned to remove toxic-metal ions.
- Learn other methods for purifying water supplies through physical means.

What Do You Think?

Toxic metals are often a result of human interactions with the environment. Rivers in mining regions can become heavily polluted with a variety of toxic-metal ions such as lead, mercury, zinc, and arsenic.

- **In what ways do toxic metals get into the water supply?**
- **What do you think are the best ways to remove toxic-metal cations from the water supply?**

Record your ideas about these questions in your *Active Chemistry* log. Be prepared to discuss your responses with your small group and the class.

Investigate

Part A: Precipitating Insoluble Sulfides

To precipitate a number of toxic metals, you can create insoluble sulfide salts using a solution of hydrogen sulfide. At high concentrations, most toxic metals will precipitate out of solution with a treatment of hydrogen sulfide.

Safety goggles and a lab apron must be worn *at all times* in a chemistry lab.

1. You will investigate three toxic-metal solutions: copper (II) chloride, cadmium (II) chloride, and nickel (II) chloride.

   a) Write each chemical formula in your *Active Chemistry* log.

b) Write a balanced equation for the reaction between each metal solution and hydrogen sulfide. Include states of matter for each substance in the reaction.

2. Your teacher has prepared a saturated hydrogen sulfide solution using the following decomposition reaction.

   $CH_3CSNH_2(aq) + 2H_2O(l) \rightarrow$
   $CH_3COO^-(aq) + NH_4^+(aq) +$
   $H_2S(aq)$.

   The H_2S concentration after the decomposition of thioacetamide is approximately 0.10 *M*. Add two drops of the 0.10 *M* H_2S solution to 5.0 mL of a 0.010 *M* solution of the following metal chlorides: $CuCl_2$, $CdCl_2$, and $NiCl_2$.

   a) Record the appearance of the precipitates in your *Active Chemistry* log.

3. Pick one of the metal chlorides to perform a quantitative analysis of the amount of precipitate formed with the addition of $H_2S(aq)$. Predict how much of the insoluble sulfide should precipitate from the 0.010 *M* solution of the metal chloride solution in an excess amount of hydrogen sulfide solution, assuming the reaction goes to completion.

   a) Record this value in your *Active Chemistry* log.

4. Use an excess amount of the H_2S reagent by adding 5.0 mL of 0.1 *M* H_2S to 5.0 mL of a 0.010 *M* solution of the metal chloride.

5. Filter, dry, and determine the mass of the precipitate. Be sure to record the mass of the dry piece of filter paper before you filter!

   a) Record the amount of precipitate in your *Active Chemistry* log. Compare it with what you expected to be formed if all the metal ends up in the precipitate.

6. Save the filtered solution (filtrate). Discard the precipitate as directed by your instructor.

7. In the previous steps, some of the metal cations remained in solution because the following solubility equilibrium for a metal sulfide is established.

   $MS(s) + H_2O(l) \rightarrow$
   $M^{2+}(aq) + HS^-(aq) + OH^-(aq)$

   Note: In this equation, M^{2+} represents Cu^{2+}, Cd^{2+} or Ni^{2+}.

   a) In your *Active Chemistry* log, write the solubility product expression (K_{sp}) for this equilibrium.

   b) Using LeChatelier's Principle (remember *Activity 4*), predict how the concentration would change if the pH were raised. Explain your prediction in your *Active Chemistry* log and discuss this with your group before proceeding to *Step 8*.

8. Add 0.01 *M* of the strong base sodium hydroxide (NaOH) to raise the pH of the filtered solution obtained in *Step 6*.

   a) Record your observations in your *Active Chemistry* log.

   b) Do they agree with what you predicted? Respond to this in your *Active Chemistry* log and discuss your observations with your group members.

The $H_2S(aq)$ solution that will be provided for this activity will give off fumes of $H_2S(g)$. The fumes smell like rotten eggs and are toxic. The solution and all test tubes it has been added to should be kept under a hood at all times.

While the solution of this compound is stable at room temperature, you should keep the bottle closed except when adding the solution.

Part B: Precipitating by Adjusting the pH

Some metal ions having insoluble hydroxides can be removed by raising the pH. Solubility product constants given in the appendix of this text can be used to determine the solubilities of Cr^{3+}, Pb^{2+}, Ni^{2+}, Sn^{2+} and Zn^{2+} at a pH of 10.0.

1. Determine the $[OH^-]$ at this pH by recalling that pOH $=14 - $ pH and $[OH^-] = 10 - $ pOH. If pOH is not a familiar concept, prove the statements in the question are true by using the K_w for the dissociation of water.
   a) Record your work and answer in your *Active Chemistry* log.
   b) In your *Active Chemistry* log, write the solubility product expression along with the K_{sp} value for each of the hydroxides formed from the ions listed.
   c) Solve for the solubilities of each ion, $[Cr^{3+}]$, $[Pb^{2+}]$, $[Ni^{2+}]$, $[Sn^{2+}]$, and $[Zn^{2+}]$, at a pH of 10. Record your answers and your work in your *Active Chemistry* log.
   d) Convert these equilibrium molar concentrations to a solubility of the metal hydroxide in ppm.
2. Research the maximum contaminant levels (MCL) for each toxic metal.
   a) In your *Active Chemistry* log, write a paragraph justifying that a pH of 10.0 would be sufficient to lower the concentration of these metal ions below MCL levels.

Chem Words

toxic-metal ions: the ions of heavy metals, the most common being Ag^+, Pb^{2+}, Hg_2^{2+}, Cu^{2+}, Cd^{2+}, Ni^{2+}, Cr^{3+} and Zn^{2+}.

Chem Talk

TOXIC-METAL IONS

Sources of Toxic-Metal Ions

Toxic-metal ions, which are frequently referred to as heavy-metal ions, can get into natural waters by being leached out of mineral deposits that contain the ions. However, the more common source is from human activities. They have been associated with retardation in brain development and disorders of the nervous system. Some, such as chromium and nickel, are carcinogenic (can cause cancer). Even at very low levels, they can still be dangerous over time because the body is rather ineffective at getting rid of them once they enter fatty tissue. Toxicity limits are difficult to determine accurately and often rely on extrapolations of animal studies performed at much higher concentrations than are found in water supplies. Since the U.S. government increased regulation of disposal of industrial waste following the Safe Drinking Water Act of 1974, industries have sharply curtailed the pollutants they add to natural waterways.

In less-developed countries, though, industrial discharges may be more common and regulation not as effective. Also, there are many abandoned mines and industrial sites worldwide where toxic metals continue to leach into waterways or into underground water. Types of industries that may release heavy-metal ions are petroleum refining, chemical manufacturing, steel making, power plants, and electroplating. Many industries have modified products that they manufacture to minimize use of the more toxic metals. For example, paints, gasoline, and solder once depended on having lead as a component. Mercury was once common in batteries and thermometers. Now, substitute products avoid the use of lead or mercury altogether in these items. However, exposure to the older products will continue for many years to come. For example, some older municipal plumbing used lead water lines and even fairly recent copper plumbing installations used lead-containing solder.

Mercury continues to be released to the atmosphere in large amounts as coal is burned in power plants. It settles out on land and water worldwide, and can become concentrated in the fatty tissue of animals, especially in fish that are high up in the food chain. Treatment of a water supply to remove toxic metals at water plants obviously cannot prevent their being reintroduced in water delivery lines. Hence, homeowners may resort to adding final stages of water purification to remove toxic metals. It has been found, though, that simply letting the water run for a minute or two before consuming it can reduce the lead concentration to well below the MCL.

Removing Toxic-Metal Ions through Precipitation

In this activity, you explored two methods to precipitate toxic-metal cations: adding sulfides and raising the pH. The use of sulfides is considered an economical way to remove the toxic-metal ions. The chemistry behind the removal is similar to precipitations utilized in previous activities, except the chemical equilibria achieved are more complex since they are pH dependent:

$$MS_{(s)} + H_2O_{(l)} \leftrightarrows M^{2+}{}_{(aq)} + HS^{-}{}_{(aq)} + OH^{-}{}_{(aq)}$$

According to LeChatelier's Principle, if the concentration of hydroxide ions is increased, then the equilibrium will shift to the left in response to this stress, precipitating more of the toxic-metal sulfide. If the pH was lowered, then the equilibrium would shift to the right in response to this stress, leaving more of the toxic-metal ion in solution. The result of these stresses can be seen in the diagram. Therefore, by making the water more basic (increasing the OH^- concentration), you can precipitate out more of the toxic-metal ion, leaving a much lower concentration in the water.

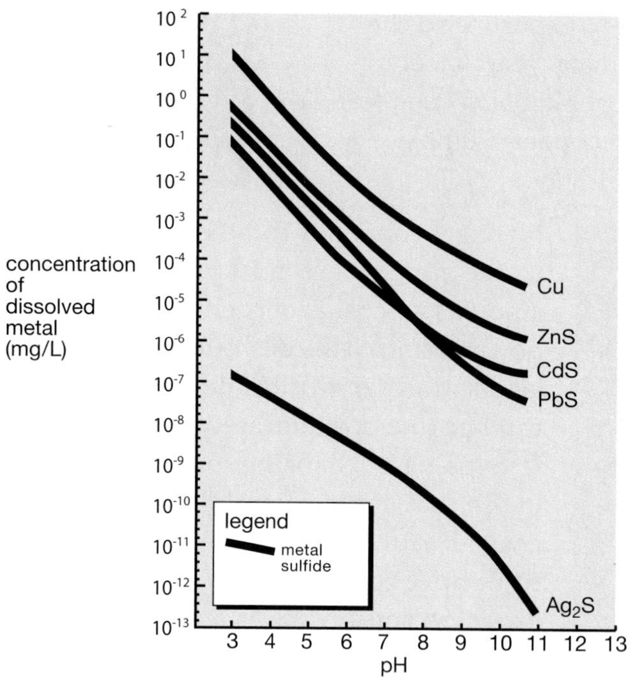
concentration of dissolved metal (mg/L)
10^2
10^1
10^0
10^-1
10^-2
10^-3
10^-4
10^-5
10^-6
10^-7
10^-8
10^-9
10^-10
10^-11
10^-12
10^-13
3 4 5 6 7 8 9 10 11 12 13
pH
Cu
ZnS
CdS
PbS
Ag2S
legend
metal sulfide

As you calculated in this activity, water-treatment plants can precipitate some toxic-metal ions simply by raising the pH so that the concentrations are less than the MCLs. In practice, the chemistry behind adjusting the pH can be very complex. The graph shown was derived from experimentation expressing the solubilities of metal ions at various pHs. No matter how you choose to adjust to the pH, though, it must be restored to a certain safe range before leaving your purification process. This will be further explored in *Activity 8*.

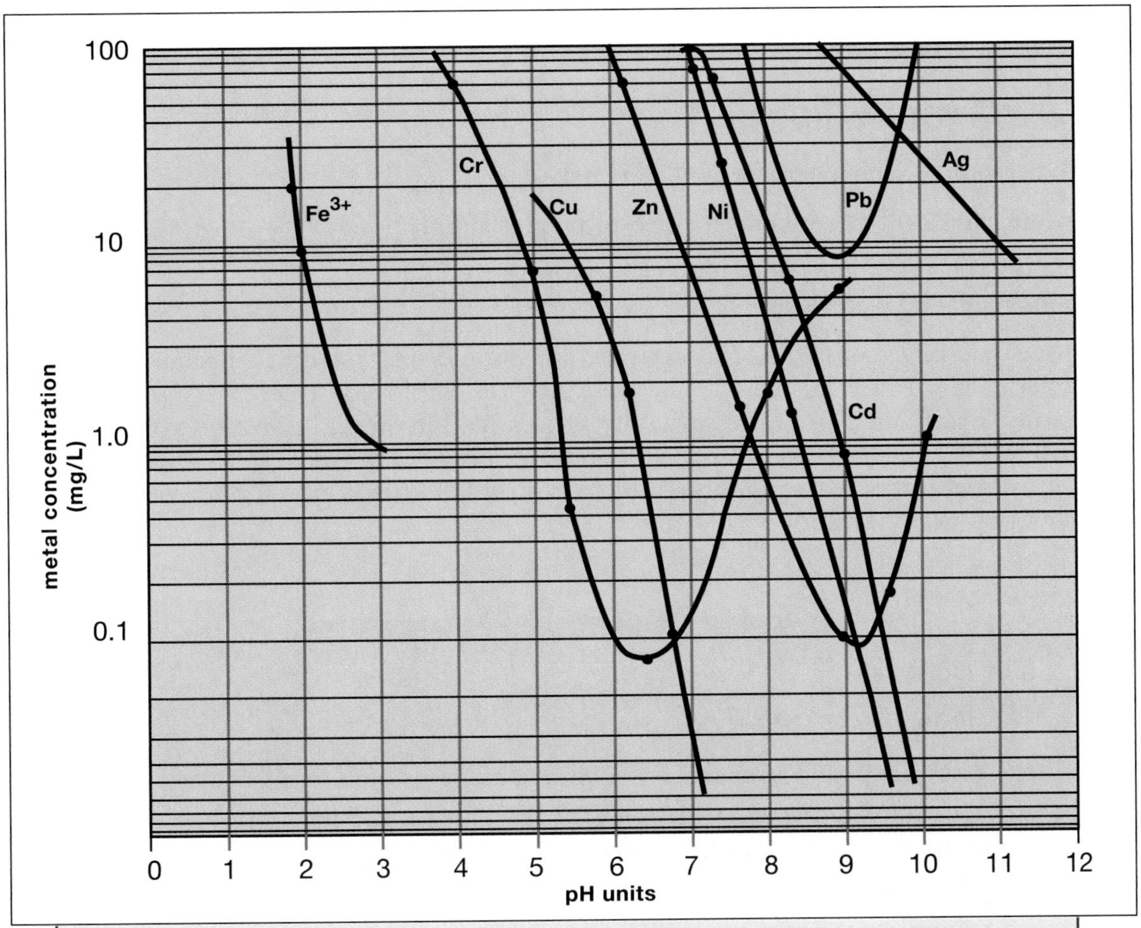

100
10
1.0
0.1
metal concentration (mg/L)
Fe3+
Cr
Cu
Zn
Ni
Pb
Ag
Cd
0
1
2
3
4
5
6
7
8
9
10
11
12
pH units

Chem Words

distillation: the separation of components in a liquid by boiling off and condensing more volatile components first.

reverse osmosis: a de-ionization technique based on using pressure to force water through a membrane that is impermeable to metal ions.

Physical Processes of Removing Toxic-Metal Ions

If one wants to remove all the metal ions from water, there are two methods available that do not give any residual amounts associated with chemical equilibria. They are **distillation** and **reverse osmosis**. In both cases, the phase that receives the metal ions will not release them back to the water. In distillation, only the water or volatile components in the water go into the gas phase as the water is boiled. The nonvolatile solids become more concentrated in the still and are discarded. The energy needed to boil the water and cool the vapor so that it condenses is considerable, and that generally makes the process too expensive to use on a large scale.

In reverse osmosis, pressure is exerted on the water to pass it through a semi-permeable membrane, which has pores that are too small to allow large ions or particles to pass through. Such a system can purify water just as well as distillation does and may be used for providing de-ionized water when it is needed in laboratories or industrial processes. *Inquiring Further* in *Activity 8* has more ideas involving membranes and their use in water purification systems.

Checking Up

1. What are two sources of toxic-metal ions?
2. How does mercury enter into the environment?
3. What is the most inexpensive water treatment to remove toxic-metal cations?
4. Describe how reverse osmosis works.

What Do You Think Now?

At the beginning of this activity you were asked:

- **In what ways do toxic metals get into the water supply?**
- **What do you think are the best ways to remove toxic-metal cations from the water supply?**

Now that you have completed this activity, you should understand that removing toxic metals is a "dirty business." The methods you employed involved using a toxic-soluble gas and a pH far outside the safe range for water. Reflect on your answers to the two questions. What do you think now is the best way to remove toxic metals from the water supply? Why do you think efforts are targeted more at prevention than at removal?

Chem Essential Questions

What does it mean?

Chemistry explains a macroscopic phenomenon (what you observe) with a description of what happens at the nanoscopic level (atoms and molecules) using symbolic structures as a way to communicate. Complete the chart below in your *Active Chemistry* log.

MACRO	NANO	SYMBOLIC
What do you see when toxic-metal ions such as Cd^{2+} are treated with: a) S^{2-} ions b) OH^{-} ions.	*Many toxic water sites have low pH. Explain how the addition of hydroxide ions and sulfide ions can help in removing toxic-metal ions from the solution.*	*Show with equations why the toxic water solution that has been treated with sulfide ions is not safe to consume and what steps must be taken to make it safe.*

How do you know?

How do you know that the addition of carbonate ions to a sample of hard water will remove Cd^{2+} ions? When answering, make specific reference to your observations and calculations from the *Investigate* section.

Why do you believe?

What toxic metal or metals had you heard of before this activity? Explain.

Why should you care?

Why is it so important to include a step removing toxic-metal ions in your water purification process?

Reflecting on the Activity and the Challenge

In this activity, you have studied ways in which toxic-metal ions can be removed from the water supply. A water-treatment plant must have sensitive detection equipment available for monitoring these contaminants. Contaminants can gradually build up in human tissue and affect human functions in many ways. The most effective way to deal with them is to reform industrial practices that account for most of their presence in water supplies. Their removal is most commonly accomplished by adding chemicals to make them precipitate. These chemicals include sulfides or hydroxides, as investigated in this activity, or other insoluble compounds such as certain chlorides. One has to consider the effect of these added chemicals on the overall water-purification process. You do not want to end up with an excessive amount of Na^+ in the water, or a pH that is too high or too low.

An alternative to precipitation reactions is the use of ion-exchange resins. However, the higher cost may make resins impractical when water needs are large. Distillation or reverse osmosis would likely be too expensive to use in water-treatment plants. They are useful, though, for producing a small amount of very pure water.

Chem to Go

1. Why is the concentration of toxic-metal ions higher in fish than it is in the water where they live?
2. Describe three pathways that toxic metals take in entering the water supply.
3. What methods can be used to remove essentially all of the metal ions from water? What limits their use?
4. Explain how pH effects the removal of toxic-metal ions through sulfide precipitation.
5. The highest acceptable pH for a water supply is 8.5.
   a) Calculate the OH^- concentration at this pH.
   b) Use K_{sp} for $Pb(OH)_2$ (1.4×10^{-20}) to find the concentration of Pb^{2+} in a saturated solution of $Pb(OH)_2$ at a pH of 8.5.
   c) Is this Pb^{2+} concentration less than the MCL for Pb^{2+}?
6. Suppose chromium and copper were both in the groundwater supply due to toxic dumping. Refer to the graph in *Chem Talk*. Would raising the pH to 10.0 remove the most of both of these toxic metals? Explain.
7. Suppose a water supply had chromium and nickel pollution. Use the graph in *Chem Talk* and the MCL values for each. What pH would you use to remove these toxic metals? Explain.

8. *Preparing for the Chapter Challenge*

   Using the information collected about your particular area, determine if there is a threat of specific toxic-metal ions in the water supply. If so, create a list of those that you anticipate you will need to remove and determine a method you will use to remove them. Note that some methods not used in this activity, such as using chloride, may also precipitate certain toxic-metal ions. Include this step in your diagram from the previous activities. Be sure to indicate the status of the water once it is filtered, including the pH.

Inquiring Further

Researching the history of toxic metals in water supplies

Toxic metals have been introduced through a variety of methods into water supplies in recent years. Some toxic metals, such as arsenic, can be found naturally in the groundwater of some areas of the world but may go unnoticed because of the lack of accurate water-quality testing. Research a particular case where toxic-metal ions have been found in a drinking-water supply. Create a presentation that explains and illustrates the case and the outcomes. Include the chemistry behind the toxic metal and the biological effects the metal has on humans and other living creatures exposed to the toxic water supply.

Activity 8 Disinfection

What Do You See?
FILTER
1
2
3
WATER
DISINFECTION
PROJECT

GOALS

In this activity you will:

- Consider biological factors affecting the water supply.
- Adjust the pH of a water supply to the accepted level for drinking water.
- Reflect on the consequences of disinfecting water and the complications involved with pH.
- Create your theoretical pathway for treating water.

What Do You Think?

You have focused your attention on keeping the water within the chemically safe guidelines of the United States Environmental Protection Agency. However, many regard disinfection, the removal of harmful organisms and viruses in natural water, as the most crucial step in the water-treatment process.

- **Why would many regard disinfection as the most critical stage in a water-treatment process, considering all you have studied thus far in the chapter?**
- **How do you think disinfection relates to basic chemistry?**

Record your ideas about these questions in your *Active Chemistry* log. Be prepared to discuss your responses with your small group and the class.

Investigate

1. Most commonly in the U.S., water-treatment plants use chlorine to kill bacteria. Three forms of chlorine may be added to water: chlorine gas, $Cl_2(g)$, sodium hypochlorite, $NaOCl$, and calcium hypochlorite, $Ca(OCl)_2$.

   a) In your *Active Chemistry* log, write balanced equations showing how each of the three compounds can react with water to produce hypochlorous acid, $HOCl(aq)$.

Safety goggles and a lab apron must be worn *at all times* in a chemistry lab.

In this activity you will be handling bacterial samples to test their growth in treated and untreated water. You must wear plastic or rubber gloves when handling the samples.

Avoid breathing fumes.

Wash your hands and arms thoroughly after the activity.

2. Obtain three 100.0 mL samples of previously untreated water from a natural source.

3. Using one of the chlorinating substances, treat the first 100.0 mL sample of natural water using a batch method. Vary amounts of the chlorinating substance used to get a variety of results throughout the class. Do not filter the water sample. Just let it sit in the batch.

4. Pour the second 100.0 mL sample in a shallow dish to treat with ultraviolet irradiation. Use a source of ultraviolet irradiation such as a mercury lamp. Expose the water sample in the shallow dish to the source of ultraviolet light for a few minutes. Vary times throughout the class or within your group to get a variety of results.

5. Do nothing to the third sample. Leave it as natural as possible.

6. Obtain an agar plate but do not open it yet. The agar plate is a sterilized petri dish with a shallow jelly protein (agar) layer. The protein will encourage the growth of any bacteria present in the water samples. Flip over the agar plate and divide the plate into three portions by writing on the glass or plastic dish bottom with a dark wax pencil. Label the three portions to represent the three samples: natural, UV, and HOCl.

7. Obtain three sterile swabs. Dip the first swab into the natural water source. Swirl it within the source and remove. Using gloves, carefully open the plate. Quickly and gently roll the swab in the section marked "natural." Be careful not to tear into the agar. Recover the agar plate as soon as you are finished swabbing.

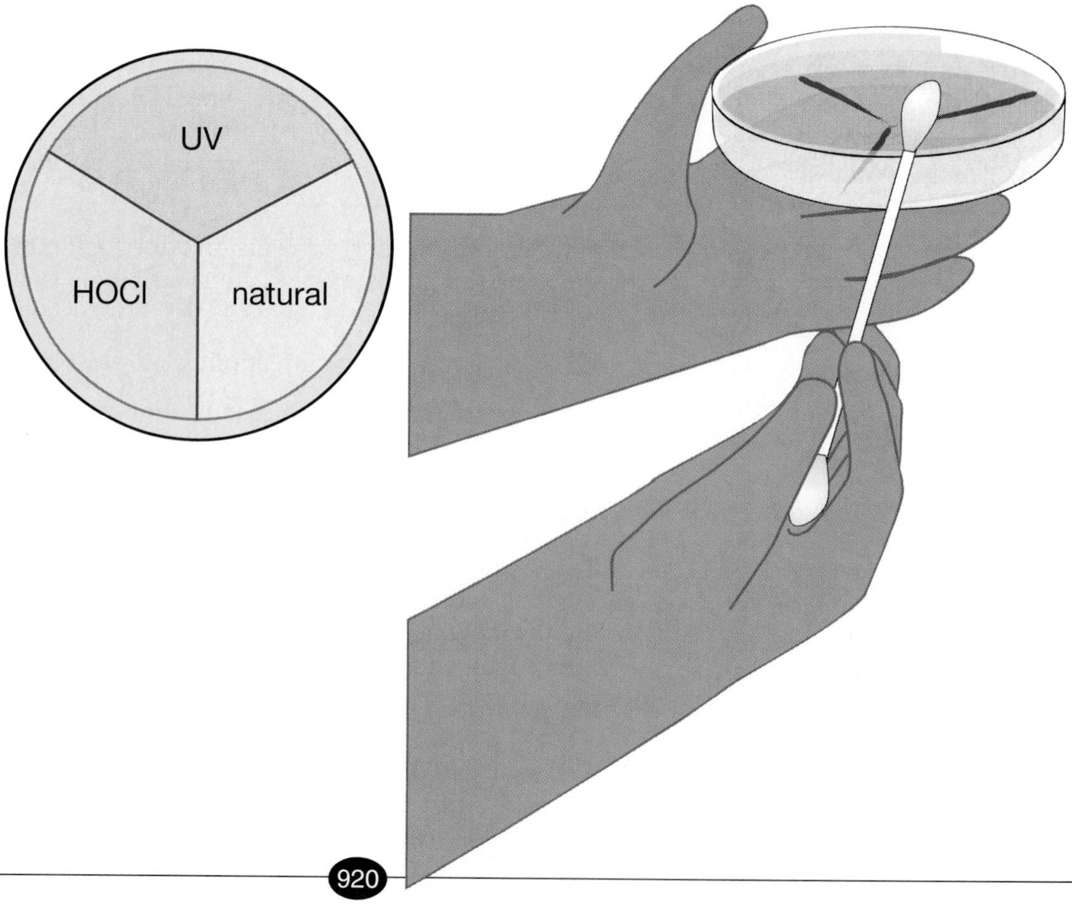
UV
HOCl
natural

8. Repeat *Step 7* for the two treated water samples.

9. Save your treated and untreated water samples for *Part B* of this activity.

10. Tape the lid so it will not fall off. Place the plate upside-down (lid-side down) in an incubator at 37°C or warm area of the room for 24 h. Observe the plate. Do not open the plate.

    a) Record your observations in your *Active Chemistry* log, noting any differences in the treated and untreated samples.

Part B: pH and Disinfection

For chlorination to be effective, HOCl must be the dominant chemical in solution. However, it too can dissociate in water:

$$HOCl(aq) = H^{+}(aq) + OCl^{-}(aq)$$

Adjusting the pH before and after treatment is an important consideration that must be included in your final process diagram for the treatment of water in your particular area of the world.

1. Copy the table below into your *Active Chemistry* log.

    a) In your *Active Chemistry* log, determine at which pH, the initial or the final, that hypochlorous acid, $HOCl(aq)$, would be present in highest concentrations. Explain your reasoning.

2. Use pH test paper or a pH probe to measure the pH of the two treated samples and one untreated sample from *Part A* of this *Investigate* section.

    a) Record the pH.

    b) Is the water sample basic or acidic in each sample?

    c) Calculate the concentration (*M*) of $H^{+}(aq)$ and $OH^{-}(aq)$ in each sample. Show your work.

3. To adjust the pH of each 100.0 mL sample to an acceptable pH (in this case you will target the neutral pH of 7.0), you will use 0.05 *M* solution of NaOH or HCl.

    a) Which source will you use to adjust the pH to 7.0?

    b) Calculate the concentration (*M*) of the appropriate solution you would add to adjust the pH to 7.0. Show the work behind your calculations.

    Have your calculations approved before moving forward to *Step 4*.

4. Using your approved calculations, conduct each neutralization reaction. Stir each sample to mix completely. Measure the new pH of your sample.

    a) Record this value in the table in your *Active Chemistry* log.

Safety goggles and a lab apron must be worn *at all times* in a chemistry lab.

Dispose of the materials as directed by your teacher. Clean up your workstation.

Wash your hands and arms thoroughly after the activity.

Sample	Initial pH	Basic or acidic?	$[H^{+}]$	$[OH^{-}]$	Source to adjust pH	Concentration of the source	Final pH
untreated							
HOCl							
UV							

Chem Talk

Chem Words

pathogens: living organisms that cause illness, disease, or death to another host organism.

disinfection: the destruction of disease-causing organisms.

trihalomethanes: compounds like chloroform, $CHCl_3$, which contain three halogen atoms bonded to carbon.

DISINFECTING WATER

Sources of Pathogens

Natural waterways are expected to have abundant amounts of both harmless and pathogenic bacteria. The closer the waterways are to livestock and cities, the more difficult it becomes to keep the **pathogens** out. Overflows of storm water from sanitary sewer systems offer an additional challenge in trying to keep sources of consumable water clean.

It is crucial that you go through disinfection steps in the water-treatment process. In this activity, you explored chlorination and ultraviolet irradiation. These, along with a treatment with ozone ($O_{3(g)}$), are the three most popular forms of disinfection, though each has its drawbacks and complications.

Disinfection

Disinfection refers to destroying disease-carrying microorganisms. There are a variety of ways water-treatment plants disinfect water, but the two of the more popular methods throughout the world are chlorination and ultraviolet disinfection. These disinfectants are popular because they are effective in killing the harmful organisms and they are inexpensive.

Many water-treatment plants in the United States use chlorine to kill bacteria. Three forms of chlorine that may be added to water are chlorine gas, $Cl_{2(g)}$, sodium hypochlorite, NaOCl, and calcium hypochlorite, $Ca(OCl)_2$. All of these produce hypochlorous acid, $HOCl_{(aq)}$, which appears to be the chemical that kills the bacteria. For example, when $Cl_{2(g)}$ is bubbled into water, the following equilibrium is established:

$$Cl_{2(aq)} + H_2O_{(l)} \rightarrow Cl^-_{(aq)} + H^+_{(aq)} + HOCl_{(aq)}$$

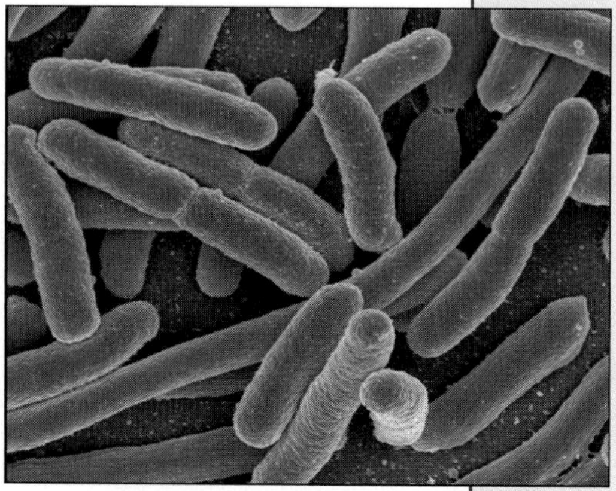

E. coli bacteria

Treating water with chlorine can lead to byproducts that may be hazardous. One class of these is called **trihalomethanes**, such as chloroform, $CHCl_3$. In chloroform three of the hydrogens of methane, CH_4, are replaced with chlorine. Chloroform, once used as an anesthetic, is a known carcinogen

or cancer-causing compound. Water-treatment facilities can minimize the amounts of these compounds in a municipal water supply by carrying out the chlorine treatment near the end of the overall water purification process and by filtration with activated carbon.

An alternative way to avoid the introduction of chlorinated organic compounds into the water supply is to kill bacteria using ultraviolet irradiation. Ultraviolet irradiation involves exposing shallow amounts of water to a minimal amount of radiation at a wavelength outside the visible spectrum, usually around 260 nm. This exposure alters the RNA and DNA of bacteria and viruses, killing them or making them unable to infect. In *Part A* you explored the effects of chlorination and ultraviolet irradiation on a sample of water and drew conclusions on how well each method kills the bacteria in natural water supplies.

Disinfection Complications

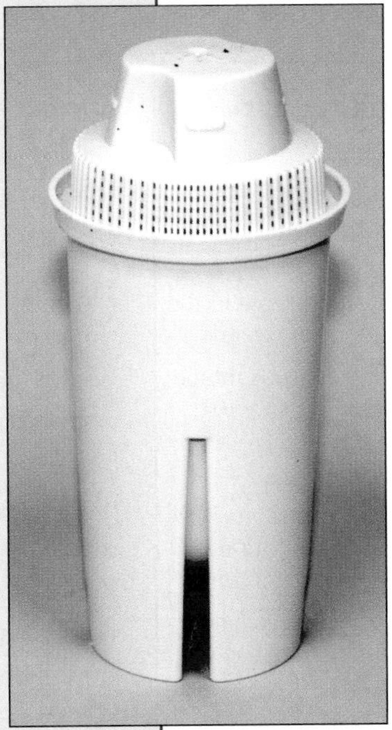

Although chlorination is the most widely used method for killing microbes in water-treatment plants in the U.S., it can create new contaminants by chlorinating organic compounds in the water. Often, water-treatment plants add chlorine both early in the process to kill large numbers of bacteria and at the end when there are many fewer organic molecules that might become chlorinated. The chlorinated forms of organic compounds may be more hazardous to human health than the original compounds were. That is because some chlorinated compounds are resistant to further reactions. Hence, when they enter the body, they remain largely intact. They will gradually accumulate in tissue and interfere with the action of many different hormones in the body. Since many agricultural and industrial products also contain chlorinated hydrocarbons, contaminants of this type would have to be dealt with even if no additional ones were formed in the chlorination of water. One technique that is used to remove such contaminants is to adsorb them on an activated carbon filter.

Chem Words

acid rain: rainfall containing sulfuric and nitric acid added through incorporation of SO_3 and NO_2 into water droplets in clouds.

The carbon, which may simply be in the form of charcoal, is activated by heating it to drive off previously adsorbed species. This purification step is expensive to perform, and the use of activated carbon might be limited in some localities to small filters in homes on just the water used for drinking and food preparation.

In order to minimize the extent of contamination by chlorinated organic compounds, ozone has been used as alternative means for killing bacteria. Ozone is frequently more lethal for bacteria than hypochlorous acid, which is the principal agent created by various chlorination techniques. Ozone can react with organic compounds to create new contaminants, but they are generally not as hazardous as the polychlorinated organic compounds, and are more readily degraded. However, alternatives to chlorination are more costly to use. Also, they cease to kill bacteria after being applied at the water-treatment plant. That contrasts with HOCl, which persists in the water supply lines where the potential always exists for more bacteria to enter the water.

pH Complications

The Public Health Service Act has mandated an acceptable pH range of 6.5 – 8.5. Water with a pH outside of this range may be corrosive to pipes or hazardous to human health. In light of all the substances that must be added to water during the purification process, it should not be surprising that the pH may need adjustment at the end of the process. For example, raising the pH was demonstrated in *Activity 6* as a means for lowering the concentration of Mg^{2+}, and in *Activity 7* for removing toxic-metals ions like Cr^{3+}, Pb^{2+}, Ni^{2+}, and Zn^{2+}. The chlorination step can also change the pH.

Natural waters differ in pH by large amounts in different parts of the country. Water supplies tend to be alkaline in areas such as the Midwest where limestone is common, particularly if groundwater is used as the water source. Rainwater, on the other hand, may be acidic in some areas because the NO, NO_2, and SO_2 emitted from coal and oil-fired power plants react with oxygen to form NO_2 and SO_3 which is absorbed by water droplets, forming sulfuric acid (H_2SO_4) and nitric acid (HNO_3). When precipitation occurs in areas polluted by these emissions, the water has a lower pH. This is **acid rain**. One of the consequences of acid rain is that lakes in many parts of the world have become increasingly acidic, even killing fish as the pH goes below 5.5. Water can also be acidified as it runs over certain minerals like pyrite, FeS_2. Coal deposits

Checking Up

1. Name three ways in which pathogens can enter the water supply.
2. What purpose does disinfection serve in the treatment of water?
3. What is a disadvantage of treating water with chlorine?
4. Describe two methods, other than chlorination, that can be used to treat water.
5. Why is activated charcoal of limited value in the water-treatment process?
6. What pH levels are considered safe for potable water?

are rich in this mineral, and acid discharges from mining areas are common and are known as **acid mine drainage**. The sequence of reactions producing acidic water with pyrite is:

$$2FeS_{2(s)} + 7O_{2(g)} + 2H_2O_{(l)} \rightarrow 2Fe^{2+}{}_{(aq)} + 4H^{+}{}_{(aq)} + 4SO_4{}^{2-}{}_{(aq)}$$

$$4Fe^{2+}{}_{(aq)} + O_{2(g)} + 10H_2O_{(l)} \rightarrow 4Fe(OH)_{3(s)} + 8H^{+}{}_{(aq)}$$

When water has been acidified in this way, it tends to dissolve toxic-metal ions, which would be insoluble under basic conditions. No matter whether the complication is natural or from the purification process, the pH must be adjusted into the acceptable range before entering the drinkable water supply.

Chem Words

acid mine drainage: the discharge of acidified water from mines.

What Do You Think Now?

At the beginning of this activity you were asked:

- **Why would many regard disinfection as the most critical stage in a water-treatment process, considering all you have studied thus far in the chapter?**
- **How do you think disinfection relates to basic chemistry?**

Look back at your answer to the questions. Would you change your answers to these two questions after performing the investigation and reading the information in the *Chem Talk* section? If so, how? If not, explain. What would be the cost if you do not consider disinfection in your part of the world?

Chem Essential Questions

What does it mean?

Chemistry explains a macroscopic phenomenon (what you observe) with a description of what happens at the nanoscopic level (atoms and molecules) using symbolic structures as a way to communicate. Complete the chart below in your *Active Chemistry* log.

MACRO	NANO	SYMBOLIC
Describe whether growth was observed on the agar plate for the untreated water sample, the treated water samples, or both.	*Explain why the ingestion of chlorine gas (Cl_2) is extremely toxic in the human body.*	*Bacteria are often eliminated from water systems by bubbling chlorine gas into the water. Explain with the equation from the* Chem Talk *section why the system should not be acidic.*

How do you know?

Make specific reference to your data from both *Part A* and *Part B* of this activity. How do you know if your treatments were effective in making the natural water supplies more drinkable?

Why do you believe?

Disinfection is something you have certainly come upon before, especially chlorination. Name something other than your tap water where chlorination is used for disinfection.

Why should you care?

Explain the significance of adjusting the pH at the end of the water treatment.

Reflecting on the Activity and the Challenge

This final activity of the chapter has brought together a number of concepts and recalled several of the purification steps introduced in earlier activities. It should be clear by now that there is not one universal prescription for purifying water. The steps chosen must depend on the characteristics of the water source, which in turn depend on the geology of the area and the extent of pollution added by agriculture, industry, a dense population, mining, and so on.

As much organic material as possible should be kept out of the water, and chlorination or other steps to kill bacteria should be put off until near the end of the water-treatment process. If disinfection were done before flocculation, a higher concentration of persistent organic pollutants would remain. After a number of precipitation and filtration steps, the hydrocarbons susceptible to chlorination should be much less abundant. Finally, all the purification steps can affect the pH, and it should be adjusted with the addition of a safe and inexpensive acid or base at the end.

Chem to Go

1. What advantage does chlorination of a water supply have over treatment with ultraviolet light or ozone?
2. How can acidifying water make it more toxic?
3. If the UV lamp is effective in killing bacteria, does it work as well in preventing new bacteria from entering the water sample as the chlorine treatment did? Explain.
4. Why is the treatment of natural water with ozone or ultraviolet irradiation not widely used in the U.S.?

5. A less expensive way to raise the pH of treated water is to use $Mg(OH)_2(s)$ or $Ca(OH)_2(s)$ as a base, and a less expensive way to lower the pH is to add $CO_2(g)$.

   a) Give the reactions or ionization steps that these components undergo in dissolving.

   b) Discuss any advantages, other than lower cost, in using these rather than NaOH and HCl.

6. HOCl is a weak acid. All weak acids dissociate into an equilibrium and have a special equilibrium constant associated with them called K_a. Hypochlorous acid dissociates into $ClO^-(aq)$ and $H^+(aq)$ and has a K_a of 2.95×10^{-5}.

   a) Write the equilibrium equation for the dissociation of HOCl.

   b) Write the equilibrium constant expression (mass-action expression) for HOCl.

   c) In a 0.0010 *M* solution of HOCl(aq), the concentration of $ClO^-(aq)$ is 8.4×10^{-4} *M*. What are the equilibrium concentrations of $ClO^-(aq)$ and $H^+(aq)$?

   d) What is the pH?

7. According to LeChatelier, what happens as the pH is raised in the dissociation of hypochlorous acid? Why is this important to consider in disinfection?

8. The most serious consequence of acid mine drainage is the dissolution of toxic metals in streams that have been acidified. Suppose that acidified water flows over $Cd(OH)_2(s)$.

   a) Calculate the equilibrium values of $[H^+]$, $[OH^-]$, and $[Cd^{2+}]$ at a pH of 6.5. For $Cd(OH)_2$, use $K_{sp} = [Cd^{2+}][OH^-]^2 = 2.5 \times 10^{-14}$.

   b) Calculate the equilibrium value of $[H^+]$, $[OH^-]$, and $[Cd^{2+}]$ at a pH of 4.5.

   c) Compare the two results. What do they mean?

9. ***Preparing for the Chapter Challenge***

   Now that you have considered biotic challenges and the importance of adjusting the pH, you are ready to complete your *Chapter Challenge*. Look back at the diagram you've been working on through the purification activities. Where would you work pH adjustments into your scheme? Why? How? Develop your disinfection treatment and justify.

Inquiring Further

Reverse osmosis and membrane processes

Membrane processes are becoming more common in water-purification processes. Membrane processes involve the use of membranes to remove small particles, molecules, and ions from water supplies. There are a number of these processes, including reverse osmosis, which vary based on the particle size you are trying to remove. These membrane processes can be employed to create drinking water from salt water, remove excess iron, nitrate, manganese, and toxic metals, filter out pathogens and viruses, and purify water of organic contaminants. Research reverse osmosis and the membrane processes. Create a poster that illustrates and explains the basic concept and lists the advantages and disadvantages of these techniques.

Chem at Work

E.P.O. Cheryl Gerken

Environmental Police Officer, DEP, Cobleskill, NY

Cheryl Gerken is on the first line of defense against water pollution, environmental crimes, and bio-terrorism. As an E.P.O. who works for the Department of Environmental Protection (a government agency), Officer Gerken is responsible for patrolling the New York City watershed.

This watershed is comprised of about 21 reservoirs, which are scattered north of the city. The reservoirs supply the nine million people in the city with drinking water. The environmental police enforce the laws that prevent chemical dumping, illegal septics, and the slaughter of wildlife in those reservoirs.

"In this kind of work you get to protect the environment and wildlife," says Gerken. "This was a way to use my law enforcement education with my lifelong interest in conservation. Being on the water and informing the public about ways to keep our ecosystem healthy is very rewarding."

Occasionally, an accident will cause a tanker to overturn, spilling oil. Quick action by environmental police can prevent the spread of pollution. In the event of such a mishap, the environmental police will set up a perimeter around the contaminated area, dispatch hazardous materials (Haz-Mat) workers to clean up the spill, and issue citations to polluters.

Officer Gerken needs a basic understanding of chemistry to perform her job effectively. For example, if she notices turbidity (milky discoloration) in the water, she will know what kind of chemical spill most likely caused it. The vigilance, knowledge and fast responses by D.E.P. police, like E.P.O. Cheryl Gerken, help keep New York City reservoirs, and the people who rely on them, healthy.

TRAILS CLOSED
DUE TO
HAZARDOUS CONDITIONS

Cristina Sanchez

Toxic Torts Attorney, Dallas, TX

Cristina Sanchez is a lawyer who practices in the field of "Toxic Torts." Toxic torts are injuries caused by negligent chemical contamination of the air, ground or water. Cristina helps those injured by contaminated groundwater. She says, "It's an important position to be in. I help cities clean up their water systems."

Jim Fickes

Sales Consultant, Culligan™, Baltimore, MD

Jim Fickes, who works for the Culligan™ water treatment company, identifies water contamination problems in private homes. He says, "The most common problems are iron, hardness, pH, nitrates or total dissolved particulates." Jim takes great pleasure in making sure people can enjoy clean, fresh drinking water at home.

H_2Woes Assessment

You have been assigned by an international health organization, like UNESCO, to improve the water supplies of a number of communities in Latin America. Because of water-borne chemicals and microbes, the communities have been forced to rely on bottled water for drinking. Many streams in the areas are suspected of being contaminated with toxic minerals and organic chemicals, possibly introduced by drainage from mines, agricultural fields or industrial sites. Naturally occurring contaminants of water sources in the areas vary widely because the minerals range from those of volcanic origin in the mountainous areas to principally sedimentary rocks in the farming or urbanized areas. You must predict the most likely contaminants in each area and specify a series of preferred steps for purifying the water. You must be prepared to explain the chemical processes that are behind these steps and why they are the best choices for assuring the purity of the water supplies.

You will need to:

- **Decide** what major water contaminants may be expected in each area, and how they got there.
- **Estimate** the amounts of contaminants that purification plants should be designed to remove.
- **Develop** a process diagram or flowchart for the water purification procedures that you will propose.
- **Explain** the chemistry behind the steps in purifying the water.

Chemistry Content

To begin, you should review all of the activities that you have completed. You can skim through the text and your *Active Chemistry* log to help remind you of the chemistry concepts in each activity.

Activity 1: Your group explored four possible substances that enter the water supply as they go through the natural water cycle. This exploration included the solubility of minerals, the forms of gases in solution, the solubility of organic compounds, and fertilizers in water.

Activity 2: You investigated how temperature changes the solubility of specific solids. You also learned about how the Gibbs free energy can help you determine if a reaction is spontaneous.

Activity 3: You learned how to quantify solutes in your specific "natural" water sample through different techniques including titration and semi-qualitative colorimetry.

Activity 4: You determined the pH and learned the basic principles behind equilibrium and the law of mass action. You also calculated a solubility product constant (K_{sp}) and an equilibrium constant (K_{eq}) from experimental data.

Activity 5: You learned your first purification technique. You created floc to remove colloidal particles in a solution. You also compared the flow and batch methods for filtering water.

Activity 6: You investigated the problems associated with hard water and determined whether precipitation reactions or ion-exchange resins reduce water hardness more. You also learned about drawbacks connected with softening water.

Activity 7: You discovered what steps can be taken to keep toxic-metal ions out of the drinking water supply. You also applied the chemical concepts from the unit to the removal of toxic-metal ions.

Activity 8: You considered biological factors that affect the water supply and how you can adjust the pH of a water supply to the accepted level for drinking water. You also reflected on the consequences of disinfecting water and the complications involved with pH.

You may want to make a chart that shows the activity number, some chemistry concepts in the activity, and some ideas as to how you can use these concepts as part of your water purification report and presentation. Your chart may include whether the activity provides content for the presentation or the report. You should pay particular attention to the *Reflecting on the Activity and the Challenge, Chem Essential Questions,* and *Preparing for the Chapter Challenge* sections. You should also compare your list with that given in the *Chem You Learned* summary.

Activity #	Chemistry concepts	How to use concepts

You may decide to do the first activity as a group to ensure that everybody understands how to proceed. After completing the first activity, each team member can be assigned two or three activities. You can then review all of the activities as a group with the activity expert reviewing each summary.

Criteria

You and your team should review the criteria by which you will be graded. Before beginning the chapter, your teacher led a class discussion to get a sense of what criteria should be used to judge the quality of work for this Water Problem and Purification Presentation. Now that you have considerable understanding of the chemistry concepts, think about and discuss what would make an informative presentation to your target group. How will you describe the possible contaminants and evidence about their existence? How will you discuss the purification processes and their effectiveness? How good do your explanations of the chemistry need to be? How much weight should be given to the presentation and how much to the accompanying written materials? How will you judge the quality of the presentations? The rubric your class develops can be a useful tool for your team to check the quality of your work and to ensure that you have included all necessary parts of the project.

Preparing for the Chapter Challenge

• Identify Your Target Audience

Your team should begin the process of creating the report by deciding what information should be provided for your target group, the international health organization. What information do you think the international health organization will be most interested in learning about?

• Write Your Explanations

Your presentation must include what you know about the chemistry of identifying contaminants and ways in which to purify water. You may decide to use the four essential questions from the activities *(What does it mean? How do you know? Why do you believe? Why should you care?)* to frame your explanations. The more chemistry content you can include, the more impressive your presentations and written materials will be.

• Chemistry content is necessary, but not enough.

You must also find an interesting and informative way of presenting your information. Remember also, that when you are presenting your ideas you are in the role of a teacher. Teachers use models that help promote learning. One model is the 7E instructional model. In the 7E model, you begin by *engaging* the audience as well as *eliciting* their prior knowledge. This means that you use a way to find out what they already know so that you can be more aware of this during the teaching and learning process. This is then followed by an *explore phase* where the participants are involved in finding out about something and experiencing some phenomenon. Following the explore phase, you can help them *explain* what they experienced. You can then *elaborate* on the concepts and describe where else they may observe similar events. You then end with an *extend* where you give the audience something to think about that is beyond what you have introduced. The last stage of the 7E model is *evaluate*. The evaluation of whether the corporate executives or marketing team understood your presentation takes place throughout the cycle—through the *engage, elicit, explore, explain, elaborate* and *extend.*

• Manage Your Time

You have a sense of how you want to proceed and what you want the final product to be. You now have to allocate the work. How much time do you have to complete the project? When is the presentation? How will you get everything done in this time frame? Who will be working on the written materials and the posters, including the description of chemistry concepts? Create a time chart for the challenge. Divide the responsibilities. Some work can be done individually as homework. Leave time to review each other's work. Planning a project well does not ensure success, but poor planning almost always leads to disappointment.

Engineering/Technology Design

Reflect on the engineering/technology design process. Recall the successes and disappointments from the *mini-challenge*. How can you use the feedback that you received to improve your presentation and report to your target audience? At this point, you are starting the design cycle again.

Make an impact with your H_2Woes report!

Chem You Learned

- The **solubility** of a compound depends on solubility **factors**, such as the relative polarity of the solute compared to the solvent, temperature of the solvent, and, for gases, the pressure of the system.
- **Enthalpy** is a thermodynamic property which is a measure of the heat content of a system.
- **Entropy** is a thermodynamic property which is a measure of the disorder in a system.
- **Gibbs free energy** calculations can be used to determine if a reaction is spontaneous and involves two factors: **enthalpy** and **entropy.** $\Delta G = \Delta H - T\Delta S$.
- **Water hardness** is primarily due to the presence of magnesium, calcium and iron ions.
- A **dynamic equilibrium** is achieved when the concentrations of reactants and products are constant because they are changing at the same rate.
- The **solubility product constant** is an equilibrium constant for a solid ionic compound that is in equilibrium with its dissolved ions.
- **The Law of Mass Action** states that the amount or mass of the products will be the same as the amount or mass of the reactants.
- **LeChatelier's Principle** states that a system in dynamic equilibrium which is disturbed by a change in temperature, pressure or concentration will change in a direction that opposes the change and return to a dynamic equilibrium.
- A **colloid** is a homogeneous mixture with small, suspended particles that will not settle out of the medium. Fog and milk are examples of a colloid.
- When a beam of light passes through a colloid, the light can be visually seen. This observation is called the **Tyndall Effect.**
- Most water softeners use an **ion-exchange resin** to remove unwanted hard water cations, such as calcium and magnesium ions.
- **Toxic-metal ions** or heavy-metal ions are found to be toxic even at very low concentrations. Chromium and nickel are classified as being **carcinogenic**.
- **Distillation** is the process of separating components in a mixture by evaporating the more volatile components and then condensing them.
- **Chlorination** of water is a technique used to disinfect water that may contain pathogens and viruses.

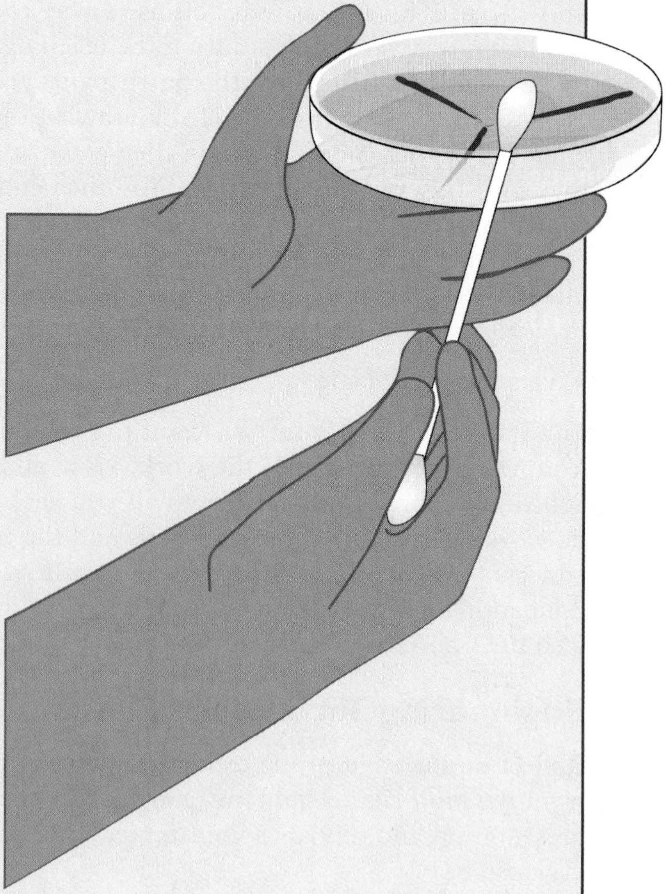

TABLES

Tables

Prefixes Used in the Metric System

Prefix	Meaning	Example
tera (T)	10^{12}	1 terameter (Tm) = 1×10^{12} m
giga (G)	10^{9}	1 gigameter (Gm) = 1×10^{9} m
mega (M)	10^{6}	1 megameter (Mm) = 1×10^{6} m
kilo (k)	10^{3}	1 kilometer (km) = 1×10^{3} m
deci (d)	10^{-1}	1 decimeter (dm) = 1×10^{-1} m = 0.1 m
centi (c)	10^{-2}	1 centimeter (cm) = 1×10^{-2} m = 0.01 m
milli (m)	10^{-3}	1 millimeter (mm) = 1×10^{-3} m = 0.001 m
micro (μ)	10^{-6}	1 micrometer (μm) = 1×10^{-6} m
nano (n)	10^{-9}	1 nanometer (nm) = 1×10^{-9} m
pico (p)	10^{-12}	1 picometer (pm) = 1×10^{-12} m

Physical Constants

Avogadro's number (N_A)	6.0221×10^{23}
atomic mass unit (amu)	1.6605×10^{-27} kg
molar gas constant (R)	$8.3145 \frac{\text{J}}{\text{mol} \cdot \text{K}}$ or $0.08206 \frac{\text{L} \cdot \text{atm}}{\text{mol} \cdot \text{K}}$
Faraday constant (F)	96,500 C/mol of e^-
molar volume of ideal gas (*V*m) (at STP: 0°C, 1 atm)	22.414 L
Planck's constant (h)	6.6262×10^{-34} J·s
electron charge (e)	1.6022×10^{-19} C
electron mass	9.1094×10^{-28} g
proton mass	1.6726×10^{-24} g
neutron mass	1.6749×10^{-24} g
speed of light (c)	2.9979×10^{8} m/s
Boltzmann's constant (k)	1.3807×10^{-23} J/K

Quantity Symbols and Unit Abbreviations

α	alpha (particles from radioactive materials, helium nuclei)
β	beta (particles from radioactive materials, electrons)
γ	gamma (rays from radioactive materials, high-energy quanta)
Δ	delta (change in)
λ	lambda (wavelength)
ρ	rho (momentum)
Ω	ohm (resistance in electric circuit)
°C	Celsius degree
°F	Fahrenheit degree
A	ampere (electric current)
amu	atomic mass unit
C	coulomb (quantity of electricity)
c	speed of light
cal	calorie
c_p	specific heat
D	density
f or υ	nu (frequency)
g	gram (mass)
G	free energy
H	enthalpy
h	Planck's constant
Hz	hertz (frequency)
J	joule
K	kelvin

K_a	ionization constant of acids
K_b	ionization constant of bases
K_{eq}	equilibrium constant
K_{sp}	solubility product
K_w	water dissociation constant
L	liter (volume)
m	meter (length)
m	mass
m	molality
M	molarity
mol	mole
N	newton (force)
n	number of moles
N_A	Avogadro's number
ppm	parts per million
P	pressure
Pa	pascal (pressure)
q	heat
R	ideal gas law constant
s	second
S	entropy
T	temperature (absolute)
V or E	volt (electromotive force)
V	volume
W	watt (power)
X	mole fraction

Activity Series of Metals

Metal	Oxidation reaction
lithium	$Li(s) \rightarrow Li^{+}(aq) + e^{-}$
potassium	$K(s) \rightarrow K^{+}(aq) + e^{-}$
barium	$Ba(s) \rightarrow Ba^{2+}(aq) + 2e^{-}$
calcium	$Ca(s) \rightarrow Ca^{2+}(aq) + 2e^{-}$
sodium	$Na(s) \rightarrow Na^{+}(aq) + e^{-}$
magnesium	$Mg(s) \rightarrow Mg^{2+}(aq) + 2e^{-}$
aluminum	$Al(s) \rightarrow Al^{3+}(aq) + 3e^{-}$
manganese	$Mn(s) \rightarrow Mn^{2+}(aq) + 2e^{-}$
zinc	$Zn(s) \rightarrow Zn^{2+}(aq) + 2e^{-}$
chromium	$Cr(s) \rightarrow Cr^{3+}(aq) + 3e^{-}$
iron	$Fe(s) \rightarrow Fe^{2+}(aq) + 2e^{-}$
cadmium	$Cd(s) \rightarrow Cd^{2+}(aq) + 2e^{-}$
cobalt	$Co(s) \rightarrow Co^{2+}(aq) + 2e^{-}$
nickel	$Ni(s) \rightarrow Ni^{2+}(aq) + 2e^{-}$
tin	$Sn(s) \rightarrow Sn^{2+}(aq) + 2e^{-}$
lead	$Pb(s) \rightarrow Pb^{2+}(aq) + 2e^{-}$
hydrogen	$H_2(g) \rightarrow 2H^{+}(aq) + 2e^{-}$
copper	$Cu(s) \rightarrow Cu^{2+}(aq) + 2e^{-}$
silver	$Ag(s) \rightarrow Ag^{+}(aq) + e^{-}$
mercury	$Hg(l) \rightarrow Hg^{2+}(aq)) + 2e^{-}$
platinum	$Pt(s) \rightarrow Pt^{2+}(aq) + 2e^{-}$
gold	$Au(s) \rightarrow Au^{3+}(aq) + 3e^{-}$

↑ oxidation increases

Common Ions
Names, Formulas, and Charges

Cations	Anions
aluminum (Al^{3+})	acetate (CH_3COO^-)
ammonium (NH_4^+)	arsenate (AsO_4^{3-})
antimony(III), antimonous (Sb^{3+})	arsenite (AsO_3^{3-})
arsenic(III), arsenious (As^{3+})	benzoate ($C_6H_5COO^-$)
bismuth (Bi^{3+})	borate (BO_3^{3-})
cadmium (Cd^{2+})	carbonate (CO_3^{2-})
cerium(IV), ceric (Ce^{4+})	chlorate (ClO_3^-)
cerium(III), cerous (Ce^{3+})	chlorite (ClO_2^-)
chromium(III), chromic (Cr^{3+})	chromate (CrO_4^{2-})
chromium(II), chromous (Cr^{2+})	cyanate (CNO^-)
cobalt(III), cobaltic (Co^{3+})	cyanide (CN^-)
copper(II), cupric (Cu^{2+})	dichromate ($Cr_2O_7^{2-}$)
copper(I), cuprous ($Cu+$)	dihydrogen phosphate ($H_2PO_4^-$)
gallium(III) (Ga^{3+})	hydride (H^-)
gold(III), auric (Au^{3+})	hexacyanoferrate(III), ferricyanide ($Fe(CN)_6^{3-}$)
gold(I), aurous (Au^+)	hexacyanoferrate(II), ferrocyanide ($Fe(CN)_6^{4-}$)
hydrogen (H^+)	hydrogen carbonate, bicarbonate (HCO_3^-)
hydronium (H_3O^+)	hydrogen oxalate, bioxalate ($HC_2O_4^-$)
iron(III), ferric (Fe^{3+})	hydrogen phthalate, biphthalate ($HC_8H_4CO_4^-$)
iron(II), ferrous (Fe^{2+})	hydrogen sulfate, bisulfate (HSO_4^-)
lead(IV), plumbic (Pb^{4+})	hydrogen sulfide, bisulfide (HS^-)
lead(II), plumbous (Pb^{2+})	hydrogen sulfite, bisulfite (HSO_3^-)
manganese(II), manganous (Mn^{2+})	hydroxide (OH^-)
mercury(II), mercuric (Hg^{2+})	hypochlorite (ClO^-)
mercury(I), mercurous (Hg_2^{2+})	iodate (IO_3^-)
nickel(II) (Ni^{2+})	monohydrogen phosphate (HPO_4^{2-})
silver (Ag^+)	nitrate (NO_3^-)
thallium(III), thallic (Tl^{3+})	nitrite (NO_2^-)
thallium(I), thallous (Tl^+)	orthosilicate (SiO_4^{4-})
tin(IV), stannic (Sn^{4+})	oxalate ($C_2O_4^{2-}$)

Common Ions
Names, Formulas, and Charges

Cations	Anions
tin(II), stannous (Sn^{2+})	perchlorate (ClO_4^-)
titanium(IV), titanic (Ti^{4+})	periodate (IO_4^-)
titanium(III), titanous (Ti^{3+})	permanganate (MnO_4^-)
vanadium (V^{3+})	peroxide (O_2^{2-})
zinc (Zn^{2+})	phosphate (PO_4^{3-})
	phosphite (PO_3^{3-})
	pyrophosphate ($P_2O_7^{4-}$)
	silicate (SiO_3^{2-})
	sulfate (SO_4^{2-})
	sulfide (S^{2-})
	sulfite (SO_3^{2-})
	thiocyanate (SCN^-)
	thiosulfate ($S_2O_3^{2-}$)

Standard Heat of Formation (ΔH°_f) Standard Entropy (S°) and Gibbs Free Energy (ΔG°) of some Common Compounds at 25°C

Substance	ΔH°_f (kJ/mol)	S° (J/mol•K)	ΔG° (kJ/mol)
$Al(s)$	0	28.5	0
$AlCl_3(s)$	– 704	110.7	– 630
$Al_2O_3(s)$	– 1676	51.0	– 1582
$Al_2SO_4(s)$	– 3441	239	– 3100
$Ba(s)$	0	66.9	0
$BaO(s)$	– 558.1	70.3	– 525
$BaCO_3(s)$	– 1219	112	– 1139
$BaCl_2(s)$	– 860.2	125	– 811
$Ba(NO_3)_2(s)$	– 992	214	– 795
$BaSO_4(s)$	– 1465	132	– 1353
$BeCl_2(s)$	– 468.6	89.9	– 426
$Ca(s)$	0	41.4	0
$CaCO_3(s)$	– 1207	92.9	– 1129
$CaCl_2(s)$	– 795.8	104.6	– 748
$CaO(s)$	– 635.5	39.8	– 604
$Ca(OH)_2(s)$	– 986.6	76.1	897
$Ca_3(PO_4)_2(s)$	– 4119	241	– 3852
$CaSO_4(s)$	– 1433	107	– 1320
$CaSO_4(s) \cdot \frac{1}{2}H_2O(s)$	– 1573	131	– 1435
$CaSO_4(s) \cdot 2H_2O(s)$	– 2020	194	– 1796
C(s, graphite)	0	5.7	0
C(s, diamond)	1.88	2.4	2.8
$CO(g)$	– 110	197.9	– 137
$CO_2(g)$	– 394	213.6	– 395
$CH_4(g)$	– 74.9	186.2	– 51
$C_2H_2(g)$	+ 227	201	209
$C_2H_4(g)$	+ 51.9	220	68
$C_3H_8(g)$	– 104	269.9	– 23
$C_4H_{10}(g)$	– 126	310.2	– 17

Substance	ΔH°_f (kJ/mol)	S° (J/mol•K)	ΔG° (kJ/mol)
$CH_3OH(l)$	– 238	126.8	–166
$C_2H_5OH(l)$	– 278	160.7	–175
$CH_3COOH(l)$	– 487	159.8	–392
$Cu(s)$	0	33.1	0
$CuCl_2(s)$	– 172	119	–132
$CuSO_4(s)$	– 771.4	109	–662
$CuSO_4(s) \cdot 5H_2O(s)$	– 2279.7	300.4	–1880
$H_2(g)$	0	130.5	0
$HBr(g)$	– 36	198.5	53
$HCl(g)$	– 92.5	186.7	–95
$HCl(aq)$	– 167.2	56.5	–131
$HI(g)$	+ 26	206	1.3
$H_2O(l)$	– 286	70.0	–237
$H_2O(g)$	– 242	188.7	–228
$H_2O_2(l)$	– 187.8	109.6	–120
$Fe(s)$	0	27.2	0
$Fe_2O_3(s)$	– 822.2	87.4	–741
$Fe_3O_4(s)$	– 1118.4	146.4	–1015
$Mg(s)$	0	32.6	0
$MgCO_3(s)$	– 1113	65.7	–1029
$MgCl_2(s)$	– 641.8	89.5	–592
$MgCl_2(s) \cdot 2H_2O(s)$	– 1280	180	–1118
$MgO(s)$	– 601.7	26.9	–569
$Mg(OH)_2(s)$	– 924.7	63.1	–834
$Mn(s)$	0	31.8	0
$MnO_2(s)$	– 520.9	53.1	–466
$N_2(g)$	0	191.6	0
$NH_3(g)$	– 46.0	192.5	–17
$NH_4Cl(s)$	– 314.4	94.6	–203

Standard Heat of Formation (ΔH°_f) Standard Entropy (S°) and Gibbs Free Energy (ΔG°) of some Common Compounds at 25°C

Substance	ΔH°_f (kJ/mol)	S° (J/mol•K)	ΔG° (kJ/mol)
$NO(g)$	+ 90.4	210.6	87
$NO_2(g)$	+ 34	240.5	52
$HNO_3(l)$	– 174.1	155.6	– 80
$O_2(g)$	0	205.0	0
$O_3(g)$	+ 143	238.8	163
P(s, white)	0	41.0	0
P(s, red)	– 17.6	22.6	– 13
$P_4(g)$	+ 314.6	163.2	278
PH_3 (g)	+ 5.4	210.0	13
$PCl_3(g)$	– 287	311.8	– 268
$PCl_5(g)$	– 374.9	364.6	– 305
$H_3PO_4(s)$	– 1279	110.5	– 1119
K(s)	0	63.6	0
KCl(s)	– 436.8	82.6	– 409
KBr(s)	– 393.8	95.9	– 381
KI(s)	– 327.9	106.3	– 325
KOH(s)	– 424.8	78.9	– 379
Ag(s)	0	42.7	0
AgCl(s)	– 127.1	96.2	–110
AgBr(s)	– 100.4	107.1	– 97
AgI(s)	– 61.9	115.5	– 66
$AgNO_3(s)$	– 124	141	– 32
Na(s)	0	51.0	0
NaF(s)	– 571	51.5	– 545
NaBr(s)	– 360	83.7	– 349
NaI(s)	– 288	91.2	– 286
$NaHCO_3(s)$	– 947.7	155	– 852
$Na_2CO_3(s)$	– 1131	136	– 1048
NaOH(s)	– 426.8	64.5	– 380

Heat of Combustion

Substance	Reaction	Heat of Reaction
carbon (graphite)	$C(graphite) + O_2(g) \rightarrow CO_2(g)$	$\Delta H = -394$ kJ/mol
methane	$CH_4(g) + 2O_2(g) \rightarrow CO_2(g) + 2H_2O(l)$	$\Delta H = -890.4$ kJ/mol
ethane	$2C_2H_6(g) + 7O_2(g) \rightarrow 4CO_2(g) + 6H_2O(l)$	$\Delta H = -3119$ kJ/2mol
propane	$C_3H_8(g) + 5O_2(g) \rightarrow 3CO_2(g) + 4H_2O(l)$	$\Delta H = -2220$ kJ/mol
butane	$2C_4H_{10}(g) + 13O_2(g) \rightarrow 8CO_2(g) + 10H_2O(l)$	$\Delta H = -5760$ kJ/2mol
octane	$2C_8H_{18}(l) + 25O_2(g) \rightarrow 16CO_2(g) + 18H_2O(l)$	$\Delta H = -11040$ kJ/2mol
cyclopropane	$2C_3H_6(g) + 9O_2(g) \rightarrow 6CO_2(g) + 6H_2O(l)$	$\Delta H = -3922$ kJ/2mol
cyclobutane	$C_4H_8(g) + 6O_2(g) \rightarrow 4CO_2(g) + 4H_2O(l)$	$\Delta H = -2570$ kJ/mol
cyclohexane	$C_6H_{12}(l) + 9O_2(g) \rightarrow 6CO_2(g) + 6H_2O(l)$	$\Delta H = -3703$ kJ/mol
cyclooctane	$C_8H_{16}(l) + 12O_2(g) \rightarrow 8CO_2(g) + 8H_2O(l)$	$\Delta H = -4962$ kJ/mol
methanol	$2CH_3OH(l) + 3O_2(g) \rightarrow 2CO_2(g) + 4H_2O(l)$	$\Delta H = -1430$ kJ/2mol
ethanol	$C_2H_5OH(l) + 3O_2(g) \rightarrow 2CO_2(g) + 3H_2O(l)$	$\Delta H = -1370$ kJ/mol
propanol	$2C_3H_7OH(l) + 9O_2(g) \rightarrow 6CO_2(g) + 8H_2O(l)$	$\Delta H = -4020$ kJ/2mol
ethene (ethylene)	$C_2H_4(g) + 3O_2(g) \rightarrow 2CO_2(g) + 2H_2O(l)$	$\Delta H = -1323$ kJ/mol
ethyne (acetylene)	$2C_2H_2(g) + 5O_2(g) \rightarrow 4CO_2(g) + 2H_2O(l)$	$\Delta H = -2600$ kJ/2mol

Units Used in Expressing Concentration

Name	Symbol	Units	Applications
molality	m	$\frac{\text{mol of solute}}{\text{kg of solvent}}$	colligative properties such as boiling point elevation and freezing point depression
molarity	M	$\frac{\text{mol of solute}}{\text{1 L of solution}}$	stoichiometric calculations in quantitative analysis
mole fraction	X	$\frac{\text{mol of solute}}{\textit{total}\text{ moles of solution}}$	thermodynamic calculations in solutions of liquids or gases
parts per million	ppm	$\frac{\text{g of solute}}{1 \times 10^6 \text{ g of solution}}$	small amount of particles dissolved in either a liquid or gas
parts per billion	ppb	$\frac{\text{g of solute}}{1 \times 10^9 \text{ g of solution}}$	extremely small amount of particles dissolved in a liquid or gas
mass percent of component	$\frac{m}{m}$ %	$\frac{\text{mass of substance in solution}}{\text{total mass of solution}} \times 100$	determining the percent of a substance contained in a compound
volume percent of component	$\frac{v}{v}$ %	$\frac{\text{volume of solute}}{\text{volume of solution}} \times 100$	determining the percent of a liquid substance contained in a solution

Ionization Constants for Acids at 25°C

Acid	Formula	K_a	K_a =	pK_a
acetic	CH_3COOH	1.8×10^{-5}	$\frac{[H^+][CH_3COO^-]}{[CH_3COOH]}$	4.7
ascorbic	$H_2C_6H_6O_6$	8×10^{-5}	$\frac{[H^+][HC_6H_6O_6^-]}{[H_2C_6H_6O_6]}$	4.1
hydrogen ascorbate ion	$HC_6H_6O_6^-$	1.6×10^{-12}	$\frac{[H^+][C_6H_6O_6^{2-}]}{[HC_6H_6O_6^-]}$	11.8
benzoic	C_6H_5COOH	6.5×10^{-5}	$\frac{[H^+][C_6H_5COO^-]}{[C_6H_5COOH]}$	4.2
carbonic	H_2CO_3	4.3×10^{-7}	$\frac{[H^+][HCO_3^-]}{[H_2CO_3]}$	6.4
hydrogen carbonate ion	HCO_3^-	5.6×10^{-11}	$\frac{[H^+][CO_3^{2-}]}{[HCO_3^-]}$	10.3
citric	$H_3C_6H_5O_7$	7.1×10^{-4}	$\frac{[H^+][H_2C_6H_5O_7^-]}{[H_3C_6H_5O_7]}$	3.1
dihydrogen citrate ion	$H_2C_6H_5O_7^-$	1.7×10^{-5}	$\frac{[H^+][HC_6H_5O_7^{2-}]}{[H_2C_6H_50_7^-]}$	4.8
monohydrogen citrate ion	$HC_6H_5O_7^{2-}$	4.1×10^{-7}	$\frac{[H^+][C_6H_5O_7^{3-}]}{[HC_6H_5O_7^{2-}]}$	6.4
hydrofluoric	HF	6.6×10^{-4}	$\frac{[H^+][F^-]}{[HF]}$	3.2
hydrogen sulfide	H_2S	9.1×10^{-8}	$\frac{[H^+][HS^-]}{[H_2S]}$	7.0
hydrogen sulfide ion	HS^-	1.0×10^{-19}	$\frac{[H^+][S^{2-}]}{[HS^-]}$	19
hypochlorous	$HOCl$	2.95×10^{-5}	$\frac{[H^+][OCl^-]}{[HOCl]}$	4.5
nitrous	HNO_2	7.1×10^{-4}	$\frac{[H^+][NO_2^-]}{[HNO_2]}$	3.1
oxalic	$H_2C_2O_4$	5.9×10^{-2}	$\frac{[H^+][HC_2O_4^-]}{[H_2C_2O_4]}$	1.2
hydrogen oxalate ion	$HC_2O_4^-$	6.4×10^{-5}	$\frac{[H^+][C_2O_4^{2-}]}{[HC_2O_4^-]}$	4.2
phenol	C_6H_5OH	1.3×10^{-10}	$\frac{[H^+][C_6H_5O^-]}{[C_6H_5OH]}$	9.9
phosphoric acid	H_3PO_4	7.5×10^{-3}	$\frac{[H^+][H_2PO_4^-]}{[H_3PO_4]}$	2.1
dihydrogen phosphate ion	$H_2PO_4^-$	6.2×10^{-8}	$\frac{[H^+][HPO_4^{2-}]}{[H_2PO_4^-]}$	7.2

Ionization Constants for Acids at 25°C

Acid	Formula	K_a	$K_a =$	pK_a
monohydrogen phosphate ion	HPO_4^{2-}	4.2×10^{-13}	$\frac{[H^+][PO_4^{3-}]}{[HPO_4^{2-}]}$	12.4
sulfuric	H_2SO_4	$>10^2$	$\frac{[H^+][HSO_4^-]}{[H_2SO_4]}$	~ –2
hydrogen sulfate ion	HSO_4^-	1.2×10^{-2}	$\frac{[H^+][SO_4^{2-}]}{[HSO_4^-]}$	1.9
sulfurous	H_2SO_3	1.7×10^{-2}	$\frac{[H^+][HSO_3^-]}{[H_2SO_3]}$	1.8
hydrogen sulfite ion	HSO_3^-	6.4×10^{-8}	$\frac{[H^+][SO_3^{2-}]}{[HSO_3^-]}$	7.2
water	H_2O	1.0×10^{-14}	$[H^+][OH^-]$	14.0

Ionization Constants for Bases at 25°C

Base	Formula	K_b	$K_b =$	pK_b
ammonia	NH_3	1.8×10^{-5}	$\frac{[NH_4^+][OH^-]}{[NH_3]}$	4.7
aniline	$C_6H_5NH_2$	4.2×10^{-10}	$\frac{[C_6H_5NH_3^+][OH^-]}{[C_6H_5NH_2]}$	9.4
hydroxylamine	NH_2OH	6.6×10^{-9}	$\frac{[NH_3OH^+][OH^-]}{[NH_2OH]}$	8.2
methylamine	CH_3NH_2	5.0×10^{-4}	$\frac{[CH_3NH_3^+][OH^-]}{[CH_3NH_2]}$	3.3
pyridine	C_5H_5N	1.5×10^{-9}	$\frac{[C_5H_5NH^+][OH^-]}{[C_5H_5N]}$	8.8

Classes and Functional Groups of Organic Compounds

Family	Group	General formula	Examples
alkane	alkyl (R–)	R-H	methane (CH_4) ethane (CH_3CH_3) propane($CH_3CH_2CH_3$) butane ($CH_3CH_2CH_2CH_3$)
alkene	alkenyl ($R_2C=R\langle_R$)	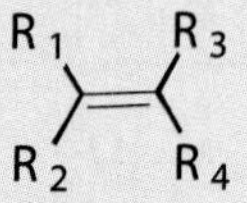	ethene ($CH_2=CH_2$) propene($CH_2=CHCH_3$) 1-butene ($CH_2=CHCH_2CH_3$)
alkyne	alkynyl (R–C≡C–)	(RC≡CR)	ethyne (CH≡CH)
alcohol	hydroxyl (–OH)	R-OH	methanol (CH_3OH) ethanol (CH_3CH_2OH) 1-propanol ($CH_3CH_2CH_2OH$)
carboxylic acid	carboxyl (–COOH)	RCOOH	acetic acid (CH_3COOH) propanoic acid (CH_3CH_2COOH)
ketone	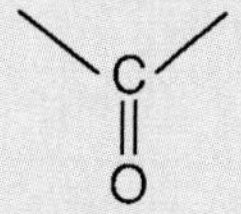	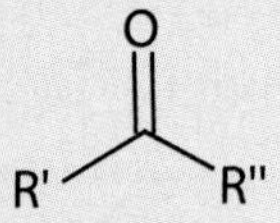	acetone 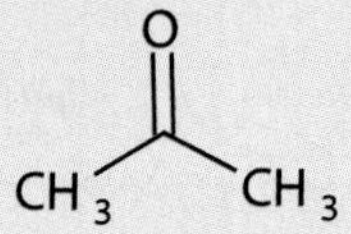
ester	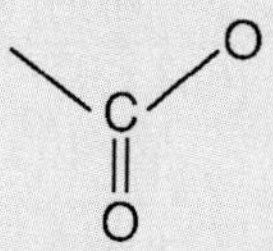	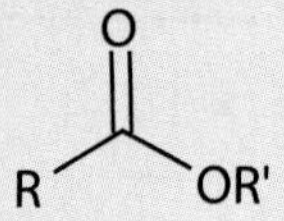	methyl acetate 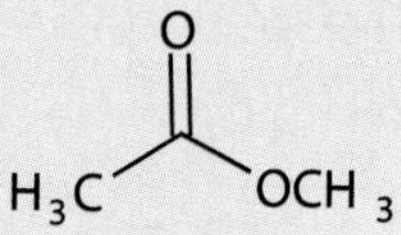
amine	$–NR_2$	$R–NR_2$	methanamine ($Ch_3–NH_2$)
amide	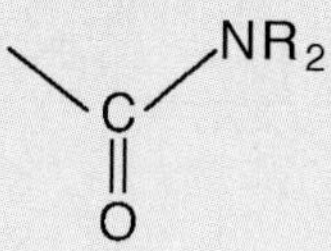	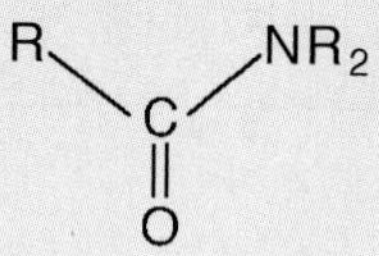	ethanamide 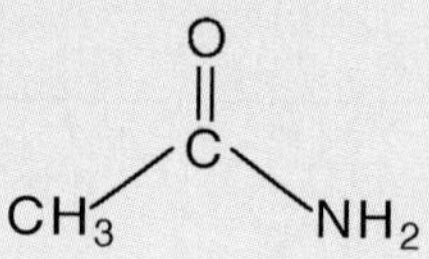
R = H, alkyl group			

Standard Reduction Potentials at 25°C

Reduction half-reaction	E°(V)
$F_2(g) + 2e^- \rightarrow 2F^-(aq)$	+ 2.87
$Co^{3+}(aq) + e^- \rightarrow Co^{2+}(aq)$	+ 1.82
$H_2O_2(aq) + 2H^+(aq) + 2e^- \rightarrow 2H_2O(l)$	+ 1.77
$Ce^{4+}(aq) + e^- \rightarrow Ce^{3+}(aq)$	+ 1.61
$MnO_4^-(aq) + 8H^+(aq) + 5e^- \rightarrow Mn^{2+}(aq) + 2H_2O(l)$	+ 1.51
$Au^{3+}(aq) + 3e^- \rightarrow Au(s)$	+ 1.50
$Cl_2(g) + 2e^- \rightarrow 2Cl^-$	+ 1.36
$O_2(g) + 4H^+(aq) + 4e^- \rightarrow 2H_2O(l)$	+ 1.23
$Br_2(l) + 2e^- \rightarrow 2Br^-(aq)$	+ 1.07
$NO_3^-(aq) + 4H^+(aq) + 3e^- \rightarrow NO(g) + 2H_2O(l)$	+ 0.96
$2\ Hg^{2+}(aq) + 2e^- \rightarrow Hg_2^{2+}(aq)$	+ 0.92
$Hg_2^{2+}(aq) + 2e^- \rightarrow 2Hg(l)$	+ 0.85
$Ag^+(aq) + e^- \rightarrow Ag(s)$	+ 0.80
$Fe^{3+}(aq) + e^- \rightarrow Fe^{2+}(aq)$	+ 0.77
$O_2(g) + 2H^+(aq) + 2e^- \rightarrow H_2O_2(aq)$	+ 0.68
$MnO_4^-(aq) + 2H_2O(l) + 3e^- \rightarrow MnO_2(s) + 4OH(aq)^-$	+ 0.59
$I_2(s) + 2e^- \rightarrow 2I^-(aq)$	+ 0.53
$O_2(g) + 2H_2O(l) + 4e^- \rightarrow 4OH^-(aq)$	+ 0.40
$Cu^{2+}(aq) + 2e^- \rightarrow Cu(s)$	+ 0.34
$Cu^{2+}(aq) + e^- \rightarrow Cu^+(aq)$	+ 0.15
$Sn^{4+}(aq) + 2e^- \rightarrow Sn^{2+}(aq)$	+ 0.13
$2H^+(aq) + 2e^- \rightarrow H_2(g)$	0.00
$Pb^{2+}(aq) + 2e^- \rightarrow Pb(s)$	− 0.13

Reduction half-reaction	E°(V)
$Sn^{2+}(aq) + 2e^- \rightarrow Sn(s)$	− 0.14
$Ni^{2+}(aq) + 2e^- \rightarrow Ni(s)$	− 0.25
$Co^{2+}(aq) + 2e^- \rightarrow Co(s)$	− 0.28
$Cd^{2+}(aq) + 2e^- \rightarrow Cd(s)$	− 0.40
$Fe^{2+}(aq) + 2e^- \rightarrow Fe(s)$	− 0.44
$Cr^{3+}(aq) + 3e^- \rightarrow Cr(s)$	− 0.74
$Zn^{2+}(aq) + 2e^- \rightarrow Zn(s)$	− 0.76
$2H_2O(l) + 2e^- \rightarrow H_2(g) + 2OH^-(aq)$	− 0.83
$Mn^{2+}(aq) + 2e^- \rightarrow Mn(s)$	− 1.18
$Al^{3+}(aq) + 3e^- \rightarrow Al(s)$	− 1.66
$Mg^{2+}(aq) + 2e^- \rightarrow Mg(s)$	− 2.37
$Na^+(aq) + e^- \rightarrow Na(s)$	− 2.71
$Ca^{2+}(aq) + 2e^- \rightarrow Ca(s)$	− 2.87
$Sr^{2+}(aq) + 2e^- \rightarrow Sr(s)$	− 2.89
$Ba^{2+}(aq) + 2e^- \rightarrow Ba(s)$	− 2.90
$K^+(aq) + e^- \rightarrow K(s)$	− 2.93
$Li^+(aq) + e^- \rightarrow Li(s)$	− 3.05

Solubility Product Constants

Name	Formula	K_{sp} (25°C)	K_{sp} =
aluminum hydroxide	$Al(OH)_3$	1.9×10^{-33}	$[Al^{3+}][OH^-]^3$
aluminum phosphate	$AlPO_4$	9.8×10^{-21}	$[Al^{3+}][PO_4^{3-}]$
barium carbonate	$BaCO_3$	2.6×10^{-9}	$[Ba^{2+}][CO_3^{2-}]$
barium chromate	$BaCrO_4$	2.1×10^{-10}	$[Ba^{2+}][CrO_4^{2-}]$
barium fluoride	BaF_2	1.7×10^{-6}	$[Ba^{2+}][F^-]^2$
barium hydroxide octahydrate	$Ba(OH)_2 \cdot 8\ H_2O$	2.6×10^{-4}	$[Ba^{2+}][OH^-]^2$
barium sulfate	$BaSO_4$	1.1×10^{-10}	$[Ba^{2+}][SO_4^{2-}]$
cadmium carbonate	$CdCO_3$	1.8×10^{-14}	$[Cd^{2+}][CO_3^{2-}]$
cadmium fluoride	CdF_2	6.4×10^{-3}	$[Cd^{2+}][F^-]^2$
cadmium hydroxide	$Cd(OH)_2$	2.5×10^{-14}	$[Cd^{2+}][OH^-]^2$
cadmium oxalate trihydrate	$CdC_2O_4 \cdot 3\ H_2O$	1.4×10^{-8}	$[Cd^{2+}][C_2O_4^{2-}]$
cadmium sulfide	CdS	8.0×10^{-28}	$[Cd^{2+}][HS^-][OH^-]$
calcium carbonate	$CaCO_3$	8.7×10^{-9}	$[Ca^{2+}][CO_3^{2-}]$
calcium fluoride	CaF_2	3.9×10^{-11}	$[Ca^{2+}][F^-]^2$
calcium hydroxide	$Ca(OH)_2$	6.5×10^{-6}	$[Ca^{2+}][OH^-]^2$
calcium oxalate monohydrate	$CaC_2O_4 \cdot H_2O$	2.3×10^{-9}	$[Ca^{2+}][C_2O_4^{2-}]$
calcium phosphate	$Ca_3(PO_4)_2$	2.0×10^{-29}	$[Ca^{2+}]^3[PO_4^{3-}]^2$
calcium sulfate	$CaSO_4$	2.4×10^{-5}	$[Ca^{2+}][SO_4^{2-}]$
chromium(III) hydroxide	$Cr(OH)_3$	1.6×10^{-30}	$[Cr^{3+}][OH^-]^3$
copper(I) bromide	$CuBr$	6.3×10^{-9}	$[Cu^+][Br^-]$
copper(I) chloride	$CuCl$	1.7×10^{-7}	$[Cu^+][Cl^-]$
copper(I) iodide	CuI	1.3×10^{-12}	$[Cu^+][I^-]$
copper(I) sulfide	Cu_2S	2.3×10^{-48}	$[Cu^+]^2[HS^-][OH^-]$
copper(II) hydroxide	$Cu(OH)_2$	1.6×10^{-19}	$[Cu^{2+}][OH^-]^2$
copper(II) oxalate	CuC_2O_4	4.4×10^{-10}	$[Cu^{2+}][C_2O_4^{2-}]$
copper(II) phosphate	$Cu_3(PO_4)_2$	1.4×10^{-37}	$[Cu^{2+}]^3[PO_4^{3-}]^2$
copper(II) sulfide	CuS	6.0×10^{-37}	$[Cu^{2+}][HS^-][OH^-]$
iron(II) carbonate	$FeCO_3$	3.5×10^{-11}	$[Fe^{2+}][CO_3^{2-}]$
iron(II) fluoride	FeF_2	2.4×10^{-6}	$[Fe^{2+}][F^-]^2$
iron(II) hydroxide	$Fe(OH)_2$	7.9×10^{-16}	$[Fe^{2+}][OH^-]^2$
iron(II) sulfide	FeS	6.0×10^{-19}	$[Fe^{2+}][HS^-][OH^-]$
iron(III) hydroxide	$Fe(OH)_3$	6.3×10^{-38}	$[Fe^{3+}][OH^-]^3$
iron(III) phosphate dihydrate	$FePO_4 \cdot 2H_2O$	9.9×10^{-29}	$[Fe^{3+}][PO_4^{3-}]$
lead(II) bromide	$PbBr_2$	6.6×10^{-6}	$[Pb^{2+}][Br^-]^2$
lead(II) carbonate	$PbCO_3$	1.5×10^{-13}	$[Pb^{2+}][CO_3^{2-}]$
lead(II) chloride	$PbCl_2$	1.6×10^{-5}	$[Pb^{2+}][Cl^-]^2$
lead(II) chromate	$PbCrO_4$	2.8×10^{-13}	$[Pb^{2+}][CrO_4^{2-}]$
lead(II) fluoride	PbF_2	7.1×10^{-7}	$[Pb^{2+}][F^-]^2$
lead(II) hydroxide	$Pb(OH)_2$	1.4×10^{-20}	$[Pb^{2+}][OH^-]^2$
lead(II) iodide	PbI_2	1.4×10^{-8}	$[Pb^{2+}][I^-]^2$

Solubility Product Constants

Name	Formula	K_{sp} (25°C)	K_{sp} =
lead(II) oxalate	PbC_2O_4	8.5×10^{-10}	$[Pb^{2+}][C_2O_4^{2-}]$
lead(II) sulfate	$PbSO_4$	6.3×10^{-7}	$[Pb^{2+}][SO_4^{2-}]$
lead(II) sulfide	PbS	3.0×10^{-28}	$[Pb^{2+}][HS^-][OH^-]$
magnesium carbonate	$MgCO_3$	3.5×10^{-8}	$[Mg^{2+}][CO_3^{2-}]$
magnesium fluoride	MgF_2	6.6×10^{-9}	$[Mg^{2+}][F^-]^2$
magnesium hydroxide	$Mg(OH)_2$	1.8×10^{-11}	$[Mg^{2+}][OH^-]^2$
magnesium, oxalate dihydrate	$MgC_2O_4 \cdot 2\ H_2O$	1.7×10^{-7}	$[Mg^{2+}][C_2O_4^{2-}]$
magnesium phosphate	$Mg_3(PO_4)_2$	6.3×10^{-26}	$[Mg^{2+}]^3[PO_4^{3-}]^2$
mercury(I) bromide	Hg_2Br_2	6.4×10^{-23}	$[Hg_2^{2+}][Br^-]^2$
mercury(I) carbonate	Hg_2CO_3	8.9×10^{-17}	$[Hg_2^{2+}][CO_3^{2-}]$
mercury(I) chloride	Hg_2Cl_2	1.3×10^{-18}	$[Hg_2^{2+}][Cl^-]^2$
mercury(I) fluoride	Hg_2F_2	3.1×10^{-6}	$[Hg_2^{2+}][F^-]^2$
mercury(I) oxalate	$Hg_2C_2O_4$	1.8×10^{-13}	$[Hg_2^{2+}][C_2O_4^{2-}]$
mercury(I) sulfate	Hg_2SO_4	8.0×10^{-7}	$[Hg_2^{2+}][SO_4^{2-}]$
mercury(II) hydroxide	$Hg(OH)_2$	2.6×10^{-26}	$[Hg^{2+}][OH^-]^2$
mercury(II) iodide	HgI_2	1.1×10^{-28}	$[Hg^{2+}][I^-]^2$
mercury(II) sulfide	HgS	3.0×10^{-53}	$[Hg^{2+}][HS^-][OH^-]$
nickel(II) carbonate	$NiCO_3$	1.3×10^{-7}	$[Ni^{2+}][CO_3^{2-}]$
nickel(II) hydroxide	$Ni(OH)_2$	5.5×10^{-16}	$[Ni^{2+}][OH^-]^2$
nickel(II) phosphate	$Ni_3(PO_4)_2$	4.7×10^{-32}	$[Ni^{2+}]^3[PO_4^{3-}]^2$
nickel(II) sulfide	NiS	3.0×10^{-20}	$[Ni^{2+}][HS^-][OH^-]$
palladium(II) sulfide	PdS	2.0×10^{-58}	$[Pd^{2+}][HS^-][OH^-]$
platinum(II) sulfide	PtS	9.9×10^{-74}	$[Pt^{2+}][HS^-][OH^-]$
silver acetate	$AgCH_3COO$	1.9×10^{-3}	$[Ag^+][CH_3COO^-]$
silver bromide	$AgBr$	5.0×10^{-13}	$[Ag^+][Br^-]$
silver carbonate	Ag_2CO_3	8.1×10^{-12}	$[Ag^+]^2[CO_3^{2-}]$
silver chloride	$AgCl$	1.8×10^{-10}	$[Ag^+][Cl^-]$
silver chromate	Ag_2CrO_4	1.2×10^{-12}	$[Ag^+]^2[CrO_4^{2-}]$
silver iodide	AgI	8.3×10^{-17}	$[Ag^+][I^-]$
silver oxalate	$Ag_2C_2O_4$	5.4×10^{-12}	$[Ag^+]^2[C_2O_4^{2-}]$
silver phosphate	Ag_3PO_4	8.9×10^{-17}	$[Ag^+]^3[PO_4^{3-}]$
silver sulfate	Ag_2SO_4	1.5×10^{-5}	$[Ag^+]^2[SO_4^{2-}]$
silver sulfide	Ag_2S	1.0×10^{-49}	$[Ag^+]^2[HS^-][OH^-]$
tin(II) hydroxide	$Sn(OH)_2$	2.0×10^{-26}	$[Sn^{2+}][OH^-]^2$
tin(II) sulfide	SnS	1.0×10^{-26}	$[Sn^{2+}][HS^-][OH^-]$
zinc carbonate	$ZnCO_3$	1.0×10^{-10}	$[Zn^{2+}][CO_3^{2-}]$
zinc fluoride	ZnF_2	3.0×10^{-2}	$[Zn^{2+}][F^-]^2$
zinc hydroxide	$Zn(OH)_2$	4.5×10^{-17}	$[Zn^{2+}][OH^-]^2$
zinc sulfide	ZnS	3.0×10^{-23}	$[Zn^{2+}][HS^-][OH^-]$

Physical Properties of some Elements

Element	Symbol	At. No.	Atomic Mass (g/mol)	Melting Point (°C) at STP	Boiling Point (°C) at STP	Density (g/cm^3) at STP	First Ionization energy (kJ/mol)	ΔH_{fusion} (kJ/mol)	ΔH_{vap} (kJ/mol)	Specific heat (J/g · °C)
Aluminum	Al	13	26.9815	660.42	2467	2.702	578	10.79	293.40	0.90
Antimony	Sb	51	121.75	630.79	1587	6.684	834	19.87	77.14	0.21
Argon	Ar	18	39.948	-189.15	-185.85	1.782×10^{-3}	1520	1.188	6.447	0.520
Arsenic	As	33	74.922	816 (>1 atm)	615 (sublimes)	5.72	946	27.7	32.4	0.33
Barium	Ba	56	137.33	725	1850	3.51	503	7.75	142	0.20
Beryllium	Be	4	9.01218	1278.0	2970.0	1.8477	601	11.71	297	1.825
Bismuth	Bi	83	208.98	271.4	1564	9.8	703	11.3	172	0.12
Bromine	Br	35	79.904	-7.15	59.6	3.12	1140	5.29	15.44	0.473
Boron	B	5	10.811	2092	4002	2.34	801	22.6	507.8	1.026
Cadmium	Cd	48	112.41	321	765	8.65	868	6.19	99.57	0.23
Calcium	Ca	20	40.08	839.05	1494	1.55	590	8.54	153.6	0.63
Carbon	C	6	12.0107	3500.0	4827.0	2.62	1086.5	104.6	711	0.709
Cerium	Ce	58	140.12	804	3470	6.78	527	5.46	414	0.19
Cesium	Cs	55	132.91	28.45	705	1.87	376	2.092	67.74	0.24
Chlorine	Cl	17	35.4527	-100.93	-33.95	3.214×10^{-3}	1251	3.203	10.20	0.48
Chromium	Cr	24	51.996	1857	2690	7.19	653	16.90	344.3	0.45
Cobalt	Co	27	58.9332	1495	3100	8.90	758	16.19	376.50	0.42
Copper	Cu	29	63.546	1083.4	2570	8.96	745	13.05	300.3	0.38
Curium	Cm	96	(247)	1340	--	13.5	581	15	--	--
Fluorine	F	9	18.9984	-219.6	-188.0	1.696×10^{-3}	1681	0.2552	3.2698	0.82
Francium	Fr	87	(223)	24	650	--	384	--	--	--
Gallium	Ga	31	69.723	29.83	2403	5.907	579	5.59	258.7	0.37
Germanium	Ge	32	72.59	937.45	2850	5.323	762	36.94	330.90	0.32
Gold	Au	79	196.97	1064.48	2808	19.32	890	12.55	334.4	0.13
Helium	He	2	4.00260	-270.0	268.6	1.785×10^{-4}	2373	0.02	0.084	5.193
Hydrogen	H	1	1.00794	-259.14	-252.87	8.99×10^{-5}	1312	0.117	0.4581	14.304
Iodine	I	53	126.90	113.55	184.35	4.93	1008	7.82	20.75	0.21
Iron	Fe	26	55.847	1535	2750	7.86	759	13.80	349.6	0.44
Krypton	Kr	36	83.80	-156.55	-153.8	3.708×10^{-3}	1351	1.64	9.05	0.25
Lead	Pb	82	207.2	327.55	1751	11.34	716	4.80	178	0.13
Lithium	Li	3	6.941	180.54	1347.0	0.53	520	3.0	147.1	3.582

Physical Properties of some Elements

Element	Symbol	At. No.	Atomic Mass (g/mol)	Melting Point (°C) at STP	Boiling Point (°C) at STP	Density (g/cm^3) at STP	First Ionization energy (kJ/mol)	ΔH_{fusion} (kJ/mol)	ΔH_{vap} (kJ/mol)	Specific heat (J/g · °C)
Magnesium	Mg	12	24.305	648.8	1105	1.738	738	9.954	127.4	1.02
Manganese	Mn	25	54.938	1244	2060	7.43	717	12.05	226	0.43
Mercury	Hg	80	200.59	-38.82	357	13.55	1007	2.30	59.23	0.14
Molybdenum	Mo	42	95.94	2617	4650	10.2	685	32	598	0.25
Neon	Ne	10	20.17	-248.6	-246	9×10^{-4}	2081	0.3317	1.7326	0.904
Nickel	Ni	28	58.71	1453	2920	8.90	737	17.47	370.40	0.44
Nitrogen	N	7	14.0067	-209.9	-195.8	1.251×10^{-3}	1403	0.72	2.7928	1.042
Niobium	Nb	41	92.91	2468	4758	8.57	664	26.40	682	0.26
Oxygen	O	8	15.994	-218.4	-183	1.429×10^{-3}	1314	0.22259	3.4099	0.92
Palladium	Pd	46	106.42	1554	2940	12.02	805	17.6	357	0.24
Phosphorus	P	15	30.9738	44.15	280.6	1,82	1012	0.657	12.13	0.77
Platinum	Pt	78	195.09	1769	3827	21.45	870	19.6	510	0.13
Potassium	K	19	30.0983	63.35	765.55	0.0862	419	2.334	79.87	0.75
Radium	Ra	88	226.03	700	1140	5	509	8.37	115.	0.12
Radon	Rn	86	(222)	-71	-61.8	9.73×10^{-3}	1037	2.89	16.4	0.1
Rhodium	Rh	45	102.91	1965	3760	12.4	720	21.50	493	0.24
Rubidium	Rb	37	85.467	38.94	688	1.53	403	2.19	72.22	0.36
Selenium	Se	34	78.96	217	685	4.79	941	6.69	26.32	0.32
Silicon	Si	14	28.0855	1410	3280	2.33	786	50.55	384.22	0.71
Silver	Ag	47	107.868	961.95	2155	10.5	731	11.3	251	0.24
Sodium	Na	11	22.9898	97.86	881.4	0.971	496	2.598	96.96	1.23
Strontium	Sr	38	87.62	769	1381	2.6	550	8.30	144	0.30
Sulfur	S	16	32.06	112.85	444.75	2.07	1000	1.7175	10	0.71
Thallium	Tl	81	204.37	303.55	1457	11.85	589	4.14	164.1	0.13
Tin	Sn	50	118.69	232	2623	7.30	709	7.03	296	0.23
Titanium	Ti	22	47.90	1660	3285	4.50	658	14.45	421	0.52
Tungsten	W	74	183.85	3410	5500	19.3	770	35.4	824	0.13
Uranium	U	92	238.03	1130	3930	18.9	584	8.52	477	0.12
Vanadium	V	23	50.94	1890	3350	5.8	650	22.8	446.7	0.49
Xenon	Xe	54	131.30	-111.85	-108	5.88×10^{-3}	1170	2.30	12.64	0.16
Zinc	Zn	30	65.38	419.63	907	7.14	906	7.322	115.3	0.39

Solubility Rules for Common Ionic Compounds in Water at 25°C

Soluble compounds	Exceptions
ammonium ion (NH_4^+)	
nitrate ion (NO_3^-)	
alkali metal ions (Li^+, Na^+, K^+, Rb^+, Cs^+)	
hydrogen carbonate ion (HCO_3^-) (common name is bicarbonate ion)	
acetate ion (CH_3COO^-)	
chlorate ion (ClO_3^-)	
halide ions (Cl^-, Br^-, and I^-)	Ag^+, Pb^{2+}, Hg_2^{2+}, Cu^+
sulfate ion (SO_4^{2-})	Ag^+, Ca^{2+}, Sr^{2+}, Ba^{2+}, Pb^{2+}, Hg_2^{2+}

Insoluble compounds	Exceptions
hydroxide ion (OH^-)	alkali metal ions and ammonium ion
carbonate ion (CO_3^{2-})	alkali metal ions and ammonium ion
phosphate ion (PO_4^{3-})	alkali metal ions and ammonium ion
chromate ion (CrO_4^{3-})	alkali metal ions and ammonium ion
sulfide ion (S^{2-})	alkali metal ions and ammonium ion
hydroxide ion (OH^-)	alkali metal ions and ammonium ion Ca^{2+}, Ba^{2+}, Sr^{2+}

GLOSSARY

Glossary

A

absolute temperature scale: a temperature scale that sets zero as absolute zero and is the basis for all thermodynamic calculations. It uses the SI temperature unit which is expressed in kelvin (K). K = °C + 273.

absolute zero: a temperature of 0 K at which all molecular motion is at a minimum.

accuracy: a measure of the closeness between a measured value and the accepted or true value.

acid: a compound or substance that releases hydrogen ions in water solution (Arrhenius); a proton donor (Brønsted-Lowry); an electron-acceptor (Lewis).

acid-base indicator: a weak organic acid that can change color to indicate the pH of a solution. Phenolphthalein is colorless in acid solution and pink or red in basic solution.

activated complex: in a reaction, a state that shows transitional bonding that is intermediate between reactant and product.

activation energy: in chemical reactions, it is the energy required to break chemical bonds to allow the reaction to proceed to products.

activity series of metals: a list of the metals from the most easily oxidized metallic element to the least easily oxidized. Elements high on the list will lose their valence electrons more easily than lower elements. Example: Zinc oxidizes more easily than copper.

alcohol: an organic molecule that contains the hydroxyl group bonded to carbon, R-OH.

alkali metals: Group 1A elements of the periodic table (Li, Na, K, Rb, Cs).

alkaline earth metals: Group 2A elements of the periodic table (Be, Mg, Ca, Sr, Ba).

alkane: an organic compound that consists of only carbon and hydrogen atoms with single bonds between the carbon atoms. Examples: methane, ethane, propane, butane.

alkene: an organic compound that consists of only carbon and hydrogen atoms with one or more double bonds between carbon atoms. Examples: ethane, propene, butane.

alkyne: an organic compound that consists of only carbon and hydrogen atoms with one or more triple bonds between the carbon atoms. Examples: ethyne and propyne.

alloy: a homogeneous mixture (solution) of two or more metals. Example: alloys of copper and zinc are called brass.

alpha particle: a helium-4 nucleus (He or $^{4}_{2}He$ or $^{4}_{2}\alpha$) with a charge of +2 that consists of two protons and two neutrons, but lacks the valence electrons.

amino acid: the building block of proteins; a compound that contains both a carboxyl group –COOH and an amine group, $-NH_2$.

anhydrate: a compound that has had water molecules removed from its natural hydrated crystalline structure.

anion: a negatively charged atom or molecule. Examples: Br^-, S^{2-}, $SO_4{}^{2-}$.

anode: the negative battery electrode that removes electrons in an electrical circuit. In an electrochemical cell, oxidation takes place at the anode terminal.

atom: the smallest part of a chemical element that retains the properties of the element.

atomic mass: determined by adding the mass of the protons and neutrons of the atom.

atomic mass unit (amu): a unit of mass defined as one-twelfth of the mass of a carbon-12 atom or 1. In terms of mass, 1 amu = 1.661×10^{-24}g.

atomic number: the number of protons contained in an element.

atomic symbol: one or more letters that represent each element in the periodic table.

atmospheric pressure: the variable pressure exerted by Earth's atmosphere. Standard conditions are: 1 atmosphere supports a column of mercury 76 cm high and equals 760 millibars and 100,000 pascals.

Avogadro's Gas Law: a gas law that states that gases at the same temperature and pressure have the same number of molecules.

Avogadro's number: a large number that equals the number of particles in a mole, 6.022×10^{23}.

B

balanced chemical equation: an equation in which the numbers and types of atoms on both sides of the reaction arrow are the same.

base: a compound or substance that produces hydroxide ions in water solution (Arrhenius); a proton acceptor (Brønsted-Lowry); an electron-donor (Lewis).

batch method: a process in which an operation is carried out on a fixed amount of material to allow time for chemical or physical transformations to go to completion. The batch method for purifying water allows time for sedimentation followed by filtration.

binary compound: a compound formed from the combining of two different elements. Example: NaCl.

boiling point: the temperature at which a liquid's vapor pressure equals the atmospheric pressure. At this temperature, the liquid phase is changing to the gas phase.

bounce: the ability of an object to rebound to its original position when dropped from a given height.

Boyle's Law: one of the basic gas laws that says, if the mass of a gas and its temperature are held constant, the volume of the gas will vary in an inverse proportion to the pressure of the gas. $P_1V_1 = P_2V_2$.

C

calorie: the amount of heat needed to raise the temperature of one gram of water by one degree Celsius. 1 cal = 4.184 J.

calorimeter: a device for experimentally determining the quantity of heat energy released or absorbed in a chemical or physical change.

catalyst: a substance that speeds up a chemical reaction, but itself does not undergo any permanent chemical change.

cathode rays: the rays emitted from the negative electrode in a gas discharge tube. These negative particles are also called electrons and β–particles.

cation: a positively charged atom or molecule. Examples: Na^+, NH_4^+, and Fe^{2+}.

celsius degrees: a metric temperature scale based on water freezing at 0°C and boiling at 100°C. This scale is converted to kelvins by K = °C + 273 and to Fahrenheit by F = 1.8°C + 32.

Charles's Law: a gas law that states that when the pressure and the amount of a gas sample are constant, the volume of the gas will vary directly with the change in temperature. $V_1 \div T_1 = V_2 \div T_2$, where T is measured in kelvins.

chemical change: also called a chemical reaction; the process of substances being chemically changed into other substances through the reorganization of atoms.

chemical formula: a shorthand method for representing the exact composition of a compound in which the atomic symbols are used with a subscript. Example: H_2O.

chemical group: a family of elements in the periodic table that have similar electron configurations and properties. Example: The halogens (F, Cl, Br, I) are in Group VIIA or Group 17.

chemical property: the manner in which substances change structure when rearranging during a chemical change.

chemiluminescence: a chemical reaction that releases energy as light or electromagnetic radiation.

chromatography: a separation technique that uses a solid phase and a liquid phase to purify individual components of a mixture.

***cis*-double bond:** a geometric arrangement of a carbon to carbon double bond where two hydrogen atoms are located on the same side of the double bond.

coagulation: a clumping together of particles suspended in a colloid so that they will settle out. A precipitate of $Al(OH)_3$ is used to coagulate fine particles in a water supply.

colloid: a mixture containing particles larger than solute molecules but small enough to remain suspended without settling out. This is also called a colloidal dispersion.

Combined Gas Laws: a law that states if the amount of gas (moles) is held constant then Boyle's and Charles's Laws can be combined to give: $P_1V_1 \div T_1 = P_2V_2 \div T_2$, where T is measured in kelvins.

combustion: a chemical change where a substance burns in the presence of oxygen, most often accompanied by the production of heat and light. A hydrocarbon reacts with oxygen to form the products carbon dioxide and water.

composite: a solid heterogeneous mixture of two or more substances that make use of the properties of each component. Example: Concrete.

compound: a substance that consists of two or more elements chemically bonded together in definite proportion. Example: Sodium chloride is always NaCl.

concentration: a measured amount of solute dissolved in a definite amount of solvent. Molarity (M, moles per liter) is an example of concentration.

condensation point: the temperature at which a gas becomes a liquid at a specified pressure.

conduction: the transfer and distribution of heat energy from atom to atom within a material, such as copper wire or a frying pan.

conductivity: the property of transmitting heat or electricity through a substance.

convection: the transfer of heat by the physical motion of masses of fluid (liquids and gases) by changes in density of the fluid.

Coulomb's Law of Electrostatics: a law that states that the force between two charged objects (q_1 and q_2) is inversely proportional to the square of the distance (d) between the two charged particles.

$F = k\,\frac{q_1 q_2}{d_2}$, $k = 9.0 \times 10^9$ N-m^2/C^2

covalent bond: a chemical bond formed by the sharing of a single pair, two pairs, or three pairs of electrons between the two atoms.

crystalline structure: in solids, it is the regular arrangement of the oppositely charged ions of the compound (salts), molecular packing pattern (compounds), or the packing of atoms (metals).

current: the rate at which electric charge passes through a conductor. The unit used is the ampere (A) = 1C/s.

D

decomposition reaction: a chemical reaction where a compound breaks down into two or more simpler substances. For example, $H_2CO_3 \rightarrow H_2O + CO_2$.

denaturation: the breaking down of the three-dimensional structure of a protein resulting in the loss of its function.

density: an intensive physical property of a substance described by its mass divided by its volume, such as g/cm^3.

deposition: the conversion of a gas into a solid, without first condensing into a liquid; or, the formation of a thin layer of metal on an object by electrolysis.

diatomic molecule: a molecule that consists of two atoms. Examples: hydrogen (H_2), nitrogen (N_2), oxygen (O_2), fluorine (F_2), and chlorine (Cl_2).

digestion: the physical and chemical breakdown of food into smaller nutrient particles.

diffusion: the spreading of a substance within another substance. Example: A drop of food dye will spread out in a glass of water until the solution is homogeneous.

dilution: a process of making a solution less concentrated by adding more solvent, such as water, to the original solution.

dimensional analysis: a process used in problem-solving by carrying dimension units throughout a set of calculations.

dipeptide: two amino acids that are linked together with a peptide bond.

dislocation: an atom misplaced in the crystalline structure, especially a metal.

disaccharide: a sugar composed of two simple sugars that can be hydrolyzed back to those two simple sugars. Examples: Lactose, sucrose, and maltose are disaccharides.

disinfection: the removal or destruction of harmful organisms and viruses.

dispersion forces: weak attractive forces (also called London forces) resulting when small dipoles occur on the surface of a molecule due to the transient distribution of the electrons about the nuclei.

dissolution: the process of dissolving through the interaction of one substance with another. It is also referred to as solvation.

distillation: separation of components in a liquid by evaporating the components with lower boiling point and then condensing them.

double bond: a bond that contains the sharing of two pairs of electrons between the two atoms.

double-replacement reaction: a reaction in which two reactants trade ions to form a precipitate. Example: $Na_2SO_{4(aq)} + Ba(NO_3)_{2(aq)} \rightarrow BaSO_{4(s)} + 2\ NaNO_{3(aq)}$.

ductile: a property of a substance, typically metal, whereby it can be pulled into a wire.

E

effusion: the process where a contained gas flows through a small opening in the container.

elasticity: the property of a material to resist deformation and return to its normal size or shape after a force has been applied to it.

electrochemical cell: a laboratory system that produces an electric current through an oxidation-reduction reaction.

electrode: a substance or material that is used as a terminal in an electrochemical cell or battery.

electrolysis: a process using electricity to cause a chemical change.

electrolyte: a solution that contains ions and will conduct an electric current.

electromagnetic spectrum: the complete spectrum of electromagnetic radiation, such as radio waves, microwaves, infrared, visible, ultraviolet, x-rays, and gamma rays.

electron: a negatively charged subatomic particle located outside of the nucleus of the atom. An electron's charge is equal to but opposite to that of a proton. Its mass is 9.109389×10^{-28} g and charge is -1.6×10^{-19} C.

electron configuration: the systematic distribution of electrons in the energy levels of an atom.

electronegativity: in a covalent bond, a measure of the ability of an atom to attract the electrons of that bond.

electroplating: the deposition of a thin layer of metal on an object by electrolysis.

element: a substance that cannot be broken down into simpler substances by chemical means. An element is composed of atoms with identical atomic numbers.

emollient: an additive to soap that helps to retain water or prevent water from escaping from the skin.

emulsion: a colloid or colloidal dispersion of one liquid suspended in another.

endothermic process: a process where energy is absorbed by the system from the surroundings. Examples: Evaporation and melting.

endpoint of a titration: the stage in a titration where the moles of reactant added from a buret is equal to the moles of a second reactant in a beaker. The beaker contains no reactants, only products.

endothermic reaction: a chemical reaction that requires heat to be added in order for it to occur and has a positive value of ΔH.

energy diagram: a graphical representation of the energy changes in a reaction, going from reactants to products.

energy level: a specific amount of energy that an electron possesses in an atom. Example: The ground-state energy level of the hydrogen electron is -2.18×10^{-18} J/atom.

energy of hydration: the energy change when a substance is solvated by liquid water.

enthalpy: change in heat energy for a process that occurs at constant pressure; symbolized by ΔH.

entropy: a thermodynamic property (symbolized by ΔS) of a substance associated with the degree of disorder in the substance. A substance is more ordered as a solid than it is as a liquid, and it is more ordered as a liquid than it is as a gas.

enzyme: a protein that acts as a catalyst by speeding up a chemical reaction that occurs in living things.

equilibrium: a condition that exists when the forward reaction rate equals the reverse reaction rate, such that there appears to be no change in the concentration of products or reactants.

equilibrium constant: for a reaction at dynamic equilibrium, the product of the product concentrations divided by the product of the reactant concentrations.

ester: the reaction of an organic acid with an alcohol forms an ester. Example: beeswax is a long-chain ester and fats are trimesters, commonly called triglycerides.

etching: the removal of metal atoms from a metallic surface with a corrosive liquid.

excited state: a condition where an electron of an atom or molecule has absorbed energy so that the electron is now at a higher energy level than its ground state.

exothermic reaction: a chemical reaction where energy is released from the system to the surroundings and has a negative value of ΔH.

extensive property: a property that depends on how much matter is being considered. Examples: Length and volume are extensive properties of matter.

F

fatty acid: a long-chain carboxylic acid, typically having 12-20 carbon atoms.

fission: the process of breaking large nuclei into smaller nuclei with the release of a large amount of energy.

floc: a process used to remove suspended particles from water. A gel can be made for this purpose by combining aluminum sulfate with calcium oxide.

flow method: a process in which an operation is carried out on a continuously moving stream of material. In the flow method for purifying water, the water flows continuously through multiple stages of filtration.

fluorescence: the emission of visible light from a substance after it absorbs higher energy radiation, such as ultraviolet light.

freezing point: the temperature at which a liquid solidifies under a specified pressure.

frequency: in electromagnetic radiation, the number of waves per second or cycles per second (hertz, Hz).

functional group: in organic chemistry, that part of a molecule that gives the molecule its characteristic physical and chemical properties. Example: The carboxylic acid group is represented by the fragment –COOH.

fusion: the process where two nuclei of lighter atoms combine to form a nucleus with greater mass while releasing a large amount of energy.

G

galvanic cell: an electrochemical cell in which oxidation and reduction take place.

gamma ray: high-energy radiation with a short wavelength, usually coming from radioactive substances.

gas pressure: force per unit area created by particles of a confined gas colliding with the inside surface of a container.

Gibbs free energy: a thermodynamic property that can be used to predict whether a process, such as dissolution of a substance, will occur spontaneously at constant temperature and pressure.

Graham's Law of Effusion: a mathematical statement that compares the rate of effusion of different gases.

$$\frac{\text{rate of effusion of gas}_1}{\text{rate of effusion of gas}_2} = \sqrt{\frac{\text{mass of gas}_2}{\text{mass of gas}_1}}$$

grain: the arrangement of atoms in a solid such as a metal.

ground state: the lowest energy level that an electron of an atom or molecule can occupy.

group: a column of elements or family of elements in the periodic table. Example: Alkali metals are in Group 1A.

H

half-cell: in electrochemical batteries each of two cells that contains an electrode surrounded by a solution. Two half-cells are connected by a salt bridge.

half-life: the period of time required for the mass of a radioactive substance to become one-half of its original mass due to disintegration of its atoms. Example: The half-life of uranium-238 is 4.5 billion years.

half-reaction: two separated parts of a redox reaction. One part is the oxidation reaction and the other part is the reduction reaction.

hard water: relatively high concentrations of Mg^{2+} and Ca^{2+} in water, which react with soap to form insoluble soap scum. It is expressed as milligrams of $CaCO_3$ per liter of water.

halogens: Group VIIA (17) in the periodic table consisting of fluorine, chlorine, bromine, iodine, and astatine.

heat energy: a form of energy related to the motion of atoms and molecules. It can be transferred by conduction, convection, or radiation.

heat of condensation: the quantity of heat released (or enthalpy change) when a unit mass of a gas becomes a liquid.

heat of crystallization: the quantity of heat released (or enthalpy change) when a unit liquid mass of a substance freezes.

heat of fusion: the quantity of heat required (or enthalpy change) to melt a unit mass of a solid at a specified temperature.

heat of vaporization: the quantity of heat required (or enthalpy change) to convert a unit liquid mass at a specified temperature into vapor.

Heisenberg uncertainty principle: the principle that states that the position of an electron and its momentum cannot be simultaneously predicted.

hydrate compound: a compound that is loosely bonded to water molecules in its crystalline structure. The formula for a hydrate will always contain a specific number of water molecules. Example: $CuSO_4{\cdot}5H_2O$.

hydrocarbon: an organic compound composed of only hydrogen and carbon atoms.

hydrogen bond: a very strong type of dipole-dipole attraction in which a hydrogen atom is bridged between two highly electronegative atoms, usually F, O, or N. The hydrogen is covalently linked to one of the electronegative atoms, and the hydrogen bond results from the strong electrostatic attraction to the other electronegative atom.

hydrogenation: the addition of molecular hydrogen to a double or triple bond in a chemical reaction, usually with a catalyst.

hydrologic cycle: the cyclic pathway that water takes in moving throughout the environment. It includes condensation, infiltration, runoff, evaporation, and precipitation.

hydrolysis: the process of chemically breaking down a substance into smaller molecules through the reaction with water.

hydrophilic: a substance that is attracted to water and is soluble in water, usually polar substances.

hydrophobic: a substance that is not attracted to water and is insoluble in water, usually non-polar substances.

I

ideal gas: a gas that would have zero intermolecular attraction forces, no volume, and all collisions of its particles would be perfectly elastic.

ideal gas constant: a proportionality constant used in the ideal gas equation and the constant R in the ideal gas equation, $PV = nRT$. $R = 8.021 \times 10^{-2}$ L·atm/mol·K or 8.315 J/mol·K.

indicator: a substance that changes color at a certain pH. Indicators are commonly added to a solution to help visually follow the course of a titration.

inner-transition metal: elements that contain *f* orbital electrons and are called the lanthanides and actinides series.

inorganic compound: a compound not based on molecular compounds of carbon.

intensive property: a property that does not depend on how much matter is being considered. Example: Density and temperature are intensive properties.

intermolecular forces: the forces that exist between molecules and include dipole-dipole forces and London dispersion forces.

ion: an atom or molecule that has acquired a charge by either gaining (anion) or losing (cation) electron(s).

ion-exchange resin: a polymeric material that has negative sites on its surface where various positive ions are adsorbed. Positive ions of higher charge are more strongly adsorbed, but still may be replaced by ions of lower charge if the concentration is sufficiently high.

ionic bond: an ionic bond is formed when one atom (usually a metal) loses a valence electron to a second atom, often a nonmetal. The resulting cation and anion are electrostatically bonded by their opposite charges.

ionic compound: a compound that contains cations and anions that are held together by electrostatic forces. Example: A salt is an ionic compound.

ionization energy: the energy required to remove an electron from a gaseous atom at ground state.

isomers: organic compounds that have the same chemical formula but different structural formulas.

isotope: atoms of the same element with identical atomic numbers but different atomic masses due to different number of neutrons in the nucleus.

J

joule: a unit of energy which is equal to newtons × meters, or $kg \cdot m^2/s^2$.

K

kelvin : the SI unit of temperature; 0 K = absolute zero. (°C + 273.15 = K)

kinetic energy: energy available because of the motion of an object. $KE = 1/2mv^2$.

Kinetic Molecular Theory of Gases: a model that explains the gas behavior in terms of particles in constant random motion that move in straight lines until collisions occur between them.

L

latent print: in forensics, fingerprints that cannot be seen by the naked eye.

lattice energy: the energy needed to separate a crystalline ionic compound into gas phase ions.

Law of Combining Volumes of Gases: when two gases react, the ratio of their volumes will be small, whole numbers, temperature and pressure being equal.

Law of Conservation of Energy: the total amount of energy in the universe is conserved. Energy can neither be created nor destroyed, only changed.

Law of Conservation of Mass: in a chemical reaction, mass is neither created nor destroyed. The total mass of the reactants equals the total mass of the products.

Law of Conservation of Matter: the number and type of atoms present during a chemical change remains the same. An atom of one element cannot be changed into another element.

Law of Definite Proportions: the composition of a pure substance is always the same, or the elements of the compound always combine in the same proportion by mass.

LeChatelier's Principle: a change in any factor of a system at equilibrium will cause the system to adjust in a direction that allows it to return to an equilibrium state.

Lewis structure: a system of representing chemical structure in which the valence electrons of an atom are placed around the element's symbol. Single bonds between atoms can be shown as a pair of dots or as a line, and unused valence electrons are shown as dots.

limiting reagent: the reactant that will be used up first and determines how much product can be produced.

luster: the reflection of light from the surface of a material described by its quality and intensity.

lustrous: a non-quantitative description of how much a metal shines.

M

malleable: a characteristic property of a metal that describes the ease of flattening it with a hammer.

mass: the amount of matter being considered.

mass number: the mass of an atom that is the sum of its protons and neutrons (atomic mass).

matter: anything that has mass.

melting point: temperature at which a solid becomes a liquid at a specified pressure.

metalloid: an element that possesses both metal and nonmetal characteristics. Examples: Silicon, arsenic, and germanium are metalloids.

metals: a class of materials that exhibit the properties of conductivity, malleability, and ductility. Metals are shiny, have basic oxides, and readily lose electrons to form positive ions.

micelle: a clump of soap ions around a non-polar particle of "dirt." The hydrophobic ends are on the interior to attract the "dirt," and the hydrophilic ends are on the exterior to help it dissolve in water.

minutiae: in forensics, the study of the types of ridge patterns of fingerprints.

mixture: a combination of two or more substances.

mobile phase: in chromatography, the fluid that carries the mixture to be analyzed along the solid phase. Example: Water is often the mobile phase in paper chromatography.

molar mass: the mass of one mole of a pure substance.

molarity: solute concentration in a solution expressed in moles per liter (*M*) of solution. Example: 1 *M* NaCl = 1 mol of sodium chloride contained in 1 L of solution.

molar volume: the volume occupied by 1 mol of a substance in the gas phase.

mole: the number equal to the number of carbon atoms in exactly 12 of pure ^{12}C; Avogadro's number: One mole represents 6.022×10^{23} units (atoms, molecules, etc.).

molecular formula: the exact formula of a molecule, giving the types of atoms and the number of each type of atom present.

molecular shape: the geometric shape of a molecule. The geometric shape of methane is a tetrahedron.

monomer: the smallest repeating unit of a polymer. Example: Ethylene is the smallest repeating unit in polyethylene.

monosaccharide: a simple sugar consisting of 3 to 9 carbon atoms that cannot be hydrolyzed to smaller molecules. Examples: Glucose, fructose, and galactose.

monounsaturated lipids: molecules with carbon chains that have only one carbon to carbon double bond. Examples: Olive oil and canola oil.

N

nanometer: one-billionth of a meter. 1 nanometer (nm) = 1×10^{-9} m.

net ionic equation: an ionic equation that has had the spectator ions removed from the reactant side and product side.

neutralization: the reaction between an acid and a base to form water and a salt (usually the reaction between hydrogen ions and hydroxide ions).

neutron: a neutral particle located in the nucleus with a charge of zero. A neutron's mass is 1.675×10^{-24} g or about 1 amu.

Newtonian liquid: a liquid that flows easily or has low viscosity, such as water.

noble gas: a member of a family of elements (Group 18 or VIIIA) of the periodic table (also called rare gas or inert gas). Examples: He, Ne, Ar, Kr, Xe, and Rn are noble gases.

nonbonding electron pairs or lone-pair electrons: valence electrons that are not used to form a bond in a molecule. The oxygen atom of water has two lone pairs of electrons not used to bond to hydrogen.

nonmetals: elements that do not exhibit the properties of conductivity, malleability, and ductility. They are generally gases or soft, brittle solids. These elements tend to form negative ions and their oxides are acidic.

non-polar bond: a bond between two atoms of similar electronegativity which share the electrons more or less equally.

non-polar molecule: a molecule that does not have a dipole moment.

normal boiling point: the temperature at which a liquid's vapor pressure is equal to one atmosphere.

normal freezing point: at one atmosphere pressure, the temperature at which a substance changes from a liquid state to its solid state.

normal melting point: at one atmosphere pressure the temperature at which a substance changes from a solid state to its liquid state.

nuclear strong force: a very strong attractive force that acts at extremely small distances. This force is found in the nucleus and interacts with the neutrons and protons.

nucleon: a constituent of an atomic nucleus; either a proton or a neutron.

nucleus: the dense core of an atom. It contains the protons and neutrons.

O

octet rule: a rule that states that atoms with eight electrons in the valence shell attain a stable condition. Atoms with fewer than eight electrons in the valence shell will form bonds in order to achieve that stability. Smaller atoms (H, He, Li, Be) are exceptions.

orbit: the path of the electron in its motion around the nucleus of Bohr's hydrogen atom.

orbital: an energy state of an electron determined by a specific arrangement based on the quantum numbers. These arrangements are represented in the *s*, *p*, *d*, and *f* orbitals.

organic compound: a molecular compound based on carbon.

oxidation: the loss of one or more electrons by an atom, molecule, or ion with a resulting gain in positive charge.

oxidation number: a positive or negative number assigned to each atom in a compound to help keep track of the electrons in a chemical reaction. Elements are zero.

oxidation-reduction (redox) reaction: a chemical reaction where an atom, molecule, or ion transfers electron(s) to another atom, molecule, or ion. Both oxidation and reduction must occur and the electron transfer must be balanced.

P

patina: a surface coating that develops on exposed metals and protects them from further corrosion.

peptide bond: a bond between the nitrogen atom of one amino acid and the carboxylic carbon atom of a second amino acid.

period: a row of the periodic table. Example: 2nd period starts with the element lithium and ends with neon.

pH: a measure of the acidity or alkalinity of a solution. Solutions with pH less than 7 are acidic, solutions with pH greater than 7 are basic. Mathematically, $pH = -\log[H+]$.

phase change: a change of the physical state of a substance in going from one state (solid, liquid, or gas) to a different state.

phosphorescence: the ability of some substances to absorb light energy and release it slowly over a period of time after the original light source is removed, to "glow in the dark."

photoelectric effect: the emission of electrons from the surface of metal when light is shined on the surface.

photon: a quantum or discrete packet of electromagnetic radiation.

physical change: a change in the state, phase, or appearance of a material without forming new materials through chemical reaction.

physical property: any property of matter that doesn't change its chemical composition. Examples: Density, boiling point, mass, and temperature.

plastic deformation: a change in form that is not reversible, such as when metal is stamped with a hard blow.

polar bond: a covalent bond in which the two atoms have a difference in electronegativity, causing one atom to be slightly negative and the other slightly positive.

polar covalent bond: a bond between two atoms of different electronegativity. The center of electron density is found nearer the more electronegative atom.

polar molecule: a molecule that has a negative region (dipole) and positive region (dipole) due to the arrangement of the polar bonds. It is more soluble in a polar solvent like water than a non-polar molecule.

polyatomic ion: an ion that consists of two or more atoms that are covalently bonded. Examples: OH^-, NO_3^-, SO_4^{2-}, NH_4^+.

polymer: a substance that is a macromolecule consisting of many identical small units (monomers) covalently bonded together in long chains.

polymerization: a chemical reaction that converts small molecules (monomers) into large molecules (polymers).

polypeptide: a polymer formed from a few amino acids up to hundreds, bonded together by peptide linkages.

polyunsaturated lipid: fat and oil that has more than one double bond in the carbon chain (such as corn oil or soybean oil).

potential energy: energy of a material as a result of its position in an electric, magnetic, or gravitational field.

precipitate: the formation of an insoluble substance from a chemical or physical change, or, the insoluble substance itself.

precision: the degree of agreement among individual measurements or experimental measurements. This is different than accuracy.

pressure: force per unit area. In the SI system, its units are pascals (Pa). $1\ Pa = 1\ N/m^2$.

primary protein structure: the sequence in which the amino acids are linked together to form a protein chain.

products: the substances formed from reactants as a result of a chemical reaction. Products are found on the right-hand side of a chemical equation.

protein: a biologically active polymer made up of hundreds of amino acids linked together to form a long chain.

proton: a positively charged subatomic particle located in the nucleus of an atom. A proton's charge is equal and opposite to that of an electron (+ 1.6×10^{-19} C) and it has a mass of 1.672623×10^{-24} g.

pure substance: a substance that contains only one kind of particle and cannot be separated into simpler components without chemical change.

Q

qualitative analysis: general observations of or determination of the identities of substances in a sample without measurement for each substance that is present.

quantitative analysis: observations that involve measurements that produce numerical data as to the quantity of a substance that is present in a sample.

R

radiation: electromagnetic waves that directly transport energy in all directions through space.

radioactive decay: a natural process where an atom that has an unstable nucleus will spontaneously emit alpha particles, beta particles, positrons, or gamma rays in order to achieve a more stable nucleus.

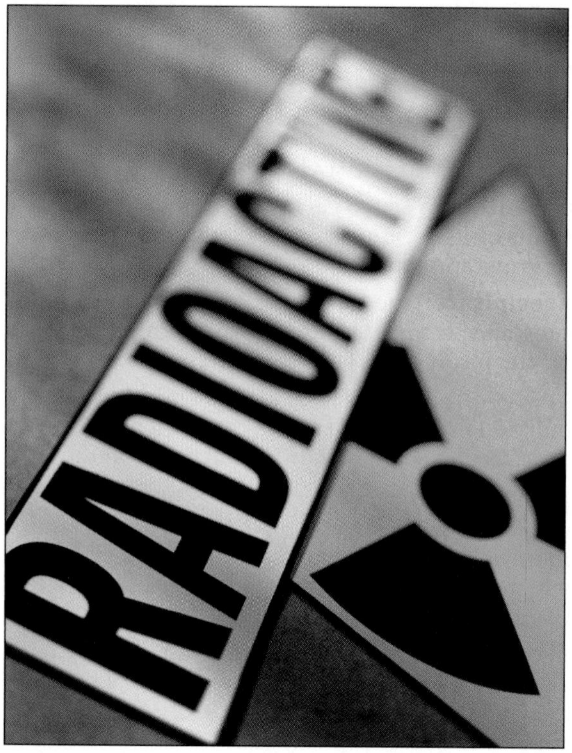
RADIOACTIVE

reactivity: a property that describes how readily a substance will react with other substances.

reactants: the starting materials in a chemical reaction that are transformed into products during chemical reactions. In the equation, reactants are on the left side.

reduction: the gain of one or more electrons by an atom, molecule, or ion, resulting in a greater negative charge.

representative element: the elements of the periodic table final electron is placed in either an *s* or *p* orbital. Example: All of the elements of the 2nd period are representative elements.

reverse osmosis: a de-ionization technique using pressure to force water through a membrane that is impermeable to metal ions as in the purification of sea water.

R_f: in chromatography, the retention factor. The R_f is the ratio of the distance that a component moved on the solid phase compared to the distance that the mobile phase moved.

S

salt: an ionic compound that is produced by the neutralization of an acid with a base.

saponification: the hydrolysis of a triglyceride with a strong base to make soap.

saturated compound: an organic compound that only contains single bonds between the carbon atoms and no double or triple bonds.

scientific notation: expressing a number to the correct number of significant digits using powers of 10 and real numbers between 1 and 10.

secondary protein structure: the three-dimensional structure of a protein chain. Three common orientations of the structure are the α-helix, random coil, or pleated sheet.

SI units: the accepted international units of measurements. Example: The SI unit for mass is the kilogram, kg.

significant figures: the precision of a calculation or measurement as reflected in the recorded number. For example, 10.45 exhibits 4 significant figures and indicates that the true value is closer to 10.45 than 10.46 or 10.44.

single-replacement reaction: a chemical reaction that involves an element replacing a cation in a solution of an ionic compound. Example: $Zn_{(s)} + CuCl_{2(aq)} \rightarrow Cu_{(s)} + ZnCl_{2(aq)}$.

slope: in a two-dimensional graph, the ratio of the change in the dependent variable to the change of the independent variable. Slope $(m) = (y_1 - y_1) \div (x_2 - x_1)$.

solubility: the solubility of the substance is the concentration of solute in a saturated solution. This is temperature dependent and is usually expressed as g/100 mL.

solubility product constant: an equilibrium constant for the dissolution of a slightly soluble ionic substance in water. It is a variation on the equilibrium constant equation but in this case, K_{sp} = [cation][anion] where the reactant is a solid and its concentration is constant.

solute: a substance in lesser concentration that interacts with a solvent to form a solution.

solution: a homogeneous mixture that consists of a solvent and at least one solute.

solvent: in a solution, the substance present in a larger amount that interacts with the solute(s).

specific heat capacity: the amount of heat necessary to raise the temperature of one gram of a substance by one degree Celsius.

spectator ions: ions that are present in solution during a chemical reaction and do not change their form. In the reaction equation, they appear unchanged on both sides.

stationary phase: the adsorbent in chromatography. Example: In paper chromatography, the cellulosic paper is the stationary phase, which retards the components of the mixture as they move with the mobile phase.

stoichiometry: the study of relationships (mass-mole-volume) among substances involved in chemical reactions.

strength: the property of how well a material withstands the application of a force.

structural formula: a formula of an organic molecule that shows not only all of the atoms but also how they are connected to each other.

sublimation: The conversion of a solid into a gas, without first becoming a liquid. Solid carbon dioxide (CO_2) sublimes at room temperature and pressure.

surface tension: the result of intermolecular forces that causes the liquid to minimize its surface area.

surfactant: a substance that lowers the surface tension of a liquid and allows wetting to occur, such as when soap is added to water.

surroundings: in thermodynamic terms, everything outside of the chemical reaction; the flask, the room, the building, etc. The chemical reaction is considered "the system" under study.

suspension: a heterogeneous mixture that contains fine solid or liquid particles in a fluid that will separate spontaneously.

synthesis reaction: a reaction in which two or more substances combine and form a single product. Example: $2Na + Cl_2 \rightarrow 2NaCl$.

system: in thermodynamics, the small part of the universe that is being studied, usually a chemical reaction. This includes the materials involved in the chemical reaction: the reactants, solvent, and products and how the heat is transferred between it and the surroundings.

T

tertiary protein structure: the overall shape of a protein, long, narrow, or globular, which is maintained by different types of intramolecular interactions.

temperature: an extensive property that is a measure of the average kinetic energy of molecules and atoms. It determines the spontaneous heat flow, which is always from hot to cold.

tetrahedral: the geometric shape of the four single bonds of a carbon atom.

texture: the characteristics of the surface of a material, such as smoothness or roughness.

thermal conductivity: the ability of an object to transfer heat from one part of itself to another by conduction. This is a result of atomic or molecular motion.

thermochemistry: a study of the quantity of heat that is absorbed or released during chemical reactions.

titration: an analytical procedure that determines the concentration of one substance by quantitatively treating a solution of it (in a beaker) with a solution of another reactant of known concentration (delivered by buret) until the precise point where the concentration of the unknown is zero. This point is usually determined by an indicator or a probe.

total ionic equation: the equation of a chemical reaction that shows all of the reactant ionic species on the left side of the equation and the product ionic species on the right side of the equation.

***trans*-double bond:** a geometric arrangement of a carbon to carbon double bond where the hydrogen atoms are located on opposite sides of the double bond.

transition metals: those elements in the periodic table that represent elements with partially filled *d*-orbitals in the 4th row and lay between Ca and Zn, that is, Sc, Ti, V, Cr, Mn, Fe, Co, Ni, Cu.

triglyceride: a triester of glycerol and a fatty acid. Example: Olive oil.

tripeptide: three amino acids that are covalently bonded together through peptide bonds.

triple bond: a bond that contains the sharing of three pairs of electrons between two atoms. Examples: carbon monoxide, C≡O and ethyne, HC≡CH.

Tyndall Effect: the scattering of a collimated beam of light by particles in a colloid where the light beam is clearly visible through light scattering.

U

uncertainty principle: the principle that states that the position of an electron and its momentum cannot be simultaneously predicted.

Universal Gas Constant: the proportionality constant used in the ideal gas equation, $PV = nRT$. $R = 8.021 \times 10^{-2}$ L·atm/mol·K or 8.315 J/mol·K.

unsaturated bond: a bond that is either a double or triple bond, usually in a carbon compound.

unsaturated hydrocarbon: an organic compound that consists only of carbon and hydrogen atoms with at least one double or triple bond between two carbon atoms.

V

valence electrons: electrons in the outermost energy level of an atom. These are the electrons involved in chemical reactions. Example: Chlorine has 7 valence electrons in the third energy level ($3s^2$ and $3p^5$).

van der Waals forces: weak intermolecular attraction forces between molecules.

vaporization: the change of state from a liquid to a gas.

viscosity: a property related to the resistance of a fluid to flow.

volt: the unit of electrical potential difference; one volt (V) = one joule/coulomb.

volume: a measure of the space occupied by matter. The SI unit of volume is the cubic meter, m^3.

W

wavelength: in electromagnetic radiation, the distance measured from crest to crest of one complete wave or cycle.

GLOSARIO

Glosario

A

ácido (acid): un compuesto o sustancia que libera iones de hidrógeno en una solución de agua (Arrhenius). Un donante de protón (Brønsted-Lowry). Un aceptador de electrón (Lewis).

ácido graso (fatty acid): una cadena larga de ácido carboxílico, típicamente teniendo de 12-20 átomos de carbono.

actividad de series de metales (activity series of metals): una lista de los metales del elemento metálico que se oxida más fácilmente al menos fácil. Los elementos altos en la lista perderán sus electrones de valencia más fácilmente que los elementos más bajos. Ejemplo: El cinc se oxida más fácilmente que el cobre.

agua dura (hard water): relativamente altas concentraciones de Mg^{2+} y Ca^{2+} en agua, las cuales reaccionan con jabón para formar una capa de suciedad insoluble de jabón. Se espera como un mg de $CaCO_3$ por litro de agua.

alcanos (alkanes): los compuestos orgánicos que consisten de solamente átomos de carbono e hidrógeno con enlaces simples entre los átomos de carbono. Ejemplos: metano, etano, propano, butano).

alcohol (alcohol): una molécula orgánica que contiene el grupo hidroxilo enlazado al carbono, R-OH.

aleación (alloy): una mezcla homogénea (solución) de dos o más metales. Ejemplo: las aleaciones de cobre y cinc son llamados bronce.

alquenos (alkenes): los compuestos orgánicos que consisten solamente de átomos de carbono e hidrógeno con uno o más enlaces triples entre los átomos de carbono. Ejemplos: etano, propano, butano).

alquinos (alkynes): compuestos orgánicos que consisten solamente de átomos de carbono e hidrógeno con uno o más enlaces triples entre los átomos de carbono. Ejemplos: etino y propino.

amino ácidos (amino acids): los bloques de construcción de proteínas; los compuestos que contienen ambos un grupo carboxilo –COOH y un grupo amino, $-NH_2$.

análisis cualitativo (qualitative analysis): observaciones generales o determinación de las identidades de sustancias en una muestra sin medida para cada sustancia que está presente.

análisis cuantitativo (quantitative analysis): observaciones que envuelven medidas que producen datos numéricos como la cantidad de una sustancia que está presente en la muestra.

análisis dimensional (dimensional analysis): un proceso usado en la solución de un problema donde se llevan a cabo unidades de dimensión a través de un conjunto de cálculos.

anhidrito (anhydrate): un compuesto que ha tenido moléculas de agua removidas de su estructura hidratada cristalina natural.

anión (aniño): un átomo o molécula de carga negativa. Ejemplo: Br^-, S^{2-}, SO_4^{2-}.

ánodo (anode): el electrodo negativo de la batería que remueve los electrones en un circuito eléctrico. En una célula electromecánica, la oxidación toma lugar en el terminal del ánodo.

átomo (atom): la parte más pequeña de un elemento químico que retiene las propiedades de ese elemento.

B

base (base): un compuesto o sustancia que produce iones de hidróxido en una solución de agua (Arrhenius), un aceptador de protones (Brønsted-Lowry) o un donante de electrones (Lewis).

C

calor de condensación (heat of condensation): la cantidad de calor liberado (o el cambio entalpía) cuando una unidad de masa de un gas se vuelve un líquido.

calor de cristalización (heat of crystallization): la cantidad de calor liberado (o el cambio entalpía) cuando una unidad de masa líquida de una sustancia se congela.

calor de fusión (heat of fusion): la cantidad de calor liberado (o el cambio entalpía) para derretir una unidad de masa de un sólido a una temperatura específica.

calor de vaporización (heat of vaporization): la cantidad de calor liberado (o el cambio entalpía) para convertir una unidad de masa líquida a una temperatura específica de vapor.

caloría (calorie): la cantidad de calor necesario para aumentar la temperatura de 1 gramo de agua por 1 grado centígrado. 1 cal = 4.184 J.

calorímetro (calorimeter): un instrumento para determinar experimentalmente la cantidad de energía de calor liberada o absorbida en un cambio químico o físico.

cambio de fase (phase change): un cambio en el estado físico de una sustancia yendo de un estado (sólido, líquido, o gaseoso) a otro diferente.

cambio físico (physical change): un cambio en el estado, fase o apariencia de un material sin formar materiales nuevos a través de una reacción química.

cambio químico (chemical change): también llamada una reacción química; el proceso de sustancias siendo cambiadas químicamente a otras sustancias a través de la reorganización de átomos.

capa electro metálica (electroplating): la deposición de una capa delgada de metal en un objeto por electrólisis.

capacidad específica de calor (specific heat capacity): la cantidad de calor necesario para aumentar la temperatura de un gramo de una sustancia por un grado centígrado.

catalítico (catalyst): una sustancia que acelera una reacción química, pero que ella misma no pasa por ningún cambio químico permanente.

catión (cation): un átomo o molécula cargada positivamente. Ejemplo: Na^+, NH_4^+ , y Fe^{2+}.

célula electromecánica (electrochemical cell): un sistema de laboratorio que produce una corriente eléctrica a través de una reacción de oxidación-reducción.

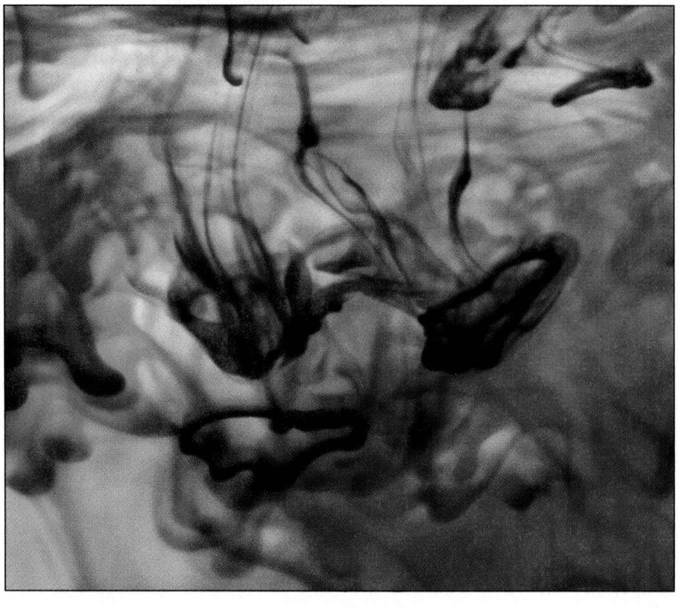

cero absoluto (absolute zero): una temperatura de 0 K y todos los movimientos moleculares están al mínimo.

ciclo hidrológico (hydrologic cycle): el sendero cíclico que toma el agua al moverse a través del ambiente. Incluye condensación, infiltración, derrame, evaporación y precipitación.

coagulación (coagulation): un grupo junto de partículas suspendidas en un coloide para que se establezcan. Una precipitación de $Al(OH)_3$ es usada para coagular partículas finas en un abastecimiento de agua.

coloide (colloid): una mezcla conteniendo partículas más grandes que moléculas de soluto pero lo suficientemente pequeñas para mantenerse suspendidas sin establecerse. Ésta también se llama una disipación coloidal.

combustión (combustion): un cambio químico donde una sustancia se quema en la presencia de oxígeno, frecuentemente acompañado por la producción de calor y luz. Un hidrocarbono reacciona con oxígeno para formar los productos dióxido de carbono y agua.

complejo activado (activated complex): en una reacción, un estado que muestra el enlace transicional el cual es intermedio entre el reactante y el producto.

compuesto (composite): una mezcla heterogénea de dos o más sustancias que pueden usar las propiedades de cada componente. Por ejemplo, concreto.

compuesto (compound): una sustancia que consiste de dos o más elementos enlazados químicamente en una proporción definida. Por ejemplo, el cloruro de sodio es siempre NaCl.

compuesto binario (binary compound): un compuesto formado de la combinación de dos elementos diferentes. Ejemplo: NaCl.

compuesto hidratado (hydrate compound): un compuesto que esta enlazado sueltamente a moléculas de agua en su estructura cristalina. La fórmula para un hidrato siempre contiene un número específico de moléculas de agua. Ejemplo: $CuSO_4{\cdot}5H_2O$.

compuesto inorgánico (inorganic compound): un compuesto que no está basado en compuestos moleculares de carbono.

compuesto orgánica (organic compound): un compuesto molecular basado en el carbono.

compuesto saturado (saturated compound): un compuesto orgánico que solamente contiene enlaces simples entre los átomos de carbono y no enlaces dobles o triples.

compuestos iónicos (ionic compounds): un compuesto que contiene cationes y aniones que están unidos por fuerzas electroestáticas. Una sal es un ejemplo de un compuesto iónico.

concentración (concentration): una cantidad medida de soluto disuelto en una cantidad definida de solvente. La molaridad (M, moles por litro) es un ejemplo de concentración.

conducción (conduction): la transferencia y la distribución de energía de calor de átomo a átomo dentro de un material, como los alambres de cobre o una sartén de freír.

conductividad (conductivity): la propiedad de trasmitir calor o electricidad a través de una sustancia.

conductividad termal (thermal conductivity): es la habilidad de un objeto a transferir calor de una parte de si mismo a otra por conducción. Este es el resultado de un movimiento atómico o molecular.

configuración del electrón (electron configuration): la distribución sistemática de los electrones en los niveles de energía de un átomo.

constante de equilibrio (equilibrium constant): para una reacción en un equilibrio dinámico, el producto de las concentraciones dividida por el producto de las concentraciones reactantes.

constante de gas ideal (ideal gas constant): una constante proporcionalmente usada en la ecuación de gas ideal y la constante R en la ecuación de gas ideal, $PV = nRT$. $R = 8.021 \times 10^{-2}$ L·atm/mol·K ó 8.315 J/mol·K.

constante de gas universal (universal gas constant): constante proporcionalmente usada en la ecuación de gas ideal, $PV = nRT$. $R = 8.021 \times 10^{-2}$ L·atm/mol·K ó 8.315 J/mol·K.

constante de producto solubilidad (solubility product constant): un equilibrio constante por la disolución de una sustancia iónica soluble levemente en agua. Es una variación en la ecuación constante de equilibrio pero en este caso, Ksp = [catión][anión] donde el reactante es un sólido y su concentración es constante.

convección (convection): la transferencia de calor por el movimiento físico de masas de fluidos (líquidos y gases) por cambios en densidad del fluido.

corriente (current): el ritmo al cual la carga eléctrica pasa a través de un conductor. La unidad usada es el amperio (A) = 1C/s.

cromatografía (chromatography): una técnica de separación que usa una fase sólida y una fase líquida para purificar componentes de una mezcla individual.

D

deformación plástica (plastic deformation): un cambio en forma que no es reversible, como es cuando un metal es estampado con un golpe duro.

densidad (density): una propiedad física intensa de una sustancia descrita por su masa dividida por su volumen, como es g/cm^3.

deposición (deposition): La conversión de un gas a sólido, sin primero condensarse en un líquido; o la formación de una capa fina de metal en un objeto por electrólisis.

descomposición radioactiva (radioactive decay): un proceso natural donde un átomo que tiene un núcleo inestable emitirá espontáneamente partículas alpha, partículas beta, positrones, o rayos gamma para poder lograr un núcleo más estable.

desinfección (disinfection): la eliminación de organismos dañinos y viruses en agua natural.

desnaturalización (denaturation): el rompimiento de la estructura tridimensional de una proteína resultando en la pérdida de su función.

destilación (distillation): la separación de los componentes en un líquido al evaporarse los componentes con el punto de ebullición bajo y entonces condensándolos.

diagrama de energía (energy diagram): una representación gráfica de los cambios de energía en una reacción, yendo de reactantes a productos.

difusión (diffusion): la dispersión de una sustancia a otra sustancia. Por ejemplo, una gota de color vegetal se esparcirá en el vaso de agua hasta que la solución es homogénea.

digestión (digestion): el rompimiento físico y químico de los alimentos a partículas nutritivas más pequeñas.

dilución (dilution): el proceso de hacer una solución menos concentrada al añadírsele más solvente, como agua, a la solución original.

dipéptido (dipeptide): dos aminoácidos que están pegados con un enlace péptido.

disacáridos (disaccharide): un azúcar compuesto de dos azucares simples el cual puede ser hidrolizado de vuelta a ser dos azucares simples. La lactosa, sucrosa y maltosa son disacáridos.

dislocación (dislocation): un átomo inoportuno en la estructura cristalina, especialmente un metal.

disolución (dissolution): el proceso de disolución a través de la interacción de una sustancia con otra. También hace referencia a la disolución.

dúctil (ductile): una propiedad de una sustancia, típicamente metales, la cual puede ser atraída en un alambre.

E

ecuación iónica neta (net ionic equation): una ecuación iónica que ha tenido los iones espectadores removidos del lado reactante y el lado productor.

ecuación iónica total (total ionic equation): la ecuación de una reacción química la cual muestra todas las especies iónicas reactantes en el lado izquierdo de la ecuación y las especies iónicas del producto en el lado derecho de la ecuación.

ecuación química equilibrada (balanced chemical equation): una ecuación en la cual los números y tipos de átomos en ambos lados de la flecha de la reacción son iguales.

efecto fotoeléctrico (photoelectric effect): la emisión de electrones de la superficie de metal cuando la luz está brillando en la superficie.

efecto Tyndall (Tyndall Effect): el esparcimiento de una emisión de luz colimada por partículas en un coloide donde la emisión de luz está claramente visible a través del esparcimiento de luz.

efusión (effusion): el proceso donde un gas contenido fluye a través de una abertura pequeña en un envase.

elasticidad (elasticity): la propiedad de un material a resistir deformación y regresar a su tamaño o forma normal después que una fuerza ha sido aplicada a ésta.

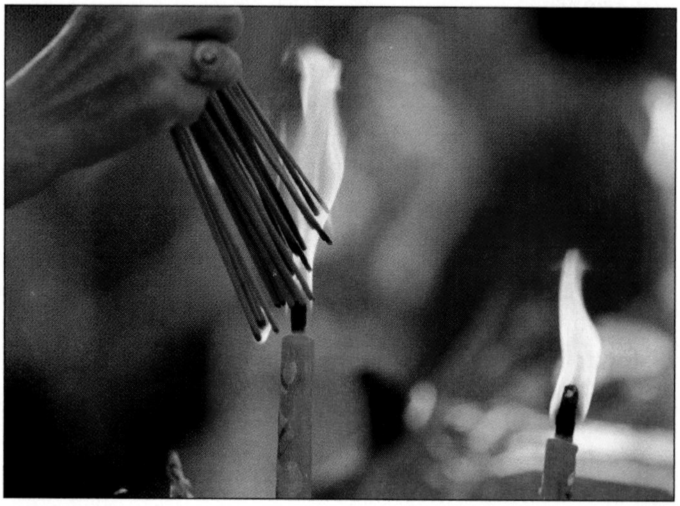

electródo (electrode): una sustancia o material que es usado como un terminal en una pila o batería electromecánica.

electrólisis (electrolysis): un proceso usando la electricidad para causar un cambio químico.

electrolito (electrolyte): una solución que contiene iones y que conducirá una corriente eléctrica.

electrón (electron): una partícula subatómica cargada negativamente localizada fuera del núcleo del átomo. La carga del electrón es igual a pero opuesta a la de un protón. Su masa es 9.109389×10^{-28} g y su carga es -1.6×10^{-19} C.

electronegatividad (electronegativity): en un enlace covalente, una medida de la habilidad de un átomo para atraer los electrones de ese enlace.

electrones de valencia (valence electrons): electrones en el nivel de energía más exterior de un átomo. Estos son los electrones envueltos en las reacciones químicas. Ejemplo: el cloro tiene 7 electrones de valencia en el tercer nivel de energía ($3s^2$ y $3p^5$).

elemento (element): una sustancia que no puede romperse en sustancias más simples por medios químicos. Un elemento que está compuesto de átomos con números atómicos idénticos.

elemento representativo (representative element): los elementos del electrón final en la tabla periódica es colocado en tanto un orbital *s* ó *p*. Ejemplo: Todos los elementos del 2do periodo son elementos representativos.

emoliente (emollient): un aditivo al jabón que ayuda a retener agua o prevenir que el agua se escape de la piel.

emulsión (emulsion): un coloide o disipación coloidal de un líquido suspendido en otro.

energía cinética (kinetic energy): energía disponible debido al movimiento de un objeto. $KE = 1/2mv^2$.

energía de activación (activation energy): en las reacciones químicas, es la energía requerida para romper los enlaces químicos para permitir la reacción de proceder a productos.

energía de calor (heat energy): una forma de energía relacionada al movimiento de átomos y moléculas. Puede ser transferida por conducción, convección o radiación.

energía de celosía (lattice energy): la energía necesaria para separar un compuesto iónico cristalino en iones de fase gaseoso.

energía de hidratación (energy of hydration): el cambio de energía cuando una sustancia es disuelta por el agua líquida.

energía gratuita Gibbs (Gibbs free energy): una propiedad termodinámica que puede ser usada para predecir si un proceso, como es la disolución de una sustancia, ocurrirá espontáneamente a una presión y temperatura constante.

energía ionizada (ionization energy): la energía requerida para remover un electrón de un átomo gaseoso en estado de tierra.

energía potencial (potential energy): la energía de un material como resultado de su posición en un campo eléctrico, magnético o gravitacional.

enlace covalente (covalent bond): un enlace químico formado al compartirse electrones entre dos átomos.

enlace por puente de hidrógeno (hydrogen bond): tipo muy fuerte de atracción dipolo-dipolo en la que un átomo de hidrógeno se encuentra entre dos átomos altamente electronegativos, por lo general, F, O, o N. El hidrógeno está covalentemente unido a uno de los átomos electronegativos y el enlace por puente de hidrógeno resulta de la fuerza de atracción electrostática hacia el otro átomo electronegativo.

enlace doble (double bond): un enlace que contiene la participación de dos pares de electrones entre los dos átomos.

enlace doble cis (*cis*-double bond): un orden geométrico de un enlace doble de carbono a carbono donde dos átomos de hidrógeno están localizados en el mismo lado del enlace doble.

enlace doble trans (*trans*-double bond): un orden geométrico de un carbono a un carbono doble donde los átomos de hidrógeno están localizados en lados opuestos del enlace doble.

enlace insaturado (unsaturated bond): un enlace que es doble o triple, generalmente en un compuesto de carbono.

enlace iónico (ionic bond): un enlace iónico es formado cuando un átomo (generalmente un metal) pierde un electrón de valencia en un segundo átomo, frecuentemente un no metal. El catión y el anión resultante son enlazados electroestáticamente por sus cargas opuestas.

enlace no polar (non-polar bond): un enlace entre dos átomos de similar electronegatividad y los cuales comparten los electrones más o menos iguales.

enlace péptido (peptide bond): un enlace entre el átomo de nitrógeno de un aminoácido y el átomo de carbono carboxílico de un segundo aminoácido.

enlace polar (polar bond): un enlace covalente en el cual dos átomos tienen una diferencia en electronegatividad, causando que un átomo sea levemente negativo y el otro levemente positivo.

enlace polar covalente (polar covalent bond): un enlace entre dos átomos de diferente electronegatividad. El centro de densidad del electrón se encuentra cerca del átomo más electronegativo.

enlace triple (triple bond): un enlace que contiene participación de tres pares de electrones entre dos átomos. Por ejemplo, el monóxido de carbono, C≡O y el etino, HC≡CH.

entalpía (enthalpy): el cambio en la energía de calor para un proceso que ocurre a una presión constante; simbolizado por ΔH.

entorno (surroundings): en términos termodinámicos, todo fuera de la reacción química; el matraz, la habitación, el edificio, etc. La reacción química es considerada “el sistema” bajo estudio.

entropía (entropy): una propiedad termodinámica de una sustancia asociada con el grado de desorden en la sustancia. Una sustancia es más ordenada como un sólido que como un líquido, y es más ordenada como líquido que como un gas.

enzima (enzyme): una proteína que actúa como un catalítico al acelerar una reacción química la cual ocurre en seres vivientes.

equilibrio (equilibrium): una condición que existe cuando el ritmo de reacción delantera iguala el ritmo de reacción inversa, parece no haber cambio en la concentración de productos o reactantes.

escala de temperatura absoluta (absolute temperature scale): una escala de temperatura que establece a cero como cero absoluto y es la base para todos los cálculos termodinámicos. Usa la unidad de temperatura del SI la cual es expresada en kelvin (K). K = °C + 273.

espectro electromagnético (electromagnetic spectrum): el espectro completo de radiación electromagnética, como son las ondas de radio, microondas, infrarrojas, visible, ultravioleta, rayos-x y rayos gamma.

estado de excitación (excited state): una condición donde un electrón de un átomo o molécula ha absorbido energía para que el electrón esté ahora a un nivel de energía más alto que el nivel de tierra.

estado de tierra (ground state): el nivel de energía más bajo que un electrón de un átomo o molécula puede ocupar.

estequiometrías (stoichiometry): el estudio de relaciones (masa-mol-volumen) entre las sustancias envueltas en las reacciones químicas.

éster (ester): la reacción de un ácido orgánico con un alcohol forma un éster. La cera es una cadena larga de éster y las grasas son ejemplos de trimestres, comúnmente llamado triglicéridos.

estructura cristalina (crystalline structure): en sólidos, es el arreglo regular de los iones cargados opuestamente en el compuesto (sales), patrones de empaque molecular (compuestos), o el empaque de átomos (metales).

estructura de proteína terciaria (tertiary protein structure): la forma total de una proteína, larga, estrecha, o globular, la cual es mantenida por diferentes tipos de interacciones intramoleculares.

estructura Lewis (Lewis structure): un sistema para representar una reacción química en la cual los electrones de valencia de un átomo están colocados alrededor del símbolo del elemento. Los enlaces simples entre los átomos pueden ser mostrados como un par de puntos o como una línea, y los electrones de valencia sin usarse son mostrados como puntos.

estructura primaria de proteína (primary protein structure): la secuencia en la cual los aminoácidos están ligados para formar una cadena de proteínas.

estructura secundaria de proteína (secondary protein structure): la estructura tridimensional de una cadena de proteínas. Tres orientaciones comunes de la estructura son la hélice-α, espiral al azar, u hoja entablada.

exactitud (accuracy): una medida de la cercanía entre un valor medido y el valor aceptado o verdadero.

extremo de volumetría / valoración (endpoint of a titration): el estado en una volumetría / valoración donde los moles del reactante añadido de una bureta es igual a los moles de un segundo reactante en un vaso de precipitación. El vaso de precipitación contiene no reactantes, solamente productos.

F

fase estacionaria (stationary phase): la absorbencia en la cromatografía. Por ejemplo, en cromatografía de papel, el papel celuloso es la fase estacionaria que atrasa los componentes en una mezcla según se mueve con la fase móvil.

fase móvil (mobile phase): en cromatografía, el fluido que carga la mezcla a ser analizada junto con la fase sólida. Un ejemplo es el agua, la cual es frecuentemente la fase móvil en cromatografía de papel.

figuras significantes (significant figures): la precisión de un cálculo o medida como es reflejada en el número registrado. Por ejemplo, 10.45 exhibe 4 figuras significantes e indica que el verdadero valor está más cerca a 10.45 que 10.46 ó 10.44.

fisión (fission): el proceso de romper grandes núcleos en pequeños núcleos y con la liberación de una cantidad grande de energía.

floculante (floc): un proceso usado para remover partículas suspendidas en el agua. Una gelatina hecha para este propósito al combinar sulfato de aluminio con óxido de calcio.

fluorescente (fluorescence): la emisión de luz visible de una sustancia después de absorber radiación de energía alta, como es la luz ultravioleta.

forma molecular (molecular shape): la forma geométrica de una molécula. La forma geométrica de metano es un tetraedro.

fórmula estructural (structural formula): una fórmula de una molécula orgánica la cual muestra no solamente a todos los átomos pero también como están conectadas una con la otra.

fórmula molecular (molecular formula): la fórmula exacta de una molécula, dados los tipos de átomos y el número de cada tipo de átomo presente.

fórmula química (chemical formula): un método abreviado para representar la composición exacta de un compuesto en el cual los símbolos atómicos son usados con un subíndice, por ejemplo, H_2O.

fortaleza (strength): la propiedad de cuán bien un material resiste la aplicación de una fuerza.

fosforescente (phosphorescence): la habilidad de algunas sustancias para absorber energía de luz y liberarla lentamente sobre un periodo de tiempo después que la fuente original de luz es removida, para "alumbrar en la oscuridad."

fotón (photon): un paquete quantum o discreto de radiación electromagnética.

frecuencia (frequency): en la radiación electromagnética, el número de ondas por segundo o ciclos por segundo (hertz, Hz).

fuerza intensa nuclear (nuclear strong force): una fuerza atractiva muy intensa que actúa en distancias extremadamente pequeñas. Esta fuerza es encontrada en el núcleo e interactúa con los neutrones y los protones.

fuerzas de disipación (dispersion forces): fuerzas débiles de atracción (también llamadas fuerzas London) que resultan cuando dipolos pequeños ocurren en la superficie de una molécula debido a la distribución transitoria de los electrones acerca de los núcleos.

fuerzas de van der Waals (van der Waals forces): fuerzas de atracción intermoleculares débiles entre moléculas.

fuerzas intermoleculares (intermolecular forces): las fuerzas que existen entre las moléculas e incluye fuerzas dipolo-dipolo y fuerzas de disipación London.

fusión (fusion): el proceso cuando dos núcleos de átomos más livianos combinados para formar un núcleo con mayor masa mientras libera una cantidad grande de energía.

G

gas ideal (ideal gas): un gas que podría tener cero fuerzas de atracción intermolecular, sin volumen y todos sus choques serían perfectamente elásticos.

gas noble (noble gas): un miembro de una familia de elementos (Grupo 18 ó VIIIA) de la tabla periódica (también llamado gas raro o gas inerte). He, Ne, Ar, Kr, Xe, y Rn son gases nobles.

grabado (etching): el remover los átomos de metal de una superficie metálica con un líquido corrosivo.

grados centígrados (celsius degrees): una escala métrica de temperatura basada en la congelación del agua a 0°C y la ebullición a 100°C. Esta escala es convertida a kelvins por K=°C + 273 y a Fahrenheit por F=1.8°C + 32.

grano (grain): el orden de átomos en un sólido como el metal.

grupo (group): una columna de elementos o familia de elementos en la tabla periódica. Ejemplo: los metales álcali están en el Grupo 1A.

grupo funcional (functional group): en química orgánica, esa parte de la molécula que da a la molécula sus propiedades químicas y físicas características. Por ejemplo, el grupo de ácido carboxílico es representado por el fragmento -COOH.

grupo químico (chemical group): una familia de elementos en la tabla periódica que tiene configuraciones y propiedades de electrones similares. Por ejemplo, los halógenos (F, Cl, Br, I) están en el Grupo VIIA or Grupo 17..

H

halógenos (halogens): el grupo VIIA (17) en la tabla periódica que consiste de flúor, cloro, bromo, iodo, y astato.

hidrocarbono (hydrocarbon): un compuesto orgánico compuesto de solamente átomos de hidrógeno y carbono.

hidrocarbono insaturado (unsaturated hydrocarbon): un compuesto orgánico que consiste solamente de átomos de carbono e hidrógeno con al menos un enlace doble o triple entre dos átomos de carbono.

hidrófilo (hydrophilic): una sustancia que es atraída al agua y es soluble en agua, generalmente sustancias polares.

hidrofóbico (hydrophobic): una sustancia que no es atraída al agua y es insoluble en agua, generalmente no es una sustancia polar.

hidrogenación (hydrogenation): la adición de hidrógeno molecular a un enlace doble o triple en una reacción química, generalmente con un catalítico.

hidrólisis (hydrolysis): el proceso de romper químicamente una sustancia en pequeñas moléculas a través de la reacción con el agua.

huella latente (latent print): en las ciencia forenses hay huellas que no se pueden ver a simple vista.

I

indicador (indicator): una sustancia que cambia de color a cierto pH. Los indicadores son comúnmente añadidos a la solución para ayudar visualmente a seguir el curso de valoración/ volumetría.

indicador a base de ácido (acid-base indicator): un ácido orgánico débil que puede cambiar de color para indicar el pH de una solución. La fenolftaleína no tiene color en una solución de ácido y es rosada o roja en una solución básica.

ión (ion): un átomo o molécula que ha adquirido una carga sea ganando (anión) o perdiendo (catión) un/unos electrón(es).

ión poli atómico (polyatomic ion): un ión que consiste de 2 o más átomos que están enlazados covalentemente. Ejemplos: OH^-, NO_3^-, SO_4^{2-}, NH_4^+.

iones espectadores (spectator ions): los iones que están presente en la solución durante una reacción química y que no cambia su forma. En la ecuación de reacción, estos parecen sin cambio en ambos lados.

isómeros (isomers): compuestos orgánicos que tienen la misma fórmula química pero diferentes fórmulas estructurales.

isótopo (isotope): átomos del mismo elemento con números atómicos idénticos pero con diferentes masas atómicas de neutrones en el núcleo.

J

julio (joule): una unidad de energía la cual es igual a newtons x metros, ó $kg\text{-}m^2/s^2$.

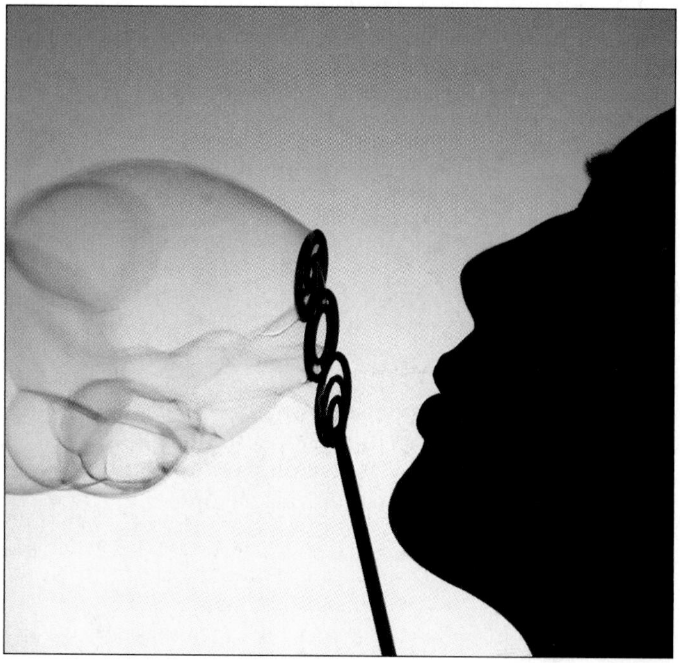

K

kelvin (kelvin): la unidad del SI de temperatura; 0 K = cero absoluto. (°C + 273.15 = K)

L

la ley de Boyle (Boyle's Law): una de las leyes de gas básica que dice, si la masa de un gas y su temperatura son mantenidos constantes, el volumen del gas variará en una proporción inversa a la presión del gas. $P_1V_1 = P_2V_2$.

la ley de gas de Avogadro (Avogadro's Gas Law): una ley de gas que dice que los gases a la misma temperatura y presión tienen el mismo número de moléculas.

ley de Charles (Charles's Law): una ley de gas que dice que cuando la presión y la cantidad de una muestra de gas son constante, el volumen del gas variará directamente con el cambio en temperatura.
$V_1 \div T_1 = V_2 \div T_2$, donde T es la medida en kelvin.

ley de combinación de volúmenes de gases (law of combining volumes of gases): cuando dos gases reaccionan, la proporción de sus volúmenes será pequeño, números enteros, temperatura y presión siendo igual.

ley de conservación de energía (law of conservation of energy): la cantidad total de energía en el universo es conservada. La energía no puede ser creada o destruida, solamente cambiada.

ley de conservación de masa (law of conservation of mass): en una reacción química, la masa no puede ser creada ni destruida. Esto significa que la masa total de los reactantes iguala la masa total de los productos.

ley de conservación de materia (law of conservation of matter): el número y el tipo de átomos presente durante un cambio químico se mantiene igual. Un átomo de un elemento no puede ser cambiado a otro elemento.

ley de efusión de Graham (Graham's Law of Effusion): una declaración matemática que compara el ritmo de efusión de diferentes gases.

$$\frac{\text{ritmo de efusión de gas}_1}{\text{ritmo de efusión de gas}_2} = \sqrt{\frac{\text{masa de gas}_2}{\text{masa de gas}_1}}$$

ley de electroestáticas de Coulomb (Coulomb's Law of Electrostatics): establece que la fuerza entre dos objetos cargados (q_1 y q_2) es proporcionalmente inversa al cuadrado de la distancia (d) entre las dos partículas cargadas.

$$F = k\frac{q_1q_2}{d_2},\ k = 9.0 \times 10^9\ \text{N-m}^2/\text{C}^2$$

ley de proporciones definida (law of definite proportions): la composición de una sustancia pura es siempre igual o los elementos de un compuesto siempre combinan en la misma proporción por la masa.

leyes de gas combinadas (combined gas laws): si la cantidad de gas (moles) es mantenida constante entonces las leyes de Boyle y Charles pueden ser combinadas para dar: $P_1V_1 \div T_1 = P_2V_2 \div T_2$, donde T es medido en kelvin.

limitación de reactivo (limiting reagent): el reactante que se usará primero y que determina cuanto producto puede ser producido.

lípidos monoinsaturado (monounsaturated lipids): las moléculas con cadenas de carbono que solamente tiene un enlace de carbono doble, como en el aceite de oliva y el aceite de canola.

lípidos poliinsaturado (polyunsaturated lipids): las grasas y aceites que tienen más de un enlace doble en la cadena de carbono (como el aceite de maíz o aceite de soya).

líquido Newtoniano (Newtonian liquid): líquidos que fluyen fácilmente o que tienen baja viscosidad, como es el agua.

lustre (luster): la reflexión de luz desde la superficie de un material descrito por su calidad e intensidad.

lustruoso (lustrous): descripción no-cuantitativa de cuanto brilla un metal.

M

maleable (malleable): una propiedad característica de un metal la cual describe la facilidad de poder ser aplanado con un martillo.

masa (mass): la cantidad de materia siendo considerada.

masa atómica (atomic mass): la masa atómica es determinada sumando la masa de los protones y los neutrones del átomo.

masa molar (molar mass): la masa de un mol de una sustancia pura.

materia (matter): cualquier cosa que tiene masa.

metal de tierra alcalina (alkaline earth metal): los elementos del Grupo 2A de la tabla periódica (Be, Mg, Ca, Sr, Ba).

metal de transición interna (inner-transition metal): elementos que contienen electrones de orbital *f* y son llamados las series lantánidos y actínidos.

metales (metals): una clase de materiales que exhiben las propiedades de conductividad, maleabilidad y ductilidad. Los metales son brillantes, tienen óxidos básicos y electrones sueltos para formar iones positivos.

metales álcali (alkali metals): los elementos del Grupo 1A de la tabla periódica (Li, Na, K, Rb, Cs).

metales de transición (transition metals): esos elementos en la tabla periódica los cuales representan elementos con orbitales-*d* parcialmente llenos en la 4ta hilera y descansan entre Ca y Zn, que son, Sc, Ti, V, Cr, Mn, Fe, Co, Ni, Cu.

metaloide (metalloid): un elemento que posee ambas características metales y no metales. El silicón, arsénico y germanio son ejemplos de metaloides.

método de flujo (flow method): un proceso en el cual una operación es llevada a cabo en un flujo continuo de movimiento de material. En el método de flujo para purificar agua, el agua fluye continuamente a través de pasos múltiples de filtración.

método de tandas (batch method): un proceso en el cual una operación es llevada a cabo en una cantidad fija de material para permitir que transformaciones químicas o físicas se completen. El método de tandas para purificar agua permite tiempo para la sedimentación seguida por la filtración.

mezcla (mixture): una combinación de dos o más sustancias.

micela (micelle): un grupo de iones de jabón alrededor de una partícula no polar de "sucio." los extremos hidrófobos están e el interior para atraer el "sucio," y los extremos hidrófilos están en el exterior para ayudar a disolverse en agua.

minucias (minutiae): en las ciencias forenses, es el estudio de los tipos de contornos de las huellas digitales.

mol (mole): el número igual al número de átomos de carbono en exactamente 12 gramos de puro^{12}C; número de Avogadro. Un mol representa 6.022×10^{23} unidades (átomos, moléculas, etc.).

molaridad (molarity): concentración de soluto en una solución expresada en moles/litro (M) de solución. Ejemplo: 1 M NaCl = 1 mol de cloruro de sodio conteniendo 1 litro de solución.

molécula diatónica (diatomic molecule): una molécula que consiste de dos átomos. Ejemplos de elementos diatónicos son el hidrógeno (H_2), nitrógeno (N_2), oxígeno (O_2), fluoruro (F_2), y cloruro (Cl_2).

molécula no polar (non-polar molecule): una molécula que no tiene un momento dipolo.

molécula polar (polar molecule): una molécula que tienen una región negativa (dipolo) y una región positiva (dipolo) debido a un arreglo en los enlaces polares. Es más soluble en un solvente polar como el agua que en una molécula no polar.

monómero (monomer): la unidad repetitiva más pequeña de un polímero. Un ejemplo es el etileno, la unidad repetitiva más pequeña en polietileno.

monosacárido (monosaccharide): un azúcar simple consistiendo de 3 a 9 átomos de carbono que no puede ser hidrolizado a moléculas más pequeños. Ejemplos de esto son la glucosa, la fructosa y la galactosa.

N

nanómetro (nanometer): una millonésima de un metro. 1 nanómetro (nm) = 1×10^{-9}m.

neutralización (neutralization): la reacción entre un ácido y una base para formar agua y una sal (generalmente la reacción entre los iones de hidrógeno y los iones de hidróxido).

neutrón (neutron): la partícula neutral localizada en el núcleo con una carga de cero. Una masa de un neutrón es 1.675×10^{-24} g ó alrededor de 1 amu.

nivel de energía (energy level): una cantidad específica de energía que un electrón posee en un átomo. Ejemplo: El estado de tierra del nivel de energía de un electrón de hidrógeno es -2.18×10^{-18} J/átomo.

no metales (nonmetals): los elementos que no exhiben las propiedades de conductividad, maleabilidad y ductilidad. Estos son generalmente gases o sólidos suaves y quebradizos. Estos elementos tienden a formar iones negativos y sus óxidos son acídicos.

notación científica (scientific notation): expresa un número al número correcto de cifras significativas usando potencias de 10 y números reales entre 1 y 10.

núcleo (nucleus): el núcleo denso de un átomo el cual contienen los protones y los neutrones.

nucleón (nucleon): un constituyente de un núcleo atómico; cualquiera protón o neutrón.

número atómico (atomic number): el número de protones contenidos en un elemento.

número de Avogadro (Avogadro's number): un número grande el cual equivale al número de partículas en una mole, 6.022×10^{23}.

número de masa (mass number): la masa de un átomo que es la suma de sus protones y neutrones (masa atómica).

número de oxidación (oxidation number): un número positivo o negativo asignado para cada átomo en un compuesto para ayudar a mantener una senda de electrones en una reacción química. Los elementos son cero.

O

onda de longitud (wavelength): en radiación electromagnética, la distancia medida de cresta a cresta de una onda o ciclo completo.

órbita (orbit): el sendero de un electrón en su movimiento alrededor del núcleo del átomo de hidrógeno de Bohr.

orbital (orbital): un estado de energía de un electrón determinado por un arreglo específico basado en los números quantum. Estos arreglos están representados en los orbitales *s*, *p*, *d*, y *f*.

osmosis invertida (reverse osmosis): una técnica de desionización usando presión para forzar agua a través de una membrana que es impermeable a los iones metales en la purificación del agua de mar.

oxidación (oxidation): la pérdida de uno o más electrones por un átomo, molécula o ión resultando con la ganancia de una carga positiva.

P

pares de electrones no enlazados o pares de electrones solitarios (nonbonding electron pairs or lone pair electrons): los electrones de valencia que no son usados para formar un enlace en una molécula. El átomo de oxígeno del agua tiene dos pares solitarios de electrones que no son usados para enlazar el hidrógeno.

partícula alpha (alpha particle): unos núcleos de helio-4 (He ó $^{4}_{2}$He ó $^{4}_{2}\alpha$) con una carga de +2 la cual consiste de dos protones y dos neutrones, pero perdiendo los electrones de valencia.

patina (patina): una capa superficial que desarrolla metales expuestos y los protege de oxidación adicional.

pendiente (slope): en una gráfica bidimensional, la proporción de un cambio en la variable dependiente al cambio de la variable independiente. Pendiente $(m) = (y_1 - y_1) \div (x_2 - x_1)$.

periodo (period): una hilera de la tabla periódica. Ejemplo: 2do periodo comienza con el elemento Litio y termina con Neón.

pH (pH): una medida de la acidez o la alcalinidad de una solución. Soluciones con pH menor que 7 son acídicos, soluciones con un pH mayor que 7 son básicas. Matemáticamente, pH = –log[H+].

pila galvánica (galvanic cell): una pila electromecánica en la cual se lleva a cabo oxidación y reducción.

pila media (half-cell): en baterías electromecánicas cada una de las dos soluciones es colocada en una pila separada y conectada a través de un puente de sal.

polimerización (polymerization): una reacción química que convierte las moléculas pequeñas (monómeros) en moléculas grandes (polímeros).

polímero (polymer): una sustancia que es una macromolécula consistiendo de muchas unidades pequeñas idénticas (monómeros) enlazadas covalentemente en largas cadenas.

polipéptido (polypeptide): un polímero formado de unos pocos aminoácidos hasta cientos, enlazados por enlaces péptido.

precipitado (precipitate): la formación de una sustancia insoluble de un cambio químico o físico, o la sustancia insoluble en si misma.

precisión (precision): el grado de acuerdo entre las medida individuales o experimentales. Esto es diferente a exactitud.

presión (pressure): fuerza por unidad de área. En el sistema de SI, sus unidades son Pascales (Pa). 1 Pa = 1 N/m^2.

presión atmosférica (atmospheric pressure): La presión variable ejercida por la atmósfera de la Tierra. Las condiciones estándares son: 1 atmósfera apoya una columna de mercurio de 76 cm de alta y es igual a 760 milibarras y 100,00 Pascales.

presión de gas (gas pressure): fuerza por unidad de área creada por partículas de un gas limitado chocando con la superficie interna de un envase.

principio de incertidumbre (uncertainty principle): un principio que declara que no podemos predecir simultáneamente la posición de un electrón o su momento.

principio de incertidumbre Heisenberg (Heisenberg uncertainty principle): este principio declara que no podemos predecir simultáneamente la posición de un electrón y su momento al mismo tiempo.

principio de LeChatelier (LeChatelier's Principle): un cambio en cualquier factor de un sistema en equilibrio causará que el sistema se ajuste en una dirección que permita su regreso a un estado de equilibrio.

proceso endotérmico (endothermic process): un proceso donde la energía es absorbida por el sistema del entorno. Por ejemplo, la evaporación o la fusión.

productos (products): las sustancias formadas de los reactantes como resultado de una reacción química. Los productos se encuentran en el lado derecho de una ecuación química.

propiedad extensiva (extensive property): una propiedad que depende en cuánta materia está siendo considerada. Por ejemplo, el largo y el volumen son propiedades extensas de la materia.

propiedad física (physical property): cualquier propiedad de la materia que no cambia su composición química. Entre éstas están las propiedades de densidad, punto de ebullición, masa y temperatura.

propiedad intensiva (intensive property): una propiedad que no depende en cuanta materia está siendo considerada. La densidad y la temperatura son propiedades intensivas.

propiedad química (chemical property): la manera en la cual la estructura de sustancias cambia cuando son reordenadas durante un cambio químico.

proteína (protein): un polímero activo biológicamente compuesto de cientos de aminoácidos enlazados juntos para formar una cadena larga.

protón (proton): una partícula subatómica cargada positivamente localizada en el núcleo de un átomo. La carga de un protón es igual y opuesta a aquella de un electrón ($+ 1.6 \times 10^{-19}$ C) y tiene una masa de 1.672623×10^{-24} g.

punto de condensación (condensation point): la temperatura en la cual un gas se convierte en líquido a una presión específica.

punto de congelación (freezing point): la temperatura a la cual un líquido se solidifica bajo una presión específica.

punto de ebullición (boiling point): la temperatura a la cual la presión de vapor del líquido iguala la presión atmosférica. En esta temperatura, la fase líquida está cambiando a la fase gaseosa.

punto de fusión (melting point): la temperatura a la cual un sólido se convierte en líquido a una presión específica.

punto normal de congelación (normal freezing point): en una presión de atmósfera, la temperatura en la cual una sustancia cambia de un estado líquido a su estado sólido.

punto normal de ebullición (normal boiling point): la temperatura que la presión de vapor de un líquido es igual a 1 atmósfera.

punto normal de fusión (normal melting point): en una presión de atmósfera, la temperatura en la cual una sustancia cambia de un estado sólido a su estado líquido.

Q

quimioluminiscencia (chemiluminescence): una reacción química que libera energía como luz o radiación electromagnética.

R

radiación (radiation): ondas electromagnéticas que transportan energía directamente en todas las direcciones a través del espacio.

rayo gamma (gamma ray): radiación de energía alta con una onda de longitud corta, generalmente viniendo de sustancias radioactivas.

rayos cátodos (cathode rays): los rayos emitidos de un electrodo negativo en un tubo de descarga de gas. Estas partículas negativas son llamadas también electrones y partículas β–.

reacción de descomposición (decomposition reaction): una reacción química donde el compuesto se rompe en dos o más sustancias más simples. Por ejemplo, $H_2CO_3 \rightarrow H_2O + CO_2$

reacción de reducción de oxidación (oxidation-reduction reaction): una reacción química donde un átomo, molécula o ión transfiere electrón(es) a otro átomo, molécula o ión. Ambos oxidación y reducción deben ocurrir y el electrón transferido debe ser equilibrado.

reacción de reemplazo simple (single-replacement reaction): una reacción química que envuelve a un elemento reemplazando un catión en una solución de un compuesto iónico. Ejemplo: $Zn_{(s)} + CuCl_{2(aq)} \rightarrow Cu_{(s)} + ZnCl_{2(aq)}$

reacción de síntesis (synthesis reaction): una reacción en la cual dos ó más sustancias se combinan y forman un solo producto. Por ejemplo, $2Na + Cl_2 \rightarrow 2NaCl$.

reacción doble de reemplazo (double-replacement reaction): una reacción en la cual dos reactantes intercambian iones para formar un precipitado. Ejemplo: $Na_2SO_{4(aq)} + Ba(NO_3)_{2(aq)} \rightarrow BaSO_{4(s)} + 2\ NaNO_{3(aq)}$

reacción endotérmica (endothermic reaction): una reacción química que requiere el añadirse calor para que ocurra y tiene un valor positivo de ΔH.

reacción exotérmica (exothermic reaction): una reacción química donde la energía es liberada del sistema del entorno y tiene un valor negativo de ΔH.

reacción media (half-reaction): en baterías electromecánicas, cada media pila representa la mitad de toda la reacción oxidación-reducción.

reactantes (reactants): los materiales de comienzo en una reacción química que son transformados en productos durante las reacciones químicas. En la ecuación, los reactantes están en el lado izquierdo.

reactividad (reactivity): una propiedad que describe cuan rápidamente una sustancia reaccionará con otra sustancia.

rebote (bounce): la habilidad de un objeto a rebotar a su posición original cuando es dejada caer de una altura dada.

reducción (reduction): la ganancia de uno o más electrones por un átomo, molécula o ión, resultando en una carga negativa más grande.

regla de octeto (octet rule): una regla que declara que los átomos con 8 electrones en la capa de valencia obtienen una condición estable. Los átomos con menos de ocho electrones la capa de valencia formará enlaces para poder lograr la estabilidad. Los átomos más pequeños (H, He, Li, Be) son excepciones.

resina de intercambio de ión (ion-exchange resin): un material polimérico que tiene lugares negativos en su superficie donde varios iones positivos son absorbidos. Los iones positivos de carga alta son absorbidos más fuertemente, pero aún pueden ser reemplazados por iones de carga baja si la concentración es suficientemente alta.

R_f (R_f): en cromatografía, el factor retención. El R_f es la proporción de la distancia que un componente es movido en la fase sólida comparada a la distancia que la fase móvil fue movida.

S

sales (salts): compuestos iónicos que son producidos por la neutralización de un ácido con una base.

saponificación (saponification): la hidrólisis de un triglicérido con una base fuerte para hacer jabón.

símbolo atómico (atomic symbol): 1 ó 2 letras que representan cada elemento en la tabla periódica.

sistema (system): En termodinámicas, la parte pequeña del universo que está siendo estudiada, generalmente una reacción química. Esto incluye los materiales envueltos en la reacción química: los reactantes, solventes y productos y como el calor es transferido entre este y sus entornos.

solubilidad (solubility): la solubilidad de una sustancia es la concentración del soluto en una solución saturada. Esta es la temperatura dependiente y se expresa generalmente como g/100 mL.

solución (solution): una mezcla homogénea que consiste de un solvente y al menos un soluto.

soluto (solute): una sustancia en menor concentración que interactúa con un solvente para formar una solución.

solvente (solvent): en una solución, la sustancia presente en una cantidad grande la cual interactúa con el/los soluto(s).

sublimación (sublimation): la conversión de un sólido a gas, sin primero convertirse en líquido. El dióxido de carbono sólido (CO_2) es sublime a la temperatura ambiente y en presión.

surfactante (surfactant): una sustancia que baja la tención de la superficie de un líquido y permite que ocurra el humedecimiento, como cuando un jabón es añadido al agua.

suspensión (suspension): una mezcla heterogénea que contienen partículas sólidas y líquidas finas en un fluido que se separará espontáneamente.

sustancia pura (pure substance): una sustancia que contiene solamente un tipo de partícula y no puede ser separada en componente más simples sin un cambio químico.

T

temperatura (temperature): una propiedad extensa la cual es una medida del promedio de la energía cinética de moléculas y átomos. Esta determina el flujo de calor espontáneo, el cual es siempre de caliente a frío.

tensión de superficie (surface tension): la atracción de moléculas en la superficie de un líquido para formar una "piel" y actuar como una hoja de líquido. Esta es la fuerza que permite a los insectos a "caminar en agua" y causa acción capilar en un tubo.

teoría molecular cinética de gases (kinetic molecular theory of gases): un modelo que explica la conducta del gas en término de partículas en constante movimiento al azar que se mueve en líneas rectas hasta que ocurren choques entre ellos.

termoquímica (thermochemistry): un estudio de una cantidad de calor que es absorbida o liberada durante las reacciones químicas.

tetraédrico (tetrahedral): la forma geométrica de los cuatro enlaces simples de un átomo de carbono.

textura (texture): las características de la superficie de un material, como es la suavidad o la aspereza.

triglicérido (triglyceride): un triéster de glicerol y un ácido graso. Por ejemplo, el aceite de oliva.

tripéptido (tripeptide): tres aminoácidos que están enlazados covalentemente juntos a través de los enlaces péptidos.

U

unidad de masa atómica (atomic mass unit [amu]): una unidad de masa definida como un doceavo de la masa de un átomo de carbono –12 ó 1. En términos de masa, esto es 1 amu = 1.661×10^{-24}g.

unidades del SI (SI units): las unidades de medidas aceptada internacionalmente. Por ejemplo, la unidad para masa del SI es el kilogramo, kg.

V

valoración/ volumetría (titration): un procedimiento analítico que determina la concentración de una sustancia al tratar cuantitativamente una solución de esta (en una vaso de precipitación) con una solución de otro reactante de concentración conocida (entregada por la bureta) hasta el punto preciso donde la concentración del desconocido es cero. Este punto es generalmente determinado por un indicador o una investigación.

vaporización (vaporization): el cambio de estado de líquido a gaseoso.

vida media (half-life): el periodo de tiempo requerido para la masa de una sustancia radioactiva convertirse la mitad de su masa original debido a la desintegración de sus átomos. Por ejemplo, la vida media del uranio-238 es 4.5 billones de años.

viscosidad (viscosity): una propiedad relacionada a la resistencia de un fluido a fluir.

voltio (volt): la unidad de diferencia potencial eléctrica, un voltio (v) = un julio/coulomb.

volumen (volume): una medida del espacio ocupado por la materia. La unidad de volumen del SI es el metro cúbico, m^3.

volumen molar (molar volume): el volumen ocupado por 1 mol de una sustancia en la fase gaseosa.

INDEX

Index

In this index, page numbers followed by "*i*" indicate illustrations; page numbers followed by "*t*" denote tables or graphs. Page ranges in bold type indicate major discussions of the topics.

B

D

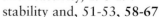

H

I

J

K

S

T

X

Z

Photo and Illustration Credits

Tomas Bunk: 3, 5, 7, 15, 26, 35, 46, 58, 68, 77, 99, 101, 110, 120, 126, 134, 144, 152, 157, 162, 177, 179, 182, 193, 201, 210, 224, 233, 241, 253, 255, 265, 274, 287, 300, 308, 318, 329, 351, 353, 361, 369, 379, 390, 401, 408, 416, 431, 433, 441, 448, 456, 468, 477, 485, 496, 509, 511, 522, 532, 544, 551, 560, 568, 575, 591, 593, 599, 608, 618, 632, 641, 650, 659, 675, 677, 685, 693, 703, 712, 722, 727, 741, 743, 751, 766, 779, 790, 799, 812, 826, 841, 843, 857, 867, 877, 892, 902, 910, 919

Unlisted Photos by Comstock, Digital Stock, iStock, photodisc/gettyimages

Chapter 1
3 top, Honolulu Community College, Distance Education SCI 122 (The Nature of Physical Science); http://honolulu.hawaii.edu/distance/sci122/Programs/p29/p29.html
19, Liberty on Line; http://libertyonline.hypermall.com/Aristotle/Default.htm
20 both, Edgar Fahs Smith Collection, University of Pennsylvania Library
24, CHF Chemistry Web Quest
30, © The Nobel Foundation
39, AIP Niels Bohr Library
54, Courtesy of the Smithsonian Institution Libraries, Washington, D.C.
63 top, © The Nobel Foundation
bottom, Courtesy of the Smithsonian Institution Libraries, Washington, D.C.
69, Courtesy of Kevin Boudreaux, Department of Chemistry, Angelo State University, San Angelo, TX
82, © The Nobel Foundation
88, Waste Isolation Pilot Plant, US Department of Energy Carlsbad Field Office. Contact the webmaster; webmaster@wipp.ws

Chapter 2
98 top, EMF Technology Ltd.
98-99 bottom, Courtesy Steve Wolf
99 top, Courtesy Steve Wolf
100, Courtesy Steve Wolf
154, Reprinted with permission from *ChemMatters* Magazine. © Dec, 2004, American Chemical Society
164, Dustin Grace, Marilyn Poon, Robert Neilson, and Jessica Todd, Dept. of Mechanical Engineering, U of Colorado; http://www.colorado.edu/MCEN.flowvis/
165 top, Life Science Trace Gas Facility; http://www.ru.nl/tracegasfacility/
171, Courtesy Steve Wolf
173, Courtesy Steve Wolf

Chapter 3
207, Courtesy Etienne Krähenbühl
214, Courtesy Ken George; http://www.potteryheart.com
215, Courtesy Ken George; http://www.potteryheart.com
216, Edgar Fahs Smith Collection, University of Pennsylvania Library
217, The W1TP Telegraph Museum; www.w1tp.com
235, Courtesy of Western New Mexico University; www.wnmu.edu
243, Copyright Hurst Gallery 2003, Cambridge, MA

Chapter 4
252 top, Illustration by Dennis Falcon
343, Department of Physics and Astronomy, University of Iowa
344, Dave Umberger, Purdue News Service

Chapter 5
378, Courtesy NASA
383, Edgar Fahs Smith Collection, University of Pennsylvania Library
417, American Art Clay Co., Inc. (Amaco®)

Chapter 6
451, Courtesy Jo Edkins

Chapter 7
578 top, Deseret Morning News

Chapter 8
650, Courtesy Pete M. Wilson
654, Courtesy Pete M. Wilson
663, Wikipedia.org; http://en-wikipedia.org/wiki/Thin_layer_chromatography

Chapter 9
687, Atlas of Gastrointestinal Endoscopy; www.EndoAtlas.com
705, Fort Crawford Museum at Prairie du Chien; contact: ftcrawmu@mhtc.net
714, Edgar Fahs Smith Collection, University of Pennsylvania Library

Chapter 10
773, Wikipedia.org; http://en-wkikpedia.org/wiki/Image:Linus Pauling.jpg

Chapter 11
839, Paulus Rusyanto, free-stockphotos.com
843, It's About Time/Jason Harris
866, It's About Time/Jason Harris
922, Rocky Mountain Laboratories, NIAID, NIH
923, It's About Time/Jason Harris

GROUP

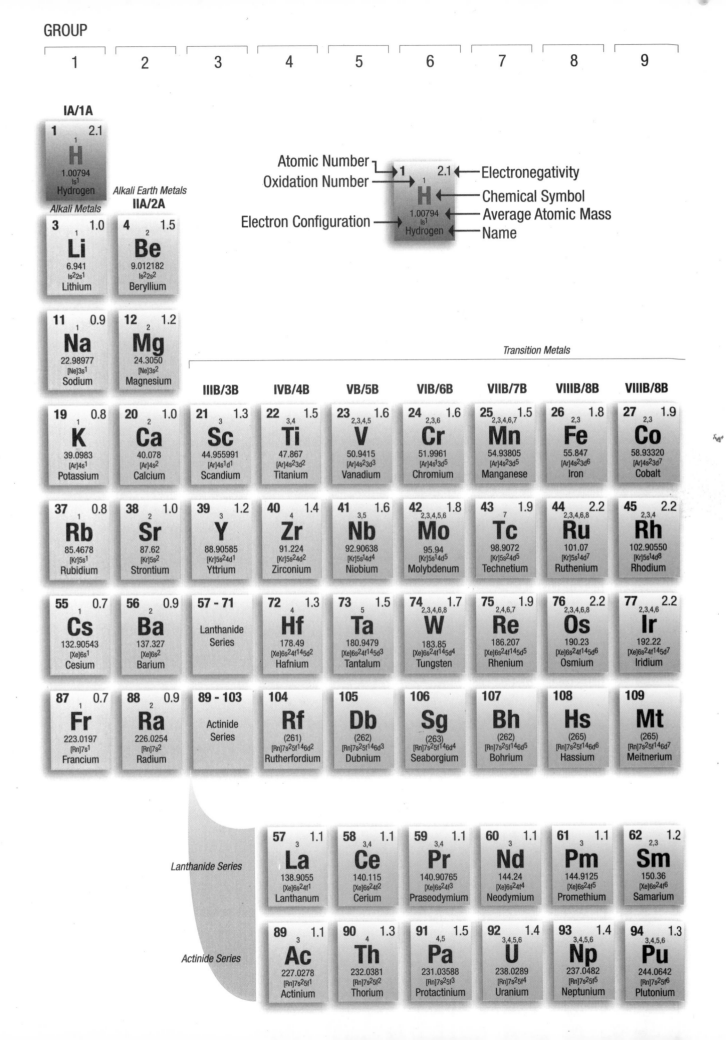

1	2	3	4	5	6	7	8	9
IA/1A								
1 2.1 1 **H** 1.00794 $1s^1$ Hydrogen								
Alkali Metals	*Alkali Earth Metals* IIA/2A							
3 1.0 1 **Li** 6.941 $1s^2 2s^1$ Lithium	4 1.5 2 **Be** 9.012182 $1s^2 2s^2$ Beryllium							
11 0.9 1 **Na** 22.98977 $[Ne]3s^1$ Sodium	12 1.2 2 **Mg** 24.3050 $[Ne]3s^2$ Magnesium							
		Transition Metals						
		IIIB/3B	IVB/4B	VB/5B	VIB/6B	VIIB/7B	VIIIB/8B	VIIIB/8B
19 0.8 1 **K** 39.0983 $[Ar]4s^1$ Potassium	20 1.0 2 **Ca** 40.078 $[Ar]4s^2$ Calcium	21 1.3 3 **Sc** 44.955991 $[Ar]4s^1d^1$ Scandium	22 1.5 3,4 **Ti** 47.867 $[Ar]4s^2 3d^2$ Titanium	23 1.6 2,3,4,5 **V** 50.9415 $[Ar]4s^2 3d^3$ Vanadium	24 1.6 2,3,6 **Cr** 51.9961 $[Ar]4s^1 3d^5$ Chromium	25 1.5 2,3,4,6,7 **Mn** 54.93805 $[Ar]4s^2 3d^5$ Manganese	26 1.8 2,3 **Fe** 55.847 $[Ar]4s^2 3d^6$ Iron	27 1.9 2,3 **Co** 58.93320 $[Ar]4s^2 3d^7$ Cobalt
37 0.8 1 **Rb** 85.4678 $[Kr]5s^1$ Rubidium	38 1.0 2 **Sr** 87.62 $[Kr]5s^2$ Strontium	39 1.2 3 **Y** 88.90585 $[Kr]5s^2 4d^1$ Yttrium	40 1.4 4 **Zr** 91.224 $[Kr]5s^2 4d^2$ Zirconium	41 1.6 3,5 **Nb** 92.90638 $[Kr]5s^1 4d^4$ Niobium	42 1.8 2,3,4,5,6 **Mo** 95.94 $[Kr]5s^1 4d^5$ Molybdenum	43 1.9 7 **Tc** 98.9072 $[Kr]5s^2 4d^5$ Technetium	44 2.2 2,3,4,6,8 **Ru** 101.07 $[Kr]5s^1 4d^7$ Ruthenium	45 2.2 2,3,4 **Rh** 102.90550 $[Kr]5s^1 4d^8$ Rhodium
55 0.7 1 **Cs** 132.90543 $[Xe]6s^1$ Cesium	56 0.9 2 **Ba** 137.327 $[Xe]6s^2$ Barium	57 - 71 Lanthanide Series	72 1.3 4 **Hf** 178.49 $[Xe]6s^2 4f^{14} 5d^2$ Hafnium	73 1.5 5 **Ta** 180.9479 $[Xe]6s^2 4f^{14} 5d^3$ Tantalum	74 1.7 2,3,4,6,8 **W** 183.85 $[Xe]6s^2 4f^{14} 5d^4$ Tungsten	75 1.9 2,4,6,7 **Re** 186.207 $[Xe]6s^2 4f^{14} 5d^5$ Rhenium	76 2.2 2,3,4,6,8 **Os** 190.23 $[Xe]6s^2 4f^{14} 5d^6$ Osmium	77 2.2 2,3,4,6 **Ir** 192.22 $[Xe]6s^2 4f^{14} 5d^7$ Iridium
87 0.7 1 **Fr** 223.0197 $[Rn]7s^1$ Francium	88 0.9 2 **Ra** 226.0254 $[Rn]7s^2$ Radium	89 - 103 Actinide Series	104 **Rf** (261) $[Rn]7s^2 5f^{14} 6d^2$ Rutherfordium	105 **Db** (262) $[Rn]7s^2 5f^{14} 6d^3$ Dubnium	106 **Sg** (263) $[Rn]7s^2 5f^{14} 6d^4$ Seaborgium	107 **Bh** (262) $[Rn]7s^2 5f^{14} 6d^5$ Bohrium	108 **Hs** (265) $[Rn]7s^2 5f^{14} 6d^6$ Hassium	109 **Mt** (265) $[Rn]7s^2 5f^{14} 6d^7$ Meitnerium

Key:

- Atomic Number → 1
- Oxidation Number → 1
- Electron Configuration → $1s^1$
- Electronegativity ← 2.1
- Chemical Symbol ← H
- Average Atomic Mass ← 1.00794
- Name ← Hydrogen

Lanthanide Series	57 1.1 3 **La** 138.9055 $[Xe]6s^2 4f^1$ Lanthanum	58 1.1 3,4 **Ce** 140.115 $[Xe]6s^2 4f^2$ Cerium	59 1.1 3,4 **Pr** 140.90765 $[Xe]6s^2 4f^3$ Praseodymium	60 1.1 3 **Nd** 144.24 $[Xe]6s^2 4f^4$ Neodymium	61 1.1 3 **Pm** 144.9125 $[Xe]6s^2 4f^5$ Promethium	62 1.2 2,3 **Sm** 150.36 $[Xe]6s^2 4f^6$ Samarium
Actinide Series	89 1.1 3 **Ac** 227.0278 $[Rn]7s^2 5f^1$ Actinium	90 1.3 4 **Th** 232.0381 $[Rn]7s^2 5f^2$ Thorium	91 1.5 4,5 **Pa** 231.03588 $[Rn]7s^2 5f^3$ Protactinium	92 1.4 3,4,5,6 **U** 238.0289 $[Rn]7s^2 5f^4$ Uranium	93 1.4 3,4,5,6 **Np** 237.0482 $[Rn]7s^2 5f^5$ Neptunium	94 1.3 3,4,5,6 **Pu** 244.0642 $[Rn]7s^2 5f^6$ Plutonium